MECHAN

For Students of B.Sc. (Pass & Hons.)

Revised as per UGC Model Curriculum

Prof. D. S. MATHUR

Formerly Head of the Physics Department
Hindu College, University of Delhi.

Revised by:

Dr. P. S. HEMNE

M.Sc. (Physics), Ph.D.
Principal and Head of Post Graduate Department of Physics,
Nevjabai Hitkarini College, Bramhapuri.
(RTM Nagpur University)

S Chand And Company Limited

(ISO 9001 Certified Company)

RAM NAGAR, NEW DELHI - 110 055

S Chand And Company Limited

(ISO 9001 Certified Company)

Head Office: 7361, RAM NAGAR, QUTAB ROAD, NEW DELHI - 110 055
Phone: 23672080-81-82, 66672000 Fax: 91-11-23677446
www.**schandpublishing.com**; e-mail: **info@schandpublishing.com**

Branches:

Ahmedabad : Ph: 27541965, 27542369, ahmedabad@schandpublishing.com
Bengaluru : Ph: 22268048, 22354008, bangalore@schandpublishing.com
Bhopal : Ph: 4209587, bhopal@schandpublishing.com
Chandigarh : Ph: 2625356, 2625546, 4025418, chandigarh@schandpublishing.com
Chennai : Ph: 28410027, 28410058, chennai@schandpublishing.com
Coimbatore : Ph: 2323620, 4217136, coimbatore@schandpublishing.com (Marketing Office)
Cuttack : Ph: 2332580, 2332581, cuttack@schandpublishing.com
Dehradun : Ph: 2711101, 2710861, dehradun@schandpublishing.com
Guwahati : Ph: 2738811, 2735640, guwahati@schandpublishing.com
Hyderabad : Ph: 27550194, 27550195, hyderabad@schandpublishing.com
Jaipur : Ph: 2219175, 2219176, jaipur@schandpublishing.com
Jalandhar : Ph: 2401630, jalandhar@schandpublishing.com
Kochi : Ph: 2809208, 2808207, cochin@schandpublishing.com
Kolkata : Ph: 23353914, 23357458, kolkata@schandpublishing.com
Lucknow : Ph: 4065646, lucknow@schandpublishing.com
Mumbai : Ph: 22690881, 22610885, 22610886, mumbai@schandpublishing.com
Nagpur : Ph: 2720523, 2777666, nagpur@schandpublishing.com
Patna : Ph: 2300489, 2260011, patna@schandpublishing.com
Pune : Ph: 64017298, pune@schandpublishing.com
Raipur : Ph: 2443142, raipur@schandpublishing.com (Marketing Office)
Ranchi : Ph: 2361178, ranchi@schandpublishing.com
Sahibabad : Ph: 2771235, 2771238, delhibr-sahibabad@schandpublishing.com

First Edition 1981
Subsequent Editions and Reprints 1984, 85, 86, 88, 90, 92, 93, 94, 95, 96, 99, 2000, 2001, 2002, 2003, 2004, 2005, 2006, 2007, 2008, 2009, 2010, 2011 (Twice), 2012
Revised Edition 2012
Reprints 2013, 2014 (Twice), 2015, 2016, 2018 (Twice)
Reprint 2019 (Twice)

ISBN : 978-81-219-0599-2 **Code :** 1016C 063

PRINTED IN INDIA

By Vikas Publishing House Pvt. Ltd., Plot 20/4, Site-IV, Industrial Area Sahibabad, Ghaziabad-201010 and Published by S Chand And Company Limited, 7361, Ram Nagar, New Delhi-110 055.

Preface to the Revised Edition

I feel a great pleasure in presenting this book on **'Mechanics'** as revised and enlarged version of the previous book **'Mechanics' by D. S. Mathur.** The book is framed in accordance with the syllabi of U.G.C. and the syllabi of most of the Indian universities. The book presents a comprehensive study of important topics of Mechanics for the undergraduate students of pure and applied sciences, particularly students of B.Sc. Pass and B.Sc. Honors classes and Engineering disciplines in a brief, coherent and lucid manner. For a beginner, the knowledge of scalar and vector is essential to understand the concept in Mechanics. Every care is now taken in elaborating each topic in a simple manner that the reader should feel comfort to grasp its principle and theory. *Basic chapters on reference frames, Newton's laws of motion, gravitational laws, relativity, dynamics of relativistic and non-relativistic particles, conservation laws, wave motion, harmonic oscillators, elasticity, fluid mechanics, production and measurement of low pressures* are incorporated.

Very large number of solved examples based on S.I. system of units are given at the end of each chapter, article-wise. This helps the students to understand each article very well. A set of questions and unsolved updated problems as Exercises are given for a better comprehension of each topic. Recent questions asked in various Indian universities in their examinations are also incorporated at the end of each chapter to enrich the book. I hope this book will also benefit the students appearing for IAS, AMIE and other competitive examinations.

The author humbly invites suggest ions from the students and teachers for further improvement of this book.

My special thanks to my wife Mrs. Vaishali for her incessant encouragement and inspiration at every step. I express my sincere thanks to S. Chand & Company Ltd. for giving me an opportunity to write this book. I acknowledge my deepest sense of gratitude to Shri Bhagirath Kaushik, Vice-president (S & M) for rendering constant encouragement, guidance, and kind support during the entire work. I place on record my thanks to the Editorial staff for designing and layouting of this book in the present form.

Revisor
Dr. P.S. Hemne

Preface

I take this opportunity to thank my readers for giving my new book such a warm reception that the second edition had to be brought out in two years time. Since the book was first published, I have recived a number of suggestions, a great deal of appreaciation and some criticisn also. I am equally thankful to my well wisher and critics for providing me guideline for considerably modifying and revising the book in the present edition, I sincerely hope my readers will be satisfied with my attempt to remove the short coming from which most first edition suffer. My endeavour will be to effect to more improvement in the forthcoming editions in the light of changing syllabuses and comments of students and teachers who I hope will continue writing to me.

15th April 1981 **D. S. Mathur**

Contents

1 Chapter

MATHEMATICAL BACKGROUND: SCALARS AND VECTORS

Brief Contents

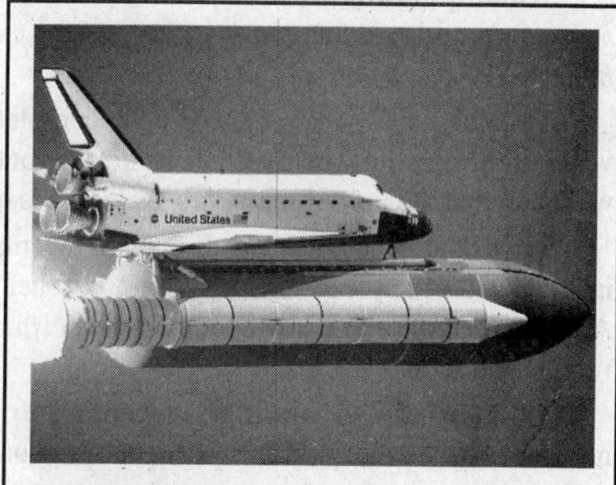

1.1 SCALAR AND VECTOR QUANTITIES

In Physics, we come across with various physical quantities like speed, velocity, acceleration, mass, volume, energy, momentum, temperature, time, speed of light and so many. These physical quantities may, in general, be divided into two main classes : (*i*) *Scalar quantities* or *Scalars*, and (*ii*) *Vector quantities* or *Vectors*.

To understand the difference between a scalar and a vector, let us take an example where the only information known is that a car is moving at 60 km per hour. The information given (60 km/hour) only refers to the car's *speed*, which is a *scalar quantity*. It does not indicate the direction the car is moving. However, when we say, the same car travelling at 60 km/hour due east indicates the *velocity* of the car because it has magnitude (60 km/hour) and direction (due east), therefore, a vector is indicated.

Scalar quantities. *Scalar quantities or scalars are those physical quantities which possess only magnitude and no direction in space*, as for example, *mass, volume, temperature, time, speed of light etc*.

A scalar quantity can, therefore, be completely specified simply by its magnitude or numerical value, indicating how many times its unit is contained in it. Thus, when we speak of a mass of 50 g, we mean that the unit of mass, the gram, (g) is contained 50 times in it.

Since, the scalar has no direction, the magnitude or measure of a scalar quantity is quite independent of any coordinate system. In other words, the coordinate system is not required at all. All such quantities are, however, obey the ordinary algebraical laws of addition and multiplication, *viz*, the following:

(*i*) Law of commutation, according to which the result of addition or multiplication of number of scalars is quite independent of the order in which they may be taken. For example,

$$A + B \equiv B + A \text{ and } A \times B \equiv B \times A$$

(*ii*) Law of association, according to which the sum of the product of a finite number of scalars is quite independent of the manner in which they may be grouped or associated. Thus,

$$A + B + C \equiv (A + B) + C \equiv A + (B + C) \equiv (A + C) + B.$$

And, similarly, $A \times (B \times C) \equiv (A \times B) \times C \equiv (A \times C) \times B$,

clearly indicating that in the case of continuous sums and products the brackets are really superfluous.

(*iii*) Law of distribution, which states that in expressions involving both addition and multiplication the result is the same as the sum of the individual term-wise products. For example,

$$A \times (B + C) = A \times B + A \times C \text{ and } (A + B) \times C = A \times C + B \times C.$$

Vector quantities. *A vector quantity or a vector is defined as a quantity that has both magnitude and direction. To work with vector quantities, one must know the method for representing these quantities.*

Magnitude, or *size* of a vector is also referred to as the vector's *displacement*. It can be thought of as the scalar portion of the vector and is represented by the length of the vector. By definition, a vector has both magnitude and direction. Direction indicates how the vector is oriented relative to some reference axis, as shown in Fig. 1.1. Using East/West and North/South reference axes, vector $\vec{A}$ is oriented in NE quadrant with a direction of 45° North of the EW axis. Giving direction to a scalar A makes it a vector, denoted by $\vec{A}$. The length of $\vec{A}$ is representative of its magnitude or displacement. This is very simple definition.

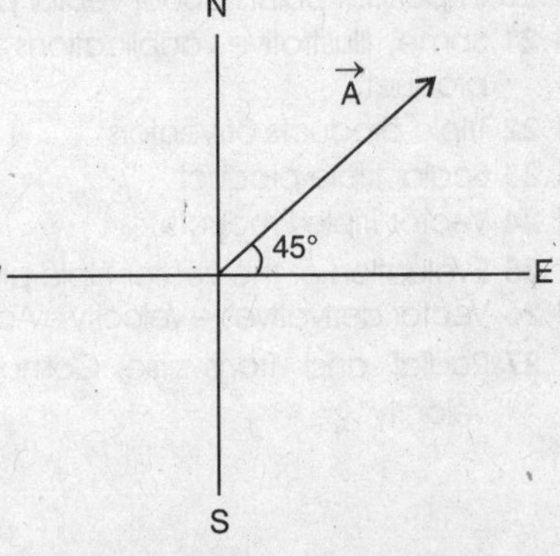

Fig. 1.1 Vector reference Axis

However, it is important to note that possessing **magnitude** and direction is not sufficient for a quantity to be vector but it must follow the parallelogram law of addition (§1.8). This condition is important because *a quantity may have magnitude as well as direction and may still not be a vector quantity*. For instance, the finite rotation of a rigid body about a given axis has magnitude (*viz.,* the angle of rotation), also direction (*viz.,* the direction of the axis) but it is not a vector quantity. This is so for the simple reason that two finite rotations of the body do not add up in accordance with the vector law of addition, *i.e.,* the resultant rotation is not the vector sum of the two finite rotations.

However, if the rotation be small or infinitesimal, it may be regardad as a vector quantity ; for, then, the arc described by the body in a small interval of time is more or less a straight line and is thus representable as a vector, and so also the transverse and angular velocities of the body. Thus, whereas small rotations, angular velocity and angular momentum are vector quantities, large or finite ones are not.

It follows, therefore, that to qualify as a vector, a physical quanitity must not only possess magnitude and direction but must also satisfy the parallelogram law of vector addition.

Vectors associated with a linear or directional effect are called *polar vectors* or, usually, simply as *vectors*, and those associated with rotation about an axis are referred to as *axial vectors*. Thus, force, linear velocity and linear momentum are *polar vectors* and a couple, angular velocity and angular momentum are axial vectors.

1.2 VECTOR NOTATION

In ordinary writing, whether on a black board or a paper, a *vector quantity A*, say, is represented by putting a wavy line underneath the letter A or a small arrow-head above it (indicating its direction), as $\vec{A}$, The magnitude of a vector $\vec{A}$ is denoted by $|\vec{A}|$ or mod $\vec{A}$.

1.3 UNIT AND ZERO VECTORS

A vector of unit magnitude is called a *unit vector* and the notation for it in the direction of $\vec{A}$, is $\hat{A}$ read as '*A*, hat or *A*, caret'. Thus, we have

$$\vec{A} = \hat{A}\,A$$

A unit vector, as will be readily seen, merely indicates direction.

A vector of zero magnitude is called a **zero** *or a* **null vector**, *denoted by* $\vec{0}$.

All zero or null vectors are taken to be equal and their directions are quite arbitrary and, indeed, quite immaterial.

Vectors other than null vectors are reffered to as *proper vectors.*

1.4 GRAPHICAL REPRESENTATION OF A VECTOR

Graphically, a vector is represented by an arrow drawn to a chosen scale, parallel to the direction of the vector. The length and the direction of the arrow thus represent the magnitude and the direction of the vector respectively. Thus, the arrow in **Fig. 1.2** (*a*) represents a vector $\vec{A}$, parallel to the *x-y* plane and making an angle θ with the axis of *x* or a line parallel to it. If the magnitude of vector $\vec{A}$ be 7 units *i.e.*, if $A = 7$, the arrow representing it is drawn 7 times the length of the arrow representing unit vector $\hat{A}$, as shown in **Fig. 1.2** (*b*).

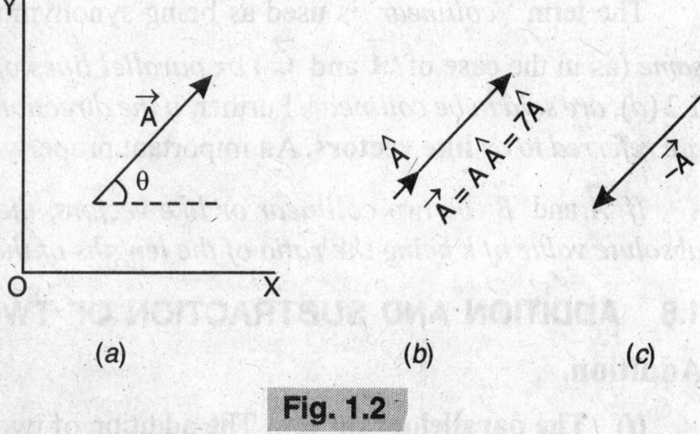

Fig. 1.2

The *negative of vector* $\vec{A}$, is the vector — $\vec{A}$, having the *same magnitude as* $\vec{A}$ but being oppositely directed to it. It is, therefore, represented by an arrow equal in length to that representing $\vec{A}$ but antiparallel to it, as shown in Fig. 1.2 (*c*).

1.5 MULTIPLICATION AND DIVISION OF VECTORS BY SCALARS

From the law of addition of vectors (§1.8) it follows that the sum $\vec{A}+\vec{A}+\vec{A}$........ to m terms gives a vector of magnitude m times that of A in the same direction with it, *i.e.*, equal to $m\vec{A}$. So that, the product of a vector $\vec{A}$ and a scalar m is a vector $m\,A$ whose magnitude is m times the magnitude of $\vec{A}$ and which is similarly or oppositely directed to $\vec{A}$ according as the scalar m is positive or negative. Thus,

$$|m\vec{A}| = mA.$$

Further, if m and n be two scalars and A and B two vectors, we have

$$(m+n)\vec{A} = m\vec{A}+n\vec{A} \text{ and } m(n\vec{A}) = n(m\vec{A}) = (m,n)\vec{A},$$

showing clearly that the multiplication of a vector by a scalar is distributive.

The division of vector $\vec{A}$ by a non-zero scallar m is defined as the multiplication of vector $\vec{A}$ by $1/m$. Thus if $\vec{A} = \hat{A}A$, we have $\hat{A} = \vec{A}/A$.

1.6 EQUALITY OF VECTORS

Although a vector may refer to a physical quantity defined at a particular point, it does not necessarily have any particular location. So that, we can compare two vectors even though they may measure physical quantities defined at quite different points of sapce and time. It follows, therefore, that *all vectors, with the same magnitude and direction, are equal despite their entirely different locations in space and remain so even if moved parallel to themselves*. Thus, in Fig. 1.2 (*d*) vectors $\vec{A}$, $\vec{B}$ and $\vec{C}$ are all equal, since they have all the same magnitude and direction, even though they are differently located in space. Such vectors are called *free vectors* to distinguish them from a localised vector which must pass through a specified point in space, such as a position vector (§1.12), and is thus a *bound vector*. Their 'invariance' *under parallel translation, i.e.*, when moved parallel to themselves, is a very important property of free vectors.

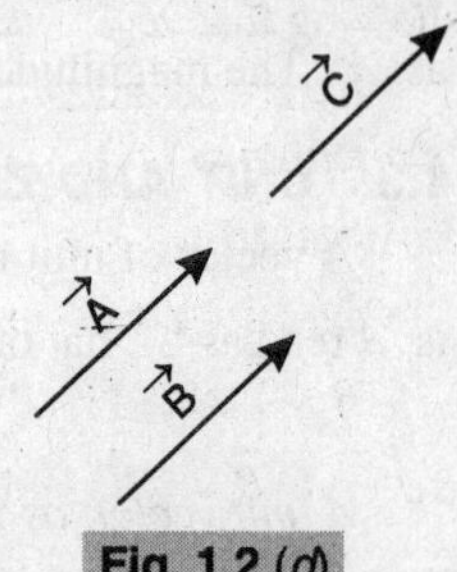

Fig. 1.2 (*d*)

1.7 COLLINEAR VECTORS

The term ' *collinear*' is used as being synonymous with *parallel*. So that, *vectors having the same* (as in the case of $\vec{A}$ and $\vec{C}$) *or parallel lines of action* (as in the case of $\vec{A}$ and $\vec{B}$) in Fig. 1.2 (*d*), *are said to be collinear*. Further, *if the directions of the two parallel vectors be the same, they are referred to as* **like vectors.** An important property of such (*i.e.*, like) vectors is the following :

If $\vec{A}$ and $\vec{B}$ be two collinear or like vectors, there exists a scalar k such that $\vec{B} = k\vec{A}$, the absolute value of k being the ratio of the lengths of the two collinear or like vectors.

1.8 ADDITION AND SUBTRACTION OF TWO VECTORS

Addition.

(*i*) **The parallelogram law.** The addition of two vectors may be effected with the help of the *parallelogram law of vector addition*, according to which the sum or the resultant $\vec{R}$ *of two vectors*

$\vec{A}$ and $\vec{B}$ *is the diagonal of the parallelogram of which* $\vec{A}$ and $\vec{B}$ *are the adjacent sides*, as shown in Fig. 1.3 (*a*), *i.e.*, $\vec{R} = \vec{A} + \vec{B}$. As will be seen, $\vec{A}$, $\vec{B}$ and $\vec{R}$ are all concurrent.

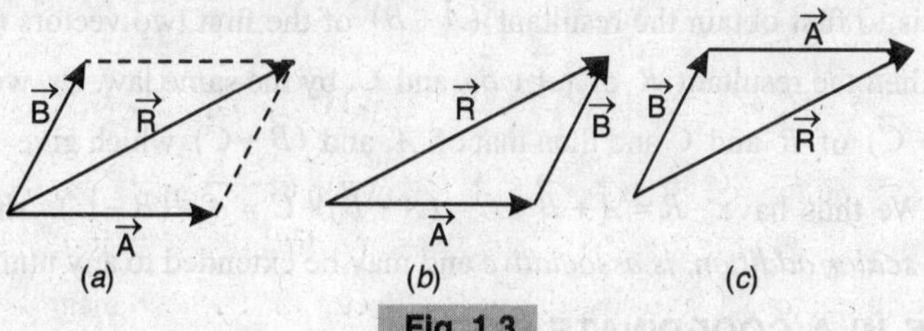

Fig. 1.3

N.B Since any side of a triangle is less than the sum of the other two, it follows that the magnitude of the resultant vector $\vec{R}$ is less than (not equal its) the sum of the magnitudes of the vectors $\vec{A}$ and $\vec{B}$.

***(ii)* The triangle law.** The triangle law of vector addition follows from the parallelogram law and states that *if the tail-end of one vector be placed at the head or the arrow-end of the other, their sum or resultant* $\vec{R}$ *is drawn from the tail end of the first to the head-end of the other*. As is evident from Figs. 1.3 (*b*) and (*c*), the resultant $\vec{R}$ is the same irrespective of the order in which the vectors ($\vec{A}$ and $\vec{B}$) are taken. So that, we have

$$\vec{R} = \vec{A} + \vec{B} = \vec{B} + \vec{A}$$

showing that *vector addition too is commutative.*

It may be noted that *vectors need not lie in the same plane for the laws of vector addition to be applicable to them.*

Subtraction.

Clearly, if the sum of two vectors $\vec{A}$ and $\vec{B}$ be equal to a vector of zero magnitude, we have $\vec{A} + \vec{B} = 0$, showing that vectors $\vec{A}$ and $\vec{B}$ are equal in magnitude but opposite in direction. So that, we have $\vec{B} = -\vec{A}$, indicating that $-\vec{A}$ *is a vector of the same magnitude as vector* $\vec{A}$ *but pointing in a direction opposite to that of* $\vec{A}$. And this at once gives us a method of subtracting a vector $\vec{B}$ from a vector $\vec{A}$ namely, the addition of the vector $\vec{A}$ to the vector $-\vec{B}$. So that, $\vec{A} + (-\vec{B}) = \vec{A} - \vec{B}$, as shown in Fig. 1.4.

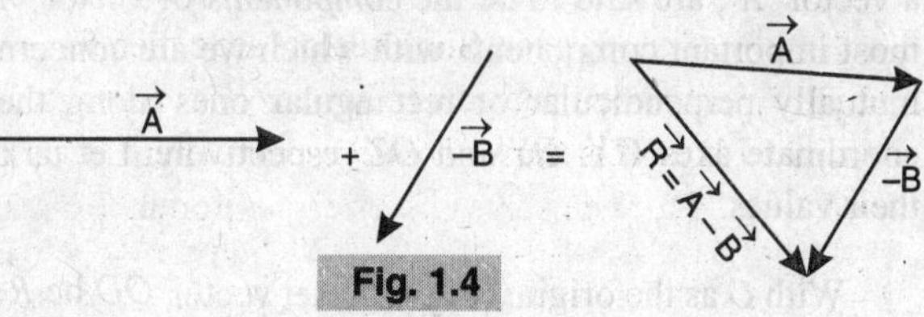

Fig. 1.4

1.9 ADDITION OF MORE THAN TWO VECTORS — (COMPOSITION OF VECTORS)

The determination of the sum or the resultant of a system of more than two vectors (not necessarily in the same plane) is called *composition of vectors*. This may be done with the help of what is called the **polygon law of vector addition** which states that if a vector polygon be drawn, placing the tail-end of each succeeding vector at the head of the arrow-end of the

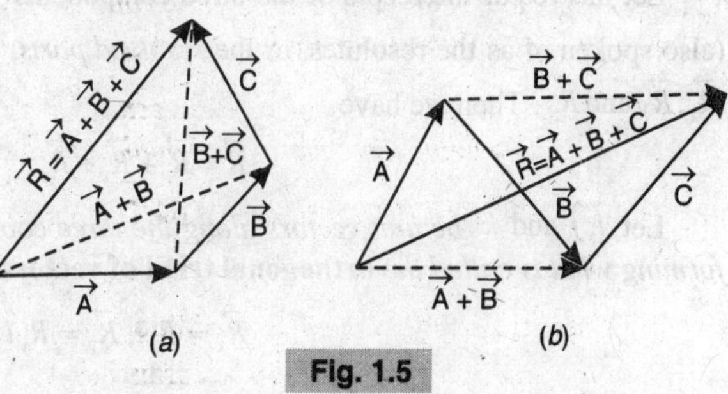

Fig. 1.5

preceding one, as shown in Fig. 1.5 (*a*) and (*b*), their resultant $\vec{R}$ is drawn from the tail-end of the first to the head or the arrow-end of the last. This follows directly from the *Triangle law*. For, what we do, in effect, is to first obtain the resultant $(\vec{A}+\vec{B})$ of the first two vectors ($\vec{A}$ and $\vec{B}$) by the triangle law and then the resultant $\vec{R}$ of $(\vec{A}+\vec{B})$ and $\vec{C}$ by the same law. Or, we could first obtain the resultant $(\vec{B}+\vec{C})$ of $\vec{B}$ and $\vec{C}$ and then that of $\vec{A}$ and $(\vec{B}+\vec{C})$ which give $\vec{R}$, the resultant of $\vec{A}$, $\vec{B}$ and $\vec{C}$. We thus have $\vec{R}=\vec{A}+\vec{B}+\vec{C}=(\vec{A}+\vec{B})+\vec{C}=\vec{A}+(\vec{B}+\vec{C})$, showing that *vector addition too, like scalar addition, is associative* and may be extended to any number of vectors.

1.10 VECTORS IN A COORDINATE SYSTEM

Although it is quite possible to deal with physical laws in terms of vectors, it is found most helpful in actual practice to represent them in a coordinate system, and the one most widely favoured is the familiar *Cartesian coordinate system* which may be right-handed or left handed. The former is shown in Fig. 1.6 (*a*) with its three mutually perpendicular axes *OX*, *OY* and *OZ* represented by the extended thumb, fore-finger and middle finger respectively of the right hand. Its mirror image (Fig. 1.6 (*b*)) forms the left handed system which is, however, not quite so convenient to use. We shall, therefore, stick to the right handed system only, in which to an observer at *O*, righthanded rotations about the axes *OX*, *OY* and *OZ* appear to be from *X* to *Y*, *Y* to *Z* and Z to *X* respectively.

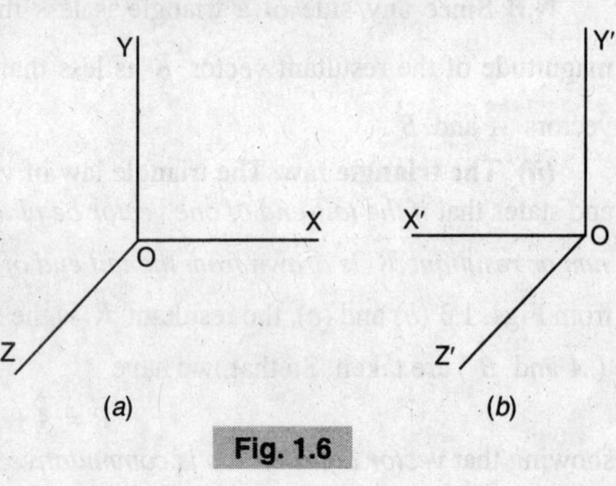

Fig. 1.6

1.11 RECTANGULAR COMPONENTS OF A VECTOR

Two or more vectors which, when compounded in accordance with the parallelogram law or the polygon law of vectors give a vector $\vec{A}$, are said to be the *components* of vector $\vec{A}$. The most important components with which we are concerned are mutually perpendicular or rectangular ones along the three coordinate axes *OX*, *OY* and *OZ* respectively. Let us deduce their values.

With *O* as the origin, (Fig. 1.7), let vector $\vec{OD}$ be $\vec{R}$. Then on *OD* as diagonal, let us construct a *rectangular parallelopiped* with its three edges along the three coordinate axes, as shown.

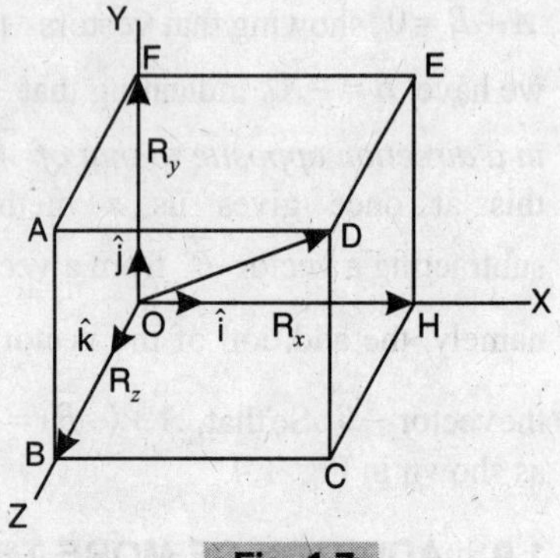

Fig. 1.7

Let the vector intercepts of the three components of $\vec{R}$, (also spoken of as the resolutes, or the *resolved parts*, of $\vec{R}$) along the three axes respectively be $\vec{R}_x, \vec{R}_y$ and $\vec{R}_z$. Then we have

$$\vec{R}=\vec{R}_x+\vec{R}_y+\vec{R}_z \qquad ...(i)$$

Let $\hat{i}, \hat{j}$ and $\hat{k}$ *be unit vectors along the three coordinate axes, chosen as the base vectors or forming what is called the* **orthogonal triad of vectors**. Then, we have

$$\vec{R}_x = R_x\hat{i},\ \vec{R}_y = R_y\hat{i} \text{ and } \vec{R}_z = R_z\hat{k}$$

So that, substituting in relation (*i*), we have

$$\vec{R} = R_x\hat{i} + R_y\hat{j} + R_z\hat{k}. \quad ...(ii)$$

Here, $R_x\hat{i}, R_y\hat{j}$ and $R_z\hat{k}$ are the orthogonal projections of $\vec{R}$ on the directions of $\hat{i}, \hat{j}$ and $\hat{k}$ respectively.

From the geometry of the figure, we have

$$OD^2 = OH^2 + OF^2 + OB^2$$

i.e.,
$$R^2 = R_x^2 + R_y^2 + R_z^2 \quad ...(iii)$$

where R is the magnitude (or modulus) of vector $\vec{R}$.

Thus, *the square of the magnitude (or modulus) of a vector is equal to the sum of the squares of its rectangular components.*

$$\therefore \quad R = \sqrt{R_x^{\,2} + R_y^{\,2} + R_z^{\,2}} \quad ...(iv)$$

And, clearly, $R_x = R\ cos\ (\vec{R}, x)$ $Ry = R\ cos\ (\vec{R}, y)$ and $R_z = R\ cos\ (\vec{R}, z)$, where the three cosines, *viz.*, $cos\ (\vec{R}, x) = R_z/R$, $\cos\ (\vec{R}, y) = R_y/R$ and $cos\ (\vec{R}, z) = R_z/R$ are referred to as the **direction cosines** of vector $\vec{R}$, since they help to determine its direction. They are quite often represented by the letter *l, m* and *n* respectively.

Dividing relation (*iii*) by R^2, we have

$$1 = R_x^2/R^2 + R_y^2/R^2 + R_z^2/R^2$$
$$= \cos^2(\vec{R}, x) + \cos^2(\vec{R}, y) + \cos^2(\vec{R}, z)$$
$$= l^2 + m^2 + n^2 \quad ...(v)$$

i.e., the sum of the squares of the three direction cosines of a vector is equal to unity.

Clearly, the unit vector along $\vec{R}$ is given by

$$\hat{R} = \frac{\vec{R}}{R} = \frac{R_x}{R}\hat{i} + \frac{R_y}{R}\hat{j} + \frac{R_z}{R}\hat{k}$$

where $R_x/R = \cos\ (\vec{R}, x)$, $R_y/R = \cos\ (\vec{R}, y)$ and $R_z/R = \cos\ (\vec{R}, z)$ are the direction cosines of $\vec{R}$.

We therefore have

$$\text{unit vector } \hat{R} = \cos\,(\vec{R}, x)\,\hat{i} + \cos\,(\vec{R}, y)\,\hat{j} + \cos\,(\vec{R}, z)\hat{k}, \quad ...(vi)$$

Further, if we have a number of vectors $\vec{R_1}, \vec{R_2}, \vec{R_3}$ *etc.*, their sum may be expressed in terms of their rectangular components in the form

$$\sum\vec{R} = (\sum R_x)\hat{i} + (\sum R_y)\hat{j} + (\sum R_z)\hat{k}.$$

So that, $\sum R_x$, is the resolute of $\sum\vec{R}$ in the direction of $\hat{i}$ and $\sum R_y$ and $\sum R_z$, its resolutes in the directions of $\hat{j}$ and $\hat{k}$ respectively.

Since the direction of $\hat{i}, \hat{j}$ and $\hat{k}$ may be chosen arbitrarily, we have the result that the *resolute of a sum of vectors in any direction is equal to the sum of the resolute of the individual vectors in that direction.*

N.B. It must be carefully noted that unit vector in different directions are not equal even though their moduli or magnitudes are naturally the same, *viz* unity.

1.12 POSITION VECTOR

The position of a point P from any assigned point, such as the origin O of the Cartesian coordinate system, for example, is uniquely specified by the vector $\vec{OP} = \vec{r}$ (Fig. 1.8), called the *position vector of point P relative to O.*

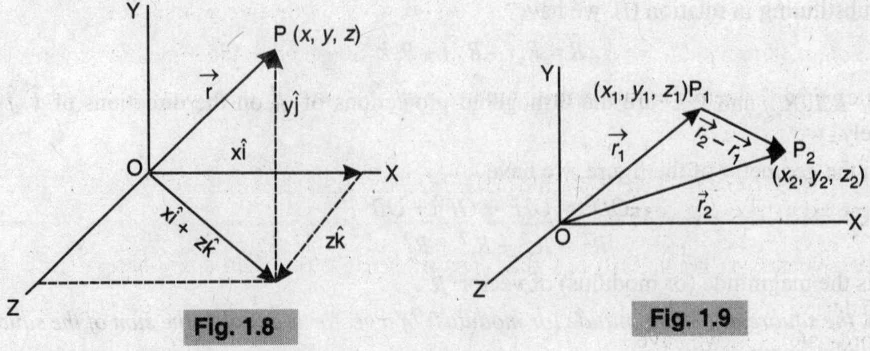

Fig. 1.8

Fig. 1.9

The coordinates of point P being (x, y, z) we have

$$\vec{r} = x\hat{i} + y\hat{j} + z\hat{k} \qquad ...(vii)$$

where $\quad |\vec{r}| = \sqrt{x^2 + y^2 + z^2}$.

The direction cosines of $\vec{r}$ obviously x/r, y/r and z/r. Such a point, with a position vector r, is often spoken of as the point r. It follows from the above that if there be two points P_1 and P_2, with (x_1, y_1, z_1) and (x_2, y_2, z_2) (as their respective coordinates and $\overrightarrow{OP_1} = \vec{r_1}$ and $\overrightarrow{OP_2} = \vec{r_2}$ as their respective position vectors, Fig. 1.9), we have $\vec{r_1} = x_1\hat{i} + y_1\hat{j} + z_1\hat{k}$ and $\vec{r_2} = x_2\hat{i} + y_2\hat{j} + z_2\hat{k}$.

Therefore, $\quad \overrightarrow{P_1P_2} = \overrightarrow{P_1O} + \overrightarrow{OP_2} = -\vec{r_1} + \vec{r_2} = \vec{r_2} - \vec{r_1}$

$$= (x_2 - x_1)\hat{i} + (y_2 - y_1)\hat{j} + (z_2 - z_1)\hat{k}.$$

1.13 CONDITION FOR COPLANARITY OF VECTORS

If $\vec{A}$ and $\vec{B}$ be two vectors in the same plane, the vector $\vec{R} = m_1\vec{A} + m_2\vec{B}$ will also be coplanar with $\vec{A}$ and $\vec{B}$, irrespective of the values of the scalars m_1 and m_2.

In the case of three of more vectors, they are said to be coplanar when they are parallel to the same plane. And, any plane parallel to it is referred to as the *plane of the vectors*.

Let $\vec{A}$, $\vec{B}$ and $\vec{C}$ be three coplanar vectors. Then, it is always possible to have three scalars m_1, m_2 and m_2 such that

$$m_1\vec{A} + m_2\vec{B} + m_3\vec{C} = 0. \qquad ....(viii)$$

Conversely, if vectors, $\vec{A}$, $\vec{B}$ and $\vec{C}$ be such as to satisfy condition (*viii*) above, it can be easily shown that they are coplanar. For relation (*viii*) gives $\vec{A} = -\frac{m_2}{m_1}\vec{B} - \frac{m_3}{m_1}\vec{C}$. Since both $-m_2/m_1$ and $-m_3/m_1$ are purely arbitrary scalars, vector $\vec{A}$ must be in the same plane with vectors $\vec{B}$ and $\vec{C}$. Further, if we express vectors $\vec{A}$, $\vec{B}$ and $\vec{C}$ in terms of their rectangular components, the condition for their coplanarity [*viz*., relation (*viii*) above] takes the form

$$\begin{aligned} m_1A_x + m_2B_x + m_3C_x &= 0 \\ m_1A_y + m_2B_y + m_3C_y &= 0 \\ m_1A_z + m_2B_z + m_3C_z &= 0, \end{aligned} \qquad ....(ix)$$

which, with the elimination of m_1, m_2 and m_3, reduces to

$$A_x(B_yC_z - C_yB_z) + B_x(C_yA_z - A_yC_z) + C_x(A_yB_z - B_yA_z) = 0. \qquad ....(x)$$

Or, to give it the determinant form, we have $\begin{vmatrix} A_x & B_x & C_x \\ A_y & B_y & C_y \\ A_z & B_z & C_z \end{vmatrix} = 0$. $\qquad .....(xi)$

As we shall shortly see (under §1.22), the left hand part of the above relation stands for the volume of parallelopiped, with sides $\vec{A}, \vec{B}, \vec{C}$. And, obviously, if these lie in the same plane, the volume of the parallelopiped is zero. So that *expression (xi) really represents the condition for coplanarity of the three vectors.*

1.14 INVARIANCE OF THE MAGNITUDE OF A VECTOR ON ROTATION OF THE REFERENCE FRAME

Consider a vector $\vec{A}$ (Fig. 1.10) in a reference frame of a Cartesian coordinate system, with the orthogonal triad of unit vectors $\hat{i}, \hat{j}$ and $\hat{k}$. Then, if A_x, A_y and A_z be the components of $\vec{A}$ along the three coordinate axes, we have

$$\vec{A} = A_x\hat{i} + A_y\hat{j} + A_z\hat{k} \quad ...(i)$$

Now, keeping the direction of unchanged, *i.e.*, keeping it fixed in its position (with respect to any of the so called fixed objects) imagine the reference frame to be rigidly rotated about the origin, say, in the anticlockwise direction, with the coordinate axes now taking up the positions *OX′, OY′ and OZ′*. Then, if the new orthogonal triad of unit vectors be formed by $\hat{i}', \hat{j}'$ and $\hat{k}'$ and the components of $\vec{A}$ along the new coordinate axes be A_x', A_y' and A_z', we have

$$\vec{A} = A_x'\hat{i}' + A_y'\hat{j}' + A_y'\hat{k}' \quad ...(ii)$$

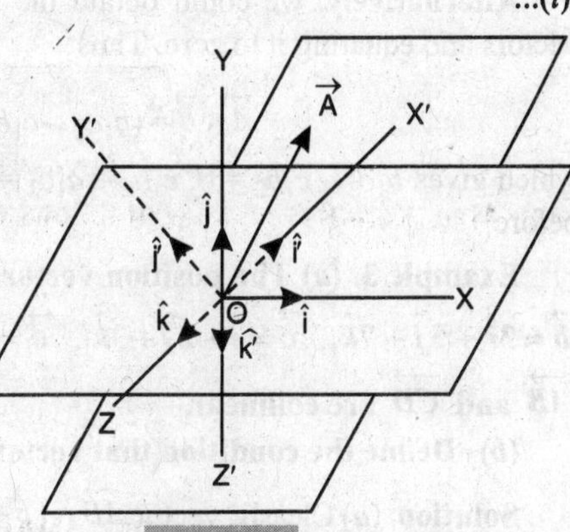

Fig. 1.10

Since the length of vector $\vec{A}$ must obviously be quite independent of the orientation of the coordinate system, or its form of reference, we have

$$A^2 = A_x^2 + A_y^2 + A_z^2 = A_x'^2 + A_y'^2 + A_z'^2$$

$$A = \sqrt{A_x^2 + A_y^2 + A_z^2} = \sqrt{A_x'^2 + A_y'^2 + A_z'^2}.$$

In other words rigid rotation of the Cartesian system (or the frame of reference) of a vector brings about no change in its form of magnitude.

Example 1.

(*a*) Obtian the magnitude and direction cosines of vectors $(\vec{A}+\vec{B})$ and $(\vec{A}-\vec{B})$, if $\vec{A} = 3\hat{i} + 2\hat{j} + \hat{k}$ and $\vec{B} = \hat{i} - 2\hat{j} + 3\hat{k}$.

(*b*) A force $\vec{F} = 2.5\hat{i} + 4.5\hat{j} - 5\hat{k}$ newton acts through the origin. What is the magnitude of this force and what angles does it make with the three coordinate axes ?

Solution.

(*a*) Obviously, $(\vec{A}+\vec{B}) = 4\hat{i} + 4\hat{k}$ and $(\vec{A}-\vec{B}) = 2\hat{i} + 4\hat{j} - 2\hat{k}$. So that, their magnitudes are

$$|\vec{A}+\vec{B}| = \sqrt{4^2+4^2} = 4\sqrt{2} \text{ and } |\vec{A}-\vec{B}| = \sqrt{2^2+4^2+2^2} = \sqrt{24}.$$

Hence, the direction cosines of $(\vec{A}+\vec{B})$ are $= \frac{4}{4\sqrt{2}} = \frac{1}{\sqrt{2}}$, 0 and $\frac{4}{4\sqrt{2}} = \frac{1}{\sqrt{2}}$ and the direction cosines of $(\vec{A}-\vec{B})$ are $\frac{2}{\sqrt{24}}, \frac{4}{\sqrt{24}}, \frac{2}{\sqrt{24}}$.

(*b*) Clearly, the magnitude of the force is given by

$$|\vec{F}| = \sqrt{(2.5)^2 + (4.5)^2 + (-5^2)} = 7.176 \text{ newton and its direction cosines are}$$

(*i*) $\cos\theta_x = 2.5/7.176 = 0.3483$ and $\therefore \theta_x = 69.6°$

(*ii*) $\cos\theta_y = 4.5/7.176 = 0.6270$ and $\therefore \theta_y = 51.2°$ and

(*iii*) $\cos\theta_z = 5/7.176 = 0.6968$ and $\therefore \theta_z = 124.2°$.

Example 2. Deduce the necessary condition for two vectors $\vec{A} = a_1\hat{i} + b_1\hat{j} + c_1\hat{k}$ and $\vec{B} = a_2\hat{i} + b_2\hat{j} + c_2\hat{k}$ to be collinear.

Solution. Obviously, to be collinear (or parallel), the direction cosines of vector $\vec{A}$ must be equal to the respective direction cosines of vector $\vec{B}$ *i.e*,. we should have $a_1/A = a_2/B$, $b_1/A = b_2/B$ and $c_1/A = c_2/B$, which gives $a_1/a_2 = b_1/b_2 = c_1/c_2 = A/B$.

Thus, the condition for collinearity of the two vectors works out to be that the ratio between the scalars a_1 and a_2, b_1 and b_2 and c_1 and c_2 must be the same, *i.e*,. $a_1/a_2 = b_1/b_2 = c_1/c_2$.

Alternatively, we could obtain the same condition by taking the cross product of the two vectors and equating it to zero. Thus

$$\vec{A}\times\vec{B} = (b_1c_2 - c_1b_2)\,\hat{i} + (c_1a_2 - a_1c_2)\;\hat{j} + (a_1b_2 - b_1a_2)\,\hat{k} = 0,$$

which gives $b_1c_2 - c_1b_2 = 0$, $c_1a_2 - a_1c_2 = 0$ and $a_1b_2 - b_1a_2 = 0$, whence, $a_1/a_2 = b_1/b_2 = c_1/c_2$, as before.

Example 3. (*a*) The position vectors of four points *A*, *B*, *C* and *D* are $\vec{a} = 2\hat{i} + 3\hat{j} + 4\hat{k}$, $\vec{b} = 3\hat{i} + 5\hat{j} + 7\hat{k}$, $\vec{c} = \hat{i} + 2\hat{j} + 3\hat{k}$, $\vec{d} = 3\hat{i} + 6\hat{j} + 9\hat{k}$ respectively. Examine whether vectors $\overrightarrow{AB}$ and $\overrightarrow{CD}$ are collinear.

(*b*) Define the condition that vectors $5\hat{i} + 7\hat{j} - 3\hat{k}$ and $2\hat{i} - b\hat{j} + c\hat{k}$ may be parallel.

Solution. (*a*) Clearly, vector $\overrightarrow{AB} = (\vec{b} - \vec{a}) = \hat{i} + 2\hat{j} + 3\hat{k}$ and vector $\overrightarrow{CD} = (\vec{d} - \vec{c}) = 2\hat{i} + 4\hat{j} + 6\hat{k}$. For collinearity of vectors, as we have been in example 2 above, the condition is that $a_1/a_2 = b_1/b_2 = c_1/c_2$. Here, $a_1/a_2 = 1/2$, $b_1/b_2 = 2/4 = 1/2$ and $c_1/c_2 = 3/6 = 1/2$, *i.e.*, the condition for collinearity is satisfied. The two vectors are thus collinear.

(*b*) For the two given vectors to be parallel (or collinear), we must have $5/2 = -7/b = -3/c$, whence, $b = -14/5$ and $c = -6/5$, which is thus the required condition.

Example 4. If a position vector $\vec{r} = 2\hat{i} + 2\hat{j} + \hat{k}$, obtain (*i*) its direction cosines, and (*ii*) its components in the *xz* and *yz* planes.

Solution. Clearly, magnitude of $\vec{r}$ given by $|\vec{r}| = r = \sqrt{2^2 + 2^2 + 1^2} = \sqrt{9} = 3$ *units* and hence

(*i*) its direction cosines are $\cos(\vec{r}, x) = 2/3$, $\cos(\vec{r}, y) = 2/3$ and $\cos(\vec{r}, z) = 1/3$, and

(*ii*) its components in the *xz* and *yz* planes are $\vec{r}_{xz} = 2\hat{i} + \hat{k}$ and $\vec{r}_{yz} = 2\hat{j} + \hat{k}$, with their mangitudes equal to $\sqrt{2^2 + 1^2} = \sqrt{5}$ and $\sqrt{2^2 + 1^2} = \sqrt{5}$ respectively.

Example 5. Show that the vectors $\vec{a} - 2\vec{b} + 3\vec{c}$, $-2\vec{a} + 3\vec{b} - 4\vec{c}$ and $-\vec{b} + 2\vec{c}$ are coplanar, where $\vec{a}, \vec{b}$ and $\vec{c}$ are unit (or any) vectors.

Solution. We have the condition for coplanarity of three vectors, namely that the

$$\text{determinant} \begin{vmatrix} A_x & B_x & C_x \\ A_y & B_y & C_y \\ A_z & B_z & C_z \end{vmatrix} = 0.$$

$$\text{Here, the determinant is} \begin{vmatrix} 1 & -2 & 3 \\ -2 & 3 & -4 \\ 0 & -1 & 2 \end{vmatrix}$$

So that, its value is 1 (6 – 4) + (–2) (+ 4) + 3 (2) = 2 – 8 + 6 = 0, indicanting that the three vectors are coplanar.

Alternatively, we could express one of the vectors in terms of the other two, equate the coefficients of $\vec{a}, \vec{b}$ and $\vec{c}$, solve any two of the three equations thus obtained and see if the same solution satisfies the third equation too. If it does, the three vectors are coplanar.

Thus, let us put $\vec{a} - 2\vec{b} + 3\vec{c} = x(-2\vec{a} + 3\vec{b} - 4\vec{c}) + y(-\vec{b} + 2\vec{c})$, where x and y are scalars.

Equating the coefficients of $\vec{a}, \vec{b}$ and $\vec{c}$ we have

$-2x = 1$ .....(*i*), $3x - y = -2$ .... (*ii*) and $-4x + 2y = 3$ .....(*iii*)

Solving (*i*), and (*ii*), we have $x = -1/2$ and $y = 1/2$.

Since these values of x and y also satisfy equation (*iii*), the three vectors are coplanar.

Example 6. If vector $\vec{A} = \hat{i} + 2\hat{j} - 2\hat{k}, \vec{B} = 2\hat{i} + \hat{j} + \hat{k}$ and $\vec{C} = \hat{i} - 3\hat{j} - 2\hat{k}$, find the magnitude and direction cosines of the vector $(\vec{A} + \vec{B} + \vec{C})$.

Solution. Vector sum

$$\vec{R} = \vec{A} + \vec{B} + \vec{C}$$
$$= \hat{i} + 2\hat{j} - 2\hat{k} + 2\hat{i} + \hat{j} + \hat{k} + \hat{i} - 3\hat{j} - 2\hat{k}$$
$$= 4\hat{i} - 3\hat{k}$$

$\therefore$ $R_x = 4\hat{i}$, $R_y = 0$ and $R_z = -3\hat{k}$

Hence magnitude of $\vec{R} = |\vec{R}| = \sqrt{4^2 + 0^2 + 3^2} = 5$

Direction cosines of $\vec{R}$ will be

$$l = \frac{R_x}{R} = \frac{4}{5}; \quad m = \frac{R_y}{R} = \frac{0}{5} = 0; \quad n = \frac{R_z}{R} = \frac{-3}{5}$$

1.15 PRODUCT OF TWO VECTORS

From the manner is which two vectors enter into combination in physics we come across two distinct kinds of products: (*i*) a number or a scalar, called the scalar product, and (*ii*) a vector, called the vector product. The process by which we obtain a product is called multiplication and each of the two vectors is called a factor of the product.

The scaler and the vector products are also called the *inner* and the *outer* products, after *Grassmann*.

1.16 SCALAR PRODUCT

The scalar product of two vectors $\vec{A}$ and $\vec{B}$ is denoted by $\vec{A} \bullet \vec{B}$ and is read as $\vec{A}$ dot $\vec{B}$. It is also. therefore, known as the *dot product of the two vectors* (also sometimes referred to as the *direct product*).

It is defined as the product of the magnitude of the two vectors $\vec{A}$ and $\vec{B}$ and the cosine of their included angle θ (Fig. 1.11), irrespective of the coordinate system used. *Thus,*

$$\vec{A} \cdot \vec{B} = AB \cos\theta \quad \text{or} \quad AB \cos(\vec{A}, \vec{B})$$

Since cos $(\vec{A}, \vec{B})$ is equal to cos $(\vec{B}, \vec{A})$, the scalar product is clearly commutative and $\vec{A} \cdot \vec{B} = \vec{B} \cdot \vec{A}$

The order of the factors may thus be reversed without in any way affecting the value of the product.

Further, since $B \cos\theta$ is the projection (or the resolute) of $\vec{B}$ in the direction of $\vec{A}$ and $A \cos\theta$, the projection (or the resolute) of $\vec{A}$ in the direction of $\vec{B}$,

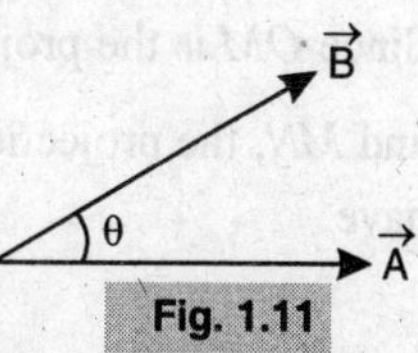

Fig. 1.11

as shown in Figs. 1.12 (*a*) and (*b*) respectively we have $\vec{A}\cdot\vec{B} = AB\cos\theta = BA\cos\theta$, *i.e., the scalar product of two vectors* ($\vec{A}$ *and* $\vec{B}$) *is the product of the magnitude of either vector and the projection* (or *the resolute*) *of the other in its direction.*

It also follows from the above that the angle between the two vectors, *i.e.*, θ is given by the relation $\cos\theta = \vec{A}\cdot\vec{B}/AB$.

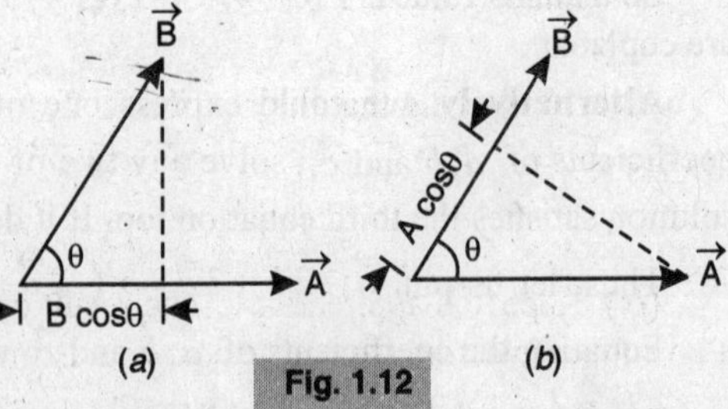

Fig. 1.12

1.17 IMPORTANT POINTS ABOUT SCALAR PRODUCT

The following points in regard to scalar product of two vectors may usefully be remembered:

(*i*) If the two vectors ($\vec{A}$ and $\vec{B}$) be perpendicular to each other, *i.e.*, $\theta = \pi/2$ and, therefore, $\cos\theta = \cos(\vec{A},\vec{B}) = 0$, *i.e.*, the scalar product $\vec{A}\cdot\vec{B} = AB\cos = AB\cos(\vec{A},\vec{B}) = 0$. This is, therefore, the condition for two vectors to be perpendicular (or orthogonal) to each other.

(*ii*) If the two vectors have the same direction, clearly θ = 0 and $\cos\theta = \cos(\vec{A},\vec{B}) = 1$. So that, the scalar product $\vec{A}\cdot\vec{B} = AB\cos\theta = AB\cos(\vec{A},\vec{B}) = AB\cos 0° = AB$, *i.e.*, the scalar product is equal to the product of the magnitude of the two vectors.

And, if $\vec{A} = \vec{B}$, *i.e.*, if the two vectors be equal, we have

$$\vec{A}\cdot\vec{A} = |\vec{A}||\vec{A}| = AA = A^2. \text{ Or, } A^2 = A^2,$$

i.e., the square of a vector is equal to the square of its magnitude (or modulus).

(*iii*) If the two vectors have opposite directions, θ = π and therefore cos θ = cos π = –1. So that $\vec{A}\cdot\vec{B} = -AB$, *i.e.*, the scalar product is equal to the negative product of their magnitudes.

(*iv*) It follows from (*ii*) above that square of any unit vector, like $\hat{i}, \hat{j}$ or $\hat{k}$ is unity.

Thus, $i^2 = j^2 = k^2 = (1)(1)\cos 0° = 1$.

Or, $$\hat{i}\cdot\hat{i} = \hat{j}\cdot\hat{j} = \hat{k}\cdot\hat{k} = 1.$$

(*v*) Since $\hat{i}, \hat{j}$ and $\hat{k}$ are orthogonal (or perpendicular to each other), we have, from (*i*) above,

$$\hat{i}\cdot\hat{j} = \hat{j}\cdot\hat{k} = \hat{k}\cdot\hat{i} = (1)(1)\cos 90° = 0.$$

(*vi*) If *either vector* ($\vec{A}$ *or* $\vec{B}$) *is multipli... ...y a scalar or a number m, the scalar product too is multiplied by that number*. Thus,

$$(m\vec{A})\cdot\vec{B} = \vec{A}\cdot(m\vec{B}) = m(\vec{A}\cdot\vec{B}) = mAB\cos\theta = mAB\cos\vec{A}\cdot\vec{B}.$$

(*vii*) If $\vec{A}\cdot\vec{B} = 0$, it means that either $\vec{A}$ *or* $\vec{B} = 0$ or $\vec{A}$ and $\vec{B}$ are perpendicular to each other.

(*viii*) The scalar product obeys the distributive law. This may be seen from the following :

In Fig. 1.13, the scalar product of vector $\vec{A}$ and the resultant $(\vec{B}+\vec{C})$ of $\vec{B}$ and $\vec{C}$ is given by $\vec{A}\cdot(\vec{B}+\vec{C}) = \vec{A}$. (projection or resolute of $(\vec{B}+\vec{C})$ in the direction of $\vec{A}$), *i.e.*,

$$\vec{A}\cdot(\vec{B}+\vec{C}) = A \times ON = A(OM + MN)$$
$$= A.\,OM + A.\,MN. \qquad ...(i)$$

Since *OM* is the projection (or resolute) of $\vec{B}$ in the direction of $\vec{A}$ and *MN*, the projection (or resolute) of $\vec{C}$ in the direction of $\vec{A}$, we have

$$A\cdot OM = \vec{A}\cdot\vec{B} \text{ and } A\cdot MN = \vec{A}\cdot\vec{C}.$$

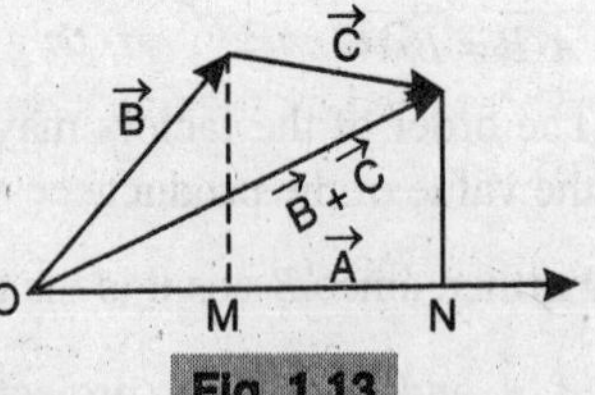

Fig. 1.13

Substituting these values in relation (*i*) above we have

$$\vec{A}\cdot(\vec{B}+\vec{C}) = \vec{A}\cdot\vec{B}+\vec{A}\cdot\vec{C}$$

clearly showing that the distributive law holds good.

It thus follows that $(\vec{A}+\vec{B})\cdot(\vec{C}+\vec{D}) = \vec{A}\cdot(\vec{C}+\vec{D}) + \vec{B}\cdot(\vec{C}+\vec{D})$

$$= \vec{A}\cdot\vec{C}+\vec{A}\cdot\vec{D}+\vec{B}\cdot\vec{C}+\vec{B}\cdot\vec{D}$$

(*ix*) Repeated application of the result obtained in (*viii*) above shows that the scalar product of two sums of vectors may be exapanded as in ordinary algebra. Thus.

$$(A+B)^2 = A^2 + 2AB + B^2 \text{ and } (A+B)(A-B) = A^2 - B^2, \textit{etc.}$$

(*x*) The distributive law also enables us to obtain an expression for the scalar product of two vectors in terms of their rectangular components. For if $\vec{A} = A_x\hat{i} + A_y\hat{j} + A_z\hat{k}$ and $\vec{B} = B_x\hat{i} + B_y\hat{j} + B_z\hat{k}$ we have, remembering that $\hat{i}, \hat{j}$ and $\hat{k}$ are mutually perpendicular,

$$\vec{A}\cdot\vec{B} = A_xB_x + A_yB_y + A_zB_z$$

i.e., the scalar product of two vectors is equal to the sum of the products of their corresponding rectangular components.

And, since $\vec{A}\cdot\vec{B} = AB\cos\theta$, we have angle θ between the two vectors given by the relation

$$\cos\theta = \frac{A_xB_x + A_yB_y + A_zB_z}{\sqrt{A_x^2 + A_y^2 + A_z^2}\sqrt{B_x^2 + B_y^2 + B_z^2}}$$

Further if $\vec{A} = \vec{B}$, we have

$$\vec{A}\cdot\vec{A} = A^2 = A^2 = A_xA_x + A_yA_y + A_zA_z = A_x^2 + A_y^2 + A_z^2$$

i.e., the square of a vector is equal to the sum of the squares of its rectangular components.

(*xi*) The magnitudes of the components of vector $\vec{A}$ along the three coordinate axes may be written as $\vec{A_x} = \vec{A}.\hat{i}$, $\vec{A_y} = \vec{A}.\hat{j}$, $\vec{A_z} = \vec{A}.\hat{k}$, for, as we know,

$$\vec{A}\cdot\hat{i} = (A_x\hat{i} + A_y\hat{j} + A_z\hat{k}).\hat{i} = A_x\hat{i}\cdot\hat{i} + A_y\hat{i}\cdot\hat{j} + A_z\hat{i}\cdot\hat{k}$$

$$= A_x + 0 + 0 = A_x.$$

Similarly $= A_y = \vec{A}\cdot\hat{j}$ and $A_z = \vec{A}\cdot\hat{k}$.

And, if U_l be the unit vector along a line L, the component of vector $\vec{A}$ along the line can be shown to be $\vec{A}\cdot\vec{U_l}$

(*xii*) A scalar product, being a number, can occur as a numerical coefficient of a vector. Thus, for example,

(*i*) $(\vec{A}\cdot\vec{B})\vec{C}$ is a vector of magnitude $(\vec{A}\cdot\vec{B})\vec{C}$ in the direction of $\vec{C}$.

(*ii*) $(\vec{A}\cdot\vec{B})\,(\vec{C}\cdot\vec{D})$ is a number obtained by the multiplication of two numbers $(\vec{A}\cdot\vec{B})$ and $(\vec{C}\cdot\vec{D})$.

1.18 SOME IILUSTRATIVE APPLICATION OF SCALAR PRODUCT

(*i*) Deduction of the cosine law. Let two vectors $\vec{A}$ and $\vec{B}$ be represented by the two sides of a triangle, as shown in Fig. 1.14. Then, the third side represents a vector $\vec{C} = -\vec{B} + \vec{A} = \vec{A} - \vec{B}$.

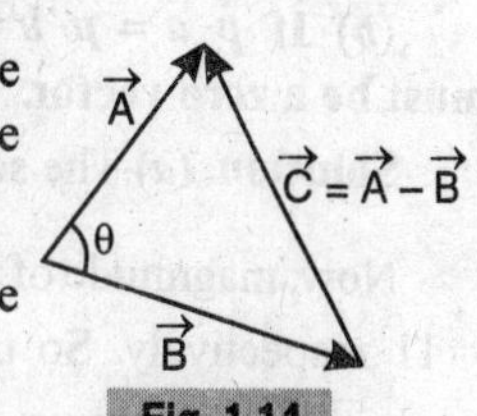

Fig. 1.14

Taking the scalar product of each side with itself, we have $\vec{C}\cdot\vec{C} = (\vec{A}-\vec{B})\cdot(\vec{A}-\vec{B})$. Or, $C^2 = A^2 + B^2 - 2AB$, because $\vec{A}\cdot\vec{B} = \vec{B}\cdot\vec{A}$.

Or, $C^2 = A^2 + B^2 - 2AB \cos(\vec{A}, \vec{B}) = A^2 + B^2 - 2AB \cos\theta.$

This is the well known trigonometric relation called the cosine law.

***(ii)* Obtaining the equation of a plane.** Let *ABCD* be the plane (Fig. 1.15) whose equation is required to be obtained. Drop a normal *N* on to the plane from an origin *O*, lying quite outside the plane and let $\vec{r}$ be the position vector (with respect to *O*) of any point *P* in the plane.

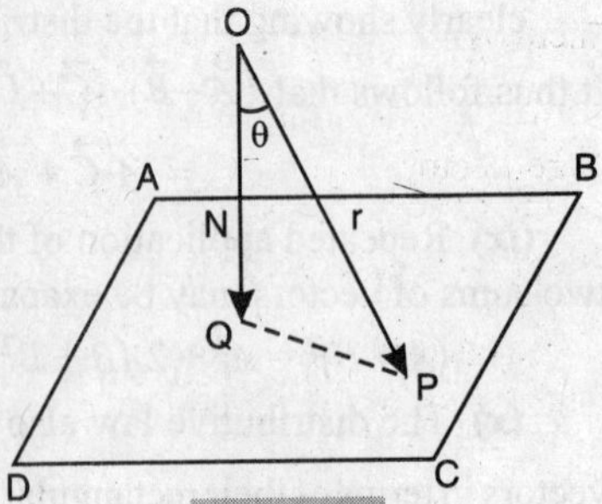

Then, since the projection of $\vec{r}$ on normal $\vec{N}$ must be equal to the magnitude *N* of $\vec{N}$, we have $N = r\cos\theta$ and $\therefore N^2 = Nr \cos\theta = Nr$, which is the required equation of the plane.

Fig. 1.15

Or, if we write $\vec{N}$ and $\vec{r}$ in terms of their rectangular components N_x, N_y, N_z and x, y, z respectively, along the three Cartesian coordinate axes, with $\hat{i}, \hat{j}, \hat{k}$ as the orthogonal triad of unit vectors along these, we have

$$\vec{N} = N_x\hat{i} + N_y\hat{j} + N_z\hat{k} \text{ and } \hat{r} = x\hat{i} + y\hat{j} + z\hat{k}$$

So that, $$N^2 = (N_x\hat{i} + N_y\hat{j} + N_z\hat{k})\,(x\hat{i} + y\hat{j} + z\hat{k} = xN_x + yN_y + zN_z)$$

which is the usual form of the equation met with in Analytical Geometry.

***(iii)* Deduction of expression for work and power.** As we know, work is said to be done by a force acting on a particle when the particle is displaced in a direction other than the one normal to the force. It is a *scalar quantity* proportional to the force and the resolved part of displacement in the direction of the force or to the displacment and resolved part of the force in the direction of displacement. If, therefore, vectors $\vec{F}$ and $\vec{d}$ represent force and displacement respectively, inclined to each other at an angle θ (Fig. 1.16) we have *work done*, $W = (F\cos\theta)\, d = \vec{F}.\vec{d}$, its value being zero only when $\vec{F}$ and $\vec{d}$ are at right angles to each other.

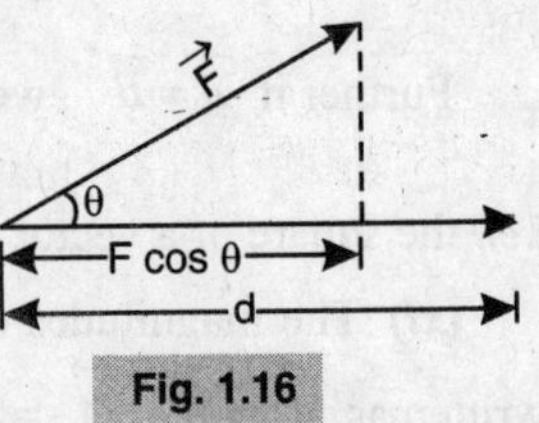

Fig. 1.16

Further if there be more than one force acting on the particle, say, $\vec{F}_1, \vec{F}_2, \vec{F}_3$, *etc.*, then, work done by them for a displacement $\vec{d}$ of the particle is respectively $\vec{F}_1\cdot\vec{d}, \vec{F}_2\cdot\vec{d} \ldots\ldots \vec{F}_n\vec{d}$. We, therefore, have *total work done*, $W = \sum_1^n \vec{F}\cdot\vec{d} = \vec{d}\cdot\sum\vec{F} = \vec{d}\cdot\vec{R}$,

i.e., the effect of all the forces taken together is the same as that of one single force $\vec{R}$ equal to their resultant.

Now, power is the rate of doing work. So that, power $P = \dfrac{dW}{dt} = \dfrac{d}{dt}(\vec{F}\cdot\vec{d}) = \vec{F}\cdot\dfrac{d}{dt}(\vec{d})$.

Since, $\dfrac{d}{dt}(\vec{d})$ is the velocity $\vec{v}$ of the particle, we have $\vec{P} = \vec{F}\cdot\vec{v}$

Example 6. (*a*) Obtain the scalar product of the vectors (6, 2, 3). (2, –9, 6) as also the angle between them

(*b*) If $\vec{p}\cdot\vec{a} = \vec{p}\cdot\vec{b} = \vec{p}\cdot\vec{c} = 0$, where $\vec{a}, \vec{b}$ and $\vec{c}$ are non-coplanar vectors, show that $\vec{p}$ must be a zero vector.

Solution. (*a*) The scalar product of the two vector is 6(2) + 2(–9) + 3(6) = 12.

Now, magnitude of the two vectors, say $\vec{A}$ and $\vec{B}$ are $\sqrt{6^2 + 2^2 + 3^2} = 7$ and $\sqrt{(2)^2 + (-9)^2 + 6^2} = 11$ respectively. So that, if θ be the angle between the two vectors, we have (from § 1.16), $\cos\theta\ \vec{A}\cdot\vec{B}/AB - 12/(7)(11) = 12/77 = 0.1559$, whence, $\theta = 81°$ very nearly.

(*b*) Suppose for a moment, that $\vec{p}$ is not a zero vector. Then, since $\vec{p}\cdot\vec{a}$ as also $\vec{p}\cdot\vec{b}=0, \vec{p}$ must be perpendicular to both $\vec{a}$ and $\vec{b}$ and must, therefore, also be normal to the plane containing them. And, since $\vec{p}\cdot\vec{c}$ is also zero, it follows that vector *c* too must be in the plane containing *a* and *b*, which is contrary to our hypothesis. Obviously, then, for the given relation to be tr[illegible], *p* must be a zero vector.

Example 7. Show that the vectors $\vec{A}=3\hat{i}-2\hat{j}+\hat{k}, \vec{B}=\hat{i}-3\hat{j}+5\hat{k}$ and $\vec{C}=2\hat{i}+\hat{j}-4\hat{k}$ form a right angled triangle. ***(Patna 2007)***

Solution. The vectors $\vec{A}, \vec{B}$ and $\vec{C}$ will form a triangle if one of the vectors is equal to the vector sum of the remaining two vectors.

Now $\quad \vec{B}+\vec{C}=\hat{i}-3\hat{j}+5\hat{k}+2\hat{i}+\hat{j}-4\hat{k}=3\hat{i}-2\hat{i}+\hat{k}=\vec{A}$

Hence, the three vectors form a triangle.

$$\vec{A}\cdot\vec{B} = (3\hat{i}-2\hat{j}+\hat{k})\cdot(\hat{i}-3\hat{j}+5\hat{k})=14$$

$$\vec{A}\cdot\vec{C} = (3\hat{i}-2\hat{j}+\hat{k})\cdot(2\hat{i}+\hat{j}-4\hat{k})=0$$

$$\vec{B}\cdot\vec{C} = (\hat{i}-3\hat{j}+5\hat{k})\cdot(2\hat{i}+\hat{j}-4\hat{k})=-21$$

As $\vec{A}\cdot\vec{C}=0$, the vectors $\vec{A}$ and $\vec{C}$ are orthogonal and triangle formed is a right angled triangle.

Example 8. A particle moves from a point (3, –4, –2) m to a point (–2, 3, 5)m under the influence of a force $\vec{F}=(-2\hat{i}+3\hat{j}+4\hat{k})$ Newton. Calculate the work done by the force. ***(Nagpur University 2008)***

Solution. Displacement of the particle.

$$\vec{r} = (-2-3)\hat{i}+(3+4)\hat{j}+(5+2)\hat{k} = (-5\hat{i}+7\hat{j}+7\hat{k})m$$

Here, $\quad \vec{F} = (-2\hat{i}+3\hat{j}+4\hat{k})N$

∴ Work done $\quad W = \vec{F}\cdot\vec{r}=(-2\hat{i}+3\hat{j}+4\hat{k})\cdot(-5\hat{i}+7\hat{j}+7\hat{k})$

$$= (10+21+28) \text{ Joules} = 59 \text{ J}$$

Example 9. If $\vec{A}=3\hat{i}-\hat{j}+2\hat{k}$ and $\vec{B}=\hat{i}-2\hat{j}+2\hat{k}$, find scalar product of two vectors. ***(Nagpur University 2006)***

Solution.

$$\vec{A}.\vec{B} = (3\hat{i}-\hat{j}+2\hat{k})\cdot(\hat{i}-2\hat{j}+2\hat{k}) = 3+2+4 = 9$$

Example 10. Find the angle between the vectors $(2\hat{i}+2\hat{j}+3\hat{k})$ and $(6\hat{i}-3\hat{j}+2\hat{k})$. ***(Nagpur University 2007)***

Solution. Let θ be the angle between the two vectors, then

$$\vec{A}.\vec{B} = AB\cos\theta$$

$$\cos\theta = \frac{\vec{A}\cdot\vec{B}}{AB}=\frac{A_xB_x+A_yB_y+A_zB_z}{\sqrt{A_x^2+A_y^2+A_z^2}\sqrt{B_x^2+B_y^2+B_z^2}}$$

$$=\frac{12-6+6}{\sqrt{4+4+9}\sqrt{36+9+4}}=\frac{12}{\sqrt{17}\sqrt{49}}=\frac{12}{7\sqrt{17}}=0.4158$$

$$\therefore \quad \theta = \cos^{-1} 0.4158 = 65.45°$$

Example 11. Obtain the projection of a vector $\vec{P} = 2\hat{i} + 3\hat{j} - \hat{k}$ along a line L which originates at point (2, 2, 0) and passes through point (–2, 4, 6).

Solution. The projection of vector $\vec{P}$ along line $L = \vec{P}.e\vec{L}$, where *eL, is the unit vector along the line.*

We must, therefore, determine first this unit vector.

Clearly, the line charges from + 2 to –2, thus undergoing a change of –2 – 2 = –4 in the direction of *x*. It similarly undergoes a change of 4 – 2 = 2 in the direction of *y* and 6 – 0 = 6 in the direction of *z*. So that, we have unit vector

$$e\vec{L} = \frac{-4}{\sqrt{(-4)^2 + (2)^2 + (6)^2}}\hat{i} + \frac{2}{\sqrt{(-4)^2 + (2)^2 + (6)^2}}\hat{j} + \frac{6}{\sqrt{(-4)^2 + (2)^2 + (6)^2}}\hat{k}$$

$$= \frac{-4}{\sqrt{56}}\hat{i} + \frac{2}{\sqrt{56}}\hat{j} + \frac{6}{\sqrt{56}}\hat{k}.$$

$\therefore$ Projection of vector P along line $L = \vec{P}.eL = 2\left(\frac{-4}{\sqrt{56}}\right) + 3\left(\frac{2}{\sqrt{56}}\right) - \left(\frac{6}{\sqrt{56}}\right)$

$$= -1.009,$$

the negative sign indicating that the projection is oppositely directed to line *L*.

Example 12. (*a*) If $\vec{A} = 4\hat{i} + 6\hat{j} - 3\hat{k}$ and $\vec{B} = -2\hat{i} - 5\hat{j} + 7\hat{k}$, find out (*i*) direction cosines of *A* and (*ii*) angle between *A* and *B*.

(*b*) Show that if (*i*) $|\vec{a} + \vec{b}| = |\vec{a} - \vec{b}|$, $\vec{a}$ and $\vec{b}$ are perpendicular, (*ii*) $\vec{a}$ and $\vec{b}$ are equal in mangitude and non-parallel, $(\vec{a} + \vec{b})$ and $(\vec{a} - \vec{b})$ are perpendicular.

Solution. (*a*) Clearly, magnitude of vector $\vec{A}$ is $A = \sqrt{4^2 + 6^2 + (-3)^2} = \sqrt{61}$ and magnitude of vector $\vec{B}$ is $B = \sqrt{(-2)^2 + (-5)^2 + 7^2} = \sqrt{78}$

Hence (*i*) direction cosines of *A* are $4/\sqrt{61}, 6/\sqrt{61}$ and $-3/\sqrt{61}$.

(*ii*) As we know, if θ be the angle between $\vec{A}$ and $\vec{B}$, we have $\cos\theta = \vec{A}\cdot\vec{B}/AB$.

Now $\vec{A}\cdot\vec{B} = 4(-2) + 6(-5) + (-3)\,7 = -8 - 30 - 21 = -59$.

So that, cos θ = (–59)/(√61) (√78) = 0.8555, whence, θ = 31.2°,

(*b*) (*i*) We know that the square of a vector is equal to the square of its magnitude [§1.17 (*ii*)]. So that, $|\vec{a} + \vec{b}|$ and $|\vec{a} - \vec{b}|$ being equal, we have $(\vec{a} + \vec{b})^2, = (\vec{a} - \vec{b})^2$, *i.e.*, $\vec{a}^2 + 2\vec{a}.\vec{b} + \vec{b}^2 = \vec{a}^2 - 2\vec{a}.\vec{b} + \vec{b}^2$, which is possible only when the dot product $a \cdot b = 0$ clearly indicating that *a* and *b* must be perpendicular to each other.

(*ii*) We have $(\vec{a} + \vec{b})\cdot(\vec{a} - \vec{b}) = \vec{a}^2 - \vec{a}.\vec{b} + \vec{b}.\vec{a} - \vec{b}^2 = \vec{a}^2 - \vec{b}^2 = 0$ $[\because \vec{a} = \vec{b}.]$

The dot product of vectors $(\vec{a} + \vec{b})$ and $(\vec{a} - \vec{b})$ being zero, they must be perpendicular to each other.

Example 13. (*a*) Find the component of a vector along and perpendicular to another vector.

(*b*) Obtain the scalar product of vectors $\vec{P} = 3\hat{i} - 2\hat{j} + 8\hat{k}$ and $\vec{Q} = -\hat{i} - 2\hat{j} - 3\hat{k}$, as also the mangnitude of the components of $\vec{P}$ and $\vec{Q}$ along each other.

Solution. (*a*) In Fig. 1.17 let $\vec{P}$ be the vector whose components along and perpendicular to another vector $\vec{Q}$ are desired to be determined.

Since, $\vec{P}=\overrightarrow{OA}=\overrightarrow{OM}+\overrightarrow{MA}$, clearly $\overrightarrow{OM}$ is the component of $\vec{P}$ along vector $\vec{Q}$ and $\overrightarrow{MA}$, its component perpendicular to $\vec{Q}$.

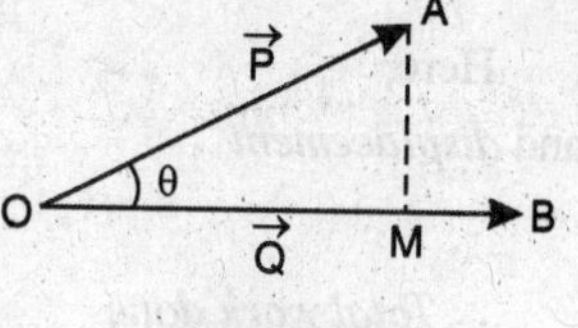

Fig. 1.17

Now, $\overrightarrow{OM}=OM\,\hat{Q}$, where $\hat{Q}$ is the unit $\vec{Q}$ vector along $\vec{Q}$, *i.e.*, $= P\cos\theta$. $Q=\vec{P}\cdot\vec{Q}$ But $\hat{Q}=\vec{Q}/Q$. So that, component of $\vec{P}$ along $\vec{Q}=(\vec{P}\cdot\vec{Q})/Q$.

And $\overrightarrow{MA}=\overrightarrow{MO}+\overrightarrow{OA}=\overrightarrow{OA}-\overrightarrow{OM}$. So that, component (MA) of $\vec{P}$ perpendicular to $\vec{Q}=\overrightarrow{OA}-\overrightarrow{OM}=\vec{P}-(\vec{P}\cdot\vec{Q})/Q$.

(*b*) The scalar product $\vec{P}\cdot\vec{Q}=3(-1)+(-2)(-2)+8(-3)=-23$. And, clearly, magnitude of $\vec{P}$ is given by $P=\sqrt{3^2+(-2)^2+8^2}=\sqrt{69}$. And clealy, magnitude of $\vec{Q}$ is given by $Q=\sqrt{(-1)^2+(-2)^2+(-3)^2}=\sqrt{14}$

$\therefore$ Unit vector along $\vec{P}$ is $\hat{P}=\frac{1}{\sqrt{69}}(3\hat{i}-2\hat{j}+8\hat{k})$, and

Unit vector along $\vec{Q}$ is $\hat{Q}=\frac{1}{\sqrt{14}}(-\hat{i}-2\hat{j}-3\hat{k})$.

Therefore, as we have seen under (*a*) above,

component of $\vec{P}$ along $\vec{Q}=(\vec{P}\cdot\vec{Q})/Q=-23/\sqrt{14}$

and component of $\vec{Q}$ along $\vec{P}=(\vec{P}\cdot\vec{Q})/P=-23/\sqrt{69}$.

Example 14. The projection velocity of a rocket is expressed as $\vec{V}=5\hat{v}_x+7\hat{v}_y+9\hat{v}_z$, where $\hat{v}_x,\hat{v}_y$ and v_z are unit velocity vectors along east, north and vertical directions respectively. Calculate the magnitude of the horizontal and vertical components of the velocity. Also deduce the change in the angle of projection if the vertical component be doubled.

Solution. Obviously, the magnitude of vector $\vec{V}$, *i.e.*, $V=\sqrt{5^2+7^2+9^2}=\sqrt{155}$, and horizontal component of the vector in $5\hat{v}_x+7\hat{v}_y$, with its magnitude $=\sqrt{5^2+7^2}=\sqrt{74}$ and vertical component of the vector is $9\hat{v}_x$, with its magnitude = 9.

If this latter (*i.e.*, the vertical) component be doubled, the new vector will be, say, $\vec{V}'=5\hat{v}_x+7\hat{v}_y+18\hat{v}_z$, with magnitude $V'=\sqrt{5^2+7^3+18^2}=\sqrt{398}$. Then, clearly angle between vectors $\vec{V}$ and $\vec{V}'$ will directly give the required change in the direction of velocity.

Now, $\vec{V}\cdot\vec{V}' = VV'\cos(\vec{V},\vec{V}')$. whence, $\cos(\vec{V},\vec{V}')=\vec{V}\cdot\vec{V}'/VV'$.

Since $\vec{V}\cdot\vec{V}' = 5(5)+7(7)+9(18)=236$ and $VV'=(\sqrt{155})(\sqrt{398})$, we have

$$\cos\vec{V},\vec{V}' = \frac{236}{(\sqrt{155})(\sqrt{398})}=0.95$$

Hence, angle $(\vec{V},\vec{V}')$ or the change in the direction of velocity $=\cos^{-1}(0.95)=18.2°$.

Example 15. A particle is displaced from the point whose position vector is $5\hat{i}-5\hat{j}-7\hat{k}$ to the point $6\hat{i}+2\hat{j}-2\hat{k}$ under the action of forces $10\hat{i}-\hat{j}+11\hat{k}$, $4\hat{i}+5\hat{j}+6\hat{k}$, $-2\hat{i}+\hat{j}-9\hat{k}$. Find the total work done.

Solution. Clearly, total work done $=\vec{F}\cdot\vec{d}$,

where $\vec{F}$ is the *resultant force on the particle and* $\vec{d}$, *its displacement.*

Here, $\vec{F} = (10\hat{i} - \hat{j} + 11\hat{k}) + (4\hat{i} + 5\hat{j} + 6\hat{k}) + (-2\hat{i} + \hat{j} - 9\hat{k}) = 12\hat{i} + 5\hat{j} + 8\hat{k},$

and *displacement* $\vec{d}$ = *position vector of second point–position vector of first point*

$$= (6\hat{i} + 2\hat{j} - 2\hat{k}) - (5\hat{i} - 5\hat{j} - 7\hat{k}) = \hat{i} + 7\hat{j} + 5\hat{k}.$$

$\therefore$ *Total work done* $= \vec{F}.\vec{d} = (12\hat{i} + 5\hat{j} + 8\hat{k}).(\hat{i} + 7\hat{j} + 5\hat{k})$

$$= 12(1) + 5(7) + 8(5) = 12 + 35 + 40 = 87 \text{ units.}$$

Example 16. The methane molecule CH_4 may be fitted in a cube such that the C atom lies at the body centre and four H atoms at non adjacent corners of the cube as shown in Fig. 1.18. Prove that the angle between any two C—H bonds is $\cos^{-1}(-1/3)$.

Solution. Let Fig. 1.18 represent a cube of each edge $2a$ with O, as its body centre where the C atom of the methane molecule lies and let the H atoms be at the four non-adjacent corners P, Q, R and S, as shown.

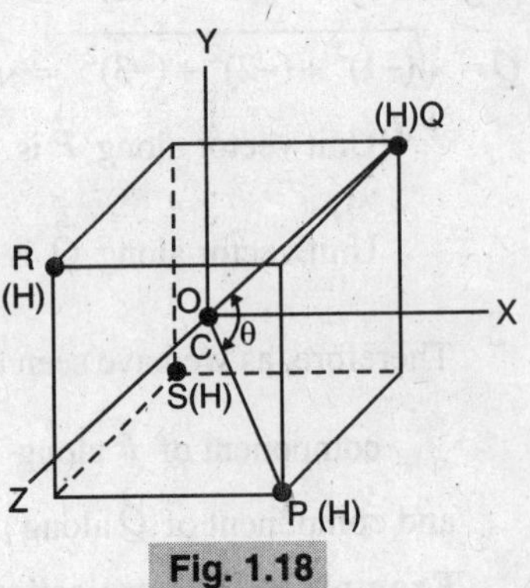

Fig. 1.18

Consider the two C—H bonds OP and OQ, with an angle θ between them. We are required to show that $\theta = \cos^{-1}(-1/3)$.

Clearly vector $\overrightarrow{OP} = a\hat{i} - a\hat{j} + a\hat{k}$ and vector $\overrightarrow{OQ} = a\hat{i} + a\hat{j} - a\hat{k}$.

So that,

$$\overrightarrow{OP}.\overrightarrow{OQ} = (OP)(OQ)\cos\theta = (a\hat{i} - a\hat{j} + a\hat{k})(a\hat{i} + a\hat{j} - a\hat{k})$$

$$= a^2 - a^2 - a^2 = -a^2.$$

And $(OP)(OQ) = (a\sqrt{3})(a\sqrt{3}) = 3a^2$

We therefore, have

$$\cos\theta = \frac{\overrightarrow{OP}.\overrightarrow{OQ}}{(OP)(OQ)} = \frac{-a^2}{3a^2} = -1/3.$$

And, therefore, $\theta = \cos^{-1}(-1/3)$.

The same can be shown to be true for any other pair of C–H bonds.

Example 17. In a tetrahedron, if two pairs of opposite edges are perpendicular, show that the third pairs are also perpendicular to each other, and the sum of the squares on two opposite edges is the same for each pair.

Solution. Let $ABCD$ be a tetrahedron (Fig. 1.19) such that taking D as the origin of reference, the position vectors of points A, B and C are $\vec{a}$, $\vec{b}$ and $\vec{c}$ respectively.

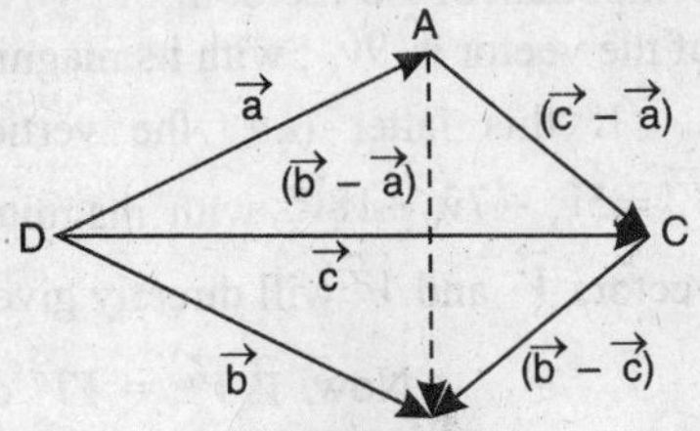

Then clearly, $\overrightarrow{AB} = (\vec{b} - \vec{a})$, $\overrightarrow{AC} = (\vec{c} - \vec{a})$ and $\overrightarrow{CB} = (\vec{b} - \vec{c})$.

Fig. 1.19

If the edge BD is perpendicular to CA, we have $\vec{b}.(\vec{c} - \vec{a}) = 0$

i.e., $\vec{b}.\vec{c} - \vec{b}.\vec{a} = 0$, or, $\vec{b}.\vec{c} = \vec{a}.\vec{b}$ ...(*i*)

Similarly, if edge DA is perpendicular to BC, we have $\vec{a}.(\vec{b} - \vec{c}) = 0$,

i.e., $\vec{a}.\vec{b} - \vec{a}.\vec{c} = 0$, or, $\vec{a}.\vec{b} = \vec{c}.\vec{a}$ ...(*ii*)

From relations (*i*) and (*ii*), therefore, $\vec{a}.\vec{b} = \vec{b}.\vec{c} = \vec{c}.\vec{a}$ So that,

$$\vec{b}.\vec{c} = \vec{c}.\vec{a} \text{ Or, } \vec{b}.\vec{c} - \vec{c}.\vec{a} = 0 \text{ Or, } \vec{c}.(\vec{b} - \vec{a}) = 0$$

showing that DC is perpendicular to BA.

Now, the sum of the squares on the opposite pair of edges BD and CA

$$= b^2 + (c - a)^2 = b^2 + c^2 + a^2 - 2ac$$

and, since $\vec{a}\cdot\vec{b} = \vec{b}\cdot\vec{c} = \vec{c}\cdot\vec{a}$, the sum of the squares on the other two pairs of opposite edges (*viz*; *DA, BC* and *DC, AB*) will also be the same.

Example 18. The position vectors of two particles ejected simultaneously from the same source are $\vec{r}_1 = 3\hat{i} + 4\hat{j} + 5\hat{k}$ and $\vec{r}_2 = 2\hat{i} + 6\hat{j} + 8\hat{k}$. Obtain (*i*) the displacement $\vec{r}$ of particle two with respect to particle one, (*ii*) the magnitudes of $\vec{r}_1, \vec{r}_2$ and $\vec{r}$, (*iii*) angles between $\vec{r}_1$ and $r_2, \vec{r}_1$ and $\vec{r}$ and $\vec{r}_2$ and $\vec{r}$ and (*iv*) projection of $\vec{r}$ *on* $\vec{r}_1$.

Solution. (*i*) Here, obviously, displacement of particles 2 with respect to particle 1,

i.e., $\quad \vec{r} = \vec{r}_2 - \vec{r}_1 = -\hat{i} + 2\hat{j} + 3\hat{k}.$

(*ii*) Magnitude of $\quad \vec{r}_1 = |\vec{r}_1| = \sqrt{9+16+25} = 5\sqrt{2} = 7.07,$

Magnitude of $\quad \vec{r}_2 = |\vec{r}_2| = \sqrt{4+36+64} = \sqrt{104} = 10.20$

and Magnitude of $\quad \vec{r} = |\vec{r}| = \sqrt{1+4+9} = \sqrt{14} = 3.74.$

(*iii*) We have $\quad \vec{r}_1\cdot\vec{r}_2 = |\vec{r}_1||\vec{r}_2|\cos\theta_{r_1r_2}$, hence, $\cos\theta_{r_1r_2} = \dfrac{\vec{r}_1\cdot\vec{r}_2}{|\vec{r}_1||\vec{r}_2|}$

$$= \frac{6+24+40}{(7.07)(10.20)} = 0.9706 \text{ and } \therefore \theta_{r_1r} = 14.0°$$

Similarly, $\quad \cos\theta_{r_1r} = \dfrac{\vec{r}_1\cdot\vec{r}}{|\vec{r}_1||\vec{r}|} = \dfrac{-3+8+15}{(7.07)(3.74)} = 0.7563 \text{ and } \therefore \theta_{r_1r} = 49.9°$

and $\quad \cos\theta_{r_2r} = \dfrac{\vec{r}_2\cdot\vec{r}}{|\vec{r}_2||\vec{r}|} = \dfrac{-2+12+24}{(10.20)(3.74)} = 0.8913 \text{ and } \therefore \theta_{r_2r} = 27.0°$

(*iv*) And, projection of $\vec{r}$ on $\vec{r}_1 = \vec{r}\cdot\vec{r}_1$ (where $\vec{r}_1$ is the unit vector in the direction of $\vec{r}_1$)

$$= \frac{\vec{r}\cdot\vec{r}_1}{|\vec{r}_1|} = \frac{20}{7.07} = 2.83$$

1.19 VECTOR PRODUCT

The vector product (or the *outer product*) of two vectors $\vec{A}$ and $\vec{B}$ is denoted by $\vec{A}\times\vec{B}$, read as '$\vec{A}$ cross $\vec{B}$'. It is, therefore, also called the *cross product* of the two vectors.

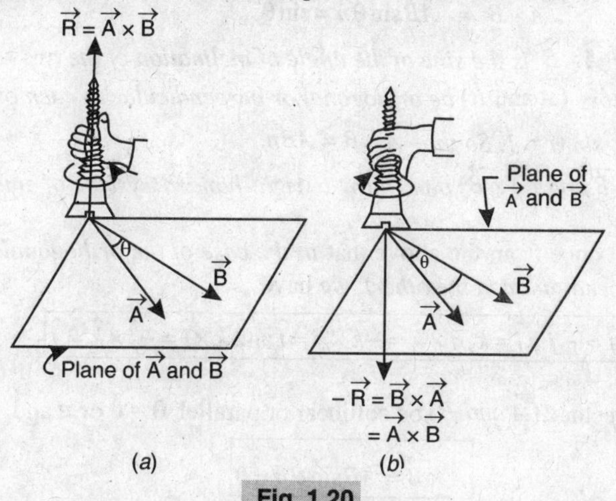

Fig. 1.20

It may also be denoted simply as $[\vec{A}, \vec{B}]$. *It is definied as a vector whose magnitude (or modulus) is equal to the product of the magnitudes of the two vectors* $\vec{A}$ and $\vec{B}$ *and the sine of their included angle* θ. This vector $\vec{R}$ is normal to the plane of $\vec{A}$ and $\vec{B}$ and points in the direction in which a right-handed screw would advance when rotated about an axis perpendicular to the plane of the two vectors in the direction from $\vec{A}$ to $\vec{B}$ through the smaller angle θ between them [Fig. 1.20 (*a*)].

Or, alternatively, we might state the rule thus:

If the fingers of the right hand be curled in the direction in which vector $\vec{A}$ *must be turned through the smaller included angle θ to coincide with the direction of vector* $\vec{B}$, *the thumb points in the direction of* $\vec{R}$, as shown in Fig. 1.20 (*a*).

Either of these rules is referred to as the right-handed screw rule.

Thus, if $\hat{n}$ be the unit vector which gives the direction of vector $\vec{R}$, we have

$$\vec{R} = \vec{A} \times \vec{B} = \vec{A}\vec{B} \sin\theta\, \hat{n}, \qquad 0 \le \theta \le 180° \text{ or } \pi,$$

1.20 IMPORTANT POINTS ABOUT VECTOR PRODUCT

(*i*) Since $0 \ge \theta \ge \pi$, sin θ and, therefore, $|\vec{R}|$ or R cannot be negative.

And, clearly, $$\sin\theta = \frac{\vec{A} \times \vec{B}}{|\vec{A}||\vec{B}|}$$

(*ii*) *A change in the order of factors* $\vec{A}$ *and* $\vec{B}$ *in the cross product obviously reverses its sign on account of the reversed/sense of rotation of the screw,* [Fig. 1.20 (*b*)]. So that, the cross product $\vec{B} \times \vec{A} = -\vec{A} \times \vec{B} = -\vec{R} = -AB\sin\theta\hat{n}$, indicating that **the vector product is not commutative.**

(*iii*) *If either vector* ($\vec{A}$ *or* $\vec{B}$) *be multiplied by number or a scalar m, their vector product too is multiplied by the same number. Thus,*

$$(m\vec{A}) \times \vec{B} = \vec{A} \times (m\vec{B}) = (m\vec{A}\vec{B}) \sin\theta\,\hat{n}.$$

Again, $$(m\vec{A}) \times (n\vec{B}) = (mA\,nB\sin\theta)\hat{n} = nA \times mB$$
$$= mnA \times B = A \times (mnB),$$ where *mn* is another scalar.

Thus, we see that the vector product is associative.

(*iv*) $\hat{A}$ and $\hat{B}$ be unit vectors, we have $A = B = 1$ and, therefore,

$$\hat{A} \times \hat{B} = AB\sin\theta\,\hat{n} = \sin\theta,$$

i.e., the magnitude of $\hat{A} \times \hat{B}$ *is the sine of the angle of inclination of the two.*

(*v*) *If the two vectors* ($\vec{A}$ and $\vec{B}$) *be orthogonal or perpendicular to each other, we have* θ = 90° *or* π/2 *and, therefore,* sin θ = 1. *So that* $\vec{A} \times \vec{B} = AB\hat{n}$.

The vectors $\vec{A}, \vec{B}$ *and* ($\vec{A} \times \vec{B}$) *thus form a right-handed system of mutually perpendicular vectors.*

It follows at once from the above that *in the case of the orthogonal triad of unit vectors,* $\hat{i}, \hat{j}$ *and* $\hat{k}$ *(each perpendidular to the other),* we have

$$\boxed{\hat{i} \times \hat{j} = -\hat{j} \times \hat{i} = \hat{k};\ \hat{j} \times \hat{k} = -\hat{k} \times \hat{j} = \hat{i} \text{ and } \hat{k} \times \hat{i} = -\hat{i} \times \hat{k} = \hat{j}}$$

(*iv*) If the two vectors ($\vec{A}$ *and* $\vec{B}$) be collinear or parallel, θ = 0 or π and, therefore, sin θ = 0.

So that, $$\boxed{\vec{A} \times \vec{B} = AB\sin\theta\,\hat{n} = 0}$$

It follows at once, therefore, that $\vec{A} \times \vec{A} = 0$, indicating that *the vector product of two parallel or equal vectors is zero* and, clearly therefore, the **vector product of a vector with its ownself is zero.**

Obviously, therefore, *in the case of orthogonal triad of unit veciors,* we have

$$\boxed{\hat{i} \times \hat{i} = \hat{j} \times \hat{j} = \hat{k} \times \hat{k} = 0}$$

Conversely, *if the vector product* $\vec{A} \times \vec{B} = 0$, we have $AB \sin\theta \hat{n} = 0$. So that, either $\vec{A} = 0$ or $\vec{B} = 0$ or sin θ and, therefore, θ = 0 or π, *i.e.,* either one of the vectors is a null (or zero) vector or the two vectors are parallel to each other.

(vii) **The distributive law holds good for the cross product of vectors.** Thus,

$$\vec{A} \times (\vec{B} + \vec{C}) = \vec{A} \times \vec{B} + \vec{A} \times \vec{C}$$

This may be seen from the following : Putting $\vec{U} = \vec{A} \times (\vec{B} + \vec{C}) - \vec{A} \times \vec{B} - \vec{A} \times \vec{C}$ and taking the scalar product with an arbitary vector V, we have

$$\vec{V}.\vec{U} = \vec{V}.[\vec{A} \times (\vec{B} + \vec{C}) - \vec{A} \times \vec{B} - \vec{A} \times \vec{C}] = \vec{V}.\vec{A} \times (\vec{B} + \vec{C}) - \vec{V}.(\vec{A} \times \vec{B}) - \vec{V}.(\vec{A} \times \vec{C}).$$

As we shall see under § 1.22, $\vec{A}.(\vec{B} \times \vec{C}) = (\vec{A} \times \vec{B}).\vec{C}$. We, therefore, have

$$\vec{V}.\vec{U} = (\vec{V} \times \vec{A}).(\vec{B} + \vec{C}) - (\vec{V} \times \vec{A}).\vec{B} - (\vec{V} \times \vec{A}).\vec{C}.$$

Or, because scalar products are distributive, we have

$$\vec{V}.\vec{U} = (\vec{V} \times \vec{A}).\vec{B} + (\vec{V} \times \vec{A})\,\vec{C} - (\vec{V} \times \vec{A}).\vec{B} - (\vec{V} \times \vec{A}).\vec{C} = 0.$$

Obviously, therefore, either $\vec{V} = 0$ or perpendicular to $\vec{U}$ or $\vec{U} = 0$.

Since $\vec{V}$ is an arbitary vector, it can be chosen to be non-zero and non-perpendicular to $\vec{U}$. Hence, $\vec{U} = 0$ and we, therefore, have

$$\boxed{\vec{A} \times (\vec{B} + \vec{C}) = \vec{A} \times \vec{B} + \vec{A} \times \vec{C}}$$

In accordance with the distributive law.

(viii) *A vector product can be expressed in terms of rectangular components of the two vectors and put in the determinant form*, as may be seen from the following:

Writing $\vec{A}$ and $\vec{B}$ in terms of their rectangular components, we have

$$\vec{A} = A_x\hat{i} + A_y\hat{j} + A_z\hat{k} \quad \text{and} \quad \vec{B} = B_x\hat{i} + B_y\hat{j} + B_z\hat{k}$$

And ∴ $\vec{A} \times \vec{B} = (A_x\hat{i} + A_y\hat{j} + A_z\hat{k}) \times (B_x\hat{i} \times B_y\hat{j} + B_z\hat{k})$

$$= (A_xB_x)\,\hat{i} \times \hat{i} + (A_xB_y)\,\hat{i} \times \hat{j} + (A_xB_z)\,\hat{i} \times \hat{k} + (A_yB_x)\hat{j} \times \hat{i} + (A_yB_y)\hat{j} \times \hat{j} + (A_yB_z)\,\hat{j} \times \hat{k}$$
$$+ (A_zB_x)\hat{k} \times \hat{i} + (A_zB_y)\hat{k} \times \hat{j} + (A_zB_z)\hat{k} \times \hat{k}.$$

Since $\hat{i} \times \hat{i} = \hat{j} \times \hat{j} = \hat{k} \times \hat{k} = 0$ and $\hat{i} \times \hat{j} = \hat{k} = -\hat{j} \times \hat{i}$, *etc.*, [See (*v*) above], we have

$$\vec{A} \times \vec{B} = (A_xB_y)\hat{k} - (A_xB_z)\hat{j} - (A_yB_x)\hat{k} + (A_yB_z)\hat{i} + (A_zB_x)\hat{j} - (A_zB_y)\hat{k}$$

This may be grouped together as

$$\vec{A} \times \vec{B} = (A_yB_z - A_zB_y)\hat{i} + (A_zB_x - A_xB_z)\,\hat{j} + (A_xB_y - A_yB_x)\hat{k}$$

Or, putting it in the easily remembered *determinant form, we have*

$$\vec{A} \times \vec{B} = \begin{vmatrix} \hat{i} & \hat{j} & \hat{k} \\ A_x & A_y & A_z \\ B_x & B_y & B_x \end{vmatrix}$$

It may be noted that the scalar components of the first vector A occupy the middle row of the determinant.

(ix) If $\vec{B} = \vec{C} + n\vec{A}$, where n is a number or a scalar, we have

$$\vec{A} \times \vec{B} = \vec{A} \times (\vec{C} + n\vec{A}) = \vec{A} \times \vec{C}. \qquad [\because \vec{A} \times (n\vec{A}) = 0.]$$

Conversely, however, if $\vec{A} \times \vec{B} = \vec{A} \times \vec{C}$, *it does not necessarily mean that B = C. All it implies is that B differs from* $\vec{C}$ *by some vector parallel to* $\vec{A}$ *which may or may not be a zero vector.*

1.21 SOME ILLUSTRATIVE APPLICATIONS OF VECTOR PRODUCT

(i) Torque or moment of a force. Let a force $\vec{F}$ be acting on a body free to rotate about *O* (Fig. 1.21) and let $\vec{r}$ be the *position vector* of any point *P* on the line of action of the force. Then, since torque = *force* × *perpendicular distance of its line of action from O,* we have *torque (or moment) of force F about O,*

i.e., $\quad T = Fr \sin\theta.$

Now, as we know, *Fr* sin θ is the magnitude of the cross of vector product $\vec{r} \times \vec{F}$. So that, in vector notation, we have

$$\text{Torque, } \vec{T} = \vec{r} \times \vec{F}$$

its direction being perpendicular to the plane containing $\vec{F}$ and $\vec{r}$.

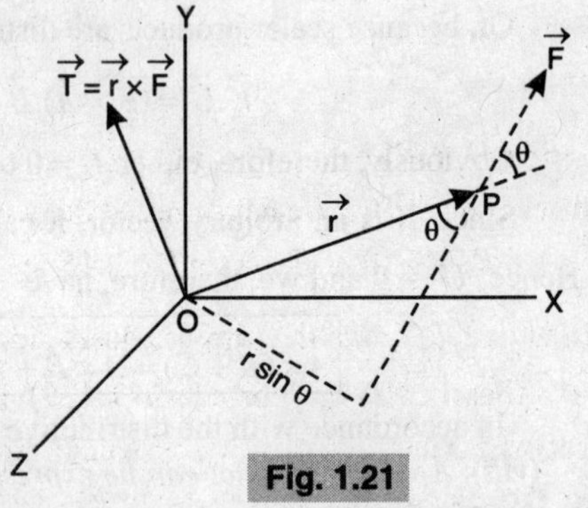

If we draw a set of three coordinate axes through *O*, as shown, we shall have

$$\vec{r} = x\hat{i} + y\hat{j} + z\hat{k},$$

where $x\hat{i}$, $y\hat{j}$ and $z\hat{k}$ are the rectangular components of $\vec{r}$ along the three axes respectively.

Similarly,

$$\vec{F} = F_x\hat{i} + F_y\hat{j} + F_z\hat{k} \text{ and } \vec{T} = T_x\hat{i} + T_y\hat{j} + T_z\hat{k}, \qquad ...(i)$$

Fig. 1.21

Now,

$$\vec{T} = \vec{r} \times \vec{F} = \begin{vmatrix} \hat{i} & \hat{j} & \hat{k} \\ x & y & z \\ F_x & F_y & F_z \end{vmatrix}$$

which, on expansion, gives

$$\vec{T} = \hat{i}(F_z y - F_y z) + \hat{j}(F_x z - F_z x) + \hat{k}(F_y x - F_x y). \qquad ...(ii)$$

Comparing expressions (*i*) and (*ii*), we have

$$T_x = F_z y - F_y z,\ T_y = F_x z - F_z x \text{ and } T_z = F_y x - F_x y,$$

where T_x, T_y and T_z are the respective scalar components of $\vec{T}$ along the three coordinate axes through *O*.

It will be easily seen that the scalar components T_x, T_y and T_z of torque $\vec{T}$ are given by the dot or the scalar products of $\vec{T}$ and the respective unit vectors along the three coordinate axes. Thus,

$$T_x = \vec{T}.\hat{i},\ T_y = \vec{T}.\hat{j} \text{ and } T_z = \vec{T}.\hat{k}. \quad \text{For, } \vec{T}.\hat{i} = (T_x\hat{i} + T_y\hat{j} + T_z\hat{k}).\hat{i}$$

$$= T_x\hat{i}.\hat{i} + T_y\hat{j}.\hat{i} + T_z\hat{k}.\hat{i}$$

And since $\quad \hat{i}.\hat{i} = 1,\ \hat{j}.\hat{i} = 0$ and $\hat{k}.\hat{i} = 0$, we have $T_x = \vec{T}.\hat{i}$.

And, similarly, $\quad T_y = \vec{T}.\hat{j}$ and $T_z = \vec{T}.\hat{k}$.

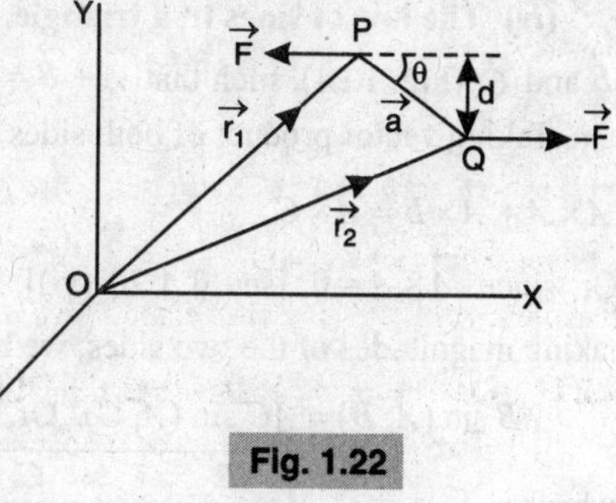

Fig. 1.22

***(ii)* Couple.** A couple, as we know, is a combination of two equal, opposite and parallel forces. Let $\vec{F}$ and $-\vec{F}$ be two such forces acting at points P and Q (Fig. 1.22) and let the position vectors of P and Q with respect to O be $\vec{r_1}$ and $\vec{r_2}$ respectively.

Then, since *moment of the couple* $\vec{C}$ with respect to O is equal to the sum of the moments, (with respect to O) of the two forces constituting the couple, we have $\vec{C} = \vec{r_1} \times \vec{F} + \vec{r_2} \times (-\vec{F}) = (\vec{r_1} - \vec{r_2}) \times \vec{F}$.

Since $\vec{r_1} - \vec{r_2} = \vec{a}$, where $\vec{a}$ lies in the same plane with $\vec{F}$, we have

$$\boxed{\vec{C} = \vec{a} \times \vec{F}}$$

Thus, *the moment of the couple,* $\vec{C}$, *is a vector lying in a plane perpendicular to that containing the two forces.*

The magnitude of couple $\vec{C} = |\vec{a} \times \vec{F}|$ or $aF \sin\theta$.

And since $a \sin\theta = d$, *the perpendicular distance between the two forces, we have magnitude of the moment of the couple, i.e.,* $C = Fd$ = *(one of the forces) (perpendicular distance between the forces).*

***(iii)* Area of a parallelogram.** Let vectors $\vec{A}$ and $\vec{B}$ form the adjacent sides of a parallelogram *OPQR*, (Fig. 1.23) inclined to each other at an angle θ. Then, If *OD* be the perpendicular dropped from *O* on to *PQ*, we have area of the parallelogram

$= PQ\ (OD) = B\ (A \sin\theta) = AB \sin\theta = AB\,(\vec{A}, \vec{B})$, which is obviously twice the area of the triangle *OPQ* with the same adjacent sides $\vec{A}$ and $\vec{B}$.

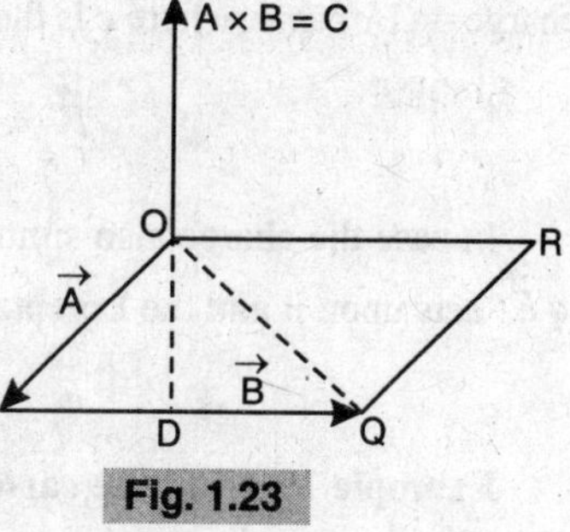

Fig. 1.23

Clearly, $AB \sin\theta$ or $AB \sin\ (\vec{A}, \vec{B})$ is the magnitude of the vector product $\vec{A} \times \vec{B} = \vec{C}$, say, whose direction is perpendicular to the plane containing $\vec{A}$ *and* $\vec{B}$, *i.e., to the plane of the parallelogram.*

Now, an area, by itself, has no sign but may be regarded positive or negative in relation to the direction in which its boundary is described. $\vec{A} \times \vec{B} = \vec{C}$, *therefore, represents a vector area which gives both the magnitude and the orientation of the area of the parallelogram.*

The direction of vector $\vec{C}$, drawn normal to the plane of the figure (*i.e.,* the parallelogram here) bears the same relation to the direction in which the boundary of the figure is described as the direction of advance of a right-handed screw does to its direction of rotation. Thus, with the parallelogram described as shown ($\vec{A}$ being taken first and $\vec{B}$ next), the normal vector $\vec{C} = \vec{A} \times \vec{B}$ is drawn pointing upwards, the area of the parallelogram being regarded as positive in relation to *this* direction of $\vec{C}$.

With this convention, therefore, any vector area (*i.e.,* the area of any plane figure) may be represented by a vector drawn normal to the plane of the figure in a direction relative to which the area of the figure is regarded as positive.

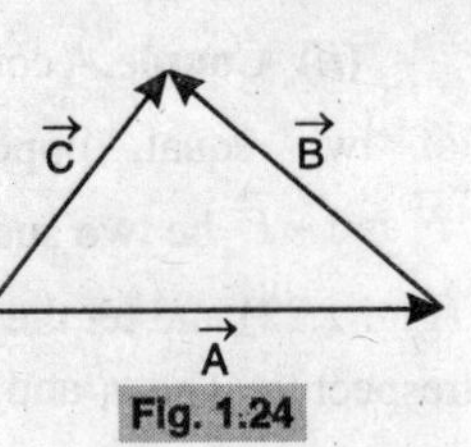

Fig. 1.24

(iv) **The law of sines in a triangle.** Consider a triangle of vectors $\vec{A}$, $\vec{B}$ and $\vec{C}$ (Fig. 1.24), such that $\vec{A}+\vec{B}=\vec{C}$.

Taking vector product of both sides of the relation with $\vec{A}$, we have

$\vec{A}\times\vec{A}+\vec{A}\times\vec{B}=\vec{A}\times\vec{C}$.

Or, since $\vec{A}\times\vec{A}=0$ [see § 1.20 (vi)], we have $\vec{A}\times\vec{B}=\vec{A}\times\vec{C}$. So that, taking magnitudes of the two sides, we have

$$AB\sin(\vec{A},\vec{B})=AC\sin(\vec{A},\vec{C}).\ \text{Or, } B\sin(\vec{A},\vec{B})=C\sin(\vec{A},\vec{C}),$$

whence,
$$\boxed{\frac{B}{\sin(\vec{A},\vec{C})}=\frac{C}{\sin(\vec{A},\vec{B})}}$$

which is the familiar law of sines in a triangle.

(v) **Force on a moving charge in a magnetic field.** Imagine a charge q to be moving with velocity $\vec{v}$ at an angle θ with a magnetic field $\vec{B}$ at any given instant (Fig. 1.25). Then, the force acting on it in a direction perpendicular to $\vec{B}$ as well as $\vec{v}$ is $F = qvB\sin\theta$, where F, v and B are the *magnitudes* of the *force, velocity* and the *magnetic field* respectively. In vector form, therefore, we may put it as

$$\vec{F}=q(\vec{v}\times\vec{B})\ \textit{emu or SI units.}$$

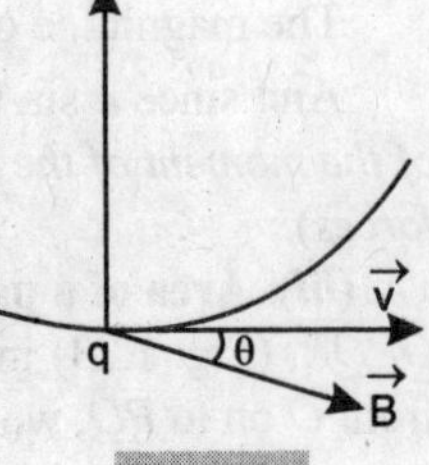

Fig. 1.25

This is called *Lorentz force law*, with the force itself referred to as the *Lorentz force.*

In most cases, q is taken in *esu* and $|\vec{B}|$ in *emu* (*i.e., gauss*). Since 1 *esu* charge = (1/c) *emu*, where c is the velocity of light in vacuo, we have q *esu* = q/c *emu* and, therefore,

$$\vec{F}=\frac{q}{c}(\vec{v}\times\vec{B})$$

In case the charge also simultaneously passes through an electric field $\vec{E}$, an additional force $q\vec{E}$ acts upon it and the Lorentz force law then takes the form

$$\vec{F}=qE+\frac{q}{c}(\vec{v}\times\vec{B})$$

Example 19. Find the cartesian components of a vector $\vec{C}$ which is perpendicular to the vectors $\vec{A}=2\hat{i}-\hat{j}-4\hat{k}$ and $\vec{B}=3\hat{i}-\hat{j}-\hat{k}$. ***(Gauhati Uni. 2000; Lucknow Uni. 2001)***

Solution.
$$\vec{C}=\vec{A}\times\vec{B}=(2\hat{i}-\hat{j}-4\hat{k})\times(3\hat{i}-\hat{j}-\hat{k})$$
$$=\begin{vmatrix}\hat{i} & \hat{j} & \hat{k}\\ 2 & -1 & -4\\ 3 & -1 & 1\end{vmatrix}=(3\hat{i}+10\hat{j}-\hat{k})$$

Example 20. ***(a)*** **Obtain the cross product of $\vec{P}=3\hat{i}-2\hat{j}+8\hat{k}$ and $\vec{Q}=-\hat{i}-2\hat{j}-3\hat{k}$.**

(b) **Show that if $\vec{a}$, $\vec{b}$ and $\vec{c}$ be three non-zero vectors, such that**

$$\vec{a}\times\vec{b}=\vec{b}\times\vec{c}=0,\ \text{then } \vec{a}\times\vec{c}=0.$$

Solution. (*a*) We have *cross product* $\vec{P}\times\vec{Q} = \begin{vmatrix} \hat{i} & \hat{j} & \hat{k} \\ 3 & -2 & 8 \\ -1 & -2 & -3 \end{vmatrix}$

$= \hat{i}\,[(-2)(-3) - (-2)\,8] + \hat{j}\,[(-1)8 - (-3)3] + \hat{k}\,[3(-2) - (-2)(-1)] = 22\hat{i} + \hat{j} - 8\hat{k}.$

(*b*) Since $\vec{a}\times\vec{b} = 0$, it is clear that $\vec{a}$ is parallel to $\vec{b}$ and, similarly, since $\vec{b}\times\vec{c} = 0, \vec{b}$ is parallel to $\vec{c}$. Obviously, therefore, a is parallel to $\vec{c}$ and hence

$$\vec{a}\times\vec{c} = 0.$$

Example 21. (*a*) Express the magnitude of $\vec{a}\times\vec{b}$ in terms of scalar products.

(*b*) If two vectors are $6\hat{i} + 0.3\hat{j} - 5\hat{k}, \hat{i} - 4.2\hat{j} + 2.5\hat{k}$, find their vector product and by calculation prove that the new vector is perpendicular to the two.

Solution. (*a*) Clearly,

$$\begin{aligned}(\vec{a}\times\vec{b})^2 &= (\vec{a}\times\vec{b}).(\vec{a}\times\vec{b}) = |a\times b|^2 \\ &= |a|^2||b|^2 \sin^2\theta = |a|^2|b|^2(1-\cos^2\theta) \\ &= a^2b^2 - |a|^2|b|^2\cos^2\theta = a^2b^2 - (a.b)^2\end{aligned}$$

(*b*) Let the two given vectors be called $\vec{a}$ and $\vec{b}$ respectively. Then,

their vector product $\vec{c}$, say, $= \begin{vmatrix} \hat{i} & \hat{j} & \hat{k} \\ 6 & 0.3 & -5 \\ 1 & -4.2 & 2.5 \end{vmatrix}$

$$\begin{aligned}&= \hat{i}\,[(0.3)(2.5) - (-5)(-4.2)] + \hat{j}\,[(-5)\,1 - 6\,(2.5)] + \hat{k}\,[6(-4.2) - (0.3)1] \\ &= -20.25\hat{i} - 20\hat{j} - 25.5\hat{k}.\end{aligned}$$

Now, taking the scalar product of the new vector $\vec{c}$ with vector $\vec{a}$, we have

$$\begin{aligned}\vec{c}\,.\,\vec{a} &= (-20.25\,\hat{i} - 20\,\hat{j} - 25.5\hat{k}).(6\hat{i} + 0.3\hat{j} - 5\hat{k}) \\ &= -121.5 - 6 + 127.5 = 0.\end{aligned}$$

This shows that $\vec{c}$ is also perpendicular to $\vec{a}$.

Similarly,

$$\begin{aligned}\vec{c}\,.\vec{b} &= \left(-20.25\hat{i} - 20\hat{j} - 25.5\hat{k}\right).\left(\hat{i} - 4.2\hat{j} + 2.5\hat{k}\right) \\ &= -20.25 + 84 - 63.75 = 0,\end{aligned}$$

This shows that $\vec{c}$ is also perpendicular to $\vec{b}$.

Example 22. Find the unit vector perpendicular to each of the vectors $\vec{a} = 3\hat{i} + \hat{j} + 2\hat{k}$ and $\vec{b} = 2\hat{i} - 2\hat{j} + 4\hat{k}$. Also determine the sine of the angle between *a* and *b*. What will be the vector perpendicular to $\vec{a}$ and $\vec{b}$ having a magnitude $4\sqrt{3}$? ***(Nagpur University. 2008)***

Solution. By its very definition, the vector product $\vec{a}\times\vec{b}$ is perpendicular to the plane of $\vec{a}$ and $\vec{b}$. So that, we have unit vector perpendicular to $\vec{a}$ and $\vec{b}$, say, $\hat{n} = \dfrac{\vec{a}\times\vec{b}}{|a\times b|}$.

Now, $\vec{a}\times\vec{b} = (3\hat{i} + \hat{j} + 2\hat{k}) + (2\hat{i} - 2\hat{j} + 2\hat{k}) = 8\hat{i} - 8\hat{j} - 8\hat{k}$

and $\therefore$ $|\vec{a}\times\vec{b}| = \sqrt{64 + 64 + 64} = 8\sqrt{3}.$

Hence unit vector $\hat{n}$, perpendicular to $\vec{a}$ and $\vec{b}$

$$= \frac{8\hat{i} - 8\hat{j} - 8\hat{k}}{8\sqrt{3}} = \frac{1}{\sqrt{3}}(\hat{i} - \hat{j} - \hat{k}).$$

Finally, since the unit vector perpendicular to $\vec{a}$ and $\vec{b}$ is $\vec{n}$, equal to $\frac{1}{\sqrt{3}}(\hat{i} - \hat{j} - \hat{k})$, we have vector of magnitude $4\sqrt{3}$ and perpendicular to $\vec{a}$ and $\vec{b} = 4\sqrt{3}\hat{n}$

$$= 4\sqrt{3}\left[\frac{1}{\sqrt{3}}(\hat{i} - \hat{j} - \hat{k})\right] = 4\hat{i} - 4\hat{j} - 4\hat{k} = 4(\hat{i} - \hat{j} - \hat{k}).$$

Example 23. (*a*) Find the area of the parallelogram determined by the vectors $\vec{a} = 3\hat{i} + 2\hat{j}$ and $\vec{b} = 2\hat{j} - 4\hat{k}$.

(*b*) Find the area of the triangle whose vertices are (1, –1, –3), (4, –3, 1) and (3, –1, 2).

Solution. (*a*) Here, vector area of the parallelogram

$$= \vec{a} \times \vec{b} = (3\hat{i} + 2\hat{j}) \times (2\hat{j} - 4\hat{k})$$

$$= 8\hat{i} - 12\hat{j} + 6\hat{k}.$$

∴ magnitude of the area of the parallelogram

$$= |8\hat{i} + 12\hat{j} + 6\hat{k}|$$

$$= \sqrt{64 + 144 + 36} = 2\sqrt{61}.$$

(*b*) Clearly, the position vectors of the vertices *A*, *B* and *C* of the triangle *ABC* are $\vec{a} = (\hat{i} - \hat{j} - 3\hat{k})$, $\vec{b} = (4\hat{i} - 3\hat{j} + \hat{k})$ and $\vec{c} = (3\hat{i} - \hat{j} + 2\hat{k})$.

∴ $$\overrightarrow{BA} = \vec{a} - \vec{b} = -3\hat{i} + 2\hat{j} - 4\hat{k} \text{ and } \overrightarrow{BC} = \vec{c} - \vec{b} = -\hat{i} + 2\hat{j} + \hat{k}.$$

Hence *vector area of the triangle* $= \frac{1}{2}\overrightarrow{BA} \times \overrightarrow{BC}$

$$= \frac{1}{2}(-3\hat{i} + 2\hat{j} - 4\hat{k}) \times (-\hat{i} + 2\hat{j} + \hat{k})$$

$$= \frac{1}{2}(10\hat{i} + 7\hat{j} - 4\hat{k})$$

and magnitude of the area of the triangle $= \frac{1}{2}|10\hat{i} + 7\hat{j} - 4\hat{k}|$

$$= \frac{1}{2}\sqrt{100 + 49 + 16} = \frac{1}{2}\sqrt{165}.$$

Example 24. Prove that the vector area of a triangle whose vertices are $\vec{a}, \vec{b}, \vec{c}$ is $\frac{1}{2}(\vec{b} \times \vec{c} + \vec{c} \times \vec{a} + \vec{a} \times \vec{b})$.

What is the condition for the collinearity of the vertices?

Solution. As in example 23 above, let the triangle be *ABC*. Then, we have

$$\overrightarrow{BC} = (\vec{c} - \vec{b}) \text{ and } \overrightarrow{BA} = (\vec{a} - \vec{b})$$

∴ *vector area of the triangle* $= \frac{1}{2}\overrightarrow{BC} \times \overrightarrow{BA} = \frac{1}{2}[(\vec{c} - \vec{b}) \times (\vec{a} - \vec{b})]$

$$= \frac{1}{2}(\vec{c} \times \vec{a} - \vec{c} \times \vec{b} - \vec{b} \times \vec{a} + \vec{b} \times \vec{b})$$

Now, $\vec{b} \times \vec{b} = 0, -\vec{c} \times \vec{b} = \vec{b} \times \vec{c}$ and $-\vec{b} \times \vec{a} = \vec{a} \times \vec{b}$

So that, the vector area of the triangle $= \frac{1}{2}(\vec{b} \times \vec{c} + \vec{c} \times \vec{a} + \vec{a} \times \vec{b})$.

If the vertices of the triangle be collinear, we shall have area of the triangle equal to zero and, therefore vector area of the triangle too equal to zero. Thus, the condition for collinearity of the vertices is that $\frac{1}{2}(\vec{b} \times \vec{c} + \vec{c} \times \vec{a} + \vec{a} \times \vec{b}) = 0$.

Example 25. Show that if the vector area of each face of a tetrahedron has the direction of the outward normal, the sum of their vector areas is zero.

Solution. Let $DABC$ be the tetrahedron (Fig. 1.19), such that taking D as the origin, the position vectors of A, B and C are $\vec{a}$, $\vec{b}$ and $\vec{c}$ respectively. Then, we clearly have vector area of face DBC $= \frac{1}{2}\vec{b} \times \vec{c}$, of face $DAB = \frac{1}{2}\vec{a} \times \vec{b}$, of face $DCA = \frac{1}{2}\vec{c} \times \vec{a}$ and of face $BAC = \frac{1}{2}(\vec{b} - \vec{a})(\vec{b} - \vec{c})$ $= \frac{1}{2}(\vec{b} \times \vec{b} - \vec{b} \times \vec{c} - \vec{a} \times \vec{b} + \vec{a} \times \vec{c}) = -\frac{1}{2}(\vec{b} \times \vec{c} + \vec{a} \times \vec{b} + \vec{c} \times \vec{a})$, all directed along their respective outward normals.

$\therefore$ Sum of the vector areas of all the faces of the tetrahedron

$$= \frac{1}{2}(\vec{b} \times \vec{c} + \vec{a} \times \vec{b} + \vec{c} \times \vec{a}) - \frac{1}{2}(\vec{b} \times \vec{c} + \vec{a} \times \vec{b} + \vec{c} \times \vec{a}) = 0.$$

Example 26. A rigid body is rotating with angular velocity 3 radians per second about an axis passing through the point $2\hat{i} - \hat{j} - \hat{k}$ and parallel to $\hat{i} - 2\hat{j} + 2\hat{k}$. Find the magnitude of the velocity of the point of the rigid body whose position vector is $2\hat{i} + 3\hat{j} - 4\hat{k}$.

Solution. Obviously, the unit vector, $\hat{n}$, say, in the direction of

$$\hat{i} - 2\hat{j} + 2\hat{k} = \frac{\hat{i} - 2\hat{j} + 2\hat{k}}{|\hat{i} - 2\hat{j} + 2\hat{k}|}$$

$$= \frac{\hat{i} - 2\hat{j} + 2\hat{k}}{\sqrt{1+4+4}} = \frac{1}{3}(\hat{i} - 2\hat{j} + 2\hat{k}).$$

$\therefore$ *angular velocity of the rigid body,* $\vec{\omega} = \omega\hat{n} = 3\left[\frac{1}{3}(\hat{i} - 2\hat{j} + 2\hat{k})\right]$

$$= \hat{i} - 2\hat{j} + 2\hat{k}.$$

Let the point whose velocity is desired to be determined be P. Then, its position vector with respect to the point $2\hat{i} - \hat{j} - \hat{k}$ on the axis is given by

$$\vec{r} = (2\hat{i} + 3\hat{j} - 4\hat{k}) - (2\hat{i} - \hat{j} - \hat{k}) = 4\hat{j} - 3\hat{k}.$$

Hence, if $\vec{v}$ be the velocity of point P, we have $\vec{v} = \vec{\omega} \times \vec{r}$

$$= (\hat{i} - 2\hat{j} + 2\hat{k}) \times (4\hat{j} - 3\hat{k}) = \begin{vmatrix} \hat{i} & \hat{j} & \hat{k} \\ 1 & -2 & 2 \\ 0 & 4 & -3 \end{vmatrix} = -2\hat{i} + 3\hat{j} + 4\hat{k}.$$

So that, magnitude of the velocity $= \sqrt{(-2)^2 + 3^3 + 4^2} = \sqrt{29}$ units.

Example 27. A Force $\vec{F} = -2\hat{i} + 3\hat{j} + 4\hat{k}$ is acting at a point $5\hat{i} + 4\hat{j} + 3\hat{k}$. Obtain the moment of the force about the origin.

Solution. Here, $\vec{r} = 5\hat{i} + 4\hat{j} + 3\hat{k}$. Therefore, moment of the force about the origin

$$\begin{aligned}\vec{r} \times \vec{F} &= (5\hat{i} + 4\hat{j} + 3\hat{k}) \times (-2\hat{i} + 3\hat{j} + 4\hat{k}) \\ &= \hat{i}\,(16 - 9) + \hat{j}\,(-6 - 20) + \hat{k}\,(15 + 8) \\ &= 7\hat{i} - 26\hat{j} + 23\hat{k}\end{aligned}$$

1.22 TRIPLE PRODUCTS OF VECTORS

Let us consider three vectors $\vec{A}, \vec{B}$ and $\vec{C}$. As we know, the cross or vector product of any two of them, say, $\vec{B}$ and $\vec{C}$, *i.e.*, $\vec{B} \times \vec{C}$ is a vector. This vector product may have with the third vector $\vec{A}$ either.

(*i*) *a dot or a scalar product* $\vec{A} . (\vec{B} \times \vec{C})$ which, being a number or a scalar, is called the *scalar triple product* (or a *mixed product*) of $\vec{A}, \vec{B}$ and $\vec{C}$; or,

(*ii*) a cross or a vector product $\vec{A} \times (\vec{B} \times \vec{C})$ which, being a vector, is referred to as the vector triple product.

Let us deal with each in a little more detail, in article 1.23.

Example 28. Prove that the vector $2\hat{i} - \hat{j} + \hat{k}, \hat{i} + 2\hat{j} + 3\hat{k}$ and $3\hat{i} - 4\hat{j} + 5\hat{k}$ are co-planar. ***(Meerut U. 2001)***

Solution. Let $\vec{A} = 2i - j + k; \vec{B} = i + 2j + 3k$ and $\vec{C} = 3\hat{i} - 4\hat{j} + 5\hat{k}$. The three vectors are co-planar if $\vec{A} . (\vec{B} \times \vec{C}) = 0$.

Now
$$\begin{aligned}\vec{A} . (\vec{B} \times \vec{C}) &= \begin{vmatrix} Ax & Ay & Az \\ Bx & By & Bz \\ Cx & Cy & Cz \end{vmatrix} = \begin{vmatrix} +2 & -1 & +1 \\ +1 & +2 & -3 \\ +3 & -4 & +5 \end{vmatrix} \\ &= 2\,(10 - 12) - 1\,(-9 - 5) + 1\,(-4 - 6) \\ &= -4 + 14 - 10 = 0\end{aligned}$$

Since $\vec{A} . (\vec{B} \times \vec{C}) = 0$, the three vectors $\vec{A}, \vec{B}$ and $\vec{C}$ are Co-planar.

1.23 SCALAR TRIPLE PRODUCT

Let the three vectors $\vec{A}, \vec{B}$ and $\vec{C}$ form a parallelopiped, as shown in Fig. 1.26. Then, if B and C be the *magnitude* of vectors $\vec{B}$ and $\vec{C}$, we have *area of the base of the parallelopiped* $= BC \sin\phi = |\vec{B} \times \vec{C}|$.

Thus, *the magnitude of the vector product* $\vec{B} \times \vec{C}$ *is the area of the base of the parallelopiped, and its direction perpendicular to this area,* as shown.

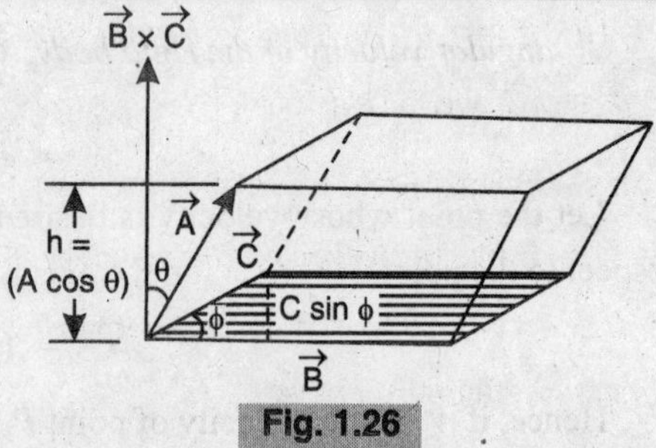

Fig. 1.26

If θ be the angle that the direction of the vector $(\vec{B} \times \vec{C})$ makes with vector $\vec{A}$ (forming one of the edges of the parallelopiped), we have altitude of the parallelopiped, $h = A \cos\theta$, where A is the magnitude of vector $\vec{A}$.

And, therefore, $\vec{A} \cdot (\vec{B} \times \vec{C}) = A \cos\theta\, (\vec{B} \times \vec{C})$ = *vertical height of parallelopiped* × *area of its base* = *volume of the parallelopiped, V*, the sign of V being positive if θ be an acute angle, *i.e.*, if $\vec{A}, \vec{B}$ and $\vec{C}$ form a right-handed system of vectors.

Thus, we see that *the scalar triple product* $\vec{A}\cdot\left(\vec{B}\times\vec{C}\right)$ *represents the volume of a parallelopiped, with the three vectors forming its three edges.*

Obviously, since any one of the faces of the parallelopiped may be taken to be its base, its volume V is also given by $\vec{B}\cdot\left(\vec{C}\times\vec{A}\right)$ *and* $\vec{C}\cdot\left(\vec{A}\times\vec{B}\right)$, *with the cyclic order of* $\vec{A}, \vec{B}$ *and* $\vec{C}$ *maintained.*

In case this cyclic order be altered, the sign of the product is changed since, as we know,

$$\vec{B}\times\vec{C} = -\vec{C}\times\vec{B}.$$

Further, since the order of the terms in a scaler product is quite immaterial, we have

$$V = \vec{A}\cdot\left(\vec{B}\times\vec{C}\right) = \left(\vec{B}\times\vec{C}\right)\cdot\vec{A} = -\vec{A}\cdot\left(\vec{C}\times\vec{B}\right) = -\left(\vec{C}\times\vec{B}\right)\cdot\vec{A}$$

$$= \vec{B}\cdot\left(\vec{C}\times\vec{A}\right) = \left(\vec{C}\times\vec{A}\right)\cdot\vec{B} = -\vec{B}\cdot\left(\vec{A}\times\vec{C}\right) = -\left(\vec{A}\times\vec{C}\right)\cdot\vec{B}$$

$$= \vec{C}\cdot\left(\vec{A}\times\vec{B}\right) = \left(\vec{A}\times\vec{B}\right)\cdot\vec{C} = -\vec{C}\cdot\left(\vec{B}\times\vec{A}\right) = -\left(\vec{B}\times\vec{A}\right)\cdot\vec{C}$$

It will thus be seen that *the value of scalar tirple product depends on the cyclic order of the vectors and is quite independent of the positions of the dots and the crosses, which may be interchanged as desired.* It is, therefore, usual to denote a scalar triple product of vector $\vec{A}, \vec{B}$ and $\vec{C}$ by $\left[\vec{A}\,\vec{B}\,\vec{C}\right]$ or $\left[\vec{A}, \vec{B}, \vec{C}\right]$, putting the three vectors in their cyclic order but without any dots or crosses.

Further points to be noted about a scalar triple product.

(*i*) *In case the three vectors be coplanar, their scalar triple product is zero,* because the vectoı $\left(\vec{B}\times\vec{C}\right)$ being then perpendicular to vector $\vec{A}$, their scalar product is zero.

Thus, the conditions for coplanarity of three vectors is that *their scalar triple product* $\left[\vec{A}\vec{B}\vec{C}\right]$ *should vanish. The condition is satisfied when two of the vectors are parallel* [see (*iii*) below].

(*ii*) *If two of the vectors be equal, the scalar triple product is zero.* For if the three vectors be $\vec{A}, \vec{B}$ and $\vec{C}$ we have $\left[\vec{A}\vec{A}\vec{B}\right] = \left(\vec{A}\times\vec{A}\right).\vec{B}$ Ans, since $\vec{A}\times\vec{A} = 0$ [the vector product of a vector with itself being zero. § 1.20 (*vi*), we have $\left[\vec{A}\vec{A}\vec{B}\right] = 0$.

(*iii*) *If two of the vectors be parallel, the scalar triple product is zero*. For, of the three vectors $\vec{A}, \vec{B}$ and $\vec{C}$, if $\vec{A}$ and $\vec{B}$ be parallel, we have, in accordance with § 1.7, $\vec{B} = k\vec{A}$, where k is some scalar, We, therefore, have

$$\left[\vec{A}\vec{B}\vec{C}\right] = \left(\vec{A}\times\vec{B}\right)\cdot\vec{C} = \left(\vec{A}\times k\vec{A}\right)\cdot\vec{C} = k\left(\vec{A}\times\vec{A}\right)\cdot\vec{C} = k\left[\vec{A}\vec{A}\vec{C}\right] = 0.$$

(*iv*) In terms of the cartesian components of the three vectors, we have

$$\vec{B}\times\vec{C} = (B_yC_z - B_zC_y)\hat{i} + (B_zC_x + B_xC_z)\hat{j} + (B_xC_y - B_yC_x)\hat{k}.$$

and ∴

$$\vec{A}\cdot\left(\vec{B}\times\vec{C}\right) = \left[\vec{A}\vec{B}\vec{C}\right] = (B_yC_z - B_zC_y)\hat{i} + (B_zC_x - B_xC_z)\hat{j} + (B_xC_y - B_yC_x)\hat{k}\,].\left(A_x\hat{i} + A_y\hat{j} + A_z\hat{k}\right)$$

$$= A_x(B_yC_z - B_zC_y) + \mathrm{Ay}(B_zC_x - B_xC_z) + A_z(B_xC_y - B_yC_x).$$

Or, $$\left[\vec{A}\vec{B}\vec{C}\right] = \begin{vmatrix} A_x & A_y & A_z \\ B_x & B_y & B_z \\ C_x & C_y & C_z \end{vmatrix}$$

which is the familiar expression for the volume of a parallelopiped with one of its corners at the origin (Fig. 1.26).

(*v*) The scaler triple product of the orthogonal vector triad is unity. For,

$$\left[\hat{i}\hat{j}\hat{k}\right] = \left(\hat{i}\times\hat{j}\right)\cdot\hat{k} = \hat{k}.\hat{k} = 1.$$

(*vi*) Since the distribution law holds good for both scalar and vector products, it also holds good for scalar triple products. Thus, for instance,

$$\left[\vec{A}, \vec{B}+\vec{D}, \vec{C}+\vec{E}\right] = \left[\vec{A}\vec{B}\vec{C}\right] + \left[\vec{A}\vec{B}\vec{E}\right] + \left[\vec{A}\vec{D}\vec{C}\right] + \left[\vec{A}\vec{D}\vec{E}\right],$$

the cyclic order of the vectors being maintained in each term.

1.24 VECTOR TRIPLE PRODUCTS

The cross product of two vectors, one of which is itself the cross product of two vectors, is called a vector triple product (for the simple reason that it is a vector). Thus, if $\vec{A}, \vec{B}$ and $\vec{C}$ be three vectors we have $\vec{A}\times\left(\vec{B}\times\vec{C}\right)$, $\vec{B}\times\left(\vec{C}\times\vec{A}\right)$ and $\vec{C}\times\left(\vec{A}\times\vec{B}\right)$ as examples of vector triple products.

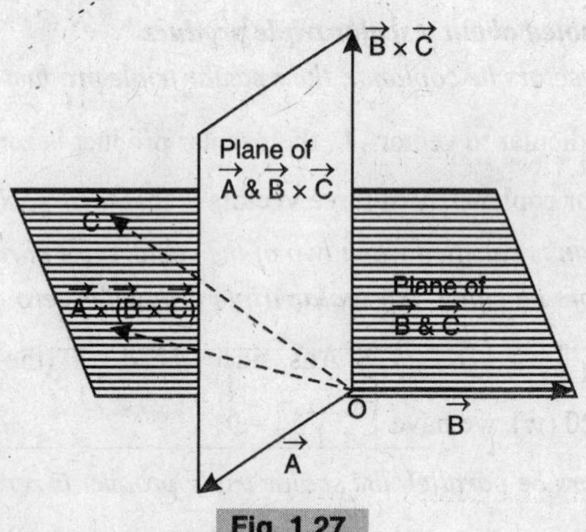

Fig. 1.27.

The vector triple product $\vec{A}\times\left(\vec{B}\times\vec{C}\right)$ is a vector lying in a plane perpendicular to that of $\vec{A}$ and $\left(\vec{B}\times\vec{C}\right)$, as explained under § 1.19. But, as we know, vector $\left(\vec{B}\times\vec{C}\right)$ lies in the plane normal to that of $\vec{B}$ and $\vec{C}$. It follows, therefore, that vector $\vec{A}\times\left(\vec{B}\times\vec{C}\right)$ lies in the plane of vector $\vec{B}$ and $\vec{C}$ and is perpendicular to that of $\vec{A}$, as shown in Fig. 1.27.

Similarly, vector $\vec{B}\times\left(\vec{A}\times\vec{C}\right)$ lies in the plane of $\vec{A}$ and $\vec{C}$ and is perpendicular to $\vec{B}$. And vector $\vec{C}\times\left(\vec{A}\times\vec{B}\right)$ lies in the plane of $\vec{A}$ and $\vec{B}$ and is perpendicular to $\vec{C}$. So that, in general,

$$\vec{A}\times\left(\vec{B}\times\vec{C}\right) \neq \left(\vec{A}\times\vec{B}\right)\times\vec{C}.$$

In other words, the associative law does not hold good in the case of vector triple products. The position of the brackets are thus of the utmost importance here.

1.25 EVALUATION OF THE VECTOR TRIPLE PRODUCT $\vec{A} \times (\vec{B} \times \vec{C})$

Let $\hat{i}, \hat{j}, \hat{k}$ be the right handed orthogonal triad of unit vectors, with unit vectors $\hat{i}$ along $\vec{B}$, $\hat{j}$ perpendicular to it in the plane of $\vec{B}$ and $\vec{C}$, and $\hat{k}$ perpendicular to $\hat{i}$ and $\hat{j}$. Then we have $B_y = 0$, $B_z = 0$ and $C_z = 0$. So that,

$$\vec{A} = A_x\hat{i} + A_y\hat{j} + A_z\hat{k}, \vec{B} = B_x\hat{i} + 0 + 0 = B_x\hat{i} \text{ and } \vec{C} = C_x\hat{i} + C_y j + 0$$

$$= C_x\hat{i} + C_y\hat{j}.$$

Hence $\qquad \vec{B} \times \vec{C} = B_x\hat{i} \times (C_x\hat{i} + C_y\hat{j}) = B_x C_y \hat{k} \; [\because \hat{i} \times \hat{i} = 0 \text{ and } \hat{i} \times \hat{j} = \hat{k}.]$

And $\qquad \vec{A} \times (\vec{B} \times \vec{C}) = A_y B_x C_y \hat{i} - A_x B_x C_y \hat{j}.$

$$[\because \hat{i} \times \hat{k} = -\hat{j}, \hat{j} \times \hat{k} = \hat{i} \text{ and } \hat{k} \times \hat{k} = 0.]$$

Adding and subtracting $A_x B_x C_x \hat{i}$ to the right-hand side, we have

$$\vec{A} \times (\vec{B} \times \vec{C}) = A_x B_x C_x \hat{i} + A_y B_x C_y \hat{i} - A_x B_x C_y \hat{j}$$

$$= (A_x C_x + A_y C_y) B_x \hat{i} - A_x B_x (C_x \hat{i} + C_y \hat{j})$$

Now, $\qquad A_x C_x + A_y C_y = \vec{A} \cdot \vec{C}, A_x B_x = \vec{A} \cdot \vec{B},$

$$[\because \hat{i} \cdot \hat{i} = \hat{j} \cdot \hat{j} = 1 \text{ and } \hat{i} \cdot \hat{j} = \hat{j} \cdot \hat{k} = 0.]$$

$$B_x \hat{i} = \vec{B} \text{ and } C_x \hat{i} + C_y \hat{j} = \vec{C}.$$

We, therefore, have $\qquad \boxed{\vec{A} \times (\vec{B} \times \vec{C}) = (\vec{A} \cdot \vec{C})\vec{B} - (\vec{A} \cdot \vec{B})\vec{C}.}$

Or to put in the determinant form, we have

$$\vec{A} \times (\vec{B} \times \vec{C}) = \begin{vmatrix} \vec{B} & \vec{C} \\ \vec{A} \cdot \vec{B} & \vec{A} \cdot \vec{C} \end{vmatrix}$$

And, proceeding in the same manner, we have

$$\vec{B} \times (\vec{C} \times \vec{A}) = (\vec{B} \cdot \vec{A})\vec{C} - (\vec{B} \cdot \vec{C})\vec{A}$$

and $\qquad \vec{C} \times (\vec{A} \times \vec{B}) = (\vec{C} \cdot \vec{B})\vec{A} - (\vec{C} \cdot \vec{A})\vec{B}$

As a *mnemonic* or aid to memory, we might call the three vectors, the *first*, the *second* and the third, taken in order. Then, the vector triple product

= first × (second × third) = [(first.third) second – (first.second) third]

Example 29. Prove that $\vec{A}\times\left(\vec{B}\times\vec{C}\right)+\vec{B}\times\left(\vec{C}\times\vec{A}\right)+\vec{C}\times\left(\vec{A}\times\vec{B}\right)=0.$

(Nagpur U. s/2009, s/2008, s/2005; Gauhati U. 2000; Meerut U. 2002)

Solution. According to tripple vector product

$$\vec{A}\times\left(\vec{B}\times\vec{C}\right) = \vec{B}\left(\vec{A}\cdot\vec{C}\right)-\vec{C}\left(\vec{A}\cdot\vec{B}\right)$$
$$\vec{B}\times\left(\vec{C}\times\vec{A}\right) = \vec{C}\left(\vec{B}\cdot\vec{A}\right)-\vec{A}\left(\vec{B}\cdot\vec{C}\right)$$
$$\vec{C}\times\left(\vec{A}\times\vec{B}\right) = \vec{A}\left(\vec{C}\cdot\vec{B}\right)-\vec{B}\left(\vec{C}\cdot\vec{A}\right)$$

Now, $\vec{A}\cdot\vec{C}=\vec{C}\cdot\vec{A}$, $\vec{A}\cdot\vec{B}=\vec{B}\cdot\vec{A}$, $\vec{B}\cdot\vec{C}=\vec{C}\cdot\vec{B}$

Adding, we get

$$\vec{A}\times\left(\vec{B}\times\vec{C}\right)+\vec{B}\times\left(\vec{C}\times\vec{A}\right)+\vec{C}\times\left(\vec{A}\times\vec{B}\right)=0$$

Example 30. If unit vectors $\hat{A}$ and $\hat{B}$ are inclined at an angle θ, then prove that

$\left|\hat{A}-\hat{B}\right| = 2\sin\theta/2.$ ***(M.D.U. 2003)***

Solution. $\left|\vec{A}-\vec{B}\right| = \sqrt{A^2+B^2-2AB\cos\theta}$

For unit Vectors, $\left|\hat{A}-\hat{B}\right| = \sqrt{1+1-2\cos\theta} = \sqrt{2(1-\cos\theta)}$

$$\left|\hat{A}-\hat{B}\right|^2 = 2(1-\cos\theta) = 2\times 2\sin^2\frac{\theta}{2}$$
$$\left|\hat{A}-\hat{B}\right| = 2\sin\theta/2$$

Example 31. If $\vec{A}+\vec{B}+\vec{C}=0$, prove that $\vec{A}\cdot\left(\vec{B}\times\vec{C}\right)=0.$ ***(Meerut University. 2003)***

Solution. If $\vec{A}\times\vec{B}\times\vec{C}=0$, the three vectors $\vec{A}, \vec{B}$ and $\vec{C}$ are co-planer. As $\vec{A}\cdot\left(\vec{B}\times\vec{C}\right)$ represents the volume of the parallelopiped enclosed by the vectors $\vec{A}\cdot\vec{B}$ and $\vec{C}$ as its edges and the three vectors are coplanar, the volume of the parallelopiped is zero. Hence,

$$\vec{A}\cdot\left(\vec{B}\times\vec{C}\right) = 0$$

Example 32. Prove that $\left(\vec{A}+\vec{B}\right).\left[\left(\vec{B}+\vec{C}\right)\times\left(\vec{C}+\vec{A}\right)\right] = 2\vec{A}.\left(\vec{B}\times\vec{C}\right).$

(Nagpur University. 2004)

Solution. $\left(\vec{A}+\vec{B}\right)\cdot\left[\left(\vec{B}+\vec{C}\right)\times\left(\vec{C}+\vec{A}\right)\right]$

$$= \left(\vec{A}+\vec{B}\right)\cdot\left[\left(\vec{B}\times\vec{C}\right)+\left(\vec{B}\times\vec{A}\right)+\left(\vec{C}\times\vec{C}\right)+\left(\vec{C}\times\vec{A}\right)\right]$$
$$= \vec{A}\cdot\left(\vec{B}\times\vec{C}\right)+\vec{A}\cdot\left(\vec{B}\times\vec{A}\right)+\vec{A}\cdot\left(\vec{C}\times\vec{C}\right)+\vec{A}\cdot\left(\vec{C}\times\vec{A}\right)$$
$$+\vec{B}\cdot\left(\vec{B}\times\vec{C}\right)+\vec{B}\cdot\left(\vec{B}\times\vec{A}\right)+\vec{B}\cdot\left(\vec{C}\times\vec{C}\right)+\vec{B}\cdot\left(\vec{C}\times\vec{A}\right)$$

Now, $\vec{A}\cdot\left(\vec{B}\times\vec{A}\right) = 0;\ \vec{A}\cdot\left(\vec{C}\times\vec{C}\right) = 0;\ \vec{A}\cdot\left(\vec{C}\times\vec{A}\right) = 0,$

$$\vec{B}.\left(\vec{B}\times\vec{C}\right) = 0;\ \vec{B}\cdot\left(\vec{B}\times\vec{A}\right) = 0;\ \vec{B}\cdot\left(\vec{C}\times\vec{C}\right) = 0$$

$$\left(\vec{A}+\vec{B}\right).\left[\left(\vec{B}+\vec{C}\right)\times\left(\vec{C}+\vec{A}\right)\right] = \vec{A}\cdot\left(\vec{B}\times\vec{C}\right)+\vec{B}\cdot\left(\vec{C}\times\vec{A}\right) = 2\vec{A}\cdot\left(\vec{B}\times\vec{C}\right)$$

Example 33. $\vec{A} = 4\hat{i} - 5\hat{j} + 3\hat{k}$, $\vec{B} = 2\hat{i} - 10\hat{j} - 7\hat{k}$ **and** $\vec{C} = 5\hat{i} + 7\hat{j} - 4\hat{k}$. **Calculate the following:** (*i*) $\vec{A}\times\vec{B}.\vec{C}$ (*ii*) $\vec{A}\times\left(\vec{B}\times\vec{C}\right)$.

Solution. We have

(*i*) $\vec{A}\times\vec{B}\cdot\vec{C}$ or $\left[\vec{A}\vec{B}\vec{C}\right] = \begin{vmatrix} 4 & -5 & 3 \\ 2 & -10 & -7 \\ 5 & 7 & -4 \end{vmatrix} = 4(40+49) - 5(-35+8) + 3(14+50)$

$$= 356 + 135 + 192 = 683$$

(*ii*) $\vec{A}\times\left(\vec{B}\times\vec{C}\right) = \vec{B}\left(\vec{A}\cdot\vec{C}\right) - \vec{C}\left(\vec{A}\cdot\vec{B}\right)$ [§ 1.25.]

$$= \left(2\hat{i} - 10\hat{j} - 7\hat{k}\right)(20-35-12) - \left(5\hat{i} + 7\hat{j} - 4\hat{k}\right)(8+50-21)$$

$$= -54\hat{i} + 270\hat{j} + 189\hat{k} - 185\hat{i} - 259\hat{j} + 148\hat{k} = -239\hat{i} + 11\hat{j} + 337\hat{k}.$$

Example 34. (*a*) **Prove that** $\vec{a}\times\left(\vec{b}\times\vec{c}\right)+\vec{b}\times\left(\vec{c}\times\vec{a}\right)+\vec{c}\times\left(\vec{a}\times\vec{b}\right) = 0.$

(*b*) **Prove that the four points** $\left(4\hat{i}+5\hat{j}+\hat{k}\right)$, $-\left(\hat{j}+\hat{k}\right)$, $3\hat{i}+9\hat{j}+4\hat{k}$ **and** $4\left(-\hat{i}+\hat{j}+\hat{k}\right)$ **are coplanar.**

Solution. (*a*) As we know (§ 1.25), $\vec{a}\times\left(\vec{b}\times\vec{c}\right) = \left(\vec{a}\cdot\vec{c}\right)\vec{b} - \left(\vec{a}\cdot\vec{b}\right)\vec{c}$ ...(*i*)

$-\vec{b}\times\left(\vec{c}\times\vec{a}\right) = \left(\vec{a}\cdot\vec{b}\right)\vec{c} - \left(\vec{b}\cdot\vec{c}\right)\vec{a}$ ...(*ii*) and $\vec{c}\times\left(\vec{a}\times\vec{b}\right) = \left(\vec{b}\cdot\vec{c}\right)\vec{a} - \left(\vec{c}\cdot\vec{a}\right)\vec{b}$. ...(*ii*)

So that, adding up the three, we have

$$\vec{a}\times\left(\vec{b}\times\vec{c}\right)+\vec{b}\times\left(\vec{c}\times\vec{a}\right)+\vec{c}\times\left(\vec{a}\times\vec{b}\right) = 0.$$

(*b*) If $4\hat{i}+5\hat{j}+\hat{k}$, $-\left(\hat{j}+\hat{k}\right)$, $3\hat{i}+9\hat{j}+4\hat{k}$ and $4\left(-\hat{i}+\hat{j}+\hat{k}\right)$ be the position vectors of four points *A*, *B*, *C* and *D* with reference to an origin *O*, clearly the points will be coplanar if the vectors $\vec{BA}, \vec{BC}$ and $\vec{CD}$ be coplanar.

Now, $\vec{BA} = \vec{OA} - \vec{OB} = \left(4\hat{i}+5\hat{j}+\hat{k}\right) - \left[-\left(\hat{j}+\hat{k}\right)\right] = 4\hat{i}+6\hat{j}+2\hat{k}$,

$$\vec{BC} = \vec{OC} - \vec{OB} = \left(3\hat{i}+9\hat{j}+4\hat{k}\right) - \left[\left(\hat{j}+\hat{k}\right)\right] = 3\hat{i}+10\hat{j}+5\hat{k}$$

And $\vec{CD} = \vec{OD} - \vec{OC} = \left(-4\hat{i}+4\hat{j}+4\hat{k}\right) - \left(3\hat{i}+9\hat{j}+4\hat{k}\right) = -7\hat{i}-5\hat{j}$

And, these vectors $\left(\vec{BA}, \vec{BC} \text{ and } \vec{CD}\right)$ will be coplanar if their scalar product is zero. Let us see if it is so.

The triple scalar product of the vectors is clearly

$$\left[\vec{BA}\ \vec{BC}\ \vec{CD}\right] = \begin{vmatrix} 4 & 6 & 2 \\ 3 & 10 & 5 \\ -7 & -5 & 0 \end{vmatrix} = 4(25) + 6(-35) + 2(55) = 0.$$

The three vactors $\vec{BA}\ \vec{BC}$ and $\vec{CD}$, and hence the four points *A*, *B*, *C* and *D*, are thus coplanar.

Example 35. The edges of a parallelopiped are given by the vectors $\hat{i} + 2\hat{j} + 3\hat{k}, 5\hat{j}$ and $4\hat{j} + m\hat{k}$. What should be the value of *m* in order that the volume of the parallelopiped be 20 units?

Solution. The volume of a parallelopiped, as we know is given by the scalar triple product of the vectors representing its three edges. So that, we have:

$$\textit{volume of parallelopiped} = \begin{vmatrix} 1 & 2 & 3 \\ 0 & 5 & 0 \\ 0 & 4 & m \end{vmatrix} = 1(5m) + 2(0) + 3(0) = 5m$$

Since the volume is given to be 20 units, we have $5m = 20$, hence, $m = 4$.

Example 36. Show that (*i*) $\left(\vec{a} \times \vec{b}\right) \times \left(\vec{c} \times \vec{d}\right) = \left[\vec{a}\,\vec{b}\,\vec{d}\right]\vec{c} - \left[\vec{a}\,\vec{b}\,\vec{c}\right]\vec{d}$.

(*ii*) $\left(\vec{a} \times \vec{b}\right) \times \left(\vec{c} \times \vec{d}\right) = \left[\vec{a}\,\vec{c}\,\vec{d}\right]\vec{b} - \left[\vec{b}\,\vec{c}\,\vec{d}\right]\vec{a}$.

Solution. (*i*) Let $\vec{a} \times \vec{b} = \vec{m}$. Then, $\left(\vec{a} \times \vec{b}\right) \times \left(\vec{c} \times \vec{d}\right) = \vec{m} \times \left(\vec{c} \times \vec{d}\right)$

$$= \left(\vec{m} \cdot \vec{d}\right)\vec{c} - \left(\vec{c} \cdot \vec{m}\right)\vec{d}$$

$$= \left[\left(\vec{a} \times \vec{b}\right) \cdot \vec{d}\right]\vec{c} - \left[\vec{c} \cdot \left(\vec{a} \times \vec{b}\right)\right]d.$$

since in the triple products $\left(\vec{a} \times \vec{b}\right) \cdot \vec{d}$ and $\vec{c} \cdot \left(\vec{a} \times \vec{b}\right)$, positions of the dots and crosses are quite immaterial and may be interchanged or omitted, as desired we have

$$\left(\vec{a} \times \vec{b}\right) \times \left(\vec{c} \times \vec{d}\right) = \left[\vec{a}\,\vec{b}\,\vec{d}\right]\vec{c} - \left[\vec{a}\,\vec{b}\,\vec{c}\right]\vec{d}.$$

(*ii*) Again, putting $\left(\vec{c} \times \vec{d}\right) = \vec{n}$, we have

$$\left(\vec{a} \times \vec{b}\right) \times \left(\vec{c} \times \vec{d}\right) = \left(\vec{a} \times \vec{b}\right) \times \vec{n} = \left(\vec{a} \cdot \vec{n}\right)\vec{b} - \left(\vec{b}.\vec{n}\right)\vec{a}$$

$$= \left[\vec{a} \cdot \left(\vec{c} \times \vec{d}\right)\right]\vec{b} - \left[\vec{b}\left(\vec{c} \times \vec{d}\right)\right]\vec{a}$$

$$= \left[\vec{a}\,\vec{c}\,\vec{d}\right]\vec{b} - \left[\vec{b}\,\vec{c}\,\vec{d}\right]\vec{a}.$$

Example 37. Obtain the value of the product $\left(\vec{A} \times \vec{B}\right).\left(\vec{C} \times \vec{D}\right)$ and show that $\vec{A} \times \left[\vec{B} \times \left(\vec{C} \times \vec{D}\right)\right] = \left(\vec{A} \times \vec{C}\right)\left(\vec{B}.\vec{D}\right) - \left(\vec{A} \times \vec{D}\right)\left(\vec{B}.\vec{C}\right)$

Solution. Since in the case of scalar products, the positions of dots and crosses are freely interchangable, we have

$$\left(\vec{A} \times \vec{B}\right) \cdot \left(\vec{C} \times \vec{D}\right) = \vec{A} \cdot \left[\vec{B} \times \left(\vec{C} \times \vec{D}\right)\right] = \vec{A} \cdot \left[\left(\vec{B} \cdot \vec{D}\right)\vec{C} - \left(\vec{B} \cdot \vec{C}\right)\vec{D}\right]$$

$$= \left(\vec{A}\cdot\vec{C}\right)\left(\vec{B}\cdot\vec{D}\right) - \left(\vec{A}\cdot\vec{D}\right)\left(\vec{B}\cdot\vec{C}\right)$$

Again, $$\vec{A}\times\left[\vec{B}\times\left(\vec{C}\times\vec{D}\right)\right] = \vec{A}\times\left[\left(\vec{B}\cdot\vec{D}\right)\vec{C} - \left(\vec{B}\cdot\vec{C}\right)\vec{D}\right]$$

$$= \left(\vec{A}\times\vec{C}\right)\left(\vec{B}\cdot\vec{D}\right) - \left(\vec{A}\times\vec{D}\right)\left(\vec{B}\cdot\vec{C}\right).$$

1.26 VECTOR DERIVATIVES – VELOCITY – ACCELERATION

Let $\vec{r}$ be a *single-valued function* of a scalar variable *t* such that for every value of *t* there exists only one value of $\vec{r}$. Then, as *t* varies continuously, $\vec{r}$ also does so.

We are particularly interested in the case in which *t* represents the time variable and $\vec{r}$ stands for the position vector of a moving particle with respect to a fixed origin *O* (Fig. 1.28). Then, as *t* varies continuously, the point moves along a continuous curve in space. So that, if $\vec{r}$ and $\vec{r}+\delta\vec{r}$ be the position vectors of the point in positions *P* and *P′* relative to origin *O* for the values *t* and $t+\delta t$ of the scalar variable, we have

change in the value of $\vec{r} = \delta\vec{r}$.

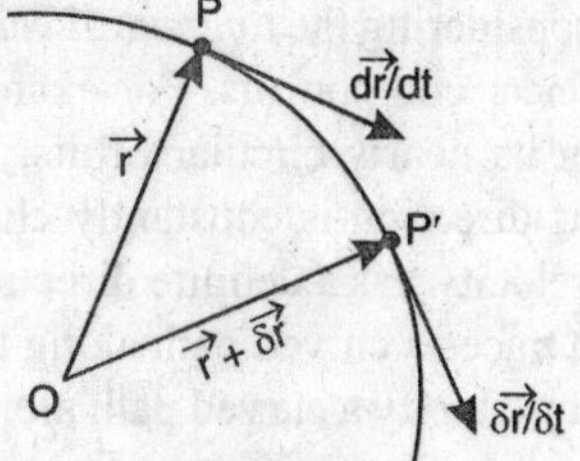

Fig. 1.28

The quotient $\delta\vec{r}/\delta t$ (of vectors $\delta\vec{r}$ by the scalar or a number δt) is also a vector. As $\delta t \to 0$, point *P′* approaches *P* and the chord *PP′* tends to coincide with the tangent to the curve at *P*.

The limiting value of $\delta\vec{r}/\delta t$ as δt tends to zero is $\delta\vec{r}/\delta t$ and is a vector whose direction is that of the tangent at *P* in the sense in which *t* increases. It is called the time derivative of $\vec{r}$ or the differential coefficient of $\vec{r}$ with respect to *t*. We thus have

$$\frac{d\vec{r}}{dt} = \underset{\delta t\to 0}{Lt}\frac{\delta\vec{r}}{\delta t}.$$

When this limit exists, the function $\vec{r}$ is said to be differentiable.

The second and third derivatives of $\vec{r}$ are respectively $d^2\vec{r}/dt^2$ and $d^3\vec{r}/dt^3$.

Clearly, $\delta\vec{r}$ represents the displacement of the particle in time inverval δt and, therefore, $\delta\vec{r}/\delta t$ gives its *average velocity* during interval δt. The limiting value of this average velocity, as $\delta t \to 0$, is the **instantaneous velocity** $\vec{v}$ of the particle. Thus, we have

$$\boxed{\vec{v} = d\vec{r}/dt}$$

along the tangent of the path of the particle.

Proceeding in the same manner if, $\delta\vec{v}$ be the increase in the velocity $\vec{v}$ of the particle during the time-interval δt, the rate of change of velocity or the average acceleration during the interval = $\delta\vec{v}/\delta t$ and therefore, instantaneous acceleration $\vec{a}$ of the particle is the limiting value $d\vec{v}/dt$ of $\delta\vec{v}/\delta t$ as $\delta t \to 0$. Thus,

$$\boxed{\vec{a} = \frac{d\vec{v}}{dt} = \frac{d^2\vec{r}}{dt^2}}$$

Now, since $\vec{r} = x\hat{i} + y\hat{j} + z\hat{k}$ and since x, y and z are funtions of time, we also have

$$\vec{v} = \frac{d\vec{r}}{dt} = \frac{dx}{dt}\hat{i} + \frac{dy}{dt}\hat{j} + \frac{dz}{dt}\hat{k}$$

and

$$\vec{a} = \frac{d^2\vec{r}}{dt^2} = \frac{d^2x}{dt^2}\hat{i} + \frac{d^2y}{dt^2}\hat{j} + \frac{d^2z}{dt^2}\hat{k}.$$

1.27 RADIAL AND TRANSVERSE COMPONENTS OF VELOCITY

Motion of a particle in a straight line is known as linear motion. However, it is possible to treat motion in a curved path by considering the *tangential velocity* or by resolving the motion into two linear components. For example, as the earth rotates around the sun in its nearly circular orbits, its speed is approximately constant but its direction is constantly changing. Yet at any particular instant, its velocity has a definite direction. If in fig. 1.29, E represents the earth, it traces a curved path along the arc EA but the instantaneous value of its velocity a curved path along the arc EA but the instantaneous value of its velocity is along the straight line EB, tangent to the path. Thus at any particular instant, its instantaneous velocity is along tangent to the path, and we refer it as tangential velocity.

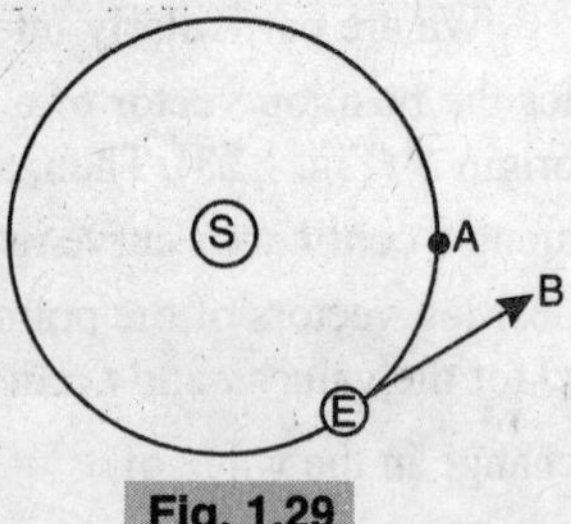

Fig. 1.29

Displacement. Consider a particle moving along a curve in a plane. The position of a point *P* in a co-ordinate system can be specified by a single *i.e.,* the displacement of the particle relative to the origin *O* of the co-ordinate system. This vector is called the *position vector* of the point and denoted by $\overrightarrow{OP} = \vec{r}$. It gives the magnitude as well as the direction of the displacement. If $\hat{r}$ is a *unit vector* along *OP i.e.,* along the direction of $\vec{r}$ then

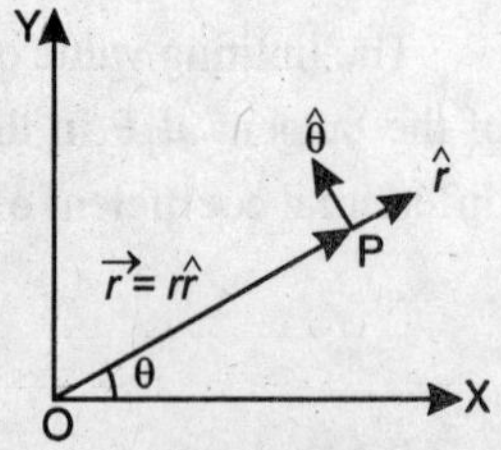

Fig. 1.30

$$\vec{r} = r\hat{r}$$

When a particle is moving along a curve in a plane it has a velocity and an acceleration.

Velocity. The velocity is the derivative of displacement $\vec{r}$ with respect to time *t*.

$$\therefore \quad \text{Velocity } \vec{v} = \frac{d}{dt}(\vec{r}) = \frac{d}{dt}(r\hat{r}) = \frac{dr}{dt}\hat{r} + r\frac{d\hat{r}}{dt} = \frac{dr}{dt}\hat{r} + r\frac{d\hat{r}}{d\theta}\frac{d\theta}{dt}$$

But

$$\frac{d\hat{r}}{d\theta} = \hat{\theta}$$

$$\therefore \quad \text{Velocity } \vec{v} = \frac{d\vec{r}}{dt} = \dot{r}\hat{r} + r\dot{\theta}\hat{\theta} \quad \text{...(i)}$$

where

$$\dot{r} = \frac{dr}{dt} \text{ and } \dot{\theta} = \frac{d\theta}{dt}$$

or

$$\vec{v} = \vec{v}_r + \vec{v}_\theta \quad \text{...(ii)}$$

Components of velocity. The quantity $\vec{v}_r = \dot{r}\hat{r}$ is known as the *radial velocity* and is due to the change in magnitude of r, θ remaining constant and $\vec{v}_\theta = r\dot{\theta}\hat{\theta}$ is known as *transverse velocity* and is due to the change in θ, *r* remaining constant.

The magnitude of radial velocity $|\vec{v}_r| = \dot{r}$

and the magnitude of transverse velocity $|\vec{v}_\theta| = r\dot{\theta}$

if $\dot{\theta}$ = a constant = ω the angular velocity, then $|\vec{v}_\theta| = r\omega$

The magnitude of velocity $\vec{v}$ is

$$|\vec{v}| = \left[|\vec{v}_r|^2 + |\vec{v}_\theta|^2\right]^{\frac{1}{2}} = [\dot{r}^2 + r^2\dot{\theta}^2]^{1/2}$$

Acceleration. *Acceleration is the derivative of velocity $\vec{v}$ with respect to time t.*

$$\therefore \quad \text{Acceleration } \vec{a} = \frac{d\vec{v}}{dt} = \frac{d}{dt}\left(\dot{r}\hat{r} + r\dot{\theta}\hat{\theta}\right)$$

$$= \ddot{r}\hat{r} + \dot{r}\left(\frac{d\hat{r}}{dt}\right) + \dot{r}\dot{\theta}\hat{\theta} + r\ddot{\theta}\hat{\theta} + r\dot{\theta}\left(\frac{d\hat{\theta}}{dt}\right)$$

$$= \ddot{r}\hat{r} + \dot{r}\left(\frac{d\hat{r}}{dt}\right) + \dot{r}\dot{\theta}\hat{\theta} + r\ddot{\theta}\hat{\theta} + r\dot{\theta}\left(\frac{d\hat{\theta}}{d\theta}\cdot\frac{d\theta}{dt}\right)$$

But $\quad \dfrac{d\hat{r}}{d\theta} = \hat{\theta}$ and $\dfrac{d\hat{\theta}}{d\theta} = -\hat{r}$

$$\therefore \quad \vec{a} = \ddot{r}\hat{r} + \dot{r}\dot{\theta}\hat{\theta} + \dot{r}\ddot{\theta}\hat{\theta} - r\dot{\theta}^2\hat{r}$$

$$= \left(\ddot{r} - r\dot{\theta}^2\right)\hat{r} + \left(r\ddot{\theta} + 2\dot{r}\dot{\theta}\right)\hat{\theta}$$

or $$\vec{a} = \vec{a}_r + \vec{a}_\theta = a_r\hat{r} + a_\theta\hat{\theta}$$

Components of acceleration. The quantity $\vec{a}_r$ is known as *radial acceleration*. Its magnitude $|\vec{a}_r| = \ddot{r} - r\dot{\theta}^2$ and its direction is along $\hat{r}$. It consists of two parts.

(i) The quantity $\ddot{r}$ gives the acceleration due to change in magnitude of $\dot{r}$. It has a positive sign as it is directed *away from* the centre.

(ii) The quantity $r\dot{\theta}^2$ gives the *centripetal acceleration* (if $\dot{\theta}$ = a constant = ω, $r\dot{\theta}^2 = r\omega^2$) due to change in θ. It has a negative sign as it is directed *towards* the centre.

The quantity $\vec{a}_\theta$ is known as *transverse acceleration*. Its magnitude $|a_\theta| = r\theta + 2r\theta$ and its direction is along θ. This also consists of two parts :

(i) The quantity $r\ddot{\theta}$ gives the angular acceleration due to change in $\dot{\theta}$.

(ii) The quantity $2\dot{r}\theta$ arises due to the interaction of linear and angular velocities due to changes in r and θ respectively. This is similar to **coriolis acceleration.**

$\vec{a}_r$ and $\vec{a}_\theta$ are perpendicular to each other. The magnitude of $|\vec{a}|$ is given by

$$|\vec{a}| = \left[|\vec{a}_r|^2 + |\vec{a}_\theta|^2\right]^{1/2}$$

1.28 COMPONENTS OF VELOCITY IN CARTESIAN COORDINATE SYSTEM

(Two dimensional)

If x and y are cartesian co-ordinates of the point P having polar co-ordinates (r, θ) in a two dimensional system, then

$$x = r\cos\theta \text{ and } y = r\sin\theta$$

$$\cos\theta = \frac{x}{y};\ \sin\theta = \frac{y}{r} \text{ and } r = (x^2+y^2)^{1/2}$$

Differentiating $x = r\cos\theta$ and $y = r\sin\theta$ with respect to t we have

$$\dot{x} = \dot{r}\cos\theta - r\sin\theta\dot{\theta} \quad \text{...(i) where } \dot{x} = \frac{dx}{dt}$$

and

$$\dot{y} = \dot{r}\sin\theta + r\cos\theta\dot{\theta} \quad \text{...(ii) where } \dot{y} = \frac{dy}{dt}$$

Multiplying (*i*) by $\cos\theta$, (*ii*) by $\sin\theta$ and adding, we get

$$\dot{x}\cos\theta + \dot{y}\sin\theta = \dot{r}(\cos^2\theta + \sin^2\theta) = \dot{r}$$

$$\therefore \quad \dot{r} = \dot{x}\cos\theta + \dot{y}\sin\theta = \frac{\dot{x}x + \dot{y}y}{(x^2+y^2)^{1/2}}$$

or

$$|\vec{v}_r| = \frac{\dot{x}x + \dot{y}y}{(x^2+y^2)^{1/2}}$$

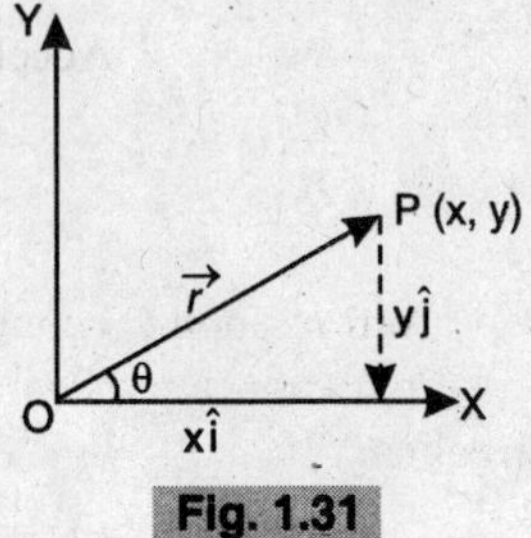

Fig. 1.31

Multiplying (*i*) by $\sin\theta$, (*ii*) by $\cos\theta$ and subtracting (*i*) from (*ii*) we have

$$\dot{y}\cos\theta - \dot{x}\sin\theta = r(\cos^2\theta + \sin^2\theta)\ \dot{\theta}$$

$$\therefore \quad \dot{\theta} = \frac{\dot{y}\cos\theta - \dot{x}\sin\theta}{r} = \frac{\dot{y}x - \dot{x}y}{r^2} = \frac{\dot{y}x - \dot{x}y}{x^2+y^2}$$

$$|\vec{v}_\theta| = r\dot{\theta} = \frac{\dot{y}x - \dot{x}y}{(x^2+y^2)^{\frac{1}{2}}} = \frac{\dot{y}x - \dot{x}y}{r} \quad \text{...(iii)}$$

1.29 DIFFERENTIAL COEFFICIENTS OF SUMS OF VECTORS

The differential coefficient of the sum $\vec{A} + \vec{B}$ of two differentiable vectors, both of which are functions of t, is equal to the sum of their individual differential coefficients, as shown below :

If, for an increase δt in the value of t, the corresponding increases in the values of $\vec{A}$ and $\vec{B}$ be $\delta\vec{A}$ and $\delta\vec{B}$ respectively, we have

$$\delta(\vec{A}+\vec{B}) = (\vec{A}+\delta\vec{A}+\vec{B}+\delta\vec{B}) - (\vec{A}+\vec{B}) = \delta\vec{A}+\delta\vec{B}$$

and hence the quotient $\dfrac{\delta(\vec{A}+\vec{B})}{\delta t} = \dfrac{\delta\vec{A}}{\delta t} + \dfrac{\delta\vec{B}}{\delta t}$.

Or, taking the limiting values on either side as $\delta t \to 0$, we have

$$\frac{d}{dt}(\vec{A}+\vec{B}) = \frac{d\vec{A}}{dt} + \frac{d\vec{B}}{dt}.$$

What applies to the sum of two vectors applies equally well to the sum of any number of them.

1.30 DIFFERENTIAL COEFFICIENTS OF PRODUCTS OF VECTORS

As in the case of an algebraic product, so also here, the differential coefficient of a product of vectors in the sum of the quantities obtained by differentiating one single vector at a time, leaving the others unchanged.

(*i*) Product of a scalar and a vector. Let us consider the product $u\vec{r}$ of a vector $\vec{r}$ with a scalar *u*, both being differentiable functions of the variable *t*.

If, for the increase in the value of *t*, from *t* to $t + \delta t$, the corresponding increases in the value of *u* and $\vec{r}$ be δu and $\delta\vec{r}$, we have

$$\delta(u\vec{r}) = (u+\delta u)(\vec{r}+\delta\vec{r}) - u\vec{r} = \delta u\vec{r} + u\delta\vec{r} + \delta u\delta\vec{r}.$$

Dividing throughout by δt, we have

$$\frac{\delta(u\vec{r})}{\delta t} = \frac{\delta u}{\delta t}\vec{r} + u\frac{\delta\vec{r}}{\delta t} + \frac{\delta u}{dt}\delta\vec{r}.$$

Or, in the limit, $$\frac{d}{dt}(u\vec{r}) = \frac{du}{dt}\vec{r} + u\frac{d\vec{r}}{dt}. \quad ...(i)$$

From relation (*i*) coupled with the results obtained earlier, it follows that the components of *the differential coefficient* (*or derivative*) of a vector are the derivatives of its components for fixed directions.

Thus, if vector $\vec{r}$ be expressed in terms of its rectangular component vectors, we have $\vec{r} = x\hat{i} + y\hat{j} + z\hat{k}$ (where $\hat{i}$, $\hat{j}$ and $\hat{k}$ are, as we know, constant vectors and *x*, *y*, *z*, functions of time), and the differential coefficient of $\vec{r}$ is given by

$$\vec{v} = \frac{d\hat{r}}{dt} = \frac{dx}{dt}\hat{i} + \frac{dy}{dt}\hat{j} + \frac{dz}{dt}\hat{k},$$

with *dx*/*dt*, *dy*/*dt* and *dz*/*dt* respectively representing the magnitudes of the components of vector $\vec{v}$, here representing velocity.

And, in the same manner, we have

$$\text{acceleration } \vec{a} = \frac{d\vec{v}}{dt} = \frac{d^2\vec{r}}{dt^2} = \frac{d^2x}{dt^2}\hat{i} + \frac{d^2y}{dt^2}\hat{j} + \frac{d^2z}{dt^2}\hat{k},$$

where d^2x/dt^2, d^2y/dt^2 and d^2z/dt^2 represent respectively the magnitudes of the components of acceleration $\vec{a}$.

(*ii*) Scalar Product of two vectors. Let us now try to obtain the differential coefficient of a scalar product $\vec{A}\cdot\vec{B}$ Proceeding as in case (*i*), if $\delta\vec{A}$ and $\delta\vec{B}$ be the increments in $\vec{A}$ and $\vec{B}$ respectively corresponding to an increase δt in *t*, we have increase in the scalar product given by

$$\delta(\vec{A}\cdot\vec{B}) = (\vec{A}+\delta\vec{A})\cdot(\vec{B}+\delta\vec{B}) - \vec{A}\cdot\vec{B} = \delta\vec{A}\cdot\vec{B} + \vec{A}\cdot\delta\vec{B} + \delta\vec{A}\cdot\delta\vec{B}$$
$$= \delta\vec{A}\cdot\vec{B} + \delta\vec{B}\cdot\vec{A},$$

neglecting $\delta\vec{A}\cdot\delta\vec{B}$ compared with other terms.

So that, dividing throughout by δt and proceeding to the limit $\delta t \to 0$, we have

$$\frac{d}{dt}(\vec{A}\cdot\vec{B}) = \frac{d\vec{A}}{dt}\cdot\vec{B} + \vec{A}\cdot\frac{d\vec{B}}{dt},$$

where the order of the factors in any of the terms is quite immaterial.

(iii) Vector product of two vectors. Let us now consider the vector product $\vec{A}\times\vec{B}$ Proceeding exactly as above, we have

$$\delta(\vec{A}\times\vec{B}) = (\vec{A}+\delta\vec{A})\times(\vec{B}\times\delta\vec{B}) - \vec{A}\times\vec{B}$$

$$= \delta\vec{A}\times\vec{B} + \vec{A}\times\delta\vec{B} + \delta\vec{A}\times\delta\vec{B}.$$

$$= \delta\vec{A}\times\vec{B} + \vec{A}\times\delta\vec{B},$$

whence, as before, $$\frac{d}{dt}(\vec{A}\times\vec{B}) = \frac{d\vec{A}}{dt}\times\vec{B} + \vec{A}\times\frac{d\vec{B}}{dt},$$

where, the order of the factors in each term must not be changed unless accompanied also by change of sign.

(iv) Triple products. In the case of triple products too, we proceed as before to obtain the differential coefficients. Thus,

(*a*) in the case of a scalar triple product $[\vec{A}\vec{B}\vec{C}]$, we have

$$\frac{d}{dt}[\vec{A}\vec{B}\vec{C}] = \left[\frac{d\vec{A}}{dt}\vec{B}\vec{C}\right] + \left[\vec{A}\frac{d\vec{B}}{dt}\vec{C}\right] + \left[\vec{A}\vec{B}\frac{d\vec{C}}{dt}\right],$$

where the cyclic order in each term must be maintained.

And (*b*) in the case of a vector triple product $\vec{A}\times(\vec{B}\times\vec{C})$, we have

$$\frac{d}{dt}[\vec{A}\times(\vec{B}\times\vec{C})] = \frac{d\vec{A}}{dt}\times(\vec{B}\times\vec{C}) + \vec{A}\times\left(\frac{d\vec{B}}{dt}\times\vec{C}\right) + \vec{A}\times\left(\vec{B}\times\frac{d\vec{C}}{dt}\right),$$

where, again the order of the factors in each term must be maintained.

Example 38. The path of a projectile is defined by the equation $r = 3t - t^2/30$ and $\theta^2 = (1600 - t^2)$. Find its velocity and acceleration after 30 sec.

Solution. Given $$r = 3t - \frac{t^2}{30}$$

At $$t = 30\ s;\ r = 3\times 30 - \frac{30^2}{30} = 60\text{ m}$$

$\therefore$ $$r = 60\text{ m}$$

$$\dot{r} = \frac{dr}{dt} = 3 - \frac{t}{15}$$

At $$t = 30\ s;\ \dot{r} = 3 - \frac{30}{15} = 1\text{ ms}^{-1}$$

$\therefore$ $$\dot{r} = 1\text{ ms}^{-1}$$

$$\ddot{r} = \frac{d(\dot{r})}{dt} = -\frac{1}{15}$$

$\therefore \qquad \ddot{r} = -\frac{1}{15}\ \text{ms}^{-2}$

Given $\qquad \theta^2 = 1600 - t^2$

At $\qquad t = 30$ s; $\quad \theta^2 = 1600 - 900 = 700$

$$\theta^2 = 700$$

and $\qquad \theta = \sqrt{1600 - t^2}$

At $\qquad t = 30\ s;\ \theta = \sqrt{1600 - 900} = 10\sqrt{7}$

$\therefore \qquad \theta = 10\sqrt{7}$ rad

Differentiating $\qquad \theta^2 = 1600 - t^2$

we get $\qquad 2\theta\dot{\theta} = -2t$

$\therefore \qquad \dot{\theta} = -\frac{t}{\theta}.$

At $\qquad t = 30\ s;\ \dot{\theta} = -\frac{30}{10\sqrt{7}} = -\frac{3}{\sqrt{7}}$

$$\dot{\theta} = -\frac{3}{\sqrt{7}}\ \text{rad sec}^{-1}$$

Differentiating $\qquad \dot{\theta} = -\frac{t}{\theta}$, we get

$$\ddot{\theta} = -t \times -10^{-2}\,\dot{\theta} - \frac{1}{\theta} = \frac{t}{\theta^2}\,\dot{\theta} - \frac{1}{\theta}$$

At $\qquad t = 30\ s,\ \ddot{\theta} = -\frac{30}{700} \times \frac{3}{\sqrt{7}} - \frac{1}{10\sqrt{7}}$

$$= -\frac{9}{70\sqrt{7}} - \frac{1}{10\sqrt{7}} = -\frac{16}{70\sqrt{7}}$$

$\therefore \qquad = -\frac{16}{70\sqrt{7}}$ rad sec^{-2}

Now velocity $\vec{v} = \dot{r}\hat{r} + r\dot{\theta}\hat{\theta}$

$$= \hat{r} - 60 \times \frac{-3}{\sqrt{7}}\hat{\theta} = \hat{r} - \frac{180}{\sqrt{7}}\hat{\theta}.$$

Also acceleration $\qquad \vec{a} = (\ddot{r} - r\dot{\theta}^2) + (r\ddot{\theta} + 2\dot{r}\dot{\theta})\hat{\theta}$

or $\qquad \vec{a} = \left(-\frac{1}{15} - 60 \times \frac{9}{7}\right)\hat{r} + \left(60 \times \frac{-16}{70\sqrt{7}} + 2 \times 1 \times \frac{-3}{\sqrt{7}}\right)\hat{\theta}$

$$= -\left(\frac{8107}{105}\right)\hat{r} - \left(\frac{96}{7\sqrt{7}} + \frac{6}{\sqrt{7}}\right)\hat{\theta}$$

$$= -\left(\frac{8107}{105}\right)\hat{r} - \left(\frac{138}{7\sqrt{7}}\right)\hat{\theta} = -\left[\frac{8107}{105}\hat{r} + \frac{138}{7\sqrt{7}}\hat{\theta}\right]$$

Example 39. A point moving in a plane has co-ordinates $x = 3, y = 4$ and has components of speed $\dot{x} = 5$ m/sec, $\dot{y} = 8$ m/sec at some instant of time. Find the components of speed in polar co-ordinates r, θ along directions $\hat{r}$ and $\hat{\theta}$.

Solution. Component of speed along $\hat{r}$

$$|\vec{v}_r| = \frac{\dot{x}x + \dot{y}y}{(x^2+y^2)^{1/2}} = \frac{5\times3+8\times4}{(9+16)^{1/2}} = 9.4 \text{ m/s}$$

Component of speed along $\hat{\theta}$

$$|\vec{v}_\theta| = \frac{\dot{y}x - \dot{x}y}{(x^2+y^2)^{1/2}} = \frac{8\times3-5\times4}{(9\times16)^{1/2}} = 0.8 \text{ m/s}$$

Example 40. Establish the kinematic relations $\vec{v} = \vec{u} + \vec{a}t$,

$$\vec{s} = \vec{u}t + \frac{1}{2}\vec{a}t^2 \text{ and } \vec{v}^2 - \vec{u}^2 = 2\vec{a}\vec{S}.$$

Solution. We know that acceleration $\vec{a} = d\vec{v}/dt$. So that $d\vec{v} = \vec{a}\,dt$, which, on integration gives $\vec{v} = \vec{a}t + C_1$, where C_1 is a constant of integration.

Since, at $t = 0$, $v = C_1$, clearly stands for the initial velocity $\vec{u}$.

We, therefore, have $\vec{v} = \vec{a}t + \vec{u}$ or $\vec{v} = \vec{u} + \vec{a}t$.

Now, $\vec{v} = d\vec{S}/dt = \vec{u} + \vec{a}t$. or, $d\vec{S} = (\vec{u} + \vec{a}t)\,dt$.

Integrating, we have $\vec{S} = \vec{u}t + \frac{1}{2}\vec{a}t^2 + C_2$, where C_2 is another constant of integration.

Since at $t = 0$, $\vec{S} = 0$ and $\therefore C_2 = 0$, we have $\vec{S} = \vec{u}t + \frac{1}{2}\vec{a}t^2$

Finally, taking the scalar product of $\vec{a}$ with $\vec{v}$, we have

$$\vec{v}\cdot\vec{a} = \vec{v}\cdot\frac{d\vec{v}}{dt} \text{ or, } \frac{d\vec{S}}{dt}\cdot\vec{a} = \vec{v}\cdot\frac{d\vec{v}}{dt}. \left[\because \vec{a} = \frac{d\vec{v}}{dt} \text{ and } \vec{v} = \frac{d\vec{S}}{dt}\right].$$

Integration gives $\vec{S}\cdot\vec{a} = \frac{1}{2}\vec{v}\cdot\vec{v} + C_3$, ($a$ being a constant).

where C_3 is yet another constant of integration.

Since $\vec{v}\cdot\vec{v} = \vec{v}^2 = v^2$, we have $\vec{S}.\vec{a} = \frac{1}{2}v^2 + C_3$. Again, when $S = 0$, $v = u$ and we have $0 = \frac{1}{2}v^2 + C_3$, whence, $C_3 = -u^2/2$

So that, $\vec{S}\cdot\vec{a} = \frac{1}{2}v^2 - \frac{1}{2}u^2$ whence, $\vec{v}^2 - \vec{u}^2 = 2\vec{a}\vec{S}$ $[\because v^2 = \vec{v}^2 \text{ and } u^2 = \vec{u}^2]$

Example 41. If the acceleration of moving particle at any instant be given by $\mu\vec{r}\times\vec{v}/r^3$ show that (*i*) it has a constant speed and that (*ii*) its angular momentum consists of two components, one constant in magnitude and direction and the other constant in magnitude in the direction of r.

Solution. (*i*) Clearly, the equation of motion of the particle is

$$\frac{d^2\vec{r}}{dt^2} = \frac{\mu\vec{r}\times\vec{v}}{r^3} = \frac{\mu\vec{r}}{r^3}\times\frac{d\vec{r}}{dt} \quad ...(i)\ [r = |\vec{r}|.$$

Taking the scalar product of relation (*i*) with $d\vec{r}/dt^2$, we have

$$\frac{d\vec{r}}{dt}\cdot\frac{d^2\vec{r}}{dt^2} = \frac{\mu\vec{r}}{r^3}\times\frac{d\vec{r}}{dt}\cdot\frac{d\vec{r}}{dt} = 0.$$

This, on integration, gives $(d\vec{r}/dt)^2$ = constant,

indicating that the speed $d\vec{r}/dt$ of the particle is constant.

(*ii*) Obtaining the vector product of (*i*) with $\vec{r}$, we have

$$\vec{r}\times\frac{d^2\vec{r}}{dt^2} = \frac{\mu}{r^3}\vec{r}\times\left(\vec{r}\times\frac{d\vec{r}}{dt}\right) = \frac{\mu}{r^3}\left[\left(\vec{r}\cdot\frac{d\vec{r}}{dt}\right)\vec{r} - (\vec{r}\cdot\vec{r})\frac{d\vec{r}}{dt}\right]$$

$$= \frac{\mu}{r^3}\left[\vec{r}\frac{d\vec{r}}{dt}r - r^2\frac{d\vec{r}}{dt}\right] = -\mu\frac{d}{dt}\left(\frac{\vec{r}}{r}\right),$$

which, on integration, gives $\vec{r}\times\dfrac{d\vec{r}}{dt} = -\mu\dfrac{\vec{r}}{r} + \vec{a}$, where $\vec{a}$ is a *constant vector.*

Clearly, $\vec{r}\times\dfrac{d\vec{r}}{dt}$ is the angular velocity of the particle and hence its angular momentum is given by $m\left(\vec{r}\times\dfrac{d\vec{r}}{dt}\right) = -m\mu\vec{r}/r + m\vec{a}$.

It clearly consists of two components, *viz,* (*i*) a component $-m\mu\vec{r}/r$ whose magnitude is the constant $|-m\mu|$ and whose direction is that of $\vec{r}$ and (*ii*) the component $m\vec{a}$, which is constant both in magnitude and direction.

1.31 CIRCULAR MOTION

Let us try to obtain expression for the velocity and acceleration of a particle P moving at a constant speed along a circular path in the *x-y* plane, say, of constant radius r (Fig. 1.32).

The position vector $\vec{r}$, a function of the scalar variable t, moving with constant angular velocity (or angular frequency) of magnitude ω may, at any given instant t, be expressed in terms of its components along the axes of x and y. Thus, if $\hat{i}$ and $\hat{j}$ be the *unit vectors* along the two axes respectively, we have

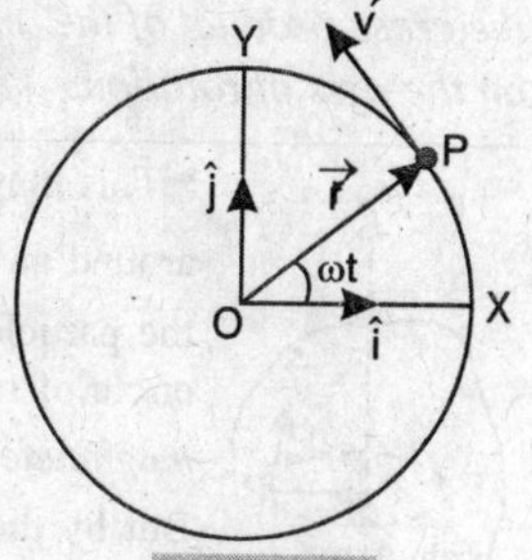

Fig. 1.32

$$\vec{r} = x\hat{i} + y\hat{j},\ i.e.,\ \vec{r} = r\cos\omega t\hat{i} + r\sin\omega t\hat{j}$$
$$= r(\cos\omega t\hat{i} + \sin\omega t\hat{j})$$

The velocity $\vec{v}$ of particle P is thus given by

$$\vec{v} = \frac{d\vec{r}}{dt} = r\frac{d\vec{r}}{dt} + \hat{r}\frac{dr}{dt}$$

where $\hat{r}$ is the unit vector along the direction of $\vec{r}$.

Now, r being constant for the circular path, $dr/dt = 0$. So that, we have

$$\vec{v} = r\frac{d\vec{r}}{dt} = r\left(\frac{d}{dt}\cos\omega t\hat{i} + \frac{d}{dt}\sin\omega t\hat{j}\right)$$

Or, $\vec{v} = r(-\omega\sin\omega t\,\hat{i} + \omega\cos\omega t\,\hat{j}) = \omega r(-\sin\omega t\,\hat{i} + \cos\omega t\,\hat{j})$.

Therefore, with v as the magnitude of the velocity of P, we have

$v^2 = \vec{v}\cdot\vec{v} = \omega r(-\sin\omega t\,\hat{i} + \cos\omega t\,\hat{j}).\ \omega r(-\sin\omega t\,\hat{i} + \cos\omega t\,\hat{j})$,

which, from our knowledge of scalar products and the fact that $\hat{i}\cdot\hat{j} = 0$, gives

$v^2 = \omega^2 r^2(\sin^2\omega t + \cos^2\omega t) = \omega^2 r^2$, where, $v = \omega r$.

Now, since acceleration $\vec{a}$ is the rate of change of velocity, we have

$\vec{a} = d\vec{v}/dt = \omega^2 r(-\cos\omega t\,\hat{i} - \sin\omega t\,\hat{j}) = -\omega^2 r(\cos\omega t\,\hat{i} + \sin\omega t\,\hat{j})$

And since $r(\cos\omega t\,\hat{i} + \sin\omega t\,\hat{j}) = \vec{r}$, we have

$$\vec{a} = -\omega^2\vec{r}.$$

Or, the *magnitude of the acceleration of particle P, i.e., $a = \omega^2 r$, its direction being $-\vec{r}$ or towards the centre of the circle,* hence the name centripetal (*i.e.*, centre-seeking) acceleration given to it.

Or, since $\omega r = v$, we may also put $a = r(v/r)^2 = v^2/r$.

Hence the force, called *centripetal force,* acting on the particle is given by *mass × acceleration* $= mv^2/r$ and is also directed towards the centre of its circular path.

Further, since the angle swept out by the radius vector in one complete revolution = 2π radians, we have *time period* of the particle given by $T = 2\pi/\omega$ and its frequency by $n = 1/T = \omega/2\pi$, whence, $\omega = 2\pi n$.

1.32 ANGULAR VELOCITY VECTOR

The angular velocity of a particle, having magnitude as well as direction, is obviously a *vector*. To obtain its value, we note that the linear velocity $\vec{v}$ of the particle is at any instant, perpendicular to both the angular velocity $\vec{\omega}$ and the radius vector $\vec{r}$. So that, the vector equation corresponding to the relation $v = \omega r$ comes out to be $\vec{v} = \vec{\omega}\times\vec{r}$ * showing that *the linear velocity of the particle is the cross product of the angular velocity vector and the position vector with respect to a fixed point on the axis of rotation.*

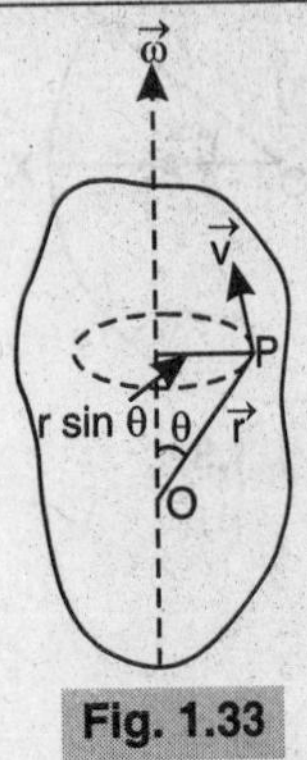

Fig. 1.33

* This may be seen from the following: Consider, a particle P in a rigid body, revolving around an axis with an angular velocity $\vec{\omega}$ (Fig. 1.33). Let $\vec{r}$ be the position vector of the particle with respect to any point O on the axis. Then, since the particle describes a circle of radius $r\sin\theta$, lying in the plane perpendicular to the axis of rotation, we have *magnitude of its linear velocity* (or of the velocity vector) $|\vec{v}| = \omega r\sin\theta$.

But by the definition of cross product, $\vec{\omega}\times\vec{r}$ has also the same magnitude $\omega r\sin\theta$ and is perpendicular to the plane containing $\vec{r}$ and $\vec{\omega}$.

We, therefore, have $\vec{v} = \vec{r}\times\vec{\omega}$.

$= \frac{4}{\sqrt{10}}(\hat{i} + 3\hat{j} + 9\hat{k})$ and its magnitude $= \frac{4}{\sqrt{10}}\sqrt{1+9+81} = 4\sqrt{\frac{91}{10}}$.

$=12$ *units very nearly.*

The cross product of this with $\vec{r}$ gives

$$\vec{r}\times\vec{v} = \vec{r}\times(\vec{\omega}\times\vec{r}) = \vec{\omega}(\vec{r}.\vec{r}) - \vec{r}(\vec{r}\cdot\vec{\omega}) = r^2\,\vec{\omega},$$

(because $\vec{r}\cdot\vec{\omega} = 0$, $\vec{r}$ and $\vec{\omega}$ being perpendicular to each other),

whence, $\vec{\omega} = \vec{r}\times\vec{v}/r^2$ and can be easily evaluated, its direction being parallel to the axis of rotation in the positive sense relative to the direction of rotation (*i.e.*, in accordance with the right-handed screw rule).

Example 42. A rigid body is spinning with an angular velocity of 4 radians/about an axis parallel to $3\hat{j}-\hat{k}$ passing through the point $\hat{i}+3\hat{j}-\hat{k}$. Find the velocity of the particle at the point $4\hat{i}-2\hat{j}+\hat{k}$.

Solution. Let $\hat{n}$ be the *unit vector* in the direction of $3\hat{j}-\hat{k}$. Then,

$$\hat{n} = \frac{3\hat{j}-\hat{k}}{\sqrt{0+9+1}} = \frac{1}{\sqrt{10}}(3\hat{j}-\hat{k})$$

$\therefore$ Angular velocity of the particle P, say, $\vec{\omega} = \omega\hat{n} = \dfrac{4}{\sqrt{10}}(3\hat{j}-\hat{k})$.

The position vector of P with reference to point $\hat{i}+3\hat{j}-\hat{k}$, *i.e.*,

$$\vec{r} = (4\hat{i}-2\hat{j}+\hat{k}) - (\hat{i}+3\hat{j}-\hat{k}) = 3\hat{i}-5\hat{j}+2\hat{k}.$$

Hence *velocity* (*linear*) *of particle* $P = \vec{r}\times\vec{\omega} = (3\hat{i}-5\hat{j}+2\hat{k})\times\dfrac{4}{\sqrt{10}}(3\hat{j}-\hat{k})$.

$= \dfrac{4}{\sqrt{10}}(\hat{i}+3\hat{j}+9\hat{k})$ and its magnitude $= \dfrac{4}{\sqrt{10}}\sqrt{1+9+81} = 4\sqrt{\dfrac{91}{10}} = 12$ units very nearly.

Example 43. A particle describes a circle in the $\hat{i}, \hat{j}$ plane with a uniform speed in 12 seconds in the direction $\hat{i}$ to $\hat{j}$. If the initial position of the radius vector relative to the centre of the circle be $\hat{i}$, determine its position at the end of the 3rd second from the start. What will be its velocity vector then?

Solution. Let OX and OY be the rectangular coordinates in the plane of the circle through its centre O (Fig. 1.34) and let $\hat{i}$ and $\hat{j}$ be the unit vectors along the two axes respectively. Then, taking the circle to be of unit radius, we have $OA = OB = 1$, where A and B are the points in which the circle meets the two axes respectively.

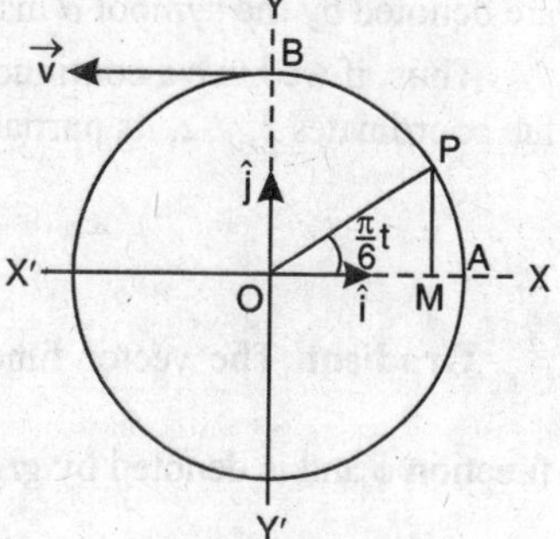

Fig. 1.34

Let A be the initial position of the particle and P, its position after t second from start. So that, the angular velocity of the particle being $2\pi/12$ or $\pi/6$ *radian/s*, angle $XOP = (\pi/6)\,t$.

If PM be the perpendicular dropped from P on to OA, we have

$$\vec{OP} = \vec{OM} + \vec{MP}. \text{ or, } \vec{OP} = \left(OP\cos\frac{\pi}{6}t\right)\hat{i} + \left(OP\sin\frac{\pi}{6}t\right)\hat{j}.$$

Or, since $OP = 1$ and $t = 3$, we have $\vec{OP} = \left(\cos\dfrac{3\pi}{6}\right)\hat{i} + \left(\cos\dfrac{3\pi}{6}\right)\hat{j}$

$$= (\cos\pi/2)\,\hat{i} + (\sin\pi/2)\,\hat{j} = \hat{j}.$$

Thus, the position of the radius vector will, after 3 seconds, be along *OB*. And, the *velocity vector* of the particle will, therefore, be $-\pi\hat{i}/6$, the velocity $\vec{v}$ being tangential to the circle at *B*, as shown.

1.33 SCALAR AND VECTOR FIELDS

A physical quantity, expressed as a continuous function of the position of a point in a region of space is referred to as a *point function* (or *function of position*). The region of space concerned is known as a **scalar field** or **a vector field** according as the physical quantity in question is a scalar or a vector one, expressed as a continuous single-valued function, $\phi(x, y, z)$ or $F(x, y, z)$ respectively, of position in that region. In actual practice, *the two functions of positions themselves are spoken of as the scalar and vector fields respectively.*

As examples of scalar fields may be mentioned the distribution of temperature or magnetic and electrostatic potentials in a given region of space. The field here consists of a series of surfaces, (isothermal or equipotential, as the case may be), each having a fixed and definite value of temperature or magnetic or electrostatic potential, *i.e.*, of the function $\phi(x, y, z)$. Such surfaces are referred to as **level surfaces**, each level surface having its own constant value of $\phi(x, y, z)$ all over.

And, as examples of vector fields, we have distribution of magnetic and electric intensity or the distribution of velocity in a moving (continuous) fluid. At any given point, in this case, the single-valued vector function $\vec{F}(x, y, z)$ is specified by a vector having a definite magnitude and direction, both of which continuously change from point to point throughout the field.

Starting from any desired point in the field and proceeding through infinitesimal distances from point to point in the direction of the field, we obtain, in general, a curved line, called the **line of flow,** the **flux line** or the **vector line,** the tangent to which at any point gives the direction of the vector at that point. The measure or magnitude of the vector is given by the number of flux lines passing per unit area of a surface normal to their direction.

1.34 PARTIAL DERIVATIVES—GRADIENT

Partial derivatives. The differentiation of a function such as $\phi(x_1, x_2, x_3...)$ of two or more independent variables, x_1, x_2, x_3 *etc.*, with respect to one of them, keeping the others constant, is called *partial differentiation*. The derivatives thus obtained are referred to as *partial derivatives* and are denoted by the symbol ∂ instead of *d*.

Thus, if we have a continuously differentiable scalar point function $\phi(x, y, z)$, *i.e.*, a function of the coordinates *x*, *y*, *z*, its partial derivatives along the three coordinate axes are

$$\frac{\partial\phi}{\partial x}, \frac{\partial\phi}{\partial y} \text{ and } \frac{\partial\phi}{\partial z}.$$

Gradient. The vector function $\hat{i}\frac{\partial\phi}{\partial x} + \hat{j}\frac{\partial\phi}{\partial y} + \hat{k}\frac{\partial\phi}{\partial z}$ is called the *gradient* of the scalar point function ϕ and is denoted by *grad* ϕ. Thus,

$$grad\,\phi = \hat{i}\frac{\partial\phi}{\partial x} + \hat{j}\frac{\partial\phi}{\partial y} + \hat{k}\frac{\partial\phi}{\partial z}.$$

$\therefore$ differential

$$d\phi = \frac{\partial\phi}{\partial x}dx + \frac{\partial\phi}{\partial y}dy + \frac{\partial\phi}{\partial z}dz$$

$$= (\hat{i}dx + \hat{j}dy + \hat{k}dz)\left(\hat{i}\frac{\partial\phi}{\partial x} + \hat{j}\frac{\partial\phi}{\partial y} + \hat{k}\frac{\partial\phi}{\partial z}\right).$$

or,

$$d\phi = dr\; grad\,\phi.$$

It can easily be shown that grad ϕ at any point is quite independent of the choice of the coordinate axes. It follows, therefore, that *the gradient of a scalar point function is a vector point function.*

If ϕ be a constant, obviously the partial derivatives $\partial\phi/\partial x$, $\partial\phi/\partial y$ and $\partial\phi/\partial z$ will all be zero and hence *grad* $\phi = 0$. And, conversely, if *grad* $\phi = 0$, the partial derivatives are all zero and hence function ϕ is a constant. Thus, *grad* $\phi = 0$ *only if* ϕ *be constant.*

1.35 THE OPERATOR $\vec{\nabla}$

We have in vector algebra a differential operator, denoted by $\vec{\nabla}$ (*i.e.*, inverted Δ). It is called **'del'** or **"nabla'**. *It operates distributively and is formally assumed to have the character of a vector.* And since it is assumed to have the character of a vector, *its product* $\vec{\nabla}\phi$ *with a scalar* ϕ *is a vector.*

If we use Cartesion orthogonal coordinates, we may write

$$\vec{\nabla} = \hat{i}\frac{\partial}{\partial x}+\hat{j}\frac{\partial}{\partial y}+\hat{k}\frac{\partial}{\partial z}.$$

So that,

$$grad\,\phi = \hat{i}\frac{\partial\phi}{\partial x}+\hat{j}\frac{\partial\phi}{\partial y}+\hat{k}\frac{\partial\phi}{\partial z}$$

$$= \left(\hat{i}\frac{\partial}{\partial x}+\hat{j}\frac{\partial}{\partial y}+\hat{k}\frac{\partial}{\partial z}\right)\phi = \vec{\nabla}\phi, \text{ a vector.}$$

N.B. It may be remembered with advantage that *the operator* $\vec{\nabla}$ *obeys the same conventions as the differential notation.* Thus, what is to be differentiated must be placed on its right, like $\vec{\nabla}\phi$ for instance. Putting it the other way, like $\phi\vec{\nabla}$, means next to nothing; $\phi\nabla$ still remains just an operator. On the other hand, $\vec{\nabla}\phi$ stands for a physical vector with a definite meaning.

1.36 MAGNITUDE AND DIRECTION OF $\vec{\nabla}\phi$

Let us consider two level surfaces L_1 and L_2 through two close points A and C, distance dr apart (Fig. 1.35), with the values of the scalar function ϕ and $(\phi + d\phi)$ respectively. And let $AB = dn$ be the normal to the surface L_1 and A.

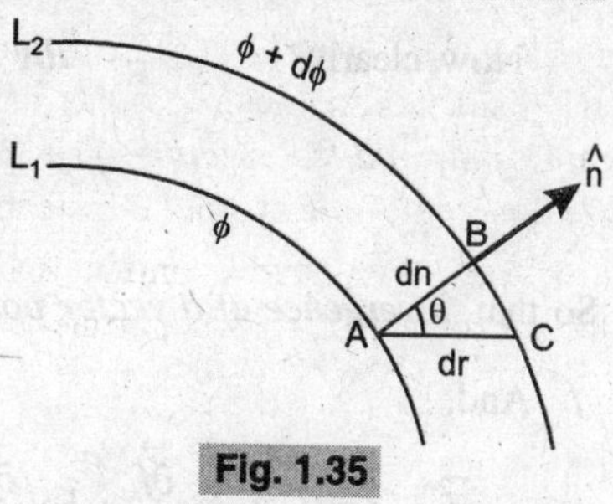

Fig. 1.35

Since L_2 is a level surface, the value of the scalar function is the same [*viz.*, $(\phi + d\phi)$] at B as at C. Obviously, therefore, the *rate of change of* ϕ along the normal AB is the highest (this being the shortest distance between the two surfaces) and is equal to $\partial\phi/\partial n$.

Now, we may put $dn = dr\cos\theta = \hat{n}.\vec{dr}$ where $\hat{n}$ is the unit vector normal to the surface L_1 at A. So that,

$$d\phi = \frac{\partial\phi}{\partial n}dn = \frac{\partial\phi}{\partial n}\hat{n}.\vec{dr}.$$

As we know,

$$\vec{\nabla}\phi\cdot d\vec{r} = \left(\hat{i}\frac{\partial\phi}{\partial x}+\hat{j}\frac{\partial\phi}{\partial y}+\hat{k}\frac{\partial\phi}{\partial z}\right)\cdot\left(\hat{i}dx+\hat{j}dy+\hat{k}dz\right)$$

$$= \frac{\partial\phi}{\partial x}dx+\frac{\partial\phi}{\partial y}dy+\frac{\partial\phi}{\partial z}dz = d\phi.$$

Or,

$$d\phi = \vec{\nabla}\phi\cdot d\vec{r} = \frac{\partial\phi}{\partial n}\hat{n}\cdot d\vec{r},$$

whence, $$\vec{\nabla}\phi = \left(\frac{\partial \phi}{\partial n}\right)\hat{n},$$

i.e., **vector $\vec{\nabla}\phi$ or *grad* ϕ has a magnitude equal to the maximum rate of change of ϕ and is directed along this maximum rate of change, *i.e.*, along the normal to the level surface L_1 (with ϕ constant).**

1.37 DIVERGENCE AND CURL

We have seen § 1.34 how from a scalar point function ϕ we can obtain a vector point function grad ϕ. Similarly, from a vector point function $\vec{f}$ we can obtain two more point funcuons : a scalar one, called *divergence* and a vector one, called *curl* (or *rotation*).

Thus, if $\vec{f}$ represents a vector field, *i.e.*, if $\vec{f}$ be a *continuously differentiable vector point function*, the function

$$\hat{i}\cdot\frac{\partial\vec{f}}{\partial x} + \hat{j}.\frac{\partial\vec{f}}{\partial y} + \hat{k}\cdot\frac{\partial\vec{f}}{\partial z},$$

which is a *scalar*, is called divergence of $\vec{f}$ and is writen as *div* $\vec{f}$. And the function

$$\hat{i}\times\frac{\partial\vec{f}}{\partial x} + \hat{j}\times\frac{\partial\vec{f}}{\partial y} + \hat{k}\times\frac{\partial\vec{f}}{\partial z},$$

which is a *vector*, is called curl of $\vec{f}$ and is written as *curl* $\vec{f}$.

It can easily be shown that both *div* $\vec{f}$ and curl $\vec{f}$ are quite independent of the orthogonal unit triad (*i.e.*, unit vectors) that may be chosen. They are thus *essentially point functions*.

Now, clearly, $$div\,\vec{f} = \hat{i}\cdot\frac{\partial\vec{f}}{\partial x} + \hat{j}\cdot\frac{\partial\vec{f}}{\partial y} + \hat{k}\cdot\frac{\partial\vec{f}}{\partial z}$$
$$= \left(\hat{i}\frac{\partial}{\partial x} + \hat{j}\frac{\partial}{\partial y} + \hat{k}\frac{\partial}{\partial z}\right)\cdot\vec{f} = \vec{\nabla}\cdot\vec{f}.$$

So that, *divergence of a vector point function $\vec{f}$ is the scalar produced of the Del operator with $\vec{f}$*. And,

$$curl\quad \vec{f} = \hat{i}\times\frac{\partial\vec{f}}{\partial x} + \hat{j}\times\frac{\partial\vec{f}}{\partial y} + \hat{k}\times\frac{\partial\vec{f}}{\partial z} = \left(\hat{i}\frac{\partial}{\partial x} + \hat{j}\frac{\partial}{\partial y} + \frac{\partial}{\partial z}\right)\times\vec{f} = \vec{\nabla}\times\vec{f},$$

i.e.*, *curl of a vector point function $\vec{f}$ is the vector product of the Del operator with $\vec{f}$. The term, $\vec{\nabla}\times$, [read as Del cross (or Nabla cross)], is therefore also used in place of the term 'curl'.

Both divergence and curl of $\vec{f}$ may be expressed in terms of the components of vector $\vec{f}$, as shown below:

If $\vec{f} = \hat{i}f_x + \hat{j}f_y + \hat{k}f_z$, we have

$$div\;\vec{f} = \Sigma\hat{i}\cdot\frac{\partial\vec{f}}{\partial x} = \Sigma\hat{i}\cdot\left[\hat{i}\frac{\partial f_x}{\partial x} + \hat{j}\frac{\partial f_y}{\partial x} + \hat{k}\frac{\partial f_z}{\partial x}\right]$$

$$= \frac{\partial f_x}{\partial x} + \frac{\partial f_y}{\partial y} + \frac{\partial f_z}{\partial z}.$$

and $$curl\,\vec{f} = \Sigma \hat{i} \times \frac{\partial \vec{f}}{\partial x} = \Sigma \hat{i} \times \left[\hat{i}\frac{\partial f_x}{\partial x} + \hat{j}\frac{\partial f_y}{\partial x} + \hat{k}\frac{\partial f_x}{\partial x} \right]$$

$$= \hat{i}\left(\frac{\partial f_z}{\partial y} - \frac{\partial f_y}{\partial z}\right) + \hat{j}\left(\frac{\partial f_x}{\partial z} - \frac{\partial f_z}{\partial x}\right) + \hat{k}\left(\frac{\partial f_y}{\partial x} - \frac{\partial f_x}{\partial y}\right)$$

$$= \begin{vmatrix} \hat{i} & \hat{j} & \hat{k} \\ \frac{\partial}{\partial x} & \frac{\partial}{\partial y} & \frac{\partial}{\partial z} \\ f_x & f_y & f_z \end{vmatrix}$$

N.B. 1. The term 'rotation' is also sometimes used for '*curl*', after *Maxwell*.

2. It may be mentioned again here for ready reference that

(*i*) $\vec{\nabla}\phi = grad\,\phi$ is a *vector*; (*ii*) $\vec{\nabla} \cdot \vec{f} = \text{div}\ \vec{f}$ is a *scalar*, and

(*iii*) $\vec{\nabla} \times \vec{f} = \text{curl}\ \vec{f}$ is a *vector*.

1.38 APPLICATIONS OF DIVERGENCE AND CURL

(*i*) **Rate of flow of flux (or a fluid).** Let $\vec{v}$ be a vector point function (or the value of the vector field) representing the *velocity* of a fluid at any given instant *t* at a point *P* inside a small parallelopiped, *with edges δx, δy, and δz parallel to the three coordinate axes*, as shown in Fig. 1.36.

Let $$\vec{v} = v_x\hat{i} + v_y\hat{j} + v_z\hat{k}.$$

Then, *velocity component along the x-axis at any point of the face ABCD normal to this axis.*

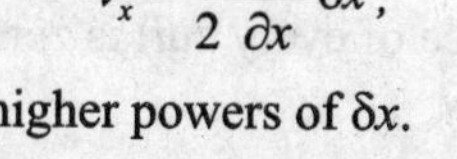

$$= v_x - \frac{1}{2}\frac{\partial v_x}{\partial x}\delta x,$$

neglecting the second and the higher powers of δx.

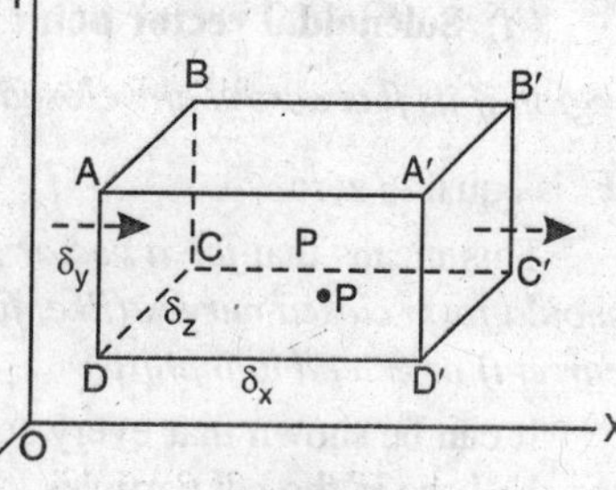

Fig. 1.36

∴ *flux (or fluid) entering per second through face ABCD of the parallelopiped.*

= (*component of velocity normal to the face*) (*area of the face*)

$$= \left(v_x - \frac{1}{2}\frac{\partial v_x}{\partial x}\delta x\right)\delta y\,\delta z.$$

Similarly, *flux (or fluid) leaving per second through the opposite face A′B′C′D′ of the parallelopiped*

$$= \left(v_x + \frac{1}{2}\frac{\partial v_x}{\partial x}\delta x\right)\delta y\,\delta z.$$

Thus, *volume of the flux (or fluid) passing per second through faces ABCD and A′B′C′D′ of the parallelopiped, i.e. along the directioin of x.*

$$= \left(v_x + \frac{1}{2}\frac{\partial v_x}{\partial x}\delta x\right)\delta y\,\delta z - \left(v_x - \frac{1}{2}\frac{\partial v_x}{\partial x}\delta x\right)\delta y\,\delta z = \frac{\partial v_x}{\partial x}\partial x\,\partial y\,\partial z$$

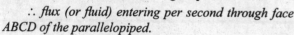

Considering the other faces of the parallelopiped also, we have *total volume of flux (or fluid) moving out of the parallelopiped per second*

$$= \left(\frac{\partial v_x}{\partial x} + \frac{\partial v_y}{\partial y} + \frac{\partial v_z}{\partial z}\right) \delta x \, \delta y \, \delta z$$

$$= (\vec{\nabla} \cdot \vec{v}) \delta x \, \delta y \, \delta z \text{ or } (\text{div } \vec{v}) \, \delta x \, \delta y \, \delta z.$$

The volume of the paralleloped being $\delta x \, \delta y \, \delta z$, we find that in the limit when δx, δy and δz tend to zero, *the volume of flux (or fluid) flowing past (or diverging from) point P (x, y, z) is* $\vec{\nabla} \cdot \vec{v}$ *ordiv* $\vec{v}$.

This means, in other words, that *if* $\vec{v}$ *be the velocity of the fluid at a point its rate of divergence per unit volume from that point is given by div* $\vec{v}$ *or* $\vec{\nabla} \cdot \vec{v}$.

A positive value of the *div* $\vec{v}$ may be interpreted to mean either that the fluid is undergoing expansion (with its density falling proportionately) or that the point itself is the **source** of the fluid.

Similarly, a negative value of *div* $\vec{v}$ may be interpreted to mean the reverse, *viz.*, that either the fluid is undergoing contraction (with its density rising proportionately or that the point serves as **a sink** (or a *negative source*) of the fluid.

If, however, *div* $\vec{v} = 0$, the fluid entering and leaving the element (or the parallelopiped) is the same. *i.e.*, there is no change in the density of the fluid indicating that it is *incompressible.* In this case, therefore if ρ be the density of the fluid, we have mass *of the fluid per unit volume that flows through a point* $(x, y, z) = \rho$ *div* $\vec{v}$.

(ii) **Solenoidal vector point function,** A *vector point function* $\vec{F}$ *is said to be solenoidal in a region if its flux across any closed surface in that region be zero*, which will happen only when *div* $\vec{F}$ is equal to zero.

This means that *for a vector point function to be solenoidal, either the lines of flow of its flux should form closed curves (like, for example, the lines of forces in the magnetic field of an electric current) or extend to infinity.*

It can be shown that every solenoidal vector function is the curl of some function. Further, as we shall see in the next articles, the divergence of every curl is zero. It follows, therefore, that *the curl of every function is necessarily solenoidal.*

1.39 SOME USEFUL RESULTS

As we have seen in Articles 1.34 and 1.37 the gradient of a scalar point function ϕ is a vector point function and so is the curl of a vector point function $\vec{f}$. We may also, therefore, obtain their divergence and curl, as given below:

(i) div grad $\phi = \vec{\nabla} \cdot \vec{\nabla}\phi = \dfrac{\partial^2 \phi}{\partial x^2} + \dfrac{\partial^2 \phi}{\partial y^2} + \dfrac{\partial^2 \phi}{\partial z^2} = \nabla^2$

where ∇^2 is the **Laplacian operator** (and a scalar). (See §1.40 below).

(ii) curl grad $\phi = \vec{\nabla} \times \vec{\nabla}\phi = 0$, because the cross product of two equal vectors is zero, [*see* §1.20, (*vi*)] and here both the vectors or $\vec{\nabla}$*'s* are equal since they operate on the same function ϕ.

It follows from this that if *we have a vector field* $\vec{f}$ *such that its curl is zero, i.e.,* $\vec{\nabla} \times \vec{f} = 0$, $\vec{f}$ *is certainly the gradient of some scalar field* ϕ, *i.e., if* $\vec{\nabla} \times \vec{f} = 0$, *we have* $\vec{f} = \vec{\nabla}\phi$.

(*iii*) *div curl* $\vec{f} = \vec{\nabla}\cdot\vec{\nabla}\times\vec{f} = 0$, because, as we know, it is a combination similar to $\vec{A}\cdot\vec{A}\times\vec{B}$ where $\vec{A}\times\vec{B}$ is perpendicular to $\vec{A}$ and has no component in the direction of $\vec{A}$.

It follows, therefore, that *if the divergence of a vector field* $\vec{D}$ *is zero, then,* $\vec{D}$ *is clearly the curl of some vector field* $\vec{f}$ *i.e.*, if $\vec{\nabla}\vec{D} = 0$, we have $\vec{D} = \vec{\nabla}\times\vec{f}$.

(*iv*) *curl curl* $\vec{f} = \vec{\nabla}\times(\vec{\nabla}\times\vec{f}) = \vec{\nabla}\vec{\nabla}\cdot\vec{f} - \nabla^2\vec{f}$ *grad div* $\vec{f} - \nabla^2\vec{f}$.

We may have two more combinations viz.,

(*v*) $\vec{\nabla}(\vec{\nabla}.\vec{f})$ and (*vi*) $(\vec{\nabla}\cdot\vec{\nabla})\vec{f} = \nabla^2\vec{f}$. There is, however nothing special about them. They represent just vector fields which we may possibly come across sometimes.

1.40 THE LAPLACIAN OPERATOR

If $\vec{\nabla}$ be the Del or Nabla operator, we have

$$\nabla^2 = \vec{\nabla}\cdot\vec{\nabla} = \left(\Sigma\hat{i}\frac{\partial}{\partial x}\right)\cdot\left(\Sigma\hat{i}\frac{\partial}{\partial x}\right) = \frac{\partial^2}{\partial x^2}+\frac{\partial^2}{\partial y^2}+\frac{\partial^2}{\partial z^2},$$

where ∇^2 is referred to as the *Laplician operator*. Being the *dot* or scalar product of two vectors $(\vec{\nabla})$, it is a *scalar operator* and is also called *del squared* or *Nabla squared* for the obvious reason that $\vec{\nabla}$ is a del operator.

Thus, *div grad* ϕ in §1.39 above could also be spoken of as *del squared* (or *Nabla squared*) ϕ.

1.41 INTEGRATION OF VECTORS

(*i*) **Line integral.** Let dl be an element of length at a point on a smooth curve *AB* drawn in a vector field and $\vec{F}$, a continuous vector point function, or vector, inclined at an angle θ to $\vec{dl}$, as shown in Fig. 1.37, such that it continuously varies in magnitude as well as direction as we proceed along the curve. Then, the integral

$$\int_A^B \vec{F}\cdot\vec{dl} = \int_A^B F\cos\theta\, dl\,.$$

is referred to as the *line integral of vector* $\vec{F}$ *along the curve AB*.

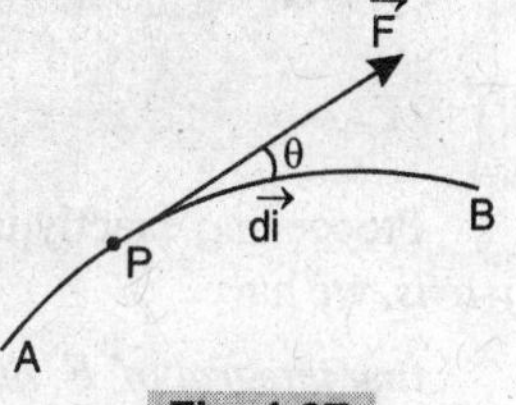

Fig. 1.37

In terms of the components of $\vec{F}$ of along the three Cartesian coordinates, we have

$$\int_A^B \vec{F}.\vec{d\,l} = \int_A^B (F_x\, dx + F_y\, dy + F_z\, dz),$$

Thus, if $\vec{F}$ represents the force acting on a particle moving along the curve from *A* to *B*, the line integral. $\int_A^B \vec{F}.\vec{dl}$ represents the total work done by the force during the motion of the particle over its entire path from *A* to *B*.

If the value of the line integral depends only upon the location of the two points in the vector field and not upon the actual path taken between them, the vector field is referred to as a **conservative field**. *Familiar examples of such fields are the electrostatic, magnetic and gravitational fields.*

If, therefore, $\vec{F}$ represents the value of the electric (or magnetic) field intensity at the point P, the line integral $\int_A^B \vec{F}.\vec{dl}$ represents the work done on unit charge (or unit pole) during its motion from A to B (*i.e.*, the potential difference between A and B) *irrespective of the path taken.*

In Hydrodynamics, the line integral of continuous vector point function or vector ($\vec{F}$ along a closed curve is called the circulation of $\vec{F}$ along the curve. And, if the circulation of a vector point function along every closed curve in a region be zero, it is said to be irrational in that region.

Relationship between line integral and curl. There is a definite relationship between the curl of a vector field $\vec{F}$ as a point and its integral along the boundary O of an infinitesimal plane area around and including that point. To clearly bring this out, let us, for convenience, calculate the line integral of F around and infinitesimal plane rectangular area $ABCD$, of sides $AB = \delta x$ and $BC = \delta y$ in the x-y plane (Fig. 1.38) surrounding and including a point P.

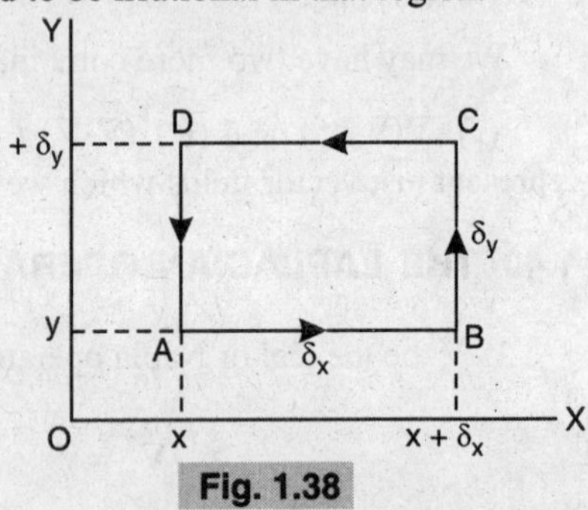

Fig. 1.38

Let the components of $\vec{F}$ along the axes of x and y be F_x and F_y respectively. Then, since the sides of the rectangle are small, the average values of these components along them may respectively be taken to be the same as those at their mid-points. So that, we have

average value of x componel along the path AB $= F_x + \frac{\partial F_x}{\partial x} \cdot \frac{\delta x}{2}$

and average value of x-components along the path CD

$$= F_x + \frac{\partial F_x}{\partial x} \cdot \frac{\delta x}{2} + \frac{\partial Fx}{\partial y} \delta y.$$

Remembering that the path CD is oppositely directed to the x-axis, we have *line integral of* $\vec{F}$ *along AB + line integral of* $\vec{F}$ along BC given by

$$\int_A^B \vec{F}.\vec{dl} + \int_C^D \vec{F}.\vec{dl} = \left(F_x + \frac{\partial F_x}{\partial x} \frac{\delta x}{2} \right) \delta x - \left(F_x + \frac{\partial F_x}{\partial x} \frac{\delta x}{2} + \frac{\partial F_x}{\partial y} \delta y \right) \delta x$$

$$= -\frac{\partial Fx}{\partial y} \delta x \, \delta y \qquad \text{...(i)}$$

Proceeding exactly in the same manner and remembering that DA is oppositely directed to the *y-axis*, we have

line integral of $\vec{F}$ *along BC + line integral of* $\vec{F}$ *along DA* given by

$$\int_B^C \vec{F}.\vec{dl} + \int_D^A \vec{F}.\vec{dl} = \frac{\partial Fy}{\partial x} \delta x \, \delta y \qquad \text{...(ii)}$$

Thus, adding relations (*i*) and (*ii*), we have

line integral over the entire boundary C of the rectangle $ABCD$ given by

$$\oint_{ABCD} \vec{F}.\vec{dl} = \oint_C \vec{F}.\vec{dl} = \left(\frac{\delta Fy}{\partial x} - \frac{\partial Fx}{\partial y} \right) \delta x \delta y$$

Now, the x-component of curl $\vec{F}$ at the point being the above line integral per unit area, we have,

$$\left(\frac{\partial Fy}{\partial x} - \frac{\partial Fx}{\partial y}\right) = \left[(curl\,\vec{F}).\hat{k}\right] = \left(curl\,\vec{F}\right)z^*$$

So, that, if the small area $\delta x \delta y$ be regarded as the vector area $\delta s_z \hat{k}$ (where $\hat{k}$ is the unit vector along the axis of z), we have

$$\oint_{ABCD} \vec{F}.d\vec{l} = \oint_C \vec{F}.d\vec{l} = (curl\,\vec{F})_z.\delta s_z \hat{k}.$$

It follows, therefore, that if we have an infinitesimal plane area at the point in question given by $\delta \vec{s} = \delta s_x \hat{i} + \delta s_y \hat{j} + \delta s_z \hat{k}$, with a boundary C and ted in any direction, we have

$$\oint_C \vec{F}.d\vec{l} = curl\,\vec{F}.\delta\vec{s},$$

the maximum value of $\oint \vec{F}.d\vec{l}$ being $|\,curl\,\vec{F}\,|\,\delta s$.

We thus see that *the magnitude of curl* $\vec{F}$ *at a point is the maximum value of the line integral of* $\vec{F}$ *per unit area along the boundary C of an infinitesimal plane area* (δs) *at that point*. And the direction of the curl is perpendicular to the plane of the infinitesimal area (when the value of the line integral is maximum) in accordance with the right handed screw rule.

N.B. It has been mentioned earlier that the curl of a conservative vector field is zero at all points in space. This may be seen from the following.

The line integral between any two points P and Q in the case of a conservative vector field is, as we know, a constant property of those points, irrespective of the path taken between them. It follows, therefore, that if we choose two different paths I and II between the two points, as indicated in fig. 1.39, we shall have

$$\underset{Path\ I}{\int_P^Q \vec{F}.d\vec{l}} = \underset{Path\ II}{\int_P^Q \vec{F}.d\vec{l}}$$

If Q be brought nearer and nearer to P, path I becomes shorter and in the limit when Q is made to coincide with P, path I is reduced to zero hence the integral along this, or any other path too, is reduced to zero. Thus, the line integral of $\vec{F}$ along any closed path (also called circulation of field $\vec{F}$ around the closed path), beginning and ending at the same point, is zero in the case of conservative field, *i.e.*,

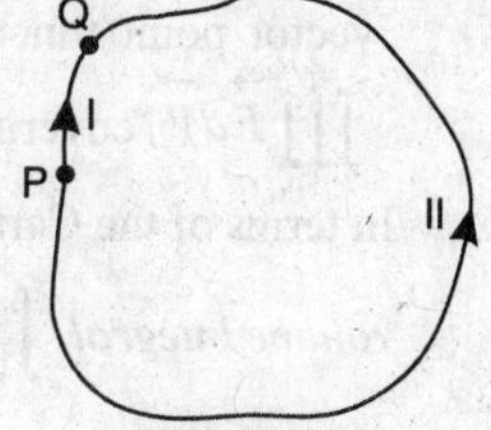

Fig. 1.39

$$\oint_{closed\ path} \vec{F}.d\vec{l} = 0,$$

* We similarly have x-component of $\vec{F}$, *i.e.*,

$$(curl\,\vec{F})_x = \left(\frac{\partial F_z}{\partial y} - \frac{F\partial_y}{\partial_z}\right) \text{ and } (curl\,F)_y = \left(\frac{\partial F_x}{\partial z} - \frac{\partial F_z}{\partial_x}\right)$$

So that, $curl\,\vec{F} = \hat{i}(curl\,F)_x + \hat{j}(curl\,F)_y + \hat{k}(curl\,F)_z$.

Or, $curl\,\vec{F} = \left(\frac{\partial F_z}{\partial y} - \frac{\partial F_y}{\partial z}\right)\hat{i} + \left(\frac{\partial F_x}{\partial z} - \frac{\partial F_z}{\partial x}\right)\hat{j} + \left(\frac{\partial F_y}{\partial x} - \frac{\partial F_x}{\partial y}\right)\hat{k}$,

as shown in §1.37.

Since the relation holds good for all conservative fields irrespective of the closed path chosen, these fields must have zero curl at all points in space. That is why they are referred to as curl-free or non-curl fields.

(*ii*) **Surface integral.** Imagine a smooth surface S (Fig. 1.40) drawn in a vector field and a continuously varying vector point function or vector $\vec{F}$ at a point P in a small element $d\vec{S}$ of the surface, at an angle θ with the normal to the surface, at the point (drawn outwards if the surface be closed and always towards the same side otherwise). Then, the integral $\iint_S \vec{F}.d\vec{S} = \iint_S F\cos\theta dS$ over the entire surface is called the normal surface inregral, or generally, simply the **surface integral** of vector $\vec{F}$ over the surface.

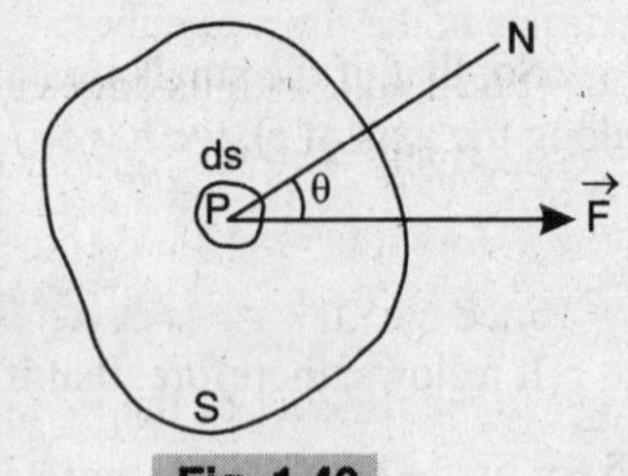

Fig. 1.40

In terms of the Cartesian components of $\vec{F}$ we have

$$\iint_S \vec{F}.d\vec{S} = \iint (F_x dS_x + F_y dS_y + F_z dS_z)$$

The surface integral of the normal component of a continuous vector point function $\vec{F}$ over a closed surface S is called the flux of across $\vec{F}$ the surface*. As we have seen before (*ii*) if the flux of a vector point function across every closed surface in a region be zero, it is said to be solenoidal in that region.

Examples (*i*) If $\vec{F}$ represents the electric or magnetic induction at the point P, the surface integral $\iint_S \vec{F}.d\vec{S}$ represents the total *normal induction over the surface.*

(*ii*) If the surface S be drawn over a region of a moving or a flowing fluid such that its velocity $\vec{v}$ varies from point to point the surface integral of $\vec{v}$ viz., $\iint \vec{v}.d\vec{S}$ gives the *value rate of flow of the fluid across the surface.*

(*iii*) **Volume integral.** Suppose we have a surface enclosing a region of volume V and that $\vec{F}$ is a vector point function at a point in a small element $d\vec{V}$ of the region. Then, the integral $\iiint_v \vec{F} d\vec{V}$, covering the entire region, is called the volume integral of vector over the surface.

In terms of the Cartesian components, we have

$$\text{volume integral } \iiint_v \vec{E}.d\vec{V} = \hat{i}\iiint^{\hat{V}} F_x\, dxdydz + \hat{j}\iiint^{\hat{V}} F_y dxdydz + \hat{k}\iiint^{\hat{V}} F_z\, dxdydz.$$

1.42 GAUSS'S THEOREM OF DIVERGENCE

The theorem states that the normal surface integral of a function $\vec{F}$ over the boundary of a closed surface S (i.e. the flux across S) is equal to the volume integral of the divergence of the function over the volume V enclosed by the surface, i.e.,

$$flux = \iint_S \vec{F}.d\vec{S} = \iiint^{\hat{V}} div\, \vec{F}\, dV = \iiint^{\hat{V}} (\vec{\nabla}.\vec{F})\, dV.$$

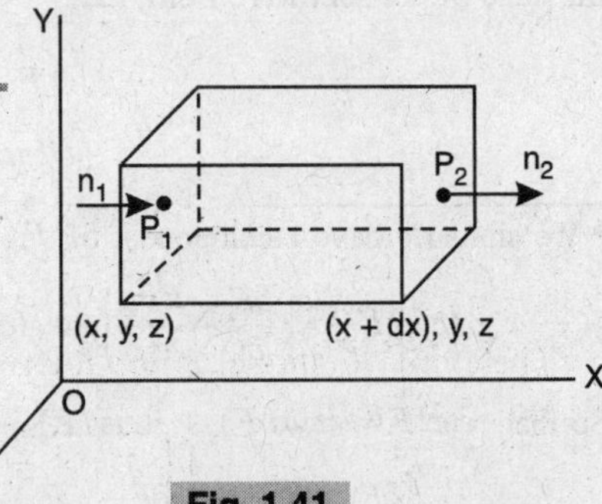

Fig. 1.41

* It is by no means necessary that the vector snould represent the flow of something. Even if it does not represent the flow of anything, the surface integral of its normal component is still called its flux across the surface.

This may be easily shown as follows:

Let the surface S enclosing a volume V be divided up into a very large number of elementary volumes in the form of cubes or rectangular parallelopipeds adjoining each other. Imagine one such cube (Fig. 1.41). with its edges along the three Cartesian coordinate axes and their lengths d_x, d_y and d_z respectively. The flux outwards through the left face is obviously given by $-\int F_x d_y d_z$, where F_x is the x-component of the vector field and the integral extends over the area of the face.

Since the cube considered is an infinitesimal one, this integral may be taken to be very nearly equal to the product of the x-component of $\vec{F}$ at the centre P_1 of the face and the area $dydz$ of the face. So that, denoting the x-component of $\vec{F}$ at the centre of the face by $F_x(P_1)$, we have

flux through left face of the cube $= -F_x(P_1)\, dydz$

Similarly, *flux through right face of the cube* $= F_x(P_2)\, dydz$, the component $F = (P_2)$ now being positive.

Taking $F_x(P_2) = F_x(P_1) + \frac{\partial F_x}{\partial x} dx$, we have

$$\textit{flux through right face of the cube} = \left[F_x(P_1) + \frac{\partial F_x}{\partial x} dx\right] dydz.$$

$\therefore$ *flux though the left and right faces*

$$= \left[F_x(P_1) + \frac{\partial F_x}{\partial x} \cdot dx\right] dydz - F_x(P_1) dydz = \frac{\partial Fx}{\partial x} dxdydz.$$

Similarly, *flux through top and bottom faces of the cube*

$$= \frac{\partial F_y}{\partial y} dxdydz$$

and *flux through the remaining faces of the cube*

$$= \frac{\partial F_x}{\partial z} dxdydz$$

Therefore, flux though all the face of the cube is given by the sum of all these. So that,

$$\iint_{\substack{\text{Surface} \\ \text{of tube}}} \vec{F}.d\vec{S} = \left(\frac{\partial F_x}{\partial x} + \frac{\partial F_y}{\partial y} + \frac{\partial F_z}{\partial z}\right] dxdydz,$$

where $d\vec{S}$ is the area of the surface of the cube.

Now $$\frac{\partial F_x}{\partial x} + \frac{\partial F_y}{\partial y} + \frac{\partial F_z}{\partial z} = \vec{\nabla}.\vec{F} \text{ or } div\, \vec{F}$$

and $$dxdydz = dV, \text{ volume of the cube.}$$

We, therefore, have $$\iint_{\substack{\text{Surface} \\ \text{of cube}}} \vec{F}.d\vec{S} = (\vec{\nabla}.\vec{F}) dV.$$

Therefore, summing up the fluxes through all the elemental cubes into which the surface is divided up, we have

$$\iint_S \vec{F}.d\vec{S} = \iiint \hat{V}(\vec{\nabla}.\vec{F})\, dV = \iiint \hat{V}(div\, \vec{F}) dV,$$

which is Gauss's theorem.

Perhaps, more rigorously, it may be written as

$$\iint_S \vec{F}\cdot\hat{n}\, dS = \iiint_{\hat{V}} (\vec{\nabla}.\vec{F})\, dV = \iiint_{\hat{V}} (div\,\vec{F})\, dV,$$

where $\hat{n}$ is the *unit outward drawn normal vector*.

It may be noted that $\iint_S \vec{F}.d\vec{S}$ gives the surface integral of $\vec{F}$ over the area of $\vec{F}$ the bounding surface *S* enclosing volume *V*, because surface of the elemental cubes other than those forming part of surface *S* itself are common to two adjacent cubes and their surface integrals thus all cancel out in view of their oppositely directed normals.

Obviously, since $\vec{F}.d\vec{S} = F_x dS_x + F_y dS_y + F_z dS_z = F_x dydz + F_y dzdx + F_z dxdy$, we can express Gauss's theorem in terms of the Cartesian coordinates as

$$\iint_S (F_x dS_x + F_y dS_y + F_z dS_z) = \iiint_{\hat{V}} \left(\frac{\partial F_x}{\partial x} + \frac{\partial F_y}{\partial y} + \frac{\partial F_x}{\partial z}\right) dxdydz.$$

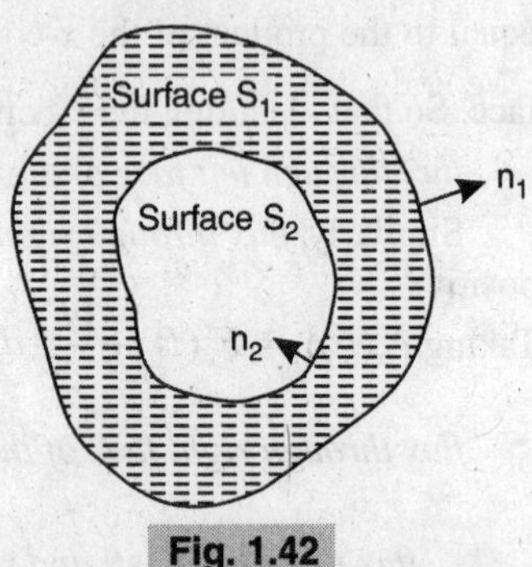

Fig. 1.42

It may as well be mentioned here that Gauss's theorem applies also to a volume bounded by two closed surfaces, as shown in Fig. 1.42 (and, indeed by any number of closed surfaces). Only, it must be remembered that the outward drawn normals (n_1 and n_2) at any points on the surfaces concerned must point away from the enclosed volume as shown.

1.43 STOKES' THEOREM

This theorem states that the line integral (or the circulations*) of a vector field $\vec{F}$ around any closed curve *O* is equal to the normal surface integral of the curl of $\vec{F}$ taken over any surface *S* of which curve *C* forms the contour or the boundary, *i.e.*,

$$\oint_C \vec{F}.d\vec{l} = \iint_S curl\ \vec{F}.d\vec{S} = \iint_S (\vec{\nabla}\times\vec{F}).d\vec{S}.$$

This may be shown as follows:

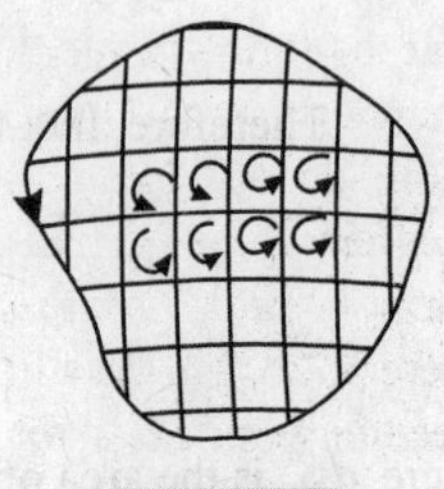
Fig. 1.43

Let a closed curve forming the boundary of a surface *S* of whatever shape (Fig. 1.43) be divided up into a very large number of small loops, infinitesimal in size and squarish in shape, all lying on the surface. These loops enclose small areas dS_1, dS_2 etc. inside them which are all flat, in view of the small size of the loops.

Considering one such small squarish loop enclosing area dS_1, we have

line integral (or circulation) of vector $\vec{F}$ around it, *i.e.*, $\oint \vec{F}.\vec{dl} = curl\ \vec{F}.\vec{dS_1}$ [§ 1.41], the direction of the curl being perpendicular to the plane of area $d\vec{S}$ in accordance with right-handed screw rule.

Now, if we sum up the left hand side, *i.e.*, the circulation around all these small loops into which the curve has been divided, we find that the contributions due to all the bounding lines of the loops, other than those that form part of the curve itself, cancel out since these contributions are all in the form of equal and oppositely directed pairs. So that, the summation simply gives the circulation or the line integral of the vector around the original closed curve alone.

* For, as mentioned under NB, page, 53 the line integral of a vector field along a closed path is also called circulation of the vector field around the path.

And, summation on the right hand side of the expression obviously gives the surface integral of curl $\vec{F}$ over the entire surface S enclosed by the curve. So that, we have

$\oint c\, \vec{F}.\vec{dl} = \iint_S curl\, \vec{F}.\, \vec{dS}$, which is the required theorem.

1.44 APPLICATION OF GAUSS'S AND STOKES' THEOREM

1. To show that the curl of the gradient of a scaler function ϕ is equal to zero, *i.e.,* $\vec{\nabla}\times\vec{\nabla}\phi = 0$.

We know that the line integral of the gradient $\vec{\nabla}\phi$ of the function along a closed loop is zero, *i.e.* $\int_{loop} \vec{\nabla}\phi.\ dl = 0$.

Now in accordance with stokes' theorem, this line integral of the vector $\vec{\nabla}\phi$ along a closed loop is equal to the surface integral of the curl of the vector over the surface S bounded by the loop, *i.e.,*

$$\oint \vec{\nabla}\phi.\vec{dl} = \iint_S \vec{\nabla}\times(\vec{\nabla}\phi).\vec{dS}$$

It follows, therefore, that the integral $\iint \hat{S}\,\vec{\nabla}\times(\vec{\nabla}\phi).\vec{dS} = 0$ over any surface. And, since the integral is zero, the integrand must-necessarily be zero. *i.e.,*

$$\vec{\nabla}\times\vec{\nabla}\phi = 0.$$

a result we had obtained by vector algebra earlier in § 1.39.

2. To show that the the divergence of the curl of a vector function $\vec{f}$ is zero. *i.e.,* $\vec{\nabla}.\vec{\nabla}\times\vec{f} = 0$. We know that according to stokes' theorem, the normal surface integral of the curl of a vector $\vec{f}$ over the closed loop that the forms the boundary of the surface. It follows, therefore that as the boundary, or the loop, decreases, *i.e.,* as the surface becomes more and more closed, (Fig. 1.44), the line integral of the vector around the loop, and hence the normal surface integral of the curl of the vector over the surface, must progressively decrease until, when the loop decreases to a mere point, *i.e.,* the surface becomes closed, the line and the surface integral become zero. Thus, *for a closed surface.*

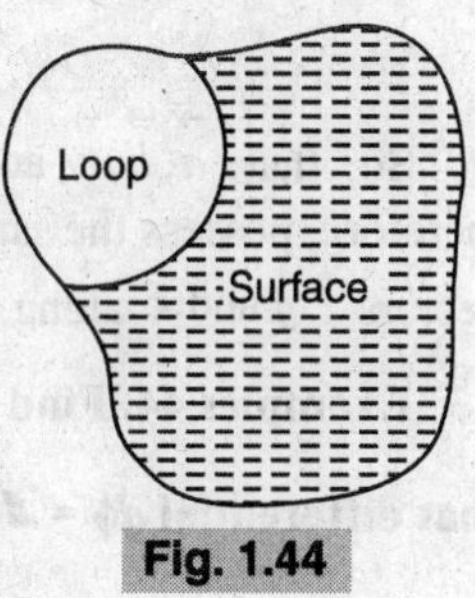

Fig. 1.44

$$\iint_S (\vec{\nabla}\times\vec{f}).\vec{dS} = 0.$$

But, in accordance with Gauss's theorem, this normal surface integral of a function over the boundary of a closed surface S is equal to the volume integral of the divergance of the function over the volume V enclosed by the surface. We, therefore, have

$$\iint_{\hat{S}} (\vec{\nabla}\times\vec{f}).\vec{dS} \times \iiint_V \vec{\nabla}.(\vec{\nabla}\times\vec{f}).\vec{dV}.$$

Obviously, therefore, $\iiint \hat{V}\,\vec{\nabla}.(\vec{\nabla}\times\vec{f}).\vec{dV} = 0$ for any vector field $\vec{f}$. And, since this is so for any volume, it follows that at every point in space the

$$\text{integrand } \vec{\nabla}.(\vec{\nabla}\times\vec{f}) = 0.$$

which, again, is a result we had arrived at earlier in § 1.39 (*iii*) by vector algebra.

1.45 RECIPROCAL SYSTEM OF VECTORS

If vectors $\vec{a}', \vec{b}'$ and $\vec{c}'$ be defined by the equations.

$$a' = \frac{\vec{b} \times \vec{c}}{[abc]},\ b' = \frac{\vec{c} \times \vec{a}}{[abc]} \text{ and } c' = \frac{\vec{a} \times \vec{b}}{[abc]},$$

they are said to be reciprocal vectors to $\vec{a}, \vec{b}$ and $\vec{c}$ which are assumed to be non-coplaner so that the product $[abc] = 0$. The planes of $\vec{a}, \vec{b}$ and $\vec{c}$ are respectively perpendicular to those of $\vec{b}, \vec{c}$; $\vec{c}, \vec{a}$ and $\vec{a}, \vec{b}$.

Since, obviously, the dot products $\vec{a}.\vec{a}' = \vec{b}.\vec{b}' = \vec{c}.\vec{c}' = 1$ the name *reciprocal vectors* for $\vec{a}', \vec{b}'$ and $\vec{c}'$ is only natural.

The dot product of any other pair, one from each system, is zero. Thus, $\vec{a}, \vec{b}' = 0$ because $\vec{a} \cdot \vec{b}' = \vec{a}\,\vec{c}\,\vec{a} / \vec{a}\,\vec{b}\,\vec{c}$ and the numerator, being a triple product containing two equal or identical vectors ($\vec{a}$ and $\vec{a}$) is equal to zero. Similarly, $\vec{c}.\vec{b}' = \vec{b}.\vec{a}' = \vec{b}.\vec{c}' = \vec{c}.\vec{a}' = \vec{a}.\vec{c}' = 0$.

It can be shown that

$$\vec{a} = \frac{\vec{b}' \times \vec{c}'}{[\vec{a}'\vec{b}'\vec{c}']},\quad \vec{b} = \frac{\vec{c}' \times \vec{a}'}{[\vec{a}'\vec{b}'\vec{c}']} \text{ and } \vec{c} = \frac{\vec{a}' \times \vec{b}'}{[\vec{a}'\vec{b}'\vec{c}']}$$

So, that $\vec{a}, \vec{b}, \vec{c}$, and $\vec{a}', \vec{b}', \vec{c}'$ are really reciprocal system of vectors to each other. They, therefore, possess the same sign *i.e.*, they are either both right-handed or both left-handed. The unit vectors $\hat{i}, \hat{j}$ and $\hat{k}$ along the three coordinate axes are, however, their own reciprocals.

Examples 44. Find grad r^m where r is the distance of any point from the origin. Also show that differential $d\phi = \vec{dr}$. grad ϕ.

Solution. We have $\phi(x, y, z) = r^m = (x^2 + y^2 + z^2)^{m/2}$

$$\left[\begin{array}{l} \because r^2 = x^2 + y^2 + z^2 \\ \text{and } \therefore r = (x^2 + y^2 + z^2)^{1/2} \end{array}\right]$$

$$\therefore \qquad \frac{\partial \phi}{\partial x} = mx\,(x^2 + y^2 + z^2)^{\frac{m}{2} - 1} = mxr^{m-2}$$

Similarly, $$\frac{\partial \phi}{\partial y} = myr^{m-2} - 2 \text{ and } \frac{\partial \phi}{\partial z} = mzr^{m-2}$$

Hence, $$\text{grad } r^m \text{ (or } \vec{\nabla}\, r^m) = \sum \hat{i}\frac{\partial \phi}{\partial x} = mr^{m-2} \sum \hat{i}\, x = mr^{m-2}\, \vec{r}, \qquad ...(i)$$

where $\vec{r}$ is the position vector of the point.

or, since $\vec{r} = r\hat{r}$, where r is the magnitude of $\vec{r}$ and $\hat{r}$, the unit vector along $\vec{r}$, we have $\hat{r} = r / r$.

So that, $$\textit{grad } r^m \text{ also} = mr^{m-1}\,(\vec{r}/r) = mr^{m-1}\hat{r} \qquad ...(ii)$$

Now, differential $$d\phi = \frac{\partial\phi}{\partial x}dx + \frac{\partial\phi}{\partial y}dy + \frac{\partial\phi}{\partial z}dz$$

$$= (\hat{i}dx + \hat{j}dy + \hat{k}dz).\left(\hat{i}\frac{\partial\phi}{\partial x} + \hat{j}\frac{\partial\phi}{\partial y} + \hat{k}\frac{\partial\phi}{\partial z}\right) = d\vec{r}\,.grad\,\phi.$$

Example 45. Show that the curl of the velocity of any particle of a rigid body is equal to twice the angular velocity of the body.

Solution. We have the relation $\vec{v} = \vec{\omega} \times \vec{r}$, where $\vec{v}$ is the velocity of any particle of the body, with $\vec{r}$ the position vector relative to a fixed point and $\vec{\omega}$ the angular velocity of the body.

Obviously, $\vec{v}$ is a vector point function and vector $\vec{\omega}$ is the same for all the particles.

Now, $$curl\ \vec{v} = curl(\vec{\omega} \times \vec{r}) = \sum \hat{i}\frac{\partial}{\partial x}(\vec{\omega} \times \vec{r}) = \sum \hat{i}\left(\vec{\omega} \times \frac{\partial \vec{r}}{\partial x}\right) = \sum \hat{i} \times (\vec{\omega} \times \hat{i})$$

$$= \sum(\hat{i}.\hat{i})\vec{\omega} - \sum(\hat{i}.\vec{\omega})\,\hat{i} = 3\vec{\omega} - \vec{\omega} = 2\vec{\omega}.$$

Example 46. Establish the results: (*i*) *div* $(\phi \vec{A}) = \phi$ *div* $\vec{A} + \vec{A}$. *grad* ϕ and

(*ii*) *div* $(\vec{A} \times \vec{B}) = \vec{B}$. *curl* $\vec{A} - \vec{A}$ *curl* $\vec{B}$.

Solution. (*i*) We have $$div\ (\phi\vec{A}) = \sum \hat{i}.\frac{\partial(\phi\vec{A})}{\partial x} = \Sigma\hat{i}\left(\phi\frac{\partial\vec{A}}{\partial x} + \frac{\partial\phi}{\partial x}\vec{A}\right)$$

$$= \sum \hat{i}.\phi\frac{\partial\vec{A}}{\partial x} + \sum \hat{i}.\frac{\partial\phi}{\partial x}\vec{A} = \phi\sum \hat{i}.\frac{\partial\vec{A}}{\partial x} + \left(\sum \hat{i}\frac{\partial\phi}{\partial x}\right)\vec{A}.$$

$$= \phi\ div\ \vec{A} + \vec{A}\,.\,grad\,\phi.$$

(*ii*) $$div\ (\vec{A} \times \vec{B}) = \sum \hat{i}.\frac{\partial(\vec{A} \times \vec{B})}{\partial x} = \sum \hat{i}\left(\frac{\partial\vec{A}}{\partial x} \times \vec{B} + \vec{A} \times \frac{\partial\vec{B}}{\partial x}\right)$$

$$= \sum \hat{i}.\frac{\partial\vec{A}}{\partial x} \times \vec{B} + \sum \hat{i}.\vec{A} \times \frac{\partial\vec{B}}{\partial x}$$

$$= \sum \hat{i} \times \frac{\partial\vec{A}}{\partial x}.\vec{B} - \sum \hat{i} \times \frac{\partial\vec{B}}{\partial x}.\vec{A}$$

$$= \left(\sum \hat{i} \times \frac{\partial\vec{A}}{\partial x}\right).\vec{B} - \left(\sum \hat{i} \times \frac{\partial\vec{B}}{\partial x}\right).\vec{A} = curl\ \vec{A}.\vec{B} - curl\ \vec{B}.\vec{A}$$

$$= \vec{B}\,.\,curl\ \vec{A} - \vec{A}\,.\,curl\ \vec{B}.$$

Example 47. Obtain *div grad* r^m. Also show that *curl grad* $r^m = 0$.

Solution. We have seen in Example 44 above that

$$grad\, r^m = \vec{\nabla} r^m = mr^{m-2}\, \vec{r} = mr^{m-2}(\hat{i}x + \hat{j}y + \hat{k}z)$$

$$\therefore \quad div\ grad\ r^m \text{ or } div\ \vec{\nabla} r^m = \frac{\partial}{\partial x}(mr^{m-2}x) + \frac{\partial}{\partial y}(mr^{m-2}y) + \frac{\partial}{\partial z}(mr^{m-2}z).$$

Now, $\frac{\partial}{\partial x}(mr^{m-2}x) = m(m-2)\, r^{m-2}\frac{\partial r}{\partial x} + mr^{m-2} = m(m-2)\, r^{m-1}x^2 + mr^{m-2}$, because $\partial r/\partial x = x/r$.

Similarly, $\frac{\partial}{\partial y}(mr^{m-2}y) = m(m-2)\, r^{m-1}y^2 + mr.^{m-2}$

and $\frac{\partial}{\partial z}(mr^{m-2}z) = m(m-2)\, r^{m-1}z^2 + mr.^{m-2}$

$$\therefore\ div\ grad\ r^m = div\ \vec{\nabla} r^m = m(m-2)\, r^{m-1}r^2 + 3\, mr^{m-2} = m(m+1)r^{m-2}$$

And
$$curl\ grad\ r^m = \begin{vmatrix} \hat{i} & \hat{j} & \hat{k} \\ \frac{\partial}{\partial x} & \frac{\partial}{\partial y} & \frac{\partial}{\partial z} \\ mr^{m-2}x & mr^{m-2}y & mr^{m-2}z \end{vmatrix}$$

So that coefficient of $\hat{i}$ in *curl grad* $r^m = \frac{\partial}{\partial y}mr^{m-2}z - \frac{\partial}{\partial z}mr^{m-2}y$

$$= m(m-2)\, r^{m-3}\frac{\partial r}{\partial y}z - m(m-2)\, r^{m-3}\frac{\partial r}{\partial z}y$$

$$= m(m-2)\, r^{m-3}\frac{yz}{r}z - m(m-2)\, r^{m-3}\frac{zy}{r} = 0.$$

Hence $\quad Curl\ grad\ r^m = \vec{\nabla}\times\vec{\nabla} r^m = 0.$

Example 48. Show that $\iint_S \vec{F}\times\hat{n}_d\, S = -\iint_V curl\ \vec{F}\, dV$

Solution. Let us put $\vec{f} = \vec{a}\times\vec{F}$, where $\vec{f}$ is a vector function and $\vec{a}$, an *arbitrary constant vector*. Then, applying Gauss's theorem to $\vec{f}$, we have

$$\int_S \vec{a}\times\vec{F}.\vec{n}\, dS = \int_V div(\vec{a}\times\vec{F})\, dV. \quad \text{... (i)}$$

Now, $\quad \vec{a}\times\vec{F}.\vec{n} = \vec{a}.\vec{F}\times\vec{n} \quad$ ...(*ii*)

and $\quad div(\vec{a}\times\vec{F}) = \vec{\nabla}.(\vec{a}\times\vec{F}) = -\vec{a}.\vec{\nabla}\times\vec{F}. \quad$ ...(*iii*)

So that, using relations (*ii*) and (*iii*), relation (*i*) may be put as

$$\int_S \vec{a}.\vec{F}\times\hat{n}dS = -\int_V \vec{a}.\vec{\nabla} + \vec{F}\, dV.$$

or, $\quad a\int_S \vec{F}\times\hat{n}dS = -\vec{a}\int_V \vec{\nabla}\times d\vec{F}\, V.$

or, $\quad a\left[\int_S \vec{F}\times\hat{n}dS + \int_V \vec{\nabla}\times\vec{F}_d\, V\right] = \mathbf{0}.$

since $\vec{a}$ is just an arbitrary vector, we have $\int_S \vec{F} \times \hat{n} dS + \int_V \vec{\nabla} \times \vec{F} dV = 0.$

or,
$$\int_S \vec{F} \times \hat{n} dS = -\int_V \vec{\nabla} \times \vec{F} dV = \int_V curl\,\vec{F} dV.$$

Example 49. Verify Stokes' theorem for the functions $\vec{F} = x(\hat{i}x + \hat{j}y)$, integrated round the square in the plane $z = 0$, whose sides are along the lines $x = 0, y = 0, x = a, y = a$.

Solution. Referring to the square shown in Fig. 1.45, we clearly have

$$\oint_O \vec{F}.\vec{dl} + \int_{OA} \vec{F}.\vec{dl} + \int_{AB} \vec{F}.\vec{dl} + \int_{BC} \vec{F}.\vec{dl} + \int_{CO} \vec{F}.\vec{dl},$$

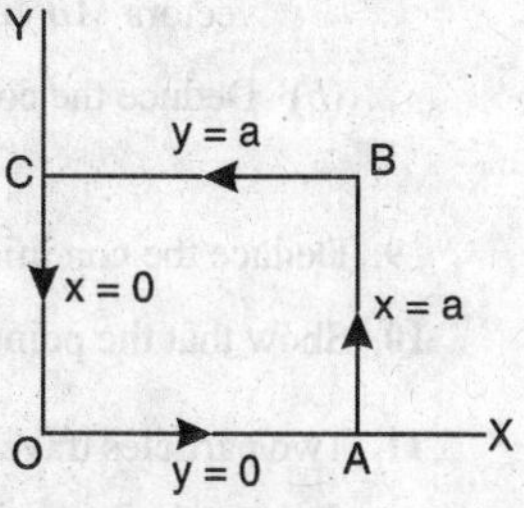

where,
$$\int_{OA} F.\vec{dl} = \int_o^a x(\hat{i}x + \hat{j}y).\hat{i}dx = \int_o^a x^2 dx = \frac{1}{3}a^3,$$

$$\int_{AB} \vec{F}.\vec{dl} = \int_o^a x(\hat{i}x + \hat{j}y).\hat{j}dy = \int_o^a ay\,dy = \frac{1}{2}a^3,$$

$$\int_{BC} \vec{F}.\vec{dl} = \int_a^o x(\hat{i}x + \hat{j}y).\hat{i}dx = -\int_o^a x^2 dx = -\frac{1}{3}a^3 \text{ and}$$

$$\int_{CO} \vec{F}.\vec{dl} = \int_a^o x(\hat{i}x + \hat{j}y).\hat{j}dy = 0$$

Fig. 1.45

So that,
$$\oint_c \vec{F}.\vec{dl} = \frac{1}{3}a^3 + \frac{1}{2}a^3 - \frac{1}{3}a^3 + 0 = \frac{1}{2}a^3.$$

Now, in accordance with *Stokes' theorem,* $\oint_c \vec{F}.\vec{dl} = \iint_S curl\,\vec{F}.\vec{dS}.$

Since curl $x\;(\hat{i}x + \hat{j}y) = \hat{k}y$ we have

$$\iint_S curl\,\vec{F}.\vec{dS} = \iint_S curl\,x(\hat{i}x + \hat{j}y)\,dS = \int_o^a \int_o^a \hat{k}y.\hat{k}d\,xdy$$

$$= \int_o^a \int_o^a ydxdy = \frac{1}{2}a^3.$$

Stokes' theorem thus stands verified.

EXERCISE

1. What is *(i) a polar vector (ii) an axial vector (iii) unit vector (iv) a zero vector*? What do you understand by the term orthogonal unit vector triad?
2. What is meant by the *position vector* of a point? Express the position vector of a point in terms of the orthogonal unit vector triad. What is the modulus of the vector $\vec{r}$?
3. What are *direction cosines*? Show that if a unit vector be resolved in terms of *i*, *j* and *k* are the direction cosines of that vector.
4. What angle does the vector $\hat{i} + \sqrt{2}\hat{j} + 3\hat{k}$ make with the axis of *z* and what is the value of its component in the $y - z$ plane? **[Ans.** 30°. $\sqrt{11}$ **]**
5. If vectors $\vec{A}$ and $\vec{B}$ be respectively equal to $3\hat{i} - 4\hat{j} + 5\hat{k}$ and $2\hat{i} + 3\hat{j} - 4\hat{k}$, obtain the magnitudes of vectors $\vec{A} + \vec{B}$ and $\vec{A} - \vec{B}$. What will be the unit vectors parallel to $\vec{A} + \vec{B}$ and $\vec{A} - \vec{B}$ respectively?

[Ans. $\sqrt{27}; \sqrt{131}; \frac{1}{\sqrt{27}}(5\hat{i} - \hat{j} + \hat{k}); \frac{1}{\sqrt{131}}(\hat{i} - 7\hat{j} + 9\hat{k})$ **]**

6. (*a*) If $\vec{A} = 3\hat{i} + 4\hat{j} + 4\hat{k}$ and $\vec{B} = \hat{i} + 4\hat{j} + 4\hat{k}$, obtain the direction cosines of $\vec{A} + \vec{B}$ and $\vec{A} - \vec{B}$.

[**Ans.** 1/3, 2/3, 2/3, 1,0,0.]

(*b*) What should be the vector which, on addition to vectors $-2\hat{i} + 3\hat{j} - 4\hat{k}$ and $-2\hat{j} + 4\hat{k}$ will give a unit vector along the axis of *y*? [**Ans.** $2\hat{i}$]

7. If $\vec{a}$ and $\vec{b}$ are the vectors $\vec{AB}, \vec{BC}$ determined by the adjacent sides of a regular hexagon, what are the vectors determined by the other sides, taken in order?

[**Ans.** $(\vec{b} - \vec{a}). - \vec{a}, - \vec{b}, (\vec{a} - \vec{b})$]

8. (*a*) The points *A*, *B* and *C* are respectively $\hat{i} + 2\hat{j} - 3\hat{k}, 3\hat{i} - 4\hat{j} + 5\hat{k}$ and $5\hat{i} - 10\hat{j} + 13\hat{k}$. Show that vectors $\vec{AB}$ and $\vec{BC}$ are collinear.

(*b*) Deduce the condition for the vector $2\hat{i} + 3\hat{j} - 4\hat{k}$ and $3\hat{i} - a\hat{j} + b\hat{k}$ to be parallel (or collinear).

[**Ans.** $a = - 9/2, b = -6$]

9. Deduce the condition for the coplanarity of three vectors $\vec{A}, \vec{B}$ and $\vec{C}$.

10. Show that the points *A* (4, 5, 1), *B* (0, –1, –1), *C* (3, 9, 4), and *D* (–4, 4, 4) are coplanar.

11. Two particles travel along the axes of x and y with velocities $\vec{v}_1 = 3\hat{i}$ and $\vec{v}_2 = 4\hat{j}$ respectively. If at the start their positions be $x_1 = -4$ cm, $y_1 = 0$ and $x_2 = 0, y_2 = -5$ cm, obtain the position vector *r* giving the relative position of the second particle with respect to the first.
When will the two particles be the closest together?

[**Ans.** $\vec{r} = (4t - 5)\,\hat{j} - (3t - 4)\,i$; 1.28 s after start]

[**Hint.** At time *t*, $\vec{r}_1 = (3t - 4)\hat{i}$ and $\vec{r}_2 = (4t - 5)\hat{j}$ and $\therefore\ \vec{r} = (\vec{r}_2 - \vec{r}_1)$]

The particles will be the closest when $|\vec{r}|$ or $|\vec{r}|^2$ is the least, *i.e.*, when

$$\frac{d}{dt}|\vec{r}|^2 = \frac{d}{dt}[3t - 4]^2 + (4t - 5)^2 = 0,$$ whence *t* can be easily calculated.]

Scalar Product

12. What is meant by the scalar product of two vectors? Show that it is *commutative* as well as *distributive*. Use the concept of scalar product to deduce the *Cosine law*.

13. If $\vec{a}$ and $\vec{b}$ are two vectors given by $\vec{a} = a_x\hat{i} + a_y\hat{j} + a_z\hat{k}$ and $\vec{b} = b_x\hat{i} + b_y\hat{j} + b_z\hat{k}$ show that $\vec{a}.\vec{b} = a_xb_x + a_yb_y + a_zb_z$.

14. Obtain the scalar product of vectors $(6\hat{i} + 2\hat{j} + 3\hat{k})$ and $(2\hat{i} - 9\hat{j} + 6\hat{k})$ and also the cosine of the angle between them.

[**Ans.** 12; 12/77]

15. Define scalar and vector products of two vectors. If $\hat{i}\ \hat{j}, \hat{k}$ are unit vectors along *x*, *y* and *z* axes respectively, show that $\hat{i}.\hat{i} = 1$ and $\hat{i}.\hat{j} = 0$.

16. (*a*) Show that vectors $\vec{A} = 2\hat{i} + 3\hat{j} - 4\hat{k}$ and $\vec{B} = 5\hat{i} + 2\hat{j} + 4\hat{k}$ are perpendicular to each other.

(*b*) Under what condition will the vectors $\vec{A} = 3\hat{i} - 5\hat{j} + 5\hat{k}$ and $\vec{B} = 5\hat{i} - \hat{j} + b\hat{k}$ be perpendicular to each other? [**Ans.** When $b = -4$.]

17. (*a*) If $|\vec{A}+\vec{B}|=|\vec{A}-\vec{B}|$,show that $\vec{A}$ and $\vec{B}$ are perpendicular to each other.

(*b*) What conclusions can you draw from the fact that the scalar product $\vec{A}.\vec{B}=0$?

18. Forces acting on a particle have magnitudes 5, 3, 1 lb wt and act in the directions of the vectors $6\hat{i}+2\hat{j}+3\hat{k}, 3\hat{i}-2\hat{j}+6\hat{k}, 2\hat{i}-3\hat{j}-6\hat{k}$ respectively. These remain constant while the particle is displaced from the point $A(2, -1, -3)$ to $B(5, -1, -1)$. Find the work done by the forces, the unit of length being 1 ft.

[**Ans.** 33 ft. lb.]

[**Hint.** Here. Clearly, the three forces are $5(6\hat{i}+2\hat{j}+3\hat{k}), 3(3\hat{i}-2\hat{j}+6\hat{k})$ and $1(2\hat{i}-3\hat{j}-6\hat{k})$ respectively. So that, their resultant is $(41\hat{i}+\hat{j}+27\hat{k})$. For the rest, see worked example 11].

19. Show that if the scalar product of a vector $\vec{r}$ with each of three non-coplanar vectors be zero, then $\vec{r}$ must be zero vector.

[**Hint.** See worked example 6 (*b*)]

20. Show that if $\vec{a}$ and $\vec{b}$ are equal in magnitude and non-parallel, $\vec{a}+\vec{b}$ and $\vec{a}-\vec{b}$ are perpendicular.

21. Find the cosine of the angle between the vectors $\vec{a}=3\hat{i}+\hat{j}+2\hat{k}$ and $\vec{b}=2\hat{i}-2\hat{j}+4\hat{k}$. Find also the unit vector perpendicular to both $\vec{a}$ and $\vec{b}$. [**Ans.** $3/\sqrt{21}; \frac{1}{\sqrt{3}}(\hat{i}-\hat{j}-\hat{k})$]

Vector Product

22. If two vectors are $6\hat{i}+0.3\hat{j}-5\hat{k}$ and $\hat{i}-4.2\hat{j}+2.5\hat{k}$, find the vector product and by calculation prove that the new vector is perpendicular to the two.

23. What is the unit vector perpendicular to each of the vectors $\vec{a}=2\hat{i}-\hat{j}+\hat{k}$ and $\vec{b}=3\hat{i}+4\hat{j}-\hat{k}$ Calculate the sine of the angle between these vectors. ***(Utkal; A.M.I.E)***

[**Ans.** $\frac{1}{\sqrt{155}}(-3\hat{i}+5\hat{j}+11\hat{k})$]

24. Show that the vector product is (*i*) *associative*, (*ii*) *not commutative*.

25. (*a*) Write down the values of (*i*) $\hat{i}\times\hat{i}, \times\hat{j}\times\hat{j}, \hat{k}\times\hat{k}$ (*ii*) $\hat{i}\times\hat{j}, \hat{j}\times\hat{k}$ and $\hat{k}\times\hat{i}$.

(*b*) Show that if $\vec{b}=\vec{c}+m\vec{a}$ where m is any scalar, $\vec{a}\times\vec{b}=\vec{a}\times\vec{c}$, but that if $\vec{a}\times\vec{b}=\vec{a}\times\vec{c}, \vec{b}$ is not necessary eual to $\vec{c}$.

26. Express the magnitude of $\vec{a}\times\vec{b}$ in terms of the scalar product.

[Delhi (Hons):]

[**Ans.** $(\vec{a}\times\vec{b})^2=a^2b^2-(\vec{a}\cdot\vec{b})^2$.]

27. Show that if $\vec{a}, \vec{b}, \vec{c}$ be three vectors. We have $\vec{a}\times(\vec{b}+\vec{c})=\vec{a}\times\vec{b}+\vec{a}\times\vec{c}$.

[Delhi (Hons); Panjab; Rajasthan: Vikram]

28. Obtain the vector area of a triangle whose vertices are $\vec{a}, \vec{b}$ and $\vec{c}$. What is the condition for collinearity of the three points ?

Ans. *Vector area* $=\frac{1}{2}(\vec{b}\times\vec{c}+\vec{c}\times\vec{a}+\vec{a}\times\vec{b}); \vec{a}\times\vec{b}+\vec{b}\times\vec{c}+\vec{c}\times\vec{a}=0.$

29. Find the area of the parallelogram determined by vectors $\hat{i}+2\hat{j}+3\hat{k}$ and $-3\hat{i}-2\hat{j}+\hat{k}$.

(Allahabad; Lcuknow)

What is the sine of the angle between the two vectors?

[Ans. $6\sqrt{5}$ sq. units; $3\sqrt{5}/7$]

30. Find the torque about the point $\hat{i}+2\hat{j}-\hat{k}$ of a force represented by $3\hat{i}+\hat{k}$ acting through the point $2\hat{i}-\hat{j}+3\hat{k}$.

(Rajasthan)

[Ans. $-3\hat{i}+11\hat{j}+9\hat{k}$]

31. Deduce the unit vector which is perpendicular to both the vectors $\vec{P}=3\hat{i}-3\hat{j}$ and $\vec{Q}=6\hat{j}+5\hat{k}$

[Ans. $\frac{3}{\sqrt{774}}(5\hat{i}+5\hat{j}-6\hat{k})$]

32. A proton of velocity $(3\hat{i}+2\hat{j})$ 10^8 cm/s enters a magnetic field $2000\hat{j}+3000\hat{k}$ *gauss*. Calculate the acceleration. Also deduce the simultaneous electric field which will keep the particle undeflected.

[Ans. 2.8 × 10^{15} $(2\hat{i}-3\hat{j}+2\hat{k})$ cm/s^2; $-20\hat{i}+30\hat{j}-20\hat{k}$ *esu*.]

[Hint. $\vec{F}=\frac{q}{c}(\vec{v}\times\vec{B})$; If $\vec{E}$ be the required electric field, $\vec{F}=\frac{q}{c}(\vec{v}\times\vec{B})+q\vec{E}=0$].

33. If $\vec{A}=4\hat{i}-5\hat{j}+3\hat{k}, \vec{B}=2\hat{i}-10\hat{j}-7\hat{k}$ and $\vec{C}=5\hat{i}+7\hat{j}-4\hat{k}$ them find $(\vec{A}\times\vec{B})\cdot\vec{C}$ *(Nagpur Uni. 2010)*

Triple Products

34. The vectors $\hat{i}+2\hat{j}+3\hat{k}$, $-3\hat{i}+2\hat{k}$ and $-5\hat{k}$ represent the edges of a parallelopiped; obtain its volume.

[Ans. 15 *units*.]

35. (*a*) Deduce the condition for coplanarity of three vectors.

(*b*) Obtain the scalar triple product of (*i*) the vectors $\vec{a},\vec{a}$ and $\vec{b}$ (*ii*) the vectors $\vec{a},\vec{b}$ and $\vec{c}$ where $\vec{a}$ and $\vec{b}$ are parallel.

[Ans. (*i*) 0; (*ii*) 0.]

36. Vectors $\vec{A},\vec{B}$ and $\vec{C}$ are respectively given by $2\hat{i}+\hat{j}-3\hat{k}, \hat{i}+3\hat{j}+4\hat{k}$ and $5\hat{j}+m\hat{k}$. What should be the value of *m* so that (*i*) the volume of the parallelopiped, with its edges represented by the three vectors, be 15 units (*ii*) the three vectors may be coplanar? **[Ans.** (*i*) m = 15 or 8; (*ii*) m = 11.]

37. (*a*) Write down the values of (*i*) $\hat{k}\cdot\hat{k}$ (*ii*) $[\hat{i}\,\hat{j}\,\hat{k}]$, (*iii*) $\vec{a}\times(\vec{b}\times\vec{c})$, (*iv*) $\vec{b}\times(\vec{c}\times\vec{a})$, (*v*) $\vec{c}\times(\vec{a}\times\vec{b})$.

Ans. (*i*) 1, (*ii*) 1, (*iii*) $(\vec{a}\cdot\vec{c})\vec{b}-(\vec{a}\cdot\vec{b})\vec{c}$, (*iv*) $(\vec{a}\cdot\vec{b})\vec{c}-(\vec{b}\cdot\vec{c})\vec{a}$, (*v*) $(\vec{b}\cdot\vec{c})\vec{a}-(\vec{c}\cdot\vec{a})\vec{b}$.

(*b*) Show that $\vec{a}\times(\vec{b}\times\vec{c})+\vec{b}\times(\vec{c}\times\vec{a})+\vec{c}\times(\vec{a}\times\vec{b})=0$.

38. Give the three vectors $\vec{A}=5\hat{i}-7\hat{j}+3\hat{k}, \vec{B}=-4\hat{i}+7\hat{j}-8\hat{k}, \vec{C}=2\hat{i}-3\hat{j}$, deduce the following: (*i*) $\vec{A}\cdot\vec{B}\times\vec{C}$ and $\vec{A}\times\vec{B}\cdot\vec{C}$, (*ii*) A^2C.

[Ans. (*i*) –14. –14; (*ii*) 83 $(2\hat{i}-3\hat{j})$.]

Derivatives of a Vector - Circular Motion

39. A body of mass 500 g, free to move, is subjected to a force of $\hat{i}+2\hat{j}+\hat{k}$ Newton. What velocity will it acquire after 4 seconds and what distance will it have covered in that interval of time?

[Ans. $\vec{v}=(8\hat{i}+16\hat{j}+8\hat{k})$ m/s; $\vec{S}=16\hat{i}+32\hat{j}+16\hat{k}$ metre.]

40. Show that in the case of a rigid body spinning about a fixed axis, the linear velocity $(\vec{v})$ of a particle of the body is the cross product of the angular velocity $\vec{\omega}$ and the position vector $\vec{r}$ of the particle relative to a fixed point on the axis.

41. A rigid body is spinning with an angular velocity of 4 radians per second about an axis parallel to $(3\hat{j}-\hat{k})$, passing through the point $(\hat{i}+3\hat{j}-\hat{k})$. Find the velocity of the particle at the poin $4\hat{i}-2\hat{j}+\hat{k}$

[**Ans.** $\vec{v}=\frac{4}{\sqrt{10}}(\hat{i}-3\hat{j}-9\hat{k})$, its magnitude = $4\sqrt{91/10}$.]

Gradient–Divergence–Curl–(Differential Operators)

42. Obtain the values of (*i*) *grad* (1/*r*), (*ii*) [*grad f* (*r*)] × *r*. [**Ans.** (*i*) $-r/r^2$. (*ii*) 0.]

43. Given that the electric field is the negative of the gradient of potential, *i.e.*, $\vec{E}=-\nabla\vec{V}$, obtain the value of the electric field if that of the potential be – *Kxy*, where *K* is a constant. [**Ans.** $K(\hat{i}y+\hat{j}x)$]

44. If $\vec{r}=x\hat{i}+y\hat{j}+z\hat{k}$ show that (*i*) *div r* = 3, (*ii*) *curl r* = 0 (*iii*) *div* ($r^n r$) = (n + 3) r^n and (*iv*) $\nabla^2 r^{-1}=0$.

45. Show that (*a*) *curl* $\phi(r)=0$ and *curl* $(\vec{a}\cdot\vec{r})\vec{a}=0$.

46. Prove that *curl grad* $\phi=0$ and *div curl* $\vec{f}=0$.

47. The Laplacian Operator $\nabla^2=\vec{\nabla}\vec{\nabla}$. Why do we not have another operator $\vec{\nabla}\times\vec{\nabla}$?

48. What is meant by line and surface integrals? Enunciate and prove *Gauss's theorm*.

49. Show that $\iint_S \vec{F}\cdot d\vec{S}=6\vec{V}$ where *S* is a closed surface, enclosing a volume $\vec{V}$ and $\vec{F}=x\hat{i}+2y\hat{j}+3z\hat{k}$

50. Show that $\int_S (x^2\hat{i}+y^2\hat{j}+z^2\hat{k})\cdot\hat{n}dS=0$, where S denotes the surface of the ellipsoid $\frac{x^2}{a^2}+\frac{y^2}{b^2}+\frac{z^2}{c^2}=1$

51. Enunciate and prove *Stokes' theorem*.

52. Show, using either Gauss's or Stokes' theorem, that f_s curl $\hat{f}\cdot\hat{n}dS=0$, where *S* is a closed surface.

2 Chapter NEWTON'S LAWS OF MOTION-REFERENCE FRAMES

Brief Contents

INTRODUCTION

Every motion, either linear or rotational in a specific frame of reference is governed by certain laws. Mechanics deals with these laws, with respect to any frame, inertial or non-inertial, and formulates them in a scientific manner. We have devoted previous chapter of mathematical background to formulate these laws. Linear motion is a translational motion in a straight line. The concept of 'force' is fully explained by Newton through his laws of motion. Force is resposible for linear acceleration while torque for angular acceleration. The basic ideas of **state of rest** and **uniform motion** were studied by various philosophers. According to Aristotle (384-322 BC), a constant force has to be applied on a body so as to keep it in a motion with constant velocity. Later on, Galileo (1564-1642 AD) stated that no force is required for a body to move with uniform velocity. Newton (1642-1727) was the first philosopher who formulated the laws differentiating '*state of rest*' and '*state of uniform motion*'. Newton's notion of space as '*Absolute space*', isotropic nature for rotational invariance and homogeneity for translational invariance led to understand the laws of motion in inertial frame of reference. Any accelerated frame of reference is a non-inertial frame. Concepts of fictitious forces like Coriolis force and its applications are studied in this chapter.

2.1 SOME IMPORTANT TERMS

Having understood the well known mathematical terms like point, straight line, scalar and vector operations under mathematical background in the previous chapter, in Physics we frequently come across three other terms: (*i*) particle, (*ii*) event and (*iii*) observer, as we proceed further in the development of topic 'Mechanics'. It is best, therefore, to understand at the very outset their exact connotations.

(*i*) Particle. A *particle* is ideally just a piece or a *quantity of matter, having practically no linear dimensions but only a position,* the measure of this quantity of matter being the *mass* of the particle.

Such idealised particles or point-bodies are, of course, convenient mathematical fictions and have no real existence. All that is implied is that, in our actual physical problems, if we happen to be dealing with a body whose size is very much smaller than the other quantities involved, we may to a first approximation, treat the body mathematically as a point-body or a particle. Thus, for instance, the bob of a simple pendulum, in relation to the length of the string carrying it, or a planet, in relation to its distance from the sun and the stars, may be considered to be a particle. It is not always that simple, however. For, the tiny electron, very close to a charged body is not regarded as a particle. It thus depends really on the circumstances obtaining in any given case whether or not a body is to be regarded as a particle. This will become—clearer as we proceed along.

(*ii*) Event. An *event* stands in our mathewmatical model for *anything that occurs suddenly or instantaneously at a point in space.* It thus involves both, *a position* and *a time of occurrence.*

(*iii*) Observer. *A person or an equipment which can locate, record, measure and interpret an event is called an observer.*

2.2 REST AND MOTION

We are already generally familiar with these terms from our junior classes Here, therefore, we may simply emphasize the fact that *they have a meaning only in relation to a given frame of reference* (see next article). A particle is taken to be at rest or in motion in relation to the given frame of reference, according as it continues, or does not continue, to occupy the same position in that particular frame of reference.

2.3 REFERENCE FRAME

A system of coordinate axes which defines the position of a particle or an event in two or three dimensional space is called a frame of reference. The essential requirement of a frame of reference is that *it should be rigid.*

The simplest frame of reference is, of course, the familiar *Cartesian system of coordinates,* in which the position of the particle is specified by its three coordinates x, y, z along the three perpendicular axes, such that if $\vec{r}$ be the *position vector* of the particle with respect to the origin, we have

$$\vec{r} = x\hat{i} + y\hat{j} + z\hat{k},$$

where, $\hat{i}$, $\hat{j}$ and $\hat{k}$ are the *unit vectors* along the three axes.

So that, *velocity* of the particle is given by

$$\vec{v} = \frac{d\vec{r}}{dt} = \frac{dx}{dt}\hat{i} + \frac{dy}{dt}\hat{j} + \frac{dz}{dt}\hat{k},$$

and its *acceleration* by $\vec{a} = \dfrac{d\vec{v}}{dt} = \dfrac{d^2\vec{r}}{dt^2}$

The origin of the frame of reference may not always be coincident with the position of the observer. The frame of reference must, however, be at rest with respect to him.

Obviously, for complete identification of an *event* in a reference frame, *i.e.,* for determination of its exact location as well as the exact time of its occurence, we must, in addition to the usual three spatial coordinates x, y and z, have yet another coordinate, *viz.*, that of time t, perpendicular to the former three.

A reference frame, with such four coordinates, x, y, z and t, is referred to as a **space-time frame,**—the four axes defining a *four dimensional continuum,* called **space-time.**

Now, all rest and motion being relative, the position or the state of motion of the same particle (or body) may appear to be different from different frames of reference. And, we naturally prefer to use that particular frame of reference from which its motion appears to be the simplest.

Thus, for example, a stone dropped by a person from the window of a railway carriage in uniform motion appears to him to fall *vertically* down but to a person outside the carriage, it appears to take a *parabolic path,* as indicated in Fig. 2.1.

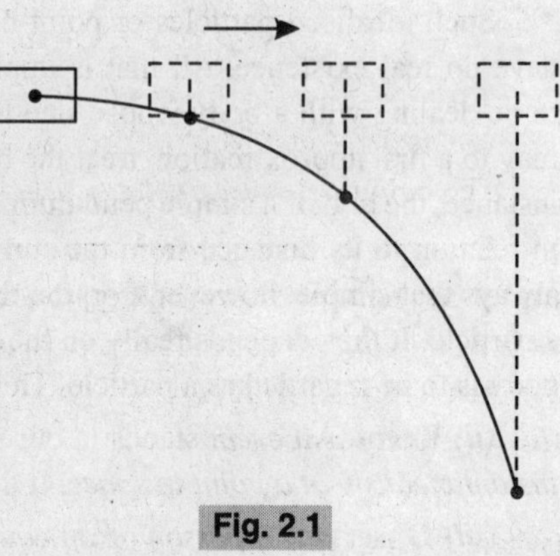

Fig. 2.1

In this case, therefore, we prefer to use a frame of reference situated in the window of the railway carriage and imagine ourself to be at its origin.

Again, if we observe the path of motion of a point on the rim of a slowly rolling wheel, we find from our frame of reference on the earth's surface that the path described by the point is a complicated, *cycloidal* one, as shown in Fig. 2.2. If, however, we have our frame of reference on the wheel itself, with its origin coincident with the centre of the wheel, and image ourself to be stationed there, we find that the motion of the point is a simple circular one. (See *Hint* under *Question* 6, Exercise 1).

Fig. 2.2

Once again, whereas the path of a projectile appears to be parabolic from the surface of the earth, it would appear to be a staright line when viewed from another projectile (see worked example 2) and so on.

Let us now make a rapid survey of Newton's laws of motion and examine their limitations if any, in regard to the frames of reference or otherwise.

Example 1. Show that the motion of one projectile as seen from another projectile will always be a straight line motion.

Solution. Since both projectiles are subject to the same acceleration—g, there g is no relative acceleration between them. They must, therefore, appear to be descending along a straight line path relative to each other, *i.e.,* the motion of one should appear to be a striaight line motion as seen from the other.

Alternatively, we may proceed as follows :

Let the trajectories of the two projectiles, projected simultaneously, be described in the x-y plane, as shown in Fig. 2.3, and let their initial velocities of projection and their angles of projection be u_1, u_2 and α_1, α_2 respectively.

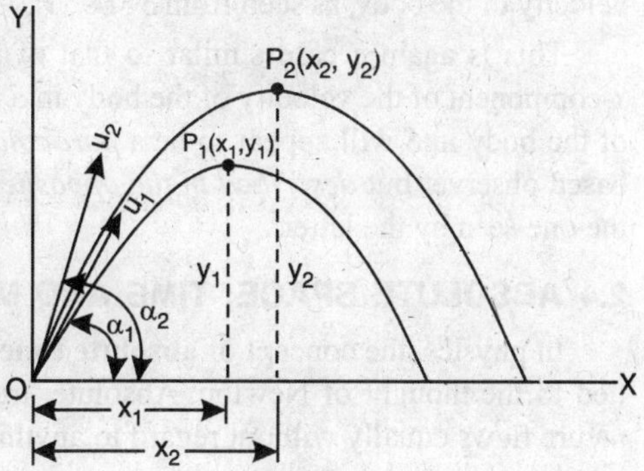

Fig. 2.3

Then, with the point of projection (O) as the origin if the position coordinates of points P_1 and P_2 at any given instant t be x_1, y_1 and x_2, y_2 respectively, we have $x_1 = u_1 \cos \alpha_1 t$, $x_2 = u_2 \cos \alpha_2 t$, $y_1 = u_1 \sin \alpha_1 t - \frac{1}{2} g t^2$ and $y_2 = u_2 \sin \alpha_2 t - \frac{1}{2} g t^2$. So that,

$$\frac{y_2 - y_1}{x_2 - x_1} = \frac{y}{x} = \frac{u_2 \sin \alpha_2 - u_1 \sin \alpha_1}{u_2 \cos \alpha_2 - u_1 \cos \alpha_1}$$

$$= m, \text{ say.}$$

whence, $y = mx$, which is the equation to a *straight line.*

The motion of one projectile, as seen from the other, is thus a straight line motion.

Example 2. To an observer, at rest on the ground, a body, thrown vertically upwards in a uniformly moving frame S, appears to describe a parabolic path. What is the path of the body as it would appear to an observer in another reference frame S' in uniform motion parallel to S, when S' has (*i*) an identical velocity with S, (*ii*) a velocity equal and opposite to that of S, and (*iii*) a velocity twice that of S?

Solution. Taking the parabolic path of the body in frame S to be described in the x-y plane (where the x-axis is along the horizontal), if the x and y-components of the velocity of the body in this frame be v_x and v_y, clearly, v_x is alos the velocity of frame S, along the x-axis.

In case (*i*), since frame S' moves with the *same* velocity as S, the x-component of the velocity of the body, as seen from S' will be, say, $v'_x = v_x - v_x, = 0$ and its y-component v'_y will obviously remain the same as that in frame S, *viz.,* v_y, since neither frame has a vertical velocity.

The path of the body, therefore, will appear to an observer in frame S' to be a *vertical straight line.*

In case (*ii*), since frame S' moves with an equal and *opposite* velocity to that to of S, the x-component of the velocity of the body, as seen from frame S', will obviously be $v'_x = v_x - (-v_x) = 2v_x$, with the y-component, $v'_y = v_y$, as in case (*i*).

So that, in time t, the *horizontal distance covered will be* $x = 2v_x t$ and the vertical distance covered will be $y = v_y t - \frac{1}{2}gt^2$. Or, eliminating t, we have

$$y = v_y \frac{x}{2v_x} - \frac{1}{2}g\frac{x^2}{4v_x^2}, \qquad \text{Or,} \quad y = \frac{v_y}{2v_x}x - \frac{g}{8v_x^2}x^2$$

which is an equation of the form $y = ax + bx^2$, the equation to a *parabola*, indicating that the path of the body is S will, in this case, appear to the observer in S' to be a *parabola, described in the same direction* as it appears to the observer at rest on the ground. Only, the x-component of the velocity of the body ($2v_x$) now appearing to be twice as much as to the stationary observer, the latus rectum of the *parabola* will be twice that of the one seen by the observer on the ground.

In case (*iii*), the frame S' having twice the velocity of S, we shall have x-component of the velocity of the body, as seen from S', *i.e.*, $v'_x = v_x - 2v_x = -v_x$ and the y-component, $v'_y = v_y$, as before.

This is again a case similar to that of the stationary observer on the ground, with only the x-component of the velocity of the body in S now reversed. To the observer in S', therefore, the path of the body in S will appear to be a *parabola,* similar in size and shape to that seen by the ground based observer but *described in the opposite direction, i.e.*, a *parabola* which is a mirror-image of the one seen by the latter.

2.4 ABSOLUTE SPACE; TIME AND MOTION

In physics, the concept of **absolute time** and **absolute space** are hypothetical concepts closely tied to the thought of Newton. Absolute, true and mathematical time of itself, and from its own nature flows equally without regard to anything external. There is another term **duration** measures relative, apparent and common time, is same sensible and external measure of duration by means of motion which is commonly used instead of true time. Using this defination, **time** runs at the same rate for all observers in the **universe** and different measures of absolute time can be scaled by multiplying by a constant.

Thus, according to Newton, '**Absolute space,** in its own nature, without regard to anything, external, remains always similar and imovable'. Relative space is some movable dimension or measure of the absolute spaces; which our senses determine by its position to bodies.

Absolute motion is the translation of a body from one absolute place into another, and relative motion, the translation from one relative place into another.

These notions imply that absolute space and time do not depend upon physical events, but are a backdrop or stage setting within which physical phenomenon occurs. Thus, every object has an absolute state of motion relative to absolute space, so that an object must be either in a state of **absolute rest** or moving at some **absolute speed.** In modern view, the absolute space is unnecessary. Hence in classical or Newtonian mechanics, the notion of absolute space is replaced by the idea of **inertial frame of reference;** that is, a preferred **set of frames of reference** that move uniformly with respect to one another. The laws of physics transform from one inertial frame to another according to **Galilean relativity.** Newton himself recognized the role of inertial frames. Thus, the motions of bodies included in a given space are the same among themselves, whether that space is at rest or moves with uniform velocity forward in a **straight line.** As a practical matter, inertial frames often are taken as frames moving uniformly with respect to the fixed stars. The best approximation to an inertial frame is the frame of reference in the intergalactic space. According to Newton, main classical properties of space are:

(*i*) Space is three dimensional. The concept of space and time is fundamental to the study of mechanics. All objects occupy space and have a length, a breadth and a height. Space is, therefore, **three dimensional.** This is why the position of a point can be specified completely by the three coordinates (x, y, z) or (r, θ, ϕ).

***(ii)* Space is flat.** Space is flat, *i.e.,* it possess Eucledian flatness. This means that the shortest distance between any two points in space is a straight line. If we take three points in space to form a triangle, the sum of angles is equal to π. If it is a right angled triangle, then the three sides are related by Pythagoras, *i.e.,* Hypotenuse^2 = Base^2 + Altitude^2.

However, according to latest theory, space is **not exactly flat** but somewhat curved. The departure from flatness is very small and can be ignored in the study of classical mechanics.

***(iii)* Space is homogeneous.** In other words, space in everywhere alike. Homogeneity of free space (a space in which fields and forces are absent) means translational invariance of its properties, *i.e.,* the result of an experiment is not altered due to linear displacement of the coordinate systems.

***(iv)* Space is isotropic.** It means that if we consider a point *O* in space and we move from this point in any direction, the properties are the same *i.e.,* there is nothing to distinguish one direction from the other. In other words, there is no preferred direction in space or one direction is as good as any other direction.

Distinction between Homogeneity and Isotropy

The **homogeneity of space** means **translational invariance** of the properties of space.

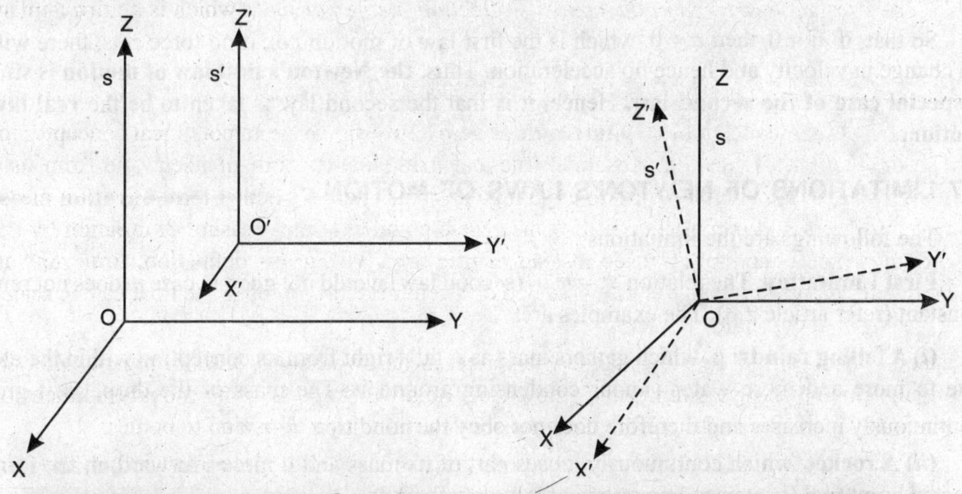

Fig. 2.4 (*a*) : Translational invariance. **Fig. 2.4 (*b*) :** Rotational invariance.

If we consider two systems *S* and *S'* (both are cartezian coordinate systems) displaced with respect to one another as shown in fig. 2.4 (*a*), then an experiment performed in system *S* will give exactly the same results as in system *S'*.

On the other hand, **isotropy** means **rotational invariance** of free space. Thus, if we have two systems *S* and *S'* rotating with respect to one another as shown in fig. 2.4 (*b*), then again an experiment performed in system *S* will give exactly the same result as in system *S'*.

2.5 NEWTON'S LAWS OF MOTION

It is our common experience, that a book or a duster tying on a table will continue to remain there (state of rest) untill we remove it or displace it. Thus, all bodies which are initially at rest will continue to remain at rest. Similary a body, moving with uniform velocity (state of uniform motion), will continue its uniform motion. These, state of rest or uniform motion will be continued for an infinite time, unless acted upon by an external force. This is nothing but Newton's first law of motion, Newton's three laws of motion are as under:

First law. *A body must continue in its state of rest or of uniform motion along a straight line unless acted upon by an external force.*

Second law. *The rate of change of momentum is proportional to the impressed force and takes place in the direction of the force.*

Third law. *To very action, there is an equal and opposite reaction.* Thus, if $\vec{F_{12}}$ and $\vec{F_{21}}$ be the force exerted on each other by two interacting bodies respectively, we have $\vec{F_{12}} = -\vec{F_{21}}$.

2.6 NEWTON'S FIRST LAW OF MOTION IS SIMPLY A SPECIAL CASE OF SECOND LAW

Newton's second law of motion gives a measures of a force as **the rate of change of linear momentum.** If $\vec{p}$ is the momentum of the particle, given by $\vec{p} = m\vec{v}$, where m is mass and $\vec{v}$ its velocity, them

$$\vec{F} = \frac{d\vec{p}}{dt} = \frac{d}{dt}(m\vec{v})$$

$$= m\frac{d\vec{v}}{dt} \qquad (\because m \text{ being constant})$$

$$= m\vec{a}$$

So that, if $\vec{F} = 0$, then $\vec{a} = 0$ which is the first law of motion *i.e.*, if no force acts, there will be no change in velocity and hence no acceleration. Thus, **the Newton's first law of motion is simply a special case of the second law.** Hence, it is that the second law is taken to be the **real law of motion.**

2.7 LIMITATIONS OF NEWTON'S LAWS OF MOTION

The followings are the limitations:

First Limitation. The relation $\vec{F} = m\vec{a}$ (second law) would not good in case m does not remain constant (refer article 2.6). The examples are:

***(i)* A falling raindrop,** which gathers mass as it falls right from its conception within the cloud, due to more and more water vapour condensing around it. The mass of the drop, as it grows, continuously increases and therefore does not obey the condition $\vec{F} = m\vec{a}$.

***(ii)* A rocket,** which continuously looses part of its mass and it moves forward, in the form of ejected burnt fuel (in succeeding stages of the rocket), and

***(iii)* Particles with relativistic velocities,** The mass of a particle is given by $m = m_0/\sqrt{1-\frac{v^2}{c^2}}$, where m_0 is the rest mass of the particle. The mass of the particle increases as its velocity becomes appreciable fraction of the velocity of light (c).

Second Limitation. Newton's third law of motion implies that the forces exerted by the two interacting bodies over each other are equal and opposite ($\vec{F_{12}} = -\vec{F_{21}}$), provided both the forces are measured simultaneously. A simultaneous measurement of the two forces is possible for ordinary practical purposes, if the time taken by the interaction is sufficiently large compared with the time taken by light signal to travel one to the other. This means that the law cases to hold good for particles of atomic dimensions, for which simultaneous measurement of two forces is almost impossible (refer Heisenberg uncertainty principle).

2.8 FRAMES OF REFERENCE: INERTIAL AND NON-INERTIAL

In article 2.6 and 2.7, we have discussed the Newton's laws of motion and their limitations. A *very important point about the first two laws is that they do not hold good in each and every frame of reference.* For a body at rest in one reference frame may not necessarily appear to be sore in another. It may, for instance, appear to be moving in a circle in a frame of reference rotating with respect to the first. It is only in a very special frame of reference that the two laws of motion hold good. Such a frame of reference is called a **Newtonian, inertial** or **Galilean frame of reference** (because it was *Galileo* who first enunciated the law of inertia which we refer to as Newton's first law of motion). The first law defines and the second identifies such a frame of reference to be *non-accelerating* and, therefore, also *non-rotating*. This means that in an inertial frame, the *acceleration* $\vec{a} = d^2\vec{r}/dt^2 = 0$ (because the force applied, $\vec{F} = m\vec{a}$ is zero), or that $d^2x/dt^2 = 0$, $d^2y/dt^2 = 0$ and $d^2z/dt^2 = 0$.

Inertial frame of reference. Newton's first law of motion is also known as the *law of inertia.* A reference frame e.g., a coordinate system in which Newton's first law of motion holds good, is known as an inertial frame of reference. In an inertial frame a body continues in its state of *rest* or of *uniform motion in a straight line* as long as no external force acts on it. All the Newton's laws of motion hold good in an inertial frame. All frames of reference moving with a *constant velocity* with respect to an inertial frame are also inertial frames of reference.

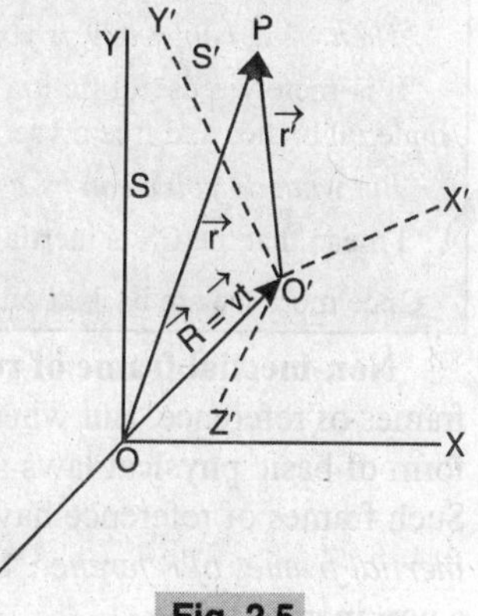

Consider an inertial frame of reference S and another reference frame S' (with or without their respective coordinate axes parallel to each other), such that their orientations in space remain fixed and are thus free to have only translatory motion with respect to one another. Suppose further that, with the origins O and O' at the two systems *initially coincident,* system S' has moved into the present position, shown in fig. 2.5 in time t, with a *constant velocity* $\vec{v}$ relative to S, so that $\overrightarrow{OO'} = R = \vec{v}\,t$.

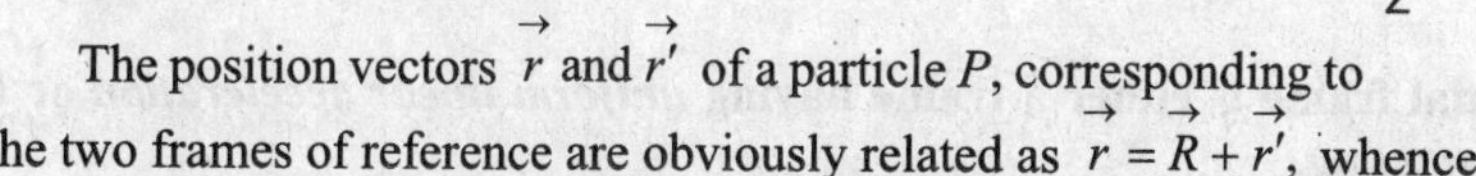

Fig. 2.5

The position vectors $\vec{r}$ and $\vec{r}'$ of a particle P, corresponding to the two frames of reference are obviously related as $\vec{r} = \vec{R} + \vec{r}'$, whence

$$\vec{r}' = \vec{r} - \vec{R} = \vec{r} - \vec{v}\,t.$$

So that, we have $d^2\vec{r}/dt^2 = d^2\vec{r}'/dt^2$ [$\vec{v}$ being constant]

Clearly, $d^2\vec{r}'/dt^2$ is the acceleration of the particle in frame S' and $d^2\vec{r}/dt^2$, its acceleration in the inertial frame S.

Thus, the acceleration of the particle is the *same* in the two frames of reference, indicating that if the particle be at rest in the inertial frame S, it would also appear to be at rest in frame S', In other words, frame S' it would also be an inertial frame.

We thus arrive at a general rule that *all frames of reference, moving with a constant velocity with respect to an inertial frame, are also inertial frames of reference.*

This means, as mentioned already, that *inertial frames are non-accelerating frames or else,* a body at rest or in uniform motion in one frame may appear to have an accelerated motion in the other.

To understand more about inertial frame of reference, listen carefully the dialogue given in the following box-1.

Box-1

In a book entitled *The Evolution of Physics,* Einstein and Infield discuss the question of the inertial system using an imaginary dialogue.

Let us interview the classical physicist and ask him some simple questions:

"What is an inertial system?"

Contd...

"It is a CS [coordinate system or what we would call a frame of reference] in which the laws of mechanics are valid. A body on which no external forces are acting moves uniformly in such a CS. This property thus enables us to distinguish an inertial CS from any other."

"But what does it mean to say that no forces are acting on a body?"

"It simply means that the body moves uniformly in an inertial CS."

Here we could once more put the question: "What is an inertial CS?"

But since there is little hope of obtaining an answer differing from the above, let us try to gain some concrete information by changing the question:

"Is a CS rigidly connected with the earth an inertial one?"

"No; because the laws of mechanics are not rigorously valid on the earth, due to its rotation. A CS rigidly connected with the sun can be regarded for many problems as an inertial CS; but when we speak of the rotating sun, we again understand that a CS connected with it cannot be regarded as strictly inertial."

"Then what, concretely, is your inertial CS, and how is its state of motion to be chosen?"

"It is merely a useful fiction and I have no idea how to realize it. If I could only get far away from all material bodies and free myself from all external influences, my CS would then be inertial."

"But what do you mean by a CS free from all external influences?"

"I mean that the CS is inertial."

Once more we are back at our initial question!

Non-inertial frame of reference. The basic laws of physics are not changed in form in inertial frames of reference. But when the frame of reference is accelerated relative to an inertial frame, the form of basic physical laws such as Newton's second law of motion become completely different. Such frames of reference having an accelerated motion relative to an inertial frame are called *non-inertial frames of reference.* Since a uniformly rotating frame has a centripetal acceleration it is also a non-inertial frame.

Example. A non-inertial frame is either a frame having *uniform linear acceleration* or a frame which is *uniformly rotating.*

As will be readily seen, the rotating frame of reference, refered to above, in which a body, which is at rest in an inertial frame, appears to be moving in a circle (and thus having an acceleration) is *not* an inertial frame of reference. This again implies, as mentioned earlier, that *inertial frames are also non-rotating frames.*

Further, since Newton's laws of motion are obeyed only in inertial frames of reference, it follows as a natural consequence that, subject to the limitations mentioned under 2.7, *i.e., mass remaining constant, the relation* $\vec{F} = m\vec{a}$ *holds good only in inertial frames,* **not** *in non-inertial ones.*

Earth: A non-inertial frame of reference. Now, an inertial frame of reference being an unaccelerated one, the question arises as to where to actually locate it. Obviously, the earth in not a suitable place for it since, as we know, apart from going round the sun, it also spins about its own axis. This imparts to a body in the frame of reference, located on the earth, a centripetal acceleration, whose value at the equator would be $\omega^2 R = (2\pi/24 \times 60 \times 60)^2 \times 6.4 \times 10^8 = 3.4$ cm/s^2, which is by no means negligible. Nevertheless, being quite small for most of our everyday purposes, it is quite often neglected, and *the earth taken to be a satisfactory inertial frame of reference.* Hence, also the interior of a vehicle (train, car etc.), moving smoothly, with constant velocity, on the earth's surface, may be taken to be an equally satisfactory inertial frame of reference.

Strictly speaking, however, the earth being not quite satisfactory for the purpose, where else can we think of locating the frame of reference? Not even the sun is at rest but revolves about the centre of our galaxy, which itself moves through space. The nearest to something fixed in space are the *fixed stars,* so called because they seem to preserve their arrangement. Not that we know them to be actually fixed in their positions in space, but their velocity from this far off distance on the earth appears to be almost negligible. *Any rigid body, therefore, situated in remote space, far from attracting matter and fixed with respect to the fixed stars, may be taken to be an inertial frame of reference.*

Now, knowing full well that, in actual practice, motion is always described in a relative frame of reference, *i.e.*, in a frame in which the position of a particle or a body is specified in relation to other material objects which may themselves be in motion relative to other objects, Newton insisted that there must exist a *fundamental or an absolute frame of reference,* which he called **absolute space,** with respect to which all motion must be measured. With the weight of his great authority behind the idea, the futile quest for this elusive absolute reference frame continued for long. But more of it later, when we deal with the special theory of relativity in the next chapter.

Here, we may simply state that for most of our purposes, the reference frame, stationary with respect to the fixed stars, is good enough as our *fixed or absolute inertial frame of reference.* All other frames of reference in uniform motion relative to it, naturally, also serve as *equivalent inertial frames,* as also any reference frame whose origin coincides with that of an inertial frame even though its coordinate axes may be inclined to those of the latter (see § 2.12).

The term *Galilean frame of reference* is used mostly in connection with *relativity.* Though here too, the earth may well be used as a Galilean frame in quite a number of cases in which its gravitational attraction is small compared with the other forces involved and its rotation is of no importance.

It only remains to be pointed out that *the concept of an inertial frame of reference is of real importance in physics for the following reasons.*

(*i*) *It is in respect of such a frame of reference that all our fundamental laws of physics have been formulated.*

(*ii*) *It is one of the basic assumptions of the special theory of relativity that the fundamental laws of physics can all be so expressed as to assume the same mathematical form in all inertial frames of reference.*

(*iii*) *It is endowed with the property of being isotropic with respect to mechanical and optical experiments ('isotropic'* meaning *same in all directions).*

2.9 GALILEAN TRANSFORMATION

An event or a physical phenomenon, observed simultaneously in two separate reference frames, will naturally have two separate sets of coordinates corresponding to the two frames of reference. Equations relating the two sets of coordinates of the event in the two systems are called **transformation equations,** because they enable the observations made in one system to be *transformed,* as it were, into those made in the other. And, if the two systems happen to be inertial or Galilean ones, the transformation is referred to as a *Galilean transformation.* Let us consider a few such transformations by way of illustration.

(*a*) Transformation of position. Let S and S' be two inertial frames of reference with observers stationed at their origins O and O' respectively, moving with a relative velocity v along the positive direction of x (Fig. 2.6). Or, what is the same thing, let S be at rest and S' move with uniform velocity v along the $+x$ direction. Needless to mention that the velocities we are considering here are all very much less than c, the velocity of light in free space, *i.e.*, $v << c$.

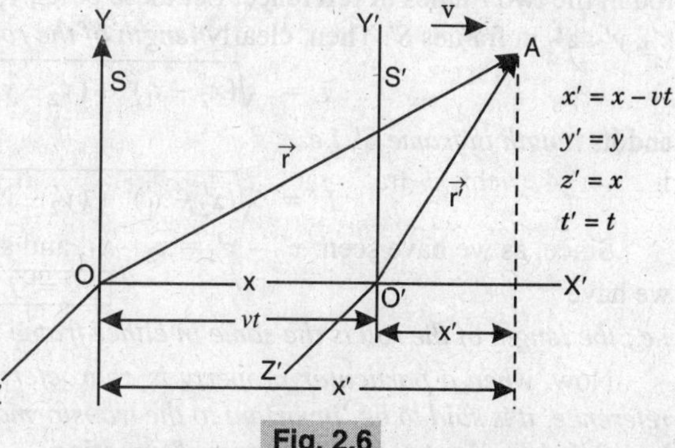

Fig. 2.6

Suppose some event occurs at A. Then, measuring time from the instant the observers were just oposite each other, *i.e.,* setting the clocks in S and S' to *zero* when origins O and O' of the two frames coincide with (or are opposite to) each other, the observer in frame S determines the position of the event by the coordinates x, y, z and the observer in S', by the coordinates x', y', z'. Since frame S' is in uniform motion relative to S, the x-measurements in S exceed those in S' by vt, the distance covered by S' in time t in the $+x$ direction. We, therefore, have $x' = x - vt$. And, since there is no relative motion between S and S' along the axes of y and z, we have $y = y'$ and $z = z'$.

Now, if we assume time to be independent of any frame of reference, we have the four transformation equations from S to S', *viz.*,

$$x' = x - vt \quad ...(i)$$
$$y' = y \quad ...(ii)$$
$$z' = z \quad ...(iii)$$
$$t' = t \quad ...(iv)$$

Or, we could express the transformation in a general form in terms of the position coordinates of A in the two reference frames, as explained in § 2.8, *viz.*, as

$$\boxed{\vec{r}' = \vec{r} - \vec{v}t}.$$

The *inverse transformation* (from S' to S) will naturally give

$$x = x' + vt, \quad y = y', \quad z = z', \quad \text{and } t = t'. \quad \text{Also, } \vec{r} = \vec{r}' + \vec{v}t.$$

(b) Transformation of distance or length. Suppose there are two events occurring simultaneously at A_1 and A_2, some distance apart, along the axis of x, such that their coordinates, as measured in the two frames of reference, are x_1, y, z; x_2, y, z and x'_1, y', z' ; x'_2, y', z' respectively. Then, clearly,

Transformation equations for the event at A_1 (from S to S') are

$$x_1' = x_1 - vt, \quad y' = y, \quad z' = z.$$

And *transformation equations for the event at* A_2 (from S to S') are

$$x_2' = x_2 - vt, \quad y' = y, \quad z' = z.$$

Hence, *distance between the two events* is given by

$$x'_2 - x'_1 = \Delta x' = (x_2 - vt) - (x_1 - vt) = (x_2 - x_1) = \Delta x,$$

indicating that *the distance between the two events, measured by the observer in either frame of reference; is the same, irrespective of the values of v and t* (which need not be known). *Only, the observations must be made simultaneously in the two frames of reference.*

It will be easily seen that if Δx be the *length L of a rod,* placed along the axis of x in frame S and $\Delta x'$, its length L' along the axis of x' in frame S', we have $L' = \Delta x' = \Delta x = L$, *i.e., it is the same in either frame of reference.*

Or, we could arrive at the same result more directly by considering the end coordinates of the rod in the two frames of reference. Let these be x_1, y_1, z_1 and x_2, y_2, z_2 in frame S and x'_1, y'_1, z'_1 and x'_2, y'_2, z'_2 in frames S'. Then, clearly *length of the rod in frame S, i.e.,*

$$L = \sqrt{(x_2 - x_1)^2 + (y_2 - y_1)^2 + (z_2 - z_1)^2}$$

and its *length in frame S', i.e.,*

$$L' = \sqrt{(x_2' - x_1')^2 + (y_2' - y_1')^2 + (z_2' - z_1')^2}$$

Since, as we have seen, $x'_2 - x'_1 = x_2 - x_1$, and similarly, $y'_2 - y'_1 = y_2 - y_1$ and $z'_2 - z'_1 = z_2 - z_1$, we have

$$\boxed{L' = L}$$

i.e., the length of the rod is the same in either frame by reference.

Now, *when a particular property is characterised by the same number in the two frames of reference, it is said to be 'invariant to the transformation'*. So that, we may say that **a distance or a length is invariant to Galilean transformation.**

(c) Trnasformation of velocity. Let us now consider the velocity measurements u and u' as made by the two observers in their respective frames of reference. For this, we consider a displacement in the $+x$ direction, say, and the time interval for it. Thus, if x_1, t and x_2, t be the coordinates of the initial and final events characterising the displacement in frame S and x'_1, t'_1 and x'_2, t'_2, the corresponding coordinates in frame S', we have

velocity relative to frame S, given by $u = \dfrac{\Delta x}{\Delta t} = \dfrac{x_2 - x_1}{t_2 - t_1}$

Or, since $x_1 = x'_1 + vt'_1$, $x_2 = x'_2 + vt'_2$, $t_1 = t'_1$ and $t_2 = t'_2$ we have

$$u = \frac{(x'_2 + vt'_2) - (x'_1 + vt'_1)}{t'_2 - t'_1} = \frac{x'_2 - x'_1}{t'_2 - t'_1} + v\frac{(t'_2 - t'_1)}{(t'_2 - t'_1)}$$

Or $$u = \frac{\Delta x}{\Delta t'} + v = u' + v. \qquad \text{Or,} \quad u' = u - v. \qquad \text{... (vi)}$$

Again, we could arrive at the same result from relation (v) above, *viz,* $\vec{r'} = \vec{r} - \vec{v}\,t$, differentiating which, we have

$$\frac{d\vec{r'}}{dt} = \frac{d\vec{r}}{dt} - \vec{v}. \quad \text{Or,} \quad \boxed{\vec{u'} = \vec{u} - \vec{v}} \qquad \text{... (vii)}$$

indicating that *the velocities measured by the observers in the two frames of reference are not the same.* We, therefore, say that **velocity is not invariant to Galilean transformation.**

The *inverse transformation* (from frame S' to S) is, obviously, given by

$$\vec{u} = \vec{u'} + \vec{v}. \qquad \text{... (viii)}$$

Here, relation (*vii*) or (*viii*) is often referred to as the **Galilean law of addition of velocities.**

(d) Transformation of acceleration. Considering accelerations $\vec{a}$ and $\vec{a'}$, as measured by the observers in their respective frames of reference, we have $\vec{a} = d\vec{u}/dt$ and $\vec{a'} = d\vec{u'}/dt$.

Since, as just seen under (*c*), above, $\vec{u} = \vec{u} - \vec{v}$, we have

$$\frac{d\vec{u'}}{dt} = \frac{d\vec{u}}{dt} - 0. \qquad (\vec{v}\text{ being a constant.})$$

Or, $$\boxed{\vec{a'} = \vec{a}}$$

indicating that *the accelerations, as measured by the two observers in the two frames of reference respectively, are the same.* **Acceleration is thus invariant to Galilean transformation.**

Example 3. A moving particle has co-ordinates $(6t + 3)$, $8t$, 5m in frame S at any time t. The frame S' is moving relative to S with a velocity $3\hat{i} + 4\hat{j}$ m/s. Find the co-ordinates and velocity of the particle in frame S.

Solution. Galelian transformation equations for space co-ordinates are

$$x' = x - v_x t \quad y' = y - v_y t \quad z' = z - v_z t$$

Now $$x = 6t + 3 \quad y = 8t \quad z = 5;\ v_x = 3\ v_y = 4\ v_z = 0$$

$\therefore$ $$x' = x - v_x t = 6t + 3 - 3t = 3t + 3$$

$$y' = y - v_y t = 8t - 4t = 4t;\ z' = z - v_z t = 5 - 0 = 5$$

$\therefore$ Co-ordinates of the particle in S' are $3t + 3$, $4t$, 5.

Velocity $x' = 3t + 3 \quad \therefore \quad \dfrac{dx'}{dt'} = \dfrac{dx'}{dt}\cdot\dfrac{dt}{dt'} = \dfrac{dx'}{dt} \qquad \cdots \left[\begin{array}{l}\because t' = t\\ dt' = dt\end{array}\right]$

Hence $\dfrac{dx'}{dt} = 3$ or $\vec{u'_x} = 3\hat{i}$

Similarly $\dfrac{dy'}{dt'} = \dfrac{dy'}{dt} = 4$ or $\vec{u'_y} = 4\hat{j} \qquad \dfrac{dz'}{dt'} = \dfrac{dz'}{dt} = 0$

$\therefore$ Velocity in frame S', $\vec{u'} = \vec{u'_x} + \vec{u'_y} + \vec{u'_z} = 3\hat{i} + 4\hat{j}$

Example 4. The position vector of a point in the frame S' moving with constant velocity of 10cm/sec along X-axis is given by (11, 9, 8) cm. Calculate the position with respect to the frame S if the two frames were coincident only $\frac{1}{2}$ sec earlier. ***(P.U. 2001, 2000)***

Solution. As the position co-ordinates are given in the frame S' which is moving with constant velocity of $v = 10$ cm s^{-1} along $+X$-axis, the position co-ordinates in the frame S are given by inverse Galelian transformations

$$x = x' + vt; \quad y = y'; \quad z = z'; \quad t = t'$$

Here $\quad x' = 11 \text{ cm} \quad y' = 9 \text{ cm} \quad z' = 8 \text{ cm} \quad t' = \frac{1}{2}\text{sec.}$

$\therefore \quad x = x' + vt = 11 + 10 \times \frac{1}{2} = 6 \text{ cm}; \quad y' = 9 \text{ cm}; z' = 8 \text{ cm}$

$\therefore$ The position co-ordinates of the point in the frames S are (16, 9, 8) cm.

Example 5. A frame S' is moving with velocity $5\hat{i} + 7\hat{j}$ m/s relative to an inertial frame S. A particle is moving with velocity $(t+5)\hat{i} + 9\hat{j}$ m/s with respect to S. Find the acceleration of the particle in the frame S'.

Solution. Velocity of the particle in frame S, $\vec{u} = (t+5)\,\hat{i} + 9\hat{j}$ ms^{-1}

Velocity of frame S' relative to S, $\quad \vec{v} = 5\hat{i} + 7\hat{j}$

According to Galelian transformation equations for velocity,

Velocity of the particle with respect to frame S',

$$\vec{u'} = \vec{u} - \vec{v} = (t+5)\,\hat{i} + 9\hat{j} - (5\hat{i} + 7\hat{j}) = t\,\hat{i} + 2\hat{j} \text{ ms}^{-1}$$

$\therefore$ Acceleration of the particle in the frame S', $\vec{a'} = \dfrac{d\vec{u'}}{dt} = \dfrac{d\vec{u'}}{dt}$ ...[$\because dt' = dt$]

$$= \frac{d}{dt}[t\hat{i} + 2\hat{j}] = \hat{i} \qquad \therefore \ \vec{a'} = \hat{i} \text{ ms}^{-2}$$

Example 6. The pilot of an airplane wishes to reach a point 200 km east of his present position. A wind blows 30 km/hr from the north west. Calculate his vector velocity with respect to the moving air mass if his schedule requires him to arrive at his destination in 40 minutes. (Take $\sqrt{2} = 1.4$).

Solution. Let O be the position of the pilot at the given instant (Fig. 2.7). Since he reaches the desired point 200 km due east in 40 min., his velocity in this direction is 200 × 60/40 = 300 km/hr.

The problem thus reduces to this, that 300 km/hr is the *resultant* of the *wind velocity* v_w and the *pilot's own velocity* v_p, say. By the Triangle law of vectors, therefore, $\vec{OA}$ represents the *winds velocity vector* $\vec{v_w}$, $\vec{AP}$, the *velocity vector* $\vec{v_p}$ *of the pilot* and $\vec{OP}$ the *resultant velocity vector* $\vec{R}$. So, that, $\vec{R} = \vec{v_w} + \vec{v_p}$, whence,

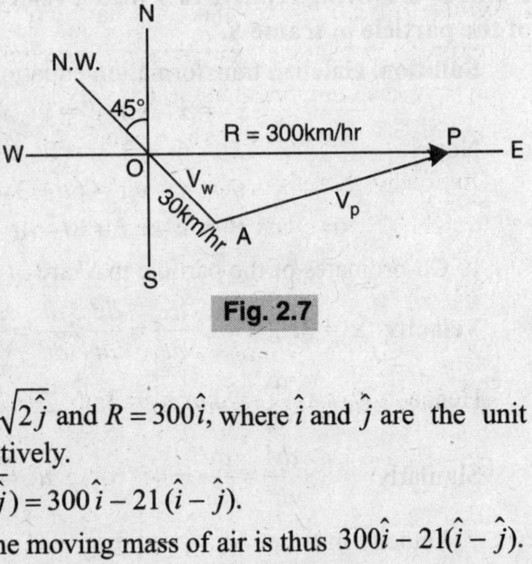

$$\vec{v_p} = \vec{R} - \vec{v_w}.$$

Fig. 2.7

Now, $\vec{v_w} = 30\sin 45\hat{i} - 30\cos 45\hat{j} = 15\sqrt{2}\hat{i} - 15\sqrt{2}\hat{j}$ and $R = 300\hat{i}$, where $\hat{i}$ and $\hat{j}$ are the unit vectors along the east and the north directions respectively.

We, therefore, have $\vec{v_p} = 300\,\hat{i} - (15\sqrt{2}\hat{i} - 15\sqrt{2}\hat{j}) = 300\,\hat{i} - 21\,(\hat{i} - \hat{j})$.

The vector velocity of the pilot with respect to the moving mass of air is thus $300\hat{i} - 21(\hat{i} - \hat{j})$.

Example 7. A reference frams S' is moving with a constant velocity v with respect to an inertial frame S. If at $t = 0$, the position vector of O' (the origin of the moving frame S') with respect to O (the origin of the inertial frame S) be R, show that the position vectors $\vec{r}$ and $\vec{r'}$ of a point P with respect to frames S and S' respectively are related by the equation $\vec{r} = \vec{R} + \vec{v}t + \vec{r'}$.

Solution. Since the reference frame S' is moving with a constant velocity with respect to the inertial frame S, *it is also an inertial frame.* The problem thus reduces to one of Galilean transformation of the position vector of a point in one Galilean frame of reference to that in the other.

Since, initially, at time $t = 0$, the position vector of the origin O' of the moving frame S' with respect to the origin O of the inertial frame S, is $\vec{R}$, it would be $(\vec{R} + \vec{v}t)$ in time t, when the former would have covered an additional distance $\vec{v}\,t$. So that, vector $\overrightarrow{OO'}$ would be equal to $\vec{R} + \vec{v}\,t$.

Referring to Fig. 2.3 which depicts the whole situation except that $\overrightarrow{OO'}$ now represents $(\vec{R} + \vec{v}\,t)$ instead of $\vec{R}$ (because, in the case shown, O' coincided with O at $t = 0$), let us consider to position vectors $\vec{r}$ and $\vec{r'}$ of a point P with respect to the origins of the two frames of reference. It is clear at once that vector $\overrightarrow{OP}$ = vector $\overrightarrow{OO'}$ + vector $\overrightarrow{O'P}$,

i.e., $$\vec{r} = \vec{R} + \vec{v}\,t + \vec{r'}.$$

Example 8. The velocity vector of an object in uniform circular motion with a speed of 50 cm/s changes direction by 30° in 2 seconds. Calculate (*i*) the change in velocity, (*ii*) the average acceleration, and (*iii*) the centripetal acceleration. How do you explain the fact that (*ii*) and (*iii*) have identical values ?

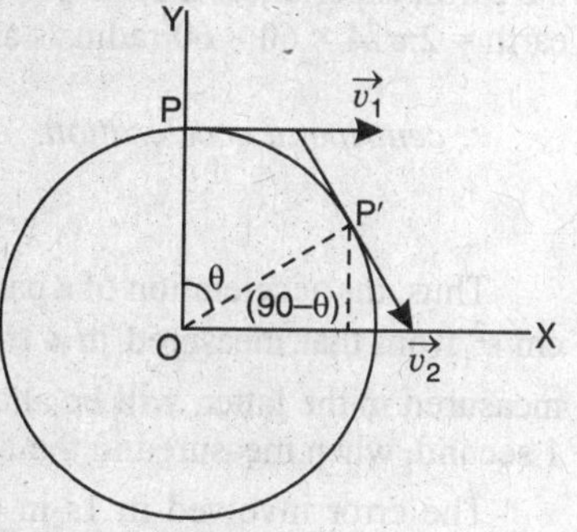

Fig. 2.8

Solution. (*i*) Let the object be moving along the circle shown in Fig. 2.8 and, taking the coordinate axes OX and OY, with the centre (O) of the circle as the origin, let P be its position at a given instant and P', its position after 2s when the velocity vector has changed direction by an angle θ. Then, the velocities of the object at P and P' are clearly $\vec{v}_1$ and $\vec{v}_2$, tangential to OP and OP' respectively, as shown.

Since only the direction of the velocity changes, *its magnitude remaining the same,* we have $|\vec{v}_1| = |\vec{v}_2| = v$, say. So that, expressing $\vec{v}_1$ and $\vec{v}_2$ in terms of their components along the axes of x and y, we have

$\vec{v}_1 = v\hat{i}$, the component along the y-axis being *zero*.

and $\vec{v}_2 = -v\sin\theta\,\hat{j} + v\cos\theta\,\hat{i} = v\cos 30\hat{i} - v\sin 30\hat{j}$

Obviously, therefore, *change in velocity,* $\Delta v = v_2 - v_1$

$$= v\cos 30\hat{i} - v\sin 30\,\hat{j} - v\hat{i}.$$

Or, $$\Delta\vec{v} = v(\cos 30 - 1)\,\hat{i} - v\sin 30\,\hat{j} = v\left(\frac{\sqrt{3}}{2} - 1\right)\hat{i} + \frac{1}{2}v\hat{j}.$$

Or, since $v = 50$ cm/s, we have $\Delta\vec{v} = 50\,(0.134)\,\hat{i} - 25\,\hat{j} = -6.7\,\hat{i} - 25\,\hat{j}$

∴ *magnitude of the change in velocity* $= \sqrt{(6.7)^2 + (25)^2} = 25.92$ or 26 cm/s.

(*ii*) Clearly, *average acceleration* $= \dfrac{\text{Change in velocity}}{\text{time}}$. Or, $\vec{a} = \dfrac{\Delta\vec{v}}{\Delta t}$

$$= \frac{-6.7\hat{i} - 25\hat{j}}{2} = -3.35\hat{i} - 12.5\hat{j}.$$

$\therefore$ *magnitude of the average acceleration*

$$= \sqrt{(3.35)^2 + (12.5)^2} = 12.94 \quad \text{or} \quad 13.0 \text{ cm/s.}$$

(iii) Finally the *centripetal acceleration of the object* = v^2/r, where r is the radius of its circular path.

Now, $v = r\omega$ and $\therefore$ $r = v/\omega$, where $v = 50$ cm/s (given) and to determine ω, we note that the object describes an angle of 30° or $30 \times \pi/180 = \pi/6$ radians in 2 seconds. It will, therefore, describe an angle of $\pi/12$ radian in 1 second *i.e.*, $\omega = \pi/12$. So that,

$$r = 50 / \frac{\pi}{12} = 600/\pi = 191 \text{ cm.}$$

$\therefore$ *centripetal acceleration of the object* $= \frac{v^2}{r} = \frac{50 \times 50}{191} = 13.09 \text{ or } 13.0 \text{ cm/s}^2$.

The reason why the values of (*ii*) average acceleration and (*iii*) centripetal acceleration agree is that although average acceleration means the average of the total acceleration consisting of (*a*) *radial* and (*b*) *angular* accelerations, here, in this case, the motion being a *uniform circular* one; the question of angular acceleration does not arise. So that, the only acceleration (or the total acceleration) is the centripetal acceleration.

Example 9. The earth, revolving around its own axis, is not, strictly speaking, an inertial frame of reference. If, however, we take it to be so, what would be the error involved in 1 second, in the position of a particle close to its surface ? (Radius of the earth = 6.4×10^8 cm).

Solution. Obviously, due to rotation about its own axis, a particle on, or close to, the surface of the earth, experiences a centripetal acceleration equal to $\omega^2 R$, where ω is the *angular velocity* of the earth = $2\pi/24 \times 60 \times 60$ radius/s and R, its *radius* = 6.4×10^8 cm (given).

$\therefore$ *centripetal acceleration,* $\quad a = \left(\frac{2\pi}{24 \times 60 \times 60}\right)^2 \times 6.4 \times 10^8 \text{ cm/s}^2$.

$$= 3.385 \text{ or } 3.4 \text{ cm/s}^2.$$

Thus, the acceleration of a particle, measured in the earth's frame of reference, will differ by 3.4 cm/s^2 from that measured in a truly inertial frame of reference, and the position of a particle, as measured in the latter, will be altered by a distance $\frac{1}{2}at^2$ in t seconds or by $\frac{1}{2}a \times 3.4$ or 1.7 cm in 1 second, when measured in the former.

The error involved in 1s in the position of the particle, as measured in the earth's frame of reference, would thus be 1.7 cm.

Example 10. The initial positions of two particles are x_1 = 10 cm, y = 0 and x_2 = 0, y = 10 cm respectively. If the velocity of the first particle be $-5 \times 10^5\, \hat{i}$ m/s calculate that of the second at the instant that the two just collide with each other. What is then the relative velocity of th first particle with respect to the second?

Solution. Suppose the two particles collide after time t second. Then clearly, *position vector of the first particle after time t, i.e.,* $\vec{r}_1(t) = \vec{r}_1 + \vec{v}_1 t = 10\hat{i} + (-5 \times 10^5 \hat{i})t$

$$= 10\hat{i} - 5 \times 10^5 \hat{i}t.$$

And *position vector of the second particle after time t, i.e.,* $\vec{r}_2(t) = \vec{r}_2 + \vec{v}_2 t = 10\hat{j} + \vec{v}_2 t$.

In order that the two particles may collide, we must, obviously, have

$$\vec{r}_1(t) = \vec{r}_2(t).$$

Or, $\vec{r}_1(t) - \vec{r}_2(t) = 0$, *i.e.*, $(10\hat{i} - 5 \times 10^5 \hat{i}) - 10\hat{j} - \vec{v}_2 t = 0$.

Or, $(10 - 5 \times 10^5 t)\hat{i} - 10\hat{j} - \vec{v}_2 t = 0$, whence, $\vec{v}_2 t = (10 - 5 \times 10^5 t)\hat{i} - 10\hat{j}$.

Since the second particle has only a velocity along the y-axis, the x-component of its velocity is *zero, i.e.,* $10 - 5 \times 10^5 t = 0$, whence,

$$t = 10/5 \times 10^5 = 2 \times 10^{-5}\ \text{s},$$

So that, $\vec{v}_2 t = -10\hat{j}$. Or, $\vec{v}_2 = -\frac{10}{t}\hat{j} = -\frac{10}{2\times10^{-5}}\hat{j} = -5\times10^5\hat{j}$ cm/s.

The *velocity of the second particle at the time of collision is thus* $-5\times10^5\hat{j}$ cm/s.

And, *the relative velocity of the first particle with respect to the second* is, obviously,

$$\vec{v}_r = \vec{v}_1 - \vec{v}_2 = -5\times10^5\hat{i} + 5\times10^5\hat{j} = 5\times10^5(\hat{j}-\hat{i})\ \text{cm/s}.$$

2.10 FRAMES OF REFERENCE WITH LINEAR ACCELERATION

In Fig. 2.5 let frame S' be moving with a linear acceleration $\vec{a}_0$ with respect to the *inertial frame* S. Then, particle A or, in fact, any other particle at rest with respect to frame S will clearly appear to be moving with an acceleration $-\vec{a}_0$ with respect to frame S' and, therefore, a particle having an acceleration $\vec{a}$ with respect to the inertial frame S will appear to have an acceleration $\vec{a}' = \vec{a} - \vec{a}_0$ in frame S'. So that, if m be the *mass* of the particle (assumed to remain unaltered in either frame), we have

observed force on the particle in frame S' given by

$$\vec{F} = m\vec{a}' = m(\vec{a} - \vec{a}_0) = m\vec{a} - m\vec{a}_0.$$

where $m\vec{a} = \vec{F}$ is clearly the *force on the particle in the inertial frame S.*

We, therefore, have $\vec{F}' = \vec{F} - m\vec{a}_0$

Or, putting $m\vec{a}_0 = \vec{F}_0$ we have $\vec{F}' = \vec{F} - \vec{F}_0$

And if $\vec{F} = 0$, $\vec{F}' = -\vec{F}_0$

Thus, even when no force is acting on the particle in frame S, a force $\vec{F}_0 = m\vec{a}_0$ appears to be acting on the particle in frame S' which is, therefore, a **non-inertial frame.** (see also § 2.14)

Incidentally, the relation $\vec{a}' = \vec{a} - \vec{a}_0$ or $\vec{a} = \vec{a}' + \vec{a}_0$ is called the **Galilean law of composition of accelerations.**

2.11 CLASSICAL RELATIVITY–GALILEAN INVARIANCE

In one of the corollaries to his laws of motion, *Newton* says : ***'the motions of bodies included in a given space are the same among themselves whether that space is at rest or moves uniformly forward in a straight line'.*** This clearly implies that if we are drifting along at a uniform speed in a closed space ship, *all the phenomena observed, and all the experiments performed inside the ship, will appear to be the same as if the ship were not in motion.* This is the *concept of Classical or Newtonian relativity,* usually referred to as *Galilean invariance.* It clearly means that *the fundamental physical laws and principles are all invariant* to Galilean transformation.* Or, in plain and simple language, *the fundamental physical laws and principles are identical in all inertial frames of reference.* Let us see if this is so.

***(i)* Newton's law of motion.** Considering the second law of motion which in the *real* law of motion and includes also the first law, let F be the force acting on a mass m in frame S (Fig. 2.5). Then, we have $F = ma$, where a is the acceleration produced in the mass. *Assuming the mass to be independent of velocity,* if F' be the force acting on it in frame S', we have $\vec{F} = m\vec{a}$, where $\vec{a}'$ is the acceleration produced in it in this frame. Since, as we know, $\vec{a} = \vec{a}'$ in the two inertial frames, we have

$$\vec{F} = \vec{F}', \quad \text{... (i)}$$

indicating that *the law is invariant to Galilean transformation.*

---

* When something does not change, one says it is invariant. Covariance means no change in form, usually used for equations.

(ii) The law of conservation of momentum. The momentum of a body or a particle of *mass m* and *velocity* $\vec{v}$ is as we know, given by $\vec{p} = m\vec{v}$. And, the *law of conservation of momentum* merely states that *if a number of particles collide against each other, their total momentum after collision is the same as their total momentum before collision, irrespective of the collisian being elastic or inelastic.* Only, in the particles before collision appears as their kinetic energy after collision and, in the case of an inelastic collision, part of the kinetic energy particles before collision appears in the form of heat (or some such sort of internal excitation energy) after the collision and only the balance as kinetic energy of the particles.

Thus if we consider only two particles of masses m_1 and m_2 in frame S (Fig. 2.5), moving with velocities $\vec{u_1}$ and $\vec{u_2}$ respectively before collision and with velocities $\vec{v_1}$ and $\vec{v_2}$ after collision, the law of conservation of momentum demands that

$$m_1\vec{u_1} + m_2\vec{u_2} = m_1\vec{v_1} + m_2\vec{v_2}. \qquad \text{... (ii)}$$

Taking the masses to remain unaltered in the two inertial frames, if the law of conservation of momentum is to be invariant to Galilean transformation, it should assume, in frame S', the form

$$m_1\vec{u_1'} + m_2\vec{u_2'} = m_1\vec{v_1'} + m_2\vec{v_2'}. \qquad \text{... (iii)}$$

where $\vec{u_1'}, \vec{u_2'}$ and $\vec{v_1'}, \vec{v_2'}$ are the respective velocities of the particles before and after collision in frame S'.

This is actually found to be the case. For, as we know, [§ 2.9 (*c*)].

$\vec{u_1} = \vec{u_1'} + \vec{v}, \vec{u_2} = \vec{u_2'} + \vec{v}, \vec{v_1} = \vec{v_1'} + \vec{v}$, and $\vec{v_2} = \vec{v_2'} + \vec{v}$, where v is the relative velocity of frame S' with respect to frame S.

Substituting these values in relation (*ii*) above, we have

$$m_1(\vec{u_1'} + \vec{v}) + m_2(\vec{u_2'} + \vec{v}) = m_1(\vec{v_1'} + \vec{v}) + m_2(\vec{v_2'} + \vec{v}).$$

Or, $$m_1\vec{u_1'} + m_2\vec{u_2'} + \vec{v}(m_1 + m_2) = m_1\vec{v_1'} + m_2\vec{v_2'} + \vec{v}(m_1 + m_2).$$

Or, $$m_1\vec{u_1'} + m_2\vec{u_2'} = m_1\vec{v_1'} + m_2\vec{v_2'}. \qquad \text{... (iv)}$$

showing that *the law of conservation of momentum is also invariant to Galilean transformation. i.e., holds good in all inertial frames of reference.*

It may be carefully noted that *although the values of momenta and changes of momentum of the individual particles are different in the two frames of reference, the total momentum of the two is conserved in either frame. Thus, whereas momentum, by itself, is not invariant to Galilean transformation, the principle of conservation is.*

(iii) The law of conservation of energy. Again, consider a collision between two particles in the inertial frame S (Fig. 2.5). Taking their respective masses to be m_1 and m_2 and their respective velocities to be $\vec{u_1}, \vec{u_2}$ and $\vec{v_1}, \vec{v_2}$ before and after collision, we have, in accordance with the law of conservation of energy,

$$\frac{1}{2}m_1\vec{u_1}^2 + \frac{1}{2}m_2\vec{u_2}^2 = \frac{1}{2}m_1\vec{v_1}^2 + \frac{1}{2}m_2\vec{v_2}^2 + E, \qquad \text{... (v)}$$

where, E is part of the energy of the particles (before the collision) appearing in some other form, like hleat etc.

Let the velocities of the two masses in frame S' before and after collision be $\vec{u}, \vec{u_2'}$ and $\vec{v_1'}, v_2'$ respectively. Then, with the values of the masses (m_1 and m_2) remaining unaltered and with E remaining the same (as established by actual experiment), the law of conservation of energy must assume the form

$$\frac{1}{2}m_1u_1'^2 + \frac{1}{2}m_2u_2'^2 = \frac{1}{2}m_1\vec{v_1'}^2 + \frac{1}{2}m_2\vec{v_2}^2 + E, \qquad \text{... (vi)}$$

if it is to be invariant to Galilean transformation.

That this is actually so may be easily seen by substituting in relation (v) above, the values of $\vec{u}_1$, $\vec{u}_2$, $\vec{v}_1$ and $\vec{v}_2$ obtained by Galilean transformation [§ 2.9 (c)], as in case (*ii*) above, when we have

$$\frac{1}{2}m_1(\vec{u}_1'^{2}+\vec{v})^2+\frac{1}{2}m_2(\vec{u}_2'+\vec{v})^2 = \frac{1}{2}m_1(\vec{v}_1'+\vec{v})^2+\frac{1}{2}m_2(\vec{v}_2'+\vec{v})^2+E,$$

where v, as we know, is the relative velocity of frame S' with respect to S.

$$\text{Or,}\quad \frac{1}{2}m_1\vec{u}_1'^{2}+\frac{1}{2}m_2\vec{u}_2'^{2}+\vec{v}(m_1\vec{u}_1'+m_2\vec{u}_2')$$

$$= \frac{1}{2}m_1(\vec{v}_1'^{2}+\vec{v}^{2}+2\vec{v}_1'\vec{v})+\frac{1}{2}m_2(\vec{v}_2'^{2}+\vec{v}+2\vec{v}_2'\vec{v})+E.$$

$$\text{Or,}\quad \frac{1}{2}m_1\vec{u}_1'^{2}+\frac{1}{2}m_2\vec{u}_2'^{2}+\vec{v}\,(m_1\vec{u}_1'+m_2\vec{u}_2')$$

$$= \frac{1}{2}m_1\vec{v}_1'^{2}+\frac{1}{2}m_2\vec{v}_2'^{2}+v(m_1\vec{v}_1'\,m_2\vec{v}_2')+E.$$

Since momentum remains conserved in frame S', we have

$$m_1\vec{u}_1'+m_2\vec{u}_3' = m_1\vec{v}_1'+m_2\vec{v}_2'.$$

$$\text{And, therefore,}\quad \frac{1}{2}m_1\vec{u}_1'^{2}+\frac{1}{2}m_2\vec{u}_2'^{2} = \frac{1}{2}m_1\vec{v}_1'^{2}+\frac{1}{2}m_2\vec{v}_2'^{2}+E,$$

showing that energy is also conserved in frame S'.

In other words, *the law of conservation of energy (like that of conservation of momentum) is invariant to Galilean transformation.*

Now, simply because any two reference frames, moving with constant relative velocity, can be connected by means of a Galilean transformation, we should not rush to the conclusion that the fundamental laws of Physics are invariant or identical in all reference frames that can be so connected. There is a snag here, namely, we have assumed both *mass* and *time* to be invariant to Galilean transformation. There is little or no justification for it, as we shall see later when we are faced with invariance of the velocity of light (c) in free space. More correctly, the statement should be that *the fundamental physical laws are invariant or identical in all reference frames that can be connected, not by Galilean, but by Lorentz transformations* (§ 3.6) which takes due account of the invariance of the value of c. For non-relativistic velocities (*i.e.*, for velocities very much less than c) Lorentz transformations too reduce to Galilean ones.

2.12 TRANSFORMATION EQUATIONS FOR A FRAME OF REFERENCE INCLINED TO AN INERTIAL FRAME

Let S be an inertial or a Galilean frame of reference and S', a frame of reference with its origin coinciding with that of S but with its coordinate axes inclined to those of the latter, as shown in Fig. 2.9.

Consider a particle at P, whose position vector is $\vec{r}$ with respect to the origin of either frame of reference. Its coordinates are obviously x, y, z in frame S and x', y', z' in frame S'.

We have x' = *sum of the components of x, y, z along the axis OX', i.e.*, $= x \cos XOX' + y \cos YOX' + z \cos ZOX'$.

Or, representing $\cos XOX'$ by $\cos (X, X')$ or C_{xx}', $\cos YOX'$ by $\cos (Y, X')$ or C_{yx}' and $\cos ZOX'$ by $\cos (Z, X')$ or C_{zx}, we have

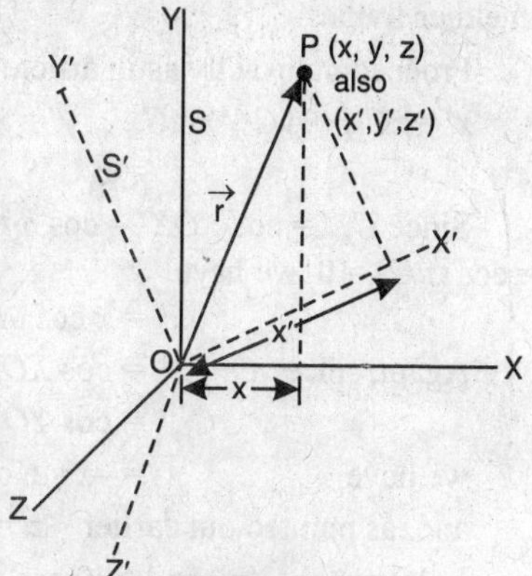

Fig. 2.9

$$x' = xC_{xx}' + yC_{yx}' + zC_{zx}' \qquad ...(i)$$

Similarly, $$y' = xC_{xy}' + yC_{yy}' + zC_{zy}' \qquad ...(ii)$$

and $$z' = xC_{xz}' + yC_{yz}' + zC_{zz}'. \qquad ...(iii)$$

These are clearly the *transformation equations* from frame S to S'. Differentiating expression (*i*) *twice* with respect to t, we have

$$\frac{d^2x'}{dl^2} = \frac{d^2x}{dl^2}C_{xx}' + \frac{d^2y}{dt^2}C_{yx}' + \frac{d^2z}{dt^2}C_{zx}'. \qquad ...(iv)$$

Since S is an *inertial frame,* and no force is acting on the particle at P, we have $d^2x/dt^2 = 0$, also $d^2y/dt^2 = 0$ and $d^2z/dt^2 = 0$.

Substituting these values in relation (*iv*), therefore, we have

$$d^2x'/dt^2 = 0.$$

In exactly the same manner we can show that

$$d^2y'/dt^2 = 0 \text{ and } d^2z'/dt^2 = 0.$$

Obviously, then, **the reference frame S' is also an inertial frame** and hence the transformation equations (*i*), (*ii*) and (*iii*) above are *Galilean transformation equations from the inertial or Galilean frame S to the inertial or Galilean frame S'*.

The *inverse Galilean transformation equations* (from S' to S) will obviously be

$$x = x'C_{xx}' + y'C_{yx}' + z'C_{zx}', \; y = x'C_{xy}' + y'C_{yy}' + z'C_{zy}'$$

and $$z = x'C_{xz}' + y'C_{yz}' + z'C_{zz}'.$$

2.13 TRANSFORMATION EQUATIONS FOR A ROTATING FRAME OF REFERENCE

Consider an inertial frame of reference S and another reference frame S' whose origin and coordinate axes coincide with those of S.

Now, with the origins of the two frames still coinciding, let S' start rotating with a uniform angular velocity ω about the common axis of z, so that in time t, the axes OX' and OY' of S' have turned through angle ωt each with respect to axes OX and OY of S, as shown in Fig. 2.10.

As in article 2.12 above, we have to determine the relation between the coordinates, x, z and x', y', z' of a particle P in the two frames of reference respectively, its position vector with respect to the origin being the same $\vec{r}$ in either frame.

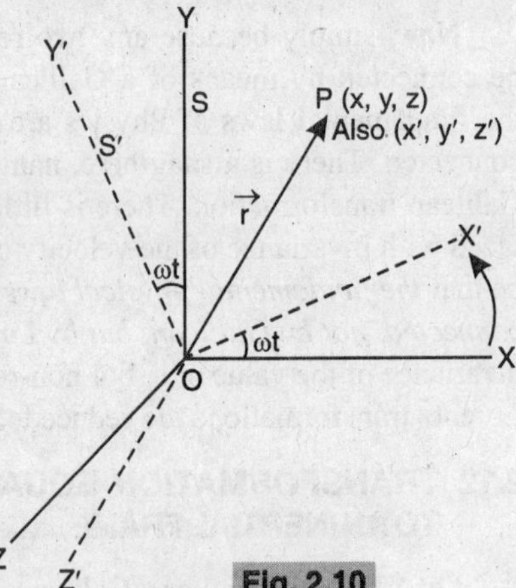

Fig. 2.10

Proceeding exactly as in article 2.12, we have

$x' = xC_{xx}' + yC_{yx}' + zC_{zx}'$, $y' = xC_{xy}' + yC_{yy}' + zC_{zy}'$ and, of course,

$$z' = z.$$

Since $C_{xx}' = \cos XOX' = \cos \omega t$, $C_{yx}' = \cos YOX' = \cos(\pi/2 - \omega t) = \sin \omega t$ and $C_{zx}' = \cos XOZ' = \cos(\pi/2) = 0$, we have

$$x' = x \cos \omega t + y \sin \omega t, \qquad ...(v)$$

Again, since $C_{xy}' = \cos XOY' = \cos(\pi/2 + \omega t) = -\sin \omega t$,

$C_{yy}' = \cos YOY' = \cos \omega t$ and $C_{zy}' = \cos ZOY' = \cos(\pi/2) = 0$,

we have $$y' = -x \sin \omega t + y \cos \omega t, \qquad ...(vi)$$

and, as pointed out earlier $z' = z$. ...(*vii*)

Relations (*v*), (*vi*) and (*vii*) are, therefore, the *transformation equations* in the case of the frame of reference S', rotating with a uniform angular velocity ω relative to the inertial frame S.

The inverse transformation equations (from S' to S) will obviously be

$x = x' \cos \omega t - y' \sin \omega t$, $y = x' \sin \omega t + y' \cos \omega t$ and $z = z'$.

Now, frame S is an inertial frame, and so force is applied to particle P. We, therefore, have

$$\frac{d^2 x}{dt^2} = 0, \quad \frac{d^2 y}{dt^2} = 0 \quad \text{and} \quad \frac{d^2 z}{dt^2} = 0.$$

On the other hand, differentiating expressions (v), (vi) and (vii) for x', y' and z' respectively with respect to t, we have

$$\frac{dx'}{dt} = -\omega x \sin \omega t + \omega y \cos \omega t + \frac{dx}{dt} \cos \omega t + \frac{dy}{dt} \sin \omega t.$$

Or, since $-x \sin \omega t + y \cos \omega t = y'$ [relation (vi), above], we have

$$\frac{dx'}{dt} = \omega y' + \frac{dx}{dt} \cos \omega t + \frac{dy}{dt} \sin \omega t. \quad ...(viii)$$

Similarly,

$$\frac{dy}{dt} = -\omega x \cos \omega t - \omega y \sin \omega t - \frac{dx}{dt} \sin \omega t + \frac{dy}{dt} \cos \omega t.$$

Or, since $x \cos \omega t + y \sin \omega t = x'$ [relation (v) above], we have

$$\frac{dy}{dt} = -\omega x' - \frac{dx}{dt} \sin \omega t + \frac{dy}{dt} \cos \omega t. \quad ...(ix)$$

And, of cource,

$$\frac{dz'}{dt} = \frac{dz}{dt}. \quad ...(x)$$

Differentiating expressions ($viii$), (ix) and (x) once again, with respect to t, we have

$$\frac{d^2 x}{dt^2} = \omega \frac{dy'}{dt} - \omega \frac{dx}{dt} \sin \omega t + \omega \frac{dy}{dt} \cos \omega t.$$

Since from relation (ix) above,

$$-\frac{dx}{dt} \sin \omega t + \frac{dy}{dt} \cos \omega t = \left(\frac{dy'}{dt} + \omega x' \right), \text{ we have}$$

$$\frac{d^2 x'}{dt^2} = \omega \frac{dy'}{dt} + \omega \left(\frac{dy'}{dt} + \omega x' \right) = 2\omega \frac{dy}{dt} + \omega^2 x', \quad ...(xi)$$

Similarly,

$$\frac{d^2 y'}{dt^2} = -\omega \frac{dx'}{dt} - \omega \frac{dx}{dt} \cos \omega t - \omega \frac{dy}{dt} \sin \omega t.$$

Since from relation ($viii$) above, $\dfrac{dx}{dt} \cos \omega t + \dfrac{dy}{dt} \sin \omega t = \left(\dfrac{dx'}{dt} - \omega y' \right)$,

$$\text{we have } \frac{d^2 y'}{dt^2} = -\omega \frac{dx'}{dt} - \omega \left(\frac{dx'}{dt} - \omega y' \right) = -2\omega \frac{dx'}{dt} + \omega^2 y'. \quad ...(xii)$$

And

$$\frac{d^2 z'}{dt^2} = \frac{d^2 z}{dt^2} \quad ...(xiii)$$

It is thus clear from relations (xi) and (xii) above, that even though no force is acting on particle P in frame S, a force *seems* to be acting on it in frame S', producing an acceleration in it. *Frame S' is, therefore, a non-inertial frame of reference.* (See also § 2.14).

2.14 NON-INERTIAL FRAMES–FICTITIOUS FORCES

We have seen that (i) a frame of reference in accelerated translational motion with respect to an inertial frame (§ 2.10 and (ii) a reference frame in uniform rotation about an inertial frame (§ 2.13), are both *non-inertial* frames. Let us consider them a little more in detail.

***(i)* The accelerated frame of reference.** It has been shown in § 2.10 how if a force $\vec{F} = m\vec{a}$ be acting on a particle in an inertial frame S, the force acting on it in a reference frame S', moving with an acceleration $\vec{a}_0$ with respect to S, in $\vec{F}' = (m\vec{a} - m\vec{a}_0)$.. Frame S' is, therefore, a non-inertial frame since Newton's second law of motion, obviously, does not hold good in its case. For, putting $-m\vec{a}_0 = \vec{F}_0$, with $m\vec{a}$, of course, equal to $\vec{F}$, we have $-\vec{F}' = \vec{F} + \vec{F}_0$. And, as we have seen already, if $\vec{F}' = \vec{F}_0 = -m\vec{a}_0$, *i.e.*, even when no force actually acts on the particle in the inertial frame S, a force equal to $\vec{F}_0$ *appears to be acting on it in frame S'.*

This force $\vec{F}_0 = m\vec{a}_0$ *does not actually exist but appears to come into being purely in consequence of the acceleration of frams S' with respect to S.* It is, therefore, a aptly called a **fictitious** or a **pseudo (false) force.** And, clearly, *it is equal to mass times the acceleration of the non-inertial frame, with its sign reversed.*

Or, *fictitious force* $\vec{F}_0$ = *mass (acceleration of non-inertial frame, with sign reversed).*

Or, $$\vec{F}_0 = m(-\vec{a}_0) = -m\vec{a}_0$$

As will be easily seen, *it is the force which, when added to the true force* $(\vec{F})$ *in the inertial frame S, gives the observed force* $\vec{F}'$ *in the non-inertial or accelerated frame S'.*

This means, in other words, that Newton's second law of motion will also hold good in the non-inertial frame S' which will, therefore, also behave as an inertial frame of reference, *if we add to the true force* $\vec{F}$ *a fictitious force* $\vec{F}_0 = -m\vec{a}_0$.

Examples of Fictitious force.

A familiar example of a fictitious force in an accelerated frame of reference is that on a particle *at rest* with respect to a lift which is descending with an acceleration equal to g, if m be the mass of the particle, the fictitious force acting on it is $F_0 = -mg$. So that, the resultant force on it, as observed by an observer in the lift (the moving frame) is given by F' = *true force acting on it, (i.e., mg) + the fictitious force, – mg*, Or, $F' = mg - mg = 0$, *i.e.*, the particle is weightless and thus remains suspended in the air, –*a* condition that obtains in artificial satellites.

Exactly similarly, a body on the palm of our hand appears to our palm to be weightless during the small fraction of time that we are jumping down from a table on to the ground. For, here too, the body is initially at rest with respect to our palm which moves down with an acceleration equal to q.

Another interesting point about a fictitious force is that it enables us to determine whether or not a given frame of reference is accelerated. For, if two frames be in uniform relative motion (zero acceleration), with respect to each other, they are obviously inertial frames, and it is impossible to find out which one is at rest and which one in motion. If, however, one of them be accelerated with respect to the other, fictitious forces come into play inside the accelerated frame. These forces are obviously different from the true or real forces. For, unlike the latter, which go on diminishing rapidly with distance and are almost zero at a large distance from a body, the former arise precisely due to the accelerated motion of the frame of reference and go on increasing with its acceleration. So that, whereas the real forces on particles or bodies at large distances from other bodies are negligible, the fictitious forces may have appreciable values. *If, therefore, we find a body or*

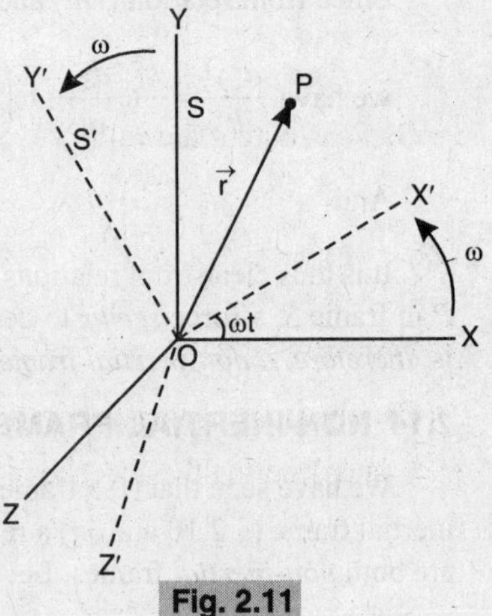

Fig. 2.11

a particle, far away from other material bodies, to be acted upon by an appreciable force, we can safely declare that its frame of reference is an accelerated one.

(ii) The rotating frame of reference-Coriolis acceleration and force. Let us now consider a reference frame S' (shown dotted) rotating with a *uniform angular velocity* $\vec{\omega}$ with respect to an *inertial frame* S (Fig. 2.11). To make matters simpler, let us assume the two frames of reference to have a common origin O and the axis of rotation of S' about S to be passing through O.

Suppose now we have a moving particle P (like, for instance, a fly or an ant walking on a rotating piece of cardboard). The value of its position vector r at any given instant t will, obviously, be the same in either frame of reference, though its components along the three axes will naturally be different.

If the particle (*i.e.,* the fly or the ant on the card board) be at rest with respect to the inertial frame S, it would appear to be moving with a relative linear velocity $-\vec{\omega} \times \vec{r}$ in the non-inertial, rotating frame S'. And, therefore, if its linear velocity in frame S be $\vec{v} = d\vec{r}/dt$, it will apear in frame S' to be $\vec{v'} = \dfrac{d\vec{r}}{dt} - \vec{\omega} \times \vec{r}$

So that, we have $\left(\dfrac{d\vec{r}}{dt}\right)S' = \left(\dfrac{d\vec{r}}{dt}\right)S - \vec{\omega} \times \vec{r}$. Or, $\vec{v'} = \vec{v} - \vec{\omega} . \vec{r}$,

whence, $$\left(\frac{d\vec{r}}{dt}\right)S = \left(\frac{d\vec{r}}{dt}\right)S' + \vec{\omega} \times \vec{r}. \qquad ...(i)$$

Or, $$\vec{v} = \vec{v} + \vec{\omega} \times \vec{r}.$$

This gives the linear velocity $(\vec{v})$ of the particle in the inertial frame S at any given instant in terms of its velocity $(\vec{v'})$ in the rotating frame S' and its position vector r at that instant.

Now, equation (*i*) above, *relating the rate of change of a vector* ($\vec{r}$ *in this case*) *in two given frames of reference* (*S and S'*) *is clearly a general one,* applicable to *any* vector and may, therefore, be put in the form of an *operator equation* $\left(\dfrac{d}{dt}\right)S = \left(\dfrac{d}{dt}\right)S' + \vec{\omega} \times \vec{r}$. ...(*ii*)

Applying this to the velocity vector v, in order to deduce a relationship between the accelerations of the particle in the two frames of reference, we have

$$\left(\frac{d\vec{v}}{dt}\right)S = \left(\frac{d\vec{v}}{dt}\right)S' + \vec{\omega} \times \vec{r},\ \ i.e.,\ \ \frac{d\vec{v}}{dt} = \frac{d\vec{v'}}{dt} + \vec{\omega} \times \vec{v}.$$

Or, substituting the value of $\vec{v}$, we have

$$\left(\frac{d\vec{v}}{dt}\right)Sa = \frac{d}{dt}[(\vec{v'} + \vec{\omega} \times \vec{r})]S' + \vec{\omega} \times (\vec{v'} + \vec{\omega} \times \vec{r'})$$

Or, $$\frac{d\vec{v}}{dt} = \frac{d\vec{v'}}{dt} + \frac{d\vec{\omega}}{dt} \times \vec{r} + \vec{\omega}\left(\frac{d\vec{r}}{dt}\right)S + \vec{\omega} \times \vec{v'} + \vec{\omega} \times (\vec{\omega} \times \vec{r}).$$

Clearly $d\vec{v}/dt$ is the acceleration of the particle, as observed in the inertial frame S. Denoting it by $\vec{a}$, and denoting the acceleration $d\vec{v'}/dt$ in the rotating frame S' by $\vec{a'}$, we have

$$\vec{a} = \vec{a'} + 2\vec{\omega} \times \vec{v} + \frac{d\omega}{dt} \times \vec{r} + \vec{\omega} \times (\vec{\omega} \times \vec{r}) \qquad [\because (d\vec{r}/dt)S' = \vec{v'}.]$$

Since the angular velocity $\vec{\omega}$ is uniform, $d\vec{\omega}/dt = 0$. We, therefore, have

$$\vec{a} = \vec{a'} + 2\vec{\omega} \times \vec{v'} + \vec{\omega} \times (\vec{\omega} \times \vec{r}).$$

Here, $2\vec{\omega} \times \vec{v'}$ is what is called Coriolis acceleration, after *G*. Coriolis, who first discovered it, and $\vec{\omega} \times (\vec{\omega} \times \vec{r})$, the familiar **centripental acceleration.** So that, we have

$$\frac{\textit{acceleration in}}{\textit{the inertial frame}} = \frac{\textit{observed acceleration}}{\textit{in the rotating frame}} + \frac{\textit{Coriolis}}{\textit{acceleration}} + \frac{\textit{centripetal}}{\textit{acceleration.}}$$

Coriolis force

Hence, if *m* be the *mass* of the particle, we have *force acting on the particle in the rotating frame* = $m\vec{a'} = \vec{F'}$ and the *true force acting on it in the inertial frame* = $m\vec{a} = \vec{F}$.

And, therefore, $m\vec{a'} = m\vec{a} - 2m\vec{\omega} \times \vec{v'} - m\vec{\omega} \times (\vec{\omega} \times \vec{r})$.

Or, $\vec{F'} = \vec{F} - 2m\vec{\omega} \times \vec{v'} - m\vec{\omega} \times (\vec{\omega} \times \vec{r})$.

But, as we know, the *force* acting in a non-inertial frame, *i.e.*,

$$\vec{F'} = \vec{F} + \vec{F_0}$$

where $\vec{F_0}$ is the *fictitious force* acting in the non-inertial frame.

So, that, here, *fictitious force* $\vec{F_0} = -2m\vec{\omega} \times \vec{v'} - m\vec{\omega} \times (\vec{\omega} \times \vec{r})$,

where $-2m\vec{\omega} \times \vec{v'}$ is the *Coriolis force* and $-m\vec{\omega} \times (\vec{\omega} \times \vec{r})$, the *centrifugal force.*

Thus, here, *fictitious force* $\vec{F_0}$ = *Coriolis force* + *centrifugal force.*

It will thus be seen that the centrifugal force is a fictitious force *which acts on a particle at rest relative to a rotating frame of reference.* Being responsible for keeping the particle at rest in the rotating frame, *it is mumerically equal to the centripetal force,* $m\omega^2 \times \vec{r_n}$, where $\vec{r_n}$ is the distance of the particle from the centre of rotation (or the component of $\vec{r}$ normal to the axis of rotation) *but is oppositely directed, i.e.,* outwards, away from the axis of rotation, Fig. 2.12).

It will also be seen that *Coriolis force too is a fictitious force, which acts on a particle in motion relative to a rotating frame of reference.* It is proportional to the angular velocity ($\vec{\omega}$) of the rotating frame and to the velocity $\vec{v'}$ of the particle relative to it. Its direction is always perpendicular to that of $\vec{v'}$ and is obtained by a rotation through 90° in the opposite sense to that of $\vec{\omega}$, as will be clear from Fig. 2.11.

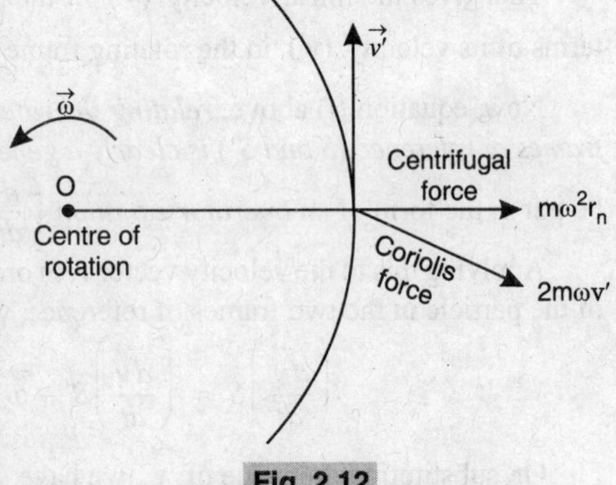

Fig. 2.12

It will obviously be zero if either $\vec{v'}$ *or* $\vec{\omega}$ *is zero, i.e., if the particle is at rest relative to the rotating frame* (in which case the only fictitious force acting on the particle will be the centrifugal force) *or if the reference frame be a non-rotating one.*

It will further be seen that particle *P* (Fig. 2.11) will move relative to the rotating frame *S'* in accordance with Newton's law of motion *if we add to the true force* $\vec{F}$, *these two fictitious forces.*

2.15 EFFECTS OF CENTRIFUGAL AND CORIOLIS FORCES DUE TO EARTH'S ROTATION

Since the earth is rotating uniformly about its own axis, from west to east, a reference frame fixed on it is clearly a rotating frame of reference. As a result, the two fictitious forces, *viz.*, the

Centrifugal force. and the Coriolis *force* must act on a particle, *at rest and in motion respectively,* relative to the rotating frame or reference. Let us see the effect of these two forces.

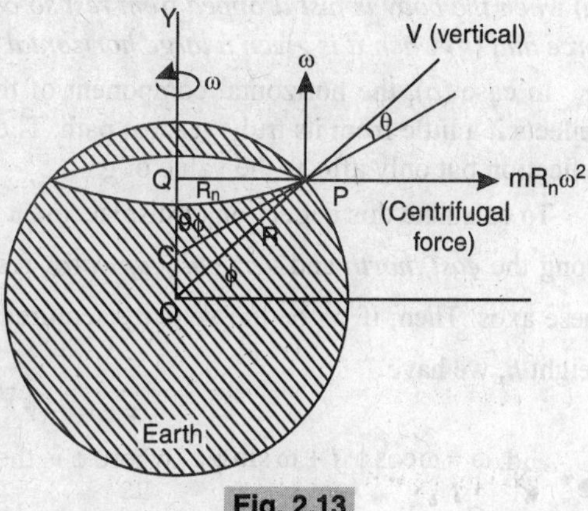

Fig. 2.13

***(i)* Effect of centrifugal force.** Let us consider a particle P at rest on the surface of the earth, in latitude ϕ (Fig. 2.13). Then, because the particle is at rest in the rotating frame of reference of the earth, *there is no Coriolis force acting on it.* The only fictitious force effective is therefore, the centrifugal force = $m\omega \times (\omega \times \mathbf{R}_n)$, where $\mathbf{R}_n$ is the component of the radius R of the earth, perpendicular to its axis (or the distance of the particle P from the axis). Hence, if the *observed or apparent acceleration of the* particle, in latitude ϕ, be directed towards C, and *its true acceleration, g,* towards the centre (o) of the earth, we have

$$g_\phi = g - \omega' \times (\omega \times R_n).$$

Now, if we take the axes, OY and OX, *along* and *perpendicular* to ω respectively, with $\hat{i}$ and $\hat{j}$ as the unit vectors along OX and OY as usual, we have

$$\vec{g} = -g(\cos\phi\hat{i} + \sin\phi\hat{j}),\ \vec{w} = \omega\hat{j} \text{ and } \vec{R}_n = R\cos\phi\hat{i}.$$

Substituting in the expression for g_ϕ above, therefore, we have

$$\vec{g}_\phi = -g(\cos\phi\,\hat{i} + \sin\phi\,\hat{j}) - \omega\hat{j} \times (\omega\hat{j} \times R\cos\phi\,\hat{i})$$

$$= -g(\cos\phi\,\hat{i} + \sin\phi\hat{j}) + \omega^2 R\cos\phi\,\hat{i},$$

i.e., the *magnitude of the apparent acceleration* is

$$g_\phi = \sqrt{(g\cos\phi - \omega^2 R\cos\phi)^2 + g^2\sin^2\phi}.$$

Since ω is small, we may neglect terms involving ω^4.

So that, we have

$$g_\phi = \sqrt{(g^2\cos^2\phi - 2g\omega^2 R\cos^2\phi + g^2\sin^2\phi} = \sqrt{g^2 - 2g\omega^2 R\cos^2\phi}.$$

Or, $$g_\phi = g\left(1 - \frac{2\omega^2 R\cos^2\phi}{g}\right)^{\frac{1}{2}} = g\left(1 - \frac{\omega^2 R\cos^2\phi}{g}\right)$$

very nearly,

i.e., $$g_\phi = g - \omega^2 R\cos^2\phi.$$

This acceleration, as mentioned above, is directed towards C instead of O, the centre of the earth. So that, if the angle that this *apparent direction PC* makes with the *true direction PO* be θ, we have

$$\theta = \tan^{-1}\frac{g\cos\phi - \omega^2 R\cos\phi}{g\sin\phi} = \tan^{-1}\left[\left(1 - \frac{\omega^2 R}{g}\right)\cot\phi\right].$$

Thus, the effect of centrifugal force, due to rotation of the earth, is to reduce the effective value of g on its surface as also to slightly change its direction from the truly vertical,—towards the north and the south respectively in the two hemispheres.

Obviously, θ gives the deflection of a plumb line from the true direction of the gravitational force and will have its maximum value in latitude $\phi = 45°$.

***(ii)* Effect of Coriolis force.** In case a body is in motion relative to the rotating frame of reference of the earth, the fictitious Coriolis force comes into play and two cases of interest arise :

(*a*) *when the body is just dropped from rest so as to fall freely under the action of the gravitational force and* (*b*) *when it is given a large horizontal velocity* (case of a *projectile*).

In case (*a*), the horizontal component of the Coriolis force acting on the freely falling body deflects it a little from its truly vertical path. The vertical component, obviously, produces no south deflection but only affects the value of g.

To calculate this deflection or displacement of the falling body, let us take the axes of x, y and z along the *east, north* and *vertically upwards* respectively and $\hat{i}, \hat{j}$ and $\hat{k}$ as the unit vectors along these axes. Then, if $\vec{v}$ be the velocity acquired by the body in time t taken by it to fall through a height h, we have

$$\vec{v} = -v\,\vec{k} \qquad (\because \text{ the velocity is directed } \textit{downwards})$$

and $\omega = \omega\cos\phi\; j + \omega\sin\phi\; \hat{k}$, where ϕ is the *latitude* at the place.

$\therefore$ *Coriolis acceleration,* say, $\vec{a}_c = -2\vec{\omega}\times\vec{v}$

$$= -2\omega\,(\cos\phi\,\hat{j} + \sin\phi\,\hat{k})\times(-v\hat{k})$$

$$= 2\omega v\,(\cos\phi\,\hat{i} - 0) = 2\omega\, v\cos\phi\,\hat{i},$$

i.e., the Coriolis acceleration on the body in latitude ϕ is $2\omega v \cos\phi$ along the positive direction of the axis of x or *is directed towards the east.*

The equation of motion of the body may, therefore, be put as

$$d^2x/dt^2 = 2\omega v\cos\phi.$$

Since v is the velocity acquired by the body in time t, we have $v = 0 + gt = gt$, since its initial velocity is *zero* and the acceleration due to gravity, g. So that,

$$d^2x/dt^2 = 2\omega gt\cos\phi.$$

$\therefore$ *x-component of the velocity of the body,* say,

$$v_x = dx/dt = \int 2\omega gt\cos\phi\, dt.$$

Or, $v_x = 2\omega g\cos\phi\, t^2/2 + C$, where C is the constant of integration.

Since v_x is zero at the very start, when $t = 0$, we have $C = 0$.

And $\therefore$ $\qquad v_x = \omega g\cos\phi\, t^2.$

Integrating once again, we have

displacement along the axis of x, i.e., $x = \int \omega g\cos\phi\, t^2 dt$

$$= \omega g\cos\phi\left(\frac{t^3}{3}\right) + C'.$$

where C' is another **constant of integration.**

Again, since at $t = 0$, there is no displacement, *i.e.*, $x = 0$, we have $C' = 0$.

Hence, $\qquad x = \dfrac{1}{3}\omega g\cos\phi\, t^3.$

Now, t is the time taken by the body to fall through a height h. So that, its initial velocity being zero, we have $h = \frac{1}{2}gt^2$ whence, $t = \sqrt{2h/g}$. Substituting this value of t in the expression for x above, we have

$$x = \frac{1}{3}\omega g\cos\phi\,(2h/g)^{\frac{3}{2}} = \left(\frac{8}{9g}\right)^{\frac{1}{2}} h^{\frac{3}{2}}\,\omega\cos\phi\,.$$

Thus, the horizontal displacement of the body due to Coriolis force (*i*) *in latitude* ϕ is equal to $(8/9g)^{1/2}\, h^{3/2}\, \omega\cos\phi$ and (*ii*) *at the equator,* since $\phi = 0$, or $\cos\phi = 1$, it is equal to $(8/9g)^{1/2}\, h^{3/2}\, \omega$

(*i.e.*, the *maximum*). And *it is always directed along the positive direction of the x-axis or towards the east.*

In case (*b*), if the horizontal velocity of the body, (or the projectile) be sufficiently large, so that it covers fairly large horizontal distances, the small *Coriolis force* gets sufficient time to act upon it, making the position vector turn at a constant rate of $-\omega \sin \phi$. Since *in the Northern hemisphere,* ϕ is positive, this rotation, as viewed from above, is *clockwise* (and hence the projectile gets deflected towards the right) and in the Southern hemisphere, it is *anticlockwise* (and the projectile thus gets deflected towards the left). This is known as **Ferel's law.**

Example 11. Calculate the fictitious force and the observed (or total) force on a body of mass 5 kg in a frame of reference moving (*i*) vertically upwards, (*ii*) vertically downwards, with an acceleration of 4m/s². (Take $g = 9.8$ m/s²).

Solution. Taking the *earth to be an inertial frame of reference* and the *upward direction as positive,* we have

Case (I) *True weight of the body or the true force acting on it, i.e.,* $F = mg = 5\,(-9.8) = -49.0$ *newton, i.e.,* 49.0N *in the downward direction.*

And, the *fictitious force acting on it, i.e.,* F_0 = *mass* (*reversed acceleration of the non-inertial frame*) $= m\,(-a_0) = 5\,(-4) = -20$ *newton, i.e.,* 20N *in the downward direction.*

$\therefore$ *observed or total force on the body,* $\vec{F'} = \vec{F} + \vec{F_0} = 49.0 + 20.0 = 69.0$N *in the downward direction,* (*i.e., the same as in a lift or elevator moving upwards with an acceleration of* 4 *m/s²*)

Thus, the fictitious force in the body is 20 N and the observed (or total) force on it, 69 N, *both acting downwards.*

Case (II). True force acting on the body, as before, $\vec{F} = mg = 5\,(-9.8) = -49.0$ *newton* = 49.0N *downwards.*

And, *the fictitious force acting on the body,* $\vec{F_0} = m\,(-a_0) = 5\,[-(-4)]$
$= 20.0$ N upwards.

$\therefore$ *observed or total force on the body.* $\vec{F'} = \vec{F} + \vec{F_0} = -49.0 + 20.0$
$= -29.0$ newton
$= 29.0$ N downwards,

(*i.e., the same as in a lift or elevator, moving downwards with an acceleration of 4 m/s²*).

Thus, in this case, *fictitious force on the body is 20N upwards and the observed* (*or total*) *force on it, 29 N downwards.*

Example 12. Calculate the total force acting on a freely falling body of mass 5 kg with reference to a frame moving with a downward acceleration of 2 ms⁻².

Solution. The force $\vec{F'}$ acting on a body in a non-inertial frame is given by $\vec{F'} = \vec{F_i} - \vec{F_0}$ where is the force on the same body in an inertial frame and $\vec{F_0}$ is the fictitious force due to the accelerated motion of the non-inertial frame. As the body is falling freely, downward force on it in the inertial frame of the earth $\vec{F_i} = 0$

$$\therefore \qquad \vec{F'} = -\vec{F_0} \quad \text{or} \quad \vec{F} = -m\vec{a_0}$$

where $\vec{a_0}$ is the acceleration of the non-inertial frame and m the mass of the body.

As the reference frame is moving downward with acceleration of $2\,\text{m/s}^2$ $\vec{a_0} = -2\,\text{ms}^{-2}$

$\therefore \quad \vec{F'} = -m\vec{a_0} = -(-2 \times 5) = +10\text{N}$

The positive sign indicates that the fictitious force is acting upward.

Example 13. A frame of reference is moving with an acceleration of 5 m/sec^2 downward. Find the apparent force and total force acting on a body of mass 10 kg falling freely relative to the frame.

Solution. Apparent force = Total force = – (–5 × 10) = 50 N (upward).

Example 14. Calculate the effective weight of an astronaut ordinarily weighing 60 kg when his rocket moves vertically upward with 5*g* acceleration.

Solution. As the rocket moves vertically upward with an acceleration 5*g*, it is a non-inertial frame and therefore the total force on the astronaut is given by $\vec{F'} = \vec{F_i} - \vec{F_0}$

where is the force on the astronaut in an inertial frame and $\vec{F_0}$ is the fictitious force on the astronaut due to the acceleration of the rocket.

Now $\quad \vec{F_i} = 60 \text{ kg. } wt = 60.g \text{ N}$

and $\quad \vec{F_o} = -m\vec{a_0} = -60 \times 5.g \text{ N} = -300.g \text{ N}$

$\therefore$ Effective weight of the astronaut

$$\vec{F} = \vec{F_i} - \vec{F_0} = 60g - (-300\,g)$$
$$= 360g \text{ N} = 360 \text{ kg.}$$

Example 15. How much faster than its present speed should the earth rotate so that bodies lying on the equator may fly off into space ?

Solution. The centrifugal force acting on a body of mass *m* at the equator is equal to $m R\omega^2$ where *R* is the radius of the earth and ω its angular velocity. If *g* is the acceleration due to gravity when the earth is at rest, then *g′* the acceleration when the earth has an angular velocity ω is given by

$$g' = g - R\omega \cos^2\lambda = g - R\omega^2 \quad [\because \lambda = 0, \cos\lambda = 1 \text{ and } \cos^2\lambda = 1]$$

For the body to fly off into space the new angular speed ω′ should be such that

$$g - R\omega'^2 = 0 \text{ or } \frac{R\omega'^2}{g} = 1 \qquad ...(i)$$

but $$\frac{R\omega^2}{g} = \frac{1}{291} \qquad ...(ii)$$

Dividing (*i*) by (*ii*), we have $\dfrac{\omega'^2}{\omega^2} = 291$ or $\dfrac{\omega'}{\omega} = \sqrt{291} = 17.06$

Hence the earth should have about seventeen times the present angular velocity so that bodies lying on the equator may fly into space.

Example 16. If the earth were to cease rotating about its axis what will be the change in the value of g at a place of latitude 45° assuming the earth to be a sphere of radius 6.38 × 10^8 cm?

Solution. We know that $\quad g' = g - R\omega^2\cos^2\lambda$ or $g - g' = R\omega^2\cos^2\lambda$

Now $\quad \lambda = 45°; R = 6.38 \times 10^8$ cm, $\omega = 2\pi/60 \times 60 \times 24$

Substituting, we have $$g - g' = \frac{6.38 \times 10^8 \times 4\pi^2}{60 \times 60 \times 60 \times 60 \times 24 \times 24}\cos^2 45°$$
$$= 3.372 \times \frac{1}{2} = 1.686 \text{ cm/sec}^2.$$

Example 17. Find the magnitude and direction of Coriolis force that acts on a 800 kg van running due north at 144 km hr^{-1} at a place where latitude is 30°N. ***(G.N.D.U. 2004)***

Solution. Mass of the van $m = 800$ kg

Velocity $\vec{v} = 144 \text{ km hr}^{-1} = \dfrac{144 \times 1000}{60 \times 60} = 40 \text{ ms}^{-1}$ due North

Latitude of the place $\lambda = 30° \text{ N} \quad \therefore \sin\lambda = \sin 30 = \dfrac{1}{2}$

$$\omega \text{ for the earth} = \frac{2\pi}{24 \times 60 \times 60} \text{ rad/sec.}$$

The *X*-axis is taken towards the East, *Y*-axis towards the North and *Z*-axis in the vertically upward direction.

Coriolis force is given by $\vec{F}_{cor} = -2m(\vec{\omega} \times \vec{v}_a)$

Horizontal component of Coriolis force

$$(\vec{F}_{cor})_{Horizontal} = +2m\omega \sin\lambda\,(v_y \hat{i} - v_x \hat{j})$$

and vertical component

$$(\vec{F}_{cor})_{Vertical} = 2\,m\omega\, v_x \cos\lambda\,\hat{k}$$

As the van is running due North (along + *Y*-axis) the component of its velocity due East (along + *x*-axis) *i.e.,* $v_x = 0$ and $v_y = \vec{v}_a = \vec{v}$

$\therefore$ Vertical component of Coriolis force = 0

Horizontal component of Coriolis force,

$$(\vec{F}_{cor})_H = +2m\,\omega \sin\lambda v_y\,\hat{i}$$

$$= 2 \times 800 \times \frac{2\pi}{24 \times 60 \times 60} \times \frac{1}{2} \times 40$$

$$= 7 \text{ Newton}$$

This force will act along $+\hat{i}$, *i.e.,* towards East.

Note. If the latitude of the place is 30°S, the force will acting $-\hat{i}$, *i.e.,* towards the West.

Example 18. A bullet is fired horizontally with a velocity 500 ms^{-1} at 60°N colatitude, (*a*) Eastwards (*b*) Northwards. Calculate the magnitude of the Coriolis acceleration due to rotation of earth. **(*P.U. 2001*)**

Solution. Velocity of the bullet $\vec{v} = 500 \text{ ms}^{-1}$

Co-latitude $\phi = 60° \quad \therefore$ Latitude $\lambda = (90 - \phi) = 30°$ and $\sin\lambda = \sin 30 = \dfrac{1}{2}$.

The *X*-axis is taken towards the East, *Y*-axis towards the North and *Z*-axis in the vertically upward direction.

Coriolis acceleration is given by $\vec{a}_a = -2\vec{\omega} \times \vec{v}_a$

Horizontal component of Coriolis acceleration $(\vec{a}_a)_H = 2\omega \sin\lambda\,(v_y \hat{i} - v_x \hat{j})$

and Vertical component of Coriolis acceleration $(\vec{a}_a)_V = 2\omega\, v_x \cos\lambda \hat{k}$

(*a*) Bullet fired Eastward. Then $v_x = \vec{v} = 500 \text{ ms}^{-1}$; $v_y = 0$

$\therefore$ Horizontal component of Coriolis acceleration.

$$(\vec{a}_a)_H = -2\omega \sin\lambda v\,\hat{j}$$

$$= 2 \times \frac{2\pi}{24 \times 60 \times 60} \times \frac{1}{2} \times 500 = 0.036 \text{ ms}^{-1}$$

along $-\hat{j}$ *i.e.,* $-Y$ direction or towards South.

Vertical component of Coriolis acceleration

$$(\vec{a}_a)_V = 2\omega\, v_x \cos\lambda \hat{k}$$

$$= 2 \times \frac{2\pi}{24 \times 60 \times 60} \times \frac{\sqrt{3}}{2} \times 500 = 0.036\sqrt{3}$$

along $+\hat{k}$ *i.e.*, $+Z$ direction or vertically upwards.

∴ Magnitude of the resultant acceleration

$$|\vec{a}_a| = \sqrt{|(\vec{a}_a)_H|^2 + |(\vec{a}_a)_V|^2} = \sqrt{(0.036)^2 + (0.036\sqrt{3})^2} = 0.072 \text{ ms}^{-1}$$

(*b*) Bullet fired Northwards. Then $v_y = \vec{v} = 500 \text{ ms}^{-1}$; $v_x = 0$

∴ Horizontal component of coriolis acceleration $(\vec{a}_a)_H = 2\omega \sin\lambda v \hat{i} = 0.036 \text{ ms}^{-1}$ along $\hat{i}$ *i.e.*, $+X$ direction.

Vertical component of coriolis acceleration $(\vec{a}_a)_V = 2\omega v_x \cos\lambda \hat{k} = 0$

∴ Resultant acceleration = 0.036 ms^{-1} along $+X$ direction.

Example 19. Calculate the magnitude and direction of Coriolis acceleration of a rocket moving with a velocity of 2 km s^{-1} at 60° South latidude.

Solution. For a body moving in a vertical direction, Coriolis force is given by

$$\vec{F}_{cor} = -2m(\vec{\omega} \times \vec{v}) = -2m \begin{vmatrix} \hat{i} & \hat{j} & \hat{k} \\ 0 & \omega_y & \omega_z \\ 0 & 0 & \dot{z} \end{vmatrix}$$

$$\therefore \quad \vec{F}_{cor} = -2m\omega_y \dot{z}\, \hat{i}$$

For a rocket moving vertically *upwards* at 60° South latitude (λ)

$$\dot{z} = +v \quad \text{and} \quad \omega_y = -\omega\cos\lambda \quad \therefore \quad \vec{F}_{cor} = +2m\omega v \cos\lambda\, \hat{i}$$

The Coriolis force, therefore acts towards the positive direction of x-axis *i.e.*, towards the East. The magnitude of Coriolis acceleration = $\omega\, v \cos\lambda$

$$= 2 \times \frac{2\pi}{24 \times 60 \times 60} \times 2 \times 10^3 \times \cos 60 = 14.58 \times 10^{-2} \text{ m/s}^2.$$

Example 20. Find latitude of a place where the plane of vibration of Foucalt's pendulum rotates once a day.

Solution. The period of rotation of a Foucault's pendulum at a latitude λ is given by

$$T = \frac{2\pi}{\omega \sin\lambda}. \quad \text{Now } \frac{2\pi}{\omega} = 24 \text{ hours}$$

For a place where plane of vibration of a Foucault's pendulum rotates once a day T = 24 hours.

$$\therefore \quad \sin\lambda = 1 \text{ or } \lambda = \frac{\pi}{2}, \text{ i.e., at a latitude } \lambda = \frac{\pi}{2} \text{ or at the poles.}$$

Example 21. Calculate the rate of rotation of the plane of oscillation of a pendulum at latitude 30° and hence obtain the time it will take to turn through (*i*) a full right angle and (*ii*) 60°. ***(P.U., 2001)***

Solution. At a latitude $\lambda = 30°; \sin\lambda = \frac{1}{2}$

∴ The period of rotation $T = \dfrac{2\pi}{\omega \sin\lambda} = \dfrac{2\pi}{\omega \frac{1}{2}} = 24 \times 2 = 48$ hours.

Hence rate of rotation $= \dfrac{2\pi}{48}$ radian/hour

and time taken to turn through (*i*) a full right angle or $\pi/2$ radian $= \dfrac{\pi/2}{2\pi/48} = \dfrac{48}{4} = 12$ hours

and (*ii*) through $60° = \dfrac{\pi/3}{2\pi/48} = \dfrac{48}{6} = 8$ hours.

Example 22. Imagine two non-inertial frames *S'* and *S"* to be initially coincident with an inertial frame *S*, with *S'* at rest and S" having a velocity *v* along the axis of *x* and both subjected to the same acceleration *a* along this axis (Fig. 2.14). Obtain

(*i*) the positions of the origins *O'* and *O"* of the two non-inertial frames with respect to the origin *O* of the inertial frame after time *t*;

(*ii*) the relations between the respective positions *x'* and *x"* of a particle, in frames *S'* and *S"*, and its position *x* in frame *S*;

(*iii*) the equation of motion of a particle of mass *m*, subjected to a constant force *F* in frame *S* and hence also its equations of motion in frames *S'* and *S"*, indicating any point of interest the emerges :

(*iv*) the relative velocity of frames *S"* with respect to frame *S'*.

What conclusion, if any, do you draw from the results obtained in regard to non-inertial frames, in general, moving with a constant relative velocity ?

Solution. (*i*) Initially, the origins *O, O'* and *O"* of the three reference frames are coincident. Therefore, the initial velocity of frame *S'* being *zero* and its acceleration along the *x*-axis, ***a***, the position vector of its origin *O'* after time *t* is given by

$$\overrightarrow{OO'} = \vec{r_0'} = \frac{1}{2}at^2\,\hat{i},$$

where $\hat{i}$ is the unit vector along the axis of *x*.

i.e., displacement of O' from O, along the x-axis, is $x' = \dfrac{1}{2}at^2$, (Fig. 2.14).

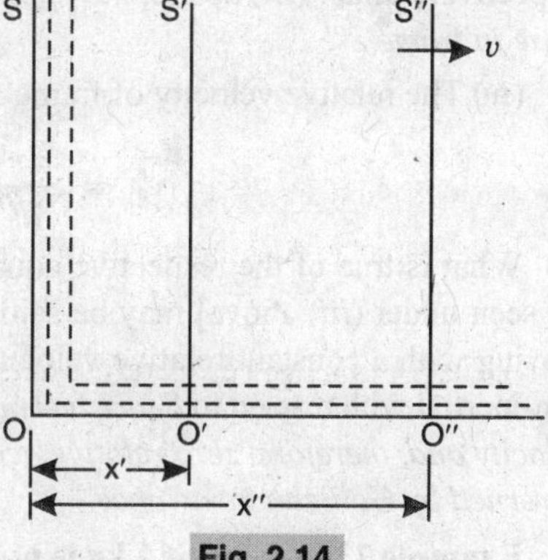

Fig. 2.14.

And, since frame S" has an initial velocity $\vec{v}$ along the *x*-axis, as also an acceleration $\vec{a}$ along it, its position after time *t* is given by $\overrightarrow{OO'} = \vec{r_0''} = \left(vt + \dfrac{1}{2}at^2\right)\hat{i}$

i.e., displacement of O" from O along the x-axis is $x_0'' = vt + \dfrac{1}{2}at^2$.

(*ii*) If the positions of a particle in frames *S, S'* and *S"* be respectively *x, x'* and *x"*, we clearly have $x' = x - x_0' = x - \dfrac{1}{2}at^2$ and $x'' = x - x_0'' = x - vt - \dfrac{1}{2}at^2$.

(*iii*) The equation of motion of a particle of mass *m*, subjected to a constant force $\vec{F}$, in frame *S*, is, obviously, $\vec{F} = m\dfrac{d^2\vec{r}}{dt^2}$, where $\vec{r}$ is the position vector of the particle in frame *S*.

Similarly, if $\vec{r'}$ and $\vec{r''}$ be the position vectors of the particle in frames. *S'* and *S"* respectively, the equation of motion of the particle in frame *S'* is

$$\vec{F'} = m\frac{d^2\vec{r'}}{dt^2}.$$

and its equation of motion in frames S'', $\vec{F''} = m\dfrac{d^2\vec{r''}}{dt^2}$.

In terms of components along the three Cartesian coordinate axes, we have in frame *S'*

$$F_x' = m\frac{d^2x'}{dt^2},\ F_y' = m\frac{d^2y'}{dt^2} \text{ and } F_z' = m\frac{d^2z'}{dt^2}.$$

Since there is motion only along the x-axis (with $y' = y'' = y$ and $z' = z'' = z$), we need consider only the x-component. So that, we have

$$F'_{x0} = m\frac{d^2x'}{dt^2} = m\frac{d^2}{dt^2}\left(x - \frac{1}{2}at^2\right) = m\frac{d^2x}{dt^2} = ma.$$

Clearly, $m\frac{d^2x}{dt^2}$ is the x-component of force F on the particle in frame S. Denoting it by F_x, we, therefore, have $\quad F'_x = F_x - ma \quad$ ...(*i*)

Proceeding exactly similarly, we obtain

in frame S'', $\quad F''_x = m\frac{d^2x''}{dt^2} = m\frac{d^2}{dt^2}\left(x - u - \frac{1}{2}at^2\right) = m\frac{d^2x}{dt^2} - ma. \ [\because v = \text{constant}]$

Or, $\quad F''_x = m\frac{d^2x}{dt^2} - ma = F_x - ma. \quad$ ...(*ii*)

It will thus be seen that the same fictitious force *ma* appears in both the transformation equations I and II, in view,, no doubt, of the *same acceleration (a) of the two frames S' and S" with respect to S.*

As will be readily seen from the transformation equation (*i*) and (*ii*) for frames S' and S'' respectively under (*iii*) above, *the applied and fictitious forces in frame S' are respectively equal to those in frame S".*

(*iv*) The relative velocity of frame S'' with respect to frame S' is obviously given by

$$\vec{v_2''} = \frac{d\vec{r'}}{dt} - \frac{d\vec{r''}}{dt} = (v + at)\,\hat{i} - (at)\hat{i} = v\hat{i}.$$

What is true of the respective equality of the applied and fictitious forces in frames S' and S'' [as seen under (*iii*) above] may be said to be true, in general, in the case of all non-inertial frames moving with a constant relative velocity. This follows from the fact that all such frames, although non-inertial with respect to S, *are inertial with respect to each other in view of their constant relative velocity and, therefore, zero relative acceleration. The applied and fictitious forces in them are thus governed by Galilean invariance.*

Example 23. A mass of 1 kg is hurled horizontally due north with a velocity of 0.5 km per second in latitude 30° N. Obtain the magnitude and direction of the Coriolis force acting on the mass and its deflection in consequence thereof in a time-interval of half a second.

Solution. Taking the axes of x, y and z along the east, the north and vertically upwards respectively, with $\hat{i}, \hat{j}$ and $\hat{k}$ as the respective unit vectors along the three axes, as usual, we have

velocity of mass, $\vec{v} = 500\,\hat{j}$ m/s.

Now, the *angular velocity vector of the earth,* $\vec{v}$, due to the spinning around of the earth from west to east, in directed along the axis. It, therefore, lies towards, the north at 30° with the horizontal in the given altitude ϕ(30° N). We therefore have

$$\vec{w} = \omega\cos\phi\,\hat{j} + \omega\sin\phi\,\hat{k} = \omega(\cos 30°\,\hat{j} + \sin 30°\,\hat{k}).$$

where ω, as we know, is equal to $2\pi/24 \times 60 \times 60 = 0.727 \times 10^{-5}$ radian/s.

$\therefore$ Coriolis acceleration of the mass $= -2\,\vec{\omega} \times \vec{v} = -2\omega(\cos 30°\,\hat{j} + \sin 30\hat{k}) \times 500\,\hat{j}$

$$= 2\,(0.727 \times 10^{-5}) \times \frac{1}{2} \times 500\hat{i} = 36.35 \times 10^{-5}\,\text{m/s}^2.$$

(Or, we could have obtained the Coriolis acceleration directly from the relation $a_c = 2\omega v \sin\phi$, since the *effective angular velocity* of the earth, here, is $\omega \cos(90 - \phi) = \omega \sin\phi$).

Because the mass is 1 kg, we have Coriolis force acting on the mass

$= 1 \times 36.35 \times 10^{-3} = 36.35 \times 10^{-3}$ N towards the east.

$\therefore$ Deflection of the mass due to this force in $\frac{1}{2}s = \frac{1}{2} \times 36.35 \times 10^{-3} \times \left(\frac{1}{2}\right)^2 = 4.544 \times 10^{-3}$ m.

2.16 FOUCAULT'S PENDULUM–DEMONSTRATION OF EARTH'S ROTATIONS

A Foucault's pendulum is just a simple pendulum, with a massive *bob* carried by a very long wire suspended from a rigid support, so as to have *equal freedom of oscillation in any direction.*

It constitutes a simple device to demonstrate the rotation of the earth about its own axis and was first used by Foucault for a public demonstration of the same in the year 1851, in Paris. The suspended mass in his case was 28 kg and the suspension wire about 70 metre long, so that the time-period of the pendulum was nearly 17 sec. Such a pendulum, once set oscillating, continues to oscillate for a long enough time.

The theory underlying the experiment is as follows :

If the pendulum (Fig. 2.15) were to be set up at the North pole of the earth, it may oscillate as a simple pendulum in a vertical plane which remains fixed in an inertial or Galilean frame of reference. Since the earth under it rotates from west to east with an angular velocity ω, the plane of oscillation of the pendulum would appear to an observer on the surface of the earth to be turning with an angular velocity–ω, *i.e.,* in the opposite direction (from east to west) to that of the earth.

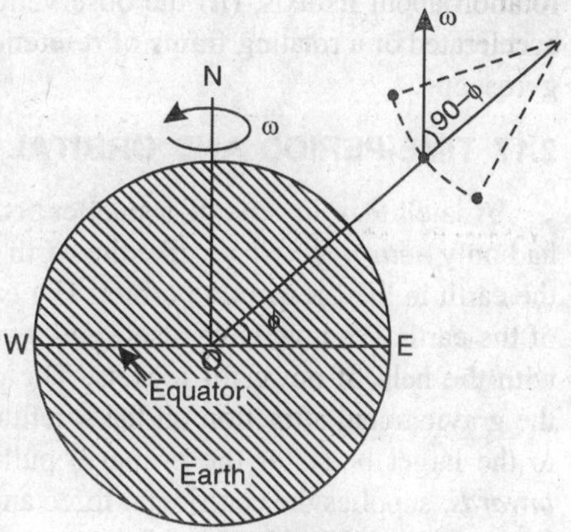

Fig. 2.15

It is by no means necessary, however, that the pendulum should be situated right at one of the poles. An apparent rotation of its plane of oscillation, due to the earth's rotation may equally well be observed *in any latitude,* except, of course, at the equator. For, it can be shown that, *if the oscillations be small, the bob describes an ellipse with its centre at the origin or the position of rest of the pendulum. The rotation of the earth* (*a rotating frame of reference*) *merely results in a Coriolis force coming into play due to the horizontal motion of the bob relative to it.* Acting, as usual, in a direction perpendicular to that of the velocity of the bob, *it causes precession of the plane of its oscillation, which thus rotates with an angular velocity –ω sin ϕ in latitude ϕ.*

Actually, however, there are two superimposed rotations of the elliptical orbit of the pendulum, one depending upon the area of the elliptical orbit and hence called the *area effect* and the other, on the angular velocity, –ω sin ϕ, due to rotation of the earth and called the *Foucault effect.* The former is a rotation in the *same* sense in which the ellipse is described (and will get reversed in sign if that sense is reversed) and the latter, a rotation *in a definite direction, viz., clockwise in the Northern, and anticlockwise in the Southern, hemisphere.*

Since we are interested only in the rotation of the ellipse in consequence of the earth's rotation or its Foucault rotation, we must eliminate the *area effect* which, in the absence of suitable precautions, may be so much greater than the *Foucault effect* as to completely mask it. This is usually done by setting the pendulum in motion *by first drawing it a little to one side with the help of a piece of thread tied to it and then burning the thread.* The angular velocity of the ellipse (*i.e.,* its rate of precession) due to the area effect is then negligible compared with its Foucault angular velocity, –ω sin ϕ. So that, in the case of a pendulum, set oscillating in this manner, the precession or the rotation of its orbit may be taken to be due entirely to Foucault effect *i.e.,* due to rotation of the earth alone.

Obviously enoght, the time taken by one full rotation of the plane of oscillation of the pendulum is given by $T = 2\pi/(Foucault\ angular\ velocity) = 2\pi/\omega \sin \pi$. Or, since time taken by the earth to complete one rotation about its axis is 24 hours, we have $2\pi/\omega = 24$ hours and, therefore, $T = 24 \sin \phi$ hours.

As already mentioned, the rotation of the plane of oscillation of the pendulum will be clockwise in the Northern hemisphere and anticlockwise in the Southern hemisphere. There is thus clearly *a relative motion between the plane of oscillation of the pendulum bob and the earth is either hemisphere.* This relative angular shift of the plane of oscillation is measured over a period of days to demonstrate the rotation of the earth about its axis.

Among other methods of demonstrating the rotation of the earth may be mentioned (*i*) the observation of the *fixed stars* which, in fact, gave us the very first indication regarding the earth's rotation about its axis, (*ii*) the observation of any fictitious forces, indicating the presence of an accelerated or a rotating frame of reference, as mentioned already under 2.14; and (*iii*) the familiar gyroscope.

2.17 TIME-PERIOD AND ORBITAL SPEED OF A SATELLITE

A satellite is, in general, a smaller body revolving around a much larger body. Until recently, we had only *natural satellites,* like the earth revolving around the sun and the moon revolving around the earth in their respective orbits. The earth is thus a satellite of the sun and the moon, a satellite of the earth. We have also *man-made* or *artificial* satellites, placed in orbit around the earth, with the help of powerful rockets. The principle underlying is the same in either case, *viz.,* that the gravitational attraction on the satellite due to the larger body (or the primary) pulling it *inwards,* supplies the centripetal force and this is just balanced by the (fictitious) centrifugal force on it, pulling it *outwards,* as shown in Fig. 2.16.

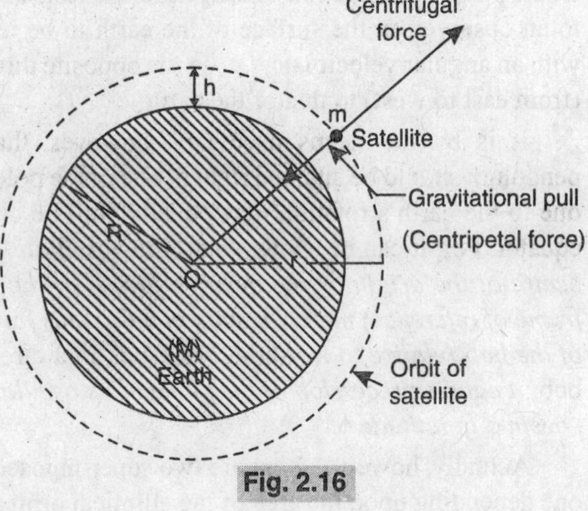

Fig. 2.16

Thus, if m be the *mass of the satellite, M,* the *mass of the earth r,* the distance between the earth and the satellite (*i.e.,* between their centres), we have

gravitational pull of the earth on the satellite (i.e., the centripetal force), inwards = $\frac{mM}{r^2}G$, where G is the *gravitational constant.*

And *centrifugal force on the satellite, outwards* = mv^2/r, where v is uniform speed of the satellite around the earth.

It ω be the *angular velocity* of the satellite, so that $v = r\omega$, we have

$$\frac{mMG}{r^2} = \frac{mv^2}{r} = \frac{m(r\omega)^2}{r} = mr\omega^2$$

whence, $\omega^2 = MG/r^3$. Or, $\omega = \sqrt{MG/r^3}$.

Since $r = (R + h)$, where *R is the radius of the earth and h,* the distance of the satellite from the surface of the earth, we have

$$\omega = \sqrt{MG/(R+h)^3}.$$

Now. if g be the acceleration due to gravity on the surface of the earth, we have

$$g = MG/R^2 \quad \text{or} \quad MG = gR^2.$$

Substituting this value of *MG* in the expression for ω above, we have

$$\omega = \sqrt{gR^2/(R+h)^3}.$$

And, therefore, *time-period of the satellite,*

$$T = \frac{2\pi}{\omega} = 2\pi\sqrt{\frac{(R+h)^3}{gR^2}}.$$

In case the orbit of the satellite lies close to the earth, *i.e.,* if $h << R$, we have $r = (R+h) = R$. So that,

$$T = 2\pi\sqrt{\frac{R^3}{gR^2}} = 2\pi\sqrt{\frac{R}{g}}$$

Let us calculate the orbital speed of such a satellite.

Remembering that, in this case, $r = (R + h) = R$ (the satellite being close to the earth), we have

$$r = r\omega = R\omega = R\sqrt{gR^2/R^3} = R\sqrt{g/R} = \sqrt{gR^2/R} = \sqrt{gR}.$$

So, that, taking $R = 6.4 \times 10^8$ cm and $g = 980$ cm/sec, we have

$$r = \sqrt{980 \times 6.4 \times 10^8} = 7.92 \times 10^5 \text{ cm/s}^2 = 7.92 \text{ km/s}.$$

Thus, *the orbital speed of an earth satellite revolving close to the earth's surface* is nearly 8 km/s.

Example 24. Find the latitude at which the plane of vibration of Foucault's pendulum does not rotate at all. ***(Pbi. U., 2003; P.U. 2003)***

Solution. When the plane of vibration of Foucault's pendulum does not rotate at all its time period is infinite.

∴ The period of rotation $T = \infty$

and $$\frac{2\pi}{\omega \sin \lambda} = \infty \text{ or } \lambda = 0$$

Thus the plane of vibration of a Foucault's pendulum does not rotate at all at the Equator.

Example 25. Foucault's pendulum is oscillating along NS direction at a place where latitude is 30°. What time must elapse before the pendulum starts oscillating along NE-SW direction ?

Solution. At a latitude

$$\lambda = 30°, \sin \lambda = \sin 30 = \frac{1}{2}$$

∴ Period of rotation $$T = \frac{2\pi}{\omega \sin \lambda} = \frac{2\pi}{\omega . \frac{1}{2}} = 24 \times 2 = 48 \text{ hours.}$$

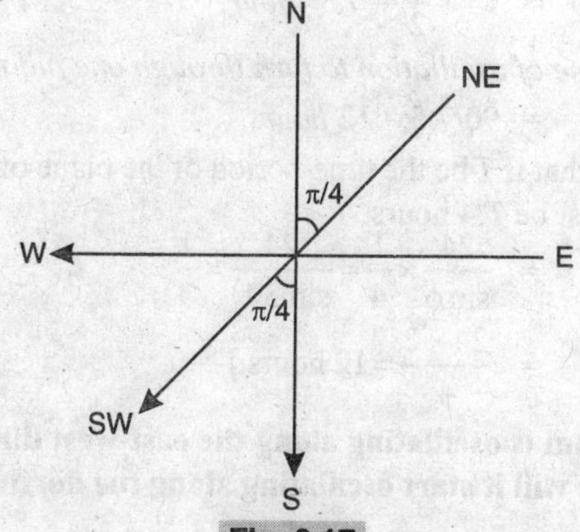

Fig. 2.17

Hence rate of rotation $= \frac{2\pi}{48}$ radius is per hour.

In turning from NS to NE-SW direction the pendulum turns through $45° = \frac{\pi}{4}$ radian as shown.

$$\therefore \qquad \text{Time taken} = \frac{\frac{\pi}{4}}{2\pi/48} = \frac{48}{8} = 6 \text{ hours}.$$

Example 26. Show that at latitude θ, the plane of oscillation of Foucault's pendulum rotates through 2π sin θ every day. Explain this physically on a pole of the earth.

Solution. The period of rotation of a Foucault's pendulum at a latitude θ is given by

$$T = \frac{2\pi}{\omega \sin\theta}$$

where $\frac{2\pi}{\omega} = 24$ hours. $\therefore \qquad T = \frac{24}{\sin\theta}$ hours

In T hours the plane rotates thorugh 2π radians.

$\therefore$ In 24 hours the plane will rotate through an angle

$$\phi = \frac{2\pi}{T} \times 24 = \frac{2\pi}{24} \sin\theta \times 24 = 2\pi \sin\theta \text{ radian}$$

At the poles $\qquad \phi = 90°, \sin\theta = \sin 90° = 1$

$\therefore \qquad \phi = 2\pi$ radians

Thus the plane of oscillation of a Foucault's pendulum rotates through 2π radians in 24 hours at the poles which means that the period of rotation of the earth about its own axis is 24 hours.

Example 27. Calculate the rate of rotation of the plane of oscillation of a pendulum in latitude 30° and hence obtain the time it will take to turn through a full right angle.

Solution. We know that the time taken by the plane of oscillation of a pendulum to make one complete rotation in latitude ϕ is given by $T = 24/\sin\phi$ hours.

Also, if a be the angular velocity of the plane of oscillation in *this* latitude, its time-period (*i.e.*, time taken for one full rotation) must be $T = 2\pi/\alpha$.

We, therefore, have $2\pi/\alpha = 24/\sin\phi$, whence, $\alpha = 2\pi \sin\phi/24$ radian/hr.

Or, *rate of rotation of the plane of oscillation of the pendulum* in latitude 30°

$$= 360° \sin\phi/24 = 15° \sin\phi \text{ per hour.}$$

Since, here, $\phi = 30°$, and therefore, $\sin\phi = \frac{1}{2}$, we have

rate of rotation of the plane of oscillation of the pendulum in latitude 30°

$$= 15 \times \frac{1}{2} = 7.5°/hour.$$

$\therefore$ *Time taken by the plane of oscillation to turn through one full right angle*

$$= 90/7.5 = 12 \text{ hours.}$$

[Or, we could have said that if T be the time-period of the plane of oscillation in hours, the time taken to turn through 90° must be $T/4$ hours.

$$= \frac{24}{\sin\phi} \times \frac{1}{4} = \frac{24}{\sin 30°} \times \frac{1}{4}$$

$$= \frac{24 \times 2}{4} = 12 \text{ hours.]}$$

Example 28. A pendulum is oscillating along the east-west direction at a place of latitude 30°N. After how much time will it start oscillating along the north west-south east direction?

Solution. The problem here, obviously, is to calculate the time the plane of oscillation of the pendulum will take to turn through an angle of 135°, (Fig. 2.18) in latitude 30° N.

Since in latitude $\phi = 30°$, the rate of rotation of the plane of oscillation of the pendulum is (as we have seen, under example 11 above) equal to $15° \sin \phi = 15° \sin 30° = 7.5°$/hr, we have, time taken by the plane of oscillation to turn through, 135° = 135/7.5 = 18 hours.

Thus, *the pendulum will start oscillating along the north west–south east direction after* 18 *hours.*

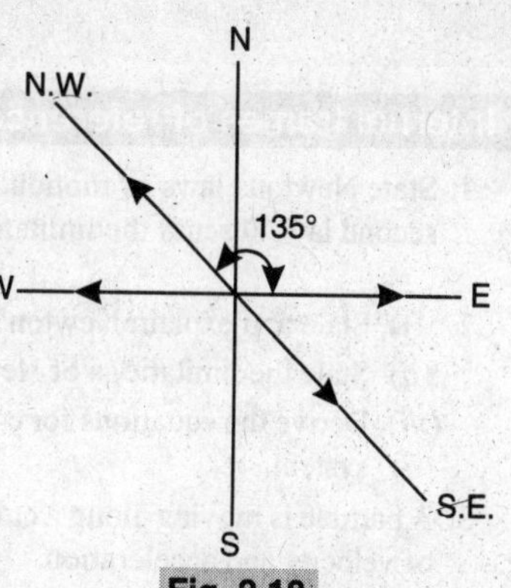

Fig. 2.18

Example 29. A satellite moves in a circular orbit around the earth at a height $R_e/2$ from the earth's surface, where R_e is the radius of the earth. Calculate its period of revolution.

Given $R_e = 6.38 \times 10^6$m, $g = 9.80$ m/s^2.

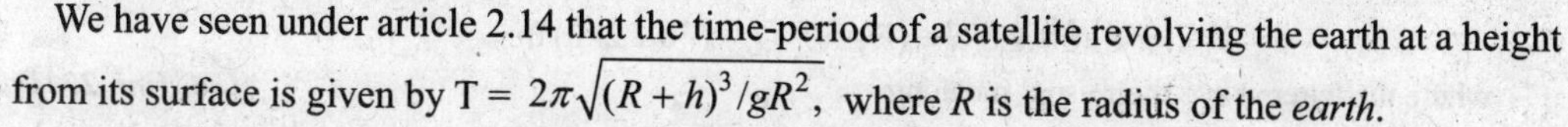

We have seen under article 2.14 that the time-period of a satellite revolving the earth at a height h from its surface is given by $T = 2\pi\sqrt{(R+h)^3/gR^2}$, where R is the radius of the *earth.*

Here, $R = R_e$ and $h = R_e/2$. So that, *time-period of revolution of the satellite,*

$$T = 2\pi\sqrt{\left(R_e + \frac{R_e}{2}\right)^3 / g(R_e)^2} = 2\pi\sqrt{27R_e/8g}.$$

Substituting the given values of R_e and g, therefore, *we have time period of the satellite,*

$$T = 2\pi\sqrt{\frac{27 \times 6.38 \times 10^4}{8 \times 9.80}} = 9.309 \times 10^3 \text{ or } 9.3 \times 10^3 \text{ s}$$

Example 30. At what height from the surface of the earth must a satellite revolve in its orbit around the earth, concentric and coplanar with the equator, such that it always appears to be at the same point over the earth's surface as viewed by an observer on the earth? (G = 6.67 × 10^{-8}e g.s units, R = 6.38 × 10^8 cm and mass of the earth = 5.98 × 10^{27} g).

Solution. Obviously, the satellite will always appear to be at the same point over the earth's surface when its angular velocity is the *same* as that of the earth,

viz., $\omega = 2\pi/24 \times 60 \times 60 = 7.27 \times 10^{-5}$ radians or 7.3 radians.

Let r be the radius of the orbit of the satellite. Then, as we have seen under article 2.14, *angular velocity of the satellite, i.e.,* $\omega = \sqrt{MG.r^3}$. Or, $\omega^2 = MG.r^3$, whence, $r^3 = MG/\omega^2$. So that, substituting the values of M, G and ω, we have

$$r^3 = \frac{5.98 \times 10^{27} \times 6.67 \times 10^{-8}}{(7.3 \times 10^{-5})^2} = 74.85 \times 10^{27}, \text{ whence, } r = (74.85 \times 10^{27})^{\frac{1}{2}} = 4.2 \times 10^9 \text{ cm.}$$

Now, $r = (R + h)$, where R is the radius of the earth and h, the height of the satellite from the surface of the earth.

We, therefore, have $h = r - R = 4.2 \times 10^9 - 6.38 \times 10^8 = 3.562 \times 10^9$ cm.

Thus, *the satellite must revolve in its orbit around the earth at a height of* 3.56 × 10^9 cm *from the surface of the earth.*

EXERCISE

I. Intertial frames of reference–Galilean invariance

1. State Newtons laws of motion. Show that Newton's first law of motion is simply a special case of the second law. Discuss the limitations of Newtons laws of motion. ***(Nagpur Uni. 2007, 2006, 2003)***

2. (*i*) State and explain Newton's second law of motion.
(*ii*) State the limitations of Newton's law of motion.
(*iii*) Derive the equations for components of a velocity, Acceleration and force in a cartesian coordinate system. ***(Nagpur Uni. 2007)***

3. A particle is moving along a curve in a plane. Derive expression for its radial and transverse components of velocity and acceleration. *(Nagpur Uni. 2007, 2006)*

4. A particle is moving along a curve in a plane. Derive expression for the radial and transverse component of velocity and acceleration. Prove that for the motion of a particle in a plane.

$$\vec{v} = r\hat{r} + r\dot{\theta}\hat{\theta} \text{ and } \vec{a} = (\ddot{r} - r\dot{\theta}^2)\, r + (\ddot{r}\theta + 2r\ddot{\theta})\,\hat{\theta}$$

where the letters have their usual meaning ***(Cal. Uni. 2003)***

5. What is meant by a frame of reference? Give examples to show that the state of motion of a body would appear to be different when viewed from different frames of reference. From which particular frame of reference would you like to study this motion and why?

6. Show that to a person at rest on the ground, the path of a particle on the rim of a slowly moving wheel of a car will appear to be a cycloid while it will apear to be circular to an observer situated at the centre of the wheel.

[**Hint.** Imagine the motion of the wheel to be along the $+x$ direction in the x–y plane, with OX along the horizontal and OY along the vertical, the origin O lying at the centre of the wheel. Let r be the radius of the wheel, $-\omega$, its angular velocity (being clockwise) and $-\theta$, the angle that a point P on its rim makes with the x-axis at O, to start with (Fig. 2.19). *i.e.*, at $t = 0$. Then, after time t, the position of the point is specified by the coordinates $x = r\cos(-\omega t - \theta) = r\cos(\omega t + \theta)$, $y = -r\sin(\omega t + \theta)$, indicating that the point moves along a *circular path* of radius r, the same as that of the wheel.

For an observer, at rest on the ground, on the other hand, the centre of the wheel has also a linear velocity rw. Hence, after time t, the position of the point is given by the coordinates $x = r\omega t + r\cos(\omega t + \theta)$, $y = r - r\sin(\omega t + \theta)$, and this is the equation of a cycloid.]

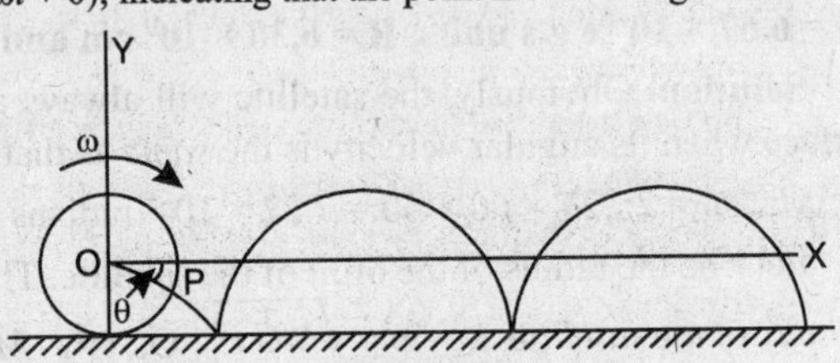

Fig. 2.19

7. Enunciate Newton's laws of motion and discuss their limitations.

8. What is an *inertial frame of reference*? Show that all other frames of reference, with constant velocity relative to it, are also inertial frames. What are the characteristic properties and importance of such frames? Can the earth be regarded as one such frame?

9. What is meant by *Galilean transformation* and *Galilean invariance*? Show that whereas length (or distance) and acceleration are invariant to Galilean transformation, velocity is not.

10. A reference frame S' is moving with a constant velocity v with respect to an inertial frame S and the position of its origin O' is given by R_0 at $t = 0$. If the position vector of a point in frame S be r, show that it will be $i + vt + R_0$ in frame S'.

11. Explain how the parabolic trajectory of a projectile would appear when observed from a frame of reference moving with (*i*) a velocity equal to the horizontal component of the velocity of the projectile, (*ii*) a velocity equal to twice the horizontal component of the velocity of the projectile, and (*iii*) a constant velocity inclined to the horizontal.

Ans. (*i*) a vertical straight line, (*ii*) original trajectory in the opposite direction (*iii*) a new parabolic trajectory.

12. Two inertial frames S and S' have their axes parallel and the position of the origin O' of frame S' relative to origin O of frame S is given by $\vec{r_0} = \hat{i} + 2\hat{j} + 3\hat{k}$. Show that, if the position of a point P in frame S be (2, 3, 4), its position if frame S' would be $(\hat{i} + \hat{j} + \hat{k})$.

13. If the respective axes of two frames S and S' be inclined to each other, with their origins coinciding, obtain the usual transformation equations and show that if frame S be inertial, frame S' too is inertial.

14. If in question 13 above, the position vector of the origin O' of frame S' with respect to the origin O of frame S be R_0, show that $x = x_0 + x'C'_{xx} + y'C'_{yx} + z'C'_{zx}$; $y = y_0 + x'C'_{xy} + y'C'_{yy} + z'C'_{zy}$ and $z = z_0 + x'C'_{xz} + y'C'_{yz} + z'C'_{zz}$.

15. Enunciate the laws of conservation of momentum and conservation of energy and show that they are both invariant to Galilean transformation.

16. A particle of mass m_1 moving with velocity v collides *head on* against a particle of mass m_2 at rest. Taking the collision to be an *elastic* one obtain the velocities of the two particles and the fraction of the total kinetic energy acquired by the second particle after the collision. How will this fraction change if $m_1 = m_2$?

[**Ans.** $v_1 = \dfrac{m_1v - m_2v_2}{m_1}$; $v_2 = \dfrac{2v}{1 + m_1/m_2}$; $\dfrac{4m_1m_2}{(m_1 + m_2)}$; the fraction will change to 1, *i.e.*, the entire energy of m_1 will be transferred to m_2.]

17. In question 16 above, if the collision be an *inelastic* one, so that the two particles coalesce together on collision, obtain their common velocity after the collision and the loss of kinetic energy suffered.

[**Ans.** Common velocity $= \dfrac{m_1v}{m_1 + m_2}$; loss of energy suffered $= \dfrac{1}{2}m_1v\dfrac{m_2}{m_1 + m_2}$.]

18. In a *head-on* collision, a particle with an initial speed v_0 strikes a stationary particle of the same mass. Find the velocities v_1 and v_2 of the two particles respectively after the collision if (*a*) half the original kinetic energy is lost, (*b*) the final kinetic energy is 50% greater than the original kinetic energy.

[**Ans.** (*a*) $v_1 = v_2 = \frac{1}{2}v_0$, (*b*) $v_1 = \frac{1}{2}v_0(1 + \sqrt{2})$, $v_2 = \frac{1}{2}v_0(1 - \sqrt{2})$.]

19. The position vectors of two particles are respectively $\vec{r_1} = 4\hat{i} + 6\hat{j} + 4\hat{k}$ m. and $\vec{r_2} = 2\hat{i} + 3\hat{j} + 2\hat{k}$ m. The velocity of the first particle is $\hat{i} - 2\hat{j} + 2\hat{k}$ m/s. How much greater should the velocity of the second particle be so that the two may collide in 5 seconds? [**Ans.** $0.2\,(2\hat{i} + 3\hat{j} + 2\hat{k})$ m/s.]

II. Non-inertial frames—Fictitious forces

20. What is meant by a non-inertial frame of reference? And what is a fictitious force? Why? is it so called? Under what condition will an accelerated frame of reference serve as an inertial frame?

21. What will be the effective weight of a person carried vertically up in a rocket with an acceleration of 6g, if his actual weight on the earth is 60 kg. [**Ans.** 420 kg.]

22. A car carries a framework *ABCD*, shown in Fig. 2.20 in which a mass *P* of 200 g is supported between two springs of force constant 5000 dyne/cm each. Side *AB* is kept horizontal and is along the length of the car and the pointer attached to *P* reads zero when the car is at rest. What will the pointer read when the car has (*i*) a uniform speed of 20 m/s on a straight road, (*ii*) a uniform speed of 10 m/s on a circular road of radius 20 metres,

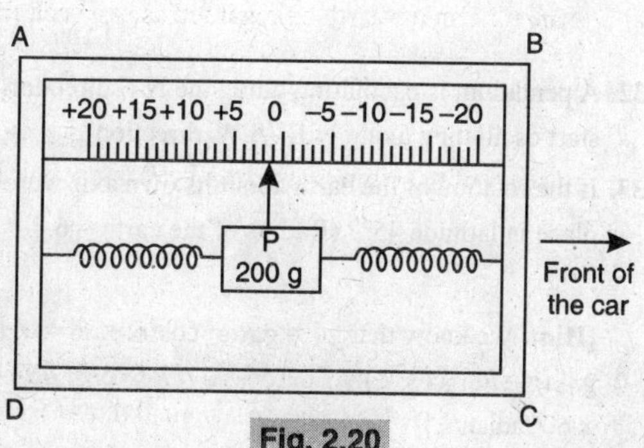

Fig. 2.20

(*iii*) uniform acceleration of 0.5 m/s on a straight road, (*iv*) a uniform acceleration of –1.0 m/s on a straight road ? [**Ans.** (*i*) 0, (*ii*) 0, (*iii*) +10 mm (*iv*) –20 mm.]

[**Hint.** (*i*) No acceleration of the mass relative to the car. Hence no fictitious force. (*ii*) Centripetal acceleration towards the centre of the circular path–hence a fictitious force, *viz.*, *centrifugal force* perpendicular to AB, *outwards,* counter balancing the centripetal force (inwards)—no change in the position of the pointer which, therefore, continues to real zero. (*iii*) Acceleration *forwards*—hence fictitious force = *ma*. (*iv*) Here, since *a* is negative the fictitious force = +*ma*].

23. A person weights 50 kg on the earth. Calculate the fictitious force acting on him and his effective weight in a lift when the lift is moving (*i*) down, (*ii*) up, with an acceleration of 4m/s.

[**Ans.** (*i*) 200 N, upwards; 29.6 kg, (*iii*) 200 N, downwards, 70.4 kg.]

24. What is *Coriolis force?* Under what conditions does it come into play? Discuss in general terms the effect of the Coriolis force produced as a result of the earth's rotation. What is *Ferel's law*?

25. Calculate the values of the centrifugal and the Coriolis forces on a mass of 20 g placed at a distance of 10 cm from the axis of a rotating frame of reference, if the angular speed of rotation of the frame be 10 radians per second. [**Ans.** 2×10^4 dyne; 4×10^4 dyne.]

26. A mass of ice, weighing 500,000 tons near the North pole moves west at the rate of 5 miles a day. Neglecting the curvature of the earth, find the magnitude and direction of the Coriolis force. Express the magnitude in tons weight (Take $g = 32$ m/s). [**Ans.** 0.7 *tons weight, due north.*]

27. A reference frame *a* rotates with respect to another reference frame *b* with uniform angular velocity ω. If the position, velocity and acceleration of a particle in frame *a* are represented by R, v_a and f_a respectively, show that the acceleration of that particle in frame *b* is given by $f_b = f_a + 2\omega \times v_a + \omega \times (\omega \times R)$. Interpret this equation with reference to the motion of bodies on the earth's surface.

28. Obtain an expression for the horizontal displacement of an object falling freely under the action of gravity in latitude ϕ. Hence calculate the displacement suffered by a stone dropped from the top of a tower 100 metres high (*i*) in latitude 60°N, (*ii*) at the equator. (Angular velocity of the earth about its axis = 7.2×10^{-5} m/s and g = 9.8 m/s^2). [**Ans.** (*i*) 1.085 cm; (*ii*) 2.17 cm.]

29. Calculate the fictitious acceleration of the sun relative to a reference frame fixed on the surface of the earth. (Distance between the sun and the earth = 1.5×10^{12} cm).

[**Ans.** 7.8×10^4 cm/s^2, *directed towards the earth.*]

III. Foucalt's pendulum—Earth satellites

30. What is a Faucault pendulum? How does it enable us to demonstrate the rotation of the earth about its own axis?

31. What will be the period of rotation of the plane of oscillation of Foucault's pendulum (*i*) in latitudes 30° and 45°, (*ii*) at the North pole, (*iii*) at the equator?

[**Ans.** (*i*) 12 hours and 33.94 hours (*ii*) 24 hours, (*iii*) Infinite.]

32. A pendulum is oscillating along the N-S direction at a place in latitude 30° N. How long will it take to start oscillating along N.E.–S.W. direction? [**Ans.** 6 hours.]

33. If the rotation of the earth about its own axis were to cease suddenly, how will it effect the value of g at place in latitude 45°? (Radius of the earth = 6.4×10^8 cm?

[**Ans.** Increase of 1.69 cm/s^2 in the value of g.]

[**Hint.** We know that $g\phi = g.R\omega^2 \cos^2\phi$. If $\omega = 0$, the value of $g\phi$ becomes g, *i.e.*, increases by $g - g\phi = g - (g - R\omega^2 \cos^2 \phi) = R\omega^2 \cos^2 \phi = R\omega^2 \cos^2 45° = R\omega^2/2$, where, $R = 6.4 \times 10^8$ cm and $\omega = 2\pi/24 \times 60 \times 60$ radian/s.]

34. Assuming the law of gravitation, find an expression for the period of revolution of a satellite.

Calculate the mass of the earth and the time of revolution of a satellite describing a circular orbit close to the earth's surface from the following data: $G = 6.6 \times 10^{-8}$ *c.g.s.* units, $g = 981$ cm./s^2 and *radius of the earth,* $R = 6.37 \times 10^8$ cm.

[**Ans.** 6.30×10^{27} cm.; 5060 s^2.]

35. Considering the earth to be homogeneous sphere of mass density 6, show that the period of revolution of a satellite in an orbit lying just outside the equator depends only upon the density σ.

[**Hint.** We know that the period of revolution of a satellite is given by $T = 2\pi\sqrt{(R+h)^3/gR^2}$ Putting $gR^2 = MG$, $T = 2\pi\sqrt{(R+h)^3/MG}$, where M is mass of the earth and R its radius. Since the satellite is close to earth's surface $(R + h) \cong R$. Hence $T = 2\pi\sqrt{R^3/MG}$ Clearly $M = \frac{4}{3}\pi R^3$.

Therefore, $T = 2\pi\sqrt{3R^3/4\pi R^3 G\sigma} = \sqrt{3\pi/\sigma G}$, showing that T depends only upon σ, G being universal constant].

Chapter 3

RELATIVITY

Brief Contents

INTRODUCTION

The most frequently used terms 'space', 'time', 'mass' and 'motion' very simple for an ordinary person, perturbed the minds of scientists for the past so many centuries. Answers did come, in various stages, sometimes contradicting to one another. However, scientists always gave up the lesser satisfactory explanations and accepted only experimentally verified ones. The Newtonian principle of relativity* talks about two philosophic
al concepts, namely, absolute space, and absolute time. Newton realised that in practical problems one is always concerned with relative motion. Then question comes in mind is that 'relative to what?'. Hence, the idea of absoluteness was abandoned and concept of inertial frame of reference was accepted. In this frame of reference, Newton's laws of motion are valid. Galilean transformation equations were successfuly employed to transform coordinates of a particle from one inertial frame to another inertial frame. Distance between two points is found to be invariant under Galilean transformation. However, this principle of relativity, though held for mechanics, was no longer true for electrodynamics and optics. This has been verified by Michelson-Morley experiment.

Einstein started with a radically new idea that the motion through ether is a meaningless concept, while motion relative to material bodies alone has a physical significance. Einstein formulated his relativity principle, without reference to any absolute frame. According to him, the relativity principle was valid in all frames of reference, in uniform rectilinear motion, relative to one another. Further, the postulated that the relativity principle must be applicable to both the laws of mechanics, as well as laws of electro-magnetism (Maxwell's equations). Thirdly, he considered the velocity of light to be same in all inertial frames. It does not depend upon the velocity of the observer or that of its source. This revolutionary new theory, in 1905 was proposed by Einstein, known as "Special Theory of Relativity."

3.1 ALBERT EINSTEIN : A LUMINOUS STAR IN PHYSICS

The twentieth century has undoubtedly been the most significant for the advance of science, in general, and *Physics*, in particular. It has seen yet another luminous star, in the person of **Albert Einstein,** appear on the firmament among the all-time great that includes *Newton* and *Maxwell*. Few, indeed, if any, have so completely shaken the world of science, since *Newton*, by the sheer boldness and profoundness of their ideas. He literally created an upheavel by the publication, in quick succession, in the year 1905, two epoch-making papers, on the concept of the *photon* and on the *Electrodynamics of moving bodies* respectively, with yet another on *the mathematical analysis of Brownian motion* thrown in, in between. By far the most revolutionary of them is the one on the electrodynamics of moving bodies which demolishes at one stroke some of the most cherished and supposedly infallible laws and concepts and gives the breath-takingly new idea of the relativity of space and time.

Truly it may be said that just as the enunciation of Newton's laws of motion heralded emancipation from the age-old Aristotlean ideas of motion, so also did Einstein's theory of relativity make a proclamation, loud and clear, of emancipation from the crippling bondage to lumineferous ether and the confused notions of absolute space and time.

As to an introduction to the theory of relativity, we can do no better than to listen reverently to what *Einstein* himself says with his characteristic humility. This is quoted in the box 1.

* 'Absolute motion, which is the translation of a body from one absolute space to another absolute space, can never be detected for translatory motion. It can only be perceived in the form of the motion, relative to the other material bodies.'

Box - I

I am anxious to draw attention to the fact that this theory of relativity is not speculative in origin; it owes its invention entirely to the desire to make physical theory fit observed fact as well as possible. We have here no revolutionary act but the natural continuation of a line that can be traced through centuries. The abandonment of a certain concept connected with space, time and motion hitherto treated as fundamental must not be regarded as arbitrary but only conditioned by observed facts. The law of the constant velocity of light in empty space which has been confirmed by the development of electrodynamics and optics and the equal legitimacy of all inertial systems (special theory of relativity) which was proved in a particularly incisive manner by Michelson's famous experiment, between them made it necessary, to begin with, that the concept of time should be made relative, each inertial system being given its own special time .... It is, in general, one of the essential features of the theory of relativity that it is at pains to work out the relations between general concepts and empirical facts more precisely. The fundamental principle here is that the justification for a physical concept lies exclusively in its clear and unambiguous relation to facts that can be experienced.

We shall see in what follows the gradual development of the subject and how Einstein ultimately arrived at the conclusions he did.

3.2 SEARCH FOR A FUNDAMENTAL FRAME OF REFERENCE

It has already been pointed out in the last chapter (2.7) that it was on account of Newton's insistence as to the existence of a *fundamental* or *absolute frame of reference*, called *absolute space*, that the search for it was carried on. This search resulted in the discovery, or rather the invention, of that monstrosity of a medium, *luminiferous ether*, as the following brief account will show.

As we know, **Maxwell** clearly demonstrated, in the year 1864, the inter-relationship between electricity, magnetism and light when, from the known properties of electricity and magnetism, he formulated his celebrated *theory of electromagnetic radiation* and gave the well known *equations of electromagnetic field* which, bear his name and are identical with those that represent a wave phenomenon. He thus established the presence of electromagnetic waves in space, travelling with the speed of light. In other words, he *proved light to be an electromagnetic wave.*

Since waves known hitherto (like sound and water waves) all required a material medium (air and water respectively) for their propagation, it was supposed that there must also be a suitable medium to carry these newly found electromagnetic waves which travelled even through empty space between the stars and the earth. This intangible medium, though no one knew what it actually was, came to be referred to as *luminiferous ether*, pervading all space, empty or otherwise.

Further, to enable it to transmit light, a transverse wave motion, the ether had to be a *rigid solid* and in view of the tremendous velocity of light, it had to have a *large shear modulus* and yet all material objects, like the earth and the planets and stars etc, were to continue in their regular courses through it without encountering the slightest resistance. Utterly incredible as it seems to us today, no one seemed to object to its existence. On the other hand, it was felt that perhaps it was the absolute space or the fundamental frame of reference Newton was looking for and in which (or in a frame of reference fixed relative to it) his laws of motion would hold *perfectly*.

On the face of it, it was such an inviting—and exciting—proposition, and many a brilliant experiment were sought to be devised to establish the existence of this elusive medium, ether, and hence that of an absolute frame of reference. I was but natural that light waves should be used for the purpose, since, after all, ether was little else but just a vehicle for them.

Now, the orbit of the earth around the sun having a radius of 150 million km, its orbital velocity works out to 30 km/sec. So that, even assuming that the sun has no ether drift, the velocity of the earth through the ether must be this orbital velocity of 30 km/sec and the same must, therefore, also be the velocity of the resulting ether drift. Since the velocity of light is 3×10^5 km/sec, it will be easily seen that the velocity of the expected ether drift is just $30/3 \times 10^5 = 10^{-4}$ of the velocity of light. Obviously, therefore, a very sensitive apparatus was called for, if the experiment was to succeed.

Maxwell had actually despaired of any terrestrial methods being sensitive enough for the purpose and started looking for any astronomical evidence that may come his way in support. But **A.A. Michelson**, of the USA, when the learnt about it in the year 1879, accepted the challenge and, along with his colleague **E.W. Morley** (at the *Case Institute of Technology* in Cleveland), succeeded in performing, in the year 1887, one of the most famous experiments in the history of physics, (see next article) which gave a null result, striking at the very root of the ether hypothesis.

3.3 MICHELSON—MORLEY EXPERIMENT

The apparatus used by *Michelson* and *Morley* is known as *interferometer* since it depends upon the principle of interference of light and is shown diagrammatically in Fig. 3.1.

Here, S is a source of monochromatic light, a parallel beam from which falls upon a thin, parallel-sided glass plate P_1, thinly silvered on the back surface. The incident beam is thus split up into two parts at A at right angles to each other and of *equal intensity, viz.*, a reflected one, travelling upwards and a refracted one, travelling along the original direction. The former suffers reflection at mirror M_1 at T along its own path and gets refracted through P_1 on to the telescope T. The latter similarly gets reflected back as it falls normally on mirror M_2 at C and is then reflected downwards from the back surface of P_1 along the same path as the former to enter the telescope. The two mirrors (M_1 and M_2) are heavily silvered on the front face (to avoid multiple reflections) and are arranged at right angles to each other at the same distance D from plate P_1.

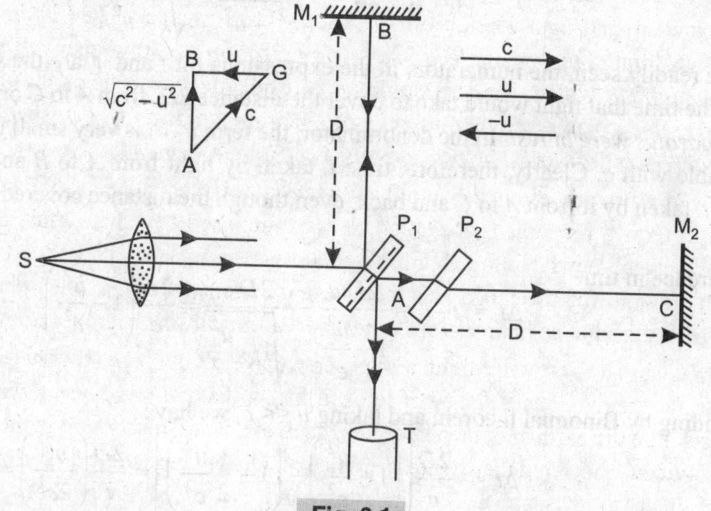

Fig. 3.1

As will be easily seen, the beam reflected upwards to M_1 traverses the thickness of plate P_1 *thrice* whereas the one refracted on to mirror M_2 does so only *once*. To make their paths through glass and air equal, therefore, a *compensating plate* P_2, identical with P_1, is arranged parallel to it, as shown.

If the beam of light be exactly parallel and if distances AB and AC from plate P_1 to the two mirrors respectively be the same (D), the two parts of the beam from M_1 and M_2 arrive at the telescope *in phase* and the field of view appears bright. If, however, their paths differ by an odd number of half wavelengths, they arrive at the telescope *out of phase, i.e.*, in opposing phases, and the field of view appears dark.

Since the beam of light incident on P_1 is almost always a slightly divergent one, some of the rays reaching the telescope from M_1 and M_2 are in phase and some out of phase, so that what we observe through the telescope is an *interference pattern of dark and bright fringes.*

Now, if u be the velocity of the apparatus (*i.e.*, of the earth), relative to the ether, from *left to right,* the drift velocity of the ether must be $-u$, *i.e., in the opposite direction,* from *right to left.* So that, if c be the actual velocity of light its relative velocity with respect to the apparatus, *along AC* $= (c - u)$ and, therefore, time taken to cover the distance D from A to C, say, $t_1 = D/(c - u)$. And, on the return journey, from C to A, the relative velocity of light $= (c + u)$ and, therefore, time taken to cover the same distance D from C to A, say, $t_2 = D/(c + u)$.

∴ *Total time taken by light to travel from A to C and back,* say, t, is given by

$$t = t_1 + t_2 = \frac{D}{(c-u)} + \frac{D}{(c+u)} = \frac{2cD}{(c^2-u^2)} = \frac{2D/c}{1-u^2/c^2}.$$

And the beam proceeding upwards from A to B must obviously be moving along the direction AG (as shown in the inset), so that the resultant of its velocity c and that of the ether drift $(-u)$ is along AB. This resultant velocity will thus clearly be $\sqrt{c^2-u^2}$ and the time taken to cover the distance D from A to B thus equal to $D/\sqrt{c^2-u^2} = t_1'$, say. On the return journey too from B to A, the resultant velocity of light will be the same $\sqrt{c^2-u^2}$, so that, again, time taken to cover the distance D from B to $A = t_1' = D/\sqrt{c^2-u^2}$.

∴ *total time taken by light to travel from A to B and back* say,

$$t' = t_1' + t_1' = 2t_1' = \frac{2D}{\sqrt{c^2-u^2}} = \frac{2D/c}{\sqrt{1-u^2/c^2}}$$

As will be readily seen, the numerators in the expressions for t and t' are the *same, viz.*, $2D/c$, and represent the time that light would take to cover the distance $2D$, from A to C or from A to B and back, *if the apparatus were at rest.* In the denominator, the term u^2/c^2 is very small unless u happens to be comparable with c. Clearly, therefore, time t' taken by light from A to B and back is a little less than time t, taken by it from A to C and back, even though the distance covered is the same D in either case.

This difference in time

$$\Delta t = t - t' = \frac{2D/c}{1-\frac{u^2}{c^2}} - \frac{2D/c}{\sqrt{1-\frac{u^2}{c^2}}} = \frac{2D}{c}\left(1-\frac{u^2}{c^2}\right)^{-1} - \frac{2D}{c}\left(1-\frac{u^2}{c^2}\right)^{-\frac{1}{2}}.$$

Or, expanding by Binomial theorem and taking $u \ll c$, we have

$$\Delta t = \frac{2D}{c}\left[\left(1+\frac{u^2}{c^2}\right)-\left(1+\frac{1}{2}\frac{u^2}{c^2}\right)\right] = \frac{2D}{c}\left(\frac{u^2}{2c^2}\right) = \frac{Du^2}{c^3}.$$

And, therefore, distance covered by light in time Δt

$$= \Delta t \times c = \frac{Du^2}{c_3}c = D\frac{u^2}{c^2},$$

indicating that the *optical path AC* is longer by Du^2/c^2 than the optical path AB or that this is the *path difference introduced* between the two parts of the incident beam (reflected from M_1 and M_2 respectively) *due to motion of the apparatus.*

The apparatus is now turned through 90° so that AB comes into the line of motion and AC, perpendicular to it, so that the optical path AB is now longer than the optical path AC by the same amount Du^2/c^2. The total path difference introduced between the two beams is thus 2 Du^2/c^2. Naturally, therefore, the interference pattern in the field of view of the telescope will shift a little, say, through n fringes. Since for a path difference equal to one wavelength, λ, the pattern shifts through 1 fringe, its shift through n fringes indicates a path difference $n\lambda$. We, therefore, have

$$n\lambda = 2\,Du^2/c^2,$$

whence,

$$n = 2\,Du^2/c^2\,\lambda.$$

Michelson and Morley had effectively increased distance D to nearly 11 metres (by repeated reflections) and, in order that the apparatus may be rotated without producing any strain, it was mounted on a stone slab, floated in mercury and kept rotating slowly at about 10 rotations per hour.

Thus, with *orbital velocity u of the earth, and hence that of the apparatus,* equal to 18.5 miles or 30 km/sec or 3×10^6 cm/sec, the *velocity of light*, $c = 3 \times 10^{10}$ cm/sec and with the wavelength of light used, $\lambda = 6 \times 10^{-5}$ cm, the expected value of n, in accordance with the expression above, comes to

$$\frac{2 \times 1100 \times 9 \times 10^{12}}{9 \times 10^{20} \times 6 \times 10^{-5}} = 0.37 \approx 0.4,$$

which could be accurately measured, in view of the high sensitivity of the apparatus, capable of measuring a shift as small as one-hundredth of a fringe.

Negative Result

The actual shift of the interference pattern observed, however, was much too small, almost negligible, *indicating little or no relative velocity between the earth and the ether.*

The experiment has since been repeated below the earth's surface as well as at high altitudes at different times of the year and, lately, with highly monochromatic light from a *laser*, but in all cases, the result has been a negative one. Other experiments to discover the ether wind have similarly failed.

It is always hard, however, to discard an idea to which one has grown accustomed. Strenuous efforts were therefore made to explain away the negative result of the experiment. Thus, Michelson himself hazarded the suggestion that the earth dragged along with it the ether in its immediate neighbourhood and there was thus no relative motion between the two. This was, however, easily demolished by *Lodge* who, in the year 1892, measured the velocity of light near rapidly rotating bodies and came to the conclusion that not more than half a per cent of the velocity of light could thus be communicated to the ether.

The same year (1892), *Fitzgerald* and *Lorentz* put forth the suggestion that probably there was interaction between the ether and a material body moving relatively to it, and that, as a result, the body gets shortened in all its dimensions *parallel to the relative velocity,* such that if L_o be the length of the body when at rest, and if it be moving with a speed u parallel to its length, the new length L acquired by it is given by the relation, $L = L_o\sqrt{1 - u^2/c^2}$.

It will be easily seen that if we make use of this suggestion in the experiment discussed above, we shall find that whereas distance AB will remain unchanged, distance AC will get shortened to $D\sqrt{1-u^2/c^2}$. So that, substituting $D\sqrt{1-u^2/c^2}$ for D in the expression for t above, we have

$$t = \frac{(2D/c)\left(\sqrt{1-u^2/c^2}\right)}{1-u^2/c^2} = \frac{2D/c}{\sqrt{1-u^2/c^2}},$$ which is the same as t'.

This contraction hypothesis, therefore, easily explains why the *Michelson-Morley experiment* gave a negative result. It is, however, open to the objection that it has been put forward for the specific purpose of explaining away the difficulty and that it does not follow from the theory.

It was 18 years later, in 1905, that the true and simple explanation for the negative result of Michelson and Morley's experiment was furnished by **Einstein,** namely, that *the velocity of light in space is a universal constant.* In fact, he made this constancy of the velocity of light one of the basic postulates of his special theory of relativity, as we shall presently see.

Example 1. In an Michelson and Morley experiment, the length of the arm of the interferometer was 11 meters, the wavelength of light 5.5. × 10^{-7} meters and the earth's velocity 30 km/sec, calculate the amount of fringe-shift?

Solution. The required fringe shift, *i.e.*, path difference introduced is given by

$$\Delta x = \frac{2\,Du^2}{c^2}$$

and the corresponding phase difference introduced will be

$$\delta = \frac{2\,Du^2}{c^2\,\lambda}$$

Here,

$$l = 1100 \text{ cm}, \lambda = 5.5 \times 10^{-7} \text{ m} = 5.5 \times 10^{-5} \text{ cm}$$

$$u = 30 \times 10^5 \text{ cm/sec}$$

$$c = 3 \times 10^{10} \text{ cm/sec}$$

$$\therefore \quad \text{required fringe shift} = \frac{2 \times 1100 \times (3 \times 10^6)^2}{(3 \times 10^{10})^2 \times 5.5 \times 10^{-5}} = \frac{2}{5} = 0.4$$

Example 2. In the Michelson-Morley experiment, the wavelength of the monochromatic light used is 5000 Angstrom units. What will be the expected fringe-shift on the basis of stationary ether hypothesis of the effective length of each path be 5 meters? (Given velocity of the earth = 3 × 10^4 m/sec and c = 3 × 10^8 m/sec)

Solution. We know that if the fringe shift be n fringes, we have $n = 2\,Du^2/c^2\,\lambda$. Here, $D = 5$ m, $u = 3 \times 10^4$ m/sec, $c = 3 \times 10^8$ m/sec and $\lambda = 5000 \times 10^{-8}$ cm $= 5 \times 10^{-7}$ m

So that,

$$n = \frac{2 \times 5(3 \times 10^4)^2}{(3 \times 10^8)^2 \times 5 \times 10^{-7}} = 0.2 \quad \text{or} \quad 1/5.$$

Thus, *the expected fringe shift is one-fifth of a fringe-width.*

Example 3. A stream of width l is flowing with a velocity v and a person wishes to row straight across it. In what direction should he strike out and how long would it take him to cross the stream? How long would it take him to cover a distance l upstream and back?

Solution. In order to be able to row straight across the stream, the person must strike out at an angle θ upstream with the direction of flow, such that the resultant R of his own velocity V and that of the stream v is perpendicular to the latter.

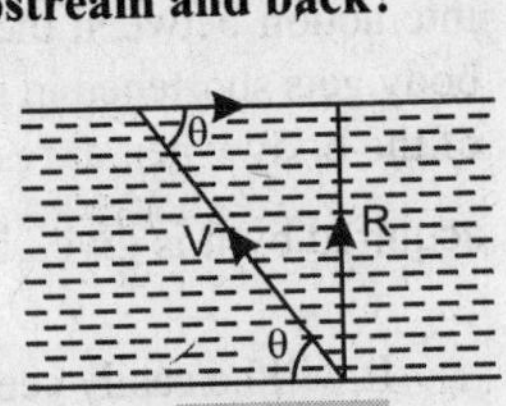

Fig. 3.2

Then, clearly, $V \cos\theta = v$, whence, $\theta = \cos^{-1} v/V$.

And the resultant velocity $R = V \sin\theta$, perpendicular to the direction of stream-flow.

∴ *time taken to row straight across the stream*

$$= \frac{l}{V\sin\theta} = \frac{l}{V\sqrt{1-\cos^2\theta}} = \frac{l}{V\sqrt{1-v^2/V^2}} = \frac{l}{\sqrt{V^2 - v^2}}$$

And, clearly, resultant velocity of the person upstream = $(V + v)$ and his resultant velocity downstream = $(V + v)$.

Hence time taken to cover a distance l upstream

$$= l/(V - v)$$

and *time taken to cover the same distance back, i.e., downstream* $= l/(V + v)$

$\therefore$ *time taken to cover a distance l upstream and back*

$$= \frac{l}{V - v} + \frac{l}{V + v} = \frac{2lv}{V^2 - v^2}.$$

3.4 EINSTEIN'S CONCEPT OF RELATIVITY

When the experiments in search of the ether drift failed, it began to be increasingly realised that there was no such thing as an *absolute* or *privileged* frame of reference and that the basic laws of physics took the same form in all inertial frames of reference. The implications of this Galilian invariance principle were emphasised by the French mathematical physicist *Henri Poincaree* when he stated that '... the laws of physical phenomena [are] the same, whether for an observer fixed or for an observer carried along in a uniform movement of translation, so that we have not and could not have any means of discerning whether or not we are carried along in such a motion'.

This simply means that if we are drifting with uniform speed in a spaceship, with all the windows closed, we shall not be able to say, with the help of any experiments we might choose to perform, whether we are at rest or in motion. If, however, we look out of a window, we shall be able to say merely that we are in motion with respect to the fixed stars but not whether we or the stars are actually in motion.

How near, indeed, had Poincare thus come to expounding the theory of relativity and yet how far he actually was form it. For, instead of grasping the implications of the failure of all ether-drift experiments, and building up a new theory on its basis, discarding older notions or space and time, he concerned himself with trying to somehow save the old classical theory by suitable adjustments and modifications in it.

Box - II

The real import of the negative results of the ether-drift experiments was clearly seen and understood by *Einstein.* For, discussing the reciprocal electrodynamic action of a magnet and a conductor where 'the experimentally observable phenomenon depends only on the relative motion of the conductor and the magnet ....',

Einstein says:

'Examples of this sort, together with the unsuccessful attempts to discover any motion of the earth relative to the 'light medium', suggest that the phenomena of electrodynamics as well as of mechanics possess no properties corresponding to the idea of absolute rest. They suggest rather that ... the same laws of electrodynamics and optics will be valid for all frames of reference for which the equations of mechanics hold good*. We will raise this conjecture (the purport of which will hereafter be called the *Principle of Relativity*) to the status of a postulate, and also introduce another postulate which is only apparently irreconcilable with the former, namely, that light is always propagated in empty space with a definite velocity c which is independent of the state of motion of the emitting body ... The introduction of a "luminiferous ether" will prove to be superfluous in as much as the view here to be developed will not require an 'absolutely stationary space' provided with special properties, ...'

Thus, from the negative results of the ether-drift experiments and from his own reasoning, *Einstein* felt fully convinced that there was no such thing as an *absolute* or *fixed* frame of reference. He examined the physical consequence of the absence of such a frame of reference and had the boldness to break away from old and traditional concepts of space and time. He knit his conclusions

* the inertial frame of reference.

and revolutionary ideas into a cogent theory which he announced to an unsuspecting world in the year 1905 as his *Special theory of relativity*. And, ten years later, in 1915, followed the second and the more complex and difficult part of it in the form of the *General theory of relativity*. The former deals with problems associated with unaccelerated frames of reference, *i.e.*, those which move with uniform relative velocity with respect to one another and the latter with those associated with accelerated ones.

We shall concern ourselves here mainly with only the **Special theory of relativity** which is not only comparatively simpler but has also produced the most profound effect on the entire field of physics.

3.5 SPECIAL THEORY OF RELATIVITY

The two **basic postulates** on which the theory rests may be stated in a precise form thus:

1. The laws of physics all take the same identical form for all frames of reference in uniform relative motion, *i.e.*, for all the inertial frames of reference.

This, it will be readily seen, is a direct consequence of the absence of an absolute or fixed frame of reference. For, if the laws of physics were to take on different forms in different frames of reference, it would be easily inferred from these differences as to which of them are at rest in space and which in motion. But, as we have seen, such distinction between the state of rest and of uniform motion is precluded by the absence of a universal frame of reference. The first postulate is thus merely a generalised statement of this observed fact.

2. The velocity of light in free space is the same (c) relative to any inertial frame of reference, *i.e.*, it is invariant to transformation from one inertial frame to another and has thus the same value (3.0×10^{10} cm or 3×10^{8} m/sec) for all observers irrespective of their state of motion.

This postulate is clearly a statement of the result of *Michelson—Morley* experiment.

The two implications of the above postulates are immediately obvious:

(*i*) Velocity being *not* invariant to Galilian transformation, it follows that if c be the velocity of light in frame S, that in frame S', moving relative to S with velocity v, must be $c' = c - v$. In accordance with the second postulate of the special theory of relativity, however, we have $c' = c$ since c must always have the same value irrespective of the state of motion of the frames of reference.

The new postulate is thus clearly at variance with Galilian transformation.

(*ii*) Again, suppose a flash of light is emitted from the origin when points O and O' of the two frames of reference S and S' (Fig. 3.3) just cross each other. Suppose further that it is possible for the two observers in the two frames of reference to see the light or rather the *wave front* (a surface of equal phase) spreading out into space. Then, in view of the constancy of the value of c, irrespective of the motion of the two frames of reference, each of the two observers at O and O' respectively will, even after drifting apart, claim to be at the centre of the spreading spherical wave front of light, as shown in Fig. 3.4, thinking that the other has moved away from the centre of the sphere.

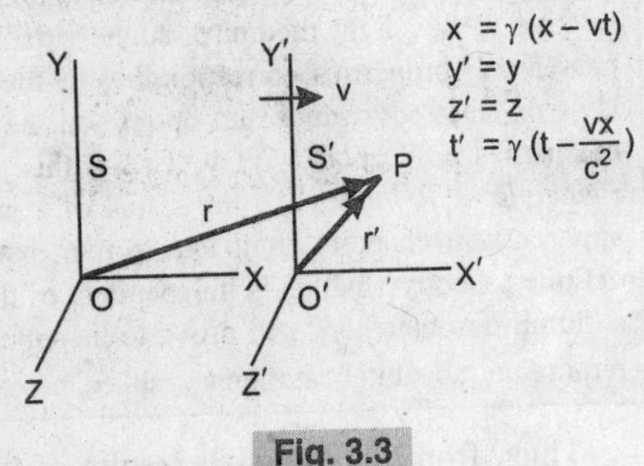

Fig. 3.3

As can be readily seen, this will not be the case if, instead of being in free space, our observers were to be in boats in water and if a stone were dropped (instead of a flash of light emitted) when they just crossed each other. The ripple pattern formed will appear to be different to each observer and they will be able to say from the very shape of it whether or not they are in motion or which one of them is in motion and which, stationary.

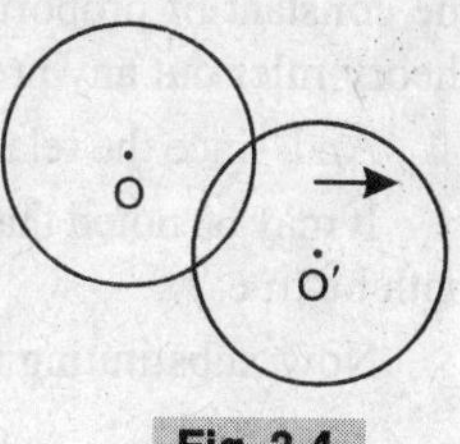

Fig. 3.4

This difference between the two cases, it may be carefully noted, is due to the fact that *whereas water functions as a frame of reference by itself, space does not,* and, again, *whereas the speed of the waves in water varies with the motion of the observer, the speed of the waves in space (i.e., of light or electromagnetic waves) is quite independent of it.*

3.6 LORENTZ COORDINATE TRANSFORMATION (OR SIMPLY, LORENTZ TRANSFORMATION)

As just mentioned in §3.5 above, the Galilian transformation is quite at variance with the velocity of light in free space being independent of the motion of the observer or the source of light. We, therefore, look for a transformation which is consistent with this new concept.

As we have seen under the article referred to, if a flash of light be emitted as the two observers just cross each other in the two frames of reference (Fig. 3.3), each thinks himself to be at the centre of a uniformly expanding spherical wave front (Fig. 3.4). Clearly, *equation of the wave front, as seen by the observer at O in reference frame S,* is

$$x^2 + y^2 + z^2 = c^2 t^2, \qquad ...(i)$$

And *equation of the wave front, as seen by the observer at O′ in reference frame S′*, is

$$x'^2 + y'^2 + z'^2 = c'^2 t'^2, \qquad ...(ii)$$

where *c*, the velocity of light is the same in either frame of reference.

In order, therefore, that both the observers may seem to be at the centre of the same expanding wave front, we should have relation (*i*) = relation (*ii*).

Now, *Galilian transformation* gives $x' = x - vt$, $y' = y$, $z' = z$ and $t' = t$.

So that, substituting for x', y', z' and t' in relation (*ii*) above, we obtain

$$x^2 - 2\,xyt + v^2 t^2 + y^2 + z^2 = c^2 t^2, \qquad ...(iii)$$

which is surely not the same as relation (*i*), showing once again, that *the Galilian transformation fails if the constancy of the value of c be assumed.*

This means clearly that in the new transformation we are looking for, the relation $x' = x - vt$ no longer holds good. Since however, the relation is quite in accord with classical mechanics, the new transformation must be such that the *x*-coordinate, in accordance with it, also reduces itself to this very value, when the relative velocity *v* is small compared with *c*.

The simplest relation for the *x*-coordinate, in accordance with the new transformation, can be

$$x' = \gamma(x - vt) \qquad ...(iv)$$

where γ is independent of the coordinates *x* or *t*, but may vary with *v*.

This relation has the merit of being a *linear* one in *x* and *t*, providing for a uniformly expanding wave front and admitting of one and only one interpretation in the system *S′* of an observation made from system *S*. A quadratic equation, on the other hand, will obviously give two; and a higher order equation, even more than two interpretations, which is simply inadmissible.

In plain and simple language, the equation $x' = \gamma(x - vt)$ will automatically give only one value of x' for a given value of *x*, without our having to impose any further conditions.

Considering the inverse transformation, connecting measurements in frame *S* with those made in frame *S′*, we shall have only the sign of *v* reversed; so that,

$$x = \gamma(x' + vt'), \qquad ...(v)$$

the constant of proportionality γ remaining the same in either case, since the first postulate of the theory rules out any preferred frame of reference.

And, since the relative motion of S and S' is confined to the x-direction, we have $y' = y$ and $z' = z$.

It may be noted that t' *can no longer be taken to be equal to t,* or else relations (*iv*) and (*v*) cannot both be true.

Now, substituting in relation (*v*) the value of x', as given by relation (*iv*), we have

$$x = \gamma[\gamma(x - vt) + vt'] = \gamma^2(x - vt) + \gamma\, vt'.$$

or,

$$\gamma\, vt' = x - \gamma^2(x - vt) = x - \gamma^2 x + \gamma^2 vt = \gamma^2 vt + x(1 - \gamma^2),$$

whence,

$$t' = \gamma t + x\left(\frac{1-\gamma^2}{\gamma v}\right) \qquad ...(vi)$$

In order to determine the value of γ, we note that the reference frame S' moves with relative velocity v in the $+x$-direction with respect to reference frame S and that the flash of light is emitted when the two observers at O and O' are opposite each other, *i.e.*, at the time the flash is emitted, $x = x' = 0$ and also $t = t' = 0$. Since the velocity of light is the same c in the two frames of reference, we have

x-coordinate of the light pulse in frame S, given by $x = ct$. ...(*vii*)

and x'-coordinate of the light pulse in frame S', given by $x' = ct'$ ...(*viii*)

Substituting in relation (*viii*) the values of x' and t' from relations (*iv*) and (*vi*) respectively, we have

$$\gamma(x - vt) = c\gamma t + cx\left(\frac{1-\gamma^2}{\gamma v}\right),$$

whence, solving for x, we obtain $x = ct\left[\dfrac{1 + v/c}{1 - (c/v)(1/\gamma^2 - 1)}\right]$.

Since $x = ct$, as shown in relation (*vii*) above, we have

$$\frac{1 + v/c}{1 - (c/v)(1/\gamma^2 - 1)} = 1. \quad \text{or,} \quad 1 + \frac{v}{c} = 1 - \left(\frac{c}{v}\right)\left(\frac{1}{\gamma^2} - 1\right),$$

whence,

$$\gamma = \frac{1}{\sqrt{1 - v^2/c^2}}$$

The factor v/c is quite often represented by β; so that,

$$\gamma = \frac{1}{\sqrt{1 - v^2/c^2}} = \frac{1}{\sqrt{1 - \beta^2}}$$

Substituting this value of γ in relations (*iv*) and (*vi*) above, we have

$$x' = \frac{x - vt}{1 - v^2/c^2} = \gamma(x - vt) \qquad ...(ix)$$

and

$$t' = \gamma\left(t - \frac{vx}{c^2}\right) = \frac{t - vx/c^2}{\sqrt{1 - v^2/c^2}} \qquad ...(x)$$

And, since, as already mentioned, S' moves along the $+x$ direction relative to S, we have

$$y' = y \qquad ...(xi)$$

and

$$z' = z \qquad ...(xii)$$

These values of x', y', z' and t', when substituted in relation (*ii*) above, give relation (*i*), precisely as it should be if the two observers are to seem to be at the centre of the same spherical wave front.

This *relativistic transformation* is referred to a **Lorentz transformation,** after *H.A. Lorentz,* a Dutch physicist, because it was he who first showed that this transformation was the only one under which the laws of electricity and magnetism have the same form in all reference frames in relative motion (*i.e.*, in all *inertial* frames), though it was *Einstein,* of course, who showed its wider significance as being the only proper transformation for *all* types of measurements, electromagnetic or otherwise.

Equations (*ix*), (*x*), (*xi*) and (*xii*) are, therefore, referred to as **Lorentz transformation equations, or Lorentz coordinate transformation equation.**

The Galilian and Lorentz (or Relativistic) transformations for an observer in reference frame S', moving with uniform velocity v relative to frame S in the $+x$-*direction*, are arranged side by side below, so that the differences between the two may become apparent at a glance:

Galilian transformations	**Lorentz (or Relativistic) transformations**
$x' = x - vt$	$x' = \dfrac{x - vt}{\sqrt{1 - v^2/c^2}} = \gamma(x - vt)$
$y' = y$	$y' = y$
$z' = z$	$z' = z$
$t' = t$	$t' = \dfrac{t - vx/c^2}{\sqrt{1 - v^2/c^2}} = \gamma\left(t - \dfrac{vx}{c^2}\right)$

N.B. If v/c be small, as it most often would be, we may take only the first two terms of the Binomial expansion of $\dfrac{1}{\sqrt{1 - v^2/c^2}}$ or $\left(1 - \dfrac{v^2}{c^2}\right)^{-\frac{1}{2}}$, namely, $\left(1 + \dfrac{1}{2}\dfrac{v^2}{c^2}\right)$ as the value of γ. This approximation is valid enough even if v/c has a value up to about 0.5.

As will be readily seen, when $v << c$, *i.e.*, when $v/c \to 0$, we have $\gamma = 1/\sqrt{1 - v^2/c^2} \approx 1$ and Lorentz (or Relativistic) transformations reduce to Galilian ones. So that, Galilian or Newtonian physics is just a particular case of Relativistic physics. In fact, v for the earth (18.5 mi/sec) being only 1/10,000 th of the value of c, is negligibly small compared with c and the Galilian or Newtonian physics is thus perfectly valid for almost all our practical purposes, the relativistic effects manifesting themselves only at very high values of v, when they are comparable with c, as in the case of electrons, protons, mesons etc.

We have, in our discussion above, assumed frame S' to be moving with velocity v in the positive direction of x relative to frame S. As seen from frame S', therefore, frame S would appear to be moving in the negative x direction *i.e.*, with velocity $-v$. Consequently, the **Inverse Lorentz transformation,** which converts measurements made in frame S' into those in frame S, may be obtained from Lorentz transformations by simply changing the sign of v from positive to negative. We shall then have

$$x = \frac{x' + vt'}{\sqrt{1 - v^2/c^2}} = \gamma(x' + vt'), y = y', z = z'$$

and

$$t = \frac{t' + vx'/c^2}{\sqrt{1 - v^2/c^2}} = \gamma\left(t' + \frac{vx'}{c^2}\right).$$

It is thus amply clear by now that *measurements of space and time are by no means absolute but are dependent upon the relative motion between the observer and the phenomenon observed.*

3.7 RESULTS FLOWING FROM LORENTZ TRANSFORMATION

Let us now examine some of the relativistic effects, *i.e.*, effects which are the result of relativistic or Lorentz transformation. Quite a few of them, as we shall see, will appear to be surprisingly new and strange because, in view of the small relative motion between the frames of reference of which we have experience in our daily life, we do not ordinarily come across any perceptible relativistic phenomena.

Let us consider a few important examples:

3.7.1 Length Contraction

The length of a rod, as measured in a frame of reference, *at rest with respect to the observer,* is called its **proper-length** and would obviously be the *same* in all stationary frames of reference. Reference frames that it will be different, depending upon their relative velocities with respect to the observer. Let us see how.

Consider a rod laid along the axis of x in a frame of reference S, at rest with respect to the observer and let x_1 and x_2 be the coordinates of its tow ends which may be noted at leisure, one after the other, the rod being at rest. Then, the *proper length* of the rod, say,

$$L_o = (x_2 - x_1).$$

If the x-coordinates of the ends of the rod in the reference frame S', moving with a uniform velocity v with respect to frame S be x_1' and x_2', *as noted simultaneously at the same instant* t', we have length of the rod in the moving reference frame S' given by $L = (x_2' - x_1')$.

To corelate L_o and L, we note that inverse Lorentz transformation gives

$$x_1 = \frac{x_1' + vt'}{\sqrt{1 - v^2/c^2}} \quad \text{and} \quad x_2 = \frac{x_2' + vt'}{\sqrt{1 - v^2/c^2}}.$$

So that,

$$L_o = x_2 - x_1 = \frac{x_2' + vt'}{\sqrt{1 - v^2/c^2}} - \frac{x_1' + vt'}{\sqrt{1 - v^2/c^2}}$$

$$= \frac{x_2' - x_1'}{\sqrt{1 - v^2/c^2}} = \frac{L}{\sqrt{1 - v^2/c^2}}$$

whence,

$$L = L_o\sqrt{1 - v^2/c^2},$$

which is clearly *shorter than its proper length* L_o. And, as will be easily seen, the higher the value of v, *i.e.*, the faster the motion of the rod (or of the reference frame carrying it), with respect to the observer, the shorter its length compared with its proper length. So that, *if* $v = c$, *i.e., if the rod be moving with the velocity of light* (*c*), *its length would be zero.*

It follows at once, therefore, that the length of the rod or any other object when $v = 0$, or *when the rod or the object is at rest with respect to the observer, i.e., its proper length, is the largest.*

There will, of course, be no shortening of the length of the rod if it lies along the axis of y or z, perpendicular to the x-direction or the direction of motion of the frame of reference carrying it, though there will, naturally be some shortening if the length of the rod be inclined to the direction of its velocity for, then, it will have a component in the latter direction.

This shortening or contraction in the length of an object along its direction of motion is known as the **Lorentz—Fitzgerald contraction,** since both *Lorentz* and the Irish physicist *G.F. Fitzgerald,* during the 1890's, independently suggested that the null result of Michelson–Morley experiment could be accounted for, if the length of a material object contracted by the fraction $\sqrt{1 - v^2/c^2}$ in its direction of motion with speed v, through ether. Of course, as we know *now*, the contraction is certainly this fraction but for entirely different reasons.

It may be pointed out that there is *reciprocity of the contraction effect, i.e.,* the contraction works both ways — a length along the x-axis in frame S being contracted for the observer in S' and a length along the x'-axis in frame S' being contracted for the observer in S. For, if the rod be at rest along the axis of x' with respect to the moving frame S', its proper length, as measured by the observer in S' (at rest with respect to it) will be $L_o = (x_2' - x_1')$, where x_1' and x_2' are the coordinates of the end-points of the rod along this axis. And if the x-coordinates of the two end-points of the rod in frame S, as noted *instantaneously, i.e.,* at the same instant t, by the observer in S', be x_1 and x_2, its length, as measured in frame S, is $L = (x_2 - x_1)$.

Since, in accordance with *Lorentz tranformation,*

$$x'_1 = \frac{x_1 - vt}{\sqrt{1-v^2/c^2}} \quad \text{and} \quad x'_2 = \frac{x_2 - vt}{\sqrt{1-v^2/c^2}}$$

We have $$L_o = x'_2 - x'_1 = \frac{x_2 - vt}{\sqrt{1-v^2/c^2}} - \frac{x_1 - vt}{\sqrt{1-v^2/c^2}} = \frac{x_2 - x_1}{\sqrt{1-v^2/c^2}}$$

$$= \frac{L}{\sqrt{1-v^2/c^2}}$$

whence, $$L = L_o\sqrt{1-v^2/c^2}, \text{ the same as before.}$$

Thus, *with relative motion between an object and observer, the length of the object, as measured by the latter, always comes out to be shorter than its proper length.*

It is for this reason that if we have two frames of reference in relative motion (one stationary and the other in motion) along the x-direction, say, a straight line parallel to this direction in one appears shorter to an observer in the other, — not, so, however, a straight line alone the y or the z-direction, perpendicular to the x-direction. Similarly, a square and a circle in one appear to the observer in the other to be a rectangle and an ellipse respectively (Fig. 3.5), the sides of the square and the radius of the circle (or their components) in the direction of motion getting shortened.

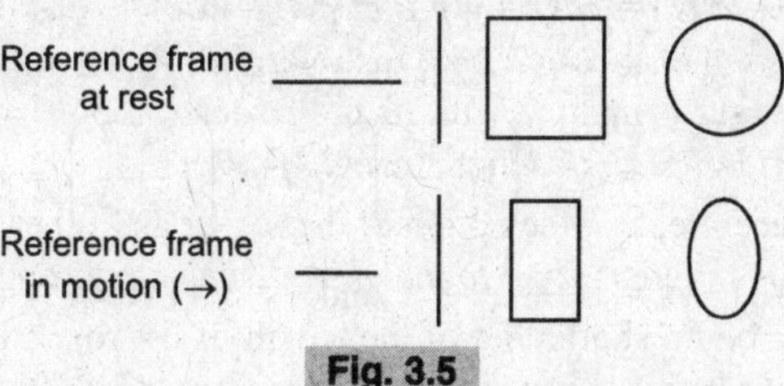

Fig. 3.5

As will be easily seen, however, for small values of v for which $v/c \to 0$, the factor $\sqrt{1-v^2/c^2} = 1$, so that $L = L_o$, a result in accordance with classical mechanics where length is treated as an absolute quantity, unaffected by rest or motion.

This is exactly the reason why at speeds with which we are ordinarily concerned (and which are an infinitesimal fraction of c), the *Lorentz-Fitzgerald* contraction is nil or negligible.

For an interesting example (and evidence) of the contraction. Phenomenon, see worked example at the end of the chapter.

Box - III

Note. It is interesting to point out that even though a fast moving object must undergo Lorentz-Fitzgerald contraction, its length, if observed visually (*i.e.,* directly by the eye) or photographically, would *not* show any such contraction. Strangely enough, this phenomenon was discovered and studied only in the year 1959, more than half a century after the publication of the special theory of relativity. It may, however, be explained thus: The light proceeding from the farthest part of the object leaves the earliest and that from its nearest part, the latest, with that from other parts at times in between these two extremes, to reach the eye or the camera *simultaneously* so as to form a composite image of the object on the retina of the eye or the film of the camera. As can well be imagined, this should actually make the moving object look larger in size in its direction of motion. It so happens, however, that this apparent increase in its length is just offset by the Lorentz-Fitzgerald contraction that it must undergo on account of its relative motion. As a result, it appears to be neither lengthened nor shortened. Thus, if the moving object be a three-dimensional one, like a *cube*, no change in its shape will come about except a rotation of its orientation, which may approach 180° as $v \to c$. And, in the case of a sphere, there will be no distortion whatsoever.

Example 4. Show that Lorentz transformations are superior to Galilean transformations.

(Kanpur 2002)

Solution. By Lorentz transformation equations are

$$x' = \beta(x - vt), y' = y, z' = z, t' = \gamma\left(t - \frac{vx}{c^2}\right)$$

where,
$$\gamma = \frac{1}{\sqrt{(1 - v^2/c^2)}}$$

If v is very small, than $(v/c) \to 0$ and so $(\beta \to 1)$.

$$x' = x - vt, y' = y, z' = z, t' = t\{t - 0(x)\}$$

This implies, $x' = x - vt, y' = y, z' = z, t' = t$

These are Galilean transformations. These facts prove that Lorentz transformations are superior to Galilean transformations.

Example 5. Show by means of Lorentz transformation equations that

$$x^{2\prime} - c^2t'^2 = x^2 - c^2t^2.$$

Solution. As we know, in accordance with Lorentz coordinate transformation,

$$x' = \gamma(x - vt) \text{ and } t' = \gamma(t - vx/c^2)$$

$$\therefore \quad x'^2 - c^2t'^2 = \gamma^2(x - vt)^2 - c^2\gamma^2(t - vx/c^2)^2$$

$$= \gamma^2(x^2 - 2xvt + v^2t^2) - c^2\gamma^2(t^2 - 2vxt/c^2 + v^2x^2/c^4)$$

$$= \gamma^2x^2\left(1 - \frac{v^2}{c^2}\right) - \gamma^2t^2c^2\left(1 - \frac{v^2}{c^2}\right) = \gamma^2(x^2 - c^2t^2)(1 - v^2/c^2)$$

Now,
$$\gamma^2 = \frac{1}{1 - v^2/c^2} \text{ and } \therefore \gamma^2(1 - v^2/c^2) = 1.$$

So that,
$$x'^2 - c^2t'^2 = x^2 - c^2t^2.$$

Example 6. Show that a four dimensional volume element *dx dy dz dt* is invariant to Lorentz transformation.

Solution. This follows straightaway from Lorentz coordinate transformation. For, if the volume element be in a stationary frame S and if a frame S' be moving with a constant velocity relative to S along the x-axis, we have in frame S',

$$dx' = \gamma dx, dy' = dy, dz' = dz \text{ and } dt' = dt.$$

$$\therefore \quad dx'\, dy'\, dz'\, dt' = \gamma dx\, dy\, dz\, dt/\gamma = dx\, dy\, dz\, dt.$$

In other words, *the four dimensional volume elements dx dy dz dt is invariant to Lorentz transformation.*

Example 7. The space-time coordinates of two events in frame S are 0, 0, 0, 0 and 5c, 0, 0, 4 respectively. Obtain the space-time interval between them, what should be the velocity of a frame S' relative to S, in which (*i*) the two events may appear to occur simultaneously, (*ii*) the second may appear to occur 2 seconds (*a*) carlier, (*b*) later, than the first even?

Solution. Here, clearly, $x_1 = 0, y_1 = 0, z_1 = 0$ and $t_1 = 0$ and $x_2 = 5c, y_2 = 0, z_2 = 0$ and $t_2 = 4$.

So that, $(x_2 - x_1) = \Delta x = 5c$, $(y_2 - y_1) = \Delta y = 0$, $(z_2 - z_1) = \Delta z = 0$, and $(t_2 - t_1) = \Delta t = 4$

Now, the (*space-time interval*)^2 is given by $S_{12}^2 = (x_2 - x_1)^2 + (y_2 - y_1)^2 + (z_2 - z_1)^2 - c^2 (t_2 - t_1)^2$.

We, therefore, have $S_{12}^2 = (5c)^2 + 0 + 0 - c^2 (4)^2 = 25c^2 - 16c^2 = 9c^2$,

whence, the *space-time interval* $S_{12} = \sqrt{9c^2} = 3c$.

Now, imagine a reference frame S' to be moving with velocity v relative to S, along the axis of x. Then, in accordance with Lorentz transformation, the interval $(t_2' - t_1') = \Delta t'$ between the two events in this frame, as it would appear to an observer in S, is given by the relation $\Delta t' = \gamma\left(\Delta t - v\dfrac{\Delta x}{c^2}\right)$

where γ, as we know, is equal to $1/\sqrt{1 - v^2/c^2}$.

Clearly, therefore,

(*i*) *For the two events to appear to occur simultaneously in frame S'*, we should have $\Delta t' = 0$, *i.e.*,

$$\gamma\left(\Delta t - \frac{v\Delta x}{cz}\right) = 0 \quad \text{or,} \quad \Delta t = \frac{v\Delta x}{c^2}$$

Or, substituting the values of Δt and Δx, we have

$$4 = \frac{v(5c)}{c^2}, \quad \text{whence,} \quad v = \frac{4}{5}c = 0.80 \text{ c}.$$

Thus, *the velocity of frame S' must be 0.80 c relative to S, along the axis of x.*

(*ii*) (*a*) *For the second event to appear to occur 2 sec* ***earlier*** *than the first in frame S'*, we should have $(t_2' - t_1') = \Delta t' = +2$. So that,

$$2 = \gamma\left(\Delta t - v\frac{\Delta x}{c^2}\right) = \frac{1}{\sqrt{1 - v^2/c^2}}\left(4 - \frac{v(5c)}{c^2}\right) = \frac{1}{\sqrt{1 - v^2/c^2}}\left(4 - 5\frac{v}{c}\right)$$

Squaring and rearranging, we obtain the quadratic equation.

$$\frac{29}{4}\frac{v^2}{c^2} - 10\frac{v}{c} + 3 = 0, \qquad \ldots(i)$$

which gives $v/c = 0.94$ or 0.44, *i.e.*, $v = 0.94\,c$ or $0.44\,c$.

The first value being inadmissible, since it gives a negative value of $\Delta t'$, we have $v = 0.44$ c.

The velocity of the frame S' must thus be 0.44 c relative to S, along the axis of x.

(*b*) *For the second event to appear to occur 2 sec* ***later*** *than the first in frame S'*, we should have $(t'_2 - t_1') = \Delta t' = -2$. So that, we now have

$$-2 = \gamma\left(\Delta t - v\frac{\Delta x}{c^2}\right) = \frac{1}{\sqrt{1 - v^2/c^2}}\left(\Delta t - v\frac{\Delta x}{c^2}\right).$$

which, on substitution of the values of Δt and Δx, squaring and rearranging, as before, again gives the same quadratic equation as (*i*) above.

So that, again, $v = 0.94\ c$ or $0.44\ c$.

Here, obviously, the second value is inadmissible, as it gives a positive value of $\Delta t'$. We, therefore, have $v = 0.94$ c.

Thus, *in this case, the velocity of frame S' must be 0.94 c relative to S, along the axis of x.*

Example 8. A body travelling at 0.9 c where c is speed of light, is shortened to $(d/d') = \sqrt{1-\frac{v^2}{c^2}}$, calculate the ratio, between d and d' in the expression, to the length at rest.

Solution.
$$\left(\frac{d}{d'}\right) = \sqrt{1-\frac{v^2}{c^2}} = \left[1-\left(0.9\frac{c}{c}\right)^2\right]^{\frac{1}{2}} = 0.436$$
$$= 43.6\% \text{ of the length at rest.}$$

Example 9. Show that the force acting on a particle, as observed by two observers in two inertial frames to reference in the same. (Given $V < C$).

Solution. The force acting on a particle as observed by the observer O in frame S is given by

$$F = \frac{d}{dt}(MV) = M\frac{dV}{dt} = Ma$$

The force acting on a particle as observed by the observer O' in the frame S' is given by

$$F' = \frac{d}{dt}(MV') = M\frac{dV'}{dt} = Ma'$$

Since both are inertial frames of reference, $a = a'$, $F = F'$.

It means, the same force will be observed by the two observers O and O' in two inertial forms of reference S and S'. This means force is invariant to Galilean transformations. It further means, Newton's second law of motion $F = ma$ is valid in all inertial frames of reference, *i.e.* the basic laws of physics are invariant in two inertial frames of reference.

Example 10. What is the length of metre stick moving parallel to its length when its mass is 3/2 of its rest mass. ***(Delhi Uni. 2003)***

Solution. Here
$$m = m_o/\sqrt{1-\frac{v^2}{c^2}} \quad \ldots(i)$$

Therefore,
$$\frac{m}{m_o} = 1/\sqrt{1-\frac{v^2}{c^2}}$$

Similarly,
$$L = L'\sqrt{1-\frac{v^2}{c^2}} \quad \ldots(ii)$$

Dividing (*ii*) by (*i*), we have
$$\frac{L}{m} = \frac{L'}{m_o}\left(1-\frac{v^2}{c^2}\right)$$
$$L = \frac{m}{m_o}.L'\left(1-\frac{v^2}{c^2}\right)$$

or
$$L = \frac{m}{m_o}L'\left(\frac{m_o}{m}\right)^2 \quad [\because \text{Eq. } (i)]$$

$$= \frac{m_o}{m} . L'$$

But $\frac{m_o}{m} = \frac{2}{3}$ and $L' = 1$ metre,

$$L = \frac{2}{3} \times 1 \text{ m} = 0.667 \text{ m}$$

Example 11. The length of a rocket ship is 100 metres on the grand. When it is in flight its length observed on the ground is 99 meters calculate the speed?

Solution. By the result of Lorentz contraction, the length will be

$$L' = L\sqrt{1 - \frac{v^2}{c^2}}$$

Hence $$99 = 100\left[1 - \frac{v^2}{c^2}\right]^{\frac{1}{2}}$$

$$\left(\frac{99}{100}\right)^2 = 1 - \frac{v^2}{c^2} \qquad \text{(as } L' < L\text{)}$$

$$\frac{v^2}{c^2} = \frac{199}{10^4}$$

$$\frac{v}{c} = \frac{\sqrt{199}}{100}$$

or $$v = \frac{(199)^{1/2}}{100} \times 3 \times 10^8 \text{ m/sec} = 3 \times 10^6 \times (199)^{1/2}$$

$$= 42.3 \times 10^6 \text{ ms}^{-1}$$

Example 12. A rod has a length 100 cm when rod is in a satellite moving with velocity 0.8*c* relative to laboratory, what is the length of the rod as determined by an observer, (*a*) in the satellite and (*b*) in the laboratory?

Solution. (*a*) The observer in the satellite is at rest-relative to the rod as the rod is in the satellite. So the length of the rod relative to the observer is 100 cm.

(*b*) Now the observer in the laboratory. So that the rod is in motion w.r.to the observer.

$$L' = L\sqrt{1 - \frac{v^2}{c^2}}$$

$$= 100[1 - (0.8)^2]^{1/2} = 100 \times 0.6 = 60 \text{ cm}$$

Example 13. Calculate the length of a rod moving with a velocity of 0.8*c* in a direction inclined at 60° to its own length. Proper length of rod is given to be 100 cm.

Solution. Suppose the rod is moving with velocity $v = 0.8c$ along *x*-axis and the rod as inclined at 60° with *x*-axis.

Contraction will take place only in *x*-direction and not in *y*-direction. Hence $l_x = l \cos 60°$, $l_y = l \sin 60°$.

$$\vec{l} = \hat{i}\, l_x = \hat{j}\, l_y$$

$$l'_x = l_x\sqrt{1 - \frac{v^2}{c^2}},\ l'_y = l_y = l \sin 60° = \left(\frac{\sqrt{3}}{3}\right) l,$$

$$l'_x = [(l\cos 60°)\sqrt{(1-(0.64))}] = l\left(\frac{1}{2}\right)(0.6) = 0.3\,l$$

$$l' = [(l'_x)^2 + (l_y)^2]^{\frac{1}{2}} = l[0.09 + (3/4)]^{\frac{1}{2}}$$

$$= 0.916\,l = 0.916 \times 100 = 91.6$$

Here l = length of the rod at rest, and

l' = length of the moving rod.

∴ Length of the rod in motion = 91.6 cm.

Example 14. Calculate the percentage contraction in the length of a rod in a frame of reference, moving with velocity 0.8*c* in a direction (*a*) parallel to its length (*b*) at an angle of 30° with its length. What is the orientation of the rod in the moving frame of reference in case (*b*)?

Solution. (*a*) Let L_0 be the length of the rod, placed along the axis of x, in a reference frame S, at rest. Then, its length in a frame S', moving with velocity $0.8c$ relative to S in a direction parallel to its length, *i.e.*, along the axis of x is given by

$$L' = L_0\sqrt{1-v^2/c^2} = L_0\sqrt{1-\frac{(0.8c)^2}{c^2}} = L_0\sqrt{1-0.64},$$

whence,
$$L' = L_0\sqrt{0.36} = 0.60L_0$$

∴ *percentage contraction produced in the length of the rod* $= \dfrac{(L_0 - 0.60\,L_0)}{L_0} \times 100 = 40$

(*b*) In this case, the *component of the length of the rod along its direction of motion.*

$$= L_0 \cos 30° = \frac{\sqrt{3}}{2} L_0.$$

and the *component of its length, perpendicular to this direction* $= L_0 \sin 30° = 0.5\,L_0$.

Only the former component undergoes a change in length and not the latter (being perpendicular to the direction of motion).

If, therefore, L_0'' be the length of the former component in the moving frame S', we have

$$L_0'' = \frac{\sqrt{3}}{2} L_0 \sqrt{1-\frac{(0.8c)^2}{c^2}} = \frac{\sqrt{3}}{2} L_0 \times 0.60 = 0.52\,L_0.$$

Since the other component remains unchanged at $0.5\,L_0$, we have *total length of the rod in frame S'*, say. $L'' = \sqrt{(0.52\,L_0)^2 + (0.5\,L_0)^2} = 0.7228\,L_0$.

∴ *percentage contraction produced in the length of the rod* $= \dfrac{0.7228\,L_0}{L_0} \times 100 = 22.72$

Clearly, if θ be the angle that the length of the rod appears to make with the direction of velocity v of frame S', we have

$$\tan\theta = \frac{\text{length component} \perp v}{\text{length component} \parallel v} = \frac{0.5\,L_0}{0.52\,L_0} = 0.96$$

Or,
$$\theta = \tan^{-1}(0.96) = 43°50'.$$

Thus, *the rod makes an angle of 43°50′ with its direction of motion.*

Example 15. A circular lamina moves with its plane parallel to the *x* – *y* plane of a reference frame *S* at rest. Assuming its motion to be along the axis of *x* (or *y*), calculate the velocity at which its surface area would appear to be reduced to half to an observer in frame *S*.

Solution. Taking the motion of the lamina to be along the axis of x of the reference frame S, with velocity v, it is clear that its radius R along this axis will contract to, say, R', whereas the radius perpendicular to its *i.e.,* along the axis of y, will remain unaltered. So that, the circular lamina will appear to have assumed an elliptical shape, with its major and minor axes equal to R and R' along the axes of y and x respectively. Its surface area will, therefore, appear to be $\pi RR'$. The original surface area of the circular lamina being πR^2, we have

$$\pi RR' = \frac{1}{2}\pi R^2, \text{ whence, } R' = R/2.$$

But, as we know, R' must be equal to $R\sqrt{1-v^2/c^2}$, where v is the velocity of the circular lamina with respect to the reference frame S.

$$\therefore \quad \frac{R}{2} = R\sqrt{1-v^2/c^2}. \quad \text{Or} \quad \frac{1}{4} = 1 - \frac{v^2}{c^2},$$

whence, $\quad v^2/c^2 = 3/4$. Or, $v/c = \sqrt{3/2}$. Or, $v = (\sqrt{3/2})c = 0.866c$.

Thus, *the velocity of the circular lamina relative to frame S must be* 0.866*c*.

Example 16. A rod 1 metre long is moving along its length with a velocity 0.6*c*. Calculate its length as it appears to an observer (*a*) on the earth (*b*) moving with the rod itself.

Solution. Here, obviously, 1 metre is the proper length L_0 of the rod in its own moving frame of reference.

(*a*) If, therefore, L' be its length, as it appears to an observer in the stationary reference frame of the earth, we have

$$L' = L_0\sqrt{1-v^2/c^2} = 1\sqrt{1-\frac{(0.6\,c)^2}{c^2}} = 1\sqrt{1-0.36}$$

$$= 0.8 \text{ m} = 80 \text{ cm.}$$

Thus, *the observer on the earth will estimate the length of the rod to be 80* cm.

(*b*) For an observer moving with the rod itself, its length would be the same as its proper length in the moving reference frame, *viz.*, 1 metre, because there is no relative motion between the rod and the observer (*i.e.* $v = 0$).

Example 17. Obtain the volume of a cube, the proper length of each edge of which is L_0 when it is moving with a velocity *v* along one of its edges.

Solution. Here, clearly, the only change in length, (*i.e.*, a *contraction*) will occur in the particular edge of the cube along which it is moving, the lengths of the other edges, being perpendicular to the direction of motion, remaining unaffected.

If, therefore, L_0 be the *proper length* of each edge of the cube, the length of the edge along which it is moving will become $L_0\sqrt{1-v^2/c^2}$.

And, since the other two edges of the cube remain unaffected and continue to have the same length as before, *viz.*, L_0, we have

volume of the moving cube $= L_0\sqrt{1-v^2/c^2}\,(L_0)(L_0) = L_0 3\sqrt{1-v^2/c^2}$

Example 18. How fast should a rocket ship move relative to an observer in order that its length may appear to the observer to be 99 per cent of its proper length? (Given, $c = 3 \times 10^{10}$ cm/sec.).

Solution. We have the relation $L' = L_0\sqrt{1-v^2/c^2}$, where L' is the length of the rocket ship as it would appear to an observer when it is moving with velocity v relative to him and L_0, its *proper length,* (*i.e.*, as it would appear to an observer moving with it). We, therefore, have

$$L'/L_0 = 99/100 = \sqrt{1 - v^2/c^2} \quad \text{Or,} \quad (99/100)^9 = 1 - v^2/c^2$$

Or, $v^2/c^2 = 1 - (99/100)^2 = 1 - 0.98 = 0.02$, whence, $v^2 = .02c^2$.

Or, $v = 0.1415c$,

i.e., $v = 0.1415 \times 3 \times 10^{10} = 4.245 \times 10^9$ cm/sec.

Thus, the rocket ship should have a velocity 4.245×10^9 cm/sec, with respect to the observer.

3.7.2 Time Dilation

Time intervals too, like length, are affected by relative motion. Thus, to an observer, a clock appears to run slower when in motion, than when at rest with respect to him. So that, the time interval between two events occurring at a given point in space in a frame of reference, moving with respect to the observer, appears to be greater as noted on a clock at rest with respect to him than on an identical clock in the moving frame of reference itself. This is referred to as *time dilation*, meaning *apparent lengthening of time*. Let us deduce this result from *Lorentz transformation*.

Suppose we have two frames of reference, S and S' (Fig. 3.2), the former at rest and the latter moving with a uniform velocity v relative to it, along the $+x$ direction. Suppose further that two identical clocks are carried by the two reference frames at their origins O and O', such that they both show zero time when just against each other, *i.e.,* when their origins just cross each other.

Then, if two events occur at any given point x' in frame S', at times t_1' and t_2', as noted on the clock carried by it and at times t_1 and t_2, *as noted on the clock carried by frame S*, we clearly have time interval between the two events, *as noted on the clock in the moving frame S′* given by $\Delta t' = (t_2' - t_1')$.

And, time interval between the same two events as noted on the clock in the stationary frame S given by $\Delta t = (t_2 - t_1)$.

Now according to inverse Lorentz transformation, we have

$$t_1' = \gamma\left(t_1 - \frac{v_x}{c^2}\right) \quad \text{and} \quad t_2' = \gamma\left(t_2 - \frac{v_x}{c^2}\right)$$

where $\gamma = 1/\sqrt{1-(v^2/c^2)}$

Therefore, $$\Delta t' = (t_2' - t_1') = \gamma\left(t_2 - \frac{v_x}{c^2}\right) - \gamma\left(t_1 - \frac{v_x}{c^2}\right) = \gamma(t_2 - t_1)$$

or $$\Delta t' = \gamma.\Delta t$$

Since the factor $1/\sqrt{1-v^2/c^2}$ or γ is greater than 1, we have $\Delta t' > \Delta t$.

Thus, *the time interval $\Delta t'$ between two events occurring at a given point in the moving frame S′ appears to be longer, or dilated, by a factor $1/\sqrt{1-v^2/c^2}$ or γ to the observer in the stationary frame S.*

The same will happen if frame S' were at rest and S in motion. So that, *like length contraction, time dilation too shows reciprocity effect, i.e.,* works both ways or *is independent of the direction of velocity and depends only on its magnitude.* In general, therefore, the interval between two events at the same point in a moving frame appears to be longer by a factor γ to an observer in a stationary frame.

This interval of time $\Delta t'$ between two events occurring at the same place, measured on the clock, moving with the reference frame S' in which the events occur, and hence at rest with respect to it, is called to *proper time interval* or *the proper time*, the usual symbol for which is τ. Thus, the proper time interval in a moving system is always less than the corresponding time interval, measured on a system at rest.

If follows from the above that the passage of time and hence also all physiological processes that go with it, like pulse and heart beats, and, infact, the process of ageing itself, are slowed down in a fast moving reference frame. Indeed, if the velocity of the moving frame be $v = c$, the passage of time and hence also the process of ageing will stop altogether!

The Twin Paradox

Consider two exactly identical twin brothers. Let one of the twins go to a long space journey at a high speed in a rocket and the other stay behind on the earth. The clock in the moving rocket will appear to go slower than the clock on the surface of earth (as $\Delta t' = \gamma.\Delta t$). Therefore, when he returns back to the earth, he will find himself younger than the twin who behind on the earth stayed.

Incidentally, this also shows that nothing material can really travel faster than light,– a proven fact, having the force of a *fundamental law of nature*.

In case, however, the velocity (v) of the moving frame of reference be small, as is ordinarily the case, so that $v/c \to 0$, we have $\Delta t = \Delta t'$, the time intervals between the two events in both the moving and the stationary systems are the same, – a result in accord with the absolute nature of time in Classical or Newtonian physics.

Most fundamental particles disintegrate spontaneously after a comparatively very brief spell of life, called their *life-time*. In a frame of reference S in which the particle is at rest (*i.e.*, its own frame of reference), the mean life-time is denoted by τ and is called the *proper life-time* of the particle. It is found to depend upon the velocity of the particle. Thus, in a frame of reference S' (say, the laboratory frame) in which it is moving with velocity v relative to S, the life-time gets dilated to

$$\tau' = \gamma T = \frac{\tau}{\sqrt{1 - v^2/c^2}}$$

Further, if N_o be the number of particles that undergo disintegration in the particle's own reference frame, the number of particles the survive up to time t is given by

$$N(t) = N_o e^{t/\tau}$$

Verification of Time Dilation

(*i*) **Indirect verification.** An indirect verification of the time dilation effect is afforded by the fact of $\mu^{\pm}$ *mesons or muons,* for short, produced higher up in the atmosphere, reaching the ground level in the very short span of their life-time.

These elementary particles, having a mass 215 times that of an electron, are produced in the upper reaches of the atmosphere as a result of collision of cosmic rays with the air molecules and though they do not all have the same velocity, the faster ones among them have a velocity $0.998c$, very close to that of light in free space. Even, with this high velocity, however, they can, in their whole life-time of 2.2×10^{-6} *sec* cover at the most a distance equal to $0.998c \times 2.2 \times 10^{-6} = 658.68$ *metres* before they disintegrate or decay into an *electron* and two neutrinos each (a neutrino being a particle of zero charge and zero mass). And, yet they are found copiously in the laboratory 10 km below the spot where they are produced.

How is this possible? Obviously, because of time dilation. For, whereas in their own frame of reference (*i.e.,* the frame of reference in which they are produced), their mean life-time τ is only 2.2×10^{-6} sec, for us, in the laboratory frame of reference, it is dilated to $\tau' = \gamma\tau = \frac{\tau}{\sqrt{1 - v^2/c^2}} = \frac{2.2 \times 10^{-6}}{\sqrt{1 - \frac{(0.998c)^2}{c^2}}} = 34.38 \times 10^{-6}$ sec, which is more than 15 times that in their own frame of reference. In this much longer life-time, they can easily cover a distance of $0.998c \times 34.38 \times 10^{-6} = 10.29$ km. This at once explains their presence in the laboratory, 10 km *below*, at the ground level.

(*ii*) **Direct verification.** Directly, the time dilation effect may be verified in the laboratory, using a beam of π^+ *mesons or Pions*, for short, (the products of highly energetic nuclear reactions in the upper atmosphere) which are produced artificially in the laboratory by bombarding a suitable target of carbon or beryllium by highly energetic *protons* or *α-particles* from a *synchrocyclotron*. These particles are comparatively heavier than mesons, with a mass 273 times that of an electron, but have a much shorter life-time τ of 2.6×10^{-8} *sec* in their own frame of reference, after which they disintegrate into a *Meons* and two *neutrinos* each. Though all the $\pi^{\pm}$ *mesons* do not have the same velocity, the faster ones may be assumed to have a velocity of $0.9c$. So that, their dilated life-time τ in the laboratory frame of reference should be equal to

$$\gamma\tau = \frac{2.6\times10^{-8}}{\sqrt{1-v^2/c^2}} = \frac{2.6\times10^{-8}}{\sqrt{1-\dfrac{(0.9c)^2}{c^2}}} = 5.96\times10^{-8} \text{ sec, } i.e.,$$

more than twice that in their own frame of reference (in which they are at rest).

To verify whether this is so, we obtain a beam of *pions* in the manner indicated (*i.e.,* by bombarding a ribbon target *T* of *carbon* or *beryllium* (Fig. 3.6) by α-particles or protons from a synchrocyclotron). This beam is narrowed down by passing it through a collimator slit *S*, as shown. The pions in the beam decay into *muons* and *neutrinos* and the muons thus produced are detected by a suitable device D, along side which the beam passes.

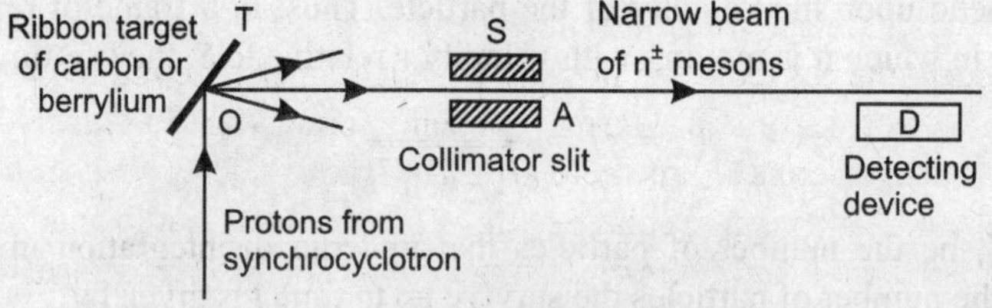

Fig. 3.6

Obviously, the number of *muons* recorded by the detecting device per second is proportional to the number of pions present in the beam in the vicinity of the device, *i.e.,* to the flux-of pions adjacent to it. By observing the recordings of the detecting device at various points along the path *OP* of the beam, therefore, the dilated life-time τ of the moving pions can be obtained.

To obtain the mean life-time or the proper life-time τ of the pions (*i.e.,* their life-time in their own frame of reference, in which they are at rest), they are brought to rest at *A* right at the beginning of their path as they emerge from the slit, by introducing a thick solid slab of a suitable material. The time interval elapsing between the entering of the points in the solid slab and the emerging of muons therefrom, noted electronically, then gives the proper life-time τ of the pions constituting the beam.

It is found that $\tau' = \gamma\tau = \dfrac{\tau}{\sqrt{1-v^2/c^2}}$ and the time dilation effect thus stands verified.

3.7.3. Simultaneity

By *simultaneity* of two events we understand their occurrence at *exactly the same time*. Thus, for example, if in a fixed frame of reference, *S*, *A* and *B* are two points distant x_1 and x_2 respectively from the origin *O* and *P*, the carefully determined *mid-point* of *AB*. Then, if a light signal is emitted at P, it will arrive at A at exactly the same time as at B, since the velocity of light (c) is the same in all directions. We, therefore, say that the two events, *viz.*, the arrival of the light signal at A and at B, occur simultaneously at time t, say, *i.e.*, one event occurs at x_1 at time t and the other at x_2 also at the same time t.

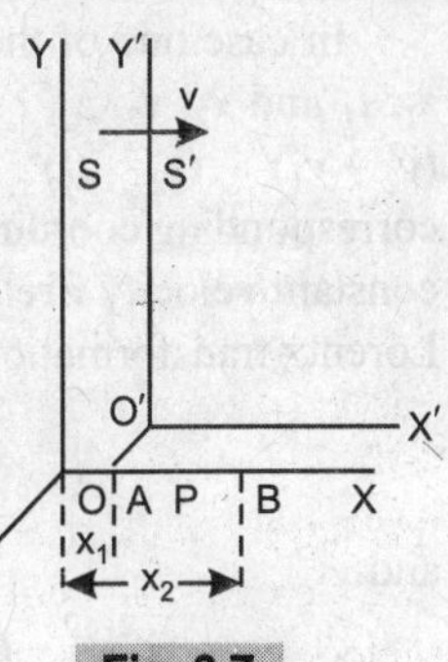

Fig. 3.7.

Let us see if the two events also appear to be simultaneous to an observer in a frame of reference S', moving relative to S, with velocity v along the positive direction of its x-axis. For the observer in S, the corresponding values of t for the events at x_1 and x_2 will, in accordance, with Lorentz transformation, be given respectively by

$$t_1' = \gamma\left(t - \frac{vx_1}{c^2}\right) \quad \text{and} \quad t_2' = \gamma\left(t - \frac{vx_2}{c^2}\right)$$

So that, the time interval between the two events, as observed by the observer in S' will be $t' = (t_2' - t_1') = \gamma v(x_1 - x_2)/c^2$, which is surely *not zero*, indicating that the two events at A and B, which appear to be simultaneous to the observer in S *do not appear so* to the observer in S' but to have a time interval t' between them, the magnitude of which depends upon both, the distance between the two events and the velocity of frame S' and relative to S.

Exactly in the same manner it can be shown that two events that appear to be simultaneous to an observer in frame S' do not appear to be so to the observer in frame S.

As can well be seen, *this failure of simultaneity in one frame of reference in relative motion with another is a direct consequence of the value of c being the same in all frames of reference and in all directions.* So that, if we accept, as we must, the postulate of *invariance of the velocity of light,* we have also to accept the consequence flowing from it, namely, the *relativity of simultaneity*, *i.e.*, the simultaneity of events, separated in space, not being something *absolute* that can be expected or accepted in all frames of reference. It is there in each frame of reference separately but there can be no question of agreement between simultaneity in one frame with that in another in relative motion with it. In short, it is only a *local affair* of each individual frame of reference, whether at rest or in motion.

3.7.4 Invariance of Space-time Interval

It has already been mentioned (§3.3) that to know the true position of a point, we must know its four space-time coordinates, *viz.*, the three spatial coordinates x, y, z and the time coordinate t. Such a point in a *space-time frame of reference*, or an occurrence there, is, as we have seen before, referred to as an *event* in the space-time language, first proposed by *H. Minkowski* in the year 1908. And, just as the familiar space vectors enable us to deduce spatial relationships between points or lines, independently of any particular coordinate system, so also, with the addition of a time vector to them, the four space-time vectors enable us to express physical law in special relativity (involving terms measured in space-time coordinates), irrespective of any particular frame of reference, *i.e.*, laws that are invariant to *Lorentz transformation*.

Now, before the advent of the theory of relativity, as we know, *space* and *time* were regarded as separate *entities* and both space as well as time intervals were invariant to Galilian transformation, their values being thus quite independent of the frame of reference ued. This is not the case with Lorentz transformation, under which neither of them is invariant. What remains invariant under this transformation is the combination $c^2t^2 - x^2 - y^2 - z^2$, as we have seen under §3.5. It is called the *space-time interval* between two points, one of which has been taken at the origin itself. It is usually denoted by the symbol S^2_{12} and, as is so obvious, it is actually the *interval squared*, though, commonly, we refer to it as the *interval*.

In case one of the points is not at the origin, and the coordinates of the two points are x_1, y_1, z_1, t_1 and x_2, y_2, z_2, t_2 respectively, the *space-time interval* is obviously $c^2(t_2^2 - t_1^2) - (x_2 - x_1)^2 - (y_2 - y_1)^2 - (z_2 - z_1)^2$. That this is invariant to Lorentz tranformation may be easily seen. For, if the corresponding coordinates of these points in a frame S', moving along the axis of x of frame S with a constant velocity v relative to it, be x_1', y_1', z_1', t_1' and x_2', y_2', z_2, t_2 we have, in accordance with Inverse Lorentz transformation,

$$S_{12}'^2 = c^2(t_2^2 - t_1^2) = c^2\gamma^2[(t_2' - t_1') + v(x_2' - x_1')/c^2]^2,$$

$$(x_2 - x_1)^2 = \gamma^2[(x_2' - x_1') + v(t_1' - t_1')]^2, \quad (y_2 - y_1)^2 = (y_2' - y_1')^2$$

and
$$(z_2 - z_1)^2 = (z_2' - z_1')^2.$$

$\therefore$
$$c^2(t_2^2 - t_1^2) - (x_2 - x_1)^2 - (y_2 - y_1)^2 - (z_2 - z_1)^2$$
$$= c^2\gamma^2[(t_2' - t_1') + v(x_2' - x_1')/c^2]^2 - \gamma^2[(x_2' - x_1') + v(t_2' - t_1')]^2 - (y_2' - y_1')^2 - (z_2' - z_1')^2$$

Or,
$$S_{12}'^2 = c^2(t_2' - t_1')^2\,\gamma^2\left(1 - \frac{v^2}{c^2}\right) - (x_2' - x_1')^2\,\gamma^2\left(1 - \frac{v^2}{c^2}\right) - (y_2' - y_1')^2 - (z_2' - z_1')^2$$

Since
$$\gamma = 1/\sqrt{1 - v^2/c^2}, \quad \text{or,} \quad \gamma^2 = 1/(1 - v^2/c^2)$$

we have
$$\gamma^2\left(1 - \frac{v^2}{c^2}\right) = 1$$

$\therefore$
$$S_{12}'^2 = c^2(t_2' - t_1')^2 - (x_2' - x_1')^2 - (y_2' - y_1')^2 - (z_2' - z_1')^2.$$

Thus, $c^2(t_2 - t_1)^2 - (x_2 - x_1)^2 - (y_2 - y_1) - (z_2 - z_1)^2 = c^2(t_2' - t_1')^2$

Or,
$$S_{12}^2 = S_{12}'^2, \qquad \text{...}(i)$$

clearly showing that the *space-time interval is invariant to Lorentz transformation.*

It may be noted again that the *space and the time-intervals, taken separately are not invariant.* For, clearly, $(x_2 - x_1)^2 + (y_2 - y_1)^2 + (z_2 - z_1)^2$ is not equal to $(x_2' - x'_1)^2 + (y_2' - y'_1)^2 + (z_2' + z_1')$ and nor is $(t_2 - t_1) = (t_2' - t_1')$.

Thus whereas in Classical physics, *time* and *space* were taken to be two different things, the Lorentz transformation equations and relation (*i*) above, proclaim clearly that *in the theory of relativity*, time **and space are equivalent** *and can be expressed one in terms of the other.* Thus, it can be seen from equation (*i*) that, *in terms of distance,* 1 *sec* is 3×10^8 *metre*, the distance covered by light in free space in 1 *sec* and, similarly, 1 *metre of time* is $1/3 \times 10^8$ *sec*, the time taken by light to cover a distance of one metre.

Thus, measuring time and space in the same units in a system in which $c = 1$, the Lorentz transformation equations, as also equation (*i*) above are greatly simplified and respectively become

$$x' = (x - vt)/\sqrt{1 - v^2}, \; y' = y, \; z' = z \;\text{ and } t' = (t - vx)/\sqrt{1 - v^2} \qquad \text{...}(ii)$$

and $(t_2 - t_1)^2 - (x_2 - x_1)^2 - (y_2 - y_1)^2 - (z_2 - z_1)^2 = (t_2' - t_1')^2 - (x_2' - x_1')^2 - (y_2' - y_1')^2 - (z_2' - z_1')^2$. ...(*iii*)

Now, if we consider two points (or particles) which, in a given co-ordinate system, have only space but no time (or zero time), we can see from relation (*iii*) that the interval squared would be negative and the interval, therefore, an *imaginary* one. Such an interval is referred to as a *space-like interval*, obviously because the interval, in this case, is more like space than like time. One the other hand, when we have two points or particles, occupying the same place in the coordinate system but having different times, the square of the time being positive and the distance *zero*, the interval squared is positive and hence the interval *real*. Such an interval is called a *time-like interval.*

Incidentally, the invariance of the space-time interval in two frames of reference means, in other words, the invariance of the value of c in the two frames.

Example 19. A certain young lady on her twenty fifth birthday that it is time to slendrize. She weights 100 kilograms. She has heard that if she moves fast enough, she will appear thinner to her stationary friends.

(*i*) How fast must she move to appear slendrize by a factor of 50%

(*ii*) At this speed, what will be her mass to be her stationary friends?

(*iii*) It she maintains her speed untill the day she calls her twenty-nineth birthday, how old will her stationary friends claim she is according to their measurements?

Solution. Given: $m_o = 100$ kg, $L = 50\%$ of $L_o = \dfrac{50}{100} L_o = \dfrac{L_o}{2}$ where L_o represents dimensions of the lady at rest and L its length when she is in motion.

$$\Delta t = 4 \text{ years. For 29 years} - 25 \text{ years} = 4 \text{ years}$$

(*i*) We have, $L = L_o\left(1-\dfrac{v^2}{c^2}\right)^{\frac{1}{2}}$ putting the values, we get

$$\frac{L_o}{2} = L_o\left(1-\frac{v^2}{c^2}\right)^{\frac{1}{2}}$$

Or $$1-\frac{v^2}{c^2} = \frac{1}{4} \quad \text{or} \quad \frac{v^2}{c^2}=\frac{3}{4}$$

Or $$V = \frac{\sqrt{3}}{2}c = 0.867\,c$$

(*ii*) $$m = \frac{m_o}{\sqrt{1-\dfrac{v^2}{c^2}}} = \frac{100}{\dfrac{1}{2}} = 200 \text{ kg}$$

(*iii*) By time dilation, $$\Delta t' = \frac{\Delta t}{\left(1-\dfrac{v^2}{c^2}\right)^{\frac{1}{2}}} = \frac{4}{\dfrac{1}{2}} = 8$$

The lady will appear to be 25 + 8 = 33 years old.

Example 20. Two twins are 25 years old when one of them sets out on a journey through a space at nearly constant speed. The twin in the spaceship measures time with an accurate watch. When he turns back to earth, he claims to be 31 years old while the twin left on the earth is then 43 years old. What was the speed of the spaceship?

Solution. The spaceship clock reads the trip to be only 6 years long while the earth clock reads it to be 18 years. Here, $\Delta t' = 6$ and $\Delta t = 18$.

$$\Delta t' = \Delta t \times \sqrt{1-\frac{v^2}{c^2}}$$

$$6 = 18 \times \sqrt{1-\frac{v^2}{c^2}}$$

$$\frac{v^2}{c^2} = 1 - 0.111 = 0.889 \text{ or } \frac{v}{c} = 0.9429$$

$$v = 0.9429 \times 3 \times 10^8 = 2.83 \times 10^8 \text{ m/sec}$$

Example 21. A man on the moon observes two spaceships coming towards him from opposite directions at speeds 0.8*c* and 0.7*c* respectively. What is the relative speed of the two spaceships as measured by an observer on either one? ***(Nagpur Uni. 2005)***

Solution. The two spaceships *A* as stationary *S* frame, the moon as the *S′* frame and the other spaceship *B* as the object whose speed u_x in the *S* frame is to be determined.

With respect to *S* frame, the moon moves with velocity *V* as shown in Fig. 3.8(*b*)

Then, $v = -0.8c,\ u'_x = -0.7c$

Now
$$u_x = \frac{u'_x + v}{1 + \frac{vu'_x}{c^2}} = \frac{-0.7c - 0.8c}{1 + \frac{(-0.8c)(-0.7c)}{c^2}}$$

$$= \frac{-1.5c}{1.56} = -0.96c$$

$$= -2.88 \times 10^8 \text{ m/sec.}$$

The minus sign shows that the spaceship *B* approaches *A*.

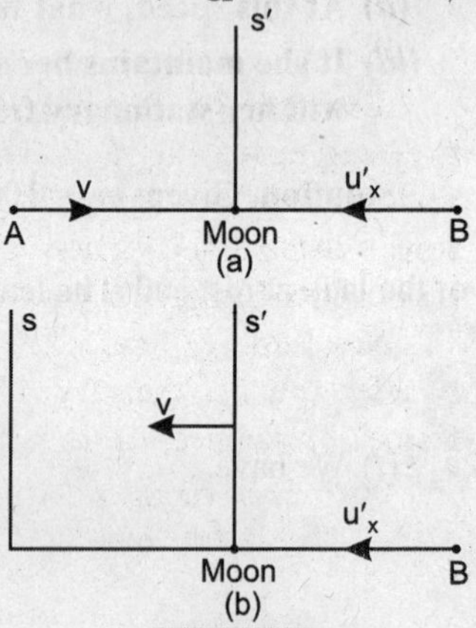

Fig. 3.8

Example 22. Two β particles *A* and *B* emitted by a radioactive source travel in opposite directions each with a velocity of 0.9*c* with respect to the source. Find the velocity of *B* with respect to *A*.

Solution. The two β-particles *A* and *B* move in opposite directions as shown in Fig. 3.9 (*a*). Now we regard the β-particle as stationary *S* frame, radioactive source *R* as the *S′* frame, and β–particle *B* as the object whose speed u_x in the frame *S* is to be determined. With respect to *S*, the radioactive source moves with velocity *v* as shown in Fig. 3.9 (*b*). Then

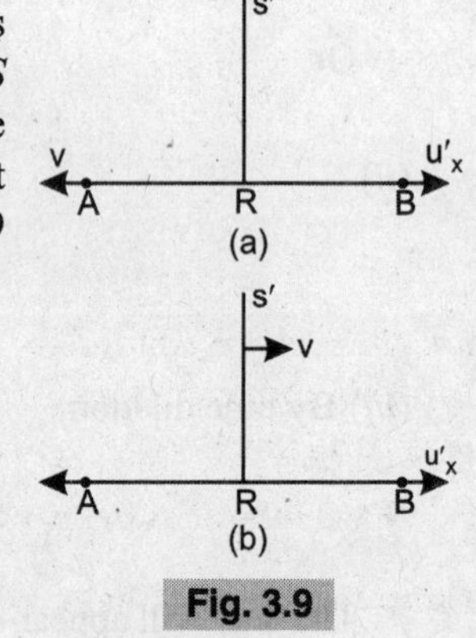

Fig. 3.9

$$v = +0.9c,\ u'_x = +0.9c$$

$$\therefore \quad u_x = \frac{u'_x + v}{1 + \frac{vu'_x}{c^2}} = \frac{0.9c + 0.9c}{1 + \frac{0.9c \times 0.9c}{c^2}}$$

$$= \frac{1.8c}{1.81} = 2.982 \times 10^8 \text{ m/sec.}$$

Example 23. (*i*) What is mean life of a burst of π^+ mesons, travelling with β = 0.73 ? (The proper mean life time τ is 2.5 × 10^{-8} sec.)

(*ii*) What distance is travelled at β = 0.73 during one mean life?

(*iii*) What distance would be travelled without relativistic effects?

Solution. Here, the proper mean life of the π^+ mesons is $\tau = 2.5 \times 10^{-8}$ *sec.*

(*i*) Therefore, their observed mean life when travelling at $\beta = v/c = 0.73$, *i.e.*, at $v = 0.73c$, is given by

$$\tau' = \gamma\tau = \frac{2.5 \times 10^{-8}}{\sqrt{1 - v^2/c^2}} = \frac{2.5 \times 10^{-8}}{\sqrt{1 - \left(\frac{0.73c}{c}\right)^2}} = \frac{2.5 \times 10^{-8}}{\sqrt{1 - (0.73)^2}} = \frac{2.5 \times 10^{-8}}{\sqrt{0.4672}}$$

$$= 3.658 \times 10^{-8} \text{ sec.}$$

Thus, *the observed mean life of the burst of* π^+ *mesons* is 3.658×10^{-8} *sec.*

(*ii*) Obviously, *distance travelled in one mean life*, at $\beta = 0.73$ or $v = 0.73\ c$

$= velocity \times observed\ mean\ life = v\tau$

$= 0.73 \times 3 \times 10^{10} \times 3.658 \times 10^{-8} = 800.9$ or 801 cm.

(*iii*) Distance travelled in one mean life, without relativistic effects, would obviously be

$=$ velocity $\times$ proper mean life $= v\tau$

$= 0.73 \times 3 \times 10^{10} \times 2.5 \times 10^{-8} = 547.4$ cm.

Example 24. The life time of mu-mesons is 2.2 × 10^{-6} sec and their speed 0.998*c*, so that they can cover only a distance of 0.998c × 2.2 × 10^{-6} or 658.6 metres in their entire life time, and yet they are found in profusion at sea level, *i.e.*, at a depth of 10 kilometer from the upper atmosphere where they are produced. How may this be explained on the basis of (*i*) Lorentz-Fitzgerald contraction, (*ii*) time dilation?

Solution. (*i*) Here, 2.2×10^{-8} sec. being the mean life time of the μ-mesons in their own frame of reference, *i.e.*, their *proper life-time*, the distance covered by them during this time in their own frame of reference, say $h_o = 658.6$ m.

The *observed distance* (as seen from *our* reference frame, *i.e.*, the earth) will, therefore, be, say,

$$h = \gamma h_o = h_o\Big/\sqrt{1 - v^2/c^2} = 658.6\Big/\sqrt{1 - (0.998c/c)^2}$$

$$= 658.6/0.064 = 10290 \text{ m} = 10.29 \text{ km}.$$

Thus, *the μ-mesons are able to cover a distance of 10 km or more despite their short life-time. This explains their presence at sea level.*

(*ii*) Here, again, the proper life-time of the μ-mesons is $\tau = 2.2 \times 10^{-6}$ *sec* and, therefore, their observed life time $\tau' = \gamma\tau = 2.2 \times 10^{-6}\Big/\sqrt{1 - v^2/c^2}$

$$= 2.2 \times 10^{-6}\Bigg/\sqrt{1 - \left(\frac{0.998c}{c}\right)^2}$$

$$= 2.2 \times 10^{-6}/0.064 = 34.38 \times 10^{-6}\ sec,$$

i.e., their observed life-time is about 16 times their proper life-time and, *in this increased or dilated life-time*, they can cover a distance $0.998c \times 34.38 \times 10^{-6} = 0.998 \times 3 \times 10^6 \times 34.38 \times 10^{-6} = 10290$ $m = 10.29$ km, as in (*i*) above. *Hence their presence at sea level.*

Example 25. A beam of particles of half life 2 × 10^{-6} sec travels in the laboratory with 0.96 times the speed of light. How much distance does the beam travel before the flux falls to $\frac{1}{2}$ times the initial flux?

Solution. Here, the proper half-life of the beam of particles, $\tau/2 = 2 \times 10^{-6}$ *sec.*

$\therefore$ their observed half-life when travelling at velocity $v = 0.96c = \tau'/2$

$= \gamma\tau/2 = 2 \times 10^{-6}\Big/\sqrt{1 - v^2/c^2} = 2 \times 10^{-6}\Big/\sqrt{1 - (0.96c/c)^2} = 2 \times 10^{-8}/0.28\ sec.$

In this time, obviously, the flux falls to half its initial value and the *distance covered during the time* $= v \times (\tau'/2)$

$= 0.96 \times 3 \times 10^{10} \times 2 \times 10^{-6}/0.28 = 2.057 \times 10^5$ cm.

Example 26. The proper mean life of the μ-meson is approximately 2 × 10^{-5} sec. Suppose that a large burst of μ-mesons produced at some height in the atmosphere travels downward with velocity *v* = 0.99*c*. The number of collisions in the atmosphere on the way down is small.

If 1 per cent of those in the original burst survive to reach the earth's surface, estimate the original height. (In the meson frame of reference, the number of particles which survive to a time t is given by

$$N_{(t)} = N_{(o)}e^{(-t/\tau)}.$$

Solution. We are given the *proper life-time of a μ-meson in its own frame of reference to* be $\tau = 2.6 \times 10^{-6}$ *sec.*

∴ Its *observed life-time in the laboratory frame of reference* is $\tau' = \gamma\tau$.

And, therefore, number of particles that survive up to time t to *reach the laboratory frame of reference* is $N_{(t)} = N_{(o)}e^{-t/\tau'} = N_{(o)}e^{-t/\gamma\tau}$.

Since 1% of the particle in the original burst survive to reach the earths' surface or the laboratory, we have $N_{(t)}/N_{(o)} = e^{-t/\gamma\tau} = 1/100$.

Taking logarithms, we have $\log_e{}^{-t/\gamma\tau} = -\log_e 100 = -2 \times 2.306$.

Or, $t = 4.6052\gamma\tau = 4.6052\tau\Big/\sqrt{1-v^2/c^2} = 4.6052 \times 2 \times 10^{-5}\Big/\sqrt{1-\left(\dfrac{0.99c}{c}\right)^2}$

Or, $t = 4.6052 \times 2 \times 10^{-5}\Big/\sqrt{1-(0.99)^2} = 4.6052 \times 2 \times 10^{-5}\Big/\sqrt{0.02} = 6.513 \times 10^{-5}$ *sec.*

∴ *estimated original height of the μ-mesons*, say,

$h = v \times t = 0.99 \times 3 \times 10^{10} \times 6.513 \times 10^{-5} = 1.934 \times 10^5 = 2 \times 10^5$ cm very nearly,

Example 27. Show from Lorentz transformation that two events simultaneous ($t_1 = t_2$) at different positions ($x_1 \neq x_2$) in a reference frame *S* are not, in general, simultaneous in another reference frame *S'*.

Solution. In accordance with *Inverse Lorentz transformation*, we have

$$t_1 = (t_1' + vx_1'/c^2) = t_2 = \gamma(t_2' + vx_2'/c^2) \qquad ...(i)$$

where v is the velocity of frame *S'* relative to *S* and t_1 and t_2', the corresponding values of t_1 and t_2, in frame *S'*.

In case of the two events are also simultaneous in frame *S'*, t_1' will be equal to t_2'. Let us see if this is so.

From relation (*i*) above, we have $t_1' = t_2' + \dfrac{v}{c^2}\left(x_2' - x_1'\right)$ ...(*ii*)

Now, in accordance with Lorentz transformation, $x_2' = \gamma(x_2 - vt_2)$ and $x_1' = \gamma(x_1 - vt_1)$. Therefore, $(x_2' - x_1') = \gamma(x_2 - vt_2) - \gamma(x_1 - vt_1)$.

Since $t_1 = t_2$, we have $(x_2' - x_1') = \gamma(x_2 - x_1)$.

Substituting this value of $(x_2' - x_1')$ in relation (*ii*) for t_1', above, we have

$$t_1' = t_2' + \frac{\gamma v}{c^2}(x_2 - x_1) \qquad ...(iii)$$

It is thus clear from relation (*iii*) that with $x_2 \neq x_1$, t_2' cannot be equal to t_1',

i.e., the two events cannot be simultaneous in frame S' also, unless of course, v/c = 0, when there are no relativistic effects at all.

Example 28. Determine the time (as measured by a clock at rest on rocket) taken by a rocket to reach a distant star and return to earth with a constant velocity $v = \sqrt{0.9996}\,c$ if the distance of the star is 4 light years. (A light year is defined as the distance travelled by a light beam in vacuum in one year).

Solution. Here, time taken by the rocket for the round trip, to the star and back, as measured by a clock on the earth, is, say, $t' = \dfrac{(4+4)c}{\sqrt{0.9999}\,c} = 8$ years.

If the time taken by the round trip, as measured on the clock carried by the rocket itself be t, clearly t is the *proper time*. So that, we have $t' = \gamma t$, whence,

$$t = t'/\gamma = t'\sqrt{1 - v^2/c^2}.$$

Since $v = \sqrt{0.9999}\,c$, we have $v/c = \sqrt{0.9999}$. Or, $v^2/c^2 = 0.9999$.

So that, $$t = 8\sqrt{1 - 0.9999} = 8\sqrt{0.001} = 8 \times 0.01 = 0.08 \text{ years.}$$

Thus the time for the round trip, as measured on the clock carried by the rocket itself is 0.08 years.

3.7.5 Transformation of Velocity—Velocity Addition

Suppose a particle has a velocity u in a frame of reference S at rest, such that its components along the three coordinate axes are $u_x = dx/dt$, $u_y = dy/dt$ and $u_z = dz/dt$ and its velocity in a frame of reference S', moving with a uniform velocity v relative to S along the positive direction of the x-axis, is u', with its components $u'_x = dx'/dt$, $u'_y = dy'/dt$, and $u'_z = dz'/dt$ along the three coordinate axes, as measured in S'. Let us see how these component velocities in the two frames of reference are related to each other.

As we know, in accordance with Lorentz transformation,

$x' = \gamma(x - vt)$, $y' = y$, $z' = z$ and $t' = \gamma(t - vx/c^2)$, where $\gamma = 1/\sqrt{1 - v^2/c^2}$.

So that, $$u'_x = \frac{dx'}{dt} = \frac{\gamma(dx - vdt)}{\gamma(dt - vdx/c^2)} = \frac{dx - vdt}{dt - vdx/c^2}$$

Dividing the numerator and the denominator on the right hand side of the equation by dt, we have

$$u'_x = \frac{dx'}{dt} = \frac{dx/dt - v}{1 - \dfrac{v}{c^2}.\dfrac{dx}{dt}}.$$

Or, substituting u_x for dx/dt, we have $u'_x = \dfrac{u_x - v}{1 - vu_x/c^2}$.

And, $$u'_y = \frac{dy'}{dt} = \frac{dy}{\gamma(dt - vdx/c^2)}.$$

Or, dividing the numerator and denominator on the right hand side of the equation by dt, as before, we have

$$u'_y = \frac{dy/dt}{\gamma\left(1 - \dfrac{v}{c^2}.\dfrac{dx}{dt}\right)} = \frac{u_y}{\gamma(1 - vu_x/c^2)}. \qquad \left[\because dy/dt = u_y \text{ and } dx/dt = u_x\right.$$

Similarly, $$u'_z = \frac{u_z}{\gamma(1 - vu_x/c^2)},$$

where u'_x, u'_y and u'_z are the components of the resultant velocity u' in frame S'.

In case velocity u is along the axis of x, its components u_y and u_z in frame S' and hence also u'_y and u'_z in frame S' are each equal to zero and we have

$$u' = \frac{u - v}{1 - uv/c^2}. \qquad \text{...}(i)$$

It will thus be seen that, as under Galilian transformation, so also here, *velocity is not invariant in the two frames of reference.*

By *inverse Lorentz transformation* (*i.e.*, replacing v by $-v$), we obtain

$$u_x = \frac{u'_x + v}{1 + vu'_x/c^2},\ u_y = \frac{u'_y}{\gamma(1 + vu'_x/c^2)} \text{ and } u_z = \frac{u'_z}{\gamma(1 + vu'_x/c^2)}.$$

Again, if the velocity of the particle, u', be directed along the x'-axis in frame S', its components u'_y and u'_z in frame S' and hence also u_y and u_z in frame S are each equal to *zero* and we have

$$u = \frac{u' + v}{1 + uv/c^2} \qquad ...(ii)$$

N.B. Quite often it is more convenient to measure and express high velocities as fractions of c rather than in cm or m/sec. So that, we divide the relations for u'_x and u_x, say, by c and put these in the form

$$\frac{u'_x}{c} = \frac{(u_x/c) - (v/c)}{1 - \frac{v}{c}\cdot\frac{u_x}{c}} \text{ and } \frac{u_x}{c} = \frac{(u'_x/c) + (v/c)}{1 + \frac{v}{c}\cdot\frac{u'_x}{c}}.$$

Other relations for u'_y, u'_z, u_y and u'_z may also be similarly expressed.

Now, the velocity u of the particle in frame S may be regarded as the resultant of its velocity u in frame S' and the velocity v of frame S' relative to S. So that, the expressions above give us a method for the addition of high or relativistic velocities (*i.e.*, velocities that approach the value of c) and constitute a **law for the addition of relativistic velocities.** Thus, from relation (*ii*) above, we may formally state the law as follows:

If a particle moves with velocity u' in a reference frame S' and if S' has a velocity v relative to a frame S, the velocity of the particle relative to S is given by $(u' + v)/(1 + u'v/c^2)$.

It may be noted that

(*i*) *If u'_x be very much less than c, so that $u'_x/c \to 0$, the above expressions all reduce to those obtained by Galilian transformation, i.e., $u_x = u'_x + v$, $u_y = u'_y$ and $u_z = u'_z$.*

(*ii*) *For higher values of u'_x, the denominator in the expression for u_x becomes greater than 1 and hence the resultant velocity u_x is smaller than $(u'_x + v)$, the value given by Galilian transformation.*

(*iii*) *If $u'_x = c$, i.e., if the velocity of the particle along the x'-axis in frame S' be equal to that of light* (*i.e., if the particle be a photon*), *we have* $u_x = \dfrac{c + v}{1 + vc/c^2} = \dfrac{c + v}{(c + v)/c} = c$, *i.e., the particle has the same velocity c in frame S.*

Thus, *this particular velocity c alone is invariant in the two frames of reference irrespective of their relative velocity v.*

But this result is only to be expected in view of the fact that *Lorentz transformation* itself has been obtained on the basic assumption of the constancy of the value of c in all reference frames, whatever their own velocities.

Incidentally, another interesting result that emerges in that, *under Lorentz transformation, no two velocities can add up to more than the value of c.* The same is not true under Galilian transformation. The following example will illustrate the point.

Suppose the relative velocity of S' with respect to S, along its x-axis, *i.e.*, $v = 3c/4$ and a particle in S moves along the $+x'$-direction with velocity $c/2$, *i.e.*, $u'_x = c/2$. Then, in accordance with Galilian transformation, the resultant velocity of the particle, relative to frame S will be

$$u_x = \frac{c}{2} + \frac{3c}{4} = \frac{5c}{4} = 1.25\ c, \text{ i.e., greater than } c.$$

But, under *Lorentz transformation,* it will be

$$\frac{u_x}{c} = \frac{(u'_x/c)+(v/c)}{1+\frac{v}{c}\cdot\frac{u'_x}{c}} = \frac{\left(\frac{1}{2}\right)+\left(\frac{3}{4}\right)}{1+\frac{3}{4}\cdot\frac{1}{2}}$$

$$= \frac{5}{4}\times\frac{8}{11} = \frac{10}{11}, \quad \text{whence, } u_x = \frac{10}{11}c\text{, i.e., less than } c.$$

Example 29. In the laboratory two particles are observed to travel in opposite directions with speed 2.8 × 10^10 cm/sec. Deduce the relative speed of the particles.

Solution. Let us call the two particles A and B, with the velocity of $A = +2.8 \times 10^{10}$ cm/sec and that of $B = -2.8 \times 10^{10}$ cm/sec along the axis of x.

Imagining particle B to be in a reference frame S at rest, the laboratory will constitute a reference frame S' in motion, with velocity $-(-2.8 \times 10^{10}) = 2.8 \times 10^{10}$ cm/sec. So that, *the velocity of the moving frame* S', *i.e.*, $v = -v_x = 2.8 \times 10^{10}$ cm/sec.

The problem thus reduces to determining the velocity of particle A in the moving frame S' of the laboratory as it would appear to an observer in the stationary reference frame S of particle B.

By *Inverse Lorentz transformation,* we have $u_x = \dfrac{u'_x + v}{1+\frac{v}{c^2}u'_x}$.

Here, velocity of particle A in the moving frame S' is $u'_x = 2.8 + 10^{10}$ cm/sec, its velocity in the stationary frame S' of particle B is u_x (to be determined), velocity of the moving frame S', *i.e.*, $v = -v_x$ and $c = 3 \times 10^{10}$ cm/sec.

Substituting these values in the expression of u_x above, we have

$$u_x = \frac{u'_x - v_x}{1-\frac{v_x}{c^2}u'_x} = \frac{2.8\times10^{10}+2.8\times10^{10}}{1-\left(\frac{-2.8\times10^{10}}{c^2}\right)(2.8\times10^{10})} = \frac{5.6\times10^{10}}{1+\left(\frac{2.8\times10^{10}}{3\times10^{10}}\right)^2}$$

$$= \frac{5.6\times10^{10}}{1+(2.8)^{2/9}} = \frac{5.6\times10^{10}}{1.8714} = 2.993\times10^{10} \text{ cm/sec.}$$

Thus, the relative velocity of the two particles is 2.993×10^{10} cm/sec.

Example 30. Show that if in the S' frame we have $v'_y = c \sin \phi$ and $v'_x = c \cos \phi$, in the frame S, $v_x^2 + v_y^2 = c$. Frame S' moves with velocity Vi with respect to the S frame.

Solution. Since frame S' is moving relative to S in the x-direction with velocity V, we have, by *Inverse Lorentz transformation.*

$$v_x = \frac{v'_x + V}{1+v'_x V/c^2}$$

and
$$v_y = \frac{v'_y}{\gamma(1+v'_x V/c)} = \frac{v_y}{(1+y'_x V/c^2)}\sqrt{1-v^2c^2}. \qquad \left[\because \gamma = \frac{1}{\sqrt{1-v^2/c^2}}\right]$$

∴ putting $v'_q = c\cos\phi$ and $v'_y = c\sin\phi$, we have

$$v_z^2 + v_y^2 = \left(\frac{c\cos\phi + V}{1+\frac{V\cos\phi}{c}}\right)^2 + \frac{(c^2\sin^2\phi)(1-V^2/c^2)}{1+\left(\frac{\gamma\cos\phi}{c}\right)^2}$$

$$= \frac{1}{1+\left(\frac{V\cos\phi}{c}\right)^2}(c^2\cos^2\phi + 2cV\cos\phi + V^2 + c^2\sin^2\phi - V^2\sin^2\phi)$$

$$= \frac{1}{\left(1+\frac{V\cos\phi}{c}\right)^2}[c^2 + 2cV\cos\phi + V^2(1-\sin^2\phi)]$$

$$= \frac{1}{\left(1+\frac{V\cos\phi}{c}\right)^2}(c^2 + 2cV\cos\phi + V^2\cos^2\phi)$$

$$= \frac{c^2}{\left(1+\frac{V\cos\phi}{c}\right)^2}\left(1+\frac{2V\cos\phi}{c}+\frac{V^2\cos^2\phi}{c^2}\right)$$

$$= \frac{c^2}{\left(1+\frac{V\cos\phi}{c}\right)^2}\left(1+\frac{V\cos\phi}{c}\right)^2 = c^2$$

or, $\quad v_x^2 + v_y^2 = c^2.$

Example 31. The velocity of a particle is $6\hat{i} + 5\hat{j} + 4\hat{k}$ in a frame of references S', moving with velocity 0.8 c along the axis of x, relative to a reference frame S at rest. What is the velocity of the particle in the latter frame?

Solution. Here, clearly, the velocity of the particle in the moving frame S' is $u' = 6\hat{i} + 5\hat{j} + 4\hat{k}$. So that, we have $u'_x = 6$ m/sec, $u'_y = 5$ m/sec and $u'_z = 4$ m/sec. and v, the velocity of frame S' relative to S is given to be $0.8\,c$, where

$$c = 3 \times 10^8 \text{ m/sec.}$$

Now, by *Inverse Lorentz transformation*, we have

$$u_x = \frac{u'_x + v}{1 + u'_x v/c^2} = \frac{6 + 0.8\,c}{1+\frac{6(0.8\,c)}{c^2}} = \frac{6+0.8\,c}{1+4.8/c} = \frac{c(6+0.8\,c)}{c+4.8}$$

$$\approx 0.8\,c = 0.8 \times 3 \times 10^8 = 2.4 \times 10^8 \text{ m/sec.}$$

$$u_y = \frac{u'_y}{\gamma\left(1+\frac{u'_x v}{c^2}\right)} = \frac{u'_y(1-y^2/c^2)}{1+\frac{u'_x v}{c^2}} = \frac{5\sqrt{1-(0.8)^2}}{1+\frac{6\times 0.8}{c}} = \frac{5\times 0.6\,c}{c+4.8}$$

$$= 3 \text{ m/sec.}$$

and
$$u_z = \frac{u_z}{\gamma\left(1+\frac{u'_z v}{c^2}\right)} = \frac{u_z(1-v^2/c^2)}{1+\frac{u'_x v}{c^2}} = \frac{4\sqrt{1-(0.8)^2}}{1+\frac{6\times 0.8}{c}} = \frac{4\times 0.6\,c}{c+4.8}$$

$$\approx 2.4 \text{ m/sec.}$$

$\therefore$ The velocity of the particle in frame S is $(2.4\times 10^8\hat{\text{i}} + 3\hat{\text{j}} + 2.4\hat{\text{k}})$ m/sec.

Example 32. Two velocities of 0.8*c* each are inclined to one another at an angle of 30°. Obtain the value of their resultant.

Solution. Here, we may imagine one of the velocities of 0.8*c* to be along the axis of *x* and the other inclined to it an angle of 30°. This is equivalent to saying that a frame of reference *S'*, say, is moving along its *x'*-axis with a velocity of 0.8*c* relative and parallel to a stationary frame *S* and a particle is moving with a velocity 0.8*c* inclined to it at an angle of 30°. it is then required to determine the resultant velocity of the particle as it would appear to an observer in frame *S*. So that, we have

velocity of frame S', relative to S, along the x'-axis = *v* = 0.8*c*,

and *velocity of the particle at an angle of 30° with its x'-axis (or the velocity v)* = *u'*.

Resolving *u'* along the *x'*-axis (or the velocity *v* of frame *S'*) and perpendicular to it, *i.e.*, along the *y'*-axis; we have

component along the y-axis, $u'_x = u' \cos 30° = 0.8\, c\,(\cos 30°)$

$$= 0.8(\sqrt{3/2}\, c) = 0.4\sqrt{3}\, c$$

and *component along the y'-axis*, $u'_y = u' \sin 30° = 0.8\text{ c}\,(\sin 30°)$

$$= 0.8\,(1/2)\, c = 0.4\sqrt{3}\, c.$$

Now, by *Lorentz transformation*, we have the values of these components, as observed in frame *S*, given by

$$u_x = \frac{u'_x + v}{1 + u'_x\, v/c^2} = \frac{0.4\sqrt{3}\, c + 0.8c}{1 + 0.4\sqrt{3}\, c(0.8c)/c^2} = \frac{c(0.4\sqrt{3} + 0.8)}{1 + 0.4\sqrt{3(0.8)}}$$

$$= \frac{c(0.4\sqrt{3} + 0.8)}{1 + 0.32\sqrt{3}} = \frac{1.493}{1.554}c = 0.96\, c.$$

and
$$u_y = \frac{u'_y}{\gamma(1 + u'_x\, v/c^2)} = \frac{u'_y\sqrt{1 - v^2/c^2}}{1 + u'_x\, v/c^2} = \frac{0.4c\sqrt{1 - (0.8\, c/c)^2}}{\frac{1 + 0.4\sqrt{3}c\,(0.8c)}{c^2}}$$

$$= \frac{0.4c\sqrt{1 - 0.64}}{1 + 0.32\sqrt{3}} = \frac{0.4c(0.6)}{1.554} = \frac{0.24}{1.554}c = 0.15c.$$

∴ resultant velocity *u* of the particle, as observed in frame $S = \sqrt{u_x^2 + u_y^2}$

$$= \sqrt{(0.96)^2 + (0.15)^2}\, c = \sqrt{0.9442}\ c = 0.97c$$

And the angle that this resultant velocity makes with the *x*-axis (or the direction of motion of frame *S'*) is, say, α, where $\tan \alpha = u_y/u_x$,

Or,
$$\alpha = \tan^{-1}(u_y/u_x) = \tan^{-1}\frac{0.15}{0.96} \text{ or } \tan^{-1}(0.1563) = 8°53'.$$

Example 33. A particle in a stationary frame *S* lies in the *X–Y* plane and has a velocity 0.8*c* inclined to 60° to the axis of *x*. What will be the velocity of the particle as observed by a person in a frame S' moving relative to *S* with a velocity 0.4*c* metres/sec?

Solution. Here obviously, velocity of frame *S'*, relative to *S*, along the axis of *x*, *i.e.*, *v* = 0.4*c*.

Component of velocity *u* (= 0.8*c*) of the particle along the *x*-axis, *i.e.*,

$$u_x = 0.8c \cos 60° = 0.8c\,(1/2) = 0.4c$$

and component of velocity u of the particle along the y-axis, *i.e.*,

$$u_x = 0.8c \sin 60° = 0.8c\,(\sqrt{3}/2 = 0.4\sqrt{3c}\,)$$

Now, by *Lorentz transformation*, we have the values of these components, as observed by a person in the moving frame S', given by

$$u_x' = \frac{u_z - v}{1 - u_x v/c^2} = \frac{0.4c - 0.4c}{1 - 0.4c(0.4c)/c^2} = 0$$

and

$$u_y' = \frac{u_y}{\gamma(1 - u_x v/c^2)} = \frac{0.4\sqrt{3c}\sqrt{1 - v^2/c^2}}{1 - 0.4c(0.4c)/c^2} = \frac{0.4\sqrt{3c}\sqrt{1-(0.4c)^2/c^2}}{1 - 0.16}$$

$$= \frac{0.4\sqrt{3}\sqrt{1-0.16}}{1-0.16}c = \frac{0.4\sqrt{3}\sqrt{0.84}}{0.84}c = 0.4\sqrt{3}/\sqrt{0.84} = 0.756c.$$

$\therefore$ resultant velocity u' as observed by a person in frame S' is given by

$$0i + 0.756\,cj = 0.756\,cj.$$

In other words, the particle will appear to the observer in frame S' to be moving with velocity $0.756c$ along the axis of y.

3.7.6 Relativistic Doppler Effect

We are already familiar with the *Doppler effect* in Sound, *viz.*, the apparent change in the frequency of sound due to motion of the source of sound and the listener relative to the medium. It bears the name of *Doppler* (an Austrian) who was the first to have worked out the theory in the case of sound waves in the year 1842*. He also called attention to the relevance of the phenomenon in the case of light.

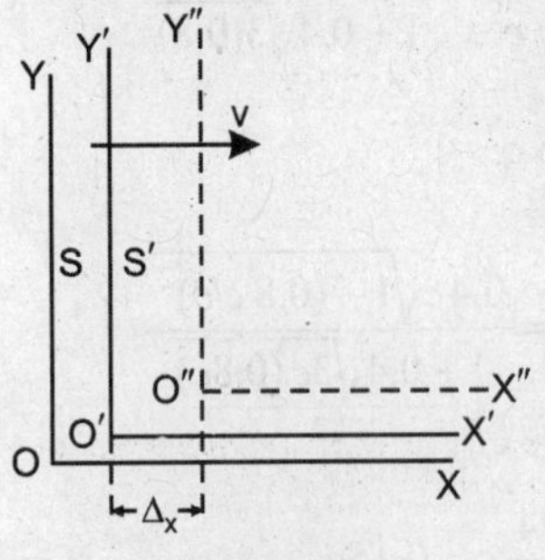

Fig. 3.10

The Doppler effect in light is, however, different from that in sound for the simple reason that, unlike sound, light requires no material medium for its propagation and hence its relative velocity is the same (c) for all observers regardless of their own state of motion. Then again, the velocity of light is so great that any apparent change in the frequency or the wavelength of a light pulse is appreciable only at relativistic speeds, *i.e.*, speeds near about c. Let us then proceed to discuss the case of light.

Imagine two reference frames S and S', where S is stationary and S' in relative motion with respect to S, with a constant velocity v along the axis of x, (Fig. 3.10).

Let two light signals or pulse be emitted from a source placed at the origin O in frame S at time $t = 0$ and $t = T$, where T is the *true time-period* of the light pulses. Suppose the interval between the reception of these pulses by an observer at the origin O' in frame S' is $\Delta t'$. Then, clearly, $\Delta t'$ is the *proper time interval* T' between the two pulses, as measured in frame S' (since they are both observed at the same point O' by an observer at rest with respect to S'). The observer will naturally interpret this interval as the time-period of the pulses received by him, *i.e.*, the apparent time-period of the pulses for the observer in frame S' will be T'.

Since the observer continues to be at O' all the time, the distance $\Delta x'$ covered by him in frame S' during the reception of the two pulses is *zero*. Let us obtain the values Δx and Δt in frame S which correspond to those of $\Delta x'$ and $\Delta t'$ in frame S'.

* It is interesting to recall that the theory was first tested in Holland, in the year 1845, by musically trained observers, who estimated by the car the apparent change in pitch (or frequency) as trumpeters rode ahead in a railroad flat car and again when the two exchanged their positions.

From Inverse Lorentz transformation equation $x = \frac{x' + vt'}{\sqrt{1 - v^2/c^2}}$

we have

$$\Delta x = \frac{\Delta x' + v\Delta t'}{\sqrt{1 - v^2/c^2}}, \text{ because the time-interval here is } \Delta t'.$$

Since $\Delta x' = 0$, we have $\Delta x = \frac{v\Delta t'}{\sqrt{1 - v^2/c^2}} = \frac{vT'}{\sqrt{1 - v^2/c^2}}$ $[\because \Delta t' = T'$.

Clearly, the second pulse has to cover this much distance more than the first pulse in frame S, along the axis of x, to be able to reach the observer at the origin O', in the moving frame S'.

Similarly, from the Inverse Lorentz transformation equation

$$t = \frac{t' + v_x'/c^2}{\sqrt{1 - v^2/c^2}}, \quad \text{we have} \quad \Delta t = \frac{\Delta t' + v\Delta x'/c^2}{\sqrt{1 - v^2/c^2}}$$

Or, since $\Delta x' = 0, \quad \Delta t = \frac{\Delta t'}{\sqrt{1 - v^2/c^2}} = \frac{T'}{\sqrt{1 - v^2/c^2}}$

This obviously includes both the actual time-period T of the pulses and the time taken $(\Delta x/c)$ by the second pulse to cover the extra distance Δx in frame S.

So that, $\Delta t = T + \Delta x/c$.

Substituting the values of Δt and Δx obtained above, we therefore have

$$\frac{T'}{\sqrt{1 - v^2/c^2}} = T + \frac{vT'}{c\sqrt{1 - v^2/c^2}},$$

whence, $T = \frac{T'}{\sqrt{1 - v^2/c^2}}\left(1 - \frac{v}{c}\right)$

If ν and ν′ be the *actual* and the *observed* (or *apparent*) frequencies of the light pulses respectively (*i.e.*, their frequencies in frames S and S'), we have $\nu = 1/T$ and $\nu' = 1/T'$. So that,

$$\frac{1}{\nu} = \frac{(1 - v/c)}{\nu - \sqrt{1 - v^2/c^2}}. \quad \text{Or,} \quad \nu' = \nu \frac{(1 - v/c)}{\sqrt{1 - v^2/c^2}}$$

$$= \nu \frac{(1 - v/c)}{\sqrt{(1 - v/c)(1 + v/c)}}$$

Or, $$\nu' = \nu\sqrt{\frac{1 - v/c}{1 + v/c}} = \nu\sqrt{\frac{1 - \beta}{1 + \beta}} \qquad \text{...I } [\because v/c = \beta].$$

This is known as *Doppler's formula* and gives the apparent frequency ν′ of the light pulses of actual frequency ν as observed in frame S'.

Since the velocity of light $c = \nu\lambda = \nu'\lambda'$, we have $\nu = c/\lambda$ and $\nu' = c/\lambda'$, where λ and λ′ are the *wavelengths* of the light pulses corresponding to frequencies ν and ν′ respectively. From relation I, therefore, we have

$$\frac{c}{\lambda'} = \frac{c}{\lambda}\sqrt{\frac{1 - v/c}{1 + v/c}} = \frac{c}{\lambda}\sqrt{\frac{1 - \beta}{1 + \beta}}. \quad \text{Or, } \lambda' = \lambda\sqrt{\frac{1 + v/c}{1 - v/c}} = \lambda\sqrt{\frac{1 + \beta}{1 - \beta}}, \qquad \text{...II}$$

which gives the *apparent* wavelength λ′ of the light pulses, of actual wavelength λ, as observed in frame S'.

In both relations I and II, v is positive or negative according as the observer is receding from, or approaching, the source of light; so that, in the former case, the apparent frequency of the pulse (ν') decreases and its apparent wavelength (λ') increases and in the latter case, the exact opposite happens, *i.e.*, the apparent frequency increases and the apparent wavelength decreases.

N.B. It will be readily seen that if we ignore the second and higher order terms in v and c, we obtain, from I above, the relation $\nu' = \nu(1 - v/c)$ for the apparent frequency. This is a case of *non-relativistic Doppler effect*, the same as in the case of sound.

Now, what we have discussed above is, in point of fact, the *longitudinal Doppler effect*. There is also a *transverse Doppler effect* in the case of light, though it has no non-relativistic counterpart in the case of sound. This effect relates to the frequency observed in a direction at right angles to that of the motion of the source, usually an atom. The apparent frequency is here given by $\nu' = \nu \sqrt{1-v^2/c^2}$, where ν is the actual frequency of the light pulse emitted by an atom in the frame of reference in which it is at rest and ν', the apparent frequency as noted in a frame of reference moving relative to it with velocity v.

Experimental confirmation of Doppler effect. The fact that there is indeed an apparent change in the frequency or the wavelength of light due to Doppler effect has been fully confirmed experimentally by *Ives* and *Stilwell* in the year 1941.

They measured spectroscopically the change of shift in the average wavelength of a particular spectral line emitted by the hydrogen atom. This they succeeded in doing by using a beam of hydrogen atoms in a highly excited state. With the help of a very strong electric field, they accelerated the atoms as molecular (H_2^+) ions and as H_3^+ *ions* to a velocity of about 0.005 c and then examined the spectrum of the atomic hydrogen, produced as a break-up product of these ions.

One particular line in the spectrum was closely studied and its wavelength obtained both in the foreward and backward direction, *i.e.*, in the direction of motion of the atoms as well as in the opposite direction – the former by receiving the spectrum directly on the slit of the spectrometer and the latter, by reflecting the spectrum on to the slit with the help of a plane mirror. Also, the wavelength of the same spectral line was obtained for such of the hydrogen atoms as were at rest, of which there will always be quite a few.

If the wavelength of the spectral line in question, for the hydrogen atoms at rest, be λ_o and its wavelengths in the forward and backward directions be respectively λ_F and λ_B, we have.

average (or mean) apparent wavelength of the displaced line,

$$\lambda_{av} = (\lambda_F + \lambda_B)/2.$$

So that, apparent change in the average wavelength of the line

$$= \lambda_{av} - \lambda_o = \frac{1}{2}(\lambda_F + \lambda_B)\lambda_o$$

But, as explained above, $\lambda_F = \lambda_o \sqrt{\dfrac{1-\beta}{1+\beta}}$ and $\lambda_B = \lambda_o \sqrt{\dfrac{1+\beta}{1-\beta}}$

$$\therefore \quad \lambda_{av} - \lambda_o = \frac{1}{2}\lambda_o\left(\sqrt{\frac{1-\beta}{1+\beta}} + \sqrt{\frac{1+\beta}{1+\beta}}\right) - \lambda_o = \frac{\lambda_o}{(1-\beta^2)^{1/2}} - \lambda_o$$

$$= \lambda_o\,(1-\beta^2)^{-\frac{1}{2}} - \lambda_o$$

$$= \lambda_o\left(1+\frac{1}{2}\beta^2+...\right) - \lambda_o = \frac{\lambda_o\beta^2}{2}, \text{ neglecting higher terms of } \beta.$$

Or,

$$\lambda_{av} - \lambda_o = \frac{\lambda_o v^2}{2c^2}.$$

Since, the shift in wavelength ($\lambda_{av} - \lambda_0$), here, depends upon v^2, it is quite independent of the sign of v, *i.e.*, is in the same direction, whether v is positive or negative.

As calculated by this relation, *Ives* and *Stilwell* obtained the value 0.072 Angstrom unit or 0.072×10^{-8} cm, whereas their observed value was found to be 0.074 *Angstrom unit* or 0.074×10^{8} cm.

The excellent agreement between the two values thus confirms the validity of relativistic Doppler effect, as expected.

The recessional red shift. Every element shows its own characteristic lines of definite wavelengths in its spectrum. The spectral lines of all known elements have, therefore, been carefully mapped out to enable us to see at a glance the position and wavelength of the spectral line or lines emitted by any given element.

Now, in the spectrum of the light received from distant stars and galaxies, the characteristic spectral lines of the various known elements present in them are all found to be shifted by various amounts from their normal positions towards the lower frequency or the high wavelength side, namely, the red end of the spectrum.

This shift is attributable to *Doppler effect*, according to which $\lambda' = \lambda\sqrt{(1+\beta)/(1-\beta)} = \lambda\sqrt{(1+v/c)/(1-v/c)}$; so that, for a positive value of velocity v of the source (*i.e.*, with the source receding from the observer), there is an apparent increase, and for a negative value of v (*i.e.*, with the source approaching the observer) there is an apparent decrease, in the wavelength of light received by the observer. In the former case, therefore, there is an apparent shift of the wavelength towards the red end, and in the latter case, towards the violet end of the spectrum. In fact, the velocity of recession or approach of the source may be easily determined from this shift in the wavelength of a spectral line.

The fact that light from the distant stars and galaxies shows this shift of the spectral line towards the red means that they are receding from us. Thus, since the shift of the spectral lines towards the red is due to the recession of the stars and galaxies from us on the earth, the phenomenon is called *recessional red shift* and lends strong support to the theory that the universe is expanding, with all bodies receding from one another. The Doppler effect has thus been instrumental in the detection, for the first time, of the apparent expansion of the universe.

On the basis of a large number of observations made on several galaxies, it is surmised that the relative velocity of a galaxy, at a distance r from us, is given by

$$V = \alpha r,$$

where α is an empirical constant, whose value is found to be near about 3×10^{-18} sec^{-1}.

Interestingly enough, *the reciprocal* of α, *i.e.*, $1/\alpha$, which has the dimensions of time and which is equal to $1/3 \times 10^{-18} = 3 \times 10^{17}$ sec $= 10^{10}$ years, is spoken of as the age of the universe and its product with c, *i.e.*, c/α, which has the dimensions of length or distance and which is equal to $3 \times 10^{17} \times 3 \times 10^{10}$ or 10^{28} years, is similarly spoken of as the *radius of the universe*, though no one yet seems to know for certain what the significance of these terms actually is.

Example 34. A motorist goes through a red light and, when challenged, claims that the colour he actually saw was green ($\lambda = 5.4 \times 10^{-7}$ m) and not red ($\lambda = 6.2 \times 10^{-7}$ m) because of the Doppler effect. What should have been his speed for his claim to be true?

We know that if λ' be the *apparent* or *observed wavelength* of light, λ, the *actual wavelength* and v, the relative speed of the observer with respect to the source of light, we have

$$\lambda' = \lambda\sqrt{\frac{1+\beta}{1-\beta}} = \lambda\sqrt{\frac{1+v/c}{1-v/c}}. \qquad \text{[See 3.7.6]}$$

Since the observer is here approaching the source of light, v is negative

We, therefore, have $$\lambda' = \lambda\sqrt{\frac{1-v/c}{1+v/c}}$$

Or, $\lambda'^2 = \lambda^2\left(\frac{1-v/c}{1+v/c}\right) = \lambda^2(1-v/c)(1+v/c)^{-1} = \lambda^2(1-v/c)^2$, neglecting higher powers of v/c.

Or, $\lambda' = \lambda(1-v/c)$. Or, $\lambda - \lambda' = \frac{v}{c}\lambda$.

Or, substituting the given values, we have

$$(6.2-5.4)\times 10^{-7} = \frac{v(6.2\times 10^{-7})}{3\times 10^8}. \quad \text{Or,} \quad 0.8\times 3\times 10^8 = 6.2v$$

whence, $$v = \frac{0.8\times 3\times 10^8}{6.2} = \frac{2.4}{6.2}\times 10^8 \text{ m/sec} = \frac{2.4\times 10^8}{6.2\times 1000} = 3871 \text{ km/sec.}$$

Thus, *for the absurd claim of the motorist to be true, his speed should have been* 3871 km/sec.

Example 35. Protons are accelerated through a potential of 20 kV, after which they drift with constant velocity through a region where neutralisation to H atoms and associated light emission takes place. The H emission (λ = 4860.33 *A* for an atom at rest) is observed in the spectrometer. The optical axis of the spectrometer is parallel to the motion of the ions. The spectrum is Doppler-shifted because of the motion of the ions in the direction of observed emission. The apparatus also contains a miror which is palced so as to allow superposition of the spectrum of light emitted in the reverse direction. (1*A* = 10^{-8} cm).

Calculate (*i*) the first order Doppler shift, depending on v/c appropriate to the forward and the backward directions and indicate the appearance of the relevant part of the spectrum on a diagram, (*ii*) the second order (*i.e.*, v^2/c^2) effect.

Solution. In plain and simple language, it simply means that as the high velocity protons get neutralised into hydrogen atoms, the characteristic H_β line of the hydrogen spectrum is emitted. Its position is noted in the spectrometer both when the ions are moving towards and (with the help of the mirror) away from the spectrometer. We are asked (*i*) to determinte the mean *Dopper shift*, using the first power alone of v/c and to represent it on a proper diagram and, (*ii*) to obtain the *Doppler shift* corresponding to the second power of v/c.

(*i*) We have the relation $\lambda' = \lambda\sqrt{\frac{1+\beta}{1-\beta}}$, where λ' is the *observed wavelength* and λ, the *actual wavelenth* emitted and $\beta = v/c$.

So that, $$\lambda' = \lambda(1+\beta)^{\frac{1}{2}}(1-\beta)^{-\frac{1}{2}} = \lambda\left(1+\frac{1}{2}\beta - \frac{1}{2}\beta^2 + ...\right)\left(1+\frac{1}{2}\beta+\frac{3}{2}\beta^2+...\right)$$

$$= \lambda\left(1+\frac{1}{2}\beta+\frac{3}{8}\beta^2+\frac{1}{2}\beta+\frac{1}{4}\beta^2-\frac{1}{3}\beta^2+...\right)$$

Or, $$\lambda' = \lambda\left(1+\beta+\frac{1}{2}\beta^2+...\right)$$

$\therefore$ restricting ourselves to only the first order terms in β, we have

$$\lambda' - \lambda = \lambda\beta = \lambda v/c.$$

Now, to obtain the value of v, we note that the protons have been accelerated through a potential of 20 *kV*. If $\therefore$ m_p be the mass of a proton and v, the velocity acquired by it, we have

$$\frac{1}{2}m_p v^2 = 20{,}000\ eV = 20{,}000\times 1.6\times 10^{-12}\ ergs, \text{ (because } 1\ eV = 1.60\times 10^{-12}\ ergs).$$

Since $m_p = 1.67\times 10^{-24}$ gm, we have $v^2 = \frac{2\times 20{,}000\times 1.6\times 10^{-12}}{1.67\times 10^{-24}}$

whence, $$v = \sqrt{\frac{2\times 20{,}000\times 1.6\times 10^{-12}}{1.67\times 10^{-24}}} = 1.957\times 10^8 = 2\times 10^8 \text{ cm/sec.}$$

When the ions are moving forward, towards the spectrometer, v is *negative*; so that,

for foward movement of the ions, $(\lambda' - \lambda) = \dfrac{-\lambda v}{c} = \dfrac{-4861.33 \times 2 \times 10^8}{3 \times 10^{10}} = -\,32.4$ A.

and *for backward movement of the ions, v being positive, we have*

$$(\lambda' - \lambda) = \frac{\lambda v}{c} = 32.4\ A.$$

Hence in *the first case* (*i.e.,* forward movement), *the wavelenth decreases to* 4861.33 – 32.4 = 4828.93 A and *in the latter case* (*i.e., backward movement*), the wavelength increases to 4861.33 + 32.4 = 4893.73 A. This may be represented diagrammatically, as shown in Fig. 3.10

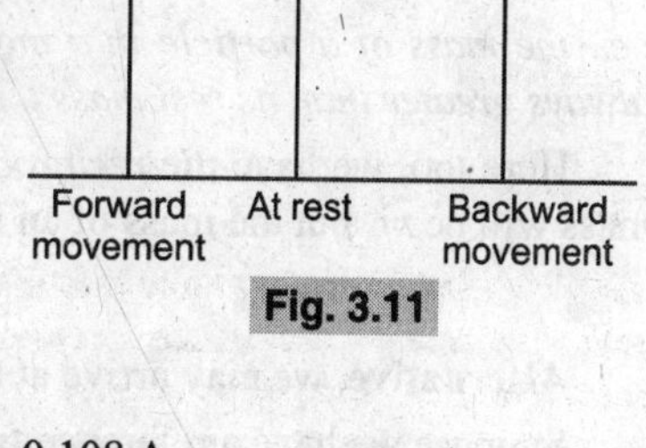

Fig. 3.11

(*ii*) In terms of the second power of β or v/c (or form 3.7.6) we have

$$\lambda' - \lambda = \frac{1}{2}\lambda\beta^2$$

$$= \frac{\frac{1}{2}(4861.33)\,(2 \times 10^8)^2}{(3 \times 10^{10})^2} = 0.108 \text{ A}.$$

Thus, *whether the movement of the ions be forward or backward, there will be an increase in the observed wavelength of the spectral line equal to* 0.108 *A* or $0.108 \times 10^8 = 1.08 \times 10^7$ cm.

3.7.7 The Relativity of Mass—Conservation of Mementum—Force.

The mass of a body too, like length (or space) and time, is dependent on the motion of the body. Its variation with velocity with velocity is, in fact, a direct consequence of the dilation of time, as will be clear from the following.

We know that for all inertial fremes, in relative motion along the axis of x, the displacements Δy and Δz of a particle along the axes of y and z respectively remain unaffected whatever the value of the relative velocity v of the moving reference frame with respect to the stationary one.

The time taken by the particle to traverse this displacement Δy, and hence also its velocity component along the y-axis will, however, depend upon the frame of reference in question (since neither time nor velocity is invariant to Lorentz transformation.)

But, again, the *proper time* $\Delta\tau$ (at noted on a clock carried by the moving frame itself) to cover the displacement Δy will, as we know, be the same in either reference frame, and so will, therefore, be the quantity $\Delta y/\Delta\tau$.

So that, if we take $\Delta y/\Delta\tau$ to be the velocity component of the particle along the axis of y in the moving frame and m_o, its *rest mass* of *proper mass, i.e.,* its mass as taken by an observer at rest with respect to it (*i.e.,* by the observer in the moving frame, in this case), we have *y-component of the momentum of the particle in the moving frame, i.e.,*

$$p_y = m_o \Delta y/d\tau.$$

Now, if Δt be the time taken to cover the displacement Δy, as noted on an identical clock by an observer in the stationary frame, we have by Lorentz transformation, $\Delta\tau = \Delta t\sqrt{1 - v^2/c^2}$, whence,

$$\Delta t/\Delta\tau = 1\Big/\sqrt{1 - v^2/c^2}$$

Thus, y-component of the velocity of the particle, as measured in the stationary frame, is $v_y = \Delta y/\Delta t$ and, therefore,

y-component of the momentum of the particle in the stationary fame = mv_y, where m is the *mass of the moving particle as taken by the observer in the stationary frame.*

Since, despite relativistic effects, the basic laws of physics in all frames of reference must have the same mathematical forms, *the low of conservation of momentum must hold good in either frame.* We, therefore, have

$$p_y = mv_y = m_o\frac{\Delta y}{\Delta\tau} = \frac{m_o\Delta y}{dt}\frac{dt}{d\tau} = m_o\frac{\Delta y}{dt}\frac{dt}{d\tau} = m_o v_y\frac{dt}{d\tau},$$

whence, $m = m_o dt/d\tau$.

or, substituting the value of $dt/d\tau$ from above, we have

$$m = \frac{m_o}{\sqrt{1 - v^2/c^2}}.$$

Since $\sqrt{1 - v^2/c^2}$ is always greater than, 1, $m > m_o$,

i.e., the mass of a particle in a moving frame, as taken by an observer in a stationary frame, is always greater than its rest mass.

Here too, we have the *reciprocity effect*; so that, for an observer moving with the particle, its mass will be m_o but the mass of an identical particle in the stationary frame will appear to be

$$m = m_o\Big/\sqrt{1 - v^2/c^2}.$$

Alternative, we may arrive at the same result as follows:

Suppose we have a reference frame Σ at rest (Fig. 3.12), in which two identical particles *A* and *B*, (two *protons,* say) are made to under go a symmetrical, glancing collision, moving with equal and opposite velocities, as shown in Fig. 3.12(*a*), such that a line (shown dotted) parallel to the *x* axis bisects the angle between their trajectories.

If the collision be a perfectly elastic one, the *x*-components of the velocities of the two particles remain the same respectively, in magnitude and direction, both before and after the collision and since the particles have equal masses, there is no change of momentum in the *x*-direction. Again, because their *y*-components, after collision are simply reversed in direction, their magnitude remaining unchanged, the change in momentum of particle *A* is equal and opposite to the change in momentum of particle *B* (their initial *y*-components being oppositely directly), so that *the change in momentum along the y-direction too is zero and the momentum of the system thus remains conserved* in accordance with Newtonian physics, under which the masses of the particles remain unaffected by their velocities.

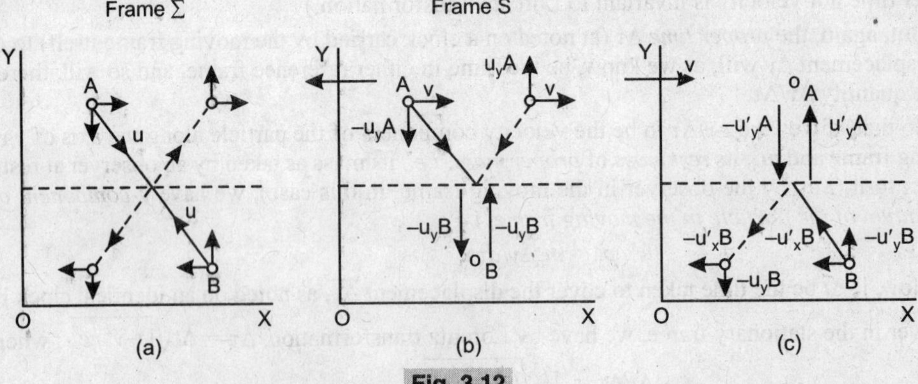

Fig. 3.12

Imagine now that we observe this collision from a frame of reference *S*, moving relative to the stationary frame Σ with a velocity *equal to the horizontal or the x-component of particle B*; so that *B* has now a vertical velocity u_yB, say, its horizontal or *x*-component having been reduced to zero. It, therefore, appears, to move up with velocity u_yB and bounce back after collision with particle *A*, with its velocity reversed, as shown in Fig. 3.12 (*b*). Particle *A*, however, has a horizontal component of velocity *v*, say, and a vertical component v_yA, the former remaining unchanged in magnitude and direction and the latter getting reversed in direction after collision.

Similarly, if we observe the collision from a frame *S'* moving with velocity *v* (equal to that of particle *A* in frame *S*), relative to frame *S*, we find that, instead of particle *B*, particle *A* now loses its horizontal or *x*-component of velocity and merely moves down with velocity $-u'_yA$, say, and bounces back after collision with particle *B*, with its velocity reversed, as shown in Fig. 3.12 (*c*).

In view of the initial symmetry of the glancing collision, the situations in frames *S* and *S'* also naturally symmetrical, with particles *A* and *B* interchanging their roles. We, therefore, have

$$u'_yA = u_yB. \qquad ...(i)$$

In accordance with Lorentz transformation,

$$u_yA = \frac{u'_yA}{\gamma(1 + vu'_xA/c^2)}, \qquad \text{[See 3.7.5]}$$

where u'_xA is the horizontal or x-component of *A* in frame *S'*, which is *zero*, in this case.

So that, $$u_yA = u'_yA/\gamma = u_yB/\gamma \qquad \text{[From relation I, above.}$$

Or, $$u_yA = u_yB/\gamma = u_yB\sqrt{1 - v^2/c^2} \qquad [\because \gamma = 1/\sqrt{1 - v^2/c^2}$$

showing that the vertical components of the velocities of particles A and B, which are equal in magnitude in the stationary frame Σ, are no longer so in the moving frame. S.

Considering the position in frame *S*, we find that the x-component of particle *A* remaining unchanged in magnitude and direction after collision, and particle *B* having *zero x*-component, *there is no change of momentum along the x-direction,* the only change thus occurring along the y-direction.

Clearly *change in the vertical velocity-component of particle A, on collision*

$$= u_yA - (-u_yA) = 2u_yA,$$

and change in the vertical velocity-component of particle *B*,

$$= -u_yB - u_yB = -2u_yB.$$

If, therefore, m_o be the mass of each particle (supposed invariant, in accordance with Newtonian physics), we have

change in momentum of the system $= 2m_ou_yA - 2m_ou_yB$,

which is obviously *not equal to zero*, since $u_yA \neq u_yB$, as we have seen above.

In order, therefore, that the low of conservation of momentum should hold, as it must, we must have the masses of particles *A* and *B* in the moving frame *S* different from their *Newtonian or rest masses* in the stationary frame Σ.

Let these be m_A and m_B respectively.

Then, for the law of conservation of momentum to hold, we must have

$$2m_Au_yA - 2m_Bu_yB = 0. \quad \text{Or,} \quad m_Au_yA = m_Bu_yB.$$

Or, Since $u_yA = u_yB/\gamma$ and, therefore, $u_yB = \gamma u_yA$, we have

Or, $$m_Au_y A = \gamma m_Bu_yA, \text{ whence, } m_A = \gamma m_B.$$

Or, $$m_A = \frac{m_B}{\sqrt{1 - v^2/c^2}}.$$

Now, if in frame *S* the vertical components u_yA and u_yB be small compared with the horizontal velocity-component *v* of particle *A*, we practically have particle *B* at rest particle *A* moving relative to it with velocity *v*. Taking the rest mass of particle, therefore, to be m_oB, we have

$$m_A = \frac{m_oB}{\sqrt{1 - v^2/c^2}}.$$

But, as we know, the two particle being *identical* in every respect, $m_oB = m_oA$, and, therefore,

$$m_A = \frac{m_o A}{\sqrt{1 - v^2/c^2}}.$$

or, representing the rest mass (or inertial mass) of a body, in general, by m_o and its mass (or, *relativistic mass*), when moving with velocity v, by m, we have

$$m = \frac{m_o}{\sqrt{1 - v^2/c^2}} = \gamma m_o,$$

which is the *mass-velocity relation of the Special theory of relativity,* indicating that *mass is no longer the absolute, invariant quantity of Classical physics but depends upon the velocity with which it is moving.*

As in the case of *length* and *time*, so also here, however, this relativistic effect in appreciable only at speeds somewhat comparable with that of light, *e.g.,* those of atomic particles. In case v is small, as it normally is, so that $v/c \to 0$, we have $m = m_o$, *i.e.,* the mass of the body is then the same as its rest mass, a result in accord with the Classical physics.

The first experimental confirmation of the relativity of mass came from *Bucherer*, in the year 1908, when he showed that the value of e/m (*ratio of charge to mass*) for fast moving electrons was smaller than for slower moving ones, due obviously to a higher value of m in the former case, the value of e being always invariant.

Again, to deflect high speed electrons in a synchroton, the magnetic field required is 2000 times as strong as the one that would serve the purpose on the basis of Newton's laws, indicating clearly that the mass of the electrons has, in the synchroton, increased to 2000 times their normal mass, or, in other words, an electron now has the mass of a proton!

The relativistic relationship for mass, together with those for length and time stand fully confirmed and accepted as important basic formulations in atomic physics.

It will be seen from the above discussion that Newton's law of conservation of momentum, $p = m_o v$, where m_o is the rest mass of the body, supposed invariant in all frames of reference, is not invariant to Lorentz transformation and cannot therefore, be acceptable as the correct law at relativistic velocities. What remains constant at these high velocities and is invariant to Lorentz transformation is $\gamma m_o v$ or $m_o v(1 - v^2/c^2)^{-1/2}$. So that, the relativistic law of conservation of momentum is

$$p = \gamma m_o v.$$

At non-relativistic velocities, $v/c \to 0$ and therefore, $\gamma = 1$, so that we have $p = m_o v$, the Newtonian law of conservation of momentum, *i.e.,* at smaller velocities compared with c, the relativistic law of conservation of momentum reduces to the newtonian law. The relativistic law is, therefore, accepted now as the *correct* law of conservation of momentum, invariant in all reference frames, the Newtonian law being a particular case of it.

For most of our ordinary purposes, however, $v << c$ and hence the Newtonian law is good enough. It is only when we deal with high speed particles, like *electrons, protons, mesons,* etc., that we have to invoke the help of the *relativistic* law.

If we were to plot the value of momentum p of a particle against velocity v, we should, according to the Newtonian or the Classical theory, obtain a straight line passing through the origin and the momentum should go on increasing with v even if v exceeds c, as shown by the dotted curve in Fig. 3.13.

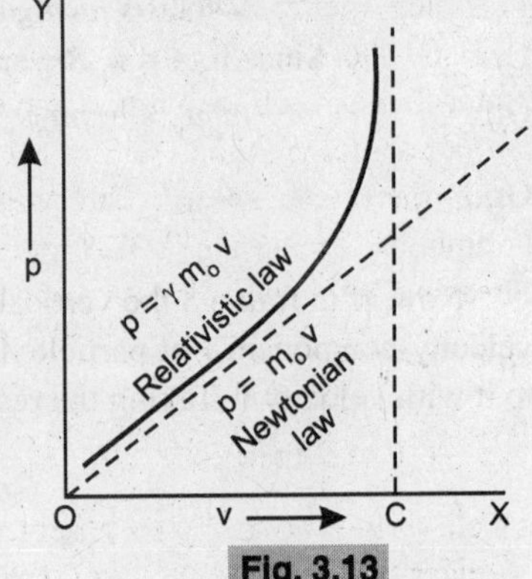

Fig. 3.13

On the other hand, if we plot p against v in accordance with the relativistic law of conservation of momentum, we obtain the full line curve shown, which shows that as $v \to c, p \to \infty$, because the mass then tends to infinity (see next article).

Force. In classical mechanics, as we know, force is defined as the *rate of change of momentum, i.e., $F = dp/dt$*. This applies equally well to relativistic mechanics. Since *mass* here means relativistic mass, the expression for force, in terms of acceleration works out to be different from the Classical expression $F = ma = mdv/dt$ *in the case of* **linear motion**, *For,*

$$F = dp/dt = \frac{d}{dt}(mv) = \frac{d}{dt}\left(\frac{m_o v}{\sqrt{1 - v^2/c^2}}\right) \quad ...(i)$$

Now, in this type of motion, *only the magnitude of the velocity changes and not its direction.* We may, therefore, put the above relation for force in the form

$$F = \frac{d}{dt}\left(\frac{m_o v}{(1 - v^2/c^2)^{1/2}}\right) = \frac{m_o (dv/dt)}{(1 - v^2/c^2)^{3/2}} \quad ...(ii)$$

Or, since $m_o/(1 - v^2/c^2)^{1/2} = m$, we have

$$F = \frac{m}{(1 - v^2/c^2)} \frac{dv}{dt},$$

where dv/dt is, obviously, the rate of change of velocity or the acceleration of the body.

This, it will readily be seen, is different from the Classical relation $F = ma = mdv/dt$.

In the case of **circular motion,** however, the direction of the velocity of the body changes continuously, its magnitude remaining constant. So that, expression *I* above takes the form

$$F = \frac{m_o}{\sqrt{1 - v^2/c^2}} \cdot \frac{dv}{dt} = mdv/dt,$$

where, as we know, dv/dt is the centripetal acceleration (v^2/r), normal to the circular path (of radius r) of the body.

$\therefore$ magnitude of the force is given by

$$F = \frac{m_o}{\sqrt{1 - v^2/c^2}} \cdot \frac{v^2}{r} = \frac{mv^2}{r}. \text{ Or, } F = ma,$$

the same relations as in the case of Classical mechanics.

Thus, in the case of circular motion, the Relativistics formula for force is identical with the Classical one ($F = ma$), if only we use relativistic mass m in place of the classical mass.

3.8 ULTIMATE SPEED OF A MATERIAL PARTICLE

In classical mechanics, there being no upper limit to velocity it is possible that as a particle is given more and more acceleration, its speed may go on increasing progressively and may well become greater than c, —in fact, it may have any velocity whatever. This is *firmly* denied by the theory of relativity. It may legitimately be asked, therefore, as to what will happen if the particle is continually accelerated. Certainly, its velocity v goes on increasing and hence also its *mass* in accordance with the mass-velocity relation $m = m_o\big/\sqrt{1 - v^2/c^2} = \gamma m_0$. But as v approaches c, $v^2/c^2 \to 1$ and therefore $\sqrt{1 - v^2/c^2} \to 0$ and the mass of the particle (m) $\to \infty$, as shown graphically in Fig. 3.14, from which it is clear that for velocities right up to $c/2$, the increase in mass

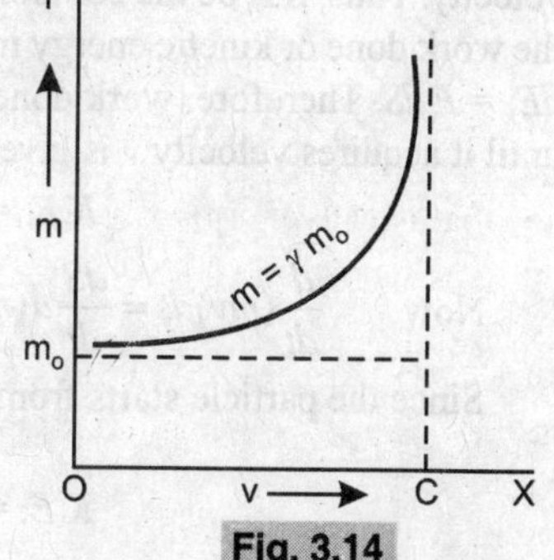

Fig. 3.14

from the value of the rest or inertial mass m_o is quite in-appreciable. Beyond this, however, the mass increases relatively more rapidly and tends *to become infinite as* $v \rightarrow c$. As will also be noted from the graph in Fig. 3.13 above, whereas momentum goes on increasing the velocity remains constant, indicating that the accelerating force applied only increases the mass and hence the momentum but not velocity.

The idea of infinity mass, however, makes no sense for a number of reasons. Thus, for example, (i) it would require an infinity force to accelerate the particle to the speed of light c, (ii) due to Lorentz-Fitzgerald contraction, its length in its direction of motion must be zero, (iii) its volume too must, therefore, be zero, and (iv) it must exert an infinite gravitational pull on all other bodies in the universe etc., etc.

So that, discarding the notion of an infinite mass, we interpret the above relationship to mean that *no material body can equal or exceed the speed of light in free space, viz.,* 3×10^{10} cm or 3×10^8 m/sec.

Now, it may perhaps be cited in apparent refutation of this statement, that a *photon*, in free space, travels with the free-space speed *c* of light. So, of course, it does, but then a photon is not a material particle since it possesses no rest mass. Also, there are, what are called phase velocities, which may even exceed the free-space speed *c* of light, but these are, again, no material particles but only abstract mathematical functions. Finally some of the atomic particles may travel in media like air, glass or water with velocities higher than that of light *in those media* but *by no means higher than its speed in free space.*

Thus, we come to the conclusion that *the ultimate speed for any material particle is the speed of light in free-space, which it can never attain or exceed.*

3.9 EQUIVALENCE OF MASS AND ENERGY

The correct way to state the second law of motion, in accordance with the Special theory of relativity, is to define force as the *time rate of change of momentum, i.e.,* as $F = \frac{d}{dt}(mv)$, since not only does it reduce to the classical second law of motion at low values of velocity but also, taken together with the third law, ensures the validity of the law of conservation of momentum in a closed system even under relativistic conditions.

This is obviously not the same definition as $F = ma$, since

$$\frac{d}{dt}(mv) = m\frac{dv}{dt} + v\frac{dm}{dt} = ma + v\frac{dm}{dt},$$

and $dm/dt \neq 0$ if v varies with time.

Now, in mechanics (Newtonian as well as Relativistic), the kinetic energy of a moving body at a given velocity v is equal to the work done in making the body move from rest and attain this velocity. Thus, if F be the component of the force applied to a body in the direction of displacement, the work done or kinetic energy imparted to the body when it is displaced through a distance dS, *i.e.,* $dE_k = F.dS$. Therefore, work done or kinetic energy imparted to it during the whole displacement S until it acquires velocity v is given by

$$K.E. = E_k = \int dE_k = \int_0^S F.ds = \int_0^S \frac{d}{dt}(mv)dS.$$

Now $$\frac{d}{dt}(mv)ds = \frac{dS}{dt}d(mv) = vd(mv) \qquad [\because dS/dt = v.]$$

Since the particle starts from rest (*i.e.,* $v = 0$) and finally acquires velocity v, we have

$$K.E. = E_k = \int_0^v vd(mv) = \int_0^v vd\left(\frac{m_o v}{\sqrt{1 - v^2/c^2}}\right) \qquad \left[\because m = \frac{m_o}{\sqrt{1 - v^2/c^2}}\right]$$

Integrating this by part*, we have

$$E_k = \frac{m_o v^2}{\sqrt{1-v^2/c^2}} - m_o \int_0^v \frac{v\,dv}{\sqrt{1-v^2/c^2}}$$

$$= \frac{m_o v^2}{\sqrt{1-v^2/c^2}} + m_o c^2 \left[\sqrt{1-v^2/c^2}\right]_0^v$$

Or,
$$E_k = -\frac{m_o c^2}{\sqrt{1-v^2/c^2}} - m_o c^2 = mc^2 - m_o c^2 = (m - m_o)c^2 = \Delta mc^2,$$

where Δm is the relativistic increase in mass with increase in velocity.

Thus, the K.E. of the body is the *product of the increase in its mass and* c^2.

Or, rewriting the equation, we have

$$mc^2 = m_o c^2 + E_k = \frac{m_o c^2}{\sqrt{1-v^2/c^2}} = \gamma m_o c^2. \quad ...(i)$$

Here, $m_o c^2$, the energy due to the rest mass of the body, *i.e.*, its energy when at rest with respect to the observer, is called its rest energy or proper energy E_o** and mc^2, the *total energy E* possessed by the body. So that, we have

total energy $E(= mc^2)$ = rest energy $(= m_o c^2)$ + *kinetic energy* $(E_k)\gamma = m_o c^2$.

This relation may also be obtained straight a way by Binomial expansion of the mass-velocity relation for values of $v/c \to 0$. Thus,

$$m = \frac{m_o}{(1 - v^2/c^2)^{1/2}} = m_o(1 - v^2/c^2)^{-1/2}$$

$$= m_o\left(1 + \frac{1}{2}\frac{v^2}{c^2} - ...\right). \text{ Or, } m = m_o + \frac{1}{2}m_o v^2/c^2, \quad ...(ii)$$

whence, $mc^2 = m_o c^2 + \frac{1}{2}mv^2$. Or, $mc^2 = m_o c^2 + E_k = \dfrac{m_o c^2}{\sqrt{1-v^2/c^2}} = \gamma m_o c^2$.

And ∴ therefore, kinetic energy is given by the relation,

$$E_k = (m - m_o)c^2 = \Delta mc^2.$$

This relativistic expression for *K.E.*, or this *mass-energy equation*, referred to as **Einstein's mass-energy relation**, is by far the most famous of the equations deduced by *Einstein* and stands fully verified and confirmed by experiment.

Box - IV

It will be easily seen that in view of the high value of c^2, *viz.*, 9×10^{20}, even a small amount of mass Δm is equivalent to a large large amount of energy. The change in the mass (Δm) in cases with which we are concerned in our every day life are, however, much too small for any energy effects to be visible. But, in the case of radioactive substances, for example, the enormous energy, thus produced by the conversion of mass, enables them to eject α and β particles with such high velocities and over such long periods. Or, again, the estimated decrease in the mass of the sun being 4×10^{12} gm/sec, it radiates out the energy equivalent of $4 \times 10^{12} \times 9 \times 10^{20} = 3.6 \times 10^{22}$ erg/sec.

---

* *i.e.*, $\int x\,dy = xy - \int y\,dx$.

**Thus the rest energy of 1 kg mass is equivalent to 9×10^{16} joules or 9×10^{22} ergs.

It will thus be noted that the classical expression $\frac{1}{2}mv^2$ for *K.E.* does give the true K.E. of the body even if we substitute the relativistic values of m and v in it.

On the other hand, the expression $E_k = mc^2 - m_oc^2$ reduces to the classical expression $E_k = \frac{1}{2}mv^2$ for values of $v << c$. For, we have

$$E_k = \frac{m_o}{\sqrt{1-v^2/c^2}} - m_oc^2 = m_oc^2\,(1 - v^2c^2)^{-1/2} - m_oc^2$$

$$= m_oc^2\left(1 + \frac{1}{2}\frac{v^2}{c^2} \ldots\ldots\right) - m_oc^2$$

$$= \frac{1}{2}m_ov^2, \quad \begin{cases}\text{The higher terms in } v/c \text{ being} \\ \text{neglible when } v/c << 1.\end{cases}$$

a result in conformity with classical physics.

We thus see that the relativistic expressions for length, *time, mass* and *energy,* all obey the same corresponding principle, *viz.,* that they get reduced to their classical forms for small values of v when $v/c \to 0$. This shows that the former are the really true expressions and the latter, merely approximations to them, valid only when v is small. Since, however, we seldom some across values of v comparable with c, except in atomic physics, the classical expressions, remain true enough for our manifold practical purposes.

Importance of mass-energy equations. It will be seen from relation (*ii*) above *viz.,* $m = m_o + \frac{1}{2}m_ov^2/c^2$, that the total inertial mass of a particle moving with velocity v relative to the observer, is the sum of (*i*) its *rest-mass* m_o, and (*ii*) *an additional mass* (or *inertia*) *equal to* E_k/c^2.

This suggests at once that the addition of energy to a system increases the inertial mass of the system. In plain and simple terms, it means that *mass may appear as energy and energy as mass*. So that, the scope of the law of conservation of energy may be widened into what may be called the *law of conservation of mass-energy*, meaning thereby that, *in any interaction, it is neither mass alone nor energy alone* that *remains conserved but mass, inclusive of energy in terms of mass, of energy inclusive of mass in terms of energy, that is really conserved.*

Here are some illustrative examples:

(*i*) When a *positron* (an elementary particle, having the same mass as an electron and a charge equal and opposite to it, *i.e.,* + *e*) and an *electron* come together, they *annihilate* one another and an equivalent amount of energy in the form of a pair of *γ-ray photons* (of energy at least 1.02 MeV) appears in their place.

The reverse of this phenomenon of annihilation of matter is that of pair production, where a *photon* of energy at least 1.02 *Mev* gives rise to a *pair of an electron and a positron* in the intense electric field near the nucleus of an atom. Here is what is called *materialisation of energy, i.e., conversion of energy into matter*.

Another example of pair production is the production of a *proton-antiproton pair*, requiring a minimum of energy 1.08 Giga *electron volts*.

The laws of conservation of momentum, mass-energy and of charge hold good in both these processes.

(*ii*) When a uranium nucleus is split up, the decrease in its total rest mass appears in the form of an equivalent amount of kinetic energy of its fragments. Thus, suppose it is split up into equal fragments, moving with velocity v, so that the mass of each is no longer its rest mass m_0 but, say m_v, which is greater than m_0. The sum of the masses of the two fragments is, therefore, $2\,m_v = M$, say, which is greater than their rest mass $2\,m_0$. The kinetic energy liberated by the splitting nucleus, or the energy due to conversion of $(M - 2\,m_0)$ of matter is thus $E_k = (M - 2\,m_0)c^2$.

As can be easily seen, it is thus possible to calculate the amount of energy that is released due to *fission* in an atomic bomb, since both M and m_0 are known. Distressingly enough, it was for jus suggesting this method of calculating the energy released by an atomic bomb that Eeinstein had been, unthinkingly and uncharitably, dubbed the world over as the 'father of the atomic bomb'.

(*iii*) In the process of *fusion* of nuclei, the total mass of the fusing nuclei is somewhat in excess of the nuclei produced as a result thereof, the difference being converted into energy in accordance with the mass-energy relation. In fact, such conversion of matter is the main source of energy of the sun and the stars, which obtain their enormous energy chiefly from what is called the '*burning*' *of protons into helium gas, i.e., the fusion of protons to form helium atoms*. The change in mass during the formation of one helium atom is given by

Δm = (*mass of 4 protons + mass of 2 electrons*) – (*mass of one helium atom*).

So that,
$$\Delta m = (4 \times 1.6725 \times 10^{-24} + 2 \times 0.911 \times 10^{-27}) - (6.647 \times 10^{-24})$$
$$\approx 0.045 \times 10^{-24} \text{ gm.}$$

Hence, *energy released per helium atom produced* $= \Delta mc^2$
$$= 0.045 \times 10^{-24} \times (3 \times 10^{10})^2 \approx 25 \text{ MeV} \qquad [\because 1 \text{ eV} = 1.6 \times 10^{12} \text{ ergs.}]$$

Again, when a number of particles, called nucleons, *i.e.*, protons and neutrons, combine to form a nucleus, there is a loss of mass Δm, *i.e.*, the mass of the nucleus is this much less than that of its constituent protons and neutrons. *The energy-equivalent of this mass-loss, i.e.,* $E = \Delta mc^2$ is called the **binding energy** of the nucleus.

It may be taken as a general rule that *an increase in mass means an increase in energy and vice versa*, though in most everyday cases, these changes in mass or energy are much too small to be discernable. Thus, a gas or a spring should, in accordance with the theory, record a greater mass in the compressed state, the increase in mass, obviously, being the work done to compress it divided by c^2. Similarly, a body when hot (and, therefore, with greater internal energy) should have a somewhat higher mass than when it is cold, and so on.

3.10 TRANSFORMATION OF RELATIVISTIC MOMENTUM AND ENERGY

Consider a particle of rest mass m_0, moving in a reference frame S. Its momentum in this frame is given by $\vec{P} = \gamma m_0\, d\vec{r}/dt$ and its energy by $E = \gamma m_0 c^2$, where $d\vec{r}/dt$ is its velocity.

As we know, an interval of time dt, as noted on a clock in the reference frame S is related to the *proper interval of time* $d\tau$, as noted on a clock carried by the particle itself, as $dt = d\tau/\sqrt{1 - v^2/c^2}$, whence $dt/d\tau = 1/\sqrt{1 - v^2/c^2} = \gamma$.

So that, if p_x, p_y and p_z be the components of the momentum of the particle along the three coordinate axes, we have

$$p_x = \gamma m_0 \frac{dx}{dt} = m_0 \frac{dx}{dt} \cdot \frac{dt}{d\tau} = m_0 \frac{dx}{d\tau} \text{ and, similarly, } p_y = m_0 \frac{dy}{d\tau}$$

$$p_z = m_0 \frac{dz}{d\tau} \quad \text{and} \quad E = m_0 c^2 \frac{dt}{d\tau} \text{ or } \frac{E}{c^2} = m_0 \frac{dt}{d\tau}.$$

Since both m_0 and τ_0 are Lorentz invariants, the quantities p_x, p_y and p_z get transformed in exactly the same manner as x, y, z and t in a reference from S', moving with velocity v relative to S along the axis of x. And, we therefore have

$$p_x' = \gamma(p_x - vE/c^2), p_y' = p_y, p_z' = p_z$$

and $$E'/c^2 = \gamma\left(\frac{E}{c^2} - \frac{v}{c^2}p_x\right) \quad \text{or} \quad E' = \gamma(E - vp_x)$$

The inverse Lorentz transformation will thus obviously be

$$p_x = \gamma(p_x' + vE'/c^2), p_y = p_y', p_z = p_z' \text{ and } E = \gamma(E' + vp_x').$$

3.11 CONSERVATION OF RELATIVISTIC ENERGY

The relativistic energy, as we know, is given by the relation $E = mc^2 = \gamma m_0 c^2$, where the value of m, equal to γm_0, has been deduced on the validity of the law of conservation of relativistic momentum. It follows, therefore, that relativistic energy too is subject to a law of conservation similar to that of momentum. Let us, however, deduce the law in a more direct manner as explained below.

Imagine a reference frame S in which two given particles, with momenta $\vec{p}_1$ and $\vec{p}_2$ and energies E_1 and E_2 respectively, undergo a collision. If their respective momenta after the collision be $\vec{p}_3$ and $\vec{p}_4$ and their energies E_3 and E_4, we have, in accordance with the law of conservation of momentum,

$$\vec{p}_1 + \vec{p}_2 = \vec{p}_3 + \vec{p}_4 .$$

Or, if we consider the x-components of their momenta only, we have

$$\vec{p}_{1x} + \vec{p}_{2x} = \vec{p}_{3x} + \vec{p}_{4x}$$

In another frame S' moving with velocity v relative to S along the *axis of x*, the components of the initial and final momenta of the particles along the x'-*axis* will respectively be $p_{1x}', p_{2x}', p_{3x}'$ and p_{4x}' and their energies before and after the collision will be E_1, E_2 and E_1', E_2'.

Since the law of conservation of momentum (being a Lorentz invariant) holds good in this frame too, we have $p_{1x}' + p_{2x}' = p_{3x} + p_{4x}'$

or, $\gamma(p_{1x} - vE_1/c^2) + \gamma(p_{2x} - vE_2/c^2) = \gamma(p_{3x} - vE_3/c^2) + \gamma(p_{4x} - vE_4/c^2).$

or, $$(p_{1x} + p_{2x}) - \frac{v}{c^2}.(E_1 + E_2) = (p_{3x} + p_{4x}) - \frac{v}{c^2}(E_3 + E_4).$$

Since, in accordance with the law of conservation of momentum,

$$(p_{1x} + p_{2x}) = (p_{3x} + p_{4x}),$$

we have $$E_1 + E_2 = E_3 + E_4,$$

i.e., the energy of the two particles is also conserved in frame S.

It may similarly be shown that $E_1' + E_2' = E_3' + E_4'$ or that *the energy of the two particles is also conserved in frame S'*.

What is true for two particles is also equally true for any number of them. We thus see that *the law of conservation of energy too, like the law of conservation of momentum, is a Lorentz invariant, i.e., holds good in all (inertial) frames of reference.*

3.12 RELATION BETWEEN RELATIVISTIC MOMENTUM AND ENERGY

A simple relation between relativistic momentum $(\vec{p})$ and relativistic energy (E) of a particle of rest mass m_0 is easily obtained from the expressions for $\vec{p}$ and E, *viz.*, $\vec{p} = \gamma m_0 \vec{v}$ and $E = \gamma m_0 c^2$. For, clearly, $\gamma m_0 = E/c^2$.

So that, $$\vec{p} = E\vec{v}/c^2,$$

which enables us to determine the velocity of the particle from the values of its momentum and energy, since, clearly, $\vec{v} = \vec{p}c^2/E$.

Another *important relation* between $\vec{p}$ and E may be obtained as follows:

Since $$p = \gamma m_0 v, \text{ we have } p^2 = \gamma^2 m_0^{\,2} v^3.$$

And since $\gamma = 1/\sqrt{1-v^2/c^2}$, we have $\gamma^2 = 1/(1-v^2/c^2) = c^2/(c^2-v^2)$,

whence, $$\gamma^2 v^2 = \gamma^2 c^2 - c^2.$$

Substituting this value of $\gamma^2 v^2$ in the expression for p^2 above, we obtain $p^2 = (\gamma^2 c^2 - c^2)m_0^2$, multiplying which by c^2 we get

$$p^2c^2 = m_0^2\gamma^2c^4 - m_0^2c^4. \quad \text{Or,} \quad m_0^2\gamma^2c^4 = p^2c^2 + m_0^2c^4.$$

Now $\gamma m_0 c^2 = E$, the total energy of the particle in question. So that,

$$E^2 = p^2c^2 + m_0^2c^4. \quad \text{Or, } E^2 - p^2c^2 = m_0^2c^4,$$

an expression connecting relativistic energy and momentum.

Since m_0 and c are both Lorentz invariants, $m_0^2c^4$ is a constant and therefore, the quantity $E^2 - p^2c^2$ too is a *Lorentz invariant* and its value remains unaltered in any inertial frame of reference.

3.13 MASS VELOCITY, MOMENTUM AND ENERGY OF PARTICLES OF ZERO REST MASS

We have just seen above that *the energy of a particle of rest mass m_0 and momentum p, is given by*

$$E = (p^2c^2 + m_0^2c^4)^{1/2}$$

If, therefore, we have a particle of rest mass zero, like a *photon* or a *nutrino*, *clearly* $m_0 = 0$ and $\therefore E = pc$, whence, $p = E/c$.

And since, as we have seen, p is also equal to Ev/c^2, we have

$$Ev/c^2 = E/c, \text{ whence, } v = c,$$

i.e., the velocity of a particle of zero rest mass is always c, the speed of light, and is, therefore, invariant and so is its rest mass (*zero*), *in all frames of reference.*

And, its energy is $$E = mc^2,$$
where m is the mass equivalent of energy E, equal to E/c^2.

To summarise then,

(*i*) *the mass of a particle of zero rest mass, i.e.,* $m = E/c^2$.

(*ii*) *its velocity is c, the same as the speed of light in free space*

(*iii*) *its momentum* $\vec{p} = mc = E/c$ and

(*iv*) *its energy* $E = mc^2 = pc$.

In case the particle be a *photon* of frequency ν, we have $E = h\nu$, where h is the well known *Planck's constant.*

So that, *for a photon, mass m* $= E/c^2 = h\nu/c^2$ and

momentum p $= E/c = h\nu/c$.

3.14 ATOMIC MASS UNIT

The basic mass unit used in atomic physics is called the *atomic mass unit* (*amu*, for short), which is $1/12^{th}$ of the rest mass of *carbon twelve* (C^{12}), *very nearly equal to the mass of a proton.* Thus, 1 *amu* $= 1.66 \times 10^{-27}$ kg.

Since, energy associated with a rest mass m_0 is $E = m_0c^2$, we have 1 *amu, in terms of energy*

$$= 1.66 \times 10^{-7} \text{ kg} \times (3 \times 10^8)^2 \text{ m}^2/\text{sec}^2 = 1.49 \times 10^{-10} \text{ joules.}$$

$$= 1.49 \times 10^{-10} \times 10^7 = 1.49 \times 10^{-3} \text{ ergs.}$$

And, since 1.60×10^{-19} *joules* = 1 eV (electron volt)*, we have

* It is the amount of energy gained by an electron moving through a potential difference of 1 volt.

$$1 \text{ amu} = \frac{1.49 \times 10^{-10}}{1.60 \times 10^{-19}} \text{ eV} = 9.31 \times 10^8 \text{ eV} = \frac{9.31 \times 10^8}{10^6}$$

$= 931$ *MeV* (mega electron volt)*.

Example 36. Find the velocity at which the mass of a particle is double its rest mass.

Solution. We have the relation $m = m_0/\sqrt{1 - v^2/c^2}$, where m_0 is the *rest mass* of a particle and *m, its mass at velocity v.*

Here, $m = 2m_0$. So that, $m_0/m = 1/2$.

Putting $v/c = \sin\theta$, we have $\sqrt{1 - v^2/c^2} = \sqrt{1 - \sin^2\theta} = \cos\theta$.

$\therefore$ $m_0/m = \cos\theta$ and we have $\cos\theta = 1/2$. Or, $\theta = \cos^{-1}(1/2) = 60°$.

$\therefore$ $\sin\theta = \sin 60° = \sqrt{3/2} = v/c$,

whence, $v = (\sqrt{3/2})c = (1.732/2)\,c = 0.866\,c = 0.866 \times 3 \times 10^8$

$= 2.598 \times 10^8$ m/sec.

Thus, *the velocity at which the mass of a particle will be double its rest mass is* 2.598×10^8 m/sec.

Example 37. A proton of rest mass 1.67×10^{-24} gm is moving with velocity 0.9 *c*. Find its mass and momentum.

Solution. We know that if m_0 be the *rest mass* of a particle, in this case, the *proton*, its mass at velocity *v* is given by

$$m = m_o/\sqrt{1 - v^2/c^2},\text{ whence, } m_0/m = \sqrt{1 - v^2/c^2}.$$

Putting $v/c = \sin\theta$, we have $\sin\theta = 0.9\,c/c = 0.9$, whence, $\theta = \sin^{-1}(0.9) = 64°9'$.

So that, $m_0/m = \sqrt{1 - \sin^2\theta} = \cos\theta = \cos 64°9' = 0.4360$

$\therefore$ $m = m_0/0.4360 = 1.67 \times 10^{-24}/0.4360 = 3.83 \times 10^{-24}$ gm.

Thus, the *mass of the proton at velocity* 0.9*c will be* 3.83×10^{-24} gm.

And $\therefore$ *momentum of the proton,* $p = mv = m \times 0.9\,c = 3.83 \times 10^{-24} \times 0.9 \times 3 \times 10^{10}$

$= 10.34 \times 10^{-14}$ gm – cm/sec.

Example 38. Calculate the speed of an electron which has kinetic energy 1.02 MeV.

Solution. Hence, we must first know the mass *m* of the electron at the final speed (*v*) acquired, before we can determine the latter by the relation $m = m_o/\sqrt{1 - v^2/c^2}$.

To determine this mass we note that the kinetic energy associated with a mass *m* is equal to mc^2.

If, therefore, Δm be the increase in the rest mass m_0 of the electron on acquiring its final speed *v*, we have Δm = (*K.E. acquired by the electron*)/c^2.

Clearly, *K.E.* acquired by the electron $= 1.02 \times 10^6$ eV $= 1.02 \times 10^6 \times 1.60 \times 10^{-19} = 1.632 \times 10^{-13}$ *joules.*

Since $c = 3 \times 10^8$ m/sec, we have $\Delta m = \dfrac{1.632 \times 10^{-13}}{(3 \times 10^8)^2} = 18.13 \times 10^{-31}$ kg.

$\therefore$ *mass of the electron on acquiring its final velocity v, i.e.,* $m = m_0 + \Delta m$

$= (9.11 + 18.13) \times 10^{-31} = 27.24 \times 10^{-21}$ kg.

---

* Strictly speaking, 1 *amu* = 931.441 MeV on the C^{12} isotope mass scale and equal to 931.441 MeV on the O^{16} scale.

Now, putting $v/c = \sin\theta$, we have $\sqrt{1 - v^2/c^2} = \sqrt{1 - \sin^2\theta} = \cos\theta$.

So that, $\quad m = m_0/\cos\theta.$

Or $\quad \cos\theta = m_0/m = 9.11 \times 10^{-31}/27.24 \times 10^{-31} = 0.3344.$

Or, $\quad \theta = \cos^{-1}(0.3344) = 70°28'$

and, $\quad \sin\theta = \sin 70°28' = 0.9425$

$$\therefore \quad \frac{v}{c} = 0.9425,$$

whence, $\quad v = 0.9425\,c = 0.9425 \times 3 \times 10^8 = 2.8275 \times 10^8$

$$\approx 2.83 \times 10^8 \text{ m/sec.}$$

Thus, *the velocity of the electron,* of *K.E.* 1.02 *MeV*, is 2.83×10^8 m/sec.

Example 39. Given a proton for which $\beta = 0.995$ measured in the laboratory. What are the corresponding relativistic energy and momentum?

Solution. The rest mass of a proton, *i.e.*, $m_0 = 1.67 \times 10^{-24}$ *gm* and $\beta = v/c = 0.995$ or $v = 0.995c$. Hence *its mass at velocity v is given by*

$$m = \frac{m_o}{\sqrt{1 - v^2/c^2}} = \frac{1.67 \times 10^{-24}}{\sqrt{1 - (0.995)^2}} \text{ gm.}$$

Hence, its *relativistic energy* $= mc^2 = \dfrac{1.67 \times 10^{-24}}{\sqrt{1 - (0.995)^2}} \times (3 \times 10^{10})^2$

$$= \frac{1.67 \times 9 \times 10^{-4}}{\sqrt{.01}} = 1.503 \times 10^{-2} \text{ ergs.}$$

Now, as we know, 1.60×10^{-12} *ergs* = 1 *eV*.

$$\therefore \textit{relativistic energy of the proton} = \frac{1.503 \times 10^{-2}}{1.60 \times 10^{-12}} = 9.39 \times 10^9 \; eV = 9.39 \text{ BeV}$$

$[\because 10^9\,eV = 1\,BeV]$

To determine the momentum (p) of the electron, we use the relation $E^2 - p^2c^2 = m_0{}^2c^4$, whence,

$pc = \sqrt{E^2 - m_o^2\,c^4}$ and $\therefore p = \sqrt{E^2 - m_o^2\,c^4}/c.$

Substituting the values of E, m_0 and c, we have

$$p = \frac{\sqrt{(1.803 \times 10^{-2})^2 - (1.67 \times 10^{-24})^2 (3 \times 10^{10})^4}}{3 \times 10^{10}} = \frac{\sqrt{2.235 \times 10^{-4}}}{3 \times 10^{10}}$$

$$= 4.983 \times 10^{-13} \text{ gm-cm/sec.}$$

Thus, *momentum of the proton* = 4.983×10^{-13} gm-cm/sec.

Example 40. (*i*) Calculate the amount of energy released when a neutron decays into a proton and an electron, (rest mass of neutron = 1.6747×10^{-24} gm) rest mass of proton = 1.6724×10^{-24} gm and rest mass of electron (or position) = 9.11×10^{-23} gm.

(*ii*) Deduce the minimum energy of a gamma ray photon (in MeV) which can cause elecron-position pair production. ($m_0 = 9.1 \times 10^{-23}$ gm)

Solution. (*i*) If Δm be the *dimunition* in mass during the decay of a *neutron* into a *proton* and an electron, we have *energy released* = Δmc^2.

Clearly, Δm = *mass of neutron – (mass of proton + mass of electron)*

$= 1.6747 \times 10^{-24} - (1.6724 \times 10^{-24} + 9.11 \times 10^{-28})$

$= (1.6747 - 1.6733) \times 10^{-24} = 0.0014 \times 10^{-24}$ gm.

$\therefore$ *energy released* $= 0.0014 \times 10^{-24} \times (3 \times 10^{10})^2 = 0.0126 \times 10^{-4}$ ergs.

Since 1.60×10^{-13} *ergs* = 1 eV, we have

energy released when a neutron decays into a proton and an electron

$$= \frac{0.0126 \times 10^{-4}}{1.60 \times 10^{-12}} = .007875 \times 10^8 = 7.875 \times 10^5\ eV \approx 0.79 \text{ MeV.}$$

(*ii*) Both the *electron* and the *positron* have the same *rest mass* $m_0 = 9.1 \times 10^{-28}$ *gm*. So that, an electron-positron pair production means the production of a mass $\Delta m = 2m_0 = 2(9.1 \times 10^{-28})$ gm

$\therefore$ *The minimum energy the γ-ray photon must possess for the production of this much mass* $= \Delta mc^2 = 2(9.1 \times 10^{-28})(3 \times 10^{10})^2 = 1.638 \times 10^{-6}$ *ergs.*

$$= \frac{1.638 \times 10^{-6}}{1.60 \times 10^{-12}} = 1.02 \times 10^{-6} \text{ eV.}$$

Thus, *the minimum energy required to produce an electron-positron pair*

$= 1.02 \times 10^6$ eV = 1.02 MeV.

Example 41.(*a*) Calculate the momentum of a photon whose energy is 1.00×10^{-12} erg. (*b*) An electron has β = 0.99. What is its kinetic energy?

Solution. (*a*) We know that the *momentum of a photon, p = E/c,* because the velocity of a photon is *c*.

So that, $$p = \frac{1.00 \times 10^{-12}}{3 \times 10^{10}} = 0.333 \times 10^{-22} = 3.33 \times 10^{-23} \text{ gm-cm/sec.}$$

Or, *the momentum of the photon* $= 3.33 \times 10^{-23}$ gm-cm/sec.

(*b*) *The kinetic energy of a particle,* K_E = *its total energy – its rest energy*

$= mc^2 - m_0c^2 = \gamma m_0 c^2 - m_0 c^2 = m_0 c^2(\gamma - 1).$

Now, m_0 *for an electron* $= 9.11 \times 10^{-28}$ gm, $c = 3 \times 10^{10}$ cm/sec.

and $\gamma = (1 - \beta^2)^{-1/2} = (1 - v^2/c^2)^{-1/2} = [1 - (0.99)^2]^{-1/2} = (1 - 0.98)^{-1/2}$

$= (0.02)^{-1/2} = 7.071.$

$\therefore$ *kinetic energy of the electron* $= 9.11 \times 10^{-28} \times (3 \times 10^{10})^2 (7.071 - 1)$

$= 9.71 \times 9 \times 10^{-8} \times 6.071 = 4.977 \times 10^{-6}$ ergs.

$= (4.977 \times 10^{-6})/(1.60 \times 10^{-12}) = 3.11 \times 10^5\ eV = 3.11$ MeV.

Example 42. (*i*) show that the momentum of a particle of rest mass m_o and kinetic energy K_E is given by the expression $p = \sqrt{\frac{K_E}{c^2} + 2m_o K_E}$.

(*ii*) A nucleus of mass *M* emits a gamma-ray quantum and recoils with velocity *r* << *c*. Find the wavelength of the gamma-ray quantum and its energy.

Solution. (*i*) We have the relation $E - p^2c^2 = m_o{}^2c^4$, whence, $E^2 = m_o{}^2c^4 + p^2c^2$.

or, $$E = (m_o^2c^4 + p^2c^2)^{\frac{1}{2}}$$

Also, we know that the *total energy E = rest energy + kinetic energy* $= m_oc^2 + k_E$.

Equating the two values of *E*, therefore, we have

$$(m_o^2c^4 + p^2c^2)^{\frac{1}{2}} = m_oc^2 + K_E.$$

Squaring both sides of the equation, we have

$$m_o^2c^4 + p^2c^2 = m_o^2c^4 + 2m_oc^4 + 2m_oc^2k_E + k_{E^2}. \text{ Or, } p^2c^2 = k_{E^2} + 2m_oc^2k_E,$$

whence, $p^2 = \dfrac{k_{E^2}}{c^2} + 2m_ok_E$ and,

$\therefore$ $p = \sqrt{\dfrac{k_{E^2}}{c^2}} + 2m_ok_E$, *the required relation*

(*ii*) Let the *momentum of the γ-ray quantum* (*or photon*) be *p*.

Then, since the momentum of the nucleus = $-Mv$, the negative sign indicating that *v* is the velocity of recoil (*i.e.*, *in the opposite direction* to that of the γ-ray quantum), we have

Total momentum $= p + (-Mv)$, which must obviously be equal to *zero*, since the initial momentum of the nucleus, before it emitted the γ-ray quantum, was *zero*.

We, therefore, have $p - Mv = 0$. Or, $p = Mv$.

$\therefore$ wavelength of the γ-ray quantum $= h/p = h/mV$.

And *its energy*, $E = hv = hc/\lambda = hc\,\dfrac{h}{Mv} = Mvc$.

Example 43. A nucleus of mass *m* emits a gamma-ray photon of frequency v_0. Show that the loss of internal energy suffered by the nucleus is not hv_0 but $hv_0\,(1 + hv_0/2mc^2)$.

Solution. Here, clearly, *energy imparted to the photon* $= hv_0$ *and, therefore, the momentum imparted to it,* $p = hv_0/c$, since the velocity of the photon is *c*.

The nucleus will naturally lose an equal amount of momentum and recoil with a velocity *v*, say, thereby losing an additional amount of energy $= \dfrac{1}{2}Mv^2$.

$\therefore$ *Total internal energy lost by the nucleus* $hv_o + \dfrac{1}{2}mv^2 = hv_o + \dfrac{(mv)^2}{2m}$.

Since *mv* is the loss of momentum of the nucleus, equal in magnitude to the gain in momentum *p* of the photon, equal to hv_0/c, we have

Total internal energy lost by the nucleus $= hv_o + \dfrac{p^3}{2m} = hv_o + \dfrac{(hv_o)^2}{2mc^2} = hv_o\left(1 + \dfrac{hv_o}{2mc^2}\right)$.

Example 44. The solar constant is the flux of solar energy per sq cm per sec at the distance of the earth from the sun. By measurement it is found that the value of the constant is 1.4×10^6 ergs/sec-cm². Show that

(*i*) the total energy generation of the sun is $\approx 4 \times 10^{33}$ ergs/sec; (*ii*) the average rate of energy generation per gm of matter on the sun is ≈ 2 ergs/gm-sec $\approx 6 \times 10^7$ ergs/gm-year; (*iii*) the energy equivalent of 1 gm of hydrogen burned to produce He^4 is $\approx 6 \times 10^{18}$ ergs and (*iv*) if the mass of the sun were one-third hydrogen and the nuclear burning process continued without change, the sun could continue to radiate at its present rate for 3×10^{10} years.

(Radius of the earth's orbit around the sun = 1.49×10^{13} cm; mass of the sun = 1.99×10^{33} gm; mass of a proton = 1.6725×10^{-24} gm; mass of an electron = 9.11×10^{-23} gm; mass of helium atom = 6.647×10^{-24} gm.

Solution. (*i*) If *E* be the *total energy* emitted by the sun *per second* and if *R* be the radius of the earth's orbit around the sun, we have *solar constant* $S = E/4\pi R^2 = 1.4 \times 10^6$ *erg*/sec-cm²(given), whence, $E = 4\pi R^2 S = 4\pi(1.49 \times 10^{13})^2\,(1.4 \times 10^6) = 4\pi \times (1.49)^2 \times 1.4 \times 10^{32} = 3.906 \times 10^{33}$ $\approx 4 \times 10^{33}$ ergs/sec.

Thus, the *total energy generation of the sun* $\approx 4 \times 10^{33}$ ergs/sec.

(*ii*) Clearly, total matter on the sun = mass of the sun = 1.99×10^{33} gm.

∴ *Average rate of energy generation per gm of matter on the sun*

$$= \frac{\text{total energy generated per sec}}{\text{mass of the sun}} = \frac{E}{m_s} = \frac{4 \times 10^{33}}{1.99 \times 10^{33}}$$

$$\approx 2 \text{ ergs/gm-sec.}$$

$$= 2 \times 3600 \times 24 \times 365 \approx 6 \times 10^7 \text{ ergs/gm-year.}$$

(*iii*) We know that 4 *protons* and 2 *electrons* constitute a helium atom. So that, *decrease in mass during the formation of a helium atom = mass of 4 protons + mass of 2 electrons-mass of a helium atom** = $4 \times 1.6725 \times 10^{-24} + 2 \times 9.11 \times 10^{-28} - 6.647 \times 10^{-24} \approx 0.045 \times 10^{-24}$ gm.

This is thus the loss of mass due to the burning of 4 protons or 4 atoms or $4 \times 1.6725 \times 10^{-24}$ gm of hydrogen to form a helium atom (because the mass of a hydrogen atom is practically the mass of its one-proton nucleus, the mass of the single revolving electron being relatively negligible).

∴ *Loss of mass due to burning of* 1 *gm of hydrogen* = $\dfrac{0.045 \times 10^{-24}}{4 \times 1.6725 \times 10^{-24}} \times 1 = 6.723 \times 10^{-3}$ gm.

And ∴ *Energy equivalent of* 1 *gm of hydrogen burned* = $6.723 \times 10^{-3}\ c^2$.

$$= 6 \times 723 \times 10^{-3} \times 9 \times 10^{20} = 6 \times 10^{18} \text{ ergs.}$$

(*iv*) If the mass of the sun were one-third hydrogen, we shall have *mass of hydrogen on the sun* $= \dfrac{1}{3}(\textit{mass of the sun}) = \dfrac{1}{3}(1.99 \times 10^{33}) = 0.667 \times 10^{33}$ gm.

As we have just seen under (*iii*) above, energy produced due to burning of 1 gm of hydrogen $= 6 \times 10^{18}$ ergs.

∴ Energy produced due to burning of the entire hydrogen on the sun

$$= 6 \times 10^8 \times 0.667 \times 10^{33} = 4 \times 10^{51} \text{ ergs.}$$

Now, the sun generates energy at the rate of 4×10^{33} ergs per sec.

∴ Time taken by the sun to generate the whole amount, *i.e.*, 4×10^{51} ergs *of energy* $= 4 \times 10^{51}/4 \times 10^{33} = 10^{18}$ sec $= 10^{18}/3600 \times 24 \times 365 = 3.17 \times 10^{10} \approx 3 \times 10^{10}$ years.

The sun will thus continue to radiate energy at its present rate for 3×10^{10} years.

Example 45. (*i*) The binding energy of an electron to the proton (*i.e.*, of hydrogen) is 13.6 eV. Find the loss of mass in the formation of 1 atom of hydrogen.

(*ii*) Calculate the binding energy of duetron.

(mass of proton (m_P) = 1.6725×10^{-24} gm, mass of neutron (m_N) = 1.6748×10^{-24} gm and mass of duetron (m_D) = 3.3433×10^{-24} gm.)

Solution. (*i*) We have *binding energy of hydrogen* = 13.6 *eV* = $13.6 \times 1.60 \times 10^{-12}$

$$\approx 22 \times 10^{-12} \text{ ergs.}$$

∴ *Loss of mass during formation of* 1 *atom of hydrogen = Binding energy/*c^2. [$\because E = mc^2$]

$$= 22 \times 10^{-12}/9 \times 10^{20} = 2.4 \times 10^{-23} \text{ gm.}$$

(*ii*) Here, *loss of mass on formation of duetron* is given by

$$\Delta m = m_P + m_N - m_D = (1.6725 + 1.6748) \times 10^{-24} - 3.3433 \times 10^{-24}$$

$$= 0.004 \times 10^{-24} \text{ gm.}$$

---

*The mass of the electrons has been taken on the left hand side of the relation to balance the mass of two electrons included in the mass of the helium atom.

$\therefore$ *Binding energy of duetron* $= \Delta mc^2 = 0.004 \times 10^{-24} \times (3 \times 10^{10})^2 = 0.225 \times 10^8$ eV

$$= \frac{0.225 \times 10^8}{10^8} = 2.25 \text{ MeV.}$$

EXERCISE

I–Michelson-Morley Experiment

1. Describe the Michelson-Morley experiment and explain the physical significance of the negative results. ***(Bombay, B.Sc. (Hons), Delhi, MSc., Kanpur, Nagpur 2010)***
2. Calculate the expected fringe shift in the Michelson-Morley experiment if the effective length of each path be 6 *meters*, velocity of the earth, 3×10^4 *m/sec* and the wavelength of the monochromatic light used, 5000 Angstrom units. **(Ans.** 0.24 fringe-width)
3. Write a brief account of the stationary ether hypothesis, explaining clearly why the medium ether was invented in the first place and discarded later.
4. The hypothetical speed of the earth through the ether is its orbital speed of 3×10^4 m/sec. If the light takes 3×10^{-7} sec to travel through the Mchelson-Morley apparatus in the direction parallel to this motion, how long will it take to travel through it in the direction perpendicular to this motion?

   (Ans. 3×10^{-7} **sec.)**
5. State the postulates of Einstein's special theory of relativity? ***(Nagpur 2010)***
6. Discuss the theory of the Michelson-Morley experiment for transmitted rays and reflected rays. Prove fringe shift = $2dv^2/\lambda c^2$ due to rotation of apparatus through 90°. ***(Nagpur 2010)***

II–Lorentz Coordinate Transformations

7. Explain the basic postulates of Einstein's special theory of relativity. Derive the Lorentz space-time transformation formulae. ***[Punjab, (supp), Agra]***
8. (*a*) A reference frame P' moves with respect to another frame P with a uniform velocity v. Write down the transformations giving x', y', z', t' in terms of x, y, z, t in Lorentz form. (The frames coincide at $t = 0$). ***(Agra)***

   (*b*) Show that for values of $v << c$, Lorentz transformation reduces to the Galilian one.
9. Show that the relativistic equations to transform space and time to system S from observations on system S' are $x = \gamma(x' + vt')$ and $t = \gamma(t' + vx'/c^2)$ respectively, where S' is moving relative to S with velocity v along the axis of x.
10. The interval S_{12} between two events is defined by the relation ${S_{12}}^2 = x^2 + y^2 + z^2 + w^2$, where $w = ict$, $i = \sqrt{-1}$. Show with the help of Lorentz transformation that S_{12} has the same value in all inertial frames, though distance and time may have different values.
11. Two events have the space-time coordinates (0, 0, 0, 0) and (4*c*, 0, 0, 3) in a given frame *S*. (*i*) What is the time-interval between them? (*ii*) Obtain the velocity of a frame in which (*a*) the two events occur simultaneously, and (*b*) the first event occurs two seconds earlier than the second.

    (Ans. (*i*) 2.645 *c*; (*ii*) (*a*) 0.75 *c*, (*b*) 0.93)

III–Length Contraction

12. What is meant by '*length contraction*' due to relativistic effect? Show that the length along the *x*-axis in frame *S* in contracted for an observer in frame S' and a length along the x'-axis in frame S' is contracted for an observer in frame *S*, where frame S' is moving with uniform velocity v with respect to *S* along the axis of *x*.

    What is meant by *proper length?*
13. The proper length of a rod is 5 *metres*. What would be its length for an observer if it be moving relative to him in a direction parallel to its own *length* (*i*) with velocity 0.8 *c*, (*ii*) with velocity *c*. (*iii*) And what would be its length for an observer who is himself moving along with it?

    (Ans. (*i*) 3 metres, (*ii*) 0, (*iii*) 5 meters)

14. How fast would a rocket ship have to go relative to an observer for its length to be contracted to 99% of its length when at rest? (**Ans.** 4.245×10^9 cm/sec.)

15. The length of the side of a square, as measured by an observer in a stationary frame of reference *S*, is *l*. What will be its apparent area, as observed by him in a reference frame *S'* moving relative to *S* wih velocity *v* along one of the sides of the square?

(**Ans.** $l^2\sqrt{1-v^2/c^2}$)

16. A frame of references is moving relative to a frame *S* with velocity $0.6\,c\hat{i}$. A vector in *S'* is represented by $5\hat{i}+8\hat{j}+4\hat{k}$. How may it be represented in frame *S*? (**Ans.** $4\hat{i}+8\hat{j}+4\hat{k}$)

17. A rod of true length 100 cm is moving with velocity 0.6 c in a direction making an angle of 30° with its length. What is the contraction produced in its length and along what direction does it appear to move? (**Ans.** 15 cm; *at an angle* $\theta = \tan^{-1}(0.72)$ *with the direction of velocity*.)

18. For suitably chosen axes in two Galilian frames *S* and *S'*, the complete Lorentz transformation is $x' = \gamma(x - vt)$, $y' = y$, $z' = z$ and $t = \gamma(t - vx/c^2)$, $\gamma = (1 - v^2/c^2)^{-1/2}$, where *v* is the relative velocity of *S* and *S'*.

A particle, as observed by an observer in *S'* describes a circle $x'^2 + y'^2 = a^2$, $z' = 0$, with constant speed. Show that to an observer in frame S, the particle appears to move in an ellipse whose centre moves with velocity *v*.

IV–Time Dilation

19. What do you understand by *time-dilation*? *What is proper interval* of time? Briefly discuss one experiment in support of time dilation in special relativity. [*Agra*, (*Supp*)]

20. On the basis of Lorentz transformation, discuss the following kinematic effects: (*a*) *Length contraction*, (*b*) *Time dilation*. **(*Punjab, Kanpur, B.Sc (Hons.), Delhi; Bombay*)**

21. State the basic postulates of the special theory of relativity and hence obtain Lorentz transformation. Discuss length contraction and time dilation.

(*B.Sc. (Hons), Delhi; M.Sc. Kanpur; Bombay; Punjab*)

22. How fast should a rocket ship move relative to an observer in order that one year on it may correspond to two years on the earth? (**Ans.** 2.598×10^{10} cm/sec.)

23. Show that if the time interval between two events occurring at the same place on the *S* Sysem be $\Delta t'$, then the time interval observed in the *S* system is $\Delta t = \gamma\Delta t'$. Is the time interval measured in S dilated or contracted with respect to that in *S'*? (**Ans.** Dilated)

24. An airplane sets out to fly at 500 miles per hour. Show that it would have to fly for more than a thousand years in order to make a difference 1/100 second between the times recorded by a clock in the airplane and a clock on the ground.

25. The half life of a particular particle, as measured in the laboratory, comes out to be 4×10^{-8} sec, when its speed is 0.8 *c* and 3×10^{-8} sec when is 0.6c. Explain this. (*Agra*)

(**Ans.** In either case, the proper half life of the particle works out to be the same *viz.*, 2.4×10^{-8} *sec, indicating that it has really a true or characteristic half life*, as measured by an observer moving along with it. It only appears different to a stationary observer at different speeds of the particle because of relativistic effec of time dilation. The faster it moves, the longer, or *more dilated*, appears to be its half life.)

26. The proper mean life-time of *pions* is 2.5×10^{-8} sec. At what velocity will they appear to have a mean life-time of 2.5×10^{-7} sec? (**Ans.** 0.995 *c*)

27. A group of muons, with a half-life of 1.5 μ sec. are produced at a height of 30 km above the surface of the earth. How long would it take the group, travelling vertically downwards, to reach the earth and what fraction of them would remain undecayed by then? (**Ans.** 100 μ sec.; practically zero.)

28. A burst of 10^4 π^+ mesons, whose proper mean life is 2.5×10^{-8} sec, cover a circular path of radius 20 metres at a speed of 0.99 *c*. (*a*) How many survive when the burst returns to the point of origin? (*b*) How many would be left in a burst that had remained at rest at the origin for the same period of time? (**Ans.** (*a*) 925; (*b*) None)

[**Hint.** (*a*) Time taken by π^+ mesons for one complete revolution in their circular path of radius $r = 20$ m or 2×10^5 cm, say $t' = 2\pi/\omega = 2\pi / \frac{v}{r} = 2\pi r/v = 2\pi \times 10^3/0.99c \approx 4.2 \times 10^{-7}$ sec.

$\therefore$ time taken for one complete revolution in their own frame of reference, say, $t = t'\gamma = t'\sqrt{1 - v^2/c^2}$

$$= 4.2 \times 10^{-7}\sqrt{1-(0.99c/c)^2} = 5.9 \times 10^{-8} \text{ sec.}$$

Now, number of π^+ mesons left after time t is given by

$$N_{(t)} = N_{(o)}e^{-t/\tau} \text{ where } \tau \text{ is their proper mean life} = 2.5 \times 10^8 \text{ sec.}$$

$$\therefore \quad N_{(t)} = 10^4 e^{-5.9\times10^{-8}/2.5\times10^8} \approx 925.$$

(*b*) Clearly, number of π^+ mesons left, in the same period of time, in the burst that had remained at rest at the origin (*i.e.*, in the laboratory itself) is given by

$$N_{(t)\text{lab}} = N_{(e)}e^{-t'/\tau} = 10^4 e^{-4.2\times10^{-7}/2.5\times10^{-9}} = 5 \times 10^{-9},$$

meaning, in other words, that none would be left.]

29. What is meant by time dilation? Derive expression for it. ***(Nagpur 2010)***

V–Velocity Transformation—Velocity Addition

30. State and deduce the mathematical expression for the law of addition of relativistic velocities. Show that in no case can the resultant velocity of a material particle be greater than *c*.

Also show that the Lorentz velocity transformation equations reduce to Galilian ones for values of $v \ll c$.

31. Two electrons move towards each other, the speed of each being 0.9*c* in a Galilian frame of reference. What is their speed relative to each other? (**Ans.** 0.994*c*)

32. In the laboratory, electrons from two accelerators are projected with the same speed of 2×10^8 m/sec but in opposite directions. What is the relative velocity of the two sets of electrons? (**Ans.** 2.77×10^8 m/sec)

33. The velocity of a particle in a reference frame *S*′, moving relative to a frame *S* with a velocity of 0.8*c* along the axis of *x*, is represented by 7i + 6j + 5k *m/sec*. What will be the velocity of the particle in frame *S*? (**Ans.** (2.4×10^8)i + 3.6j + 3k)

34. Obtain the resultant of two velocities of 0.6*c* and 0.8*c* respectively, inclined to one another at an angle of 60°. (**Ans.** 0.922c, at an angle of 29°15′ with velocity 0.6 c)

VI–Doppler Effect

35. How would you explain the existence of the Doppler effect on the basis of the special theory of relativity?

36. The wavelength 5000 *A* of a spectral line emanating from a distant star is observed in the laboratory to be 5200 *A*. Is the star approaching the earth or receding from it? Calculate its velocity of approach or recession, as the case may be.

(**Ans.** The star is receding from the earth with a velocity 1.2×10^8 cm/sec)

37. Calculate the recessional velocity of a galaxy at a distance of 3×10^9 light years. Is this velocity relativistic? (**Ans.** 8.515×10^9 cm/sec.; yes.)

[**Hint.** 1 light year = distance covered by light (in free space) in one year = $3 \times 10^{10} \times 3600 \times 24 \times 365$ cm. Therefore $r = 3 \times 10^9 \times 3 \times 10^{10} \times 3600 \times 24 \times 365$ cm.

Hence *velocity of recession of the galaxy*, $v = \alpha r$, where $\alpha = 3 \times 10^{-18}$ sec^{-1}.

VII–Relativity of Mass—Mass-Energy equivalence

38. Deduce the formula for relativistic variation of mass with velocity. Briefly explain its significance. ***(Punjab)***

Also show that the ultimate speed of a material particle is *c*.

39. (*a*) Derive the formula for the variation of the mass of a particle with velocity and describe an experiment for its verification. ***(B.Sc.(Hons), Delhi; M.Sc., Kanpur)***

(*b*) The electron beam in a television picture tube can move across the screen faster than the speed of light. Why does this not violate the special theory of relativity.

(**Ans.** Because nothing material moves across the screen)

40. (*a*) What speed must a body have for its mass to be (*i*) *three times*, (*ii*) *five times* its rest mass.

(**Ans.** (*i*) 2.828×10^8 m/sec; (*ii*) 2.94×10^8 m/sec.)

(*b*) Show that the rest mass of an electron (9.11×10^{-22} gm) is equivalent to 0.511 *MeV*.

41. What is the meaning of mass-energy equivalence? Obtain Einstein's mass-energy relation. Show that 1 *amu* = 931 *MeV*. ***(B.Sc. (Hons), Delhi, Nagpur 2010)***

42. Show that the expression $E_k = 1/2\ mv^2$ does not give the relativistic value of the kinetic energy of a body even if *m* represents its relativistic mass.

43. At what speed will a proton's mass exceed its rest mass (1.67×10^{-27} *kg*) by 1%? What kinetic energy in electron volts does this speed correspond to? (**Ans.** 4.2×10^7 m/sec; 9.3×10^6 eV)

44. Through what potential must (*i*) an electron, (*ii*) a proton be accelerated from rest in a vacuum so that its mass exceeds its rest mass by 1%? (Rest mass of electron = 9.11×10^{-28} *gm* and rest mass of proton = 1.6724×10^{-24} *gm*). (**Ans.** (*i*) 5.11×10^3 volts; 9.38×10^6 volts.)

45. (*a*) Write down the relativistic expression for kinetic energy of a body and show that for smaller speeds it reduces to the classical expression. ***(Agra)***

(*b*) The rest mass of a particle is 10 gm. What is its mass when it is moving with a velocity of 3×10^9 cm/sec? ***(Meerut)***

(**Ans.** 10.09 gm)

46. Write a note on Einstein's mass-energy relation. What is the principle of mass and energy equivalence? Explain it by giving examples. ***(Meerut)***

47. How much energy (in joules) will be produced on complete combustion of 1 *gm*. of U^{235}_{32}, taking that 1% of mass is converted into energy? (*Punjab*) (**Ans.** 9×10^{10} joules)

48. (*a*) Dynamite liberates 1.3×10^3 k.cal/kg when it explodes. What percentage of the total energy content is this? (**Ans.** 6.05×10^{-8}%)

(*b*) How much mass is lost by 1 kg of water at 0°C when it turns to ice at 0°C?

(**Ans.** 3.7×10^{-12} kg)

49. What change in mass is associated, in a chemical reaction with the (*a*) *absorption* (*b*) *release*, of 1 eV of energy? (**Ans.** (*a*) *Increase of* 0.18×10^{-32} gm, (*b*) *Decrease of* 0.18×10^{-32} gm)

50. An electron and a positron which have negligible velocities combine to produce two-photon annihilation radiation. (*a*) What is the energy of each photon? (*b*) What will be the relative direction of motion of these photons? Explain.

(**Ans.** (*a*) 0.511 MeV; *opposite each other or at an angle of* 180° *with each other*)

[**Hint.** Here, the total mass of the electron and the positron is converted into energy which appears in the form of a *pair of photons* (and *not one single photon*), each with half the total energy and moving in opposite directions, because *the initial momentum being zero, the final momentum too must be zero.* This can happen only when the two photons move with equal velocities (*c*) in opposite directions.]

51. Calculate the wavelength of the radiation emitted by the annihilation of an electron with a positron, each of rest mass 9.1×10^{-28} *gm*. ***[Punjab (Supp)]***

(**Ans.** 0.024×10^{-8} cm or 0.024 A)

[**Hint.** Since the total mass of the electron and the positron is converted into a pair of photons, each with half the total energy, we have $m_0c^2 + m_0c^2 = h\nu$, where γ is the frequency of the radiation emitted and *h*, the *Planck's constant*. Or, because $c = \nu\lambda$, where λ is the wavelength of the emitted radiation, we have $2\ m_0c^2 = 2hc/\lambda$, whence, $\lambda = hc/m_oc^2 = h/m_0c$.]

52. Show that the second law of motion can be expressed in terms of the rest mass and speed of a particle, being acted upon by a force, as

$$F = m_0(dv/dt)/(1 - v^2/c^2)^{3/2}.$$

53. An electron travelling with a speed of 2.70×10^8 *m/sec* experiences a force of 2.64×10^{-10} *dyne*. Deduce the acceleration. ***[Agra (Supp)]***

(**Ans.** If the electron be in *linear motion*, $a = 2.42 \times 10^{16}$ cm/sec^2 and if the electron be in *circular motion*, $a = 1/.27 \times 10^{17}$ cm/sec^2.)

54. (*a*) What is the recoil momentum in the laboratory of an Fe^{57} nucleus recoiling due to the emission of a 14 keV photon?

(*b*) What is the mass equivalent of the energy from an antenna radiating 1000 watts of radio energy for 24 hours? (1 *watt* = 10^7 *ergs*/sec) (**Ans.** (*a*) 7.5×10^{-9} gm cm/sec; (*b*) 9.6×10^{-7} gm)

55. A proton has a velocity equal to 0.999*c* in the laboratory. Find the energy and momentum as observed in a frame travelling in the same direction with velocity 0.990*c* with respect to the laboratory.

(**Ans.** 1.6 BeV; 1.3 BeV/c)

[**Hint.** Using Lorentz transformation, we first obtain the velocity of the proton in the moving frame, then use the relation $(E = m_p c^2)/\sqrt{1 - v^2/c^2}$ to obtain the energy of the proton in the moving frame (where $m_p = 1.6725 \times 10^{-24}$ *gm*) and hence its momentum by the relation $pc = (E^2 - m_p c^4)^{1/2}$].

56. Two particles, with proper masses m_1, m_2 move along the axis *OX* of a Galilian frame with velocities u_1 and u_2 respectively. They collide and coalesce to form a single particle. Assuming the laws of conservation of relativistic momentum and energy, prove that the proper mass m_3 and velocity u_3 of the resulting single particle are given by

$$m_3^2 = m_1^2 + m_2^2 + 2m_1 m_2 \gamma_1 \gamma_2 (1 - u_1 u_2 / c_2) \text{ and}$$

$$u_3 = (m_1 \gamma_1 u_1 + m_2 \gamma_2 u_2)/(m_1 \gamma_1 + m_2 \gamma_3),$$

where $\gamma_1^{-2} = 1 - u_1^2/c^2$ and $\gamma_2^{-2} = 1 - u_2^2/c^2$.

57. The fissioning of an atom of uranium – 235 releases 200 MeV of energy. What percent is this fission energy of the total which would have been available if all the mass of the uranium atom had appeared as energy? (**Ans.** 0.091%)

58. Write short explanatory notes from the relativistic stand stand point, on (*i*) *Mass-Energy equivalence*, (*ii*) *Ultimate speed of a material particle*, (*iii*) *Binding energy*, (*iv*) *Pair Production*, (*v*) Electron-positron annihilation.

59. A body of rest mass 100 kg changes its mass by 1 kg in a rocket ship. Calculate the speed of Rocket. ***(Nagpur U. 2010)***

60. Calculate the *K.E.* of an electron moving with a velocity of 0.98 times the velocity of light in the laboratory system. (**Ans.** 3.296×10^{-13} J)

[**Hint.** *K.E.* is $T = (m - m_0)c^2$]

4 Chapter NON-RELATIVISTIC PARTICLE DYNAMICS

Brief Contents

4.1 INTRODUCTION

According to Einstein, "The purpose of mechanics is to describe how bodies change their position in space with time" Dynamics is the study of motion of bodies and the relationship of this motion with the force producing it. It is thus an important branch of mechanics and starts with the simplest of bodies, *viz.*, particles, where particle means a quantity of matter having negligible dimensions.

Classical or Newtonian Mechanics

In dynamics, since the time of Newton, the calculations has been based on '*Newtons laws of motion*' in which we use *invariance of space* and time as well as *mass*. In other words, the assumption that the distance between two points, the interval between two events in space and the mass of a body at any point in space are *the same for all observers, irrespective of their state of rest or motion*. This system is referred as *classical* or *Newtonian mechanics*. This invariance of space, time and mass was straight way accepted and hence enjoyed complete sway right up to the end of 19th century and no doubts were raised or questions asked as to its validity and accuracy.

Relativistic or Einsteinian Mechanics

However, the concepts have been completely changed due to Einstein's revolutionary theory popularly known as '*Special theory of relativity*'. This was the year 1905, the new era in science and technology, from which the *direction of thinking* has turned. Einstein (1879-1955) in this theory catagorically stated that the speed of light (c) is constant irrespective of any relative motion between the source of light and the observer. In addition to this postulate of constancy of speed of light (c), he denied the Newton's invariance of both space and times. According to Einstein, the mass (m) of a body increases with its velocity and is γ times its *rest mass* (m_0) at velocity v, where $\gamma = 1/\sqrt{1-(v^2/c^2)}$. The Newtonian mass or momentum of a fast moving body must be multiplied by the factor γ to obtain its correct (relativistic) mass or momentum at its given speed. The system of calculations dealing with bodies moving with high velocities, approaching λ, thus came to be known as the Relativistic or Einsteinian mechanics.

Quantum or Wave Mechanics

Again, in the year 1924, the French Physicist, *Louis de Broglie*, put forward the view that 'light behaves like a wave on a macroscopic scale and as a particle (*viz.* a *photon*) on the *microscopic scale* (*i.e.*, in the absorption or emission of light). This is known as wave-matter *dual nature*, *i.e.* light behaves as corpuscles or particles as well as *waves*.

This is applicable to small and moving particles like electrons, protons, atoms, molecules and all fundamental particles, in general as well as to photons. They exhibit a similar duality of nature in the reverse sense, *i.e.*, behave as corpuscles or particles on a macroscopic scale and as waves on a microscopic scale, with a frequency and a wavelength, called *de Broglie wavelength* associated with them – this wavelength being given by $\lambda = h/mc$ for a photon (its velocity being c) and $\lambda = h/mv$ for a particle, in general, where h is the well known Plank's constant, equal to 6.62×10^{-27} erg-sec. or 6.62×10^{-34} J-sec.

Thus, with the wave-like nature of tiny particles, their behaviour cannot possibly be predicted by means of either the Classical or the Relativistic mechanics. Indeed, *Werner Heinsberg* enunciated in the year 1927 his famous **principle of uncertainty**, according to which *the position and the momentum of a particle cannot both be measured simultaneously with an equal degree of accuracy*, meaning thereby that if the position of the particle be measured accurately, the inaccuracy in the measurement of its momentum increases correspondingly and vice versa, such that *the product of the uncertainty Δr in the position of the particle at any given instant and the uncertainty Δp in its momentum at the same instant is equal, or greater than, the Plank's constant h, i.e.,*

$$\Delta r \, \Delta p \geq h?, \qquad \text{[where } h = 6.62 \times 10^{-27} \text{ erg-sec.]}$$

This uncertainty is by no means due to any want of perfection in the measuring instruments or the experiment but is *inherent* in the very nature of things,—the measurement of one (position or momentum) disturbing the other by an unknown amount.

This strange behaviour of matter on the atomic scale lies in the domain of *Quantum mechanics* (or *wave mechanics*), due to painstaking mathematical investigations of *Schrodinger*, *Heinsberg*, *Bohr* and *Dirac*, the contribution of *Dirac* being, in main, the incorporation into it of the relativistic effects in conformity with the Special Theory of Relativity.

On account of the very small value of h, however, the uncertainty in the measurement of position and momentum of a particle is appreciable only if it be of atomic size and is quite negligible for larger particles. So that, in the case of relatively larger bodies, quantum mechanics too gets reduced, for all intents and purposes, to classical mechanics.

Thus, except in the case of bodies moving very fast ($v \to c$) or having extremely small or atomic size, the classical mechanics gives results quite in conformity with experimental facts. And, since in everyday life we mostly come across bodies of relatively large size, moving with speeds far less than that of light (c), we shall concern ourselves, in general, with only the classical mechanics except in cases where it happens to be patently inapplicable.

I – DYNAMICS OF UNCHARGED PARTICLES

4.2 EQUATIONS OF MOTION OF AN UNCHARGED PARTICLE

As mentioned already, the classical mechanics is based on Newton's law of motion and the invariance of space, time and mass. So that, starting with the 2nd law, which is the *law* of motion including, as it does, both the first and the third laws, we have

force equal to rate of change of momentum, i.e.

$$F = \frac{d\vec{p}}{dt} = \frac{d}{dt}(m\vec{v}) \qquad \left[\because \vec{p} = m\vec{v}\right.$$

Since mass remains constant, we have $\vec{F} = m\frac{d\vec{v}}{dt} = m\frac{d^2\vec{r}}{dt^2} = m\vec{a}$ ...(A)

where $d\vec{v}/dt = d^2\vec{r}/dt = \vec{a}$ the acceleration of the particle.

(*i*) Now, putting relation (*A*) above as $d^2\vec{r}/dt^2 = \vec{F}/m = \vec{a}$, we have on integrating with respect to t,

velocity of the particle at instant t, i.e., $d\vec{r}/dt = \vec{a}t + C_1$ where C_1 is the constant of integration.

Since at $t = 0$, $d\vec{r}/dt\ C_1$, we have x initial velocity of the particle (*i.e.*, its velocity just before the force is applied to it) equal to C_1.

Representing the *initial velocity* by the usual notation $\vec{u}$ and the final velocity at instant t by $\vec{v}$, we therefore, have

$$\frac{d\vec{r}}{dt} = \vec{v} = \vec{u} + \vec{a}t \qquad ...(i)$$

(*ii*) Integrating equation (*i*) again with respect to t, we have *position of the particle at instant t* given by $\vec{r} = \vec{u}t + \frac{1}{2}\vec{a}t^2 + C_2$

where C_2 is another constant of integration.

Again, at $t = 0$, $\vec{r} = C_2$ where C_2 represents the *initial position vector* $\vec{r_0}$ of the particle.

So that, $\vec{r} = \vec{u}t + \frac{1}{2}\vec{a}t^2 + \vec{r_0}$ whence, $(\vec{r} - \vec{r_0}) = \vec{u}t + \frac{1}{2}\vec{a}t^2$

Clearly, $(\vec{r}-\vec{r_0}) = \vec{S}$ the *displacement vector* of the particle at instant *t*.

We, therefore, have $\qquad \vec{S} = \vec{u}\,t + \frac{1}{2}\vec{a}\,t^2 \qquad ...(ii)$

(*iii*) We have *acceleration of the particle*, $\vec{a} = d\vec{v}/dt$.

Taking its *dot product* with the velocity *v* of the particle at instant *t*,

we have, $\qquad \vec{v}\cdot\vec{a} = \vec{v}\cdot d\vec{v}/dt$

or, since $\vec{v} = d\vec{r}/dt$ we have $\frac{d\vec{r}}{dt}\cdot\vec{a} = \vec{v}\cdot\frac{d\vec{v}}{dt}$, integrating which with respect to *t*, we have

$$\int\frac{d\vec{r}}{dt}\cdot\vec{a}dt = \int\vec{v}\frac{d\vec{v}}{dt}\,dt \text{ . or, } \vec{r}\cdot\vec{a} = \frac{1}{2}\vec{v}\cdot\vec{v} + C_3\text{. or, } \vec{r}\cdot\vec{a} = \frac{1}{2}v^2 + C_3$$

where C_3 is yet another constant of integration.

At $t = 0$, clearly, $\vec{v} = \vec{u}$ and $\vec{r} = \vec{r_0}$ So that, $\vec{r}\cdot\vec{a} = \frac{1}{2}u^2 + C_3$

or, $\qquad C_3 = \vec{a}\cdot\vec{r_0} - \frac{1}{2}u^2$

Substituting this value of C_3 in the expression above, we therefore have

$$\vec{r}\cdot\vec{a} = \frac{1}{2}v^2 + \vec{a}\cdot\vec{r_0} - \frac{1}{2}u^2 \text{ or, } \frac{1}{2}(v^2 - u^2) = \vec{a}\cdot(\vec{r}-\vec{r_0})$$

or, $\qquad v^2 - u^2 = 2aS. \quad$ or, $v^2 = u^2 + 2aS. \qquad ...(iii)$

These relations, (*i*), (*ii*) and (*iii*), are the three *general equations of motion of a particle.*

Let us now consider *two particular cases.*

(*a*) **Case of a body falling freely under the action of gravity.** If we consider a body acted upon only by the gravitational force of attraction due to earth, the acceleration on it (called the *acceleration due to gravity*) acts *vertically* downwards, so that, taking the origin at the surface of the earth and the *x*-axis vertically *upwards* we have *equation of motion* of the body or the particle, $md^2x/dt^2 = -mg$.

Or, *acceleration of the particle*, $d^2x/dt^2 = -g$.

This expression, on integration with respect to *t*, gives the velocity *v* of the particle at a given instant *t*, *i.e.*, $dx/dt = v = -gt + C_1$, where C_1 is the *constant of integration.*

Since at $t = 0$, $v = u$, the initial velocity of the particle, we have $C_1 = u$, and, therefore,

$$dx/dt = v = -gt + u. \quad \text{Or,} \quad v = u - gt. \qquad ...(iv)$$

Again, integrating the above expression with respect to *t*, we have *position of the body or the particle at instant t* given by

$$x = ut - \frac{1}{2}gt^2 + C_2$$ where C_2 is another constant of integration

Again, at, $\qquad t = 0, \quad x = x_0$, so that, $C_2 = x_0$.

And therefore, $\qquad x = ut - \frac{1}{2}gt^2 + x_0$ whence, $(x_0 - x) = -ut + \frac{1}{2}gt^2$

Since $(x_0 - x) = h$, *the height through which the body has fallen*, we have

$$h = -ut + \frac{1}{2}gt^2 \qquad ...(v)$$

Finally, we have $\qquad g = -dv/dt$.

Taking the dot product of this expression with *v*, we have

$v.g = -v.\ dv\ dt$. or, $(dx/dt)\ .\ g = -v.dv/dt$, $\qquad$ [$\because v = dx/dt$.

Integrating which with respect to t, we have

$$\int \frac{dx}{dt} \cdot g \cdot dt = \int -v \cdot \frac{dv}{dt}\, dt$$

or, $x.g = -v^2/2 = C_3$,where C_3 is a constant of integration.

Since at $t = 0$, $x = x_0$ and $v = u$, we have $x_0 g = -u^2/2 + C_3$, whence, $C_3 = u^2/2 + x_0 g$.

$\therefore$ $xg = -v^2/2 + u^2/2 + x_0 g$. or, since $(x_0 - x) = h$, we have

$$v^2 = u^2 + 2gh, \qquad \ldots(vi)$$

whence, the *velocity acquired by a body starting from rest and falling freely through height h* is clearly, $v = \sqrt{2gh}$

For a body thrown vertically upwards, we simply put $-h$ in place or h in the expressions deduced above, when we obtain the following corresponding relations:

$$v = u - gt \qquad \ldots(vii),$$

$$h = ut - \frac{1}{2}gt^2 \qquad \ldots(viii)$$

and $$v^2 = u^2 - 2gh \qquad \ldots(ix)$$

So that, from relation (*ix*), *the maximum height attained by the body* (when $v = 0$) is $h = u^2/2g$ and, from relation (*vii*), *the time taken to do so* is $t = u/g$.

(*b*) **The projectile.** In the cases of motion considered above, the motion of the body or the particle takes place *along the direction of the applied force* and the problem is thus *one-dimensional*. Let us now consider a two-dimensional problem, *viz.*, the motion of a *projectile*.

A *projectile* is a body or a particle, projected at an angle to the horizontal, this angle being referred to as its *angle of elevation or projection* and the path taken by it as its *trajectory*.

Thus, suppose a particle is projected with velocity u from a point O at an angle α with the horizontal OX, (Fig. 4.1). Let OY be an up ward vertical through O and let the position of the particle at time t after projection be $P(x, y)$, as shown.

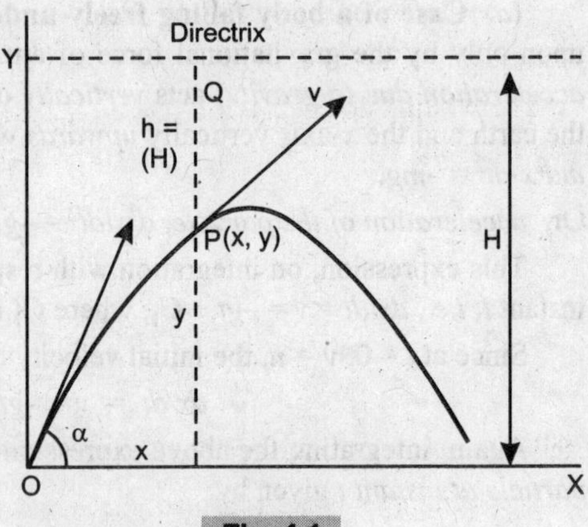

Fig. 4.1

Then, assuming no resistance due to air, the particle is throughout its motion, under the influence of the uniform acceleration due to gravity alone, acting vertically downwards. Its equations of motion along the horizontal and the vertical are, therefore, $md^2x/dt^2 = 0$ and $md^2y/dt^2 = -mg$ respectively, *i.e.* $d^2x/dt^2 = 0$ and $d^2y/dt^2 = -g$.

Since u is the velocity of projection of the particle at an angle α with the horizontal, its components *along the horizontal and the vertical* are respectively.

$$u_x = u \cos \alpha \quad \text{and} \quad u_y = u \sin \alpha.$$

Then, since the particle has no acceleration along the horizontal, its position after time t along this direction is given by

$$x = u_x t = u \cos \alpha t \qquad \ldots(x)$$

And since there is an acceleration $-g$ acting on it along the vertical, its position after time t along this direction is, in accordance with relation (*viii*) above, given by

$$y = u_y t - \frac{1}{2}gt^2 = u \sin \alpha t - \frac{1}{2}gt^2 \qquad \ldots(xi)$$

From relation (*x*), $t = x/u\cos\alpha$. Substituting this value of t in relation (*xi*), we, therefore, have

$$y = u\sin\alpha\frac{x}{u\cos\alpha} - \frac{1}{2}g\left(\frac{x}{u\cos\alpha}\right)^2$$

or,
$$y = x\tan\alpha - \frac{gx^2}{2u^2\cos^2\alpha} \qquad \text{...}(xii)$$

indicating that *the trajectory of the projectile is parabolic in shape.*

Now, relation (*xii*) may be put as

$$\frac{g - x^2}{2u^2\cos\alpha} - x\frac{\sin\alpha}{\cos\alpha} + y = 0$$

or,
$$x^2 - x\frac{\sin\alpha}{\cos\alpha}\cdot\frac{2u^2\cos^2\alpha}{g} + y\frac{2u^2\cos^2\alpha}{g} = 0$$

or,
$$x^2 - \frac{2u^2x\sin\alpha\cos\alpha}{g} + \frac{2u^2\cos^2\alpha\cdot y}{g} = 0$$

or,
$$x^2 - \frac{2u^2x\sin\times\cos\alpha}{g} + \frac{u^4\sin^2\alpha\cos^2\alpha}{g^2} = \frac{u^4\sin^2\alpha\cos^2\alpha}{g^2} - \frac{2u^2\cos^2\alpha y}{g}$$

or,
$$\left(\frac{x - u^2\sin\alpha\cos\alpha}{g}\right)^2 = -\frac{2u^2\cos^2\alpha}{g}\left(y - \frac{u^2\sin^2\alpha}{2g}\right)$$

showing that *the vertex of the parabola is at the point $u^2\sin\alpha\cos\alpha/g$, $u^2\sin^2\alpha/2g$,* and that the *length of the latus rectum is $2u^2\cos^2\alpha/g$. The directrix is thus horizontal and at a height $u^2\cos^2\alpha/2g$ above the vertex or $u^2/2g$ above the horizontal line OX.*

The *velocity of the projectile* at any instant t is given by $v^2 = v_x^2 + v_y^2$

where v_x and v_y are the velocities of the particle at time t along the axes of x and y respectively.

There being no acceleration along the x-axis, $v_x = u_x = u\cos\alpha$. And the acceleration along the axis of y being $-g$, $v_y = u_y - gt = u\sin\alpha - gt$, in accordance with relation (*vii*) above. So that,

$$v^2 = v_x{}^2 + v_y{}^2 = (u\cos\alpha)^2 + (u\sin\alpha - gt)^2.$$
$$= u^2\cos^2\alpha t + u^2\sin^2\alpha - 2u\sin\alpha\, gt + g^2t^2.$$
$$= u^2 - 2u\,g\sin\alpha t + g^2t^2 = u^2 - 2\,g\,u\sin\alpha t - \frac{1}{2}gt^2.$$

or,
$$v^2 = u^2 - 2gy,$$

whence,
$$v = \sqrt{u^2 - 2gy}$$

This velocity v is the same as that the particle would acquire in falling freely to P from a point on the directix vertically above P. (See worked example 4).

Range of the projectile. Putting $y = 0$ in relation (*xii*) above,

we have
$$\tan\alpha = gx/2u^2\cos^2\alpha.$$

or,
$$x = \frac{\sin\alpha}{\cos\alpha}\left(\frac{2u^2\cos^2\alpha}{g}\right) = \frac{\sin\alpha\, 2u^2\cos\alpha}{g}$$

or,
$$x = \frac{u^2\sin 2\alpha}{g}$$

This gives the *maximum horizontal distance covered by the projectile* or the *range of the projectile on the horizontal plane*. Denoting it by R, we therefore, have

$$R = u^2 \sin 2\alpha/g.$$

For a given range R and for a given velocity of projection, u, there are two possible angles of elevation or projection, *viz.*, α and $(\pi/2-\alpha)$ and, clearly, the *range* (R) *has its maximum value* u^2/g, when $\sin 2\alpha=1$ *i.e.*, when, $2\alpha=90°$ or $\alpha=45°$ or $\pi/4$.

Example 1. A force $\vec{F} = 25\hat{i} + 6\hat{j}$ newtons acts on a particle of mass 2.5 kg for 5 sec. If the initial position of the particle is $\vec{r}_0 = 6\hat{j} + 8\hat{k}$ metre and the initial velocity $\vec{u} = 2.5\hat{i} + 3\hat{k}$ ms^{-1} calculate (*i*) the final velocity of the particle, (*ii*) the final position of the particle, (*iii*) the work done by the force on the particle. ***(Agra,)***

Solution. (*i*) Since the *initial velocity of the particle*, $\vec{u} = 2.5\hat{i} + 3\hat{k}$ m/sec and its *acceleration* $\vec{a} = \vec{F}/m = (2.5\hat{i} + 6\hat{j})\ /2.5$ m/sec^2, we have

final velocity of the particle after time t = 5 sec, i.e., $\vec{v} = \vec{u} + \vec{a}t$

or, $\vec{v} = 2.5\hat{i} + 3\hat{k} + \left(\dfrac{25\hat{i} + 6\hat{j}}{2.5}\right)5 = 2.5\hat{i} + 3\hat{k} + 50\hat{i} + 12\hat{j} = 52.5\hat{i} + 12\hat{j} + 3\hat{k}$ m/sec

(*ii*) The *final position of the particle* is given by $\vec{r} = \vec{r}_0 + \vec{u}t + \frac{1}{2}\vec{a}t^2$

$$= (6\hat{j}+8\hat{k}) + (2.5\hat{i}+3\hat{k})\,5 + \frac{1}{2}\left(\frac{25\hat{i}+6\hat{j}}{2.5}\right)25 = 6\hat{j}+8\hat{k}+12.5\hat{i}+15\hat{k}+125\hat{i}+30\hat{j}$$

or, $$\vec{r} = 137.5\hat{i} + 36\hat{j} + 23\hat{k}$$

(*iii*) Clearly, *work done by the force on the particle, i.e.,* $W =$ (*force* × *distance through which the force is applied*) $\vec{F} = (\vec{r} - \vec{r}_0)$

$$= (25\hat{i}+6\hat{j})\,[(137.5\hat{i}+36\hat{j}+23\hat{k})-(6\hat{j}+8\hat{k})]$$

or, $$W = (25\hat{i}+6\hat{j})\,(137.5\hat{i}+30\hat{j}+15\hat{k}) = (3437.5+180) = 3617.5 \text{ joules.}$$

Example 2. The initial positions of two particles are –2, 0 and 0, –2 and they start simultaneously along the axes of x and y with uniform velocities $3i$ cm/sec and $4j$ cm/sec respectively. (*i*) Obtain the vector representing the position of the second particle with respect to the first as a function of time. (*ii*) When and where will the two particles be closest to one another?

Solution. Let the velocities of the two particles be $\vec{u}_1$ and $\vec{u}_2$ respectively. Then, we have $\vec{u}_1 = 3\hat{i}$ *cm/sec* and $\vec{u}_2 = 4\hat{j}$. And, therefore,

(*i*) Position of the *first* particle after time *t* is given by

$$\vec{r}' = \vec{r}'_0 + \vec{u}_1 t = -2\hat{i} + (3\hat{i})(t) = (3t-2)\,\hat{i}$$

and position of the *second* particle after the *same* time *t* is given by

$$\vec{r}'' = \vec{r}''_0 + \vec{u}_2 t = -2\hat{j}(4\hat{j})(t) = (4t-2)\hat{j}$$

∴ Position vector of the second particle with respect to the first is given by

$$\vec{r} = \vec{r}'' - \vec{r}' = (4t-2)\hat{j} - (3t-2)\hat{i} \text{ cm}$$

(*ii*) Obviously, the two particles will be closest together when $\vec{r}$ has the minimum value, *i.e.*, when $\dfrac{d}{dt}(r^2) = 0$ or, $\dfrac{d}{dt}[ut-2)^2 + (3t-2)^2] = 0$

i.e., when $2(4t-2)(4) + 2(3t-2)(3) = 0$, or, when $t = 28/50 = 0.56$ *sec.*

At this time, the position of the second particle with respect to the first will be given by

$$\vec{r} = (4 \times 0.56 - 2)\hat{j} - (3 \times 0.56 - 2)\hat{i} = (0.32\hat{i} + 0.24\hat{j}) \text{ cm.}$$

Thus, *the two particles will be the closest to one another after 0.56 sec when the position vector of the second particle with respect to the first is given by*

$$\vec{r} = (0.32\hat{i} + 0.24\hat{j}) \text{ cm.}$$

II – DYNAMICS OF CHARGED PARTICLES

4.3 SOME DEFINITIONS AND PRELIMINARY RELATIONS

Before proceeding with the study of the behaviour of a charged particle in an electric or a magnetic field, let us refresh our memory as to the meanings of some of the terms we shall have occasion to use so frequently in our discussion, as also recapitulate some simple preiminary relations.

(*i*) **Electric field and intensity of the field.** The area round about an electric charge q, within which its influence is perceptible, is referred to as its *electric field*, and the force experienced by a unit positive charge placed at any point in the field is called the *strength* or the *intensity* of the field at that point, or, usually, simply the *field* at that point and is denoted by the symbol E. Having both magnitude and direction, it is a *vector quantity* and hence the intensity at a point due to a number of charges is equal to the *vector sum* of the intensties there due to the individual charges.

Further, if the intensity of the field be the same at all points in it, it is said to be a *uniform electric field.*

If follows, therefore, that the force experienced by a charge q, when placed at a point where the intensity of the field is E, is equal to qE.

It may be as well be mentioned here that in the *electrostatic system of units*, q is measured in *esu* or *statcoulombs*. The *practical unit of charge* in this system is the *coulomb* = 3×10^9 *esu* or *statcoulombs*. In the *Rationalised MKS* (or the *SI*) *system*, which is now increasingly coming into vogue, the unit of charge is the *coulomb* the same as the practical unit in the electrostatic system of units.

Since the intensity of the electric field E is the force on unit charge, its unit in the *esu* system is *dyne/esu*. And since *field intensity is also defined as rate of change of potential with distance* and the unit of potential in the electrostatic system is the statvolt, *the unit of intensity in this system is also* 1 *statvolt/cm*. The *practical unit* of E in this system is *volt/cm*, where 1 volt is 1/300th of the *esu*, *i.e.*, = 1/300 *statvolt*.

In the *RMKS* (or the *SI*) *system*, the unit of electric intensity is *Newton/coulomb* (*i.e., N/C*) or 1 *volt/meter*, where 1 *newton* = 10^5 *dynes*. We, thus have 1 *N/1C* = 1 volt/1meter = 10^5 dynes/ 3×10^9 *stat coulombs* = $1/3 \times 10^4$ *statvolts*/cm.

(*ii*) **Kinetic energy of a charged particle in an electric field.** Since the potential (V) between two points in an electric field is defined as the work done in moving a unit positive charge from one point to the other (quite independently of the path taken), it is clear that the work done in taking a charge q from one point to the other (along any path) will be qV.

This work appears in the form of increased *K.E.* of the particle. So that, if m be the *mass* of the particle carrying the charge q and v, the velocity acquired by it, we have

$$\frac{1}{2}mv^2 = qV = \textit{charge} \times \textit{potential difference.}$$

Thus, a particle carrying a positive charge *gains* or *loses* energy according as it moves from a higher to a lower potential or from a lower to a higher one. Naturally, the reverse will be the case if the charge carried by the particle be negative.

In the electrostatic system, this *K.E.* is measured in *ergs* and in the *RMKS* (or the *S.I.*) system, in *joules*. More often than not, however, it is measured in *electron volts* (*eV*)* where 1 $eV = 1.60 \times 10^{-12}$ *ergs* $= 1.60 \times 10^{-19}$ *joules*.

(*iii*) **Magnetic field and strength of a magnetic field—Flux density.** The region in which magnetic effects can be detected is called a *magnetic field* and the strength of a magnetic field at any point in it is measured by the *magnetic flux density B* at that point, where flux density is defined as *the magnetic flux per unit area perpendicular to the direction of the flux*. In the *emu* or the *Gaussian system*, its unit in the *gauss* and in the *RMKS* (or the *SI*) system, it is *weber/metre*^{2} (*Wb/m*^{2}) of *tesla* (*T*), where 1 *Wb/m*^{2} (or *T*) = 10^4 *gauss*.

The flux density (*B*) is a *vector quantity*, having *magnitude* as well as *direction* (which is the same as that of the lines of magnetic flux).

(*iv*) **Force on a moving charge in a magnetic field.** We know that the force acting on a conductor of length δl carrying a current *I* in a magnetic field of strength *B* is given by $F_{mag} = BI\,\delta l \sin\theta$, where θ is the angle that the conductor makes with the direction *B*. This force is perpendicular to both the field (*B*) and the current (*I*) and its direction is given by the familiar *Fleming's left hand rule*. Putting it in vector notation, we have

$$\vec{F}_{mag} = \mathrm{I}\delta\vec{l} \times \vec{B} = \delta l\,\vec{I} \times \vec{B}$$

where $\delta\vec{l}$ and $\vec{I}$ are obviously *parallel vectors*.

If the quantities δl, *I* and *B* be measured in *emu*, F_{mag} is in dynes, but if they be measured in *RMKS* (or *SI*) units F_{mag} is in newtons (where 1 N = 10^5 dynes).

Now, as we know, *a moving charge constitutes a current* and must, therefore, experience a similar force in a magnetic field.

Lorentz force

Thus, if $\vec{v}$ be the velocity of a charge *q* moving in a direction making an angle θ with the field of $(\vec{B})$, as shown in Fig. 4.2, the distance covered by it in time $\delta t = \vec{v}\cdot\delta t$. This is equivalent to a conductor of length $\delta l = \vec{v}\cdot\delta t$ inclined to the direction of $\vec{B}$ at an angle θ and carrying a current $I = q/\delta t$ (∵ current is the rate of flow of charge).

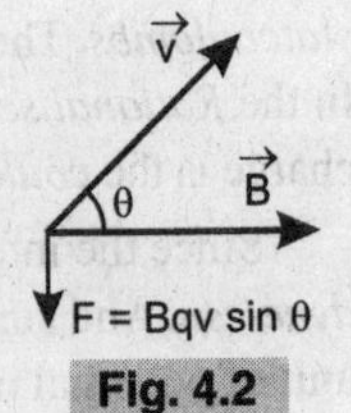

Fig. 4.2

∴ *Force acting on the charge, i.e.,*

$$F_{mag} = \frac{q}{\delta t}\vec{v}\,\delta t \times \vec{B}\sin\theta = qvB\sin\theta$$

or, *in vector notation,* $\qquad \vec{F}_{mag} = q\,\vec{v} \times \vec{B}$

This force is called *Lorentz force* and its direction, as given by the *right-handed screw rule*, is perpendicular to both $\vec{v}$ and $\vec{B}$.

If the quantities *q*, $\vec{v}$ and $\vec{B}$ be measured in *emu*, $\vec{F}_{mag}$ is in dynes, but if measured *RMKS* (or *SI*) units, it is in *newtons*.

Quite often, however, *q* and $\vec{B}$ are measured in the *Gaussian system of units, i.e., q* in esu and *B* in *emu* (or *gauss*). We have, therefore, to convert *q* into *emu* by dividing it by *c* (the speed of light in free space), because 1 *esu* of charge = 1/*c* of *emu* of charge. In such a case, then, the expression for F_{mag} becomes.

* An *electron-volt* is the energy acquired by an electron (carrying a charge $e = 4.8 \times 10^{-19}$ *esu*) on moving through a potential difference of 1 *volt* (equal to 1/300 *esu*) and is thus equal to $qV = eV = 4.8 \times 10^{-10} \times 1/300 = 1.60 \times 10^{-12}$ *ergs* or $1.60 \times 10^{-12}/10^7 = 1.60 \times 10^{-19}$ joules.

$$\vec{F}_{mag} = \frac{q}{c}\vec{v} \times \vec{B}$$

It will be noted that *for a force to act on a charged particle in a magnetic field,*

(*i*) *the particle must be in motion, i.e., $v \neq 0$,* because a stationary charge does not constitute a current.

(*ii*) *the velocity $\vec{v}$ of the particle must not be in the same direction as $\vec{B}$*, or else, under the rule of vector product, $\vec{v} \times \vec{B}$ would be equal to *zero*.

Further, since the force ($\vec{F}_{mag}$) acts in a direction perpendicular to $\vec{v}$ the velocity of the particle, *there is no change in the magnitude of the velocity but only a continuous change in its direction.*

This means, in other words, that *there is no change in the kinetic energy of a charged particle during its motion in a magnetic field.*

It may as well as be mentioned here that in case the charged particle is also simultaneously subjected to an electric field $\vec{E}$, the force on it due to the latter is $\vec{F}_{el} = q\vec{E}$. And therefore, *total force acting on the charged particle, i.e.,*

$$\vec{F} = \vec{F}_{el} + \vec{F}_{mag} = q\vec{E} + \frac{q}{c}\vec{v} \times \vec{B}$$

This force $\vec{F}$, due to the two fields together, is also called *Lorentz force.*

4.4 CHARGED PARTICLE IN A UNIFORM AND CONSTANT ELECTRIC FIELD

We have seen under §4.2 above how, in accordance with Newton's second law of motion, the force acting on a particle is given by $\vec{F} = d^2\vec{r}/dt^2$, where *m* is the *mass* of the particle (remaining constant at non-relativistic speeds) and $d^2\vec{r}/dt$ its acceleration.

Now, imagine a particle of mass *m* and carrying a charge *q* to be placed in a uniform and constant electric field $\vec{E}$. The force acting on it will obviously be $q\vec{E}$ (see §4.3 (*i*) above). If the acceleration acquired by $t^{t/1}$ particle under the action of this force be $\vec{a} = d^2\vec{r}/dt^2$,

we clearly have

$$m\vec{a} = md^2\vec{r}/dt^2 = q\vec{E} \text{ whence, } d^2\vec{r}\Big/dt^2 = \frac{q}{m}\vec{E}$$

Integrating expression (*i*) with respect to *t*, we have *velocity of the particle,* $\vec{v} = \dfrac{d\vec{r}}{dt} = \dfrac{q\vec{E}}{m}t + \vec{C}_1$ where C_1 is the constant of integration.

Clearly, at $t = 0$, $\vec{v} = \vec{u}$, the *initial velocity* of the particle. So that $C_1 = \vec{u}$. We therefore, have

$$\frac{d\vec{r}}{dt} = \vec{v} = \frac{q\vec{E}}{m}t + \vec{u}$$

As will be easily seen, this is a relation similar to $\vec{v} = \vec{u} + \vec{a}t$ for an uncharged particle, since $q\vec{E}/m$ here is equal to $\vec{a}$.

Again integrating relation (*ii*), we have

$$\vec{r} = \frac{1}{2}\frac{q\vec{E}}{m}t^2 + \vec{u}t + \vec{C}_2$$

where C_2 is another constant of integration.

Again, at $t = 0$, $\vec{r} = \vec{r}_0$ the initial position vector of the particle, and we have $\vec{r}_0 = \vec{C}_2$

So that,
$$\vec{r} = \frac{1}{2}\frac{q\vec{E}}{m}t^2 + \vec{u}t + \vec{r}_0 = \frac{1}{2}\vec{a}t^2 + \vec{u}t + \vec{r}_0 \quad ...(iii)$$

The vector diagram corresponding to it is as shown in Fig. 4.3, where $\overrightarrow{OA}$ represents the *initial position vector* $\vec{r}_0$ *at* = 0, $\overrightarrow{AB}$ *represents* $\vec{u}t$, *the distance covered in time t due to the initial velocity* $\vec{u}$ and $\overrightarrow{BC}$ represents $\frac{1}{2}\vec{a}t^2$ or $\frac{1}{2}\frac{q\vec{E}}{m}t^2$, *the distance covered on account of the acceleration acquired due to field* $\vec{E}$, directed along *BC*. The resultant displacement $\vec{r}$ of the particle is the *vector sum* of all the three and is represented by *OC*, in accordance with the polygon law of addition of vectors.

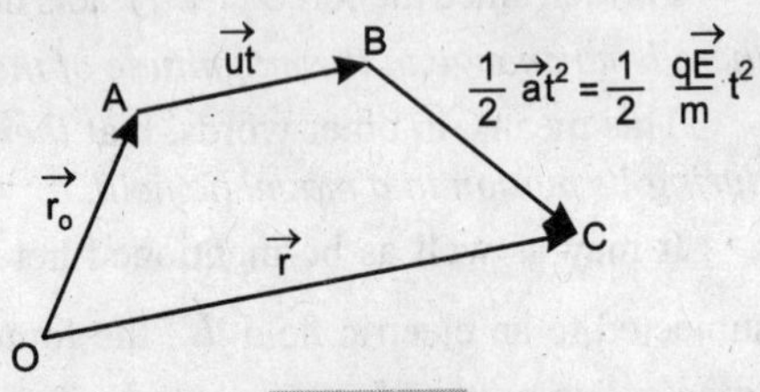

Fig. 4.3

Two particular cases. Having discussed above the general case of the motion or displacement of a charged particle when placed in an electric field, let us consider two particular cases, *viz.*, (*i*) *when the electric field acts along the direction of motion of the particle* and (*ii*) *when it acts in a direction perpendicular to it.*

(*i*) It will be easily seen that *in the case of both* $\vec{u}$ *and* $\vec{r}_0$ *being directed along the electric field* $\vec{E}$, the acceleration produced in the particle will also be directed along $\vec{E}$. The electric field is, in this case called a **longitudinal field** and the acceleration acquired by the particle, a **longitudinal acceleration**. The resultant position vector ***r*** will now also be directed along $\vec{E}$, thus making the whole problem a simple *one-dimensional* one.

Also, if $\vec{r}_0 = 0$ and $\vec{u} = 0$, *i.e., if the particle is initially at the origin and starts from rest*, we shall again have a one-dimensional problem with

$$\vec{r} = \frac{1}{2}\vec{a}t^2 = \frac{1}{2}\frac{q}{m}\vec{E}t^2 \text{ in the direction of } \vec{E},$$

exactly in the manner that the distance covered by an uncharged particle, starting from rest, is given by $\vec{S} = \frac{1}{2}\vec{a}t^2$

So that, in either case, we may replace the vectors $\vec{r}_0, \vec{r}, \vec{u}, \vec{v}$ and $\vec{E}$ by their respective scalar magnitudes.

(*ii*) Let us now discuss the case **when the electric field is a transverse one,** *i.e., in a direction perpendicular to the initial velocity of the particle.* In this case, the acceleration acquired by the particle is also referred as the **transverse acceleration.**

Thus, imagine a beam of charged particles, each of *mass m* and carrying a *charge q*, to be travelling along the axis of *x* with velocity *v* and passing in between two metallic plates P_1 and P_2 (Fig. 4.4), maintained at a constant potential difference *V*, with the upper plate positive with respect to the lower one.

Then, if *d* be the distance between the two plates, the electric field set up between them is *V*/*d* and since it is directed from the upper to the lower plate, or along the axis of *y*, let is be denoted by E_y.

As soon as the beam of charged particles enters in between the plates at the origin *O*, it is subjected to this transverse electric field E_y. Since this field

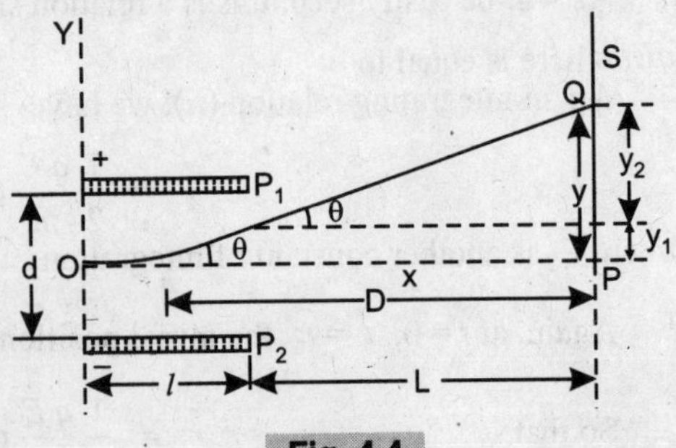

Fig. 4.4

is perpendicular to the velocity v_x of beam, the latter remains unaffected and the beam, therefore, continues to cover the horizontal distance between the plates with the same velocity v_x. If l be the length of the plates or that of the electric field set up between them, the time taken by the beam to cover this distance is l/V_x.

During this time, obviously, each particle of the beam acquires a *transverse acceleration* $a = q.E_y/m$ and hence a transverse velocity $v_y = 0 + at$.

or
$$v_y = 0 + q \cdot \frac{E_y}{m} t = \frac{qE_y}{m} \cdot \frac{1}{v_D}$$

[∵ the initial transverse velocity is *zero*.]

∴ *Transverse displacement of the beam* (upwards or downwards, according as the charge on the particles is *negative* or *positive*) during the time $t = l/v_x$ that it takes to cover the entire electric field of length l is say, $y_1 = 0 + \frac{1}{2} at^2$

i.e.
$$y_1 = \frac{1}{2} \frac{qE_y}{m} \cdot l^2 = \frac{qE_z}{2mv_x^2} \cdot l^2$$

This is clearly the equation to a parabola ($qE_y / 2mv_x^2$ being a constant quantity). So that, the beam of charged particles takes a parabolic path in between the two plates, as shown.

It will be seen that the problem here is a *two-dimensional* one, similar to that of a particle thrown horizontally and subjected to the downward acceleration due to gravity (*i.e.,* similar to that of a projectile). The important difference, however, is that, unlike the gravitational force acting on the uncharged particle, we can here alter the electric field and hence the force acting on the particle, as desired. Also, the electric field is effective only within a l, the length of the two plates, beyond which it suddenly drops to *zero* and the beam, therefore, moves straight along the direction in which it emerges from the electric field between the plates.

If there be a screen S at a distance L from the ends of the plates, the beam will strike it at, say, Q, making an angle θ with the *x-axis*, instead of at P, along it, as it would if it were undeflected. The *total vertical displacement* of the beam is thus $PQ = y$, which is clearly made up of two parts: y_1 within the plates (or the electric field) and y_2, on emergence from the plates (or the electric field).

As we have seen above,
$$y = \frac{q.E_y}{2mv_x^2} \cdot l^2$$

And
$$y = L \tan \theta,$$

where
$$\tan \theta = \frac{v_y}{v_x} = \frac{qE_y / mv_x}{v_x} = \frac{qE_y l}{mv_x^2}$$

So that,
$$y_2 = \frac{LqE_y l}{mv_x^2}$$

And, therefore, *total displacement* of the beam,

$$y = y_1 + y_2 = \frac{qE_y l^2}{2mv_x^2} + \frac{LqE_y l}{mv_x^2}$$

or,
$$y = \frac{qE_y l}{mv_x^2}\left(L + \frac{l}{2}\right)$$

Since $qE_y l/mv_x^2 = \tan \theta$ and $(L + l/2)$ = distance D of the screen from the centre C of the electric field between the plates, we have

$$y = D \tan \theta$$

This is the *principle* underlying the *cathode ray oscillograph, television picture* tubes and a host of other experiments, like determination of *e/m* (*i.e., charge to mass ratio*) for an electron etc.

In all these cases, an electron beam is obtained from a hot cathode or filament, surrounded by a hollow metallic cylinder, kept at a negative potential with respect to the cathode and called the *modulator*. This helps to make the electrons emitted by the cathode into a compact beam. The electron beam is then subjected to a high accelerating potential V', say, between the cathode and a pair of anodes, so that the energy acquired by each electron is eV', where e is the *charge* on an electron. If m be the *mass* of an electron and v_x, the velocity acquired by it along the axis of x, clearly,

$$\frac{1}{2}mv_x^2 = ev', \text{ whence, } v_x = \sqrt{2eV'/m}.$$

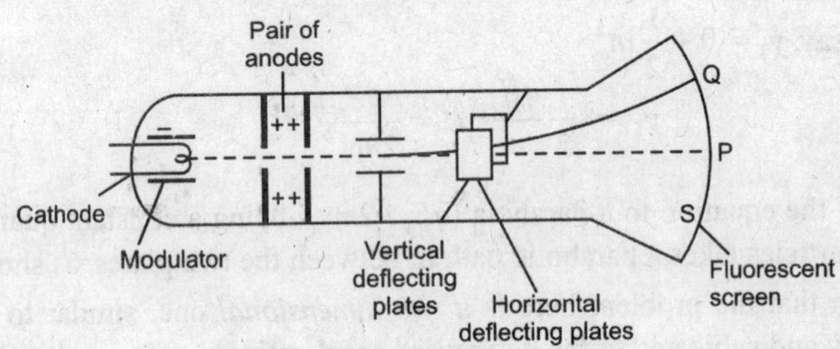

Fig. 4.5

In the case of the *cathode ray oscillograph*, (Fig. 4.5), this high velocity electron beam is passed through two pairs of plates which, when a potential difference is applied to them, have a vertical and a horizontal electric field set up in between them and thus deflect the electron beam passing through them vertically and horizontally respectively. Thus, activising any one pair of plates at a time, the beam may be deflected vertically or horizontally, as desired. The deflection of the beam is noted on fluorescent screen from the position of the bright spot produced first by the undeflected beam at P and then by the deflected beam at Q, say in the case of vertical deflection.

The cathode ray oscillograph is put to a number of of uses, one of which is to demonstrate in a spectacular manner the formation of Lissajous' figures when a particle is subjected simultaneously to simple harmonic motions at right angle to each other.

Example 3. At time $t = 0$, the velocity of an electron is $10^6 \hat{i}$ cm/sec and the initial position vector $\vec{r_0}$ = 100j cm. (*i*) Obtain the position vector after 0.1 sec. (*ii*) If the electric field by 10^{-2} *i* statvolt/cm, obtain the position and velocity vectors after 10^{-8} sec.

Solution. (*i*) The position vector after t sec will be $\vec{r} = \vec{r_0} + \vec{u}\,t$ where $\vec{u}$ is the *velocity* of the electron (supposed uniform). So that,

$$\vec{r} = 100\hat{j} + 10^6\hat{i}\,(0.1) = 10^5\hat{i} + 10^2\hat{j} \text{ cm}$$

(*ii*) In this case, the electron will have an acceleration $\vec{a}$ = (*force acting on it/its mass*) $= e\vec{E}/m$ where e is the *charge on the electron* = -4.8×10^{-10} esu and $\vec{E}$, the electric field $= 10^{-2}\hat{i}$ esu and m, the mass of the electron = 0.91×10^{-27} gm.

$\therefore$ *Velocity of the electron after* $t = 10^{-8}$ sec, *i.e.*, $\vec{v} = \vec{u} + \vec{a}\,t$

$$= 10^6\hat{i} - \frac{4.8\times10^{-10}\,(10^{-2}\hat{i})}{0.91\times10^{-27}}\times10^{-8}$$

Or, $$\vec{v} = \left(10^{-1} - \frac{4.8}{0.91}\right)10^7\hat{i} = -5.2\times10^7\hat{i}$$

And *position vector after t* = 10^{-8} *sec, i.e.,* $\vec{r} = \vec{r_0} + \vec{u}\,t + \frac{1}{2}\vec{a}\,t^2$

$$= \vec{r_0} + \vec{u}\,t + \frac{1}{2}\frac{e\vec{E}}{m}t^2$$

Or, $$\vec{r} = 100\hat{j} + 10^5\hat{i}(10^{-8}) - \frac{1}{2}\frac{4.8\times10^{-10}(10^{-2}\hat{i})}{0.91\times10^{-27}}\times(10^{-8})^2$$

$$= 10^2\hat{j} + 10^{-2}\hat{i}\,\tfrac{1}{2}\frac{4.8}{0.91}\times10^{-1}\hat{i}$$

$$= 10^2\hat{j} + 10^{-2}\hat{i}\left(1 - \frac{24}{0.91}\right) = 10^2\hat{j} + 10^{-2}\hat{i}\left(-\frac{23.09}{0.91}\right)$$

$$= 10^2\hat{j} - 25\times10^{-2}\hat{i}$$

Or, $$r = 10^2\hat{j} - 0.25\times10^{-2}\hat{i}\ \text{cm}$$

Example 4. The adjoining figure shows a particular charge distribution $\frac{1}{2}q, -q, \frac{1}{2}q$. Show that for $r >> a$, the electric field at P is given by $3Q/r^4$, where $Q = qa^2$.

Solution. Here, clearly, *electric field at P due to the charge* $\frac{1}{2}q$ *to the left of the point O* is

$$= \frac{\frac{1}{2}q}{(r+a)^2}\vec{r} = \frac{q}{2(r+a)^2}\vec{r} \text{ directed outwards,}$$

where r is the *unit vector along OP*.

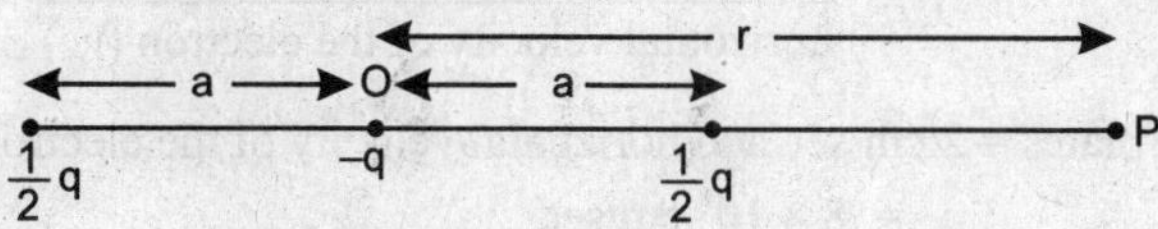

Electric field at P due to charge $\frac{1}{2}q$ *to the right of the point O*

$$= \frac{q}{2(r-a)^2}\vec{r} \text{ also directed outwards,}$$

and *electric field at P due to the charge* $-q$ *at O* = $\frac{-q}{r^2}\vec{r}$ *directed inwards.*

$\therefore$ *Resultant electric field at P due to the three charges, say* $\vec{E}$

$$= \left(\frac{q}{2(r+a)^2} + \frac{q}{2(r-a)^2} - \frac{q}{2r^2}\right)\vec{r}.$$

$$= \frac{q}{2r^2}\left[\left(1+\frac{a}{2}\right)^{-2} + \left(1-\frac{a}{2}\right)^{-2} - 2\right]\hat{r}$$

Or, expanding by Binomial Thoerem and remembering that $(a/r) << 1$ or $a << r$, or what is the same thing, $r >> a$, we have

$$\vec{E} = \frac{q}{2r^2}\left[\left(1 - \frac{2a}{r} + \frac{(-2)(-3)}{2!}\cdot\frac{a^2}{r^2}\right) + \left(1 + \frac{2a}{r} + \frac{(-2)(-3)}{2!}\cdot\frac{a^2}{r^2}\right)_{-2}\right]\vec{r}$$

$$= \frac{q}{2r^2}\left(\frac{3a^2}{r^2} + \frac{3a^2}{r^2}\right)\vec{r} = \frac{3qa^2}{r^4}\vec{r} \text{ directed outwards.}$$

Or, magnitude of the electric field at P due to the three charges

$= 3qa^3/r^4 = 3Q/r^4$ *directed outwards.* $[\because qa^2 = Q]$

Example 5. A cathode ray oseillograph has deflecting plates of length 2 cm and separation 0.5 cm. Calcualte the potential difference (in volts) between the plates which will cause angular deviatoin of 0.04 radian in an electron beam of speed 8.0 × 10³ cm/sec.

[$e/m = 5 \times 10^{17}$ esu/gm] ***(Agra 2003)***

Solution. Let the potential difference required to be applied to the plates be V volts = $V/300$ stat volts or esu.

$\therefore$ Electric field in between the plates

$$= \frac{p.d.}{\text{distance between the plates}} = \frac{V}{300 \times 0.5} = \frac{V}{150} \text{ statvolts/cm}$$

Hence *acceleration produced in an electron in between the plates*

$$= \frac{\text{force acting on the electron}}{\text{mass of the elctron}} = \frac{Ve}{150 \times \text{m}} \text{ cm/sec,}$$

where e is the *charge* on the electron and m, its *mass.*

$$= \frac{V}{150} \times 5 \times 10^{17} = \frac{V \times 10^{17}}{30} \text{ cm/sec}^2.$$

Now, the electron remain in between the plates for an interval of time

$$t = \frac{\text{length of the plates}}{\text{horizontal velocity of the electron } (v_\alpha)}$$

Here, length of the plates = 2 cm/sec and horizontal velocity of the electron

$= 8 \times 10^8$ cm/sec

So, that $$t = \frac{2}{8 \times 10^8} = 0.25 \times 10^{-6} = 2.3 \times 10^9 \text{ sec.}$$

$\therefore$ vertical velocity acquired by the electron in time, t say, v_y

$$= 0 + at = 0 + \frac{V \times 10^{17}}{30} \times 2.5 10^9 = \frac{5V}{6} \times 10^7 \text{ cm/sec}$$

$\therefore$ angular deviation of the electron, $\theta = \frac{v_y}{v_x}$ radiation = 0.04 radian (*given*)

or $$\frac{5V \times 10^7}{6 \times 8 \times 10^8} = 0.04, \text{ whence, } V = \frac{6 \times 8 \times 10^8 \times 0.04}{5 \times 10^7} = \frac{19.2}{5} = 3.84 \text{ volts.}$$

Thus, the potential difference that must be applied to the plates is 3.84 volts.

Example 6. (*a*). Calculate the intensity of the electric field which would produce in an electron an acceleration equal to that due to gravity. (Mass of an electron = 0.91 × 10⁻²⁷ gm., charge on it, e = 4.80 × 10⁻¹⁰ esu and g = 980 cm/sec²).

(b) Obtain the ratio of the electrostatic force between two electrons distant r apart and the gravitational force between them. ($G = 6.67 \times 10^{-8}$ dynes-cm²/gm²).

Solution. (a) Let $\vec{E}$ be the required intensity of the field. Then, clearly, force acting on an electron placed in this field $= \vec{E}e$ and, therefore, *acceleration produced in the electron*, $\vec{a}$ *= force/mass* $= \vec{E}e/m$ cm/sec², *i.e.*,

$$\vec{a} = \frac{\vec{E}\,(4.8 \times 10^{-10})}{0.91 \times 10^{-27}} \text{ cm/sec}^2.$$

This must be equal to the acceleration due to gravity, *i.e.*, 980 cm/sec².

We, therefore, have $\dfrac{\vec{E}\,(4.8 \times 10^{-10})}{0.91 \times 10^{-27}} = 980$, whence, $E = \dfrac{980 \times 0.91 \times 10^{-27}}{4.8 \times 10^{-10}}$

$$= \frac{980 \times 0.91}{4.8} \times 10^{-17} \text{ statvolts/cm.}$$

or, $$E = \frac{980 \times 0.91}{4.8} \times 10^{-17} \times 300 = \frac{98 \times 0.91 \times 10^{-14}}{1.6} = 5.57 \times 10^{-13} \text{ volts/cm.}$$

(b) The *electrostatic force between the two electrons,* say, $F_E = \dfrac{e.e}{r^2} = \dfrac{e^2}{r^2}$, and *gravitational force between them,* say, $F_G = \dfrac{m \times m}{r^2} G = \dfrac{m^2}{r^2} G$

∴ *Ratio of electrostatic force and gravitational force,*

$$\textit{i.e., } F_E/F_G = \frac{(4.8 \times 10^{-10})^2}{(0.91 \times 10^{-27})^2 \times 6.67 \times 10^{-8}} = 4.17 \times 10^{42}$$

Example 7. A particle of charge q and mass m enters an electric field $-E\hat{j}$ between two plates with an initial velocity $v_0\hat{i}$ (*i*) Calculate the forces acting on it in the any y directions. (*ii*) Will a force in the y-direction influence the x-component of the velocity? (*iii*) Solve for v_x and v_y as functions of time and write the complete vector equation for the velocity v acquired after time t. (*iv*) Taking the origin at the point of entry, write the complete vector equation for the position of the particle as a function of time while the particle is between the plates.

Solution. (*i*) The x-direction being perpendicular to the direction of the field which is along the y-direction, *there will be no force acting on the particle along the x-direction, i.e.,* $F_x = 0$. *In the y-direction*, naturally, *the force acting on the particle = charge on the particle × intensity of the field. So that,* $F_y = -qEj$.

(*ii*) A force in the y-direction will have no component in the x-direction and can, therefore, have *no effect* on the velocity of the particle in this direction.

(*iii*) The initial velocity of the particle is given to be $v_0\hat{i}$ along the x-direction. Since there is no force acting on the particle is this direction, its velocity in this direction remains unaltered at $v_0\hat{i}$. And, since a force $-qE\hat{j}$ acts on the particle along the y- direction, its acceleration along this direction is $a = -qE/m$. The velocity acquired by the particle along this direction in time t is, therefore, $v = 0 + at$ (the initial velocity in this direction being *zero*), *i.e.*, $v = -\dfrac{qE}{m}t$.

The *complete vector equation for the velocity of the particle* is thus $\vec{v} = v_0\hat{i} - \dfrac{qE}{m}t\hat{j}$

(*iv*) The distance covered by the particle along the x-direction in time t is $v_0 t$ and the distance covered by it along the y-direction is $ut + \dfrac{1}{2}\vec{a}t^2 = 0 + \dfrac{1}{2}\dfrac{qE}{m}t^2$

If therefore, $\vec{r}$ be the position vector of the particle after time t, we have

$$\vec{r} = \vec{r_0} + v_0 t\hat{i} - \frac{qE}{m} t^2 \hat{i}$$

Since the origin is taken at the point of entry, $r_0 = 0$. We, therefore, have *vector equation for the position of the particle,* $\vec{r} = v_0 t\hat{i} - \frac{qE}{m} t^2 \hat{j}$.

Example 8. In example 7 above, if the charged particle be an electron, having an initial energy 10^{-10} ergs, if the electric field strength be 0.01 statvolt/cm and if the length of the plates be 2 cm, find (*a*) the velocity vector as it leaves the region between the plates, (*b*) the angle (*v*, *i*) for the particle as it leaves the plates, (*c*) the displacement of the electron and (*d*) the point of intersection of the *x*-axis with its direction as it leaves the field.

Solution. (*a*) Here, if v_0 be the initial velocity of the electron, we have $\frac{1}{3} m v_0^2 = 10^{-10}$ ergs where m is the mass of electron, so that $v_0 = \sqrt{2 \times 10^{-10}}$ per $m = \sqrt{2 \times 10^{-10} / 9.1 \times 10^{-28}}$ cm/sec along the axis of x, *i.e.*, equal to v_x.

Since this velocity remains unaffected by the electric field, the time taken by the electron to cross the field-length l between the plates is given by $t = l/v_0 = 2/v_0$ sec.

∴ *Velocity acquired by the electron in time t sec, i.e.,*

$$\vec{v} = v_0\hat{i} + \frac{eE}{m}\left(\frac{l}{v_0}\right)\hat{j} = v_0\hat{i} + \frac{eE}{m}\left(\frac{l^2}{v_0^2}\right)^{\frac{1}{2}}\hat{j}$$ where eE/m is the acceleration acquired by the electron.

or, $$\vec{v} = \left(\frac{2 \times 10^{-10}}{9.1 \times 10^{28}}\right)^{\frac{1}{2}}\hat{i} + \frac{4.8 \times 10^{-10}\,(10^{-2})}{9.1 \times 10^{-28}}\left(\frac{4 \times 9.1 \times 10^{-28}}{2 \times 10^{-10}}\right)^{\frac{1}{2}}\hat{j}$$

$$= \left(\frac{2 \times 10^{18}}{9.1}\right)^{\frac{1}{2}}\hat{i} + \frac{4.8 \times 10^{16}}{9.1}(2 \times 9.1 \times 10^{-18})^{\frac{1}{2}}\hat{j}$$

or, $$\vec{v} = 4.7 \times 10^2\hat{i} + 2.25 \times 10^7\,\hat{j} \text{ cm/sec.}$$

(*b*) The angle θ that the electron makes with the *x*-axis as it leaves the plates is given by the relation $\tan\theta = v_y/v_x = 2.25 \times 10^7/4.7 \times 10^8 = 0.0475$, whence $\theta = 2°44'$.

(*c*) The displacement of the electron (see Fig. 4.4) is the distance covered by it along the *y*-direction in time *t*, *i.e.*, equal to $y = 0 + \frac{1}{2}at^2$, because the initial velocity along the *y*-direction is *zero*.

or, displacement, $$y = \frac{1}{2}\frac{E}{m}t^2 = \frac{1}{2}\frac{eE}{m}\frac{l^2}{v^2} = \frac{1}{2}\frac{4.8 \times 10^{-10} \times 10^{-}}{9.1 \times 10^{-28}}\left(\frac{4 \times 9.1 \times 10^{-28}}{2 \times 10^{-10}}\right)$$

$$= \frac{1}{2}\left(\frac{4.8 \times 10^{16}}{9.1}\right)(2 \times 9.1 \times 10^{-18}) = 4.8 \times 10^2 \text{ cm.}$$

(*d*) If *x* be the distance of the point of intersection of the direction of the electron, as it emerges from the field, with the axis of *x*, we have (see Fig. 4.4)

$$\tan\theta =, \frac{y}{l-x}, \text{ whence, } l - x = \frac{y}{\tan\theta}$$

or, $$x = l - \frac{y}{\tan\theta} = 2 = -\frac{4.8 \times 10^{-2}}{4.78 \times 10^{-2}} = 2 - 1 = 1 \text{ cm}$$

Thus, the point of intersection of the direction in which the electron emerges from the field and the axis of x lies *at a distance of 1 cm from the origin or the point of entry of the electron into the field.*

Example 9. An electron emitted with zero velocity from the hot cathode in a vacuum tube is accelerated by the electric field towards the anode. If the anode is at positive potential of 1000 V with respect to the cathode, find the velocity acquired by the electron as it reaches the anode. ($e = 1.6 \times 10^{-19}$ C, $m = 9.11 \times 10^{-31}$ kg) ***(Nagpur Uni. 2007)***

Solution. Given: $V_a = 1000$V, $e = 1.6 \times 10^{-19}$ C, $m = 9.11 \times 10^{-31}$ kg

$$\frac{1}{2}mv^2 = eV_a$$

$$v = \sqrt{\frac{2eV_a}{m}} = \sqrt{\frac{2 \times 1.6\, 10^{-19} \times 1000}{9.11 \times 10^{-31}}}$$

$$= \sqrt{\frac{2 \times 1.6 \times 10^{15}}{9.11}} = 10^7\sqrt{\frac{2 \times 16}{9.11}}$$

$$= \mathbf{1.874 \times 10^7\ m/s}$$

Example 10. A beam of electrons moving horizontally with a velocity of 10^7 m/s enters midways a uniform electric field between two horizontal parallel plates 5 cm long and 1.8 cm apart. On emerging from the plates the beam just grazes the edge of the positive plate. Calculate the potential difference V applied between them (Given $e/m = 1.8 \times 10^{11}$ C/kg). ***(Nagpur Uni. 2007)***

Solution. $v = 10^7$ m/s At $x = 5 \times 10^{-2}$ m, $y = \dfrac{1.8 \times 10^{-2}}{2} = 9 \times 10^{-3}$ m

and $d = 1.8 \times 10^{-2}$ m

The equation of the path between the plates is

$$y = \frac{eE}{2mv^2}x^2 = \frac{1}{2}\left(\frac{e}{m}\right)E\left(\frac{x}{v}\right)^2$$

$$\therefore \quad E = 2\left(\frac{m}{e}\right)\left(\frac{v}{x}\right)^2 y \quad \text{...(1)}$$

The p.d. is given by

$$V = Ed$$

$$= 2\left(\frac{m}{e}\right)\left(\frac{v}{x}\right)^2 yd$$

$$= 2\left(\frac{1}{1.8 \times 10^{11}}\right)\left(\frac{10^7}{5 \times 10^{-2}}\right)^2 9 \times 10^{-3} \times 1.8 \times 10^{-2}$$

$$= \frac{2 \times 9 \times 10^2}{25} = \mathbf{72\ V}$$

Example 11. A beam of positive ions moving along the x-axis enters a region of uniform electric field of intensity 3 KV/m along the y-axis and magnetic field of 1 Kilo Gauss along the z-axis. Calculate the speed of those ions which pass undeviated. What will happen to those ions which are moving (*i*) faster, (*ii*) slower than these ions? ***(Nagpur Uni. 2008)***

Solution. Given $E = 10^3$ V/m, $B = 10^3$ Gauss, 10^4 Gauss = 1 Wb/m^2

$$\therefore \quad B = \frac{10^3}{10^4} = 0.1\ \text{Wb/m}^2 = 0.1\ \text{Tesla}$$

For positive ions which pass undeviated

downward magnetic force = upward electric force

$$qvB = qE$$

$$\therefore \quad v = \frac{E}{B} = \frac{10^3}{0.1} = \mathbf{10^4\ m/s}$$

(*i*) The ions which move with speed *more* than this value will be deflected *downward*, and

(*ii*) the ions which move with speed less than this value will be deflected *upward*.

Example 12(a). If deflection sensitivity of a CRO is 2mm/V, calculate the deflection of the spot when a voltage of 15 V applied. ***(Nagpur Uni. 2006)***

Solution. For 1 volt, the deflection produced is 2 mm.

$\therefore$ 15 V will produce deflection = 2 × 15 = 30 mm = **3 cm.**

Example 12(b). Determine the deflection sensitivity of a signal for a CRT in which l = 2 cm, L = 30 cm, d = 0.5 cm and V_a = 2000 V. ***(Pbi. U. 2001)***

Solution. For a CRT, Electrostatic deflection sensitivity

$$S = \frac{lL}{2dV_0} \text{ m/volt}$$

Here l = 2 cm = 0.02 m; L = 30 cm = 0.3 m

d = 0.5 cm = 0.005 m ; V_a = 2000 V

$$\therefore \quad \text{Deflection sensitivity} = \frac{0.02 \times 0.3}{2 \times 0.005 \times 2000}$$

$$= 3 \times 10^{-4} \text{ m/V} = \mathbf{0.3\ mm/V}$$

Example 13. The length of deflecting plates in a *C.R.O.* is 5 cm. They are separated by 4 mm. The distance of the fluorescent screen from the nearest edge of the deflecting plates is 15 cm. A d.c voltage of 25 V is applied to the deflecting plates. If the accelerating potential difference is 1000 volt find the displacement of the spot on the screen. ***(Bangalore. U. 2001)***

Solution. For a CRT, total deflection due to electrostatic field is given by

$$\text{Total deflection} = \frac{lL}{2d}\frac{V_d}{v_a}$$

and the displacement of the spot on the screen is equal to total deflection. Referring to Fig. 9.10, we have

$$l = 5 \text{ cm} = 0.05 \text{ m; d} = 4 \text{ mm} = 0.004 \text{ m; D} = 15 \text{ cm}$$

$$L = \left[\frac{l}{2d} + D\right] = 2.5 + 15 = 17.5 \text{ cm} = 0.175 \text{ m}$$

$$V_d = 25 \text{ V}; V_a = 1000 \text{ V}.$$

$$\therefore \quad \text{Total deflection} = \frac{0.05 \times 0.175 \times 25}{2 \times 0.004 \times 1000}$$

$$= 27.34 \times 10^{-3} \text{ m} = \mathbf{27.34\ mm}$$

4.5 CHARGED PARTICLE IN AN ALTERNATING ELECTRIC FIELD

Suppose we have a particle of *mass m* and carrying a *charge q* placed in an alternating electric field whose intensity E at any instant t is given by $E = E_0 \sin \omega t$, where E_0 is the *maximum or the peak value* of E, *i.e.*, the amplitude of the electric field vector. and $2\pi/\omega$, its time-period.

If, therefore, the acceleration produced in the particle under the action of this field be d^2r/dt^2, we have

$$m\frac{d^2r}{dt^2} = qE = qE_0 \sin \omega t, \text{ whence, } \frac{d^2r}{dt^2} = \frac{qF_0}{m} \cdot \sin \omega t \quad ...(i)$$

indicating that *the acceleration of the particle too, like the applied electric field, varies sinusoidally with time,* as shown in Fig. 4.6, *having an amplitude (or peak value)* qE_0/m, and *the same time-period* $2\pi/\omega$ *as that of the applied field.*

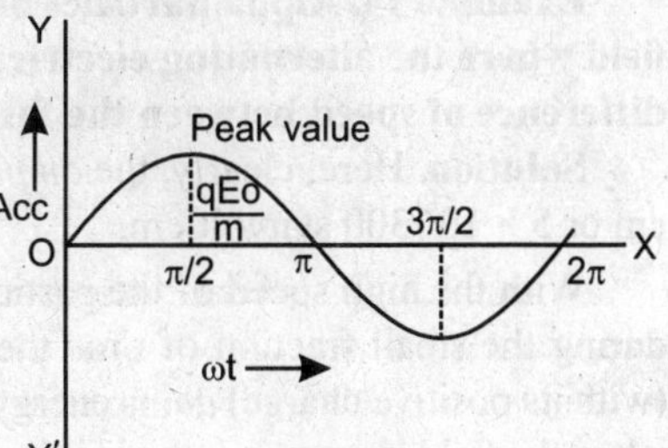

Fig. 4.6

Integrating relation *I* with respect to time, we have,

$$\frac{dr}{dt} = v = \frac{qE_0}{m\omega} \cos \omega t + C_1$$

where C_1 is the constant of integration to be determined from the initial or boundary conditions.

Initially, i.e., at $t = 0$, when the electric field (E) is *zero*, the initial velocity of the particle too is *zero* and we have

$$0 = -\frac{qE_0}{m\omega} + C_1 \quad \text{Or,} \quad C_1 = qE_0/m\omega.$$

So that, $$\frac{dr}{dt} = v = \frac{-qE_0}{m\omega} \cos \omega t + \frac{qE_0}{m\omega}$$

or, $$\frac{dr}{dt} = v = \frac{-qE_0}{m\omega}(1 - \cos \omega t) + \frac{2qE_0}{m\omega} \sin^2 \omega t \quad ...(ii)$$

indicating that *the velocity of the particle at any given instant is always positive, in the direction of* E_0, and hence **unidirectional,** *though it varies after the manner of a* $\sin^2$ *– curve*, as shown in Fig. 4.7, and has an *amplitude or peak value* $2qE_0/m\omega$.

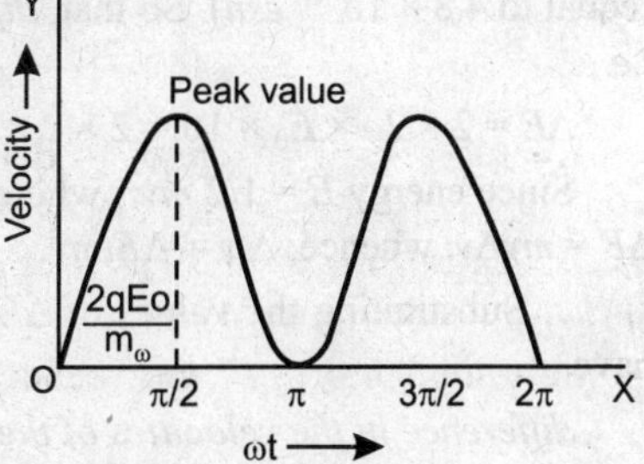

Fig. 4.7

Again, integrating relation *II*, with respect to *t*, we have

$$r = \left(\frac{qE_v}{m\omega}\right)t - \left(\frac{qE_v}{m\omega}\right) \sin \omega t + C_2 \quad ...(iii)$$

where C_2 is another constant of integration.

Since at $t = 0$, $r = r_0$, the *initial position vector*, we have

$$r = \left(\frac{qE_0}{m\omega}\right)t - \left(\frac{qE_0}{m\omega}\right) \sin \omega t + r_0 \quad ...(iii)$$

where r_0 may be *zero* or have a finite value, depending upon the choice of the origin.

However, if $r = 0$ at $t = 0$, we have $r_0 = 0$. In that case, therefore,

$$r = \left(\frac{qE_0}{m\omega}\right)t - \left(\frac{qE_0}{m\omega^2}\right) \sin \omega t \quad ...(iv)$$

It will thus be seen that under the initial or boundary condition chosen here (*viz.*, $r = 0$ at $t = 0$), *the displacement vector* (r) *is the sum of two vectors, with the value of one varying linearly, and that of the other, sinusoidally, with time.* In consequence, *the resulting motion of the particle is a simple harmonic oscillation of time-period* $2\pi/\omega$ *(the same as that of the applied electric field) and amplitude* $qE_0/m\omega^2$, *super-imposed on a constant drift velocity* $qE_0/m\omega$, as shown in Fig. 4.8. This is obvious from the fact that in this particular

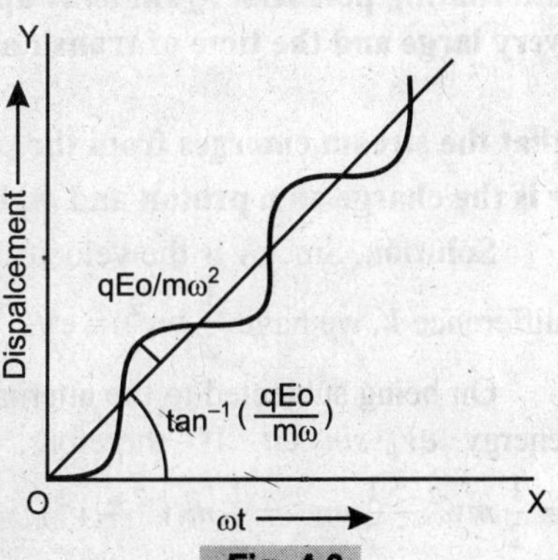

Fig. 4.8

case ($r = 0$ at $t = 0$) the expression for the velocity has no sine or cosine term attached to it, indicating that the velocity does not get reversed at any time (*i.e.*, remains unidirectional throughout) and the particle continues to advance in one and the same direction

Example 14. Alpha particles of speed $v_x = 2.0 \times 10^9$ cm/sec pass through 10 cm length of a field where the alternating electric field $E_x = 5 \times 10^3 \sin(\omega t + \phi)$ volts/cm exists. Calculate the difference of speed between the fastest and slowest particle emerging from the field.

Solution. Here, clearly, the *amplitude* or the *peak value* of the field, *i.e.*, $E_0 = 5 \times 10^3$ volts *per* cm or $5 \times 10^3/300$ statvolt/cm.

With the high speed of the particles, the value of the field may be assumed to remain the same during the small fraction of time they take to cross just 10 cm length of it. So that, an α-particle (with its positive charge) gains energy when the field is positive and loses an equal amount of energy when the field is negative, the maximum gain or loss obviously occurring when the field has its peak value.

∴ Assuming the field to be as its peak positive value, we have

force acting on the α-particle $= q \times E_0$ and hence

energy gained by the particle in crossing 10 cm of the field $= q \times E_0 \times 10$,

The particle will, therefore, have the maximum speed.

Similarly, when the field is at its peak negative value, the *energy lost by the particle in traversing 10* cm *of the field* $= q \times E_0 \times 10$. So that, the particle will now have the minimum speed.

The difference in the energies of the fastest and the slowest particles will thus be $2q \times E_0 \times 10$.

Now, an α-particle carries a positive charge of magnitude $2e$, where e is the charge on a proton (equal to 4.8×10^{-10} *esu*). So that, *difference in the energies of the fastest and the slowest particles, i.e.,*

$$\Delta E = 2 \times 2e \times E_0 \times 10 = 2 \times 2 \times 4.8 \times 10^{-10} \times (5 \times 10^3/300) \times 10 = 3.2 \times 10^7 \text{ ergs.}$$

Since energy $E = 1/2\, mv^2$, where m is the mass and v, the *velocity* of the α-particle, we have $\Delta E = mv\Delta v$, whence, $\Delta v = \Delta E/mv$.

∴ Substituting the values of ΔE, m (equal to 4 times the mass of a proton) and v (given), we have

difference in the velocities of the fastest and the slowest particles, i.e.

$$\Delta v = \frac{3.2 \times 10^7}{4 \times 1.6725 \times 10^{-24} \times 2.0 \times 10^9} = \frac{3.2 \times 10^8}{4 \times 1.6725 \times 2} = \frac{0.4 \times 10^8}{1.6725} = 2.39 \times 10^7 \text{ cm/sec}$$

Example 15. A stream of protons is first accelerated through a potential difference V until it acquires a constant velocity v and then passed through two parallel plates to which an alternating potential $v_o \sin \omega t$ is applied. If the frequency of the alternating potential be not very large and the time of transit of the stream through the plates comparatively small, show that the stream emerges from the plates with a velocity equal to $\left[\frac{2e}{m}(V + V_0 \sin \omega t)\right]^{\frac{1}{2}}$, where e is the charge on a proton and m, its mass.

Solution. Since v is the velocity acquired by a proton on being accelerated through a potential difference V, we have $\frac{1}{2}mv^2 = \text{e}V$.

On being subjected to the alternating potential $V_0 \sin \omega t$, the proton will acquire an additional energy $eV_0 \sin \omega t$. If, therefore, v' be its velocity *now*, clearly, *increase in its energy* $= \frac{1}{2}mv'^2 - \frac{1}{2}mv^2 = \frac{1}{2}m(v'^2 - v^2)$.

We, therefore, have $\frac{1}{2}m(v'^2 - v^2) = eV_0 \sin \omega t$. Or, $mv'^2 = 2eV_0 \sin \omega t + mv^2$

$$= 2eV_0 \sin \omega t + 2eV,$$

whence, $$v'^2 = \frac{2eV_0 \sin \omega t}{m} + \frac{2eV}{m} = \frac{2e}{m}(V + V_0 \sin \omega t)$$

Or, *velocity of the proton stream on emerging through the plates, i.e.,*

$$v' = \left[\frac{2e}{m}(V + V_0 \sin \omega t\right]^{1/2}$$

4.6 LINEAR ACCELERATOR

For the study of nuclear reactions, charged particles having energies of many million electron-volts (MeV) are required. It is difficult to generate direct voltages of the order of 10 million volts mainly due to insulation difficulties. To obtain linear acceleration of a charged particle in excess of 10 MeV, some indirect methods are used. The first type is known as '*Drift tube accelerator*' and the second type as '*Wave guide accelerator*'. Let us discuss first type *i.e.*, as '*Wave guide accelerator*'. Let us discuss first type *i.e.*, a linear accelerator.

A linear accelerator (or a *Linac*) is a device which accelerates charged particles in a straight line by means of oscillating electric field that provides either a series of steady accelerating steps in correct phase at a series of gaps between electrodes or accompanies the charged particles as a travelling wave.

In a linear accelerator, a moderate accelerating potential is applied a number of times so that the charged particles are accelerated along a straight line. A simple form of the linear accelerator is shown in Fig. 4.9. The charged particles or ions travel through an aperture A and move along the axis of a series of coaxial cylindrical electrode 1, 2, 3, 4 etc. These cylindrical electrodes are known as *drift tubes*. The drift tubes are connected to an *A.C.* source of very high frequency say a high frequency (H.F.) oscillator so that alternate tubes have potentials of opposite sign. Thus, in *one-half* cycle if tubes 1 and 3 are positive, 2 and 4 will be negative. After half a cycle the polarities are reversed *i.e.*, 1 and 3 will be negative and 2 and 4 positive.

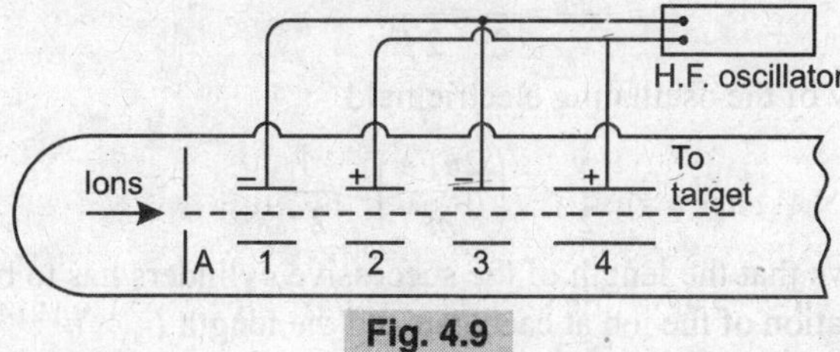

Fig. 4.9

Suppose a positive ion leaves *A* and is accelerated during the half cycle when the drift tube No. 1 is negative with respect to *A*. If *V* is the potential of drift tube 1 with respect to *A*, then velocity v_1 of the ion on reaching the drift tube is given by

$$\frac{1}{2}mv_1^2 = Ve$$

Or $$v_1 = \sqrt{\frac{2Ve}{m}}$$

where *e* is the charge and *m* the mass of the ion. It is supposed that v_1 is small as compared to *c* the velocity of light so that the change in mass due to relativity effect is negligible. The ions are accelerated in the gap between the tubes but travel with constant velocity in the *field free space* within the tubes themselves. The length of the tube 1 is so adjusted that as the positive ions come out of it, the tube has a positive potential and the next tube No. 2 has a negative potential, *i.e.*, the potential change sign. The positive ion is again accelerated in the space between the tubes 1 and 2 and on reaching the tube 2 its velocity v_2 is given by

$$\frac{1}{2}mv_2^2 = 2Ve$$

Or
$$v_2 = \sqrt{2}\sqrt{\frac{2Ve}{m}} = \sqrt{2}\, v_1$$

This shows that v_2 is $\sqrt{2}$ times v_1. In order that this ion on coming out of tube 2 may fine tube 3 just negative and the tube 2 positive, it must take the same time to travel through the tube 2. As the velocity is $\sqrt{2}v_1$ the length of tube 2 must be $\sqrt{2}$ times the length of tube 1. For successive accelerations in successive gaps the tubes 1, 2, 3, 4, etc., must have lengths proportional to 1, $\sqrt{2}$, $\sqrt{3}$, $\sqrt{4}$ etc., to a first approximation.

Energy of the ion. If n is the number of gaps that the ion travels in the accelerator and v_n is the final velocity acquired by it, then

Velocity of the ion as it emerges out of the nth tube

$$v_n = \sqrt{n}\sqrt{\frac{2Ve}{m}}$$

$\therefore$ Kinetic energy of the ion $\frac{1}{2}mv_n^2 = nVe = nVe$

The final energy of the ions when they strike the target depends upon the overall length of the accelerator *i.e.*, the total number of gaps and on the energy gained in each gap. The beam striking the target consists of pulses of particles. The number of pulses per second is equal to the frequency of the alternating voltage applied to the drift tubes.

Length of the cylinder. As the ion is accelerated in the gap between two cylindrical electrodes, the time taken by the ion to travel through the cylinder should be equal to half the time period of the high frequency voltage so that each time the ion comes out of the cylinder the polarity changes.

If v_n is the velocity of the ion, the time of passage through the nth cylinder of length L_n

$$t = \frac{L_n}{v_n} = \frac{T}{2} = \frac{1}{2f}$$

where f is the frequency of the oscillating electric field.

$$L_n = \frac{v_n}{2f} = \left(\frac{2nVe}{m}\right)^{1/2}\frac{1}{2f}$$

This equation shows that the length of the successive cylinders has to be increased in order to get a resonance acceleration of the ion at each gap and the length $L_n \propto n^{1/2}$

Limitations:

The limitations of linear accelerator are:

(*i*) The length of the accelerator becomes inconveniently large and it is difficult to maintain vacuum in such a large chamber.

(*ii*) The ion current is available in the form of pulses of short duration.

Circular Accelerator

A *circular accelerator* is another example of drift tube accelerator. Circular accelerator is a device which can accelerate charged particles by passing them again and again in a radio-frequency (*r.f.*) electric field along a closed path. Familiar examples are (*i*) ***cyclotrons*** which accelerates protons, deutrons and α-particles and (*ii*) ***Betatrons*** which accelerates electrons.

Wave Guide Accelerator

Wave Guide Accelerator makes use of electromagnetic radiations (waves) travelling in a wave guide to accelerate charged particles. A wave guide is a hollow pipe (cylindrical or rectangular) of conducting material in which oscillating electro-magnetic fields of the order of 10^5 MHz an be established. If the electro-magnetic wave is fed at one end of the wave guide and there is an electrical conductor at the other end, the advancing and the reflected waves super impose to form *standing* or *stationary* wave. But if the wave gets completely absorbed at the other end the result is a *travelling wave*. For this purpose, the wave guide is terminated at its end by an impedance equal to its characteristic impedance so that the travelling wave is maintained from one end to the other.

To accelerate the charged particle, the speed of the *e.m. wave is synchronised with that of the particle*. The particle, therefore, gains energy from the (axial) *electric field component* of the *e.m. wave* but the *magnetic field component* remains ineffective being at right angles to the path of the particle.

The *R.F.* signal is obtained from a standard master oscillator and is amplified at each feeding station using *Klystron amplifier.*

Acceleration of electrons. To accelerate the electrons a *disc loaded wave guide system* is used. The beam of electrons is injected along the axis of the metallic tube of the wave guide and the *phase velocity* of the *e.m. waves is matched* with that of electrons.

After the electrons have attained their maximum kinetic energy, they automatically emerge out of the accelerator in the form of a fine collimated beam.

Acceleration of protons. Wave guide accelerators can be used for protons. But the design of such accelerator is very different. The electrons being light particles travel most of the time with a velocity very close to the velocity of light. On the other hand, protons gain speed along its total path. As the protons have a *much lower injection velocity*, disc loaded wave guides are not found practicable for phase velocities as low as 0.1 *c* but in its place *long cylindrical resonant cavity has to be used*

Example 19. Protons are accelerated in a cyclotron in which the magnetic field strength is 1 Wb/m². What must be the frequency of the oscillator supplying power to the dees? (Given: mass of proton = 1.67 × 10⁻²⁷ kg, electronic charge = 1.6 × 10⁻¹⁹ C) ***(Nagpur U. 2009)***

Solution.

$$B = 1\ \text{Wb/m}^2,\ m_p = 1.672 \times 10^{-27}\ \text{kg}$$

$$q = e = 1.6 \times 10^{-19}\ \text{C}$$

$$T = \frac{2\pi m}{qB}$$

$$f = \frac{1}{T} = \frac{qB}{2\pi mp}$$

$$= \frac{1.6\times10^{-19}\times1}{2\times3.14\,1.672\times10^{-27}} = \frac{1.6\times10^{8}}{2\times3.14\times1.672}$$

$$= 0.1524 \times 10^8\ \text{Hz}$$

$$= 15.24 \times 10^6\ \text{Hz} = \mathbf{15.24\ MHz}$$

Example 20. Deutrons are to be accelerated with a cyclotron. If its magnets produce a flux density of 2.475 T, what must be the frequency of the oscillating potential applied to the Dee's? Mass of $_1H^2$ = 2 a.m.u. ***(P.U. 2001; Nagpur U. 2009)***

Solution. Mass of $_1H^2$ atom $= 2$ a.m.u $= 2 \times 1.66 \times 10^{-27}$ kg $= 3.32 \times 10^{-27}$ kg

$$e = 1.6\times10^{-19}\ \text{C},\ B = 2.475\ \text{T}$$

Frequency of the applied field (or oscillating potential) $f = \frac{Be}{2\pi m}$

$$= \frac{2.475 \times 1.6 \times 10^{-19}}{2\pi \times 3.32 \times 10^{-27}} = 18.98 \times 10^6 \text{ Hz} = \mathbf{18.98\ MHz}$$

Example 21. A cyclotron with dees of radius 90 cm has a transverse magnetic field of 0.8 Tesla. Calculate the energies to which (*i*) a proton and (*ii*) deutron are accelerated. (Given mass of the proton = 1.67 × 10^{-27} kg. Mass of the deutron = 3.34 × 10^{-27} kg.)

Solution. (*i*) Proton.

Mass of the proton $m = 1.67 \times 10^{-27}$ kg

Charge on the proton $e = 1.6 \times 10^{-19}$ C.

Energy of the emergent proton $E = \frac{1}{2}\frac{B^2e^2r^3}{m}$

$$= \frac{0.8 \times 0.8 \times 1.6 \times 10^{-19} \times 1.6 \times 10^{-19} \times 0.9 \times 0.9}{2 \times 1.67 \times 10^{-27}}$$

$$= 0.3973 \times 10^{-11} \text{ j} = \frac{0.3973 \times 10^{-11}}{1.6 \times 10^{-13}} \text{ MeV}$$

$$= 24.8 \text{ MeV.}$$

(*ii*) Deutron.

Mass of the deutron $m = 3.34 \times 10^{-27}$ kg

Charge on the deutron $e = 1.6 \times 10^{-19}$ C.

∴ Energy of the emergent deutron $= \frac{0.8 \times 0.8 \times 1.6 \times 10^{-19} \times 1.6 \times 10^{-19} \times 0.9 \times 0.9}{2 \times 3.34 \times 10^{-27}}$

$$= 0.1986 \times 10^{-11} \text{ J}$$

$$= \mathbf{12.4\ MeV.}$$

Example 22. A cyclotron has a magnetic field of 10^4 Gauss and radius of 80 cm. Calculate the frequency of the alternating electric field that must be applied and to what energy deutrons can be accelerated? (Mass of deutron = 2 a.m.u.) **(*P.U. 2000*)**

Solution. $B = 10^4$ Gauss = 1 T; r = 80 cm = 0.8 m

m = 2 *a.m.u.* = 2 × 1.66 × 10^{-27} kg = 3.32 × 10^{-27} kg;

$e = 1.6 \times 10^{-19}$ C.

∴ Frequency of alternating electric field

$$f = \frac{Be}{2\pi m} = \frac{1 \times 1.6 \times 10^{-19}}{2\pi \times 3.32 \times 10^{-27}}$$

$$= 7.7 \times 10^6 = 7.7 \text{ MHz}$$

Energy $E = \frac{1}{2}\frac{B^2e^2r^2}{m}$

$$= \frac{1 \times 1 \times 1.6 \times 10^{-19} \times 1.6 \times 10^{-19} \times 0.8 \times 0.8}{2 \times 3.32 \times 10^{-27}} = 24.67 \times 10^{-13} \text{ J}$$

$$= \mathbf{15.4\ MeV}$$

Example 23. Between the Dee's of a cyclotron 1.5 metre in diameter an alternating potential difference of 15 mega cycles is applied. Calculate the energy in MeV of the protons issuing out of the cyclotron. (Mass of proton = 1.672 × 10^{-27} kg.)

Solution. In terms of frequency of the applied field and radius of cyclotron Dee's the energy is given by

$$E = 2\pi^2 mf^2 2^2_{max}$$

Mass of proton $= 1.672 \times 10^{-27}$ and $f = 15 \times 10^6$

$$\therefore \quad E \text{ (in MeV)} = \frac{2\pi^2 \times 1.672 \times 10^{-27} \times 15 \times 10^6 \times 15 \times 10^6 \times .75 \times .75}{1.6 \times 10^{-13}}$$

$$= \mathbf{26.11\ MeV}$$

Example 24. A cyclotron with Dee's diameter 1.8 *m* has a magnetic field of 0.8 tesla. Calculate the energy to which the doubly ionised helium ion He^{++} can be accelerated. Also calculate the number of revolutions the particle makes in attaining this energy.

(Mass of He^{++} = 6.68 × 10^{-27} kg.)

Solution. Mass of the α-particle (He^{++})

$$m = 6.68 \times 10^{-27} \text{ kg}$$

Charge on He^{++} ion, $e = 2 \times 1.6 \times 10^{-19}$ C

Now $$E = \frac{B^2 e^2 r^2}{2m}$$

$$B = 0.8 \text{ Tesla};\ r = 0.9 \text{ m}$$

$$\therefore \quad E = \frac{0.8 \times 0.8 \times 2 \times 1.6 \times 10^{-19} \times 2 \times 1.6 \times 10^{-19} \times 0.9 \times 0.9}{2 \times 6.68 \times 10^{-27}}$$

$$= 0.397 \times 10^{-11} \text{ J} = \frac{0.397 \times 10^{-11}}{1.6 \times 10^{-13}} = \mathbf{24.8\ MeV.}$$

The frequency of the alternating electric field is given by

$$f = \frac{Be}{2\pi m} = \frac{0.8 \times 2 \times 1.6 \times 10^{-19}}{2\pi \times 6.68 \times 10^{-27}} = 0.061 \times 10^8 = 6.1 \times 10^6 \text{ s}^{-1}$$

This gives the number of times the He^{++} ion comes out of the gap between the dees each time undertaking a semi-circular path.

∴ Number of complete revolution made by He^{++} ion in attaining the above energy

$$= \frac{f}{2} = \frac{1}{2} \times 6.1 \times 10^5 \times 6.1 \times 10^6 = \mathbf{3.05 \times 10^6\ s^{-1}}$$

Example 25. Deutrons in a cyclotron describe a circle of radius 0.32 m just before emerging out of the Dee's. The frequency of the applied e.m.f. is 10 MHz. Find the flux density of the magnetic field and the velocity of the deutrons emerging out of the cyclotron. (Mass of deutron is 3.32 × 10^{-27} kg and charge 1.6 × 10^{-19} C.) ***(Bang. U. 2000)***

Solution. The frequency of the applied electric field is given by

$$f = \frac{Be}{2\pi m} \quad \therefore B = \frac{2\pi mf}{e}$$

Here $m = 3.32 \times 10^{-27}$ kg; $f = 10$ MHz $= 10 \times 10^6$ Hz;

$$e = 1.6 \times 10^{-19} \text{ C}$$

$$B = \frac{2\pi \times 3.32 \times 10^{-27}\ 10^7}{1.6 \times 10^{-19}} = 1.304 \text{ Tesla}$$

Radius of the circle just before deutrons emerge $r_{max} = 0.32$ m

Now $$Bev = \frac{mv^2}{r_{max}}$$

$\therefore$ $$v = \frac{Ber_{max}}{m} = \frac{1.304 \times 1.6 \times 10^{-19} \times 0.32}{3.32 \times 10^{-27}}$$

$$= \mathbf{2.01 \times 10^7\ ms^{-1}}$$

Example 26. A cyclotron of radius 0.462 *m* is used to accelerate deutrons. The oscilator frequency is 25 MHz. Find the magnetic flux density needed and also energy acquired by the deutron. (Given *m* = 3.32 × 10⁻²⁷ kg.) ***(Bang. U.* 2004)**

Solution. $m = 3.32 \times 10^{-27}$ kg. $f = 25$ MHz $= 25 \times 10^6$ Hz

$e = 1.6 \times 10^{-19}$ C

$$B = \frac{2\pi mf}{e} = \frac{2\pi \times 3.32 \times 10^{-27} \times 25 \times 10^6}{1.6 \times 10^{-19}} = 3.26\ \text{T}$$

$$E = 2\pi^2 mf^2 r_{max}^2$$

$$= 2\pi^2 \times 3.32 \times 10^{-27} \times 25 \times 10^6 \times 25 \times 10^6 \times 0.462 \times 0.462$$

$$= 87.4 \times 10^{-13}\ \text{J} = \frac{87.4 \times 10^{-13}}{1.6 \times 10^{-13}} = \mathbf{54.6\ MeV.}$$

Example 27. A cyclotron oscillator frequency 1 MHz is used to accelerate protons. If the radius of the dees is 60 cm, find the magnetic field in Tesla. **(*Nagpur Uni.* 2008; *H.P.U.* 2002)**

Solution. $m = 1.67 \times 10^{-27}$ kg; $f = 1$ MHz $= 10^6$ Hz

$e = 10^6 \times 10^{-19}$ C

$$B = \frac{2\pi mf}{e} = \frac{2 \times 3.142 \times 1.67 \times 10^{-27} \times 10^6}{1.6 \times 10^{-19}} = \mathbf{6.56\ T}$$

Example 28. The dees of a cyclotron, used for accelerating protons, have radii of 50 cm, each and an alternating potential difference of frequency 10 megacycles per second and maximum value 10⁴ volts is applied to them. Obtain (*i*) the strength of the magnetic field of the cyclotron, (*ii*) the velocity and the kinetic energy acquired by a proton, (*iii*) the maximum number of revolutions made by the proton and (*iv*) the time spent by the proton inside the dees.

Solution (*i*). We have *cyclotron frequency*, $n = qB/2\pi mc$, where q is in *esu* and B in *emu* or *gauss*. So that,

$$\textit{Magnetic field } B = \frac{mc}{q} 2\pi n = \frac{1.67 \times 10^{-24} \times 3 \times 10^{10} \times 2\pi \times 10 \times 10^7}{4.8 \times 10^{-10}}$$

$$= \frac{1.67 \times 3 \times 2\pi}{4.8} \times 10^3 = 6557\ \text{Gauss.}$$

(*ii*) We know that the maximum velocity of the proton (corresponding to the radius of its orbit, *i.e.*, the outer radius of the dees) is given by $v = qBr/mc$ (using *Gaussian units*, as here). So that,

$$\textit{velocity acquired by the proton, } v = \frac{4.8 \times 10^{-10} \times 6557 \times 50}{1.67 \times 10^{-24} \times 3 \times 10^{10}} = \frac{8 \times 6557}{1.67} \times 10^5$$

$$= 3.142 \times 10^9 \approx 3 \times 10^9\ \text{cm/sec.}$$

And $\therefore$ *Energy acquired by the proton,* $E = \frac{1}{2}mv^2 = \frac{1}{2}(1.67 \times 10^{-24})\,(3 \times 10^2)^2\, mv^2$

$$= \frac{15.03}{2} \times 10^{-6} = 7.5 \times 10^{-6} \text{ ergs.}$$

$$= \frac{7.5 \times 10^{-6}}{1.6 \times 10^{-12}} = 4.7 \times 10^{6} = 4.7 \times 10^{6} \text{ eV.}$$

(*iii*) If N be the number of rotations made by the proton inside the dees before emerging out, we have *energy gained by it* = $2NeV$ *ergs*, because in one rotation it crosses the gap between the dees two times and each time acquires an energy eV *ergs*.

Since $2NeV$ *ergs* = $2NV$ *electron volts*, we have $2NV = 4.7 \times 10^6$,

whence, $N = \dfrac{4.7 \times 10^6}{2V} = = 2.35 \times 10^2 = 235.$

Thus, the *number of revolutions made by the proton inside the dees* = 235.

(*iv*) The frequency of the alternating potential difference applied to the two dees being 10 megacycles per second, the time spent by the proton inside the dees during one rotation $= 1/10 \times 10^6$ sec.

Hence, *time spent by the proton inside the dees in 235 rotations*

$$= 235/10 \times 10^6 = 2.35 \times 10^{-5} \text{ sec}$$

4.7 CHARGED PARTICLE IN A UNIFORM AND CONSTANT MAGNETIC FIELD

We have seen under § 4.3 (*iii*) how when a particle carrying a charge q moves with velocity $\vec{v}$ in a magnetic field $\vec{B}$, it is acted upon by a *Lorentz force* $\vec{F} = q\vec{v} \times \vec{B}$ in *emu*, *RMKS* or *SI* units, or equal to $\frac{q}{c}\vec{v} \times \vec{B}$ in *Gaussian units* (*i.e.*, with q in *esu* and B in *emu*).

In the absence of any other force, therefore, (the force due to gravity being negligible compared with the Lorentz force), if m be the *mass* of the particle, and $d^2\mathbf{r}/dt^2$, its acceleration we have

$$m\frac{d^2\vec{r}}{dt^2} = m\frac{d\vec{v}}{dt} = q\,\vec{v} \times \vec{B} \text{ in } emu, RMKS \text{ or } SI \text{ units} \qquad \ldots(i)$$

Or $$= (q\,\vec{v}/c) \times \vec{B} \text{ in } Gaussian \text{ units.}$$

Now, if the velocity of the particle, $\vec{v}$ be perpendicular to the magnetic field the *Lorentz force* $\vec{F} = q\,\vec{v} \times \vec{B}$ in *emu*, *RMKS* or *SI* units, or, equal to $(qv/c) \times B$ in Gaussian units, acts upon it in a direction perpendicular to $\vec{v}$; so that, although it does not change the magnitude of the velocity, it continuously changes its direction, resulting in the particle moving in a circular path with the force $\vec{F}$ directed towards its centre, as shown in Fig. 4.10 (*a*). If r be the *radius* of this circular path, clearly, the balancing *centrifugal force*, acting on the particle *outwards*, (away from the centre) $= mv^2/r$.

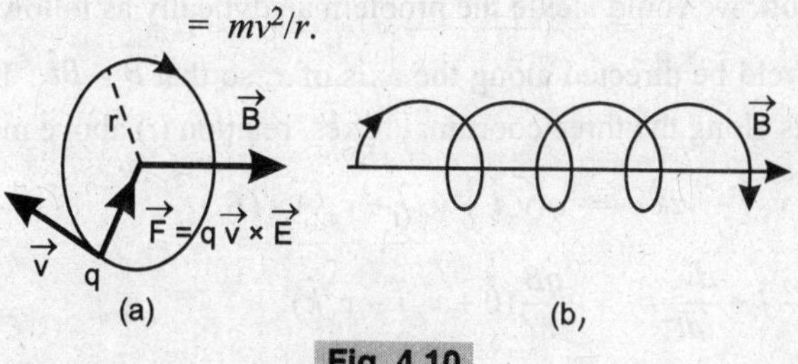

Fig. 4.10

So that, $$mv^2/\vec{r} = \overrightarrow{qv} \times \vec{B}$$

whence, $\vec{r} = m\,\vec{v}/q\,\vec{B}$, if *emu*, *RMKS* or *SI* units be used or $\vec{r} = m\,\vec{v}\,c/q\,\vec{B}$ if Gaussian units be used. ...(*ii*)

If, however, the velocity $\vec{v}$ of the particle be inclined to the magnetic field at an angle other than 90° (*i.e., be not normal to the field*), it may be resolved into a component $\vec{v_1}$, *parallel to the field,* and a component $\vec{v_2}$, *at right angles to it.* The *Lorentz force acting on the particle* will then be $q\vec{v_2} \times \vec{B}$ in *emu*, ***RMKS*** or ***SI*** units, or $(q\vec{v_2}/c) \times \vec{B}$ in Gaussian units, making the particle move in a circular path of radius $\vec{r} = m\vec{v_2}/q\vec{B}$, if *emu*, ***RMKS*** or ***SI*** units be used or, $\vec{r} = m\vec{v_2}\,c/q\vec{B}$ if *Gaussian units* be used.

And, since the component $\vec{v_1}$ of the velocity, parallel to the field *B* makes the particle move in the direction of the field, the combined effect of the circular and the linear horizontal motion is to produce a *helical motion* (or a *moving circle*), as shown in Fig. 4.10 (*b*) the direction of the magnetic field $(\vec{B})$ as axis. ...(*iii*)

The radius *r* of the circular, or the helical path, described by a charged particle in a uniform magnetic field is sometimes called **gyro radius** or **cyclotron radius.**

N.B. It will be noted that in expressions (*ii*) and (*iii*) above, for *r,* the terms *mv* and mv_2 denote the momentum of the particle in the plane perpendicular to B. The relations would, therefore, hold good even in the case of relativistic velocities if we use the appropriate value of the momentum (*p*) in place of *mv* or mv_2. These relations may, therefore, be used to obtain the value of *p* for high energy particles.

If ω be the angular velocity of the particle in circular or helical motion in the magnetic field, we have $\omega = v/r$ (or v_2/r) $= qB/m$ (or qB/mc *if Gaussian units* be used).

Therefore, *time-period of the particles* (or *the time taken by it to describe one full circle*) is given by $T = 2\pi/\omega = 2\pi m/qB$ (or $2\pi mc/qB$ in *Gaussian system of units*).

The distance through which the particle advances forward as it completes one full rotation (in case of helical motion) or the linear distance it covers in one full time-period *T* is called the *pitch of the helix* and is clearly equal to $v_1T = 2\pi m/qBv_1$ (or $2\pi mc/qBv_1$ in *Gaussian system of units*)

And, the *frequency of the particle* or the number of rotations made by it per second, here called **gyro frequency** or **cyclotron frequency,** $n = 1/T = qB/2\pi m$ [or $qB/2\pi mc$ in *Gaussian system of* units].

As will be readily seen, *the gyro frequency or* **cyclotron frequency,** *of a particle is quite independent of the velocity, and hence also of the energy, of the particle* so long as the *velocity lies in the non-relativistic region, i.e., so long as* $v \ll c$. This, as shall see in the next article, is the principle underlying the cyclotron.

This expression for frequency no longer holds good as $v \to c$, for then the mass of the particle varies in accordance with the relation $m = m_0/\sqrt{1 - v^2/c^2}$, where m_0 is the *rest mass* of the particle.

Alternative method. we could tackle the problem analytically as follows:

Let the magnetic field be directed along the axis of *x*, so that $\vec{B} = B\hat{i}$. Then, expressing $\vec{v}$ in terms of its components along the three coordinate axes, relation (*i*) above may be put in the form

$$m\frac{d}{dt}(v_x\hat{i} + v_y\hat{j} + vz\hat{k}) = q(v_x\hat{i} + v_y\hat{j} + v_z\hat{k}) \times (B_i)$$

or,
$$\frac{dv_x}{dt}\hat{i} + \frac{dv_y}{dt}\hat{j} + \frac{dv_z}{dt}\hat{k} = \frac{qB}{m}(0 + v_z\hat{j} - v_y\hat{k}) \qquad ...(iv)$$

Equating the coefficients of $\hat{i}$ on either side of the equation, we have

$$\frac{dv_x}{dt} = 0 \qquad ...(v)$$

indicating that *the particle does not accelerate in the direction of the field or that v_x, the velocity of the particle in this direction (i.e., along the field) remains constant.*

This velocity, in our earlier discussion above, we have denoted by v_1. So that,

$$v_x = v_1.$$

Similarly, equating the coefficients of **j** and **k** on either side, we have

$$\frac{dv_y}{dt} = \frac{qB}{m}v_z \ldots(vi) \quad \text{and} \quad \frac{dv_z}{dt} = -\frac{qB}{m}v_y \quad \ldots(vii)$$

Differentiating relation VI with respect to t, we have

$$\frac{d^2v_y}{dt^2} = \frac{qB}{m}\frac{dv_z}{dt}$$

∴ Substituting the value of dv_2/dt from relation (*vii*) above, we have,

$$\frac{d^2v_y}{dt^2} = -\left(\frac{qB}{m}\right)^2 v_y$$

Or, puting $qB/M = \omega$, we have $\frac{d^2v_y}{dt^2} = -\omega^2 v_y$

As will be readily seen, this an equation similar to that for the *simple harmonic motion* of a particle expect that in place of the *displacement y of the particle, we have here its velocity* v_y. On that analogy, therefore, that solution of this equation is

$$v_y = A\sin(\omega t + \phi)\dagger \quad \ldots(ix)$$

where the values of the constant A and ϕ can be obtained directly from the intial or boundary conditions.

From relation (*vi*), therefore, we have

$$\frac{d}{dt}[A\sin(\omega t + \phi)] = \frac{qB}{m}v_z = \omega v_z$$

i.e., $A\,\omega\cos(\omega t + \phi)\ \omega v_z$.

Or, $$v_z = A\cos(\omega t + \phi). \quad \ldots(x)$$

Squaring and adding relations *ix* and *x*, we have

$$v_y^2 + v_z^2 = A^2 \quad \ldots(xi)$$

But we have, in our earlier discussion, taken the velocity of the particles in the Y–Z plane to be v_2. So that $A^2 = V_2^2$ Or, $A = v_2$.

Since $v_y = dy/dt$ and $A = v_2$, we have from relation (*ix*),

$$dv_y/dt = v_2\sin(\omega t + \phi) \quad \ldots(xii)$$

Equation (*xi*) and (*xii*), on integration, respectively yield

† In case Gaussian units be used, *i.e.*, with q in esu and B in emu, q must every where be replaced by q/c, sicne q esu of charge = q/c cmu of charge.

† Or, this equation may be obtained thus:

Multiplying both sides of equation viii by $2d/dt$ and integrating, we have

$$\left(\frac{dv_y}{dt}\right)^2 = (\omega v_y)^2 + C = C - (\omega v_y)^2 \text{ where, } C \text{ is a constant of integration. So, that}$$

$$\frac{dv_y}{dt} = \sqrt{C - (\omega v_y)^2} \quad \text{or} \quad \frac{dv_y}{\sqrt{C - (\omega v_y)^2}} = dt \text{ which, on integration, gives,}$$

$$\frac{1}{\omega}\sin^{-1}\left(\frac{\omega v_y}{\sqrt{C}}\right) = t + C' \text{ where } C' \text{ is another constant of integrator}$$

$$\text{i.e. } v_y \frac{\sqrt{C}}{\omega}\sin(\omega t + \omega C') = \text{Or putting } \sqrt{C/\omega} = A \text{ and } \omega C' = \phi \text{ we have}$$

$$v_y = A\sin(\omega t + \phi)$$

$$y = -\frac{v_2}{\omega}\cos(\omega t + \phi) \text{ and } z = \frac{v_2}{\omega}\sin(\omega t + \phi)$$

squaring and adding which, we have

$$y^2 + z^2 = \frac{v_2^{\ 2}}{\omega^2} = r^2$$

This is the equation to a circle of radius r in the Y – Z plane,

where $$r = v_2 / \omega = v_2 / \frac{qB}{m} = mv_2 / qB$$

which is thus the value of *gyro radius* or the *cyclotron radius*. Since the particle has also a constant horizontal velocity v_1 along the axis of x (or the direction of the field), the resultant motion of the particle is *helical*, with the axis of the helix lying along the direction of the field (B).

Note. It may be mentioned again that if we use *Gaussian units*, *i.e.*, if we take q in *esu* and B in emu (or gauss), we must use q/c instead of q in all the expression obtianed above, since q *esu* of charge = q/c *emu* of charge.

Example 16. Calculate radius of path of an electron is a magnetic field of induction 10^{-4} wb/m^2 perpendicular to its path. (Velocity of the elctron = 1.9×10^5 m/s, m = 9.1×10^{-31} kg, $e = 1.6 \times 10^{-19}$ C) ***(Nagpur Uni. 2008)***

Solution.

$$R = \frac{mv}{eB} = \frac{9.1 \times 10^{-31} \times 1.9 \times 10^{8}}{1.6 \times 10^{-19} \times 10^{-4}}$$

$$= \frac{9.1 \times 1.9}{1.6}$$

$$= \mathbf{10.81\ m}$$

Example 17. An elctron having kinetic energy 2×10^5 *eV* enters a uniform magnectic field of induction 3×10^{-3} Wb/m^2 in a direction perpendicular to the field. Find the radius of the electron path in the field.

Solution. Given

$$m = 9 \times 10^{-31} \text{ kg}, e = 1.6 \times 10^{-19}\text{C}, 1eV = 1.6 \times 10^{-19} \text{ J},$$

$$B = 3 \times 10^{-3} \text{ Wb/m}^2, \text{K.E.} = 2 \times 10^5 \times 1.6 \times 10^{-19} \text{ J}$$

$$\frac{1}{2}mv^2 = \text{Kinetic energy k say}$$

$$\therefore \quad v = \sqrt{\frac{2\kappa}{m}}$$

Radius of the path is given by

$$R = \frac{mv}{eB} = \frac{m}{eB}\sqrt{\frac{2\kappa}{m}}$$

$$= \sqrt{\frac{2\kappa m}{eB}}$$

$$= \frac{\sqrt{2 \times 2 \times 10^5 \times 1.6 \times 10^{-19} \times 9 \times 10^{-31}}}{1.6 \times 10^{-19} \times 3 \times 10^{-3}}$$

$$= \frac{\sqrt{4 \times 1.6 \times 9 \times 10^{-45}}}{1.6 \times 3 \times 10^{-22}} = \frac{\sqrt{4 \times 16 \times 9 \times 10^{-46}}}{48 \times 10^{-23}}$$

$$= \frac{24}{48} = 0.5 \text{ m}$$

Example 18. What would be the length of the last drift tube in a linear accelerator which produces 120 MeV C^{12} ions, using frequency of 70 MHz?

(1 eV = 1.6 × 10^{-19} J, and 1 amu = 1.66 × 10^{-27} kg) ***(Nagpur U. 2009)***

Solution.

$$E_n = 120 \text{ MeV} = 120 \times 1.6 \times 10^{-19} \times 10^6 \text{ J}$$
$$= 1.2 \times 1.6 \times 10^{-11} \text{ J} \quad m = 12 \times 1.66 \times 10^{-27} \text{ kg}$$
$$f = 70 \text{ MHz} = 70 \times 10^6 \text{ Hz} = 7 \times 10^7 \text{ Hz}$$

Let l_n be the length of the last tube.

We have,

$$\frac{1}{2} m v_n^2 = E_n$$

$$\therefore \qquad v_n = \sqrt{\frac{2E_n}{m}}$$

According to the condition of synchronous acceleration

$$\frac{l_n}{v_n} = \frac{T}{2} = \frac{1}{2f}$$

$$l_n = \frac{v_n}{2f} = \frac{1}{2f}\sqrt{\frac{2E_n}{m}}$$

$$= \frac{1}{2 \times 7 \times 10^7}\sqrt{\frac{2 \times 1.2 \times 1.6 \times 10^{-11}}{12 \times 1.66 \times 10^{-27}}}$$

$$= \frac{1}{14 \times 10^7}\sqrt{\frac{2 \times 1.2 \times 1.6 \times 10^{-11}}{12 \times 1.66 \times 10^{-27}}}$$

$$= \frac{1}{14 \times 10^7}\sqrt{\frac{2 \times 1.6 \times 10^{15}}{1.66}}$$

$$= \frac{10^7}{14 \times 10^7}\sqrt{\frac{2 \times 1.6 \times 10}{1.66}}$$

$$= \frac{1}{14} \times 4.391 = 0.3136 \text{ m}$$

$$= \mathbf{31.36 \text{ cm}}$$

4.8 THE CYCLOTRON

The α and β- particles given out by natural radioactive substances neither possess sufficiently large speeds not their speeds are under control. It was, therefore, felt necessary to accelerate charged particles to very high velocities by the application of electron of electric and magnetic fields. Cockroft and Walton produced fast moving protons by electronic voltage multiplication device. The best arrangement was, however, made by Lawrence and Livingstone in 1935 and called a *cyclotron*. This arrangement won the Nobel prize for Lawrence.

Construction. The cyclotron essentially consist of two semicircular hollow cylindrical boxes. D, and D_2 usually of copper and called the dees on account of their shape like the letter D. These are placed in an evacuated cylindrical steel tank, with their edges parallel but with a small diametrical gap G between them as shown in fig. 4.11 (*a*)

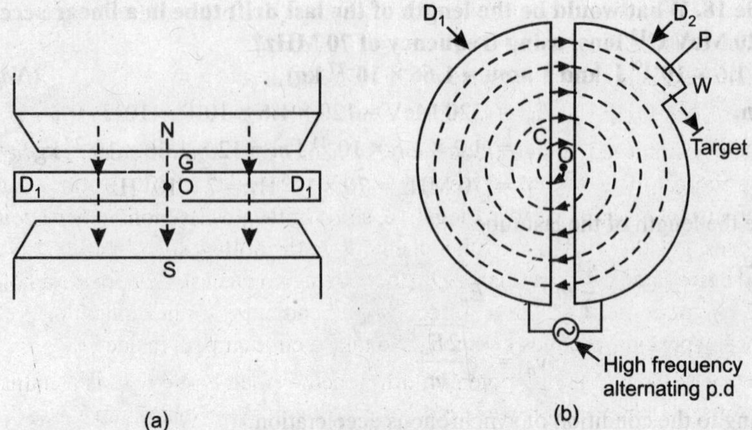

Fig. 4.11

Role of Electric and Magnetic field. Simultaneous application of electric field and magnetic field plays an important role in the working of cyclotron.

Magnetic field. The basic function of the magnetic field is to move the charged particle into a *semi-circular path with the dees*.

The whole assembly is arranged to lie in between the pole-pieces of large and powerful electromagnet NS, of about the same diameter as that of the two dees; so that, magnetic field is parallel to tha axis of the tank and perpendicular to its base adn hence also to the plane of the dees, with a flux of the order of 1.5 weber-metre^2 or 15000 gauss.

Electric field. The primary function of the electric field is to provide a potential difference between the dees of the cyclotron to *accelerate the charged particles*. Thus, an alternating electric field having a frequency such that the time taken by the particle to travel through the semi-circular path within the dees is equal to half the time period of the alternating electric field is required.

The dees, also referred to as the *electrodes*, are connected to a radio frequency oscillator in order to produce a high alternating potential difference across them, of the order of 10^4 *volts*,or more and a very high frequency in the neighbourhood of 10 MHz.

The positive ions to be accelerated may be obtained in one of the following ways:

(*i*) The required gas, (for example, *hydrogen* for obtaining *protons*, *heavy hydrogen* for obtaining *deutrons* and *helium* for obtaining *α-particles*) is filled into the steel tank at a low pressure of about 10^{-3} mm of mercury and a filament, at or near the centre of the tank, *just outside the dees,* is heated. With a small potential difference applied between the filament and the tank, the eletrons emitted by the hot filament acquire sufficient engery to be able to ionise some of the atoms of the gas and thus produce a vertical column of positive ions. Some of these positive ions then find their way into the gap between the two dees.

(*ii*) Alternatively, what is known as a *capillary ion source* is used. The ions here too are produced in the same manner as indicated under (*i*) above, but *in a separate or an auxiliary chamber* and led from there into the steel tank through a narrow opening or a capillary tube which is so directed that there is again a narrow vertical column of positive ions near the centre *O* of the gap *G* between the two dees.

Both the methods have their advantages and disadvantages in to which, however, we need not go here.

Principle. The cyclotron is a *magnetic resonance type positive ion* accelerator. The charged particle to be accelerated placed at a centre point 0 of the Dee, rapidly passes through an alternating electric field along a closed path, its energy being increased each time. A strong magnetic field is used to control the motion of the particles and to return them periodically to the region of the acceleration electric field. The particle passes definite points of the alternating electric field almost in union when the field is in the same phase *i.e.* in *resonance*.

The resonance condition is discussed below along with the cyclotron resonance equation.

Working. On account of the high frequency alternating potential difference applied to the dees D_1 and D_2, they alternately acquire positive and negative potentials about 10^7 time in a second. So that, if at a given instant D_1 happens to be negative, some of the positive ions, say *protons*, in the gap G between the dees, get attracted towards it and enter into the hollow space within it. Now, although the electric field cases to be effective inside D_1 (there being no electric field inside a hollow charged conductor), the magnetic field acts in a direction perpendicular to their plane of motion and the positive ions, or the protons, are thus compelled to take a circular path inside D_1.

The frequency of the alternating potential difference applied to the dees is so adjusted that not only does the potential changes direction but has also its peak or maximum value V when, after covering their semi-circular path through D_1, the positive ions or the protons, emerge out into the diametrical gap G; so that, they now find D_2 to be negative and D_1 positive, and therefore cross over from D_1 to D_2 *each acquiring an amount of energy* qV *in the process* (where q is the charge on it). Hence, as under the action of the magnetic field perpendicular to them, they again describe a semi-circular path inside D_z they emerge out into the gap G with a higher velocity.

If this frequency of the alternating potential difference be further equal to the gyro frequency or the cyclotron frequency $qB/2\pi m$ (by suitable adjustment of the magnetic field B), the frequency of rotation of the ions or the protons then being quite independent of their velocity inside the dees, they always emerge out into the gap from either dee to find that the dees have, in the meanwhile, changed their signs of potential. The motion of the ions through the dees is thus in resonance with the alternating potential applied. Every time, therefore, the ions gain an amount of energy qV each as they cross over from one dee to the other, with the result that they continue to move in circular paths of continually increasing radii inside the two dees, thus describing an ever-expanding spiral, as shown in Fig. 4.11 (*a*), unit the radius of their path becomes nearly the same as the outermost radius of either dee.

By this time, the ion beam acquires a sufficient high velocity and is brought out of dee D_2 through a thinly covered window W by means of a deflecting plate P which is maintained at negative potential. To make sure that this negative potential is with respect to the earth, it is *so arranged that the window W lies at right angles to the diametrical gap G between the dees, i.e., OW* is perpendicular to the gap G, because then, the instantaneous potential difference across the gap G is *zero* at the time that the ions or the protons emerge out at W. (This is so because the time taken by the ions to cover the distance from the gap to W, inside D_2, is one-quarter of their time-period and since the potential difference acorss the gap had its peak or maximum value when the ions crossed the gap from D_1 to D_2 it must, after a quarter of a time-period, have an instantaneous value *zero*). Thus, deflected by the negative plate P the high energy beam of positive ions (or protons) is allowed to fall on the target, placed in an evacuated side-tube attached to the steel tank.

Resonance condition: As we have discussed above, cyclotron is a resonance device. In a cyclotron the value of the magnetic field strength depends upon the frequency of the oscillating electric field applied between the dees. It is so chosen as to give *resonance* between the arrival of the charged particle in the gap and reversal of the voltage between the dees. This is done by adjusting the time taken by the charged particle to describe a semi-circular path equal to half the time period of oscillation of the applied high frequency electric field *i.e.*

$$\frac{\pi}{\omega} = \frac{T}{2}$$

The frequency

$$f = \frac{1}{T} = \frac{\omega}{2\pi} = \frac{Be}{2\pi m}$$

This gives the *cyclotron resonance condition* for charged particles of a given value of $\frac{e}{m}$. If this condition is not satisfied there will be no resonance between the arrival of the charged particle in the gap and the reversal of the voltage between the dees. The particle will go out of step and will not be accelerated. This is why is it said that a cyclotron is a *resonance device.*

Theory. If a positive ion is generated at a point 0, as shown in Fig. 4.11(*b*), within the gap at a time when D_2 is at positive potential and D_1 at a negative potential, it will be accelerated across the gap to D_1 and and enter the hollow segment D_1 with velocity v given by

$$Ve = \frac{1}{2}mv^2$$

where, V is the applied voltage and e and m are charge and mass of the particle respectively. When it is inside the conductor, it will not acted upon by the electric field but under the influence of the applied magnetic field having a flux density B, it will travel along a circular path, the radius of which is given by

$$\frac{mv^2}{r} = Bev$$

and finally emerges at C in the direction indicated.

The time taken by the positive ion to travel the semicircular path

$$t = \frac{\pi}{\omega} = \frac{\pi r}{v} = \frac{\pi m}{Be}$$

where ω is the angular velocity of the ion in the circular path and

$$\omega = \frac{Be}{m}$$

The value of t is a constant being independent of the velocity of the ion and the radius in which it travels. If the frequency of the applied voltage is adjusted in such a manner that it is reversed as soon as the particle comes out of D_1, the particle at C will be accelerated across the gap to D_2 and and will describe a further circular path in D_2. The radius of the semi-circle as well as speed of the particle will, now, be greater than that in the first case, but as proved above, the time taken by the particle to travel the semi-circular path in D_2 will be the same. Everytime the particle emerges out of the dees, the direction of the voltage is reversed and the particle is accelerated across the gap. The path of the particle will be a spiral and it will finally come out of the Dees is the direction indicated, through the window W.

Maximum kinetic energy of the particle. The final energy E of the charged particle is give by

$$E = \frac{1}{2}mv_{max}^2$$

where v_{max} is the maximum velocity gained by the charged particle in its final orbit of radius r_{max}

Now

$$\frac{mv_{max}^2}{r_{max}} = Bev_{max}$$

$$r_{max} = \frac{Be}{m}r_{max}$$

Hence,

$$E = \frac{1}{2}mv_{max}^2 = \frac{1}{2}m\frac{B^2e^2}{m^2}r_{max}^2$$

$$= \frac{1}{2}\frac{B^2e^2r_{max}^2}{m^2}$$

This relation gives the maximum kinetic energy of the charged particle in terms of applied *magnetic field* and *dee radius*.

The condition for optimal acceleration of the ion in the inter dee gap is that the time taken by the ion to travel the semi-circular path (t) is equal to half the time period (T) of oscillation of the applied high frequency electric field

i.e.,
$$t = \frac{T}{2}$$

or
$$\frac{\pi m}{Be} = \frac{T}{2}$$

or
$$T = \frac{2\pi m}{Be}$$

If f is the frequency of the oscillating electric field, then

$$f = \frac{1}{T} = \frac{Be}{2\pi m}$$

This is the basic cyclotron resonance equation.

Hence, in terms of f the maximum energy of the charged particle

$$E_{max} = \frac{1}{2}\frac{B^2 e^2 r_{max}^2}{m}$$

$$= \frac{1}{2}4\pi^2 m \frac{B^2 e^2}{4\pi^2 m^2} r_{max}^2$$

$$= 2\,\pi^2 m f^2 r_{max}^2$$

The particles are ejected out of the cyclotron as pulse streams and not continuously.

With a comparatively small potential difference of the order of 50,0000 volts, very fast moving particles can be produced. For example, if the particle makes 200 revolutions before emerging out it will gain a velocity equivalent to a total fall through a potential of

$$2 \times 50000 \times 200 = 20 \text{ million volts}$$

If heavy hydrogen is used instead of ordinary hydrogen, a beam of high energy deuterons is obtained. As their mass is double they possess greater energy and are more useful as atomic projectiles.

Maximum radius of curvature. If V is the average voltage applied between the dees of a cyclotron and the charged particle crosses the gaps between the dees n times to reach the orbit of maximum radius, then energy acquired by the ion having a charge e is given by

$$E_{max} = neV$$

But
$$E_{max} = \frac{1}{2}\frac{B^2 e^2 r_{max}^2}{m}$$

$\therefore$
$$\frac{B^2 e^2 r_{max}^2}{2\,m} = neV$$

or
$$r_{max} = \frac{1}{B}\left(\frac{2mV}{e}\right)^{1/2} n^{1/2}$$

If the values of B and V are kept constant, r_{max} is directly proportional to the square root of the number of time the particles crosses the gap between the dees.

Limitations of the cyclotron

(*i*) The energy to which a particle can be accelerated in a cycloron is limited due to change in mass with velocity. The mass of a particle, when moving with a velocity v is given by

$$m = \frac{m_0}{\sqrt{1-\frac{v^2}{c^2}}}$$

where m_0 is the rest mass and c the velocity of light. As already proved, the time taken by a particle to travel the semi-circular path is $\frac{\pi m}{Be} = \frac{T}{2}$

$\therefore$ Frequency
$$f = \frac{1}{T} = \frac{Be}{2\pi m}$$
$$= \frac{Be\sqrt{1-\frac{v^2}{c^2}}}{2\pi m_0}$$

Hence the frequency of rotation of the charged particle decreases as the velocity increases. As a result it takes a longer time to complete its semi-circular path and the particle continuously goes on lagging the applied alternating potential difference till a stage is reached when it can no longer be accelerated further. This discrepancy is optimised by the following two methods:

***(i)* Field variation.** The frequency of the ion can be kept constant by taking $B\sqrt{1-\frac{v^2}{c^2}}$ a constant. For this purpose the value of the magnetic field B should increase as the velocity of the ion increases so that the product remains unchanged.

***(ii)* Frequency modulation.** In the alternative method, the frequency of the applied $A.\ C$ is varied so that it is always equal to the frequency of rotation of the ion. The machine in which the frequency of electric field is kept constant and magnetic field is varied is called **Synchrotron.** whereas a machine in which magnetic field is kept constant and the frequency of the applied electric field is varied is known as a **Frequency modulated cyclotron** or **Synchro-cyclotron.**

(2) A cyclotron cannot be used to produce high energy electron beams. The reason for the same is that there is an appreciable increase in the mass of the electron at fairly low energies. For example, a 10% increase in the rest mass of the electron take place at an energy of 50 KeV only. Electron being a very light particle there is an appreciable increase in its velocity at low energies which is not the case with massive particles like the proton or the α-particle.

(3) Neutron can not be accelerated by a cyclotron. A neutron carries no charge; it can not be accelerated by the electric field between the two Dee's. It can also be not acted upon by the magnetic field so that its path within the dees cannot be regulated.

4.9 MAGNETIC FIELD FOCUSSING

An appropriate configuration of non-uniform electric field, is used for focussing of electrons. An electron beam can also be focussed with the help of magnetic field. Depending upon the nature of the magnetic field and the direction of its application, two different types of focussing are obtained.

(*i*) Longitudinal magnetic field focussing, and

(*ii*) Transverse magnetic field focussing.

4.9.1 Longitudinal Magnetic Field Focussing

Charged particles like electrons can be focussed at a point by employing a uniform magnetic field acting along the direction of motion of beam of charged particles; as shown in fig. 4.12. The path of an electron.

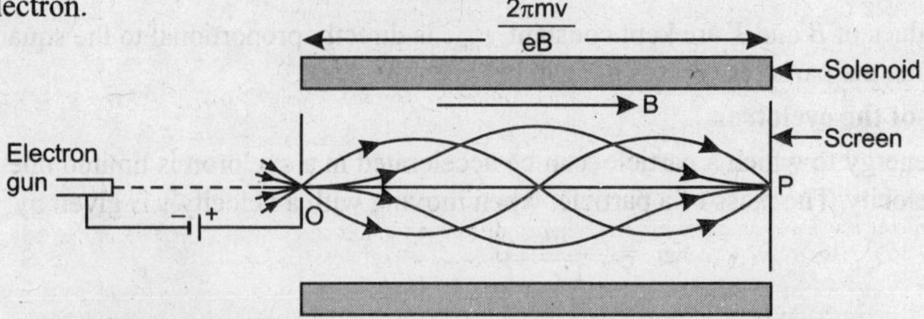

Fig. 4.12 Focusing of charged particles in a longitudinal magnetic field.

in a uniform magnetic field would be a helix if electrons enter at an angle ϕ, the path (p) of the helix is given by

$$p = \frac{2\pi mv}{eB} \cos\phi \qquad ...(i)$$

Suppose a beam of electrons enters at point O with a small angle ϕ and with a velocity v. If ϕ is taken too small ($\phi \leq 10°$), cos ϕ may by taken as unity. In time T, the charged particles come to focus at point P, the length $OP = l$ is given by

$$l = \frac{2\pi mv}{eB} \qquad ...(ii)$$

Therefore, the beam of electron entering the field B making a small angle of divergence ϕ come to focus at a distance l or any point which is located at a distance of integral multiple of l *i.e.* nl.

4.9.2 Transverse Magnetic Field Focussing (180°)

Particle carrying the *same charge* (q) and having the *same momentum* (p), even if moving in different directions, can all be brought to focus at very nearly the same point on a screen by means of a suitably applied magnetic field. This is called *magnetic focussing*, and since the particles come to common focus after describing an angle of 180° from their point of entry into the magnetic field, we quality it as **180° magnetic focussing.**

If, on the other hand, the particles carry the same charge but have different momenta, they are brough to focus at different points on the screen.

To take the second case first, if a beam of particles, each carrying a charge q, enters normally, through a slit S in a screen, [Fig. 4.13 (*a*)], into a magnetic field of flux density B perpendicular to the beam (*i.e.*, perpendicular to the plane of the paper in the case shown), a particle of the beam is acted upon by a force equal to qvB, where v is the velocity of the particle. Under the action of this force, the particle takes a circular path, such that if m be the mass of the particle and r, the radius of its circular path, we have

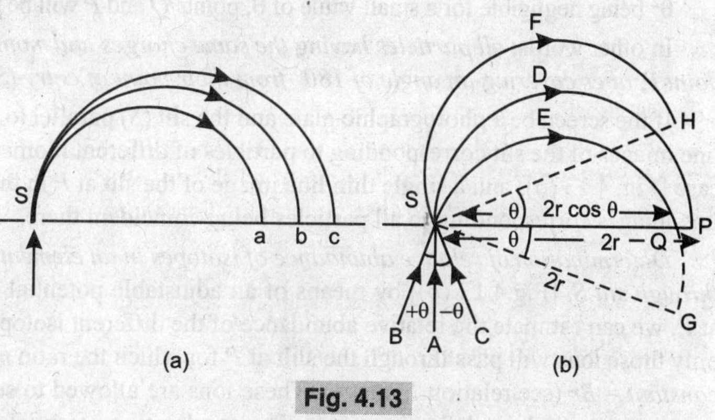

Fig. 4.13

$$mv^2/r = qvB, \text{ whence, } r = mv^2/qvB = mv/qB. \qquad ...(i)$$

Now, q and B being constants, *i.e.*, the same for each particle, r varies withe momentum $p = mv$ of the particles. So that particle's having different momenta come to focus at different points a, b, c on the screen. The device thus acts a **momentum selector.**

Obviously, even if the velocities of the particles in the beam be arranged to the *same*, their momenta will still be *different* on account of their different masses. So that, particle of *different masses* will then come to focus at different points. This is the principle underlying the mass spectrographs, like the *Bainbridge mass spectrograph, for the separation of isotopes*, i.e., elements having the same atomic number and chemical properties but different atomic weights.*

* **Isotopes:** Isotopes are nuclei having the same atomic (proton) number Z but different atomic mass A. The isotopes of an element contain the same number of protons but different number of neutrons. For example: Oxygen has two isotopes $^{16}O_8$ and $^{17}O_8$. Hydrogen has three isotope: (*i*) Hydrogen $^1H_1$ (*ii*) Deuterium $^2H_1$ and (*iii*) Tritium $^3H_1$. Neon has two isotopes $^{20}Ne_{10}$, $^{22}Ne_{10}$ Chlorine also has two isotopes $^{35}Cl_{17}$ and $^{37}Cl_{17}$. At present about 297 different isotopes are knwon .

Let us now consider the first case, *viz.*, the case of particles carrying the same charge and having the same momentum.

Thus, suppose we have a conical beam of particles, all carrying the same charge q and having the same momentum $p = mv$, entering the magnetic field through a slit S as shown in Fig. 4.13(b). Then the particles entering the slit normally along AS describe, under the action of the magnetic field, the trajectory SDP, thus covering an angle of 180° from S and coming to focus on the screen at P, such that the diameter of the circular path taken is $SP = 2r$.

The particles entering the slit along BS at a angle $+\theta$ with AS describe the trajectory SEQ and come to focus at Q, such that the diameter SG of their circular path is also inclined to SP at an angle θ, and therefore, the chord $SQ = 2r\cos\theta$.

Similarly, the particles entering the slit along CS at an angle $-\theta$ with AS describe the trajectory SFQ and also come to focus on the screen at Q, with the diameter SH of their circular path inclined to SP at an angle θ.

Thus, the particles of the conical beam are all spread over the small distance QP on the screen, where

$$QP = SP - SQ = 2r - 2r\cos\theta = 2r(l - \cos\theta)$$

Or, Since $\cos\theta = 1 - \frac{\theta^2}{2!} + \frac{\theta^4}{4!} \ldots = 1 - \frac{\theta^2}{2}$, neglecting the higher power of θ, we have

$$OP = 2r[1 - (1 - \theta^2/2)] = 2r.\theta^2/2 = r\theta^2.$$

θ^2 being negligible for a small value of θ, points Q and P will be practically coincident or the same.

In other words, *all particles having the same charges and momentum came to focus at the same point P, after covering an angle of 180° from their point of entry (S) into the magnetic field.*

If the screen be a photographic plate and the slit (S) parallel to the magnetic field, we shall have line images of the slit corresponding to particles of different momenta at point like a, b, c in the first case [Fig. 4.13 (a)] and a single thin line image of the slit at P in the second case, [Fig. 4.13(b)], the line images corresponding to all particles being coincident there.

Determination of relative abundance of isotopes in an element. Accelerating the ions of a given through slit S. [Fig 4.13 (b)] by means of an adjustable potential difference and using another slit at P, we can estimate the relative abundance of the different isotopes in the element. For, obviously only those ions will pass through the slilt at P for which the ratio *momentum to charge, i.e., mv/q is constant* = Br (see relation I, above). These ions are allowed to send a current through a sensitive galvanometer and the deflection noted. The accelerating potential is now altered so that another set of ions, with a slightly different value of m/q now enter the slit $\underline{S}$ and emerge through the slit of P, producing a slightly different deflection in the galvanometer. These deflections in the galvanometer being proportional to the number of ions present in the beam and responsible for the current through it, we can easily estimate from them the relative abundance of the different ions present in the beam and hence that of the different isotopes present in the given element.

Example 29. An electron describes a helix of radius 10 cm and pitch 3 cm in a magnetic field of 50 gauss. Calculate the components of its velocity along and perpendicular to the field. (Take mass of electron = 9×10^{-28} gm)

Solution. Let the components of the velocity of the electron along and perpendicular to the magnetic field be v_1 and v_2 respectively, the former responsible for its forward motion along the direction of the field and the latter for its rotation, making its resultant path a helix.

The radius of the helix, therefore, is given by the relation $r = mv^2c/qB$(see §4.7).

whence, $v_2 \left(\frac{qB}{mc}\right) r = \left(\frac{4.80 \times 10^{-10} \times 50}{9 \times 10^{-28} \times 3 \times 10^{10}}\right) 10 = (8.9 \times 10)^8 10 = 8.9 \times 10^9$ cm/sec.

And, since *pitch of the helix* $= \frac{2\pi mc}{qB} v_1 = 3$, we have

$$v_1 = \frac{3}{2\pi}\left(\frac{qB}{mc}\right) = \frac{3}{2\pi}(8.9 \times 10^8) = 4.25 \times 10^8 \text{ cm/sec.}$$

Thus, the *components of the velocity of the electron along and perpendicular to the magnetic field are respectively 4.25 × 10^8 cm/sec and 8.9 × 10^9 cm/sec.*

Example 30. An electron of energy 20 electron volts moving in a direction perpendicular to a magnetic field *B* = 10^2 Wb/m^2 describes a circle of radius r. Calculate the value of *r*, (1 ev = 1.6 × 10^{-19}) joules, mass of electron may be taken to be 9 × 10^{-31}kg.

Solution. Let *v* be the velocity of the electron perpendicular to the magnetic field. Then if *m* be its mass, we have

$$\frac{1}{2}mv^2 = 20\ eV = 20 \times 1.6 \times 10^{-19} \text{ joules}$$

whence

$$v = \left(\frac{2 \times 20 \times 1.6 \times 10^{-19}}{m}\right)^{\frac{1}{2}} \left(\frac{64 \times 10^{-19}}{m}\right)^{\frac{1}{2}} \text{ m/sec.}$$

Now, as we know, the radius of the circle described by a charged particles in a uniforms magnetic field (§4.7) or the gyro (or cyclotron) radius, as it is called, is given by $r = mv/qB$†. So, that, we have

$$r = \frac{m(64 \times 10^{-19})^{\frac{1}{2}}}{\sqrt{m} \times q \times B} = \frac{\sqrt{m}\,(64 \times 10^{-19})^{\frac{1}{2}}}{q \times B} = \frac{(9 \times 10^{-31} \times 64 \times 10^{-19})^{\frac{1}{2}}}{1.6 \times 10^{-19} \times 10^2}$$

$$= \frac{3 \times 8}{1.6} \times 10^{-8} = 15.0 \times 10^{-8} \text{ metre.}$$

Thus, the radius of the circular path described by the electron = 15.0 × 10^{-8} metre.

Example 31. An electron of velocity $\vec{v} = (2\hat{i} + 3\hat{j})10^2$ cm/sec enters a region of uniform magnitude field *B* = 500 $\hat{i}$ gauss, so that its path become helical.

(*i*) In what direction does the axis of the helix lie? (*ii*) Calculate the radius of the helix. (*iii*) Calculate the number of rotations as the electron advance 10 cm along the axis of the helix.

[*Agra* (supp)]

Solution. Here, the velocity *v* of the electron may be resolved into two rectangular components, $\vec{v_1} = 2 \times 10^8 \hat{i}$ cm/sec. along the direction of the magnetic field $\vec{B} = 500\hat{i}$ = gauss and $\vec{v_2} = 3 \times 10^8 \hat{j}$ cm /sec, perpendicular to it, the former component being responsible for the forward motion of the electron along the field and the latter for circuar motion (see § 4.7).So that,

(*i*) *the axis of the helix lies along the direction of the magnetic field, i.e., along the axis of x:*

(*ii*) *the radius of the helix is given by $r = mv_2c/qB$. Taking m* = 9 × 10^{-28} *gm.* q = 4.80 × 10^{-10} *esu,* v_2 = 3 × 10^8 *cm/sec and B* = 500 *gauss (given)*

we have

$$r = \frac{9 \times 10^{-28} \times 3 \times 10^8 \times 3 \times 10^{10}}{4.80 \times 10^{-10} \times 500} = \frac{81}{4.80 \times 500} = 0.03375 \approx 00.34 \text{ cm}$$

(*iii*) *The forward distance covered by the electron in one full rotation, i.e. pitch of the helical path*

$$\frac{2\pi mc}{qB} v_1 = \frac{2\pi \times 9 \times 10^{-28} \times 3 \times 10^{10}}{4.80 \times 10^{-10} \times 500} \times 2 \times 10^8$$

† $r = mvc/qB$ if Gaussian units be used , i;e;, if *q* be in esu and Bin emu or gauss.

∴ *number of rotations made by the electron as it advance through a distance of 10 cm*

$$= \frac{10}{\text{pitch of the helix}} = \frac{10 \times 4.80 \times 10^{-10} \times 500}{2\pi \times 9 \times 10^{-28} \times 3 \times 10^{10} \times 2 \times 10^{8}}$$

$$= \frac{4.8 \times 5}{2\pi \times 54} \times 10^3 = 70.74.$$

Example 32. For a proton initially travelling with velocity $v_x = 5 \times 10^8$ cm/sec, calculate the following: (*i*) Force experienced in a magnetic field $\vec{B} = 2000\hat{j} + 4000\hat{k}$ gauss. (*ii*) Acceleration acquired in an electric firld $\vec{E} = 200\hat{i} + 100\hat{j}$ volts/cm (*iii*) Transverse deflection in travelling a length $L_z = 10$ cm in an electric field $E_y = 200$ volts/cm. (*Agra 2002*)

Solution. (*i*) We know that force acting on a charge q moving perpendicular to a magnetic field $\vec{B}$ with velocity $\vec{v}$ is given by, $\vec{F} = \frac{q}{c}(\vec{v} \times \vec{B})$ using *Gaussian units*. So that,

$$\vec{F} = \frac{q}{c}(5 \times 10^8 \hat{i})(2000\hat{j} + 4000\hat{k})$$

Here $q = e = 4.8 \times 10^{-10}$ *esu* and $v = v_x = 5 \times 10^8$ cm/sec. We, therefore, have

$$\vec{F} = \frac{4.8 \times 10^{-10}}{3 \times 10^{10}} \times 5 \times 10^8 \times 2000\,(\hat{k} - 2\hat{j}) = 1.6 \times 10^8\,(\hat{k} - 2\hat{j}) \text{ dyne}$$

or *magnitude of the force*, $F = 1.6 \times 10^{-8}\sqrt{5} = 3.578 \times 10^{-8}$ dynes

and its *direction consines*, clearly $0, -2\sqrt{5}$ and $1\sqrt{5}$

(*ii*) We know that the force experienced by a particles carrying a charge q in an electric field E is equal to qE. Therefore, if m be the mass of the particle and a, the acceleration produced in it, we have

$$m\vec{a} = q\vec{E} \quad \text{whence,} \quad \vec{a} = q\vec{E}/m$$

So that acceleration of the proton in the electric field. *i.e.*,

$$\vec{a} = \frac{4.8 \times 10^{-10}}{1.67 \times 10^{-24}}\left(\frac{200\hat{i} + 100\hat{j}}{300}\right) = \frac{4.8 \times 10^{-10}}{1.67 \times 10^{-24}}\left(\frac{2\hat{i} + \hat{j}}{3}\right)$$

∴ *magnitude of the acceleration* $a = \frac{4.8 \times 10^{-10}}{1.67 \times 10^{-24} \times 3}\sqrt{5} = \frac{1.6 \times \sqrt{5}}{1.67} \times 10^{14}$

$$= 2.142 \times 10^4 \text{ cm/sec}^2,$$

and *its direction consines*, $2\sqrt{5}, 1\sqrt{5}$ and 0.

(*iii*) The *transverse displacement of the particle* will clearly be y, where acceleration $a =$ (charge × electric field)/mass $= qE_y/m$ and $t = L_x/v_x$.

$$\text{So that, } y = \frac{1}{2}\frac{4.8 \times 10^{-10}}{1.67 \times 10^{-24}} \times \frac{200}{300} \times \left(\frac{10}{5 \times 10^8}\right)^2 = \frac{1.6}{1.67 \times 25} = 0.0383 \text{ cm}$$

Example 33. (*a*) A stream of protons and deutrons in a vacuum chamber enters a uniform magnetic field. Both protons and deutrons have been subjected to the same accelerating potential; hence kinetic energies of the particles are the same if the ion stream is perpendicular to the magnetic field and the protones move in a circular path of radius 15 cm., find the radius of the path traversed by the duterons. Given that the mass of a duetron is twice that of a proton. (*Agra*)

(*b*) Calculate the Lorentz force on a proton moving with velocity $(2\hat{i} + 3\hat{j})10^8$ cm/sec in an electric field of intensity $(\hat{i} + 2\hat{j} + 3\hat{k})$ statvolts/cm and a magnetic field of $(300\hat{j} + 300\hat{k})$ gauss.

Solution. (*a*) We know that the radius of the path traversed by a charged particle in a magnetic field is given by $\vec{r} = mvc/q\vec{B}$ using. Gaussion units.

So, *that, radius of the path of proton* $\vec{r_P} = m_p v_p c/q\vec{B}$ and radius of the path of the deutron $\vec{r_D} = m_D v_D c/q\vec{B}$.

$$\therefore \qquad \frac{\vec{r_D}}{\vec{r_P}} = \frac{m_D v_D c}{q\vec{B}} \times \frac{q\vec{B}}{m_P v_P c} = \frac{m_D v_D}{m_P v_P}$$

Now, we are given that $m_D = 2m_P$. And, since the kinetic energies of the two particles are the same, their velocities must be inversely proportional to the square roots of their masses. For, $\frac{1}{2}m_D v_D{}^2 = \frac{1}{2}m_P v_P{}^2$ and $\because \quad v_D/v_P = \sqrt{m_P/2m_P} = 1/\sqrt{2}$. or $v_D = v_P/\sqrt{2}$

$$\therefore \qquad r_D/r_P = 2m_p \times v_p\sqrt{2}/m_p \times v_p = \sqrt{2}$$

Since $r_P = 15$ cm (given), we have $r_D = r_P\sqrt{2} = 15\sqrt{2} = 21.21$ cm.

Thus, the *radius of the circular path of the duetron* = 21.21 cm.

(*b*) As we know, *Lorents force* $\vec{F} = q\vec{E} + \frac{q}{c}\vec{v} \times \vec{B}$. Substituting the given values, therefore, we have

$$\vec{F} = 4.8 \times 10^{-10}\ (i + 2k\ 3k) + \frac{4.8 \times 10^{-10}}{3 \times 10^{10}}(2\hat{i} + 3\hat{j})\,10^2 \times (300\hat{j} + 300k)$$

$$= 4.8 \times 10^{-10}\ [\hat{i} + 2\hat{j} + 3\hat{k}) + 2\hat{k} - 2\hat{j} + 3\hat{i})] = 4.8 \times 10^{-10}(4\hat{i} + 5\hat{k})$$

$\therefore$ *magnitude of the force*, $F = 4.8 \times 10^{-10}\sqrt{16 + 25} = 4.8 \times 10^{-10}\sqrt{41} = 3.07 \times 10^{-9}$ dyne.

and the direction cosines = $4/\sqrt{41}, 0, 5/\sqrt{41}$.

Example 34. An electron enters a transverse magnetic field *B* at a point *P* with velocity *v* along the axis of *x* and describing a curved path of radius of curvature *r* under the action of the field, emerges from it at a point *Q* where the distance between the two points is *x*. Show that

(*i*) its displacement along the *y*-axis as it emerges from the field is $y = r\left[1 - \sqrt{1 - \left(\frac{x}{2}\right)^2}\right]$ **and**

(*ii*) its angular defelction $\theta = qBx/mvc$.

Solution. In Fig. 4.13 (a) let the dotted circle represents the region of the magnetic field *B* perpendicular to the plane of the paper and directed downwards, and let *P* be the point of entry of the electron into the field (in a direction perpendicular to it), *PQ*, the curved path of radius of curvature *r* described by it in the field in a direction tangential to the curved path at *Q*, such that horizontal distance between *P* and *Q* is *x*.

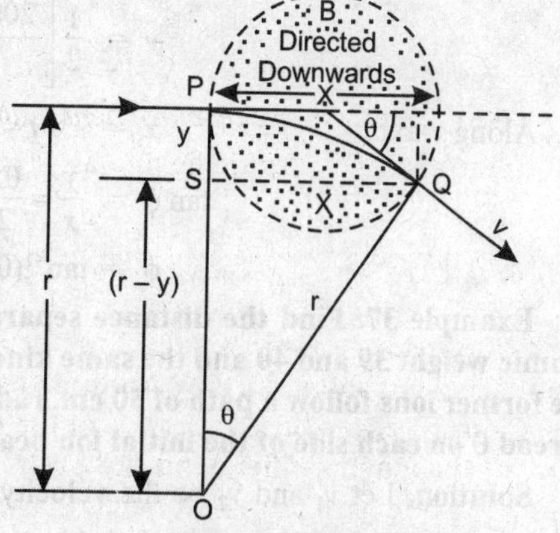

Fig. 4.13 (a)

Then, clearly, *displacement suffered* by the electron in the magnetic field is *y* and the *angular displacement* suffered by it, θ, where θ is the angle that curved path subtends at its centre of curvature *O*.

(*i*) Drop *QS* perpendicular on to *OP*. Then, $OP = r$, $SP = y$ and $OS = (r - y)$.

Now, in the right angled triangle OSQ, we have $OQ^2 = OS^2 + SQ^2$.

Or, $r^2 = (r - y)2 + x^2$,

whence, $r - y \sqrt{r^2 - x^2}$ or $y = r - \sqrt{r^2 - x^2}$

Or, displacement $y = r\left(1 - \sqrt{1 - \frac{x^2}{r^2}}\right) = r\left[1 - \sqrt{1 - \left(\frac{x}{r}\right)^2}\right]$

(*ii*) Again, from ΔOSQ, we have $x = r \sin\theta$, or $\sin\theta$ is always small, we have $x = r^{\theta}$, whence, $\theta = x/r$.

But r, as we know, is given by the relation $r = mvc/qB$. So that, angular displacement suffered by the electron, $\theta = qBx/mvc$.

Alternatively, we could obtain θ as follows: The angular velocity of the electron inside the magnetic field being $\omega = qB/mc$, we have $\theta = \omega t$ where t is the time taken by the electron to cover the distance x in the magnetic field and, therefore, equal to x/v. So that, $\theta = \omega x/v = qBx/mvc$.

Example 35. A beam of charged particles (having same charge and momentum) enters a magnetic field and is deflected by 180° in a circular path of radius 20 cm. Find the width of the focal line if beam is in the form of a cone of 6°.

Solution. $R = 20 \text{ cm} = 0.2 \text{ m}, \phi = \left(\frac{6}{2}\right)^0 = 3° = \frac{3 \times \pi}{180}$ radian

$$\text{width of the focal line} = R\phi^2$$

$$= 0.2\left(\frac{3 \times \pi}{180}\right)^2$$

$$= \mathbf{5.48 \times 10^{-4}\ m}$$

Example 36. An electron moving in a horizontal direction with a speed of 5.0 × 10⁷ m/sec enters a region where there is a uniform electric field of 2000 V/m directed upwards in the plane of its motion. Find the electrons coordinates referred to the point of entry and the direction of its motion 4 × 10⁻⁸ second later.

Solution. $z = \frac{1}{2}\left(\frac{qE}{m}\right)t^2$ Here $q = e = 1.6 \times 10^{-19}$ C

$$y = \frac{1}{2}\left[\frac{2000 \times 1.6 \times 10^{-19}}{9.1 \times 10^{-31}}\right](4 \times 10^{-8})^2 = 0.28 \text{ m}$$

Along x-axis. $x = v \times t = 5 \times 10^7 \times 4 \times 10^{-8} = 2.0$ m

$$\tan\phi = \frac{y}{x} = \frac{0.28}{2.0} = 0.14$$

$$\phi = \tan^{-1}(0.14) = 8° \text{ w.r. to horizontal axis.}$$

Example 37. Find the distance separating singly charged ions, of potassium isotopes of atomic weight 39 and 40 and the same kinetic energy, at the focus of 180° mass spectrometer if the former ions follow a path of 50 cm. radius of curvature. What is the maximum permissible spread θ on each side of the initial ion beam so that the two focal lines may not overlap?

Solution. Let v_1 and v_2 be the velocity of the two types of ions and m_1 and m_2 their atomic weight respectively. Then, since their kinetic energy is the same, we have $v_2/v_1 = \sqrt{m_1 / m_2}$

Now, $r = \frac{cmv}{qB}$ $\therefore$ $r_1 = \frac{cm_1v_1}{qB}$ and $r_2 = \frac{cm_2v_2}{qB}$

Or $$\frac{r_2}{r_1} = \frac{r_2}{50} = \frac{m_2}{m_1}\frac{v_2}{v_1} = \frac{m_2}{m_1}\sqrt{\frac{m_1}{m_2}} = \sqrt{\frac{m_2}{m_1}} = \sqrt{\frac{40}{39}},$$

whence, $$r_2 = 50\left(1+\frac{1}{39}\right)^{\frac{1}{2}} = 50\left(1+\frac{1}{2}\cdot\frac{1}{39}+...\right) = \left(50+\frac{50}{78}\right) \text{ cm}$$

$\therefore$ *Separation of the two focal lines* $= 2(r_2 - r_1) = 2\left(50+\frac{50}{78} - 50\right)$

$$= 2\times\frac{50}{78} = 1.28 \text{ cm}$$

Now, in order that the two may not overlap we must have *width of the first focal line* $r_1\theta^2 = 1.28$. Or, $50\,\theta^2 = 1.28$

where θ is the semi- angle of the cone of the ions as they enter the magnetic field. So that

$$\theta = \sqrt{1.28/50} = 0.16 \text{ radian} \quad \text{or} \quad \frac{0.16\times 180}{\pi} = 9.17°.$$

Example 38. The Uranium isotopes of atomic weight 235 and 238 may be separated by 180° magnetic focussing. Calculate the separation of their beams at the focus, brought in a magnetic field of 10^4 gauss if the radius of curvature of the heavier isotope be 100 cm when (*i*) the velocities (*ii*) the energies of the beams are equal.

Solution. The separation of the two beams at the focus is clearly equal to the difference between the diameters of their semicircular paths in the magnetic field, *i.e.*, equal to $2(r_2 - r_1)$, where r_1 and r_2 are the radii of the two semicircular paths respectively. Now,

(*i*) in case the respective velocities of the two beams be v_1 and v_2, we jave

$$r_1 = m_1v_1c/qB \text{ and } r_2 = m_2v_2c/qB,$$

whence, $r_1/r_2 = m_1v_1/m_2v_2$. Or since the velocities of the two beams are equal, we have

$$v_1 = v_2 \text{ and } \therefore r_1/r_2 = m_2/m_1 = 235/238.$$

Or $$\frac{r_2 - r_1}{r_2} = \frac{238-235}{238} = \frac{3}{238} \quad \text{Or,} \quad r_2 - r_2 = \frac{3}{238}r_2 = \frac{3}{238}\times 100$$

Hence, *separation of the two beams* $= 2(r_2 - r_1) = 2\times\frac{3}{238}\times 100 = 2.522$ cm.

(*ii*) And, when the energies of the two beams are equal, we have

$$\frac{1}{2}m_1v_1^2 = \frac{1}{2}m_2v_2^2 \quad i.e., \quad v_1/v_2 = \sqrt{m_2m_1}$$

But, as seen under (*i*) above, $r_1/r_2 = m_1v_1/m_2v_2$. So that,

$$\frac{r_1}{r_2} = \frac{m_1}{m_1}\sqrt{\frac{m_2}{m_1}} = \sqrt{\frac{m_1}{m_2}} = \sqrt{\frac{235}{238}} = \left(1-\frac{3}{238}\right)^{\frac{1}{2}} = \left(1-\frac{3}{2\times 238}\right)$$

$$\therefore \quad r_2 - r_1 = \frac{3}{2\times 238}r^2 = \frac{3}{2\times 238}\times 100$$

Hence *separation of the two beams* $\frac{2\times 3}{2\times 238}\times 100 = 1.261$ cm

4.10 CHARGED PARTICLE IN A COMBINED ELECTRIC AND MAGNETIC FIELD

Having studied the behaviour of a charged particle in an electric and a magnetic field separately, let us now see how it will behave in a combined electric and magnetic field, (*i*) when the two fields are crossed, *i.e.*, at right angles to one another, and (*ii*) when the two field are parallel (or antiparallel), it each other. Each is discussed below:

4.11 ELECTRIC AND MAGNETIC FIELDS IN CROSSED CONFIGURATION (*i.e.*, MUTUALLY PERPENDICULAR)

In atomic physics, quite often it becomes necessary to select only those particles (*viz.* electron, protons etc.) that have the same velocity, out of the bunch of particles having a wide range of velocities. This is the basis of *velocity selector* or *velocity filter* and achieved by using electric and magnetic fields in crossed configuration. When uniform electric and magnetic fields act perpendicular simultaneously over the same region, the fields are said to be in **crossed configuration.**

When electrons pass through such a region, they are deflected simultaneously by both the fields. Two metal plates seperated by a small distance, when charged set up a uniform electric field E in the y-direction and a uniform magnetic field B is also set up in the same region between the plates in z-direction. Let the magnetic field B is acting into the page. Both these fields are manually perpendicular to the direction of motion of electrons, *i.e.*, x-direction. Let the stream of electrons enter the region of crossed configuration with a velocity v [Fig. 4.14].

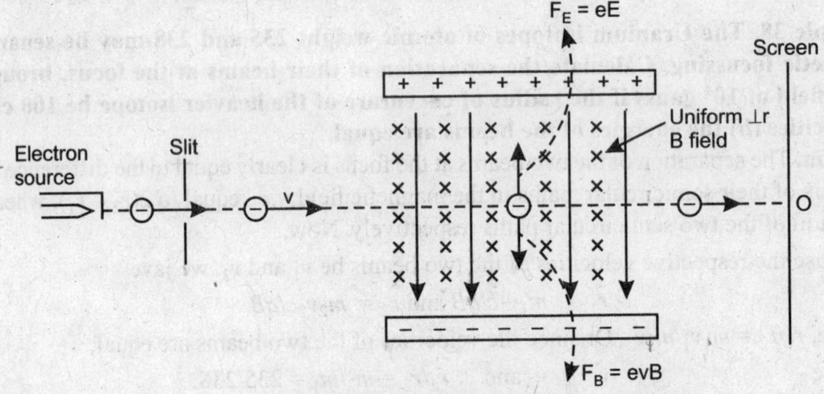

Fig. 4.14 Crossed *E* and *B* fields

The electric field E deflects the *electrons upward* with a force

$$F_E = eE \qquad \text{...(i)}$$

and magnetic field B deflects then *downwards* with a force

$$F_B = evB \qquad \text{...(ii)}$$

If the magnitudes of these two fields are adjusted such that the force acting on the electrons are equal, so that the electrons will not experience any net force. Under this condition

$$eE = evB$$

$$\therefore \quad v = \frac{E}{B}$$

The electrons experience a zero net force as the above two forces are equal and opposite thereby balance each other. Therefore, they will not deviate from their original straight line path, *i.e.*, x-axis and travel without any change in their velocity v. By knowing the value of E and B, the velocity of electrons and hence their kinetic energy can be determined. In 1897, J.J. Thomson used this method for the determination of electron beam velocity.

4.12 VELOCITY SELECTOR

Velocity selector also known as velocity filter is an electro-optic device which uses the combined effect of two mutual perpendicular fields E and B acting simultaneously over the same region. This crossed- configuration of E and B selects a stream of charged particles of single velocity from a beam of charged particles having a wide range of velocities. [Fig 4.15].

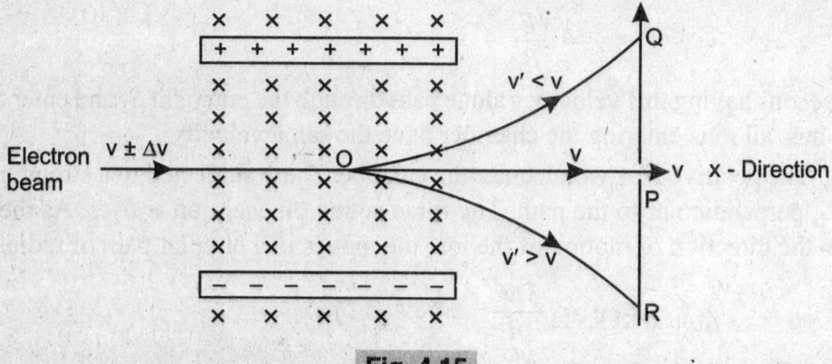

Fig. 4.15

Here the electric field E is produced in vertically downward direction ($-y$ axis) by a set of charged particles plates and a uniform magnetic field B is applied perpendicular to it, acting into the paper. If the two fields E and B are adjusted such the electric field force balances the magnetic force B acting on the electrons moving with velocities $v + \Delta v$, then those electrons are not deflected and continue to travel along the straight line, having velocity v, subsequently, they pass through the slit at P. Those electrons moving with velocity lesser than v ($v' < v$) will get deflected upward along OQ and those moving with greater velocity that v ($v' > v$) will get deflected downward along OR. Thus, a strictly homogenous single velocity electron beam travelling along OP is obtained. This arrangement is therefore, known as a **velocity selector or a velocity filter.** This forms an essential component in Bainbridge mass spectrograph.

4.13 MASS SPECTROGRAPHS

Mass spectrograph is an instrument employed to separate different isotopes from a stream of positive ions of an element and measures their individual masses as well as their relative abundances, by using electric and magnetic fields over the same region since the instrument is used to separate ions of different masses, is called as mass spectrograph.

Bainbridge's Mass Spectrograph. A schematic diagram showing the construction of a Bainbridge mass spectrograph is shown in Fig. 4.16.

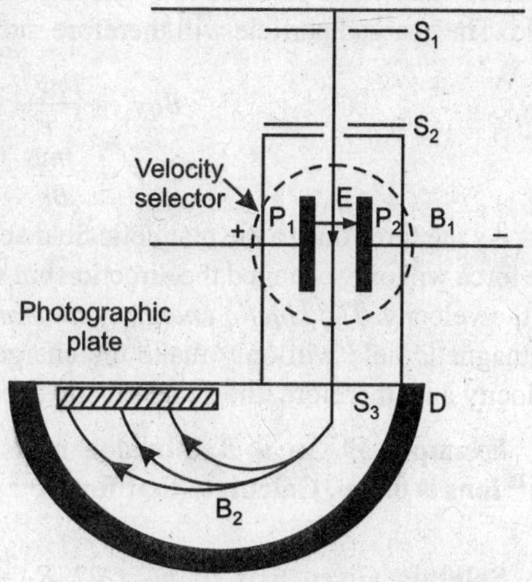

Fig. 4.16. Brainbridge's mass spectrograph

A beam of *positive ions* produced in a discharged tube is collimated into a narrow beam by the two slits S_1 and S_2. After emerging from the slit S_2, the positive ions enter a *velocity selector*.

Velocity selector. It consists of two plates P_1 and P_2 between which a steady electric field E is maintained in a direction at right angles to the ion beam. A magnetic field B_1 is produced by an electromagnet (represented by the dotted circle). The magnetic field B_1 is at right angles to the electric field E as well as the ion beam.

The electric field and the magnetic field of the *velocity selector* are so adjusted that the deflection produced by one is exactly equal and opposite to the deflection produced by the other so that, there is no net deflection for ions having a particular velocity v.

If E and B_1 are the electric field intensity and magnetic induction, then

$$eE = B_1 ev$$

or $$v = \frac{E}{B_1}$$

Only those ions having this velocity v alone pass through the entry slit S_3 and enter the evacuated chamber D. Thus, all ions entering the chamber have the same velocity.

Working. The positive ions which enter the chamber D are subjected to a strong magnetic field of intensity B_2, perpendicular to the path. The force acting on each ion is B_2ev. As the force acts at right angles to the direction of motion of the ion, the moves in a circular path of radius R given by

$$B_2ev = \frac{Mv^2}{R}$$

or $$R = \frac{Mv}{B_2e}$$

$\therefore$ $$\frac{e}{M} = \frac{V}{B_2R} = \frac{E}{B_1B_2R} \qquad \left[\because V = \frac{E}{B_1}\right]$$

As E, B_1 and B_2 are constant

$$\frac{e}{M} \propto \frac{1}{R}$$

After describing the semicircular path the ions strike a photographic plate.

Determination of mass. If e is the same for all ions, $M \propto R$.

Thus, we get a linear mass scale on the photograph plate. The ion of different mass will traverse paths of different radii and strike the photographic plates at different points, thereby giving a typical mass spectrum.

The method is very accurate as the mass scale in linear.

No change in kinetic energy of a charged particle in magnetic field. When a charged particles having a charge q, and velocity v (kinetic energy $= \frac{1}{2}mv^2$) enters a magnetic field of intensity B perpendicular to its path the force acting on the charge particles and the direction of the magnetic field. The charged particle will therefore move in a circular path of radius r, given by

$$Bqv = \frac{mv^2}{r}$$

or $$r = \frac{mv}{Bq}$$

As the force due to the magnetic field acts in direction at right angles to the direction of motion, the force will only changed the direction but will not be able to bring about a change in the magnitude of the velocity. *The kinetic energy of the particle will, therefore, remain unchanged.* The force due to magnetic field will only make the charged particle move along a circular path withe the same velocity and, therefore, the same kinetic energy.

Example 39. In a Bainbridge mass spectograph radius of curvature of the path of Ne^{20} ions is 0.2 m. Calculate that for Ne^{22} ions. Assume single ionization of both the ions.

(Nagpur Uni 2007, 2008, 2005)

Soluiton. Given $m_1 \propto 20$, $m_2 \propto 22$, $R_1 = 0.26$ m

$$R_1 = km_1$$

$$R_2 = km_2$$

$\therefore$ $$\frac{R_1}{R_2} = \frac{m_1}{m_2}$$

or $$R_2 = \frac{m_2}{m_1} \times R_1 = \frac{22 \times 0.26}{20} = \mathbf{0.286\ m}$$

Example 40. A positive ion beam moving in the x-direction enters a region in which there in an electric field E_y = 3000 volts/cm and a magnetic field B_2 = 300 gausss. Deduce the speed of those ions which may pass undeflected through the region. What will happen to ions which are (*i*) faster, (*ii*) slower than these. *[Agra (Supp),]*

Solution. As we have seen in § 4.11, the velocity v_x of a charged particles, to remain undelected in the crossed electric and magnetic fields E and B along the y-axis and z-axis respectively, must be given by the relation $v_x = E/B$. Or, if the Gaussian units be used (*i.e.*, E in stavolts/cm and B in gauss), we must have

$$v_x = \frac{cE}{B}$$

Here, $E = E_x$ = 3000 volts/cm = 3000/300 or 10 stavolts/cm, $B = B_2$ = 3000 gauss and $c = 3 \times 10^{10}$ cm/sec. So that,

$$v_x = 3 \times 10^{10} \times 10/300 = 10^2 \text{ cm/sec.}$$

Thus, the speed of the ions must be 10^2 cm/sec.

At this speed, obviously, the deflection of the + *ve* ions in the downward direction in the plane of paper *i.e.* in the $-y$ direction, due to the magnetic field is just balanced by their deflection in the $+y$ direction due to the electric field in that direction.

(*i*) If, therefore, the speed v_x of the ion-beam be higher than 10^9 cm/sec, its deflection in the $-y$ direction due to the magnetic field will exceed that in the $+y$ direction due to the electric field and *there will thus be a resultant deflection in the $-y$ direction.*

(*ii*) If, on the other hand, the speed v_x of the ion-beam be lower than 10^9 cm/sec, the deflection in the $-y$ direction due to the magnetic field will be less than that in the $+y$ direction due to the electric field and there wili, *therefore, be a resultant deflection of the beam in the $+y$ direction.*

4.14 WHEN ELECTRIC AND MAGNETIC FIELDS IN PARALLEL CONFIGURATION. (*i.e.*, E AND B ARE IN PARALLEL) – THOMSON PARABOLAS

When electricity neutral atom losses one or more electrons, it becomes a positively charged atom and is called a positive ion.

Suppose a beam of such positive ions, each of mass m and charge q moving with a velocity v enters a region in which a uniform electric field of intensity E and a uniform magnetic field of induction B are present. Both the fields E and B are parallel to each other and are at right angle to the direction of motion of the beam (fig. 4.17).

In the region of the fields, an ion experience the electric force qE in the direction of E and at the same time also experiences a magnetic force qvB in the direction perpendicular to both v and B. In the figure qvB is directed out of the plane of the paper. Therefore, during its passage through the fields, the direction of the ion due to E in the y-direction and the deflection due to B is in the x-direction.

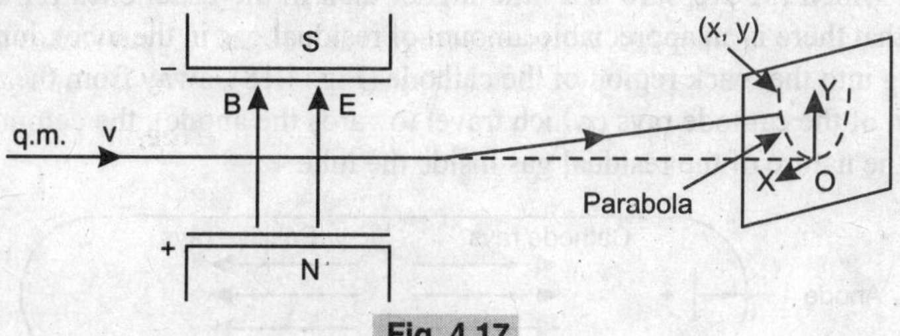

Fig. 4.17

The deflection on the screen are given by

$$S_E = \frac{qElL}{mv^2}$$

and $$S_B = \frac{qBlL}{mv}$$

where l is the length of the horizontal path through the fields and L is the distance of the screen from the centre of the fields. If x and y are the coordinates of the point on the screen where the deflected beam meets the screen, then

$$y = \frac{qElL}{mv^2} \quad ...(i)$$

$$x = \frac{qBlL}{mv} \quad ...(ii)$$

To eliminate v, we square equation (*ii*) and then dividing by equation (*i*), we get

$$\frac{x^2}{y} = \frac{q^2B^2(lL)^2}{m^2v^2} \cdot \frac{mv^2}{qElL}$$

$$= \left(\frac{lLB^2}{E}\right)\frac{q}{m}$$

Therefore, $$x^2 = \left(\frac{lLB^2}{E}\right)\frac{q}{m}y \quad ...(iii)$$

This is the equation of the parabola with its vertex at the origin O of the axes on the screen. The parabola is symmetrical about the y-axis. Thus, for constant values of l, L, B and E positive ions having the same charge to mass ratio (q/m), but moving with different velocities, will lie on the parabola represented by equation. (*iii*).

If each ion has a positive charge equal in magnitude to the electronic charge e, then equation (*iii*) is written as

$$x^2 = \left(\frac{lLB^2}{E}\right)\frac{e}{m}y \quad ...(iv)$$

or $$x^2 = C\frac{e}{m}y$$

where $$C = lLB^2/E$$

equation (*iv*) represents again a parabola, *i.e.* the path traced by a positive charge has parabolic nature. This principle was used by J.J. Thomson and he determined $\frac{e}{m}$ by using his very famous Thomson's parabola method.

4.15 DETERMINATION OF E/M FOR POSITIVE RAYS

It was first shown by *Goldstein* in the year 1886, that if a perforated cathode be used in a discharge tube in which the pressure is a little higher than in the usual ones for the production of cathode rays (so that there is an appreciable amount of residual gas in the tube), luminous streamers are seen travelling into the back region of the cathode (Fig. 4.18), away from the anode, *i.e.,* in the opposite direction of the cathode rays (which travel towards the anode), the colour of the streamers depending upon the nature of the residual gas inside the tube.

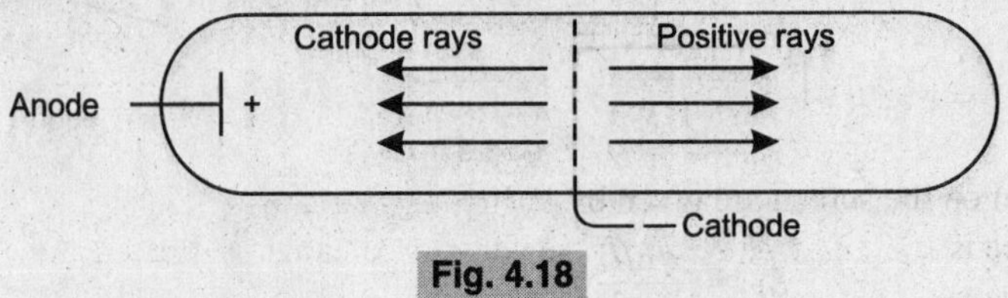

Fig. 4.18

These came to be known as *canal rays*, since they appeared to issue from the cylinderical chamels or cannels in the cathode, or *positive rays*, since they carried a positive charge on them, as evidence by their travelling away from the anode as also by the direction of their deflection by a magnetic or an electric field.

These rays, as we know, are just *stream of positive ions* produced because the fast moving electrons, rushing from the cathode towards the anode, *ionising the gas*, *i.e.*, knocking out electrons from some of the gas atoms they collide with. These positive ions carry a charge equal in magnitude to *e* (the charge on an electron) or a multiple of *e*, according as one or more electron have been knocked out of an atom.

J.J Thomson was the first to have devised a method, in the year 1911, to determine their charge to mass ratio e/m by the application of a combination of a magnetic and an electric field, parallel to each other. This is explained as under.

Example 41. A stream of ions, of charge to mass ratio 1.44 × 10¹⁴ esu/gm, travelling horizontally in vacuum, encounters vertical electric and magnetic field in the same region, on passing through which it falls on the fluorescent screen, showing a displacement of 2 cm both horizontally and vertically. What will be the horizontal displacements for a stream of ions of twice the above charge to mass ratio if the vertical displacement for it be 9 cm.

Would it be possible to distinguish between streams of deutrons and α-particles in such an experiment?

Solution. Here, again, $\dfrac{x^2}{y} = \dfrac{q}{m}, \dfrac{B^2}{E}k,$

For the stream of ions for which $q/m = 1.44 \times 10^{14}$ *esu*/gm and $x = y = 2$ cm, we, therefore have,

$$\frac{(2)^2}{2} = 2 = (1.44 \times 10^{14})\frac{B^2}{E}k, \text{ whence } \frac{B^2 k}{E} = \frac{2}{1.44 \times 10^{14}}$$

∴ For ions for which $q/m = 2(1.44 \times 10^{14})$ esu/gm and for which $y = 9$ cm, we have

$$\frac{x^2}{9} = 2(1.44 \times 10^{14})\frac{B^2}{E}k = 2(1.44 \times 10^{14})\frac{2}{(1.44 \times 10^{14})} = 4$$

or $$x^2 = 36, \text{ whence, } x = 6 \text{ cm.}$$

Thus, the horizontal displacement of this stream of ions = 6 cm.

Since, the charge to mass ratio (q/m) is the same for both a deutron and an α- particle, they will both suffer identical horizontal and vertical displacements in such an experiment and will thus be indistinguishable from the parabolas traced by them on the fluorescent screen.

Example 42. An electric field, 10³ volt/meter and a magnetic field 3.2 × 10⁻³ weber/m² are parallel to each other along the *z*- direction. In the region of this combination of fields are introduced hydrogen ions of energy 200 electron volts along the axis of *x*. How long would it takes the hydrogen ions to hit the fluorescent screen placed at a distance of 0.8 metres from the origin perpendicular to their direction of motion and what will be the coordinates of the point where the screen is hit? (Mass of proton may be taken to be 1.6 × 10⁻²⁷ kg and the charge on it equal to 1.6 × 10⁻¹⁹ coulombs).

Solution. Let v be the velocity of the hydrogen ions along the axis of x. Then $\frac{1}{2}mv^2 = 200$ eV

whence, $$= \sqrt{\frac{2 \times 200 \times 1.6 \times 10^{-19}}{1.6 \times 10^{-27}}} = 2 \times 10^{-5} \text{ m/sec.}$$

(Because 1 eV = 1.6×10^{-19} joules).

Since no force is acting along this axis, the velocity remains unaffected and hence *time taken to cover the distance x* = 0.8 *meter to the screen* = $0.8/2 \times 10^5 = 4 \times 10^{-6}$ sec.

Now a moving charge constitutes an electric current and, therefore, the force acting on the hydrogen ions due to the magnetic field B is equal to qvB* in a direction perpendicular to both B and v and, therefore, in the y-direction (in according with Fleming's left hand rule). So that, *acceleration of the ions in this direction* = qvB/m.

∴ *Distance covered by the ions in this direction in time* $t = 4 \times 10^{-6}$ sec in given by

$$y = \frac{1}{2}\frac{qvB}{m}t^2 = \frac{1}{2}\frac{1.6\times10^{-19}\times2\times10^5\times3.2\times10^{-3}}{1.6\times10^{-27}}\times(4\times10^{-10})^2 = 0.512 \text{ m}$$

because $u = 0$

Similarly, distance covered by the ions in the z- direction in time $t = 4 \times 10^{-6}$ sec is given by

$$z = \frac{1}{2}\frac{qE}{m}t^2 = \frac{1}{2}\frac{1.6\times10^{-19}\times10^3}{1.6\times10^{-27}}\times(4\times10^{-6})^2 = 0.8 \text{ m}$$

Thus, *coordinates of the point where the screen is* hit are 0.8, 0.512 and 0.8 m.

4.16 THOMSON'S PARABOLA MATHOD

(Determination of q/m of positive ions)

J.J. Thomson, in 1911, developed a method of measuring the relative masses of different atoms by employing a parallel configuration of electric field E and magnetic field B simultaneously. The experimental arrangement is shown in fig. 4.19.

F is a glass flask in which gaseous discharge is produced. The anode A is in a side tube. The cathode C is made of a tube of soft iron faced with aluminium. This tube is fixed to the neck of the flask. Along the axial hole in this tube there is a copper tube of fine bore of about 0.1 mm diameter through which positive ions produced in the flask can pass. I is the inlet for an experimental gas. An electromagnet NS with soft iron pole pieces P and Q provides a strong magnetic field in the y- direction. The pole pieces P and Q are insulted from N and S by thin micasheet GG. The electric field is set up in the same direction by applying a p.d. between P and Q. Thus, parallel electric and magnetic fields are produced at right angles to the axis of the copper tube. A vertical photographic plate P is at the end of the conical vessel V.

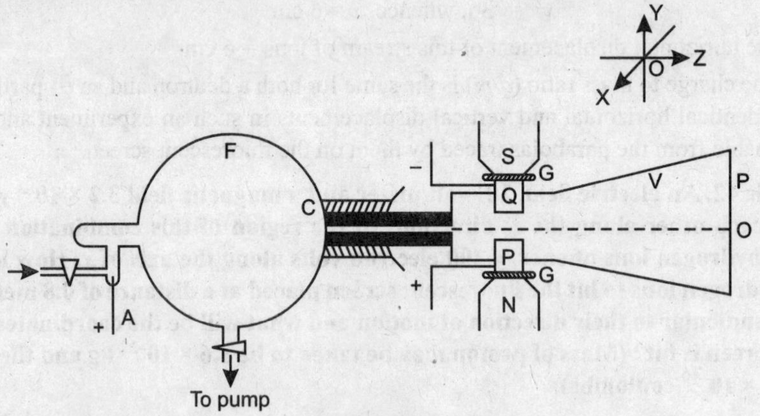

Fig. 4.19

Procedure for q/m of the isotopes of an element in gaseous state:

The flask F is evacuated of air to pressure of about 0.001 mm of Hg by means of a vaccum pump. The experimental gas at about the same pressure is now introduced into the flask through the inlet I. A high voltage of about 20000V is applied between the anode A and cathode C. Cathode

* Since the charge, the magnetic and electric field are all expressed here in RMKs (or SI) units, we need not divide the charge q by c as we do when using Gaussian units, *i.e.*, the charge in esu and the magnetic field in emu or gauss.

rays or electrons then flow form C and A and positive ions produced by ionisation of the gas-atoms flow to C. After emerging from C they pass through the region of parallel electric and magnetic field. Then the deflected ions are incident on the photographic plate P where, they produce traces of parabolas on one side of the y-axis. The fields are then reversed to obtain the parabolic traces on the other side of the y-axis.

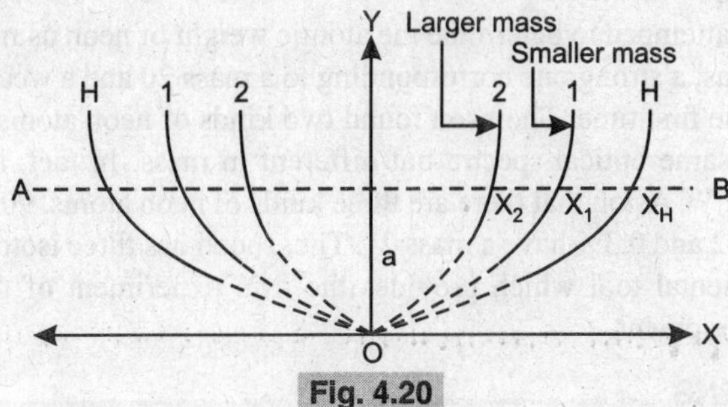

Fig. 4.20

After development of the plate parabolic traces are found on it (Fig. 4.20).

The outermost parabola H is produced by hydrogen ions because they have greatest value of q/m. (Hydrogen ions are usually present due to the residual air in the flask and the hydrogen parabola is taken as the standard). The parabolas (1) and (2) are produced by the ions of the isotopes of the gas introduced. To find q/m of the ions of the isotopes in terms of q/m of hydrogen ions a straight line $AB : y = a$; parallel to the x-axis is drawn and the x-coordinates x_H, x_1, x_2 of its point of intersection with the parabolic traces are found (Fig. 4.20). Then for hydrogenn using equation (*iv*) of article 4.14 as

$$x^2 = C\frac{q}{m}y$$

we have

$$x_H^2 = C\frac{q}{m_H}a$$

Therefore,
$$\frac{q/m_H}{x_H^2} = \frac{1}{Ca} \qquad \text{...(i)}$$

Similarly, for the isotopes

$$\frac{q/m_1}{x_1^2} = \frac{1}{Ca} \qquad \text{...(ii)}$$

$$\frac{q/m_2}{x_2^2} = \frac{1}{Ca} \qquad \text{...(iii)}$$

where m_H, m_1 and m_2 are the corresponding atomic masses. From equations (*i*), (*ii*) and (*iii*), we have

$$\frac{q/m_1}{x_1^2} = \frac{q/m_2}{x_2^2} = \frac{q/m_H}{x_H^2}$$

Hence,
$$\frac{q}{m_1} = \frac{x_1^2}{x_H^2}\left(\frac{q}{m_H}\right) \qquad \text{...(iv)}$$

and
$$\frac{q}{m_2} = \frac{x_2^2}{x_H^2}\left(\frac{q}{m_H}\right) \qquad \text{...(v)}$$

Thus the value of q/m of the ions of the isotopes in terms of that of hydrogen ions are found.

Atomic Masses:

If the ionic charge q is the same in each case, then from Eq. (*iv*) and (*v*), we have

$$m_1 = \frac{x_H^2}{x_1^2}m_H \qquad \text{...(vi)}$$

and $$m_2 = \frac{x_H^2}{x_2^2} m_H \qquad ...(vii)$$

This is how, we determine the mass of the isotopes of the desired element.

Discovery of Isotopes

In 1912, Thomson attemped to determine the atomic weight of neon using parabola method. He discovered two parabolas, a strong one corresponding to a mass 20 and a weaker one corresponding to mass 22. Thus, for the first time, Thomson found two kinds of neon atoms, identical in chemical nature and having the same optical spectra but different in mass. In fact, it was shown latter by Thomson's co-worker F.W. Aston that there are three kinds of neon atoms. 90.5% have a mass value of 20,9.2% have mass 22 and 0.3% have a mass 21. Thus, neon has three isotopes. Thomson method is an effective experimental tool which provides the firm experiment of the existence of stable isotopes of any desired element.

4.17 MAGNETIC LENS

An axially symmetric magnetic fields have a focusing property when an electron beam passes through them. Such fields are generated by using shorts solenoids. By encasing the coils in hollow iron sheilds the magnetic fields are concentrated and improved focusing action is obtain. Such Solenoids are, therefore, called as *thin magnetic lenses*.

As we know, that an electron travelling in a non-magnetic field describes a helical path of pitch.

$$p = \frac{2\pi mv}{eB}$$

The radius of the helical loop goes on progressively decreasing as the electron approaches to stronger and stronger magnetic field B. Thus, the radii of progressive solenoidal loops goes on shrinking into tighter loops and ultimately $r \rightarrow 0$ and the electron beam comes to focus at a point (Fig. 4.21). In other words, magnetic lens converges the electron beam. However, diverging action is impossible in magnetic lenses.

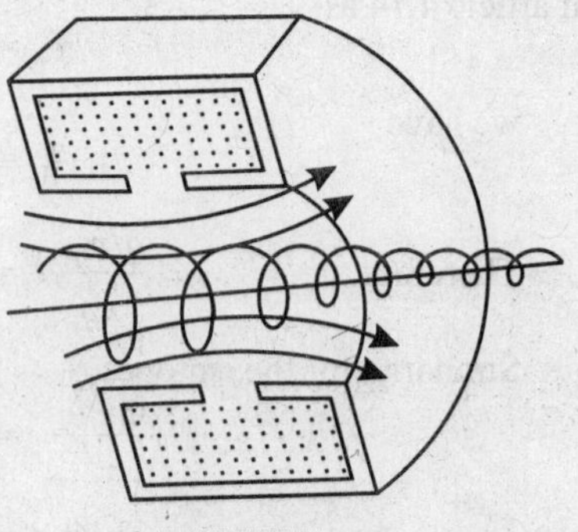

Fig. 4.21

By adjusting the current through the solenoid and the initial accelerating voltage, the focal distance of magnetic lens can be monitored.

Uses: Magnetic lenses are widely used in electron microscopes and in instruments where such an action is desired.

EXERCISE

Long Answer Questions

1. (*a*) Describe the motion of an electron subjected to a uniform electric field acting normal to the electron velocity.

   (*b*) Show that an electron moving with uniform velocity follows a parabiotic path in a transverse uniforms electric field. ***(Nagpur Uni. 2009)***

2. Show that the velocity acquired by an electron in a uniform electrostatic field varies as the square root of potential difference through which it is accelerated. ***(Nagpur Uni. 2001)***

3. Prove that an electron moves along a parabolic path, when it enters in a uniform electric field applied perpendicular to its motion. What will happen if the electric field is not uniforms?

4. (*a*) Describe the path of electron of mass '*m*' and charge '*e*' moving with velocity v in (*i*) uniforms magnetic field, and (*ii*) uniform electrostatic field. Both the fields are applied perpendicular to the direction of motion of the particle.

(*b*) Does kinetic energy of a charged particles change when it enters a magnetic field.

5. (*a*) Draw the block diagram of a cathode ray oscillograph. Describe its construction and explain its working. Give uses of CRO. ***(Pbi. U. 2004, 2002, 2000; G.N.D.U. 2004; Pat. U. 2004; Nag. U. 2002; Gharwal U. 2000)***

(*b*) Why is a sweep circuit necessary in a CRO? What will happen if fly back time is comparable to sweep time in a sawtooth voltage? ***(Nag. U. 2000)***

6. (*a*) Explain the necessity of time base circuit.

(*b*) Write the application and uses of C.R.O. ***(Pbi U. 2003; MDU 2001; Pat. U. 2004; Garhwal U. 2000)***

(*c*) Describe the working and function of electron gun in a CRO. Which type of emission is employed is it. ***(MDU 2003)***

(*d*) Describe the role of aquadag in cathod ray oscilloscope. ***(P.U. 2001)***

7. (*a*) Explain the principle of electrostatic focussing in a CRO. ***(Nagpur Uni 2007)***

(*b*) What is the difference between CRT and CRO? ***(Nagpur Uni 2007)***

(*c*) The wilemite is used on the screen of a CRO. We get (*i*) blue colour (*ii*) green colour (*iii*) red colour (*iv*) white colour.

8. (*a*) Describe dual beam cathode ray oscilloscope. ***(G.N.D.U. 2002, 2001)***

(*b*) Who Willemite is most suitable coating material for screen of C.R.T. ***(H.P.U. 2003)***

9. Explain carefully the principle of Linear accelerator

Deduce the expression for the energy of the particle and length of cylinders in terms of the constants of the apparatus. ***(Nagpur Uni 2009, 2007, 2006, GNDU 2004, 2003; H.P.U. 2001; Guahati U. 2003; P.U. 2004; K.U. 2000)***

10. (*a*) Describe the principle construction and working of a cyclotron. Derive expression for the maximum kinetic energy achieved by a particle of mass m in terms of the applied magnetic field and dee radius. Also state the relation in terms of the frequency of the applied electric field. Discuss its limitations. ***(M.D.U. 2000, KU. 2002, 2004; Nag. Uni 2010, 2007, 2006; G.N.D.U. 2002, Pbi. U. 2003; Bang. U. 2001; Kerala U. 2001; Cal. U. 2003; P.U. 2002, 2000)***

(*b*) Can we accelerate neutrons by a cyclotron?

11. (*a*) Show that the maximum radius of curvature of the path of a particle inside of the dees of a cyclotron is proportional to the square root of the number of times it crosses the gap between the dees.

(*b*) What are the primary function of (*i*) electric field and (*ii*) magnetic field in a cyclotron?

12. (*a*) A Cyclotron is a called resonance device. Explain.

(*b*) Can a cyclotron be used to accelerate electrons? If not way? ***(KU 2002; Pbi,U. 2001,2000; HPU 2002, 2001)***

13. Give theory of Thomson's parabola method to determine the specific charge of positive ions. Give the necessary theory. ***(Nagpur Uni 2007)***

14. Describe the principle, construction and working of Bainbridge's mass spectrograph. How is the nuclear mass determined using the spectrograph? ***(KU. 2002, 2000, MDU. 2002)***

15. Draw figure showing the parabolic traces obtained on the photographic place in thomson's method due to two isotopes of atomic masses m_1 and m_2 where $m_1 < m_2$. Explain how the traces are analysed to determine the atomic masses.

16. Draw a neat diagram of Thomson's apparatus for determining charges to mass ratio of positive ions. Give a brief description of the apparatus. Describe Thomson's parabola method to determine e/m of the isotope of an element in gaseous state.

17. Draw a neat diagram of cyclotron and obtain resonance condition. ***(Nagpur Uni 2002)***

18. (*a*) Explain the principle and working of cyclotron. Show that the time spent by the charged particle in the Dec of the cyclotron is independent of its velocity.

(*b*) Mention the limitations on the energy achieved by a particles in the cyclotron. ***(Nagpur Uni 2007)***

Short Answer Questions

1. Show that a charged particle does not change its energy when fired in a magnetic field.
2. Magnetic field changes the velocity of a charged particle without changing its speed. Explain. ***(Nagpur Uni. 2001)***
3. Show that the radius of orbit of a charged particle moving at right angles to magnetic field is proportional to its momentum. ***(Nagpur Uni. 2000)***
4. Consider a particles of mass m and charge q moving with velocity v. The particle enters a region where a perpendicular uniform magnetic field B acts. Show that in the region the kinetic energy of the particle is proportional to the square of the radius of its orbit.
5. Explain the working of an electrostatic electron lens.
6. What is deflection sensitivity of a cathode ray tube? Obtain expression for (*i*) electrostatic deflection sensitivity and (*ii*) magnetic deflection sensitivity. Give their importance. ***(Nagpur U. 2009; Bang. U. 2004)***
7. Explain how a CRO may be used to measure voltage. ***(Bang U. 2000)***
8. Discuss how a cathode ray oscilloscope may be used to measure the phase difference between two a.c. signals of the same frequency and amplitude. ***(Kolkata U. 2001)***
9. Explain how a CRO may be used to measure frequency. ***(Nag. U. 2002; Kolkata U. 2001; Bang. U. 2000)***
10. What is the difference between linear accelerator and circular accelerator? ***(P.U. 2001)***
11. Which accelerator makes use of electromagnetic radiations for accelerating particles? ***(G.N.D. U. 2000)***
12. What is cyclotron? Show that the maximum kinetic energy gained by a particle in a cyclotron is
$$K.E. = 2\pi^2 m f^2 r_{max}^2$$
symbols have their usual meaning.
13. What is velocity selector? Explain the function of velocity selector in Bainbridge mass spectrograph in determining the isotopes of various elements. ***(Nagpur Uni. 2008)***
14. Explain with neat diagram the working of magnetic lens. Where it is used.
15. An electric field E is applied between the vertical deflecting plates of a CRO. Obtain an expression for the displacement of an electron entering the field. ***(Nagpur Uni 2007)***
16. Obtain an expression for the deflection produced on the screen at a distance L from the centre of the plates. ***(Nagpur Uni 2007)***
17. Obtain expression for maximum K.E. of particles coming out of a cyclotron. ***(Nagpur Uni 2007)***
18. State any two limitations of a linear accelerator. ***(Nagpur Uni 2008)***
19. What is the path traced out by a beam of electrons when subjected to parallel E and B fields? ***(Nagpur Uni 2007)***
20. What is discharge tube? Describe its construction. ***(Nagpur Uni 2008)***
21. Explain the principle of 180° magnetic focusing. ***(Agra U. 2005; Nagpur U. 2008, 2006)***
22. If a charged particle passes through, mutually perpendicular electric and magnetic field, then prove that its path will be cycloid. ***(Agra U 2004)***
23. Explain the principle of velocity selector. ***(Agra U 2004)***
24. Show that in Brainbridge mass spectrograph, the radii of curvature of path of positive ions is proportional to masses of ions. ***(Nagpur U. 2009)***

I. Dynamics of uncharged particles

1. The initial position of a particle of mass 100 gm is $\vec{r}_0 = 5\hat{j} + 7\hat{k}$ cm and its initial velocity $\vec{u} = 30\hat{i} + 10\hat{k}$ cm/sec. If force $\vec{F} = 100\hat{i} + 75\hat{j}$ dynes acts upon it for 4 sec, obtain its final velocity and final position. Also calculate the work done by the force. [**Ans.** $34\hat{i} + 3\hat{j} + 10\hat{k}; 128\hat{i} + 11\hat{j} + 47\hat{k}$; 13250 ergs]

2. A particle is projected upward in a direction inclined at 60° to the horizontal. Show that its velocity when at its greatest height is half its initial velocity. (Neglect the resistance of the air)

3. Find the greatest distance that a stone can be thrown inside a horizontal tunnel 10 ft high with a velocity of projection 80 ft/sec. Find also the corresponding time of flight. **[Ans.** 120 ft; 1.58 sec.]

4. A particles P is projected with initial velocity $5\hat{i}+6\hat{j}-7\hat{k}$ m/sec. and it experience a uniforms acceleration $6\hat{j}$ m/sec^2. Another particles Q is projected from the same position 20 sec. later with initial velocity $2\hat{i}-3\hat{j}+4\hat{k}$ m/sec. and it experiences a uniform acceleration $-3\hat{j}$ m/sec^2. Deduce the position of Q relative to P, 50 sec. after P is projected. ***(Agra supp)***

[Ans. $19\hat{i}-127.5\hat{j}+47\hat{k}$]

II. Dynamics of charged particles

1. Charged particles in a uniform electric field

5. Show that when an electric field is applied at right angles to the direction of motion of a charged particle, it describes a path similar to that described by a particles thrown horizontally in the Earth's gravitational field.

6. A potential difference of 650 volts retards the motion of an electron proceeding normally from one electrode to another, parallel to it. If the initial energy possessed by the electron by 10^9 ergs, (*i*) will it be able to reach the second electrode? (*ii*) What should be the value of the retarding potential so that the electron may *just* reach the second electrode? **[Ans.** (*i*) No.; (*ii*) 625 volts]

7. Calculate (*i*) the force on a proton in an electric field of 100 statvolts/cm, (*ii*) the intensity of the electric field that can just support the weight of an electron.

[Ans. (*i*) 4.80×10^{-8} dynes; (*ii*) 1.86×10^{-15} statvolts/cm]

8. Calculate the intensity of the electric field which will produce in an alpha particles an acceleration equal to that of g (*i.e.* 980 cm/sec^2). (The mass of an alpha particle is four times that of a proton and the charge on it twice that on a proton). **[Ans.** 2.05×10^{-2} volts/cm]

9. A proton is accelerated through a potential difference V and then allowed to cross a field-free evacuated space. How long would it takes to cover the distance between two given points in this space, distance r apart. **[Ans.** $r/\sqrt{2eV/m}$]

10. In an electric field $E = 10^{-2}\hat{i}$ statvolts/cm, the velocity of an electron is $v_0 = 10^5\hat{i}$ cm/sec and its position vectors at $\vec{r_0} = 10^2 - \hat{j}$ cm at $t = 0$. Obtain its velocity and position vectors at $t = 10^{-9}$ sec.

[Ans. $\vec{v} = 5.4\times10^7\hat{i}$ cm/sec; $\vec{r} = 10^2\hat{j} - 0.25\hat{i}$ cm]

11. An electron beam is accelerated through apd. of 1000 volts, and then passed through a pair of deflecting plates 2 cm long and 0.5 cm apart. What should be the p.d. between the plates in order that the electron beam may be deflected through 5°? **[Ans.** 4.7×10^2 volts]

12. The accelerating voltage in a cathode ray oscilloscope is 2400 volts, the effective length of the deflecting plates is 3 cm, their distance apart 0.5 cm and the distance of the screen from their mid-point 30 cm. If the p,d, across the deflecting plates be 20 volts, obtain, (*i*) the velocity of an electron as it enters the deflecting field (*ii*) the time it takes to traverse this field, (*iii*) the angle of deflection due to the field and its displacement on the screen. (e/m for an electron = 5.2×10^{17} esu/ gm.

[Ans. (*i*) 2.88×10^9 cm/se, (*ii*) 1.04×10^{-9} sec, (*iii*) 1°26', (*iv*) 0.75 cm]

13. What is the energy in Joules of an electron accelerated through a potential of 1000 kV.

(Nagpur U. 2009)

[Ans. 1.6×10^{-13} J]

2. Charged particle in an alternating electric field - Linear accelerator

14. An alternating potential difference $V = 2 \sin(2\pi \times 10^8)\, t$ is applied to two plane and parallel plates A and B arranged 0.5 cm apart along the axis of x. An electron is emitted from plate A with zero velocity just when plate B is acquiring positive potential. What will be the maximum speed acquiring by the electron? **[Ans.** 6.7×10^8 cm/sec.]

[**Hint.** Here, obviously $V_0 = 2$, statvolts and $\omega = 2\pi \times 10^8$. So that, peak value of the electric field, *i.e.*,

$E_0 = V_0/0.5 = 2/0.5 = 4$ state volt/cm. Therefore, $md^2x/dt^2 = -eE_0 \sin \omega t \; d^2x/dt^2 = -(e/m)E_0 \sin \omega t$. Hence, $v = dx/dt = eE_0(1 - \cos \omega t)\; m\omega$. The value of v will be the maximum when $\cos \omega t = -1$. Thus, $v_{max} = 2\, e\, E_0/m\omega = 2 \times 4.8 \times 10^{-10} \times 4/9.1 \times 10^{-28} \times 2\pi \times 10^8 = 6.7 \times 10^9$ cms/sec.]

15. An alternating electric field of peak value 3 volts/cm and frequency 1 MHz. (*i.e.*, 10^8 c.p.s.) is established between two plane and parallel plates. Show that the electrons starting at different times with zero initial velocities in this field will acquire maximum velocities of $\pm\, 8.4 \times 10^8$ cm/sec.

[**Hint.** Proceed exactly as in problem 13 above and obtain v_{max}]

16. The energy of a C^{12} ion when it emergence from the last drift tubeof a linear accelerator is 120 MeV. What would be the energy of a O^{16} ion from the accelerator? (***Amaravati U. 2008***) [**Ans.** 160 MeV]

3. Charged particle in a magnetic field - Cyclotron

17. Show that the path of a charged particle in a uniform magnetic field is, in general, a helix. Under what condition is this path reduced to a circle?

18. A charged particles of mass M and charge q is moving in a constant magnetic field B. Show that (*i*) the component of the velocity of the particle along the axis of the magnetic field is constant, (*ii*) the magnetic field does not change the kinetic energy of the particle, (*iii*) for a uniform circular motion in a plane perpendicular to the axis of the magnetic field, the angular velocity of the particle, ω, iw given by $\omega = qB/Mc$, where c is the speed of light in free space. (***Agra***)

19. Calculate the gyroradius and gyrofrequency of an elenctron moving in a uniform magnetic field of 10^2 gauss with a velocity 3×10^9 cm/sec in a direction perpendicular to the field.

[**Ans.** 0.17 cm, $8.8 \times 10^9 \approx 9 \times 10^9$ hertz or c.p.s.]

20. An electron describes a helilx of radius 6.0 cm and pitch 2.0 cm in a magnetic field of intensity 30 gauss. Obtain the components of its velocity along and perpendicular to the magnetic field.

[**Ans.** 1.68×10^8 cm/sec, 3.39×10^9 cm/sec.]

21. Particles of charge q and mass m are projected withe velocity $a\hat{i} + b\hat{j}$ in a magnetic field $B\hat{j}$ of units.

Show that they follow a helical path. Deduce an expression for the pitch of the helix. What is the significance of the face that this is independent of the component of velocity? (***Agra***)

[**Ans.** Pitch of helix = $\dfrac{2\pi mc}{qB} b$]

22. An electron with a velocity 10^7m/sec enters a region of uniform magnetic flux density of 0.10 weber metre^2, the angle between the direction of the field and the initial path of the elctron being 25°. Find the pitch of its helical path. (e/m for an electron = 1.8×10^{11} coulomb/kg) [Ans. 0.32 cm.]

23. An electron, moving with a velocity equal to 4/5th of that of light in free space, enters a magnetic field of 300 gauss in a direction perpendicular to that of the field. Calculate the radius of the circular path described by the electron inside the field on non-relativistic as well as relativistic considerations.

[**Ans.** 4.55 cm; 7.58 cm,]

[**Hint.** Relativistically, the mass of the electron is given by $m = m_0/\sqrt{1 - v^2/c^2}$ where $m_0 = 9.1 \times 10^{-28}$ gm]

24. An alpha particle moves with velocity 10^8 cm/sec at an angle of 30° with a magnetic field of 10^2 gausss. Obtain the values of (*i*) the Lorentz force acting on it, (*ii*) the radius and the pitch of the helix described by it and (*iii*) it frequency of rotation. (Take mass of α-particle = $4 \times 1.6 \times 10^{-24}$ gm and the charge on it = $2 \times 4.8 \times 10^{-10}$ esu).

[**Ans.** (*i*) 16×10^{-16} dynes, (*ii*) 10 cm, 108.7 cm, (*iii*) $7.96 \times 10^5 \times \approx 8 \times 10^5$ *c.p.s.*]

[**Hint.** Lorentz force. $\vec{F} = \frac{q}{c}(\vec{v} \times \vec{B})$ So that, its magnitude $\frac{q}{c} v\, B \cos\theta$]

25. Explain clearly the principle underlying the working of a cyclotron. What are its drawbacks and how have they been remedied. Which is preferable, a lower or a higher radiofrequency voltage, to be applied to the dees?

26. What will be the energy of (*i*) a proton, (*ii*) an electron as it emerges from a cylotron after making 100 revolution inside it , if the p.d. across the dees be 10^2 volts? Which of these will emerge with a higher velocity? [**Ans.** (*i*) 2×10^5 eV, (*ii*) 2×10^5 eV; The electron]

27. Calculate, ignoring relativistic effects, the amount of work done on an electron in a cyclotron if, starting from rest, it finally emerges with a velocity of 4×10^9 cm/sec.
(Take mass of electron = 9×10^{-28} gm) **[Ans.** 4.5×10^2 eV]

28. (*a*) Show that the cyclotron frequency of a given kind of ions is independent of the energy. State the limiting condition, if any. ***(Agra)***
(*b*) Explain the principle of magnetic focussing. ***(Agra)***

29. The radius of the dees of a cyclotron used accelerate protons is 50 cm and they are connected to a radiofrequency supply of 10 megacycles per second at maximum value 6000 volts. Calculate (*i*) the strength of the magnetic field applied, (*ii*) the velocity and the energy of the emerging protons, (*iii*) the minimum number of rotations made by them and (*iv*) the time spent by them inside the dees.
[Ans. (*i*) 6.557×10^3 gauss, (*ii*) 3.142×10^9 cm/sec, 5.15×10^8 eV, (*iii*) 430, (*iv*) 4.3×10^{-5} sec.]

30. A particle of charged q esu and mass m gm enters a magnetic field of $2000\,\hat{i}$ gauss with a velocity $(2\hat{i} + 3\hat{i})$ 10^8 cm/sec. Deduce (*i*) radius of the helical path, (*ii*) number of rotations made by the particle while travelling forward 10 cm along the axis of the helix. ***(Agra (supp))***
[Ans. (*i*) $4.5 \times 10^{15}\left(\frac{m}{q}\right)$cm, (*ii*) $\left(\frac{q}{m}\right)(5.3\times10^{-16})$]

31. The pole pieces of a cyclotron are 1.2 m in diameter and provide a magnetic field of 1.6 Wb m^{-2}. What will be the energy of the alphas, deutron and protons in such a machine? What should be the range of oscillator frequency to cover the acceleration of the above particles? Mass of proton = 1.67×10^{-27} kg and charge 1.6×10^{-19}C. ***(Calicut Uni. 2003)*** **[Ans.** 12.20 to 24.40 MHz]

32. In a cyclotron the magnetic flux density is 1.5 m weber/m^2. A proton of mass 1.67×10^{-19} C is accelerated. The radius at which the proton leaves the system is 0.5 m. Find its maximum K.E. and the time of flight through one dee. ***(Nagpur U 2010, 2004)*** **[Ans.** 2.18×10^{-8} S]

33. A cyclotron oscillator frequency is 10 MHz. What would be the operating magnetic field for accelerating proton? If the radius of its dees is 60 cm, what is the kinetic energy of proton beam produced by the accelerator? Given: $e = 1.6 \times 10^{-19}$C. and m = 1.67×10^{-27} kg.
(Nagpur U 2008) **[Ans.** 0.656 Wb/m^2, 7.4 MeV]

III. Magnetic focusing

34. Calculate the width of the focal line obtained by 180°– magnetic focussing if the radius of curvature of the earth of the ion beam by 50 cm and the semi angle of the cone of the beam, as it enters the magnetic field, be 5°. **[Ans.** 0.38.07 cm]

35. The width of the focal line of an ion beam obtained by 180°-magnetic focussing is 0.3656 cm. If the angle of the cone of the ion beam entering the magnetic field be 4°, calculate the radius of curvature of the path taken by the beam in the magnetic field. **[Ans.** 30 cm]

IV. Charged particle in crossed electric and magnetic fields

36. A charged particle moves in a the x-direction through a region in which there is an electric field E_y and a perpendicular magnetic field B_z. What is the condition necessary to ensure that the net force on the particle will be zero? Show the v, E and B vectors on a diagram. What is the condition ofn v_x if $E_y = 10$ statvolts and $B_z = 300$ gauss?

[Ans. $F_{elec} + F_{mag} = 0$ *i.e.*, $q\vec{E} + \frac{q}{c}\vec{v} \times \vec{B} = 0$, witch leads to $v_x = cE_y/B_x$; $v_x = 1 \times 10^9$ cm/sec]

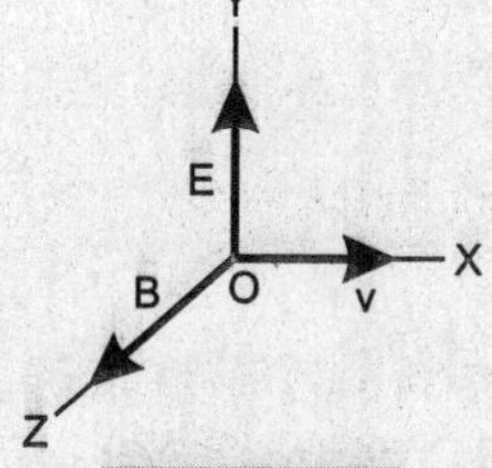

Vector diagram

37. A stram of charged particles, moving with a velocity of 6×10^9 cm/sec passes between two parallel plates 1 cm apart and having a p.d. of 27 volts across them. What should be the magnitude and direction of the magnetic field that should be applied in the region of the electric field in order that the stream of particles may remain undeflected?

[**Ans.** 0.45 gauss, perpendicular to both E and v]

38. What should be the velocity of a steam of (*i*) protons, (*ii*) deutrons in order that may remain undeflected when passing through crossed electric and magnetic fields, $E = 900$ volts/cm and $B = 600$ gauss?

[**Ans.** (*i*) 1.5×10^8 cm/sec; (*ii*) 1.5×10^8 cm/sec.]

39. Explain the principle of a velocity selector for charged particles, using crossed eletrci and magnetic feilds. ***(Agra)***

40. If the electric field in the velocity selector at a Brainbridge mass spectrograph is 10^4 V/m and magnetic flux density is 0.2 Wb/,m^2, find the speed of an ion which will go undeviated through the crossed-field.

(Nagpur 2010, 2004) [**Ans.** 5×10^4 m/s]

V. Charged particle in parallel electric and magnetic fields

41. A beam containing ions of various charges q, masses m and speeds v (along the x-axis) enters a region of uniform electric field E and magnetic field B (both along the y-axis). The ions are received on a screen after travelling a distance L_x. Show that (*i*) all ions of a given q/m value fall along a parabola irrespective of their speeds, (*ii*) all ions of a given speed fall along a straight line irrespective of their q/m value. ***(Delhi U. 2003)***

42. Ions with charge to mass ratio 2.9×10^{14} esu/gm travelling horizontally pass through a region of combined and parallel electric and magnetic fields along the vertical so as to hit a fluorescent screen on which they show horizontal and vertical displacements of 4 cm each. What will be the charge to mass ratio for charged particles which show horizontal and vertical displacements of 1 cm and 8 cm respectively? [**Ans.** 9.1×10^{12} esu/gm]

43. A beam of protons having a velocity of 2×10^7 cm/sec along the axis of x is introduced into a combination of parallel electric and magnetic fields of 100.2 volts/cm and 3.34×10^2 gauss respectively along the z-direction. Obtain the coordinates of the points where the beam will hit a photographic plate placed perpendicular to the direction of the beam at a distance of 6 cm from the rigion.

[**Ans.** 6,2,88, 4.32 cm]

44. In Thomson's parabola method, parabolic traces were obtained on the photographic plate for Neon and Hydrogen ions X-coordinates of the points of intersection of a straight line, parallel to the X-axis, with the parabolic traces were 4.77, 5, 22.4 mm. Find the atomic masses of the isotopes of neon.
(Atomic mass of $H = 1$ amu) ***(Nagpur U. 2007)***

45. Two positive ray parabolas are obtained in a particular experiment for H_2 and a gas X. At a particular y value the x values are in the ratio 4 : 1. Determine the isotopic mass of element X and identify it.
Given: $m_H = 1$ amu. ***(Nagpur U. 2009)***

[**Ans.** 16 amu]

CONSERVATION LAWS

PART I: LAW OF CONSERVATION OF ENERGY

Brief Contents

INTRODUCTION

In Physics we often deal with conservation principles this is because most physical properties abide by conservation laws. In general, a conservation law states that a ***particular measurable property of an isolated physical system does not change as the system evolves***. For example, the conservation of energy follows from the time-invariance of physical systems. At one time, scientists thought that the law of conservation of mass and the law of conservation of energy were two distinct laws. In the early part of the twentieth century, however, German-born American physicist Albert Einstein (1879-1955) demonstrated that matter and energy are two forms of the same thing He showed that matter can change into energy and that energy can change into matter. In some instances, a tiny bit of matter can be created or destroyed in a change. But the total amount of matter PLUS energy before and after a change still remains constant. This statement is now accepted as the law of conservation of mass and energy.

Examples of the law of conservation of mass and energy are common in every day life. The manufacturer of an electric heater can tell consumers how much heat will be produced by a given model of heater. The amount of heat produced is determined by the amount of electrical current ($H = I^2R$) that goes into the heater. Similarly that amount of gasoline that can be formed in the breakdown of petroleum can be calculated by the amount of petroleum used in the process. And the amount of nuclear energy produced by a nuclear power plant can be calculated by the amount of Uranium-235 used in the plant. Thus, the energy is conserved. It may take various forms, such as electrical energy, heat, light, magnetism or kinetic energy (due to its motion), sound, etc., but the relationship is always the same. The amount of energy used to initiate a change in the same as the amount of energy detected at the end of the change. In other words, energy can not be created or destroyed in a physical or chemical change, only changes the form of its manifestation. This statement summarizes the law of conservation of energy.

A partial listing of conservation laws that are said to be exact laws, or more precisely have never been shown to be violated.

- Conservation of mass-energy
- Conservation of linear momentum
- Conservation of angular momentum
- Conservation of electric charge
- Conservation of parity*

The most important consequence of the law of conservation of energy is that *perpetual motion* machines can only work perpetually if they deliver no energy to their surroundings.

5.1 SIGNIFICANCE OF CONSERVATION LAWS

In Physics, we come across various conservation laws, as mentioned above, and even though all of them may not be equally exact or accurate, they nevertheless prove helpful in many ways. Thus, for instance,

(*i*) without going into details of the trajectories or the forces involved in any particular case,

---

* Conservation laws are now widely regarded as some of the most fundamental laws in all of nature. It was a great Shock, therefore, when two American physicists, Val Lodgson Fitch (1923) and James Watson Cronin (1921) discovered mid-1960s that certain subatomic particles known as K-mesons appear to violate a conservation law. That law is known as the conservation of parity; which defines the basic symmetry of nature: that an object and its mirror image will behave the same way. Scientists have not yet fully explained this unexpected experimental result.

they give us a broad and generalised picture of the significant facts that emerge in consequence of the equations of motion:

(*ii*) even in cases where the nature of the forces involved is not clearly known, the conservation laws have been successfully invoked, particularly in the realm of what are called fundamental or elementary particles and have, indeed, helped predict the existence of quite a few more of them *viz*, conservation of parity.

(*iii*) they forewarn us of the impossibility of the occurrence of certain types of phenomena (like, for example, a perpetual motion machine) and thus prevent wastage of time and effort that we might otherwise feel tempted to devote in tackling such problems;

(*iv*) they seem to have an intimate relationship with the concept of invariance and we may often use them, with success, in exploring and unrevelling new and hitherto not well understood phenomena. Thus, as we have seen in chapter II, the principle of conservation of linear momentum has been obtained more or less as a direct consequence of Galilean invariance.

With these few examples regarding the importance of conservation laws, let us now proceed to deal with three important ones of them *viz*., those of energy, linear and angular momentum, in proper detail.

I – LAW OF CONSERVATION OF ENERGY

5.2. CONCEPTS OF WORK, POWER AND ENERGY

Before dealing with the law of conservation of energy itself, it is better to be quite clear about the concepts of work, power and energy involved in the law.

1. Work. Suppose a particle of mass *m* is acted upon by a force $\vec{F}$, (Fig. 5.1), under the influence of which it is set into motion, not necessarily in the direction of the force, its actual path depending upon its initial velocity and the magnitude and direction of the force applied. Let it be along a curve *C*, joining the points *A* and *B*. It may be noted that the magnitude and direction of the force may vary from point to point along the curve.

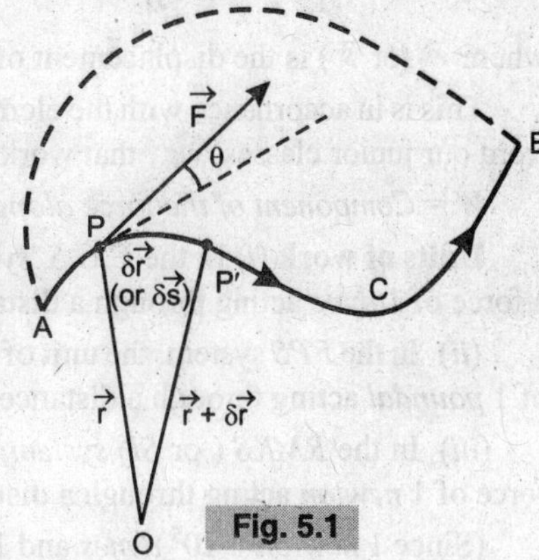

Fig. 5.1

To determine the work done in displacing the particle from *A* to *B*, let *P* and *P'* be two neighbouring points such that their position vectors are $\vec{r}$ and $\vec{r}+\delta\vec{r}$ and, therefore, $\overrightarrow{PP'} = \delta\vec{r}$ (or $\delta\vec{s}$ if we prefer to work in terms of the length of curve *C*).

Then, for a displacement of the particle (or the point of application of the force) from *P* to *P'*, we have

Work done by the force, $dW = \vec{F}\cdot d\vec{s}$

∴ *Total work done by the force* in displacing the particle along the whole length of the curve from *A* to *B*, *i.e. W*, is given by the relation

$$W = \int_A^B \vec{F}\cdot d\vec{r} = \int_A^B \vec{F}\cdot d\vec{s} = \int_A^B F\cos\theta\, ds, \quad ...(i)$$

where θ is the angle that the direction of the force makes with the tangent to the curve at the point *P* and, therefore, *F* cos θ, the tangential component of the force along the curve at the point *P*.

Such an integral evaluated along the path of the particle is called the **line integral of the force** $\vec{F}$.

We may, therefore, define work done by the force on the particles as the *line integral of the tangential component of the force evaluated along the actual path of the particle.*

If the Cartesian components of $\vec{F}$ and $d\vec{r}$ (or $d\vec{s}$) be respectively $F_x\hat{i}, F_y\hat{j}, F_z\hat{k}$ and $d_x\hat{i}, d_y\hat{j}$ and $d_z\hat{k}$, we have

$$W = \int_A^B (F_x\hat{i} + F_y\hat{j} + F_z\hat{k})(d_x\hat{i} + d_y\hat{j} + d_z\hat{k})$$

$$= \int_A^B F_x d_x + \int_A^B F_y d_y + \int_A^B F_z d_z \,. \qquad ...(ii)$$

Further, if there be a number of forces, $\vec{F_1}$, $\vec{F_2}$ etc., acting simultaneously on the particle, such that their resultant $\vec{F} = \vec{F_1} + \vec{F_2} + \vec{F_3} + ...$, we have work done on the particle given by

$$W = \int_A^B \vec{F} \cdot d\vec{r} = \int_A^B (\vec{F_1} + \vec{F_2} + \vec{F_3} + ...)\, d\vec{r}$$

$$= \int_A^B \vec{F_1} \cdot d\vec{r} + \int_A^B \vec{F_2} \cdot d\vec{r} + ..., \qquad ...(iii)$$

i.e., equal to the sum of the work done by each individual force.

In case force $\vec{F}$ be a *constant or a nonvariable* one and the displacement of the particle takes place *along a straight line*, we have

$$W = \int_A^B \vec{F} \cdot d\vec{r} \left(= \int_A^B \vec{F} \cdot d\vec{s} \right) = \vec{F} \cdot \vec{r} (= \vec{F} \cdot \vec{s}) = F \cos\theta(r) = F \cos\theta(s), \qquad ...(iv)$$

where $\vec{r}$ (or $\vec{s}$) is the displacement of the particle along the straight line.

This is in accordance with the elementary definition of work with which we are already familiar from our junior classes, *viz.,* that work done is given by

W = Component of the force along the displacement × The displacement.

Units of work (*i*) In the *C.G.S. system*, the unit of work is the **erg**, which is the work done by a force of 1 *dyne* acting through a distance of 1 cm, *i.e.,* 1 *erg* = 1 *dyne* × 1 cm.

(*ii*) In the *FPS* system, the unit of work is the **foot-poundal,** which is the work done by a force of 1 *poundal* acting through a distance of 1 *ft, i.e.,* 1 *ft-poundal* = 1 *poundal* × 1 *foot.*

(*iii*) In the *RMKS* (or *SI*) *system,* the unit of work is the **joule**, which is the work done by a force of 1 *newton* acting through a distance of 1 *meter, i.e.,* 1 *joule* = 1 *newton* × 1 *metre.*

(Since 1 *newton* = 10^5 *dynes* and 1 *metre* = 10^2 cm, 1 *joule* = $10^5 \times 10^2 = 10^7$ *ergs*).

These are called the *absolute units*. The corresponding *gravitational* units are *g times* the *absolute units*. Thus, the gravitational units of work in the three systems are (*i*) the *gm wt-cm* = 981 *ergs*, (*ii*) the *foot-pound* = 32 *foot-poundals* and (*iii*) the *kilogramme-meter* = 9.81 *joules.*

2. Power of Activity. It is defined as the *rate of doing* work and is denoted by the latter *P* or *A*.

Thus, in Fig. 5.1, since $\vec{F} \cdot d\vec{r}$ is the work done by the force in moving the particle from *P* to *P′* in time *dt*, the rate of working of the force or its *power on activity* $P = \vec{F} \cdot d\vec{r} / dt = \vec{F} \cdot \vec{V}$ ...(*v*)

where $\vec{v}$ is the *instantaneous value* of the velocity acquired by the particle.

Relation (*v*) thus gives the *instantaneous value of the power of the force*. The *average value of power* is obtained by dividing the total work done (*W*) by the total time taken (*t*), *i.e., average power* = *W*/*t*.

It will be easily seen from the above that the work done is given by

$$W = \int_A^B P.dt\,.$$

Units of power. (*i*) In the *C.G.S. system*, the unit of power is 1 *erg/sec.* (*ii*) In the *F.P.S. system*, it is 1 *foot-poundal/sec*. The unit commonly used in this system is the *horse power* (*H.P.*), equal to 550 *ft-pounds/sec* or 550 × 60 or 33,000 *ft-pounds/min.* (*iii*) In the *RMKS* or (*SI*) system, the unit of power is 1 *joule/sec*, called the **watt**, usually used to measure *electrical power*.

3. Energy. We shall deal with it later in § 5.4.

5.3 CONSERVATIVE FORCES

In the type of cases discussed under § 5.2 above, the force $\vec{F}$ generally varies from point to point and it may, therefore, appear that the work done by it (W) in moving the particle from point A to point B will depend upon the path taken between A and B. In actual fact it may or may not, depending upon the type of force we are dealing with. For, forces may, in general be divided into two broad catagories; **conservative** and **non-conservative**.

The work done by a conservative force in displacing a particle from one point to another depends only on the position of the two given points and is quite independent of the actual path taken between them. On the other hand, *the work done by a non-conservative force does depend upon the actual path taken*.

To the conservative class of forces belong most of what are called **central forces**, *i.e., forces which are directed towards, or away from, a fixed centre*, as in the case of gravitational and electrostatic forces respectively. Such forces are *position-dependent* forces, so to speak, since they depend only upon the instantaneous position of the particle with respect to the fixed centre and on nothing else.

Forces which are *velocity-dependent i.e.,* whose value depends upon the magnitude and direction of velocity, like frictional and viscous forces, are in general, *non-conservative*, though, quite a few among them too may turn out to be conservative. Thus, for example, *Lorentz force* $\frac{q}{c}(\vec{v} \times \vec{B})$, although velocity-dependent, is conservative because, acting as it does, in a direction perpendicular to both the magnetic field B and the velocity of the particle v, the work done by it, irrespective of the path taken, is always zero and thus independent of the path.

A region of space in which a particle experiences a conservative force at every point is referred to as a *conservative-force field* or a *conservative field of force*. In case the conservative force in the field happens to be a central force, it may be specified as a *central-force field*.

That a central force or a position-dependant force is a conservative force may be easily shown as follows:

Taking the origin as the fixed centre, a central force may be expressed as $\vec{F} = F(r)\hat{r}$ where $F(r)$ is a function of $\vec{r}$ only and $\hat{r}$, the unit vector along $\vec{r}$.

Clearly, work done by such a force in displacing a particle from a point A to a point B is given by

$$W_{AB} = \int_A^B \vec{F}\cdot d\vec{r} = \int_A^B F(r)\hat{r}\cdot d\vec{r}$$

As we know, $r^2 = r^2$, so that $2\vec{r}\cdot d\vec{r} = 2rdr$ and $\therefore d\vec{r} = \hat{r}dr$.

Hence $$W_{AB} = \int_A^B F(r)dr$$

an expression dependent only on the functional form of $F(r)$ and the two end-points A and B.

The force in question, *viz*, $\vec{F}$ is, therefore, a *conservative force*.

It is clear from the above that the work done by the force F in moving the particle from B to A along any path will be given by

$$W_{BA} = \int_B^A \vec{F}\cdot d\vec{r} = -\int_A^B \vec{F}\cdot d\vec{r} = -W_{AB}.$$

It follows, therefore, that the total work done in displacing a particle from A to B and back to A along whatever path (as shown dotted in Fig. 5.1) is $W_{BA} - W_{AB} = 0$, indicating that the *work done by a conservative force along a closed path, i.e., along a closed curve, is zero*. This is denoted symbolically as $\oint \vec{F}\cdot d\vec{r} = 0$, (the symbol $\oint$ standing for the *integral* over a closed path).

The is a *characteristic property of a conservative force*. In fact, *we may perhaps best define a conservative force as one by which the work done in a round trip is zero and, therefore, a non-conservative force as one by which the work done in a round trip is not zero*. In the first case, when the particle (or the body) comes back to its starting point, it has the same kinetic energy with which it started, so that its ability to do work is *conserved*. In the second case, the particle, as it comes back to its starting point, has less or more kinetic energy than the one with which it started, so that its capacity to do work is *not conserved* (*i.e.*, it is either less or more than before).

5.4 ENERGY

The energy of a particle is its *capacity to do work* and is measured by the amount of work it is capable of doing in virtue of (*i*) its motion or (*ii*) position or condition. The former is called the *kinetic energy* and the latter, the *potential energy* of the particle, represented by the symbols K (or now, more usually, T) and U (or V) respectively.

Since energy is really *work, its units are the same as those of work, viz.,* the **erg**, the **foot-poundal** (or the **foot-pound**) and the **joule** in the three systems respectively.

We shall now proceed to consider the two types of energy separately and in necessary detail.

(*i*) **Kinetic energy–Work-energy principle.** Since kinetic energy (T) of a particle is due to its motion, let us obtain a proper expression for it for a particle moving with velocity v.

Let a force $\vec{F}$ be applied to the particle in a direction opposite to that of its motion. Then, clearly, *work done by the particle against the applied force, i.e.,* $W = -\int \vec{F}\cdot d\vec{r}$. Since, in accordance with Newton's second law of motion,

$$\vec{F} = m d\vec{v}/dt,$$

Where m is *mass* of the particle, we have

$$W = -m\int \frac{d\vec{v}}{dt}\cdot d\vec{r} = -m\int \frac{dr}{dt} dv = -m\int_v^0 f\cdot dv = \frac{1}{2}mv^2.$$

Since energy of the particle is its capacity to do work, we have

Kinetic energy of the particle, $T = \frac{1}{2}mv^2$,

It may as well be noted that $dT/dt = d\left(\frac{1}{2}mv^2\right)\Big/dt = mv(dv/dt) = F.v = P$, *i.e.*, the *rate of change of energy is equal to the power or activity of the force.*

Again, invoking Newton's second law of motion, we have

$$mdv/dt = F.$$

Dot multiplying both sides by v or dr/dt and integrating with respect to t between the limits A and B (Fig. 5.1), we have

$$\int_A^B m\frac{d\vec{v}}{dt}\cdot\vec{v}\,dt = \int_A^B \vec{F}\cdot\frac{d\vec{r}}{dt}dt.$$

Or,
$$\left[\frac{1}{2}m\vec{v}\cdot\vec{v}\right]_A^B = \int_A^B \vec{F}.d\vec{r}.$$

Since $\vec{v}\cdot\vec{v} = v^2$ and v_A and v_B are the values of the initial and final velocities of the particle at points A and B respectively, we have

$$\frac{1}{2}mv_B^2 - \frac{1}{2}mv_A^2 = \int_A^B \vec{F}\cdot d\vec{r} = W$$

where W is the work done by the force in displacing the particle from point A to point B.

Since $\frac{1}{2}mv_B^2$ is the kinetic energy of the particle at point B and $\frac{1}{2}mv_A^2$, its kinetic energy at point A, we have

work done in displacing the particle from A to B = its K.E. at B–its K.E. at A

= change in energy in proceeding from A to B.

i.e. Work done by a force on a particle is equal to the change in the kinetic energy of the particle.

This is spoken of as the **work-energy principle** or the **work-energy theorem.**

As will be readily seen, the kinetic energy of the particle increases if work be done *on it* (by the force) and decreases if work be done *by it* (against the force).

(ii) **Potential energy.** We have already defined the potential energy of a particle or a body as its capacity to do work in virtue of its position (or condition). It is measured by the amount of work done by the force to restore the particle or the body from its present position (or condition) to a standard position (or condition) and is denoted by the symbol U or V. Thus, if the present or the existing position of the particle be specified by a vector $\vec{r}$ and its standard position by a vector r_0, we have

$$U = \int_r^{r_0} \vec{F}\cdot d\vec{r}.$$

It may be emphasised here that *this relationship exists only in the case of a conservative field of force*, for the work done by a conservative force alone depends on the position of the particle, irrespective of the path taken. In the case of a non-conservative force, the work done cannot be expressed in the form of potential energy since it depends on the directions of motion as also on the shape of the path taken and even, at times, on the magnitude of the velocity.

The standard position (or condition) chosen is the one in which the force acting on the particle or the body is zero, so that its *P.E.* in this position (or condition) may also be taken to be zero. The difference of *P.E.* in this position (or condition) and in the existing position (or condition) of the particle then gives its a *P.E.* in the latter position.

Thus, for example, the standard condition in the case of a spring is taken to be its normal, unstretched (or uncompressed) state. And, although for convenience we take the electrostatic and gravitational potential energies to be zero on the surface of the earth, the electrostatic and gravitational forces involved are actually governed by the inverse square law, so that the electrostatic force due to a charge or the gravitational force due to a material body is zero only at an infinite distance from it and the standard or the zero potential energy position is thus infinity. In such cases, therefore, $r_0 = \infty$ and we have

$$U = \int_r^{\infty} \vec{F} \cdot d\vec{r} \text{ or, } U = -\int_{\infty}^{r} \vec{F} \cdot d\vec{r},$$

i.e., the potential energy of a particle at a point $\vec{r}$ is given by the amount of work done in moving it from ∞ to that point.

In calculating the work we may, of course, use any convenient path since, as we know, the work done does not depend on the actual path taken but only on the positions of the end-points.

5.5 CONSERVATIVE FORCE AS NEGATIVE GRADIENT OF POTENTIAL ENERGY –CURL $\vec{F}$ = 0

We have just seen in § 5.4 above how

$U = -\int_{\infty}^{r} \vec{F} d\vec{r}$ where $\vec{F}$ is a *conservative force.*

Expressing $\vec{F}$ and $\vec{r}$ in terms of their components along the three coordinate axes, we have

$$\vec{F} = F_x\hat{i} + F_y\hat{j} + F_z\hat{k},\ \vec{r} = x\hat{i} + y\hat{j} + z\hat{k} \text{ and } d\vec{r} = d_x\hat{i} + d_y\hat{j} + d_z\hat{k}.$$

So that,
$$U = -\int_{\infty}^{r} (F_x\hat{i} + F_y\hat{j} + F_z\hat{k})(d_x\hat{i} + d_y\hat{j} + d_z\hat{k})$$
$$= -\int_{\infty}^{r} (F_x dx + F_y dy + F_z dz)$$

Which, on partial differentiation with respect to *x, y, z*, gives

$$F_x = -\partial u/\partial x,\ F_y = -\partial U/\partial y,\ F_z = -\partial U/\partial z,$$

and ∴
$$\vec{F} = F_x\hat{i} + F_y\hat{j} + F_z\hat{k} = -\left(\frac{\partial U}{\partial x}\hat{i} + \frac{\partial U}{\partial y}\hat{j} + \frac{\partial U}{\partial z}\hat{k}\right) = -\text{ grad } U$$

or $\quad -\vec{\nabla} U$

Thus, *a conservative force F is equal to the negative gradient of potential energy U.*

If instead of the three dimensions, we restrict ourselves to one dimension only, we have $F = -dU/dx$, showing that *a conservative force is the negative of the space rate of change of potential energy.*

Now, we have Curl $\vec{F} = \vec{\nabla} \times \vec{F} = -\vec{\nabla} \times \vec{\nabla} U$

$$= \begin{vmatrix} \hat{i} & \hat{j} & \hat{k} \\ \frac{\partial}{\partial x} & \frac{\partial}{\partial y} & \frac{\partial}{\partial z} \\ F_x & F_y & F_z \end{vmatrix} = -\begin{vmatrix} \hat{i} & \hat{j} & \hat{k} \\ \frac{\partial}{\partial x} & \frac{\partial}{\partial y} & \frac{\partial}{\partial z} \\ \frac{\partial U}{\partial x} & \frac{\partial U}{\partial y} & \frac{\partial U}{\partial z} \end{vmatrix}$$

$$= -\left[\hat{i}\left(\frac{\partial^2 H}{\partial y \partial z} - \frac{\partial^2 U}{\partial z \partial y}\right) + \hat{j}\left(\frac{\partial^2 U}{\partial z \partial x} - \frac{\partial^2 U}{\partial x \partial z}\right) + \hat{k}\left(\frac{\partial^2 U}{\partial x \partial y} - \frac{\partial^2 U}{\partial y \partial x}\right)\right]$$

Since, with *U* taken as a perfect differential, $\partial^2 U/\partial y \partial z = \partial^2 U/\partial z \partial y$, $\partial^2 U/\partial z \partial x = \partial^2 U/\partial x \partial z$ and $\partial^2 U/\partial y \partial x = \partial^2 U/\partial y \partial x$ we have

$$\text{Curl } \vec{F} = 0.$$

This condition (Curl $\vec{F}$ = 0) implies the existence of a potential function *U* such that $\vec{F}$ = – *grad U*. It thus follows that *curl* $\vec{F}$ = 0 is *a necessary and a sufficient condition for a conservative field of force* $\vec{F}$.

5.6. LAW OF CONSERVATION OF MECHANICAL ENERGY

It follows from § 5.5 above that

$$\vec{F}\cdot d\vec{r} = -(\partial U/\partial x)\delta x - (\partial U/\partial y)\delta y - (\partial U/\partial z)\delta z = -\delta U.$$

$\therefore$ work done in displacing a particle from A to B is given by

$$W = \int_A^B \vec{F}\cdot d\vec{r} = -\int_A^B dU = U_A - U_B.$$

But, as shown under § 5.4 (*i*)

$$W = \int_A^B \vec{F}\cdot d\vec{r} = \frac{1}{2}mv_B^{\ 2} - \frac{1}{2}mv_A^{\ 2}$$

Obviously, therefore, $U_A - U_B = \frac{1}{2}mv_B^{\ 2} - \frac{1}{2}mv_A^{\ 2}$ indicating that *what the particle loses in P.E. it gains in K.E.*

So that, $$\frac{1}{2}mv_A^{\ 2} + U_A = \frac{1}{2}mv_B^{\ 2} + U_B.$$

Or, putting T_A and T_B respectively for $\frac{1}{2}mv_A^{\ 2}$ and $\frac{1}{2}mv_B^{\ 2}$, we have

$$T_A + U_A = T_B + U_B, \text{ or }, T + U = E, \text{ a constant,}$$

showing that *the sum total (E) of the kinetic and potential energies of a particle remains unaltered as the particle moves from one point A to another point B in a conservative force field. In other words, the mechanical energy of a particle remains constant in such a field.* This is referred to as the **law of conservation of mechanical energy for conservative forces.** We shall see later that it may be easily extended to include also other forms of energy when it is called the *general law of conservation of energy.*

This is perhaps by far the most accurate of all the conservation laws and there has been found not one single exception to it so far.

It is easy enough to see that *the law holds good also for a system of particles moving in a conservative field of force* for the simple reason that it holds good for each individual particle.

The quantity $E = (T + U)$ is often spoken of as the energy function of the particle and is obviously *invariant to both changes of time and position of the particle.* This may be seen from a simple illustration of the law in the case of a falling particle.

Let the particle of mass m be at rest at a height h above the ground, so that it has only potential energy $U = mgh$, its kinetic energy T being *zero*. It *total energy* is thus $(T + U) = (0 + mgh) = mgh$.

Let it now be allowed to fall under the action of gravity, so that as it gathers speed, it acquires *K.E.* at the expense of its *P.E.*

When it has fallen to a height z above the ground, *i.e.,* through a distance $(h - z)$, acquiring a velocity v, we have $v^2 - 0 = 2g(h - z)$ and the *K.E.* gained by it is, therefore,

$$T = \frac{1}{2}mv^2 = \frac{1}{2}m[2g(h-z)] = mg(h-z).$$

And since its height from the ground is now z, the *P.E.* lost by it is $\int_h^z -mgdr = -mg(h-z)$ and

$\therefore$ its *P.E.* at this height (z) above the ground, *i.e.,* $U = mgh - [-mg(z-h)] = mgz.$

$\therefore$ *The sum total of its energy,* $E = T + U = mg\,(h - z) + mgz = mgh$, the same as at its initial height h.

And, when the particle has reached the ground, *i.e.*, when $z = 0$, its, *P.E.*, $U = mgh = 0$ and its *K.E.*, $T = mg(h - z) = mgh$.

And $\therefore$ its total energy $E = T + U = mgh + 0 = \text{mgh}$, the same as to start with.

Thus, the total energy of the particle remains the same *mgh*, in accordance with the law of conservation at any height from the ground between 0 and *h*, *indicating that the energy function* $E = T + U$ *is independent of both time and the position of the particle.*

Example 1. The position of a moving particle is at any instant given by $\vec{r} = A\cos\theta\hat{i} + A\sin\theta\hat{j}$. Show that the force acting on it is a conservative one. Also calculate the total energy of the particle.

Solution. The particle is obviously moving along a circular path of radius *A*. It must, therefore, be acted upon by a force directed towards the centre of its circular path, *i.e.*, the force acting upon it is a radial or a central one and hence necessarily *conservative*. However, this may also be show as follows:

The position vector of the particle at an instant *t* is

$$\vec{r} = A\cos\theta\,\hat{i} + A\sin\theta\,\hat{j} = A(\cos\omega t\,\hat{i} + \sin\omega t\,\hat{j})$$

Where ω is the angular velocity of the particle and $\omega t = 0$.

The *linear velocity* of the particle at the given instant is

$$\vec{v} = d\vec{r}/dt = A\omega(-\sin\omega t\,\hat{i} + \cos\omega t\,\hat{j})$$

and hence its *acceleration* $\vec{a} = d^2\vec{r}/dt^2 = -A\omega^2(\cos\omega t\,\hat{i} + \sin\omega t\,\hat{j}) = -\omega^2\vec{r}$.

$\therefore$ If *m* be the *mass* of the particle, the force acting on it is $\vec{F} = -m\omega^2\vec{r}$.

Now, if this force $(\vec{F})$ be a conservative one, we should have *curl* $\vec{F} = 0$.

Let us see if this is so.

We have $\quad Curl\ \vec{F} = \nabla \times \vec{F}$

And, $\quad \nabla \times \vec{F} = -m\omega^2 \begin{vmatrix} \hat{i} & \hat{j} & \hat{k} \\ \frac{\partial}{\partial x} & \frac{\partial}{\partial y} & \frac{\partial}{\partial z} \\ x & y & 0 \end{vmatrix}$, which is clearly equal to 0.

The *force acting on the particle is, therefore, a conservative one.*

Now, since $\vec{F}$ is a conservative force, we have $\vec{F} = -grad\ U$, where *U* is the *P.E.* of the particle at the given instant.

We, therefore, have $\quad \vec{F} = -grad\ U = -\left(\frac{\partial U}{\partial x}\hat{i} + \frac{\partial U}{\partial y}\hat{j} + \frac{\partial U}{\partial z}\hat{k}\right) = -\frac{dU}{dr}$

$$\therefore \quad U = -\int \vec{F}\cdot d\vec{r} = -\int -m\omega^2\vec{r}\cdot d\vec{r} = \frac{1}{2}m\omega^2 r.$$

And if $\vec{v}$ be the linear velocity of the particle at the given instant, we have

$$K.E.\ of\ the\ particle,\ T = \frac{1}{2}mv^2 = \frac{1}{2}m\omega^2r^2 \qquad [\because v = r\omega.]$$

$$\therefore \quad Total\ energy\ of\ the\ particle,\ E = T + U = \frac{1}{2}m\omega^2r^2 + \frac{1}{2}m\omega^2r^2 = m\omega^2r^2.$$

Or, $$E = m\omega^2(A^2\cos^2\omega t + A^2\sin^2\omega t) = m\omega^2 A.$$

Thus, the *total energy of the particle* $= m\omega^2 A$.

Example 2. Show that the following two forces are conservative:

(*i*) $\vec{F} = (y^2 - x^2)\hat{i} + 2xy\,\hat{j}$ and (*ii*) $F = (2xy + z^2)\hat{i} + x^2\hat{j} + 2xz\,\hat{k}$.

Also calculate the work done on a particle in case (*ii*) in moving it from the position 0, 1, 2 to the position 5, 6, 8.

Solution. Clearly, if the curl of each of the two forces be zero, they will be conservative.

Now, in case (*i*), $$curl\ \vec{F} = \nabla \times \vec{F} = \begin{vmatrix} \hat{i} & \hat{j} & \hat{k} \\ \frac{\partial}{\partial x} & \frac{\partial}{\partial y} & \frac{\partial}{\partial z} \\ (y^2 - x^2) & 2xy & 0 \end{vmatrix}$$

$$= \left[0 - \frac{\partial}{\partial z}(2xy)\right]\hat{i} + \left[\frac{\partial}{\partial z}(y^2 + x^2) - 0\right]\hat{j} + \left[\frac{\partial}{\partial x}2xy - \frac{\partial}{\partial y}(y^2 - x^2)\right]\hat{k}$$

$$= -\frac{\partial}{\partial z}(2xy)\hat{i} + \frac{\partial}{\partial z}(y^2 - x^2)\hat{j} + \left[\frac{\partial}{\partial x}(2xy) - \frac{\partial}{\partial y}(y^2 - x^2)\right]\hat{k}$$

$$= 0 + 0 + (2y - 2y)\hat{k} = 0.$$

Thus, *curl* $\vec{F}$ being *zero*, force $\vec{F}$ is a conservative force.

In case (*ii*), again, *curl* $$\vec{F} = \nabla \times \vec{F} = \begin{vmatrix} \hat{i} & \hat{j} & \hat{k} \\ \frac{\partial}{\partial x} & \frac{\partial}{\partial y} & \frac{\partial}{\partial z} \\ 2xy + z^2 & x^2 & 2xz \end{vmatrix}$$

$$= \left[\frac{\partial}{\partial y}(2xz) - \frac{\partial}{\partial z}(x^2)\right]\hat{i} + \left[\frac{\partial}{\partial z}(2xy + z^2) - \frac{\partial}{\partial x}(2xz)\right]\hat{j}$$
$$+ \left[\frac{\partial}{\partial x}(x^2) - \frac{\partial}{\partial y}(2xy + z^2)\right]\hat{k}$$

$$= 0 + (2z - 2z)\hat{j} + (2x - 2x)i = 0$$

Again, *curl* $\vec{F}$ being *zero, the force is a conservative one.*

Now, work done by force $\vec{F}$ in case (*ii*) in displacing a particle from A to B is given by

$$W = \int_B^A \vec{F}\cdot d\vec{r} = \int_A^B (F_x dx + F_y dy + F_z dz)$$

$$= \int_A^B [(2xy + z^2)dx + x^2 dy + 2xzdz]$$

$$= \int_A^B (2xydx + x^2 dy) + (z^2 dx + 2xzdx) = \int_A^B d(x^2 y) + d(z^2 x)$$

$$= \int_A^B d(x^2 y + z^2 x) = \left[x^2 y + z^2 x\right]_{0,1,2}^{5,6,8} = 5 \times 5 \times 6 + 8 \times 8 \times 5 - 0 - 0$$

or, $$W = 150 + 320 = 470.$$

Thus, *work done by the force* = 470 *units.*

Example 3. Show that the force $\vec{F} = yz\hat{i} + zx\hat{j} + xy\hat{k}$ is conservative force. (*Pbi. U. 2003*)

Solution. A force is said to be conservative if the curl of the force is zero.

Or, $\vec{\nabla} \times \vec{F} = 0$

Given, $\vec{F} = yz\hat{i} + zx\hat{j} + xy\hat{k}$

$$\therefore \quad \vec{\nabla} \times \vec{F} = \begin{vmatrix} \hat{i} & \hat{j} & \hat{k} \\ \frac{\partial}{\partial x} & \frac{\partial}{\partial y} & \frac{\partial}{\partial z} \\ yz & zx & xy \end{vmatrix}$$

$$= \hat{i}\left[\frac{\partial}{\partial y}(xy) - \frac{\partial}{\partial y}(zx)\right] + \hat{j}\left[\frac{\partial}{\partial z}(yz) - \frac{\partial}{\partial x}(xy)\right] + \hat{k}\left[\frac{\partial}{\partial x}(zx) - \frac{\partial}{\partial y}(yz)\right]$$

$$= \hat{i}(x-x) + \hat{j}(y-y) + \hat{k}(z-z) = 0$$

Since, $\vec{\nabla} \times \vec{F} = 0$, the force $\vec{F}$ is conservative.

Example 4. A particle lying in the $x-y$ plane is acted upon by a force directed towards the origin whose magnitude is kr where r (equal to $\sqrt{x^2 + y^2}$) is the distance from the particle to the origin. (*a*) Find the work that must be done to move the particle from the origin to the point $x = 1, y = 1$ along the radius vector to that point. (*b*) Find the work that must be done if the particle is first moved to $x = 1, y = 0$ and from there to $x = 1, y = 1$. (*c*) Is this particular force conservative or non-conservative?

Solution. (*a*) Clearly, work done in moving the particle from 0 to r is given by

$$W = \int_A^B \vec{F} \cdot d\vec{r} = \int_A^B \vec{F} \cos\theta \cdot dr = \int_0^r F dr$$

$\left[\because \text{Tangentical component of } F \right.$
$\left. F\cos\theta = F, \cos\theta \text{ being equal to } 1.\right.$

Since $F = kr$, we have $W = \int_0^r kr \cdot dr = \left[\frac{kr^2}{2}\right]_0^r = \frac{kr^2}{2}$.

Now, $r = \sqrt{x^2 + y^2} = \sqrt{1+1} = \sqrt{2}$, We, therefore, have

$$W = \frac{k(\sqrt{2})^2}{2} = k.$$

Thus, the *work done* $= k$ *units*.

(*b*) In this case, the components of force $\vec{F}$ along the x and y-axis are F_x and F_y respectively $[\because r = \sqrt{x^2 + y^2}\ ]$. And, clearly, no work is done against the component F_y in taking the particle from O to A [Fig. 5.2], along the axis of x, (where $OA = x = 1$), and similarly, no work is done against the component F_x in taking the particle from A to P along the axis of y, (where $AP = y = 1$).

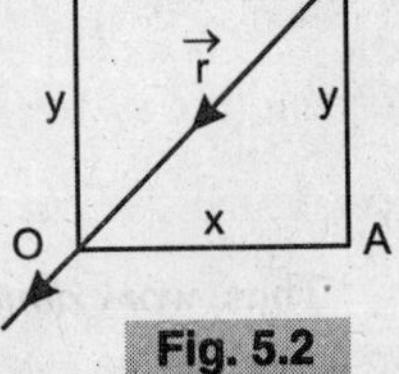

Fig. 5.2

$\therefore$ *Work done in taking the particle from the origin O to* $A(x = 1)$

$$= \int_0^1 kx \cdot dx = \frac{kx^2}{2} = \frac{k}{2}.$$

And, *work done in taking the particle from A* to $P\ (y = 1)$

$$= \int_0^1 ky \cdot dy = \frac{ky^2}{2} = \frac{k}{2}.$$

$\therefore$ *total work done in taking the particle from the origin O to A* $(x = 1, y = 0)$ *and from A to* $P(x = 1, y = 1) = k/2 + k/2 = k$, the same as in case (*i*).

(*c*) It will be easily seen that if we take the particle to P by first moving it from the origin (O) to $B(y = 1, x = 0)$ and from there to $P(y = 1, x = 1)$, we shall again have to do the same work $\int_0^1 ky\,dy + \int_0^1 kx dx = \frac{k}{2} + \frac{k}{2} = k$ as in cases (*i*) and (*ii*).

Thus, the work done in taking the particle from the origin to P is the same (k) whatever the path taken, *i.e.*, it depends only upon the position of the point P and not upon the actual path taken. The force on the particle is, therefore, a *conservative force.*

Example 5. A point-mass *m* starts from the point A of a curved track of the form shown in Fig. 5.3 with a horizontal velocity $\vec{v}_0$. The track is frictionless except for the small horizontal portion *DE* of length *L*. (*i*) Calculate the velocity of the mass at points *B* and *C*. (*ii*) What constant deceleration is required to stop the mass at *E* if the retarding frictional force starts operating at point *D*?

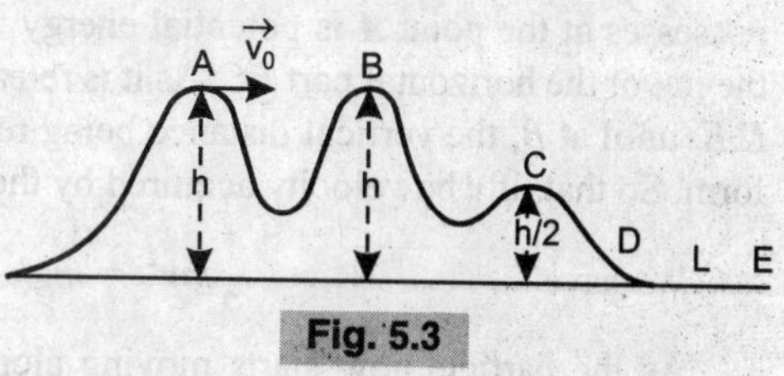

Fig. 5.3

Solution. (*i*) Clearly, the total energy possessed by the mass at the point $A = T + U = \frac{1}{2}mv_0^2 + mgh$. Since point B is also at the same height h from the horizontal as the point A, the kinetic and potential energies of the mass there too are the same as at A, *viz.*, $\frac{1}{2}mv_0^2$ and mgh respectively.

At the point C, however, which is at a height $h/2$ from the horizontal, the *P.E.* of the mass is reduced to $\frac{1}{2}mgh$. Since the total energy of the mass must remain the same as before, it follows that half the *P.E.* of the mass, *i.e.*, $\frac{1}{2}mgh$ is converted here into *K.E.* So that,

$$K.E. \text{ of the mass at } C = \frac{1}{2}mv_0^2 + \frac{1}{2}mgh$$

But if v_c be the velocity of the mass at C, its $K.\ E. = \frac{1}{2}mv_c^2$.

We $\therefore$ have $\frac{1}{2}mv_c^2 = \frac{1}{2}mv_0^2 + \frac{1}{2}mgh$, whence, $v_c = \sqrt{v_0^2 + gh}$.

Thus, the *velocity of the mass at the point* $C = \sqrt{v_0^2 + gh}$.

(*ii*) By the time the mass reaches the point D, its *P.E.* is reduced to zero, so that the whole of its energy, $\frac{1}{2}mv_0^2 + mgh$ is here converted into kinetic energy.

If therefore v_D be the velocity of the mass at D, we have

$$\frac{1}{2}mv_D^2 = \frac{1}{2}mv_0^2 + mgh, \text{ whence, } vD = \sqrt{v_0^2 + 2gh}.$$

Now, if $-a$ be the constant acceleration of the mass between the points D and E which brings it to rest at E, we have

$$0 - v_D^2 = 2(-a)(L). \text{ Or, } \quad -a = -v_D^2/2L = -\sqrt{v_0^2 + 2gh}/2L.$$

Thus, *the constant deceleration required to stop the mass at* $E = \sqrt{v_0^2 + 2gh}/2L$.

Example 6. A particle of mass *m* slides along a track with elevated ends and a flat central part, as shown in Fig. 5.4. The flat part has a length equal to 2 meters. The curved portions of the track are frictionless. For the flat part the coefficient of kinematics friction is μ = 0.20. The particle is released at point A which is at a height *h* = 1.0 metre above the flat part of the track, where does the particle finally come to rest?

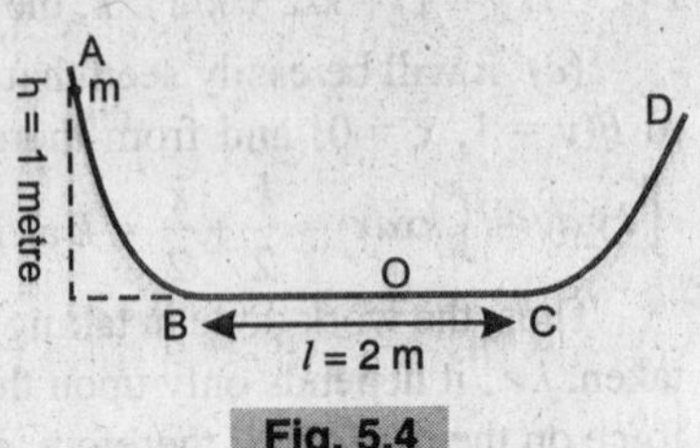

Fig. 5.4

Solution. Here, clearly, the only energy that the particle possesses at the point *A* is potential energy = *mgh*, relative to the flat or the horizontal part *BC*. As it is released at *A*, this *P.E.* naturally starts converting itself into *K.E.* until at *B*, the vertical distance being reduced to *zero*, the whole of it is present in the kinetic form. So that, if *v* be velocity acquired by the particle on reaching *B*,

We have $$\frac{1}{2}mv^2 = mgh.$$

As the particle now starts moving along the horizontal portion *BC*, it has to overcome the frictional force *F* and when the whole of its kinetic energy is used up in doing work against this frictional force over a distance *S*, say it will come to rest. We, therefore, have

$$\frac{1}{2}mv^2 = Fs.$$

Now, as we know, $F/R = \mu$ or $F = \mu R$, where *R* is the normal reaction of the horizontal surface over which the particle moves and is equal to *mg*, and μ, the coefficient of kinematic friction between the horizontal surface and the particle.

So that, $$F = \mu R = \mu mg.$$

$$\therefore \quad \frac{1}{2}mv^2 = \mu mg.s. \text{ Or, } mgh = \mu mgs, \text{ whence, } s = h/\mu.$$

Since $h = 1$ *metre* and $\mu = 0.2$, we have $s = 1/0.2 = 5$ *metres i.e.*, the particle will come to rest after transversing a 5 metre length of the flat surface.

The length of the flat surface being only 2 metres, the particle will still have some *K.E.* after travelling from *B* to *C*. It will, therefore, go up the frictionless, curved part *CD* until this *K.E.* is converted into *P.E.* It will then turn back, its *P.E.* will get converted into *K.E.* until at *C*, it will again have the same *K.E.* as before when it went up along *CD*. It will, therefore, again cover a distance of 2 metres on the flat surface from *C* to *B*, with some more part of its *K.E.* used up in doing work against the frictional force encountered. It will, however, still have some *K.E.* left and will, therefore, go up the frictionless part *BA* until this *K.E.* is converted into *P.E.* It will then turn back and its *P.E.* converted into *K.E.* until at *B* its *K.E.* will again be the same as that when it went up along *BA*. It will now, however, be able to cover a distance of only 1 metre on the flat surface, from *B* to *O*, the mid-point of the surface, for by then *it will have covered a full 5 metre length of the flat surface that it could in virtue of its initial K.E.*

The particle will thus finally come to rest at the mid-point O of the flat surface.

Example 7. The bob of a simple pendulum, initially held in the horizontal position at *A*, as shown in Fig 5.5, is released such that it goes in a circle (shown dotted) round a point *P* at a

vertical distance d below the point of suspension S of the pendulum. Show that the distance d should at least be 0.6l, where l is the length of the pendulum.

Fig. 5.5

Solution: Clearly, *K.E. gained by the bob on reaching point B = mgl, where m is the mass of the bob.*

If, therefore, v be the velocity of the bob at B, we have

$$\frac{1}{2}mv^2 = mgl, \text{ whence, } v^2 = 2gl.$$

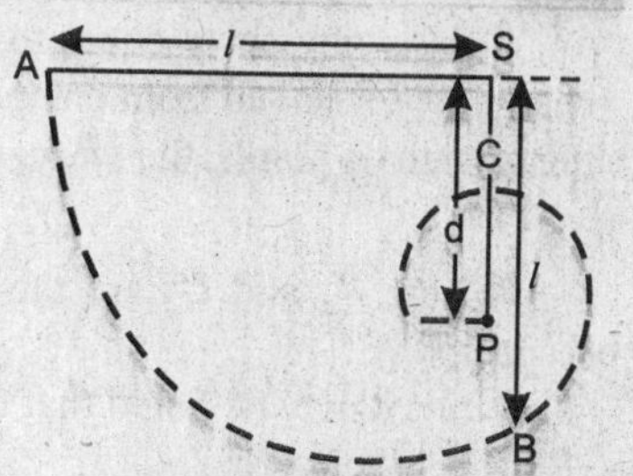

In order that the bob should go in a circle round the point P, as shown dotted, its velocity v' at the uppermost point C of the circle should be such that the centrifugal force mv'^2/r just supports the weight mg of the bob, where r is the radius of the circle, equal to $(l - d)$, *i.e.*,

$$mv'^2/r = mg. \text{ Or, } v'^2 = rg.$$

Thus, $\qquad$ *K.E. of the bob at* $C = \frac{1}{2}mv'^2$.

$\therefore$ Loss of *K.E.* in proceeding from B to $C = \frac{1}{2}mv^2 - \frac{1}{2}mv'^2$.

This must clearly be equal to the gain in *P.E.* of the bob in rising through a vertical distance BC (or $2r$), *i.e.* equal to $mg\,(2r)$.

$$\therefore \qquad \frac{1}{2}mv^2 - \frac{1}{2}mv'^2 = 2mgr. \text{ Or, } v^2 - v'^2 = 4gr.$$

Or, substituting the values of v^2 and v'^2, we have

$$2gl - rg = 4gr. \text{ Or, } 2l = 5r = 5(l - d) = 5l - 5d.$$

Or, $$5d = 3l, \text{ whence, } d = \frac{3}{5}l = 0.6\,l$$

Thus, *the least distance of point P below the point of suspension S of the pendulum must be 0.6l.*

5.7. POTENTIAL ENERGY IN AN ELECTRIC FIELD-ELECTRIC POTENTIAL

We know that the intensity $\vec{E}$ of an electric field at a point is defined as the force experienced by a unit positive charge when placed at that point in the field. It follows, therefore, that the force experienced by a charge q placed at the point will be $q\vec{E}$.

Again, the potential (V) at a point in an electric field is defined as *the amount of work done in moving a unit positive charge from ∞ (where the potential is assumed to be zero) to that point.* It is thus, in other words, *the electrostatic potential energy of a unit positive charge placed at that point.* So that, if the potential energy of a charge of $+q$ units be U at a point having position vector $\vec{r}$ in an electric field, we have

$$V = U/q = -\int_{\infty}^{r} \vec{E}\cdot d\vec{r}$$

where $\vec{E}$ is the intensity of the field at the point.

Hence, the potential difference between two points $\vec{r}_1$ and $\vec{r}_2$ is given by

$$V_2 - V_1 = \int_{r_1}^{r_2} \vec{E}\cdot d\vec{r}$$

where V_1 and V_2 are the potentials at the two points respectively.

This is obviously equal to the change in the electrostatic potential energy of a unit positive charge when moved from one point to the other. Clearly, therefore, if a charge q be moved between the two given points, the *change in electrostatic potential energy* will be

$$U_2 - U_1 = q(V_2 - V_1),$$

Where U_1 and U_2 are the electrostatic potential energies of the charge q at the two points respectively.

Now, it may be noted that the expression for potential, $V = -\int_{\infty}^{r} \vec{E} \cdot d\vec{r}$ is similar to that for the potential energy of a particle, *viz.*, $U = -\int_{\infty}^{r} \vec{F} \cdot d\vec{r}$, (§ 5.4). So that, taking

$$\vec{E} = (E_x\hat{i} + E_y\hat{j} + E_z\hat{k}) \text{ and } dr = (dx\hat{i} + dy\hat{j} + dz\hat{k})$$

and proceeding exactly as in §5.5, we obtain

$$\vec{E} = \left(\frac{\partial V}{\partial x}\hat{i} + \frac{\partial V}{\partial y}\hat{j} + \frac{\partial V}{\partial z}\hat{k}\right) = -\text{grad } V \text{ or } -V\vec{\nabla}$$

and in one dimension, $E = -dV/dx$ (only magnitude).

This enables us to defines *electric potential* in two ways, *viz.*,

(i) as the scalar quantity whose gradient with the negative sign gives the intensity of the electric field at the point in question. Or,

(ii) as the scalar quantity whose negative space rate of change in any given direction gives the component of the field intensity in that direction.

Now, in the electrostatic system of units, we have electric intensity at a point distant r from a charge q in a medium of dielectric constant K given by $\vec{E} = q\hat{r}/Kr^2$, where $\hat{r}$ is the unit vector in the direction of $\vec{r}$.

$$\therefore \quad V = -\int \vec{E} \cdot d\vec{r} = -\int \frac{q\hat{r}}{Kr^2} \cdot d\vec{r} = -\int \frac{qdr}{Kr^2} = \frac{q}{Kr} + C,$$

where C is a constant integration.

Since at $r = \infty$, $V = 0$, we have $C = 0$. And, therefore,

$$V = q/Kr \textit{ esu or statvolt.}$$

In the *RMKS* (or *SI*) system, the unit of potential is the volt, where 1 *volt* = 1 *joule*/1 *coulomb* = $10^7/3 \times 10^9$ *esu* or *statcoulomb* = 1/300 *esu*.

Based on the volt, we have a very convenient unit for the measurement of energy, namely, the **electron volt** *which is equal to the work done by an electron moving through a potential difference of 1 volt*. Thus, 1 eV = 4.80×10^{-10} *esu* × 1/300 *esu* = 1.6×10^{-12} *ergs* = 1.6×10^{-19} *joules*.

Example 8. Calculate the distance of closest approach of (*i*) two protons, each of energy 500 MeV, approaching each other from opposite directions, (*ii*) a proton of energy *V* electron volts approaching a nucleus of atomic number *Z*.

(*i*) As the two protons approach each other, they have to oppose the electrostatic force of repulsion between them and their kinetic energy is gradually converted into potential energy. Their distance of closest approach will, therefore, be that at which the whole of their kinetic energy is so converted into potential energy. Let it be r *cm*.

Then, since e is the charge on each proton, the potential energy of the two protons at distance r will be $(e)(e)/r = e^2/r$. This must be equal to their total kinetic energy,

$$2 \times 500 \text{ MeV} = 2 \times 500 \times 10^6 \text{ eV} = 2 \times 500 \times 10^6 \times 1.6 \times 10^{-12}$$

$$= 1.6 \times 10^{-3} \text{ ergs.}$$

Thus, $e^2/r = 1.6 \times 10^{-3}$, whence, $r = e^2/1.6 \times 10^{-3} = (4.8 \times 10^{-10})^2/ 1.6 \times 10^{-3}$

$$= 1.44 \times 10^{-16} \text{ cm.}$$

Or, *distance of closest approach of the two protons* = 1.44×10^{-16} cm.

(*ii*) Here, too, the proton will approach the comparatively heavier nucleus until the whole of its *K.E.* is converted into *P.E.*

Now, charge on the proton is *e* and that on the nucleus, *Ze*. So that, if *r* cm be the distance of closest approach, the *P.E.* of the proton and the nucleus = $(Ze)(e)/r = Ze^2/r$. This must be equal to the *K.E.* of the proton, given to be *V* electron volts = $V \times 1.6 \times 10^{-12}$ *ergs, i.e.,*

$Ze^2/r = V \times 1.60 \times 10^{-12}$, whence, $r = Ze^2/V \times 1.60 \times 10^{-12}$.

Or, *distance of closest approach*, $r = \dfrac{Z(4.8\times10^{-10})^2}{V\times1.60\times10^{-12}} = \dfrac{14.4Z}{V}\times10^{-3}\,cm$

$$= \frac{14.4Z}{V} A.U$$

Example 9. An electron is moving in a circular orbit of radius 2 × 10^{-8} cm about a proton. Supposed to be at rest. Calculate the velocity of the electron as also its kinetic and potential energies.

How much energy is required to ionize the system (*i.e.*, to remove the electron to an infinite distance from the proton, so as to have zero kinetic energy)? What is the value of the ionization potential?

Solution. For the electron to be moving in the circular orbit around and proton, the centrifugal force acting on it must *just* be balanced by the force of attraction between them. We, therefore, have $mv^2/r = (e)(e)/r^2$, whence, $v = \sqrt{e^2/mr}$, where *m* is the *mass* of the electron; *v*, its velocity; *r* the *radius of the orbit* and *e*, the *charge* on both the electron and the proton.

Substituting the values of *e*, *m* and *r*, therefore, we have

Velocity of the electron, $v = \sqrt{\dfrac{(4.8\times10^{-10})^2}{9.1\times10^{-28}\times2\times10^{-8}}} = \dfrac{4.8\times10^{-10}}{(18.2\times10^{-36})^{\frac{1}{2}}}$

$= 11.26 \times 10^7$ cm/sec.

∴ *Kinetic energy of the electron* = $\dfrac{1}{2}mv^2 = \dfrac{1}{2} \times 9.1 \times 10^{-28} \times (11.26 \times 10^7)^2$

$= 5.76 \times 10^{-12}$ ergs $= \dfrac{5.76\times10^{-12}}{1.6\times10^{-12}} = 3.6$ eV.

And, *potential energy of the electron* = $\dfrac{(-e)(e)}{r} = \dfrac{-e^2}{r} = -\dfrac{(4.8\times10^{-10})^2}{2\times10^{-8}}$

$= -11.5 \times 10^{-12}$ ergs $= -\dfrac{11.5\times10^{-12}}{1.6\times10^{-12}} = -7.2$ eV.

Clearly, work done in removing the electron to an infinite distance from the proton, *i.e.*, its *ionization energy = total energy of the electron at infinity – its total energy at the given distance r from the proton, i.e.,* **ionisation energy** = 0 – (*K.E. of electron at distance r from proton + P.E. of electron at distance r from proton*) = 0 – (3.6 – 7.2) = 3.6 eV = $3.6 \times 1.6 \times 10^{-12} = 5.76 \times 10^{-12}$ ergs.

Now, *ionization potential* is the potential through which the electron must be accelerated to aquire its ionization energy.

Since the ionization energy of the electron here is 3.6 *electron volts*, it must have been accelerated through a potential of 3.6/1 = 3.6 volts.

∴ **Ionisation potential** *of the electron* = 3.6 volts.

5.8 LINEAR RESTORING FORCE

As its very name indicates, a linear restoring force is the force which is proportional to the linear displacement of a particle from a fixed point – its mean position of rest or equilibrium–and is always directed towards that position (*i.e.,* opposite to that of its displacement), tending to restore the particle back to its original position. This is known as **Hooke's law.**

Thus, taking the mean position of the particle as the origin, if its displacement at a given instant be $\vec{r}$ we have

$$\vec{F} \propto (-\vec{r}) \text{ Or, } \vec{F} = -C\vec{r},$$

where C is a positive constant, called the *force constant.*

Or, since a small linear restoring force is often provided by a stretched or a compressed spring, C is also sometimes called the *spring factor.*

The negative sign of the expression for $\vec{F}$ indicates that *the force is directed oppositely to the displacement $\vec{r}$ from the mean position.* A graph between $\vec{F}$ and $\vec{r}$ will thus be a straight line passing through the origin and having a slope $-C$.

Obviously, work has to be done against this restoring force in displacing the particle from its mean position and this work is stored up in the particle in the form of potential energy.

To obtain the value (U) of this potential energy, we note that the linear restoring force is a conservative force as may be easily established by showing that *curl* $\vec{F} = 0$, this being an essential condition for a conservative force (see §5.5). We thus have

curl $\vec{F} = \vec{\nabla} \times (-C\vec{r})$ where $\vec{r} = x\hat{i} + x\hat{y} + z\hat{k}$. So that,

$$\text{curl } \vec{F} = -C\begin{vmatrix} \hat{i} & \hat{j} & \hat{k} \\ \frac{\partial}{\partial x} & \frac{\partial}{\partial y} & \frac{\partial}{\partial z} \\ x & y & z \end{vmatrix} = 0,$$

because the partial differential coefficients ($\partial z/\partial y$ *etc.*) are all equal to zero.

And since it is a conservative force, it may be expressed as the negative of the gradient of potential energy U to the particle, acquired on displacement r, *i.e.* $\vec{F} = grad\ U$, and , therefore,

$$U = -\int (F_x dx + F_z dy + F_z dz)$$

$$= \frac{C}{2}(x^2 + y^2 + z^2) + A = \frac{Cr^2}{2} + A,$$

where A is a constant of integration.

Since, with displacement zero, *i.e.* $r = 0$, the *P.E.*, U is also zero, we have $A = 0$. And, therefore,

$$U = Cr^2/2.$$

Thus, if the displacement be along the x direction, *i.e.*, if $\vec{r} = x\hat{i}$, where $\hat{i}$ is the unit vector along the axis of x, we have $U = Cx^2/2$. So that, plotting *P.E.*, (U), against displacement x, we obtain a parabola, as shown in Fig. 5.6, clearly bringing out the fact that *the work done in displacing a particle against a linear restoring force, and hence the potential energy acquired by it, is proportional to the square of its displacement from its mean or equilibrium position.*

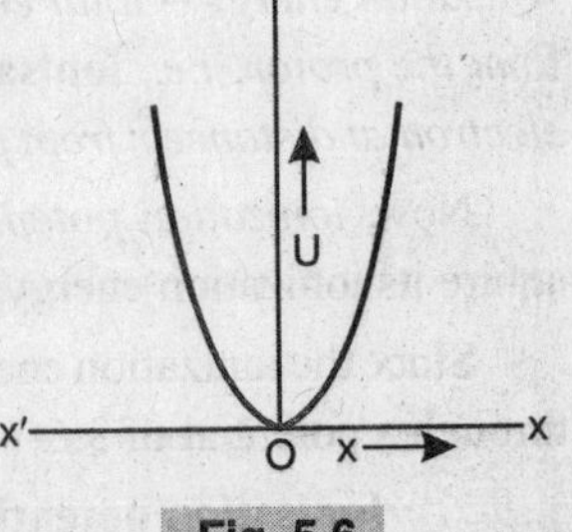

Fig. 5.6

If the *maximum displacement* of the particle be a, the *maximum potential energy acquired* by it $= \frac{1}{2}ma^2$.

Let us imagine the particle to be initially at its position of maximum displacement a, where the whole of its energy is present in the potential form and is equal to $\frac{1}{2}ma^2$. On releasing it, it will start moving towards its mean or equilibrium position under the action of the restoring force, thus acquiring kinetic energy at the expense of its potential energy. And since the restoring force, is as we have seen, a conservative force, the sum total of its energy E, at any point of its displacement, will remain constant. So that, at displacement x, if its velocity be v, we have its *kinetic energy*, $T = \frac{1}{2}mv^2$ and its *potential energy*, $U = \frac{1}{2}Cx^2$.

$\therefore$ its *total energy*, $E = T + U = \frac{1}{2}mv^2 + \frac{1}{2}Cx^2 = \frac{1}{2}Ca^2$,

whence, $\frac{1}{2}mv^2 = \frac{1}{2}C(a^2 - x^2)$ and $\therefore v = \pm\sqrt{\frac{C}{m}(a^2 - x^2)}$.

Again, as the particle reaches its mean or equilibrium position at $x = 0$, its $P.E = 0$ and its kinetic energy, the maximum, equal to $\frac{1}{2}Ca^2$. Its velocity here will therefore be the maximum, say, v_{max}.

We, therefore, have $\frac{1}{2}mv^2_{\max}\ \frac{1}{2}Ca^2$, whence, $v_{\max} = \pm\sqrt{\frac{C}{m}}a$.

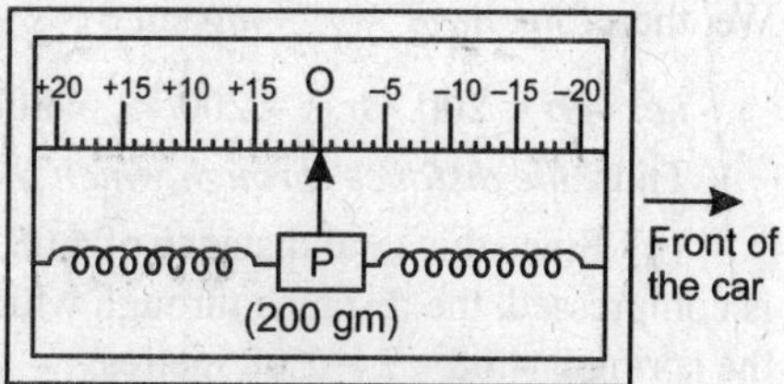

Fig. 5.7

Example 10. A car carries a framework *ABCD*, shown below (Fig. 5.7) in which a 200 gm mass *P* is supported between two springs of force constant 5000 dyne/cm each. Side *AB* is kept horizontal and along the length of the car and the pointer attached to *P* reads zero when the car is at rest. What will the pointer read when the car has (*i*) uniform speed 20 m/sec on a straight road

(*ii*) Uniform speed 10 m/sec on a circular road of radius 20 m, (*iii*) uniform acceleration of 0.5 m/sec² on a straight road, (*iv*) uniform acceleration 1.0 m/sec² on a straight road? ***(Guwahati 2002)***

Solution. (*i*) In this case, the motion of the car being unaccelerated, there is no force acting on mass P and hence *the point r attached to it continues to read zero on the scale.*

(*ii*) Here, since the car is moving with a uniform speed *along a circular path*, the centripetal force (mv^2/r) will act in a direction perpendicular to the length of the two springs, thus producing neither extension nor contraction in them. *The pointer will, therefore, again continue to read zero on the scale.*

(*iii*) The forward acceleration of the car being 0.5 m/sec² or 50 cm/sec², the force of reaction acting on the mass $P = 200 \times 50$ dynes in the backward direction. The first spring (to the left of P) will thus get compressed and the second, stretched through a distance x say. We shall, therefore, have

$200 \times 50 = -(C + C)x = -2\,Cx$. Where C is the *force constant* of each spring.

Or, $$x = -\frac{200 \times 50}{2C} = -\frac{200 \times 50}{2 \times 5000} = -1 \text{ cm} = -10 \text{ mm}$$

Thus, the mass will move 10 mm to the left and the *pointer will read* + 10 mm *on the scale, to the left of the zero mark.*

(*iv*) Here, the backward acceleration of the car being 1.0 m/sec^2 or 100 cm/sec^2, the force of reaction 200 × 100 dynes will act on the mass in the forward direction. As a result, the first spring (to the left of P) will get extended and the second, compressed by the same amount x', say. We, therefore, have

$200 \times 100 = 2 \times 5000\,x'$, whence, $x' = 200 \times 100/2 \times 5000 = +2$ cm or $+20$ mm.

The mass will thus move forward through 20 mm *and the pointer will thus read* –20 mm *on the scale, to the right of the zero mark.*

Example 11. An ideal massless spring S can be compressed 1.0 metre by a force of 100 newtons. This same spring is placed at the bottom of a frictionless inclined plane which makes an angle $\theta = 30°$ with the horizontal (Fig. 5.8). A 10 kg mass m is released from rest at the top of the incline and is brought to rest momentarily after compressing the spring 2.0 metres. (*a*) Through what distance does the mass slide before coming to rest? (*b*) What is the speed of the mass just before it reaches the spring?

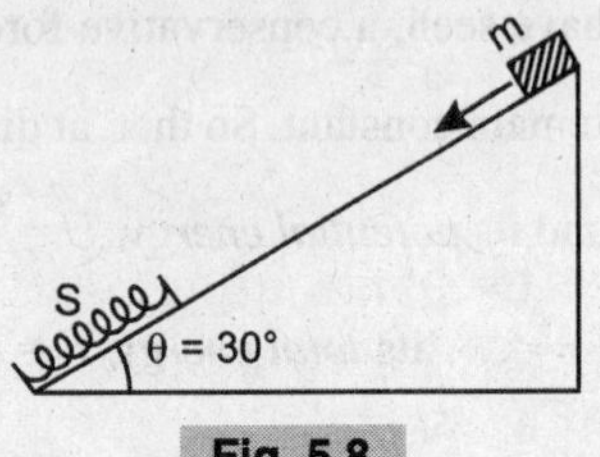

Fig. 5.8

Solution. (*a*) Let the mass m slide a *total distance s* along the inclined plane before coming to rest on compressing the spring through 2 metres. Then, clearly,

Gravitational potential energy lost by the mass = $mg \sin\theta \times s$.

This must obviously be equal to the work done in compressing the spring through a distance of 2 metres, *i.e.* equal to $\frac{1}{2}Cx^2 = \frac{1}{2} \times 100(2)^2 = 200$ joules, because $C = 100$ N/m (given)

We, therefore, have $\quad mg \sin\theta \times s = 200$. Or, $10 \times 9.8 \times \frac{1}{2} \times s = 200$,

i.e., $49s = 200$. Or, $s = 200/49 = 4.08$ m, or 4.0 metres, *say*.

Thus, *the distance through which the mass slides before coming to rest* = 4 metres.

(*b*) Since this total distance of 4.08 metres also includes the 2 metres through which the spring is compressed, the distance through which the mass slides from the top of the plane until it reaches the spring is 4.08 – 2 = 2.08 metres.

And, since its initial velocity $u = 0$ ($\because$ it starts from rest), its velocity v on covering a distance of 2.08 metres along the incline is given by the relation $v^2 - u^2 = 2\,as$. *i.e.*, $v^2 = 2 \times g \sin\theta \times 2.08 = 2 \times 9.8 \times \frac{1}{2} \times 2.08 = 20.38$, whence,

$$v = \sqrt{20.38} = 4.514 \text{ m/sec or } 4.5 \text{ metres per sec.}$$

Thus, *the speed of the mass just before it reaches the spring* = 4.5 metres/sec.

Example 12. Obtain an expression for restoring force as a function of position for a particle moving in a potential energy field $U = A - Bx + Cx^2$. At what point does the force vanish? Is this a point of stable equilibrium? If so, obtain the value of the force constant.

Solution. Clearly, *linear restoring force* $F = -dU/dx = B - 2\,Cx$.

This force will vanish when $dU/dx = 0$, or, $B - 2\,Cx = 0$, *i.e.*, when $x = B/2C$.

Now, for stable equilibrium of the particle d^2U/dx^2, *i.e.*, $2C$ must be positive.

Hence if C be a positive quantity, we shall have a *minimum potential energy position* of the particle at $x = B/2C$ and this will, therefore, be a point of stable equilibrium.

From the relation $F = B - 2\,Cx$, it is clear that the *force constant* = $2C$.

Example 13. Two ideal and identical springs S_1 and S_2, each of normal length l and force constant C are fixed at points $(-l, o)$ and $(+l, o)$ and connected together at the other end, as shown in Fig. 5.9 (*a*).

(a) Show that for the displacement, x, y, of their joined ends,

$$U = \frac{C}{2}\left[\{(x+l)^2 + y^2\}^{\frac{1}{2}} - l\right]^2 + \frac{C}{2}\left[\{(l-x)^2 + y^2\}^{\frac{1}{2}} - l\right]^2$$

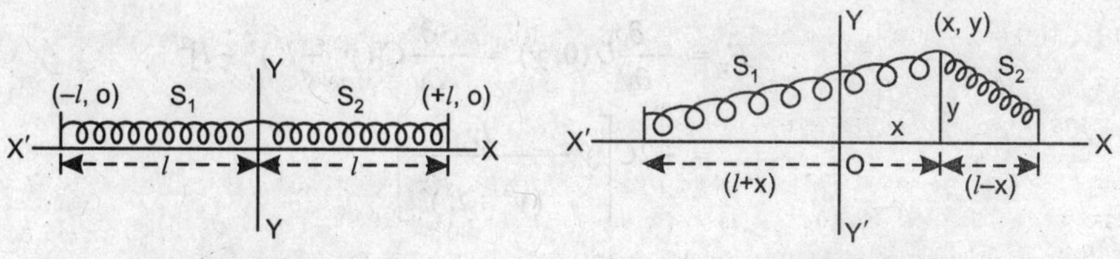

Fig. 5.9 (a) Fig. 5.9 (b)

(b) Obtain the values of the functions $U(x, o)$ and $U(y, o)$ and show that $U(x, o)$ assumes the shape of a parabola for all values of x and that if $y >> l$, $U(o, y)$ too assumes a shape which is a near parabola.

(c) Calculate the force components F_x for $y = 0$ and F_y for $x = 0$.

Solution. (a) With the joined ends of the springs given the displacement (x, y), as shown in Fig. 5.9 (b), we find that spring S_1 gets stretched and springs S_2, compressed, their increased and decreased lengths now being.

$[(l+x)^2 + y^2]^{\frac{1}{2}}$ and $[(l-x)^2 + y^2]^{\frac{1}{2}}$ respectively. So that,

increase in length of spring $S_1 = [(l+x)^2 + y^2]^{\frac{1}{2}} - l$

and *decrease in length of spring* $S_2 = [(l-x)^2 + y^2]^{\frac{1}{2}} - l$

$$\therefore \quad U(x, y) = \frac{1}{2}C[\{(l+x)^2 + y^2\}^{\frac{1}{2}} - l]^2 + \frac{1}{2}C[\{(l-x)^2 + y^2\}^{\frac{1}{2}} - l]^2.$$

(b) Obviously,

$$U(x, 0) = \frac{1}{2}C[\{(l+x)^2\}^{\frac{1}{2}} - l]^2 + \frac{1}{2}C[\{(l-x)^2\}^{\frac{1}{2}} - l]^2$$

$$= \frac{1}{2}C(l+x-l)^2 + \frac{1}{2}C(l-x-l)^2 = Cx^2,$$

indicating that $U(x, 0)$ *assumes the shape of a parabola for all values of* x.

And

$$U(0, y) = \frac{1}{2}C[(l^2 + y^2)^{\frac{1}{2}} - l]^2 + \frac{1}{2}C[(l^2 + y^2)^{\frac{1}{2}} - l]^2$$

$$= C[(y^2 + l^2)^{\frac{1}{2}} - l]^2$$

Now, if $y >> l$, we have $(y^2 + l^2)^{\frac{1}{2}} = y + \frac{1}{2}y^{-1}l^{2\dots} \approx y + l^2/2y$

$$\therefore \quad U(0, y) \approx C\left(y + \frac{l^2}{2y} - l\right)^2 \approx C\left[y\left(1 + \frac{l^2}{2y^2}\right) - l\right]^2$$

Since $y >> 1$, we have $l^2/2y^2 << 1$ and $\therefore$ $U(0, y) \approx C(y - 1)^2$

Again, y being very much greater than l, $(y - l) \approx y$. So that,

$$U(0, y) \approx Cy^2.$$

Indicating that $U(0, y)$ *too takes the shape of a near parabola.*

(c) The *force constant* F_x *for* $y = 0$ is clearly given by

$$F_x = -\frac{\partial}{\partial x}U(x, 0) = -\frac{\partial}{\partial x}Cx^2 = -2Cx.$$

And, *force constant* F_y *for* $x = 0$ is similarly given by

$$F_y = -\frac{\partial}{\partial y}U(0, y) = -\frac{\partial}{\partial y}C[(y^2 + l^2)^{\frac{1}{2}} - l]^2$$

$$= -2C\left[y - \frac{ly}{(y^2 + l^2)^{\frac{1}{2}}}\right]$$

5.9 POTENTIAL ENERGY CURVE: POTENTIAL WELL

In a conservative force field, the potential energy of a particle is, in general, a function of space and, therefore, changes from point to point. A curve, showing variation of the potential energy of a particle with its position in the field is spoken of as a *potential energy curve* and supplies a great deal of information about the motion of the particle without having to solve any equations of motion.

For the sake of simplicity, let us consider the case of a particle whose motion is only one- dimensional, restricted to only the axis of x, say. Then, a typical energy curve between the position (x) of the particle and its potential energy (U) is of the type shown in Fig. 5.10, with well-marked maxima (Q, N) and minima (C, G).

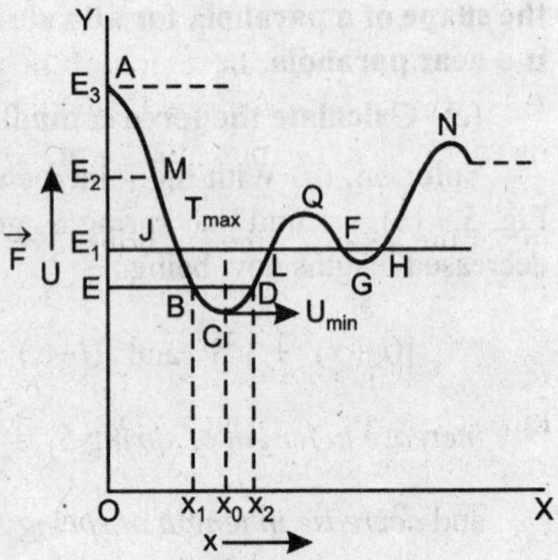

Fig. 5.10

The linear restoring force $\vec{F}$ being a conservative one, we have

$$\vec{F} = -\text{grad}\, U.$$

Since, here, the motion is restricted to the x-direction only, the potential energy (U) will be a function of the x-coordinate alone and we shall, therefore, have $\vec{F} = -dU/dx$. Thus, the slope of the curve (*i.e.*, dU/dx) at any given point gives the value of the force ($-dU/dx$) acting on the particle at that point.

It will be readily seen that for portions of the curve such as CQ and GN, where and increase in the value of x corresponds to an increase in the value of U, the slope of the curve at any point is positive and hence force F ($= -dU/dx$) acting on the particle there, negative. On the other hand, for portions of the curve, like AC and QG, where an increase in the value of x corresponds to a decrease in the value of U, the slope of the curve at any point is negative and hence the force acting on the particle there, positive. *In either case, therefore, the force acting on the particle tends to pull it into a region of lower potential energy.*

And, clearly, at points on the curve representing minima and maxima of potential energy (U), such as C, G and Q, N respectively, the slope is zero and hence no force acts on the particle when lying at any one of these points which are, for reason, referred to as **positions of equilibrium.** However, at points such as Q (or N) corresponding to a maximum of *P.E.*, the slightest displacement of the particle, either way, will result in a force acting on it, tending to move it along QDC or QFG to a position of lower potential energy C or G. These points, like Q (or N) of maximum potential energy are therefore, called **position of unstable equilibrium.** On the other hand, at points such as

C (or G) corresponding to minimum potential energy, any slight displacement of the particle, either way, results in a force acting on it, tending to bring it back into its original position C (or G).

These points (like C or G) of minimum potential energy are, therefore, called **positions of stable equilibrium.**

In case the curve has also a horizontal portion, such as shown dotted in the figure, signifying a region of *constant potential energy*, the slope of the curve, and hence the force acting on the particle at any point on it, remains zero even if slightly displaced from its initial position, so that it stays in its new position, without either tending to go further away from it or to come back to its initial position. Such a region is, therefore, called a **region neutral equilibrium.**

Bounded region or the Potential well. Let us consider again the particle at the minimum potential energy or the stable equilibrium position, C, with its total energy $E(=T+U)$ represented by the horizontal line shown, cutting the energy curve at B and D. Since the system is conservative and the energy is conserved, it follows that the *P.E.* of the particle at C being the minimum, its *K.E.* there must be the maximum, so that it moves towards either B or D. As it proceeds towards D, say, it comes under the action of the restoring force $F=-dU/dx$, so that its *K.E.* decreases and its *P.E.* increases (the sum total remaining the same, E), until when it reaches the point D, the whole of its energy is in the potential form, equal to E, its kinetic energy, and hence its velocity, now being reduced to *zero*. Here, therefore, the particle remains momentarily at rest and then start moving back under the action of the restoring force and again reaches C where its potential energy is reduced to the minimum and its kinetic energy becomes the maximum. It, therefore, continues to move towards B, its potential energy now increasing and its kinetic energy correspondingly decreasing (the sum total remaining constant at E) until at B, the whole of its energy is again in the potential form and its kinetic energy, and hence its velocity, *zero*. Again, therefore, it is momentarily at rest at B and then starts moving back towards C under the action of the restoring force.

Thus, the particle remains confined to the region BCD, oscillating (simple harmonically) between the *turning points* B and D. Such a region (between the turning points B and D) is appropriately called a bounded region or a potential well (*or potential valley*) *and always exists about a point of minimum potential energy or stable equilibrium.*

The difference of energy between the top and the botton of the well is called the *binding energy* for well and the particle confined to the well is said to be in the *bound state* or to perform a *bound motion* and, as we have seen, if its motion be one-dimensional, it is necessarily *periodic* and keeps on repeating itself after regular intervals, called its *time-period.*

It will be readily seen that

(*i*) If the total energy of the particle be E_1, the particle will have four turning points, J, L, F and H and it can oscillate in either of the two potential wells $J\,C\,L$ and $F\,G\,H$;

(*ii*) If its total energy be E_2, it will obviously have only one turning point at M and will always turn to the right from here, its speed increasing and decreasing according as its potential energy (U) decreases or increases.

(*iii*) And, if its energy be greater than E_3, there will be no turning point at all, *i.e.*, the particle will not change direction and only its speed will vary as in case (*ii*).

Now, the potential energy function $U=f(x)$ may, in general, be expanded about the position x_0 of stable equilibrium by means of *Taylor's theorem*. Thus,

$$U = U_{x_0} + \left(\frac{dU}{dx}\right)_{x_0}(x-x_0) + \left(\frac{d^2U}{dx^2}\right)_{x_0}\left(\frac{x-a}{2!}\right)^2 + \ldots,$$

where $(dU/dx)x_0$, $(d^2U/dx^2)x_0$ etc. are the differentials at the stable equilibrium position (x_0) and, as such, are constants.

If we measure displacement from the position x_0, *i.e.*, if we take x_0 as the origin, so that $(x - x_0) = (x - 0) = x$, we have

$$U = U_0 + \left(\frac{dU}{dx}\right)_0 x + \left(\frac{d^2U}{dx^2}\right)_0 \frac{x^2}{2!} + \ldots$$

Since x_0 is a point of stable equilibrium, and hence of minimum potential energy, we have $(dU/dx)_0 = 0$ and $(d^2U/dx^2)_0$, a positive quantity, say C. Then, denoting $(d^3U/dx^3)_0$....etc. by C_1 C_2...., we have

$$U = U_0 + \frac{Cx^2}{2!} + \frac{C_1x^3}{3!} + \ldots,$$

and, therefore, force acting on the particle *i.e.*, $F = -\dfrac{dU}{dx}$

Or, $$F = -Cx - \frac{C_1}{2}x^2 - \frac{C_2}{6}x^3 \ldots$$

In case the displacements be small, the higher powers of x become negligible and we, therefore, have

$$F = -Cx \text{ and } U = U_0 + \frac{1}{2}Cx^2,$$

indicating that force F is a *linear restoring force*, proportional to displacement and directed towards the position of equilibrium. The positive constant C is thus the *force constant*.

The potential energy curve (or the graph between U and x) in this region of small displacements, x_1 and x_2, say, about the position of stable equilibrium (*i.e.*, within the potential well) thus comes out to be parabolic in form (as shown in Fig. 5.11), with its vertex at x_0, U_0. In case the minimum potential energy (U_0) be assumed to be zero, the apex of the parabola will touch the x-axis at the origin O.

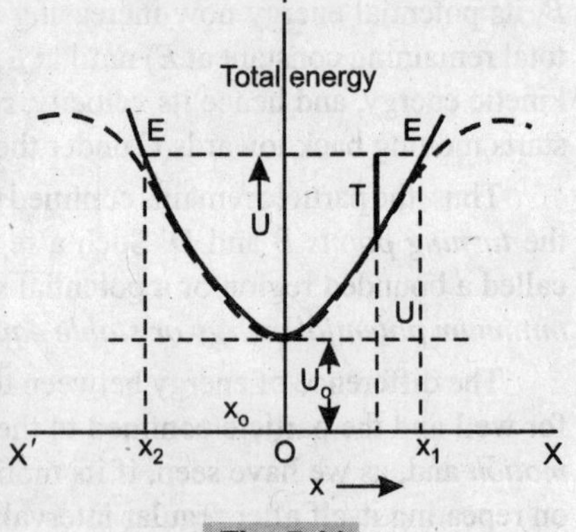

Fig. 5.11

The particle thus oscillates inside the potential well about the stable equilibrium (or minimum potential energy) position between the limits x_1 and x_2, so that its total energy $E = T + U$. It will be easily seen that the particle cannot cross the limits x_1 and x_2 for, within this region (x_1 x_2), the sum total of its energy is $E = T + U$. And at x_1 and x_2, $T = 0$ and, therefore $U = E$, *i.e.*, the entire energy is present in the potential form. Beyond x_1 and x_2, the potential energy U would be greater than this total energy E, implying thereby that, in order that $T + U$ may be equal to E, the kinetic energy T must be *negative*, which is simply absurd.

The motion of the particle thus remains restricted between x_1 and x_2 on either side of O, so long as the total energy is E and there are no non-conservative forces (like friction etc.) operating. In case the value of E be different, the values of x_1 and x_2 too will naturally be correspondingly different. This is in fact the case of a simple harmonic oscillator which we shall study in some detail later in chapter 8.

Example 14. Fig. 5.12 shows the potential energy curve of a system in arbitrary units for U and r. State the possible r-values about which the system can oscillate, also the maximum energy of oscillations in each case. If the system just escapes from the potential well at smaller r, with what kinetic energy does it go to $r \to \infty$? **(*Agra 2001*)**

If 0.1 unit be the mass of the system, calculate its velocity when it escapes from the potential well at smaller r.

Solution. As we know, the system can oscillate only about its position of stable equilibrium of minimum potential energy. As is clear from the graph, these positions occur at *A* and *B*, where the values of *r* are **2 units** and **4.5 units** respectively.

The *maximum energies of oscillation* at these positions are, obviously.

1 – (– 2.5) or **3.5 units** and 0.5 –(–1) or **1.5 units,** respectively.

And, as the system just escapes at *C* from the potential well at smaller $r = 2$ units, its *K.E.* will obviously be **1 unit.**

If *v* be the velocity of the system as it escapes from the potential well at smaller *r*, we have its $K.E. = \frac{1}{2}mv^2 = 1$ unit. So that,

$$\frac{1}{2}(0.1)v^2 = 1. \text{ Or, } v = \sqrt{20} = \mathbf{4.47\ units.}$$

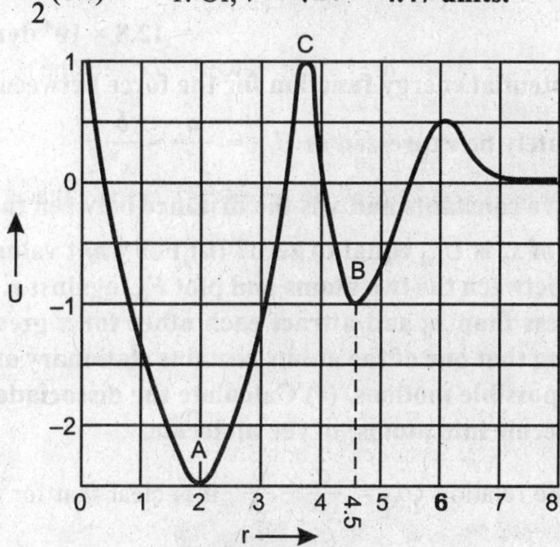

Fig. 5.12

Example 15. The figure below (Fig. 5.13) shows the potential energy diagram of a system like a diatomic molecule, potential energy *U* being plotted against inter-nuclear distance *r*.

Deduce values of the following:

(*i*) Equilibrium inter-nuclear distance r_0.

(*ii*) Binding energy E_b.

(*iii*) Force constant near the bottom of the well.

(*Agra 2003*)

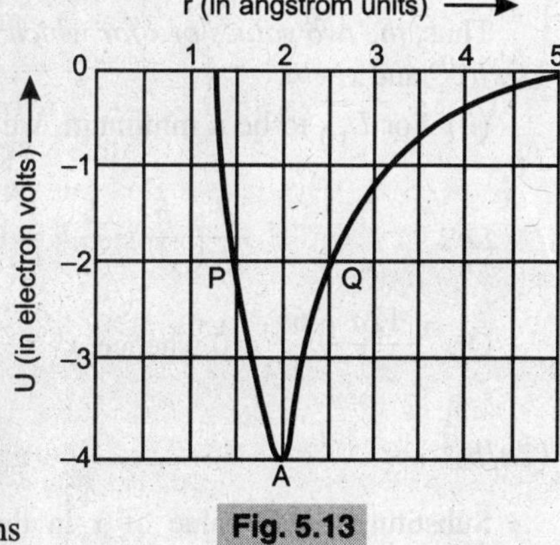

Fig. 5.13

Solution. (*i*) At the equilibrium inter-nuclear distance, the potential energy must be the minimum. As we can see from the graph supplied (Fig 5.13), this happens at the point *A* which corresponds to $r = 2$ Angstrom units. This, therefore, gives the value of r_0, Thus,

Equilibrium inter-nuclear distance, $r_0 = 2\ A.U. = 2 \times 10^{-8}$ cm.

(*ii*) Since *binding energy* is the difference between the potential energies at the top and the bottom of the potential concerned, we have

binding energy, here $E_b = 0 - (-4) = 4\text{eV} = 4 \times 1.6 \times 10^{-12} = 6.4 \times 10^{-12}$ ergs.

(*iii*) The potential energy curve near the bottom of the potential well, *i.e.*, its portion *PAQ* is *parabolic in shape* and, therefore,

$U = U_A + \frac{1}{2}(r - r_0)^2$, whence the *linear restoring force* $F = -dU/dr = -C(r - r_0)$

So that, $$C = \frac{dU/dr}{(r - r_0)} = \frac{dU}{dr(r - r_0)}$$

Considering the displacement from *A* to *Q*, therefore, we have

$dU = -2 - (-4) = 2eV = 2 \times 1.60 \times 10^{-12}$ *ergs*, $dr = 0.5$ *A.U.* $= 0.5 \times 10^{-8}$ cm and $(r - r_0)$ $= (2.5 - 2.0) = 0.5$ *A.U.* $= 0.5 \times 10^{-8}$ cm.

Hence, *force constant* $$C = \frac{2 \times 1.60 \times 10^{-12}}{(0.5 \times 10^{-8})(0.5 \times 10^{-8})} = \frac{3.20 \times 10^{-12}}{0.25 \times 10^{-16}}$$

$$= \mathbf{12.8 \times 10^4 \text{ dyne/cm.}}$$

Example 16. The potential energy function for the force between two atoms in a diatomic molecule can approximately be expressed as $U_{(x)} = \frac{a}{x^{12}} - \frac{b}{x^8}$, where *a* and *b* are positive constants and *x* is the distance between the atoms.

(*i*) For what values of *x*, is $U_{(x)}$ equal to zero? (*ii*) For what values of *x*, is $U_{(x)}$ minimum? (*iii*) Calculate the force between the two atoms and plot $F_{(x)}$ against *x*. Show that the two atoms repel each other for *x* less than x_0 and attract each other for *x* greater than x_0. What is the value of x_0? (*iv*) Assuming that one of the atoms remains stationary and the other moves along the *x*-axis, describe the possible motions. (*v*) Calculate the dissociation energy (the energy required to break the molecule into atoms) of the molecule. (*Agra* 2005)

Solution. (*i*) From the relation $U_{(x)} = \frac{a}{x^{12}} - \frac{b}{x^6}$, it is clear that for $U_{(x)}$ to be zero, we should have either (*i*) $a/x^{12} - b/x^6 = 0$, whence, $x^6 = a/b$ and, therefore,

$$x = (a/b)^{1/5}, \text{ or } (ii)\ x = \infty$$

Thus, *the two values of x for which $U_{(x)}$ will be zero are x* $= (a/b)^{1/6}$ and $x = \infty$.

(*ii*) For $U_{(x)}$ to be a minimum, we should have $dU_{(x)}/dx = 0$,

i.e., $$\frac{d}{dx}\left(\frac{a}{x^{12}} - \frac{b}{x^6}\right) = 0$$

Or, $-\frac{12a}{x^{13}} + \frac{6b}{x^7} = 0$ whence, $x^6 = \frac{2a}{b}$ and, therefore, $x = (2a/b)^{\frac{1}{6}}$

Substituting this value of *x* in the expression for $U_{(x)}$ above, we have

$$U_{(x)\min} = b^2/4a.$$

Thus, *U*(*x*) *will have the minimum value* $- b^2/4a$ *when* $x = (2a/b)^{\frac{1}{6}}$.

If, therefore, we plot a graph between *x*, the distance between the two atoms, and the potential energy $U_{(x)}$, we

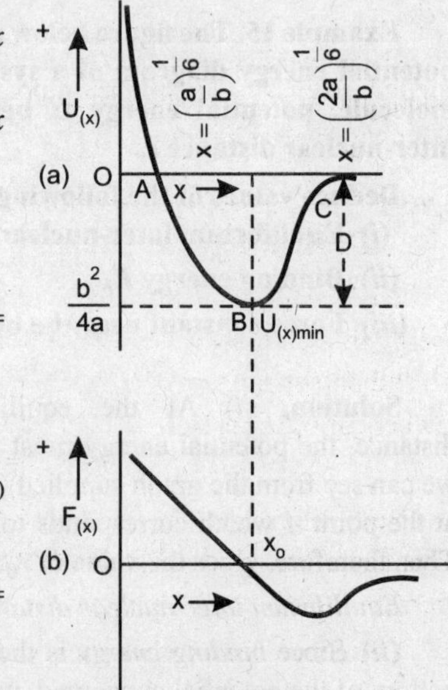

Fig. 5.14

obtain a curve of the from shown in Fig. 5.14(*a*), which shows that $U_{(x)} = 0$ both at $x = (a/b)^{\frac{1}{6}}$ and at $x = \infty$ and that $U_{(x)}$ is a minimum at $x = (2a/b)^{\frac{1}{6}}$.

(*iii*) As we know, the force between the two atoms is given by $F = -\frac{d}{dx}U_{(x)}$ which gives $F(x) = \frac{12a}{x^{13}} - \frac{6b}{x^7}$, whence,

$$F_{(x)} = 0, \text{ when } x = (2a/b)^{\frac{1}{6}}$$

This is, therefore, the point of *stable equilibrium* and we denote this value of x by x_0.

At values of x less than x_0, *i.e.*, between $x = 0$ and $x_0 = (2a/b)^{1/6}$, F will be *positive*, indicating that the force is one of repulsion or that the atoms repel each other, and that at values of x higher than x_0, *i.e.*, between $x_0 = (2a/b)^{1/6}$ and ∞, F will be *negative*, indicating that the force is one of attraction or that the atoms now attract each other.

A graph plotted between $F_{(x)}$ and x comes out to be of the form shown in Fig. 5.14 (*b*), showing $F_{(x)} = 0$ at $x_0 = (2a/b)^{\frac{1}{6}}$, positive between $x = 0$ and $x = x_0$ and negative between $x = x_0$ and $x = \infty$.

(*iv*) If one of the atoms remains stationary and the other moves along the x-axis, it will have its minimum potential energy, or stable equilibrium, position at $x_0 = (2a/b)^{1/6}$ from the stationary atom and will therefore oscillate simple harmonically about this position or within the potential well *ABC* (as explained under §5.9).

(*v*) Once one of the atoms of the molecule acquires sufficient energy to get over the potential well, it will cease to be bound to the other atom and the molecule will thus get broken or dissociated. This energy to be able to get over the potential well thus gives the *dissociation energy D* of the molecule.

The value of D is thus the difference between the potential energies at the top and the bottom of the potential well *ABC*, *i.e.*, between 0 and the minimum energy $-b^2/4a$ or equal to $0-(-b^2/4a) = b^2/4a$.

Thus, *the dissociation energy of the molecule* $= b^2/4a$, meaning thereby that if the value of the kinetic energy at the equilibrium position be $b^2/4a$ (or more), the diatomic molecule will break up into two separate atoms.

5.10 NON-CONSERVATIVE FORCES–GENERAL LAW OF CONSERVATION OF ENERGY

We have seen in §5.6 how when conservative forces alone are concerned, the mechanical energy of a particle, or a system of particles, remains conserved, *i.e.*, the sum of its kinetic energy (T) and potential energy (U) gives its total energy E which remains constant or that the charge in its total energy (ΔE) is *zero i.e.*,

$$T + U = E, \text{ a constant. Or, } \Delta T + \Delta U = \Delta E = 0.$$

Since the work done on a particle by a conservative force remains stored up in it in the form of potential energy, it follows that this work done by a conservative force, say, $W_{(c)}$ is equal to the increase in its potential energy, with the sign reversed, *i.e.*, $W_{(c)} = -\Delta U$.

Let us now see whether energy is conserved even if a non-conservative force acts on a particle,–a non-conservative force being one, the work done by which in displacing a particle from one point to another depends upon the actual path traversed between them. Frictional and viscous forces are obvious examples of such forces and, as we know, the longer the path traversed between two given points, the greater the amount of work done by the frictional force. So that, unlike the case of conservative forces, the work done here in taking a particle from a point A to another point B is not equal and opposite to the work done in taking it from B to A and the total work done from A to B and back is therefore not, zero. In fact, there is loss of kinetic energy either way, *i.e.*, in proceeding from A to B as also in proceeding back from B to A, so that the resultant kinetic energy of the particle is less than its initial value by an amount equal to the work done in performing the round trip from A back to A.

Thus, if we have both, a conservative and a non-conservative, force acting on a particle and if the work done by the two be $W_{(c)}$ and $W_{(N)}$ respectively, then if ΔT be the loss suffered by the particle in its kinetic energy, we have $W_{(c)} + W_{(N)} = \Delta T$. Or, putting $-\Delta U$ for $W_{(c)}$, we have $\Delta T + \Delta U = W_{(N)}$. Obviously, $\Delta T + \Delta U = \Delta E$, the *change in the total energy* of the particle. And, therefore, $\Delta E = W_{(N)}$.

Thus, the change in the total energy of the particle is no longer zero but $W_{(N)}$, the work done by the non-conservative force.

If the non-conservation force be a *frictional force*, the work done by it $[W_{(N)}]$ appears in the form of equivalent heat energy, say, equal to Q, where, clearly, $W_{(N)} = -Q$. We, therefore, have

$$\Delta E = -Q \text{ or } \Delta E + Q = 0,$$

i.e., the change in the total energy of the particle is zero or its total energy remains conserved.

Similarly, in the case of other non-conservative forces, the work done by them appears in some other forms of energy, like sound, light etc., but in *all cases, without exception*, the total energy is conserved. *The general law of conservation of energy thus holds good in the case of both conservative and non-conservative forces.*

EXERCISE

1. (*a*) What is meant by a conservative force? Show that if the force between two bodies is of a central kind, it is also conservative.

   (*b*) Show that in the case of a conservative force, the work done around a closed path is zero.

   (*c*) Show that *Lorentz force* is a conservative force.

2. Show that for a conservative force field $\vec{F}(r)$ we can define a scalar function $U(r)$ such that $\vec{F}(r) = \vec{\nabla} U(r)$. Also show that *curl* $\vec{F}(r) = 0$.

3. State and explain the work-energy principle and write a short note on the utility of *conservation laws*, in general.

4. Give a homely example or two of a conservative force and show that the force acting on a particle whose position at any instant t is given by $\vec{r} = a\cos\omega t\,\hat{i} + b\sin\omega t\,\hat{j}$ is a conservative force.

5. (*a*) A centripetal force of 18 N is used to keep a 2 kg ball in a uniform circular motion at the end of a string 1 m long. How much work does the force do in each revolution of the ball?

   (*b*) What is the work done by the earth's gravitational force of attraction on a satellite moving in a circular orbit around it?

   [Ans. (*a*) 0; (*b*) 0]

6. (*a*) A particle at a point (2, 1, 3) is acted upon by a force $\vec{F} = 3\hat{i} + 2xy\hat{j} + xz^2\hat{k}$. Calculate the work done in moving it to a point (4, 1, 3).

   (*b*) A particle moves along one quarter of the circumference of a circle of radius 0.5 m. If the force applied be 0.2 N, inclined at an angle of 60° with the tangent to the circle at the point, calculate the work done.

   [Ans. (*a*) 12 units; (*b*) 7.852×10^{-2} joule]

7. Investigate in two different ways whether the force $\vec{F} = (y^2 - x^2)\hat{i} + 3xy\hat{j}$ is a conservative one.

   [Ans. Non-conservative]

   [Hint. (*i*) Show that *curl* $\vec{F} \neq 0$. (*ii*) Evaluate the line integral from the point (0, 0) to the point

(x_0, y_0) along one path, made up of two straight sections (0, 0) to $(x_0, 0)$ and $(x_0, 0)$ to (x_0, y_0), as shown in Fig. 5.15, and then along the other path made up of two similar straight sections (0, 0) to $(0, y_0)$ and $(0, y_0)$ to (x_0, y_0), as shown dotted in the Figure. Show that work done along the two paths is not the same.]

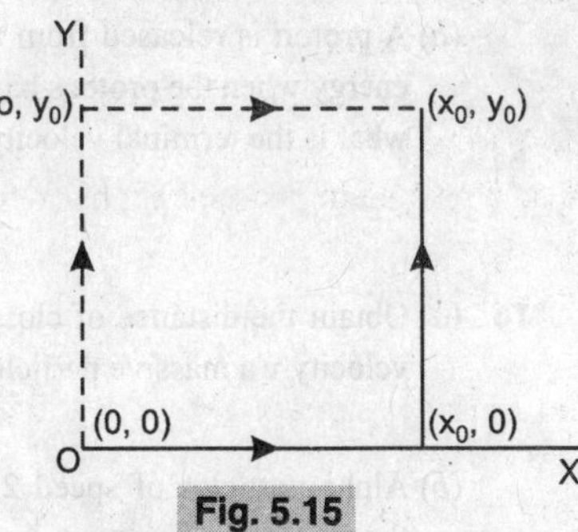

Fig. 5.15

8. (*a*) If the magnitude of the force of attraction between two particles of masses m_1 and m_2 respectively, and distance x apart, be given by $F = k\, m_1 m_2/x^2$, where k is a *constant*, find (*i*) the potential energy function and (*ii*) work required to be done to increase the separation of the masses from $x = x_1$ to $x = x_1 + d$.

[**Ans.** (*i*) $U_{(x)} = -k\, m_1 m_2/x$, if $V_{(\infty)} = 0$ (*ii*) $k\, m_1 m_2\, d/x_1\,(d + x_1)$]

(*b*) Enunciate the principle of conservation of mechanical energy and illustrate by means of a homely example.

Fall under the action of gravity

9. A particle of mass m is attached to a fixed point by means of a string of length l and hangs freely. Show that if it is projected horizontally with a velocity greater than $\sqrt{5gl}$ it will completely describe a vertical circle.

10. Show that for a given initial speed u, a projectile will have the same speed at the same elevation irrespective of its angle of projection.

11. A small block of mass m slides along the frictionless loop-the-loop track shown in Fig. 5.16. Calculate the height h at which the mass just be released on the track to be able to go round the loop of radius R. [**Ans.** $h = 5R/2$]

[**Hint.** If v be the velocity acquired by the block in falling through height h, we have $v^2 - 0 = 2gh$. Or, $v^2 = 2gh$. As the mass reaches the top of the loop, let its velocity be v', so that centrifugal force exerted by the mass on the track upwards $= mv'^2/R$. In order that the block may be able to go round the loop, this must balance the weight mg of the block. So that, $mv'^2/R = mg$, whence, $v'^2 = gR$.

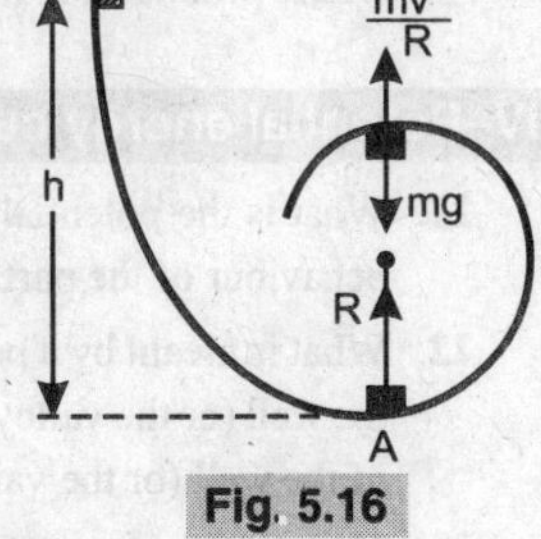

Fig. 5.16

Then, $\frac{1}{2}mv^2 - \frac{1}{2}mv'^2$ = work done by the block in covering a vertical distance $2R$ against gravity from A to B, *i.e.*, $\frac{1}{2}m(v^2 - v'^2) = 2mgR$.

Or, $v^2 - v'^2 = 4gR$.

Substituting the values of v and v', we have $2gh - gR = 4gR$.

Or, $2h = 5R$, whence, $h = 5R/2$.]

12. A light rigid rod of length l has a mass attached to its end, forming a simple pendulum. It is inverted and then released. What is its speed v at the lowest point and what is the tension T in the suspension at that instant? $\left[\textbf{Ans. } 2\sqrt{gl}; 5mg\right]$

II–Potential energy in an electric field

13. What is the energy (in electron volts and in ergs) acquired by an alpha particle accelerated through a potential difference of 10^3 volts and what is then its velocity? (Charge on an alpha particle $= +2e$ and its mass = 4 times the mass of a proton). [**Ans.** 2000 eV or 3.2×10^{-9} ergs: 3.09×10^7 cm/sec.]

14. (*a*) What is the electrostatic potential in volts due to an atomic nucleus of atomic number 10 at a distance of 2 Angstrom units from it? (*b*) What will be the energy of (*i*) an electron (*ii*) a proton, placed at that point? (Charge on the nucleus $= +10e$; 1 Angstrom unit $= 10^{-8}$ cm.)

[**Ans.** (*a*) 72 volts; (*b*) (*i*) −72 eV (*ii*) +72 eV.]

15. (*a*) Calculate (*i*) the intensity of the electric field (in volts/cm), (*ii*) the potential (in volts) at a distance of 1 *A.U.* from a proton. (Charge on a proton $= +e = 4.80 \times 10^{-10}$ esu; 1 esu of potential = 300 volts; 1 *A.U.* $= 10^{-8}$ cm.)

(*b*) A proton is released from rest at a distance of 1 *A.U.* from another proton. What is the kinetic energy when the protons have moved infinitely apart from each other? If one proton be kept at rest, what is the terminal velocity acquired by the other? (Mass of proton = 1.67×10^{-24} gm).

[**Ans.** (*a*) (*i*) 1.44×10^9 volt/cm, (*ii*) 4.8×10^{-2} esu or 14.4 volts.
(*b*) 23×10^{-12}erg; 5.25×10^6 cm/sec.]

16. (*a*) Obtain the distance of closest approach of a particle of mass *m* and charge *q*, approaching with velocity *v* a massive particle carrying a charge *Q* and supposed to remain stationary.

[**Ans.** $2Qq/mv^2$]

(*b*) Alpha particles of speed 2.0×10^9 cm/sec are shot into a thin film of gold ($Z = 79$). Deduce the distance of nearest approach between the α-particles and nuclei of gold atoms, assuming Coulomb's law to hold. [**Ans.** 2.84×10^{-12} cm]

III–Linear restoring force

17. A mass of 1 kg is supported by a spring of force constant 10^5 dynes/cm. It is pulled down through a distance of 20 cm and then released. Calculate its highest velocity. [**Ans.** 200 cm/sec]

18. A spring which does not conform to Hooke's law obeys the force law $F = -Kx^3$. Calculate the potential energy at *x*, referred to $U = 0$ at $x = 0$. Also calculate the work done in stretching the spring from $x = x_1$ to $x = x_2$.

$$\left[\textbf{Ans. } \frac{1}{4}Kx^4; \frac{1}{2}K(x_2^{\ 4} - x_1^{\ 4})\right]$$

19. An object is attached to a vertical spring and slowly lowered to its equilibrium position. This stretches the spring by an amount *d*. If the same object is attached to the same vertical spring but permitted to fall instead, through what distance does it stretch the spring? [**Ans.** 2*d*]

20. Show that a mass *M* falling freely from a vertical height *h* on a vertical spring, of force constant *C*, would produce a maximum compression y_0 in the spring, where $y_0 = \dfrac{mg}{C} + \dfrac{1}{C}\sqrt{m^2g^2 + 2mghC}$.

IV–Potential energy curve—potential well

21. What is the potential energy curve of a particle? What significant information does it give about the behaviour of the particle?

22. What is meant by a potential well (or a potential valley)? Show that for small oscillations of a particle, the well (or the valley) is parabolic in shape. What special significance attaches to this particular shape of the well (or the valley)?

23. The energy of a particle is given by $U = A - \dfrac{B}{x} + \dfrac{C}{x^2}$, where *A*, *B* and *C* are all positive constants. What is the position of stable equilibrium of the particle? What is the *force constant* for small oscillations of the particle about this position? For what values of the total energy can the motion of the particle be bounded (*i.e.*, for what values of the total energy will it be inside a potential well)?

[**Ans.** $2C/B$; $B^4/8C^3$; *for total energy* $E < A$]

24. The accompanying figure (Fig. 5.17) shows the potential energy curve of a mass of 0.25 kg, with *r* in metres and *U* in joules. Supply the following information from the curve:

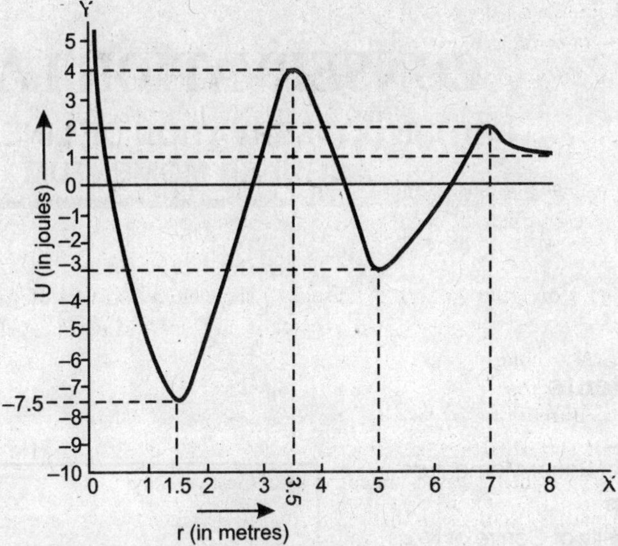

Fig. 5.17

(*i*) The positions of stable equilibrium of the particle about which it can oscillate.

(*ii*) The maximum energy of the oscillation in each case.

(*iii*) The kinetic energy with which the particle goes to $r \to \infty$ on just escaping from the potential well at the larger value of r and its velocity then.

(*iv*) The maximum total energy that would make the motion of the particle unbounded.

[**Ans.** (*i*) $r = 1.5$ m and $r = 50$ m; (*ii*) 11.5 joules and 7 joules; (*iii*) 2 joules; 4 m/sec; (*iv*) 4 jouies]

25. In Fig. 5.18, we have two potential energy curves of two diatomic molecules, with the interatomic distance (r) in *Angstrom units* and potential energy U in *electron units*. What are the intra-atomic distances (r) in *Angstrom units* and potential energy U in *electron volts*. What are the intra-atomic distances for equilibrium and the binding energies in the two cases?

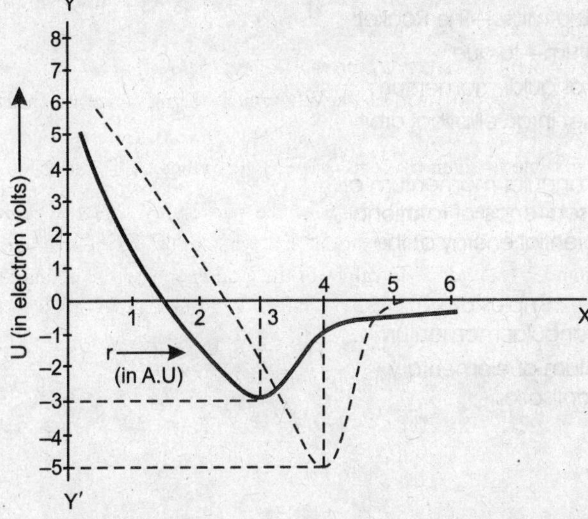

What does the narrower potential well in the second case signify?

[**Ans.** 3 *A.U.* or 3×10^{-8} cm and 4 *A.U.* or 4×10^{-8} cm; 3eV and 5eV. The narrower potential well in the second case indicates a more rapid change of gradient dU/dr and hence a larger value of the force constant]

CONSERVATION LAWS

PART II: CONSERVATION OF LINEAR AND ANGULAR MOMENTUM

Brief Contents

INTRODUCTION

In the previous chapter we have seen that the law of conservation of energy is an *impirical law* of physics. It concluded that the total amount of energy in an *isolated system* remains constant and is said to be conserved, over time. The consequence of this law is that energy can neither be created nor destroyed: it can only be transformed from one state into the other. The only thing that can happen to energy in a *closed system* is that it can change form: for instance, *Chemical energy* can become *Kinetic energy*.

However, the law of conservation of energy fails to provide complete or satisfactory solutions to a host of problems involving interaction of bodies. Let us take the most familiar example of bullet fired from a gun (or riffle). The law of conservation of energy tells us that the kinetic energies of the forward moving bullet and the backward moving or recoil of gun, along with the heat and sound energies liberated, must together be equal to the chemical energy of the explosive detonated in the gun. It does not tell us, how this total energy is distributed among the bullet, the gun and the atmosphere. And further, *energy* being a *scalar quantity*, the fact of its remaining conserved does not even suggest that the bullet and the gun must move in opposite direction. In dynamics there are many more problems in which we have no knowledge of the active forces actually involved, some additional principle of a vector nature is, therefore, obviously needed. It is the law of *conservation* of momentum, (being vector quantity) that gives the solution to above problems.

Linear and Angular Momenta

Every particle or a body can possess two types of motions, either linear or angular (*i.e.* rotational) motion. Depending upon the type of motion, a particle can have either linear momentum or angular momentum. If a particle of mass *m* is moving with a linear velocity $\vec{v}$, then it possesses linear momentum, $\vec{p}$ which is expressed as the product of its mass and velocity. Hence linear momentum, $\vec{p} = m\vec{v}$. The another type is angular momentum, denoted by $\vec{J}$ and is defined as moment of its linear momentum. Hence, $\vec{J} = \vec{r} \times \vec{p}$. We will discuss angular momentum, and its conservation at the end of this chapter in detail. Let us study the conservation of linear momentum and its applications.

6.1 CONSERVATION OF LINEAR MOMENTUM

Linear Momentum. *The linear momentum of a body is defined as the product of its mass and linear velocity.* If *m* is the mass of the body and $\vec{v}$ its velocity, then

Linear momentum, $\vec{p} = m\vec{v}$

It is a vector quantity. Its units are kg ms^{-1}.

Principle of conservation of Linear momentum. It states "The total linear momentum of a system of particles free from the action of external forces and subjected only to their mutual interaction, remains constant, no matter how complicated the forces are."

Mathematically, according to Newton's second law of motion, $\vec{F} = \dfrac{d\vec{p}}{dt}$ where $\vec{F}$ is the applied external force acting on the system. If for an *isolated system*, the external force is absent, $\vec{F} = 0$

$$\therefore \qquad \frac{d\vec{p}}{dt} = 0 \quad \text{or} \quad \vec{p} = \text{a constant}$$

i.e., the total linear momentum of the system remains constant.

Example 1. When a bullet is fired from a gun, the bullet of mass *m* moves forward with a velocity $\vec{v}$ and the gun of mass *M* kicks backward (*i.e.* recoils) with a velocity $\vec{V}$.

Soluton. Momentum of the bullet in the forward direction, $\vec{p}_1 = m\vec{v}$

Momentum of the gun in the backward direction, $\vec{p}_2 = -M\vec{V}$

Thus, the total linear momentum, after the bullet is fired

$$m\vec{v} - M\vec{V} = 0$$

Also, the linear momentum before the bullet is fired is zero. Thus, the total linear momentum of the bullet and the gun which was zero before the bullet was fired remains the same (*i.e.* zero) even after firing the bullet, *i.e.* the linear momentum is conserved.

Example 2. Imagine a rocket ship about to be fired into space (Fig. 6.1 *a*). If the rocket ship is initially at rest, its speed is 0, so its linear momentum must be zero. No matter what its mass is, the linear momentum of the rocket = mass × 0 km/hr = 0.

Solution. When the rocket is fired, then hot gases escape from the rear of the rocket ship, as shown in Fig. 6.1 (*b*). The momentum of those gases is equal to product of the total mass of the gases (m_g) and their velocity ($\vec{V}_g$) *i.e.*, $-m_g \cdot \vec{V}_g$. The negative sign indicates that the gases are escaping backward, or to the left. The law of conservation of linear momentum says, then, that the rocket has to move in the opposite direction, to the right or the +*ve* direction with a momentum $M_2\vec{V}_2$. That must be true because, then $-m_g\vec{V}_g$ (from the gases) plus ($+M_r\vec{V}_r$) (from the rocket) = 0. If you know the mass of the rocket (M_r), its velocity ($\vec{V}_r$) towards right can be calculated.

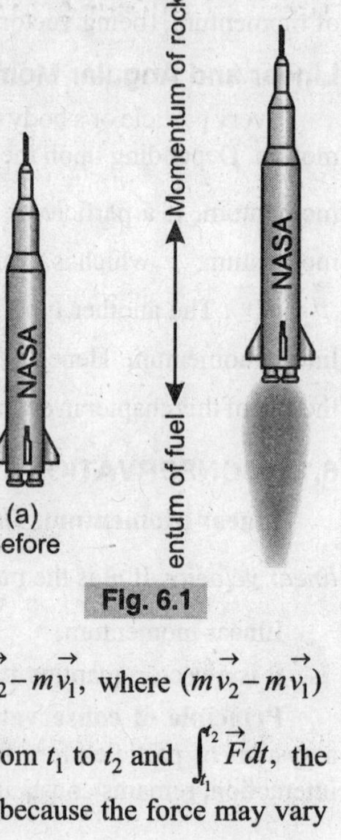

(a) Before

Fig. 6.1

Impulse. The law of conservation of linear momentum is also valid in case of an impulse, a large force acting during a small time interval. The linear momentum, $\vec{p}$ = mass × velocity = $m\vec{v}$.

Since in accordance with Newton's second law,

$$\vec{F} = d\vec{p}/dt = d(m\vec{v})dt,$$

we have

$$\vec{F}\,dt = d(m\vec{v}).$$

integrating which with respect to t, we have $\int_{t_1}^{t_2}\vec{F}dt = \int_{mv_1}^{mv_2} d(m\vec{v}) = m\vec{v}_2 - m\vec{v}_1$, where $(m\vec{v}_2 - m\vec{v}_1)$ is the change in the momentum of the particle in the interval of time from t_1 to t_2 and $\int_{t_1}^{t_2}\vec{F}dt$, the *impulse* of the force during the *same* interval (the integral being taken because the force may vary during the time interval). So that, we have

Impulse = change in momentum.

Now, in case the external force applied to a particle (or a body) be *zero*, we have

$\vec{F} = d\vec{p}/dt = d(m\vec{v})/dt = 0$, whence, $\vec{p} = m\vec{v}$ = *a constant*,

showing that *in the absence of an external force, the momentum of the particle* (*or the body*) *remains constant.*

We have already discussed under § 2.10 (*ii*) the *law of conservation of linear momentum* in the case of a system of two mutually interacting particles, so that, in the absence of an external force on the system,

$\vec{p_1} + \vec{p_2}$ or $m_1 \vec{v_1} + m_2 \vec{v_2}$ = *constant,*

i.e., *the total momentum of the particles remains conserved.*

Example 3. It would be interesting to give here an example to show that the law of conservation of momentum enables us to solve a problem which cannot be solved by a straight application of the relation $\vec{F} = m\vec{a}$.

Solution. Suppose a paritcle of mass m, initially at rest, suddenly explodes into two fragments of masses m_1 and m_2 which fly apart with velocities v_1 and v_2 respectively. Obviously, the forces resulting in the explosion of the particle must be internal forces since no external force has been applied. In the absence of the external force, therefore, the momentum must remain coserved and we should have $mv = m_1v_1 + m_2v_2$.

Since the particle was initially at rest, $v = 0$ and therefore, also $m_1v_1 + m_2v_2 = 0$, whence,

$$v_1/v_2 = -m_2/m_1.$$

showing at once that the velocities of the two fragments must be inversely proportional to their masses and *in opposite directions along the same line.* This result could not possibly be arrived at from the relation $F = ma$, since we know nothing about the forces that were acting during the explosion. Nor could we derive it from the law of conservation of energy, as already pointed out.

Principle applied to a system of particles

The law may be easily extended to any number of particles, either in fixed relative positions so as to form a rigid body or in the form of a loose conglomeration and thus being free to move into all sorts of different positions.

Let $m_1, m_2, \ldots m_n$ be the masses of the different particles and, in addition to their own interaction with each other, let there also be external forces acting on them, so that they acquire velocities $\vec{v_1}, \vec{v_2} \ldots \vec{v_n}$ respectively. Then, clearly, their total momentum $\vec{p}$, say, is the vector sum of their individual momenta $\vec{p_1}, \vec{p_2}, \vec{p_3} \ldots$etc., *i.e.*,

$$\vec{P} = \vec{p_1} + \vec{p_2} + \vec{p_3} + \ldots \vec{p_n} = m_1\vec{v_1} + m_2\vec{v_2} + m_3\vec{v_3} + \ldots m_n\vec{v_n}.$$

Differentiating with respect to t, we have

$$\frac{d\vec{p}}{dt} = \frac{d\vec{p_1}}{dt} + \frac{d\vec{p_2}}{dt} + \ldots \frac{d\vec{p_n}}{dt} = \frac{d}{dt}(\vec{p_1} + \vec{p_2} + \vec{p_3} + \ldots \vec{p_n}),$$

i.e, $$\vec{F} = \vec{F_1} + \vec{F_2} + \ldots \vec{F_n},$$

where $\vec{F_1}, \vec{F_2}, \vec{F_3} \ldots \vec{F_n}$ are the forces acting on the particles of masses $m_1, m_2, m_3 \ldots\ldots\ldots m_n$ respectively.

Now, the internal forces alone cannot bring about any changes in the momentum of the body since, forming pairs of equal and opposite forces, they give rise to equal and opposite changes of momentum which cancel out. The above forces $\vec{F_1}, \vec{F_2}, \ldots \vec{F_n}$ thus actually represent only the external forces acting on the particles and $\vec{F}$, their resultant. So that if $\vec{F} = 0$, we have $d\vec{p}/dt = 0$ and, therefore $\vec{p} = \vec{p_1} + \vec{p_2} + \vec{p_3} + \ldots \vec{p_n}$, a *constant*, implying that even though the individual values of $\vec{p_1}, \vec{p_2}$ etc. may change, *their total sum* p remains unaltered. This is the *law of conservation of linear momentum* and may formally be stated thus:

Statement:

When the vector sum of the external forces acting upon a system of particles equals zero, the total linear momentum of the system remains constant.

The conservation of linear momentum of a system is a *direct consequence* of the *translational invariance of the potential energy of the system* which, as we know, is one of the results of Galilean invariance.

Thus, considering, for the sake of simplicity, the case of two particles in one dimension, say, along the axis of x, such that their coordinates are x_1 and x_2, we have their potential energy $U(x_1, x_2)$, depending upon their positions.

Now, Galilean invariance demands that this *P.E.* should remain constant even if each particle is deplaced through the *same* distance d, *i.e.*, the potential energy $U[(x_1 + d), (x_2 + d)]$ after the displacement must be the same as before the displacement, *viz.*, $U(x_1, x_2)$. This means that if $U(x_1, x_2) = (x_1 - x_2)^2$, we should also have $U[(x_1 + d)], (x_2 + d)]$ equal to $(x_1 - x_2)^2$. Let us see if this is so.

We have $U[(x_1 + d), (x_2 + d)] = [(x_1 + d) - (x_2 + d)]^2 = (x_1 - x_2)^2 = U(x_1, x_2)$, clearly showing that *the potential energy is independent of the displacement d suffered by each particle.*

In general therefore, if the potential energy $U(\vec{r_1}, \vec{r_2})$ is a function of only $(\vec{r_1} - \vec{r_2})$, it is *translationally invariant.*

Since the force on a particle is the negative of $\partial u/\partial x$, we have

$$F_1 = -\partial u/\partial x_1 \text{ and } F_2 = -\partial u/\partial x_2.$$

But U being a function of $(x_1 - x_2)$ only, we have

$$\frac{\partial U}{dx_1} = \frac{dU}{dx}\frac{dx}{dx_1} = \frac{dU}{dx} \text{ and } \frac{\partial U}{\partial x_2} = \frac{dU}{dx}\frac{dx}{dx_2} = -\frac{dU}{dx}.$$

And, therefore, $$\frac{\partial U}{\partial x_1} = -\frac{\partial U}{\partial x_2} \text{ or, } F_1 = -F_2.$$

So that, the total force acting on the particles which interact with each other is $\vec{F} = \vec{F_1} + \vec{F_2} = 0$.

The total force acting on the system of the two particles thus being *zero*, we have, by Newton's second law, in vector form,

$$\frac{d}{dt}(m_1 \vec{v_1} + m_2 \vec{v_2}) = 0. \text{ Or, } m_1 \vec{v_1} + m_2 \vec{v_2} = constant,$$

i.e., the total momentum of the two particles remains conserved.

The same argument can be extended to any number of particles, the one and only condition being that the potential energy of the system must be translationally invariant.

The law of conservation of linear momentum is one of the fundamental conservation laws and is also applicable to atomic and nuclear physics even though Newtonian mechanics is not. It is applicable even at relativistic velocities, provided we take the relativistic value of the mass of the particles, given by $m = m_0/\sqrt{1 - v^2/c^2}$.

6.2. CENTRE OF MASS

When we consider the motion of a system consisting of a large number of particles, say, N, there is one point in it which behaves as though the entire mass of the system (*i.e.*, the sum of the masses of all the N individual particles) were concentrated there and its motion is the same as would ensue if the external forces acting on the system were applied directly to it. This point is called the *centre of mass* of the system. As we shall see as we proceed along, this concept of centre of mass has proved most useful in tackling many is problem and, in particular, those concerned with collision of particles (§ 6.6).

Taking first the simple case of a system of jus two particles of masses m_1 and m_2 and of a total mass M, with $\vec{r_1}$ and $\vec{r_2}$ as their position vectors with respect to some origin, if $\vec{R}$ be the position vector of the centre of mass, we have

$$\vec{R} = \frac{m_1\vec{r_1}+m_2\vec{r_2}}{m_1+m_2} = \frac{m_1\vec{r_1}+m_2\vec{r_2}}{M}$$

Or, $$M\vec{R} = m_1\vec{r_1}+m_2\vec{r_2},$$

i.e., the product of the total mass of the system and the position vector of the centre of mass (c.m.) is equal to the sum of the products of the individual masses and their respective position vectors.

The position of the *c.m.* of the system may thus be easily obtained.

To take a general case, if we have a system consisting of N particles, of masses $m_1, m_2, \ldots m_n$, with $\vec{r_1}, \vec{r_2} \ldots \vec{r_n}$ as their position vectors at a given instant, the position vector $\vec{R}$ of the centre of mass of the system Fig. 6.2 at that instant is given by the relation $M\vec{R} = m_1\vec{r}_1 + m_2\vec{r_2} + \ldots\ldots m_n\vec{r_n}$, where M is the total mass of the system.

Clearly, $M = m_1 + m_2 + \ldots m_n = \sum_{k=1}^{N} m_k$, where m_k is the mass of the k_{th} particle. If, therefore, $\vec{r_k}$ be the position vector of the k_{th} particle, we have

$$\vec{R} = \frac{m_1\vec{r_1}+m_2\vec{r_2}+\ldots m_N\vec{r_N}}{m_3+m_2+\ldots m_N}$$

$$= \frac{\sum_{k=1}^{N} m_k\vec{r_k}}{\sum_{k=1}^{N} nl_k} = \frac{\sum_{k=1}^{N} m_k\vec{r_k}}{M},$$

where $\sum m_k\vec{r_k}$ is called the *first moment of mass for the system.*

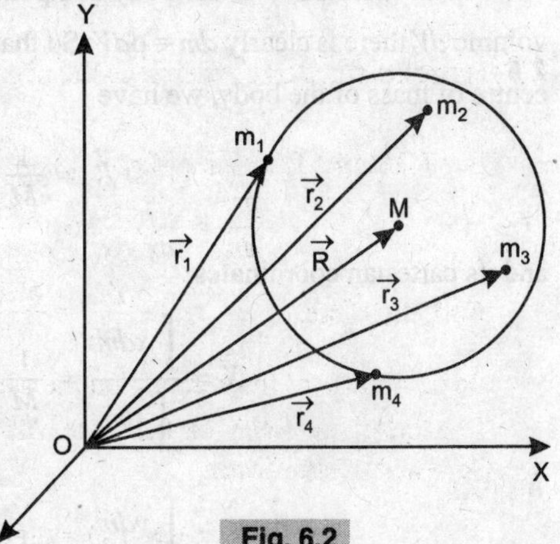

Fig. 6.2

Now, $\vec{r_k} = r_k\hat{i} + y_k\hat{j} + z_k\hat{k}$ and $\vec{R} = x\hat{i} + y\hat{j} + z\hat{k}$. So that, if X, Y and Z be the Cartesian coordinates of the centre of mass, we have

$$X = \frac{m_1x_1+m_2x_2+\ldots m_Nx_N}{m_1+m_2+\ldots m_N} = \frac{\sum_{k=1}^{N} m_kx_k}{\sum_{k=1}^{N} m_k} = \frac{\sum_{k=1}^{N} m_kx_k}{M}.$$

Or, $$X = \frac{1}{M}\sum_{k=1}^{N} m_kx_k,$$

$$Y = \frac{m_1y_1+m_2y_2+\ldots m_Ny_N}{m_1+m_2+\ldots m_N} = \frac{\sum_{k=1}^{N} m_ky_k}{\sum_{k=1}^{N} m_k} = \frac{\sum_{k=1}^{N} m_ky_k}{M}.$$

Or,
$$Y = \frac{1}{M}\sum_{k=1}^{N} m_k y_k,$$

and
$$Z = \frac{m_1 z_1 + m_2 z_2 + \ldots + m_N z_N}{m_1 + m_2 + \ldots m_N} = \frac{\sum_{k=1}^{N} m_k z_k}{\sum_{k=1}^{N} m_k} = \frac{\sum_{k=1}^{N} m_k z_k}{M}.$$

Or,
$$Z = \frac{1}{M}\sum_{k=1}^{N} m_k z_k,$$

Since a rigid body consists of a large number of particles, compactly packed together, it must also have a *centre of mass*. In view, however, of the large number of particles constituting it and the extremely small spacing between them, the distribution of mass may be deemed to be continuous throughout the body. The sign of summation used above is thus replaced by that of integration taken over the whole volume of the body.

If ρ be the density of the body at a point whose position vector is $\vec{r}$, the mass of an element of volume dV there is clearly $dm = \rho dV$. So that, proceeding as above, if $\vec{R}$ be the position vector of the centre of mass of the body, we have

$$\vec{R} = \frac{1}{M}\int \vec{r}\, dm = \frac{\int_V \vec{r}\, dm}{\int_V dm}$$

and its cartesian coordinates,

$$X = \frac{\int_V x dm}{\int_V dm} = \frac{1}{M}\int_V x dm = \frac{\int_V x\rho dv}{\int_V \rho dv},$$

$$Y = \frac{\int_V y dm}{\int_V dm} = \frac{1}{M}\int_V y dm = \frac{\int_V y\rho dv}{\int_V \rho dv},$$

and
$$Z = \frac{\int_V z dm}{\int_V dm} = \frac{1}{M}\int_V z dm = \frac{\int_V z\rho dv}{\int_V \rho dv},$$

For homogenous bodies of regular geometrical shapes, the centre of mass obviously lies on the point or the line of symmetry as the case may be, as, for example, at the centre in the case of a sphere and on the axis in the case of a cone. In fact, it is located at a point for which $\int dm\, \vec{r} = 0$ and consequently $\vec{R} = 0$. This integral also, like the summation $\sum mk\, \vec{r}_k$ (mentioned earlier) is called the *first moment of mass for the system.*

6.3 MOTION OF VELOCITY OF CENTRE OF MASS

Velocity of Centre of Mass. Let us consider the motion of the system consisting on n particles and total mass M assuming that the mass of the system remains constant *i.e.*, no mass enters or leaves the system.

$$\therefore \qquad M\vec{R} = \sum m_i \vec{r_i} = m_1 \vec{r_1} + m_2 \vec{r_2} + \ldots + \ldots + m_i \vec{r_i} + \ldots + m_n \vec{r_n}$$

Differentiating with respect to time, we get

$$M\frac{d\vec{R}}{dt} = m_1 \frac{d\vec{r_1}}{dt} + m_2 \frac{d\vec{r_2}}{dt} + \ldots + m_i \frac{d\vec{r_i}}{dt} + \ldots + m_n \frac{d\vec{r_n}}{dt}$$

But $\dfrac{d\vec{R}}{dt} = \vec{V}$ the velocity of centre of mass

and $\dfrac{d\vec{r_1}}{dt} = \vec{v_1}, \dfrac{d\vec{r_2}}{dt} = \vec{v_2} \ldots \dfrac{d\vec{r_i}}{dt} = \vec{v_i}$ and $\dfrac{d\vec{r_n}}{dt} = \vec{v_n}$

which represent the velocities of individual particles.

$$\therefore \qquad M\vec{V} = m_1 \vec{v_1} + m_2 \vec{v_2} + \ldots + m_i \vec{v_i} + \ldots + m_n \vec{v_n} = \sum m_i \vec{v_i} \qquad \ldots(i)$$

The velocity of centre of mass is given by

$$\vec{V} = \frac{m_1 \vec{v_1} + m_2 \vec{v_2} + \ldots + m_i \vec{v_i} + \ldots + m_n \vec{v_n}}{M} = \frac{\sum m_i \vec{v_i}}{M} \qquad \ldots(ii)$$

From relation (*i*) we also find the *vector sum of the linear momenta of the individual particles i.e., the total linear momentum of the system is required to the product of the total mass of the system and the velocity of centre of mass.*

In the absence of any external force, the total linear momentum of the system $\vec{P}$ is conserved

$$\therefore \qquad M\vec{V} = \sum m_i \vec{v_i} = \vec{P} = \text{a constant}$$

or $\vec{V}$ = a constant vector

Hence the velocity of the centre of mass of a system remains constant if no external force is applied to it.

Acceleration. Differentiating equation (*i*) with respect to time *t*, we have

$$M\frac{d\vec{V}}{dt} = m_1 \frac{d\vec{v_1}}{dt} + m_2 \frac{d\vec{v_2}}{dt} + \ldots + m_i \frac{d\vec{v_i}}{dt} + \ldots + m_n \frac{d\vec{v_n}}{dt}$$

or

$$M\vec{a} = m_1 \vec{a_1} + m_2 \vec{a_2} + \ldots + m_i \vec{a_i} + \ldots + m_n \vec{a_n}$$

where $\vec{a}$ is the acceleration of the centre of mass and $\vec{a_1}, \vec{a_2}$ etc. are the accelerations of individual particles.

The acceleration of the centre of mass is given by

$$\vec{a} = \frac{m_1 \vec{a_1} + m_2 \vec{a_2} + \ldots + m_i \vec{a_i} + \ldots + m_n \vec{a_n}}{M} = \frac{\sum m_i \vec{a_i}}{M} \qquad \ldots(iii)$$

According to Newton's second law of motion

$$m_1 \vec{a_1} = \vec{F_1}, m_2 \vec{a_2} = \vec{F_2} \ldots m_i \vec{a_i} = \vec{F_i} \ldots m_n \vec{a_n} = \vec{F_n}$$

The external forces acting on different particles

$$\therefore \qquad M\vec{a} = \vec{F_1} + \vec{F_2} + \ldots + \vec{F_i} + \ldots + \vec{F_n}$$

Thus the product of the total mass of a system and the vector acceleration of the centre of mass is equal to the vector sum of all the external forces acting on the individual particles of the system.

When no external force is acting

$$\therefore \quad \vec{F_1}+\vec{F_2}+\ldots+\vec{F_i}+\ldots+\vec{F_n} = \sum \vec{F_i} = 0 \quad \therefore\ M\vec{a} = 0 \text{ or } \vec{a} = 0 \text{ vector}$$

Hence in the absence of an external force, the acceleration of the centre of mass is zero and therefore the velocity is a constant vector.

6.4 TOTAL LINEAR MOMENTUM ABOUT THE CENTRE OF MASS

Let C be the centre of mass of a number of particles of mass $m_1, m_2 \ldots m_i \ldots m_n$ and $\vec{r_1}, \vec{r_2} \ldots \vec{r_i} \ldots \vec{r_n}$ their position vectors with respect to the origin O, then

Position vector of centre of mass

$$\vec{R} = \frac{m_1\vec{r_1}+m_2\vec{r_2}+\ldots+m_i\vec{r_i}+\ldots+m_n\vec{r_n}}{m_1+m_2+\ldots+m_i+\ldots+m_n} = \frac{\sum m_i\vec{r_i}}{\sum m_i} = \frac{\sum m_i\vec{r_i}}{M} \quad \ldots(i)$$

where $\quad M = m_1+m_2+\ldots+m_i+\ldots+m_n = \sum m_i$

Consider one of the particles of mass m_i having position vector $\vec{r_i}$ then its position with respect to the centre of mass C, $\vec{r_{ci}}$ is given by $\vec{R}+\vec{r_{ci}} = \vec{r_i}$

The position of all other particles with respect to the centre of mass C is also given by similar relations.

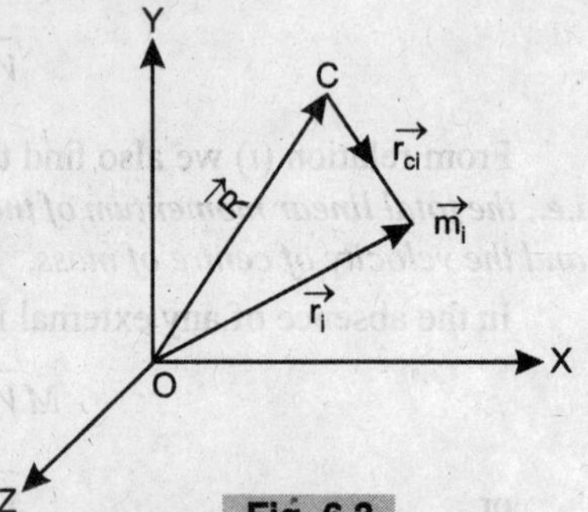

Fig. 6.3

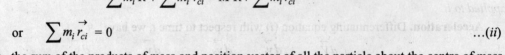

Substituting $\vec{r_i} = \vec{R}+\vec{r_{ci}}$ in Equation (*i*), we get

$$M\vec{R} = \sum m_i(\vec{R}+\vec{r_{ci}})$$

$$= \sum m_i\vec{R}+\sum m_i\vec{r_{ci}} = M\vec{R}+\sum m_i\vec{r_{ci}}$$

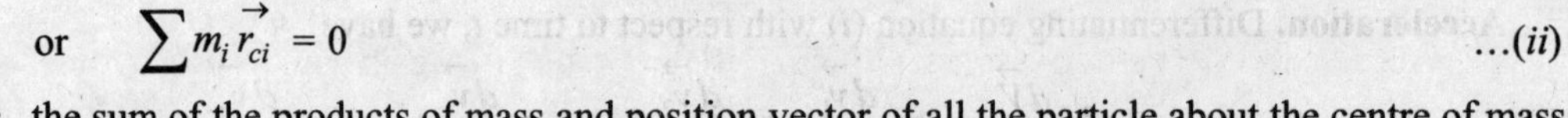

or $\quad \sum m_i\vec{r_{ci}} = 0 \quad \ldots(ii)$

i.e., the sum of the products of mass and position vector of all the particle about the centre of mass is zero.

Differentiating relation (*ii*) with respect to *t* we get $\sum m_i \dfrac{d\vec{r_{ci}}}{dt} = \sum m_i\vec{v_{ci}} = 0$

because $\dfrac{d\vec{r_{ci}}}{dt} = \vec{v_{ci}}$ = velocity of the particle of mass m_i relative to centre of mass. $\sum m_i\vec{v_{ci}}$, therefore gives the total linear momentum of all the particles about the centre of mass.

Thus the total linear momentum of the system of particles about the centre of mass is zero.

Note. The centre of mass frame is therefore, sometimes called zero momentum frame.

6.5 SYSTEM OF TWO PARTICLES

(*i*) Position vector of centre of mass. The position of centre of mass for a number of particles is mathematically given by

$$\vec{R} = \frac{\sum m_i\vec{r_i}}{\sum m_i}$$

For two mass points m_1 and m_2, $\vec{R} = \dfrac{m_1 \vec{r_1} + m_2 \vec{r_2}}{m_1 + m_2}$ ...(*i*)

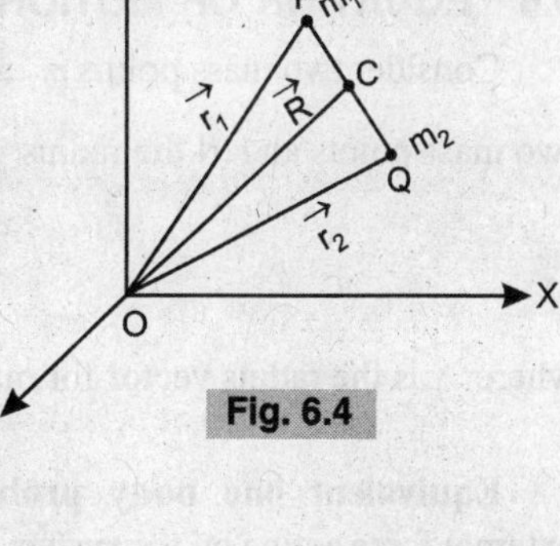

Fig. 6.4

where $\vec{r_1}$ and $\vec{r_2}$ are the vector distances of the particles of mass m_1 and m_2 respectively from the origin O.

If, however the centre of mass lies at the origin of the co-ordinate system as in Fig. 6.5.

$$\vec{R} = 0$$

$$\therefore \qquad m_1 \vec{r_1} + m_2 \vec{r_2} = 0 \text{ or } \frac{m_1}{m_2} = \frac{-\vec{r_2}}{\vec{r_1}}$$

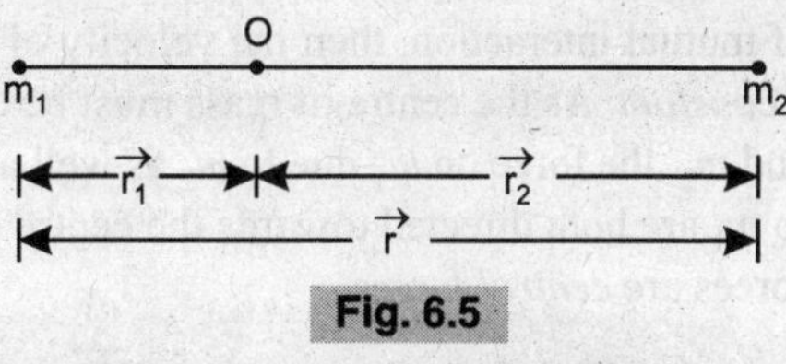

Fig. 6.5

Thus the centre of mass divides the line joining the two masses in the inverse ratio of the masses i.e., the heavier mass lies nearer the centre of mass of the two particle system. It should be noted that if O is the origin and $\vec{r_2}$ is positive, $\vec{r_1}$ must be negative.

(*ii*) Velocity of centre of mass. Rewriting equation (*i*) we have $m_1 \vec{r_1} + m_2 \vec{r_2} = (m_1 + m_2)\vec{R}$

Differentiating with respect to time we have $m_1 \dot{\vec{r_1}} + m_2 \dot{\vec{r_2}} = (m_1 + m_2)\dot{\vec{R}}$

$$\text{or Velocity of centre of mass } \dot{\vec{R}} = \frac{m_1 \dot{\vec{r_1}} + m_2 \dot{\vec{r_2}}}{m_1 + m_2} \qquad ...(ii)$$

$$\text{or} \qquad \vec{V} = \frac{m_1 \vec{v_1} + m_2 \vec{v_2}}{m_1 + m_2} \qquad ...(iii)$$

where $\vec{V} = \dot{\vec{R}}, \vec{v_1} = \dot{\vec{r_1}}$ and $\vec{v_2} = \dot{\vec{r_2}}$.

(*iii*) Acceleration of centre of mass. Differentiating equation (*ii*) again with respect to time, we have the acceleration of the centre of mass.

$$\ddot{\vec{R}} = \frac{m_1 \ddot{\vec{r_1}} + m_2 \ddot{\vec{r_2}}}{m_1 + m_2} \text{ or } \vec{a} = \frac{m_1 \vec{a_1} + m_2 \vec{a_2}}{M} \qquad ...(iv)$$

where $\vec{a} = \ddot{\vec{R}}, \vec{a_1} = \ddot{\vec{r_1}}, \vec{a_2} = \ddot{\vec{r_2}}$, and $M = m_1 + m_2$

(*iv*) Linear momentum of centre of mass. From equation (*iii*) we have

$$(m_1 + m_2)\vec{V} = m_1 \vec{v_1} + m_2 \vec{v_2}$$

$$\text{or} \qquad M\vec{V} = m_1 \vec{v_1} + m_2 \vec{v_2} \qquad [\text{where } M = m_1 + m_2]$$

$$\text{or} \qquad \vec{P} = \vec{p_1} + \vec{p_2}$$

where $\vec{P}$ is the linear momentum of the centre of mass and $m_1 \vec{v_1}$ and $m_2 \vec{v_2}$ the linear momentum of masses m_1 and m_2 respectively.

Hence the linear momentum of a system of two particles is equal to linear momentum of the centre of mass.

6.6 EQUATION OF MOTION OF CENTRE OF MASS

Consider two mass points m_1 and m_2 as shown in Fig. 6.6. If c.m. is the centre of mass for these two mass points and $\vec{R}$ the radius vector for the centre of mass, then

$$\vec{R} = \frac{m_1 \vec{r_1} + m_2 \vec{r_2}}{m_1 + m_2}$$

where $\vec{r_1}$ is the radius vector for mass point m_1 and $\vec{r_2}$ that for mass point m_2.

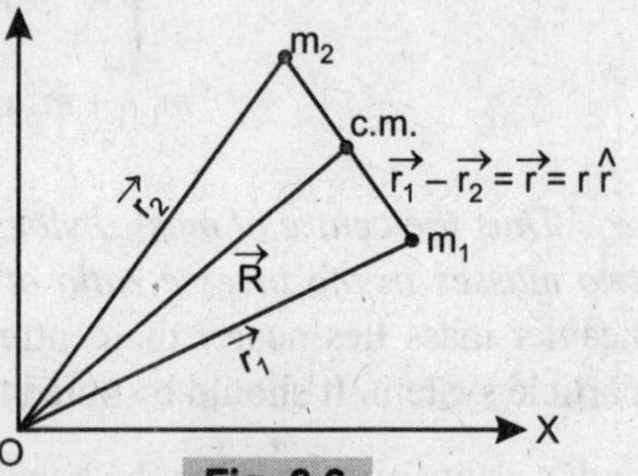

Equivalent one body problem. Suppose there is no external force acting on the system and the only forces are those of mutual interaction, then the velocity of the centre of mass is a *constant.* As the centre of mass must be on the line joining m_1 and m_2, the force on m_1 due to m_2 as well as the force on m_2 due to m_1 are both directed towards the centre of mass. Hence these forces are *central forces.*

Fig. 6.6

If we denote the force on m_1 as $\vec{F_{12}} = F(r)\,\hat{r}$ the force on m_2 being equal and opposite will be denoted by $\vec{F_{21}} = -F(r)\hat{r}$.

$$m_1 \frac{d^2 \vec{r_1}}{dt^2} = \vec{F_{12}} = F(r)\hat{r} \text{ or } \frac{d^2 \vec{r_1}}{dt^2} = \frac{1}{m_1} F(r)\hat{r} \qquad \ldots(i)$$

and

$$m_2 \frac{d^2 \vec{r_2}}{dt^2} = \vec{F_{21}} = -F(r)\hat{r} \text{ or } \frac{d^2 \vec{r_2}}{dt^2} = -\frac{1}{m_2} F(r)\hat{r} \qquad \ldots(ii)$$

Subtracting (*ii*) and (*i*) we have $\dfrac{d^2 \vec{r_1}}{dt^2} - \dfrac{d^2 \vec{r_2}}{dt^2} = \left(\dfrac{1}{m_1} + \dfrac{1}{m_2}\right) F(r)\hat{r}$

Now $$\frac{d^2 \vec{r_1}}{dt^2} - \frac{d^2 \vec{r_2}}{dt^2} = \frac{d^2}{dt^2}(\vec{r_1} - \vec{r_2}) = \frac{d^2 \vec{r}}{dt^2} \qquad [\because \vec{r} = \vec{r_1} - \vec{r_2}]$$

If we put $$\frac{1}{\mu} = \frac{1}{m_1} + \frac{1}{m_2} = \frac{m_1 + m_2}{m_1 m_2} \text{ or } \mu = \frac{m_1 m_2}{m_1 + m_2}$$

then, $$\frac{d^2 \vec{r}}{dt^2} = \left(\frac{1}{m_1} + \frac{1}{m_2}\right) F(r)\hat{r} = \frac{1}{m} F(r)\hat{r}$$

or $$\mu \ddot{\vec{r}} = F(r)\hat{r} \qquad \ldots(iii)$$

i.e. the system behaves as a single particle of mass $\mu = \dfrac{m_1 m_2}{m_1 + m_2}$. Here, μ is known as the **reduced mass** of the system and acts at the point known as **centre of mass**. The relation given by Eq. (*iii*) is known as *equation of motion* of the centre of mass of a particle having mass equal to the reduced mass (μ) at a vector distance $\vec{r}$ from one of the particles to the other and shows that two separate equations of motion (*i*) and (*ii*) have been reduced to a single equation (*iii*) involving reduced mass (μ) concept.

We have thus, reduced the two body problem to a one body problem.

6.7 MOTION OF REDUCED MASS UNDER INVERSE SQUARE FORCE

The most familiar example of inverse square force is the gravitational force. For forces of gravitational attraction between the two point masses m_1 and m_2.

$$\vec{F}(r) = -\frac{Gm_1m_2}{r^2}\hat{r} \text{ or } \mu\frac{d^2\vec{r}}{dt^2} = \mu\ddot{\vec{r}} = -\frac{Gm_1m_2}{r^2}\hat{r}$$

or,
$$\frac{m_1m_2}{m_1+m_2}\ddot{\vec{r}} = -\frac{Gm_1m_2}{r^2}\hat{r}$$

$$\therefore \quad \ddot{\vec{r}} = -\frac{GM}{r^2}\hat{r} \text{ where } M = m_1 + m_2$$

This is clearly the equation of motion of a particle of unit mass at a vector distance $\vec{r}$ (equal to the distance between the two particles) from a fixed mass $M = (m_1 + m_2)$ exerting a force of attraction on it. Further, the acceleration of one mass with respect to the other mass will appear to be the same but in opposite direction whether the observer is at mass m_1 or m_2.

6.8 LABORATORY CENTRE-OF-MASS AND FRAMES OF REFERENCE

A frame of reference carried by the centre of mass of an *isolated system* of particles (*i.e., a system not subjected to any external forces*) is called the *centre-of-mass* or the *C-frame of reference. In this frame, obviously,* $\vec{R}$ (the position vector of the centre of mass) is equal to *zero* and hence the velocity of the centre of mass, *i.e.*, $\vec{V} = d\vec{R}/dt$ also equal to zero. In consequence, the *linear momentum* $\vec{p}$ of the system too, given by $\vec{p} = M\vec{V} = \sum m_k \vec{v}_k$ is zero. The *C*-frame of reference is, therefore, also called the *zero-momentum frame.* And, since in the absence of external forces, the centre of mass, and hence the *C*-frame, moves with constant velocity, it is also an *inertial frame.* This makes it particularly useful in solving many a problem which are difficult to solve in the laboratory frame of reference, as we shall presently see. Indeed, it has become almost customary to deal with all collisions in Nuclear Physics in this frame of reference alone.

In the study of collisions between two particles we shall come across the laboratory system or laboratory frame of references and the centre of mass system or centre of mass frame of reference.

A reference frame is the space determined by a rigid body regarded as the base. The rigid body is supposed to extend in all directions as far as necessary. A point in space is located by the three coordinates taken with respect to the origin of the reference system.

If the origin of the reference system is a point rigidly fixed to the laboratory it is known as the **laboratory frame.**

The laboratory frame is inertial so long as earth is taken to be an inertial frame.

Centre of mass system (Frame of reference). *If the origin of the reference system is a point rigidly fixed to the centre of mass of a system of particles on which no external force is acting it is known as the* **centre of mass frame of reference.**

In the centre of mass reference frame the position vector of the centre of mass $\vec{R} = 0$ as the centre of mass is itself the origin of the reference system.

$\therefore$ The velocity of centre mass $\vec{V} = \dfrac{d\vec{R}}{dt} = 0$ and the linear momentum $\vec{p} = M\vec{V}$ of the system is also = 0. Hence it is known as a *zero momentum frame.*

Advantages of studying collision process in centre of mass system. (*i*) In the absence of any external force the velocity of the centre of mass is a *constant*. In other words, the centre of mass reference frame moves with a constant velocity with respect to the laboratory frame. *Hence the centre of mass frame is also an inertial frame.*

Various physical quantities measured in the two systems are related to each other by Galelian transformations provided the velocity of centre of mass is small as compared to the velocity of light.

(*ii*) A system of two particles requires six co-ordinates to describe the motion in the laboratory system. Three co-ordinates are required to describe the motion of centre of mass and three more co-ordinates are required to describe the relative motion. But in the centre of mass frame we require only three co-ordinates as the centre of mass is itself at rest in this frame.

The discussion of a collision process, therefore, becomes much simpler in the centre of mass frame of reference than in the laboratory frame.

6.9 COLLISION

When two bodies are approaching each other, a force comes into play between them for a finite time and brings about a measurable change in their velocities, momenta and energy according to the respective laws of conservation, a collision is said to have taken place.

Contrary to the meaning of the term 'collision' in our everyday parlance, in Physics it does not necessarily mean one particle (or body) 'striking' against another. Indeed, two particles may not even '*touch*' each other* and may still be said to collide. All that is implied is that as the particles approach each other, (*i*) *a large force for a relatively short time* (*i.e.*, an impulse) acts on each colliding particle, (*ii*) *the motion of a particles* (*or, at least, of one of the particles*) *is changed rather abruptly* and (*iii*) *the total momentum* (*as also the total energy*) *of the particles remains conserved.*

The essence of a collision is, in fact, *a redistribution of the total momentum of the particles.* This is the reason why the law of conservation of momentum is simply indispensable in dealing with the phenomenon of collision between particles.

During collision, the force of some interaction comes into play between the two colliding particles or systems for a finite small time which brings about a change in their relative motions. If the collision acts for a time t_0 to $t_0 + \Delta t$, then a time t less than t_0 is known as *time before collision* and a time t greater than $t_0 + \Delta t$, is called *time after collision.*

The collision is termed **scattering** if the nature of particles does not change after collision. Familiar examples of collision or scattering are the deflection of a comet as it passes near the solar system and the deflection of an α-particle by an atomic nucleus. The study of collision is of particular importance in atomic and nuclear physics. The bodies involved may be atoms, nuclei or various elementary particles such as electrons, protons, *etc.*

There are two types of collisions:

(1) Elastic Collision, and **(2)** Inelastic Collision

(1) Elastic scattering (or Elastic collision). A collision (scattering) is said to be an elastic collision if (*i*) the final particles after collision are the same as the initial particles before collision, (*ii*) the sum of the kinetic energies of the particles after collision is the same as the sum of the kinetic energies of the particle before collision.

(2) Inelastic scattering (or Inelastic collision). A collision is said to be an inelastic collision if

(*i*) The final particles after collision are the same as the initial particles before collision.

(*ii*) The sum of the kinetic energies of the particles after collision is either more or less than the sum of the kinetic energies of the particles before collision.

Some of the collisions between atomic, nuclear and fundamental particles belong to this class.

---

* As for example, in the case of an alpha particle and a nucleus of gold—due, no doubt, to the electrostatic force of repulsion between them.

In such a collision between two particles, therefore, we have $m_1u_1 + m_2u_2 = m_1v_1 + m_2v_2$ as also $\frac{1}{2}m_1u_1^2 + \frac{1}{2}m_2u_2^2 = \frac{1}{2}m_1v_1^2 + \frac{1}{2}m_2v_2^2$, where m_1 and m_2 are the respective masses of the two particles and u_1, u_2 and v_1, v_2 their velocities *before* and *after* the collision, *i.e.*, initially before the interacting forces between the particles have yet started acting and finally, after these forces have again been reduced effectively to zero.

A perfectly inelastic collision, *in which the particles stick permanently together on impact and the loss of kinetic energy is the maximum consistent with the requirements of conservation of momentum.* A bullet remaining embedded in a target is one such example.

In either case, however, since the interacting forces after the collision become effectively *zero, the potential energy of the system remains the same both before and after the collision.*

In the case of inelastic collision between larger particles, the loss of kinetic energy occurs mostly in the form of heat energy due to the increased vibrations of the constituent atoms of the particles. On the other hand, in the case of inelastic atomic collisions, an atom may absorb some energy and get into what is called an 'excited state', with one or more of its electrons moving into a higher orbit or a higher energy level, the energy so absorbed (and remaining in the potential form) being referred to as '*excitation energy*' (ξ). The final kinetic energy of the system is thus less by this much amount than the initial one, *i.e., final kinetic energy of the system* + ξ = *initial kinetic energy of the system* or, $\frac{1}{2}m_1\vec{v}_1^{\,2} + \frac{1}{2}m_2\vec{v}_2^{\,2} + \xi = \frac{1}{2}m_1\vec{u}_1^{\,2} + \frac{1}{2}m_2\vec{u}_2^{\,2}$.

In case of the atom be already in an excited state before collision, it may come into its normal state on collision, *i.e.*, the electron (or electrons) may fall back to the original orbit, thereby releasing the potential energy ξ absorbed during excitation, resulting in an increase in the kinetic energy of the system after collision. Thus, in the case, we have *final K.E. of the system* − ξ = *initial kinetic energy of the system.* Or, $\frac{1}{2}m_1\vec{v}_1^{\,2} + \frac{1}{2}m_2\vec{v}_2^{\,2} - \xi = \frac{1}{2}m_1\vec{u}_1^{\,2} + \frac{1}{2}m_2\vec{u}_2^{\,2}$

It is to be carefully noted here that in the case of inelastic collision and reaction, only the sum of the kinetic energies after collision is different from the sum of the kinetic energies before collision but the total energy of the system, including kinetic energy, potential energy and any other form of energy remains conserved.

6.10 CALCULATION OF FINAL VELOCITIES OF COLLIDING PARTICLES

The velocities of the particles after a collision can be easily calculated by solving their equations of motion if we know their velocities before collision and the forces acting during the collision. Unfortunately, these interacting forces are not always known to us. Even so, we can obtain the velocities of the particles after collision from those before collision in case (*i*) *the collision is perfectly in-elastic* and (*ii*) *the collision is elastic but one-dimensional, i.e.*, in which the relative motion of the particles before and after the collision is along the *same* line.

In case of the elastic collision be two or three-dimensional, the velocities of the particles after collision can be determined only if we also know the direction of motion of the particles after the collision. (See case (*iii*) below).

(I) Inelastic collision. In the case of a perfectly inelastic collision, if m_1 and m_2 be the masses of the two colliding particles and $\vec{u}_1$ and $\vec{u}_2$ their velocities before collision, we have

momentum of the particles before collision = $m_1\vec{u}_1 + m_2\vec{u}_2$.

After the collision, the two particles stick together and move with a velocity $\vec{v}$, say. So that,

momentum of the particles after collision = $(m_1 + m_2)\vec{v}$.

Since momentum is always conserved in a collision, we have

$(m_1 + m_2)\vec{v} = m_1\vec{u_1} + m_2\vec{u_2}$, whence $\vec{v} = \dfrac{m_1\vec{u_1} + m_2\vec{u_2}}{m_1 + m_2}$.

Thus, knowing the masses of the two particles and their initial velocities, we can easily obtain their common velocity $(\vec{v})$ after the collision.

In case the second particle be at rest, $\vec{u}_2 = 0$. So that, we shall have $(m_1 + m_2)\vec{v} = m_1\vec{u_1}$, whence, $\vec{v} = m_1\vec{u_1}(m_1 + m_2)$

That there will be a loss of *K.E.* may be easily seen from the fact that *K.E. of the particles before collision* $= \frac{1}{2}m_1\vec{u_1}^2$ [the second particle being at rest, $u_2 = 0$].

and *K.E. of the particles after collision* $= \frac{1}{2}(m_1 + m_2)v^2$,

$$\therefore \frac{K.E.\ after\ collision}{K.E.\ before\ collision} = \frac{\frac{1}{2}(m_1 + m_2)v^2}{\frac{1}{2}m_1u_1^2}$$

$$= \frac{1}{2}(m_1 + m_2)\left(\frac{m_1u_1}{m_1 + m_2}\right)^2 \frac{1}{\frac{1}{2}m_1u_1^2}$$

$$= \frac{m_1}{m_1 + m_2}, \text{ i.e.,} < 1$$

showing that *K.E. after collision* < *K.E. before collision.*

As already pointed out, this loss of *K.E.* on collision manifests itself in the form of heat energy in the system due to increased vibrations of the atoms of the two particles.

Let us now consider the problem if the two particles be in the *centre-of-mass frame of reference* in which the centre of mass remains at rest and hence the momentum both before and after the collision is *zero.*

Since the velocity of the centre of mass in the laboratory frame of reference is $\vec{v} = m_1\vec{u_1}/(m_1 + m_2)$ in accordance with relation (*iii*), § 6.3, it follows that the centre of mass frame moves this velocity $(\vec{V})$ relative to the laboratory frame. The initial velocities of the two particles in this frame. The initial velocities of the two particles in this frame are, therefore,

$$\vec{u_1'} = \vec{u_1} - \vec{V} = \vec{u_1} - m_1\vec{u_1}/(m_1 + m_2) = m_2\vec{u_1}/(m_1 + m_2)$$

and $$\vec{u_2'} = \vec{u_2} - \vec{V} = 0 - \vec{V} = -m_1\vec{u_1}/(m_1 + m_2).$$

After the collision, the two particles stick together, their combined mass being $(m_1 + m_2)$ but they must be at rest since their momentum in this frame must remain *zero*. Relative to the laboratory frame, however the, velocity of the combined mass in the centre-of-mass frame must naturally be the same as that of the frame itself, *viz.*, $\vec{V} = m_1\vec{u_1}/(m_1 + m_2)$ which, it will be readily seen, is the *same* as the velocity $\vec{v}$ of the combined mass in the laboratory frame.

(II) Elastic one-dimensional collision. Again, if m_1 and m_2 be the masses of two particles, $\vec{u_1}, \vec{u_2}$ and $\vec{v_1}, \vec{v_2}$, their respective velocities before and after a *head-on collision along the line joining their centres*, we have, *momentum equation,* $m_1\vec{u}_1 + m_2\vec{u}_2 = m_1\vec{v}_1 + m_2\vec{v}_2$ ...(*i*)

and *K.E. equation,* $\frac{1}{2}m_1\vec{u}_1^2+\frac{1}{2}m_2\vec{u}_2^2 = \frac{1}{2}m_1\vec{v}_1^2+\frac{1}{2}m_2\vec{v}_2^2$ ...(*ii*)

Or, writing these two equations as

$$m_1(u_1 - v_1) = m_2(v_2 - u_2) \quad ...(iii)$$

and $$m_1(u_1^2 - v_1^2) = m_2(v_1^2 - u_2^2) \quad ...(iv)$$

and dividing the latter by the former, we have

$$u_1 + v_1 = v_2 + u_2. \quad \text{Or,} \quad u_1 - u_2 = v_2 - v_1, \quad ...(v)$$

showing that *in an elastic one-dimensional collision, the relative velocity with which the two particles approach each other before collision is equal to the relative velocity with which they recede from each other after collision.*

As for the values of the velocities v_1 and v_2 of the particles after collision, we have from relation (*v*) above

$$v_2 = v_1 + u_1 - u_2 \text{ and } v_1 = v_2 - u_1 + u_2$$

Substituting this value of v_2 in relation (*iii*) above and solving for v_1 and, similarly, substituting the value of v_1 in (*iii*) above and solving for v_2, we have

$$v_1 = \left(\frac{m_1 - m_2}{m_1 + m_2}\right)u_1 + \left(\frac{2m_2}{m_1 + m_2}\right)u_2 \quad ...(vi)$$

and $$v_2 = \left(\frac{2m_1}{m_1 + m_2}\right)u_1 + \left(\frac{m_2 - m_1}{m_1 + m_2}\right)u_2. \quad ...(vii)$$

Now, the following special cases of interest arise:

(*a*) **When the colliding particles have the same mass.** In this case, $m_1 = m_2$. So that, from relations (*vi*) and (*vii*) we have $v_1 = u_2$ and $v_2 = u_1$, *i.e., in one-dimensional elastic collision of two particles of equal mass, the particles simply interchange their velocities on collision.*

(*b*) **If one of the particles be also initially at rest.** Let the second particle be at rest. Then, $u_2 = 0$ and, therefore, from relations (*vi*) and (*vii*), we clearly have

$$v_1 = \left(\frac{m_1 - m_2}{m_1 + m_2}\right)u_1 \quad ...(viii)$$

and $$v_2 = \left(\frac{2m_1}{m_1 + m_2}\right)u_1 \quad ...(ix)$$

and, since $m_1 = m_2$, we have $v_1 = 0$ and $v_2 = u_1$,

i.e., the first particle comes to rest on collision and the second particle acquires the initial velocity of the first.

(*c*) **If the particle at rest be very much more massive than the other.** Let the second particle, at rest, be much more massive than the first, so that m_1 is negligible compared with m_2. Then, we have, from relations (*viii*) and (*ix*),

$$v_1 \approx -u_1 \text{ and } v_2 \approx 0,$$

indicating that *when a lighter particle collides against a much more massive particle at rest the latter continues to remain at rest and the velocity of the former gets reversed.*

A common example of this type is the dropping of a steel ball on an equally hard horizontal surface on the ground. The collision thus occurs between the ball and the earth. Since the latter is very much more massive and is at rest, the velocity of the ball gets reversed on impact and it rises to the same height from which it was dropped.

(*d*) **If the particle at rest be very much lighter than the other.** Again, let the second particle be at rest and very much lighter than the first, so that now m_2 is negligible compared with m_1. Then, we have, from relations (*viii*) and (*ix*) above,

$$v_1 \approx u_1 \text{ and } v_2 \approx 2u_1$$

i.e., the velocity of the massive particle remains practically unaltered on collision with the lighter particle at rest and the lighter particle acquires nearly twice the initial velocity of the massive particle.

We can see from the above why in a reactor, hydrogen in used as a moderator for slowing down neutrons, produced by the fission of Uranium atoms, so as to enable them to produce more fissions. It is obviously because the hydrogen nucleus (*i.e.*, the proton) has nearly the same mass as a neutron and hence in a head-on collision with a hydrogen nucleus at rest, the neutrons are thus almost brought to rest or greatly slowed down. If a massive nucleus like that of lead were to be used as the target, the neutrons will simply bounce back from it with the same velocity with which they impinge on it; and if the target were a lighter one, like an electron, for example, the neutrons will simply continue to move with their original velocity after collision with it. There are, of course, other factors too in the choice of a suitable moderator but from considerations of momentum and energy, a hydrogen nucleus as a stationary target is one of the best bets.

(*iii*) **Elastic collision in two or three dimensions.** In the case of a two or three-dimensional elastic collision between two particles, the initial velocities of the particles and the conservation laws of momentum and energy alone are not enough for the determination of the velocities of the particles after collision, because the velocity of each particle has three components but we have only four known relations between them, *viz.*, three for the conservation of momentum for each of the three dimensions and one for the conservation of energy. More information is, therefore, needed to be able to calculate the final velocities of the particles and the simplest one is the angle of deflection of one of the particles.

Let us discuss the problem in both the laboratory frame of reference and the centre-of-mass frame of reference.

(*a*) **In the laboratory frame of reference.** Let a particle of mass m_1, moving with velocity $\vec{u_1}$ collide with a particle of mass m_2, initially at rest (*i.e.*, $\vec{u_2} = 0$) in the laboratory frame of reference (Fig. 6.7). Let it be deflected or *scattered* at an angle θ_1 with its initial direction, after collision, with velocity $\mathbf{v}_1$, where $\mathbf{u}_1$ and $\mathbf{v}_1$ lie in the *X-Y* plane. Obviously, then, the velocity $\mathbf{v}_2$ of m_2, after collision, making an angle θ_2 with the original direction, will have no component in the *z*-direction for the simple reason that $m_1\mathbf{u}_1$ and $m_1\mathbf{v}_1$ have no *z*-components. Now, from the law of conservation of momentum, we have

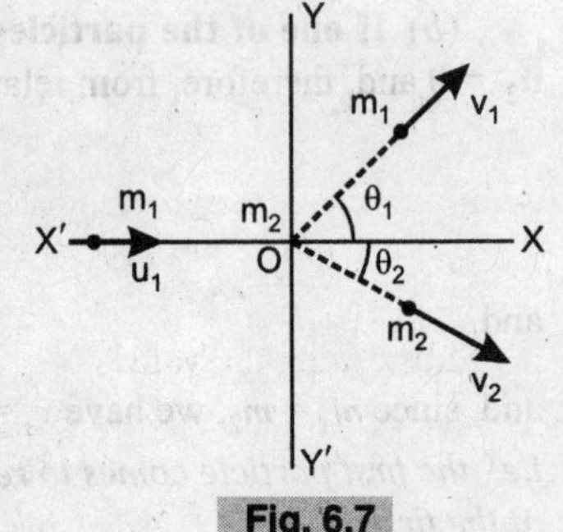

Fig. 6.7

for the x-component of the motion,

$$m_1u_1 = m_1v_1 \cos\theta_1 + m_2v_2 \cos\theta_2 \qquad ...(i)$$

and *for the y-component of the motion* $0 = m_1v_1 \sin\theta_1 - m_2v_2 \sin\theta_2$ ...(*ii*)

And, from the law of conservation of energy, we have

$$\frac{1}{2}m_1u_1^2 = \frac{1}{2}m_1v_1^2 + \frac{1}{2}m_2v_2^2. \qquad ...(iii)$$

If we know the initial conditions, *viz.*, m_1, m_2 and u_1, we have to determine four unknown quantities, *i.e.*, v_1, v_2, θ_1 and θ_2 and have only three equations connecting them. We must, therefore, be given the value of one more quantity, such as θ_1, to be able to determine the motion after collision.

Solving these equations, then, for v_1, v_2 and θ_2, in the particular case when $m_1 = m_2$, *i.e.*, when the two masses are equal, we obtain $v_1 = u_1 \cos\theta_1$ and from relation (*iii*), therefore, $v_2^2 = u_1^2 - v_1^2$, whence v_2 can be obtained.

Finally, $\sin\theta_2 = \dfrac{v_1}{v_2}\sin\theta_1$. So that, knowing v_1, v_2 and θ_1 (given), we can also determine θ_2, where the sum of θ_1 and θ_2 is always 90°, showing that the two equal masses move, after collision, in directions perpendicular to each other.

This method is somewhat lengthy and laborious. If, however, we view the problem in the centre-of-mass frame, its solution becomes very much simpler and perhaps also a little more instructive, as will be seen from the following.

(*b*) **In the centre-of-mass frame of reference.** As pointed out earlier under case (*i*) above, the centre-of-mass frame of reference moves with velocity $\vec{V} = m_1\vec{u}_1/(m_1+m_2)$ relative to the laboratory frame of reference, so that the centre of mass remains at rest in this frame. The initial and final velocities of the two particles (m_1 and m_2) in this frame of reference are thus given by

$$\vec{u}_1 = \vec{u}_1 - \vec{V},\ \vec{u}_2 = -\vec{V},\ \vec{v}_1' = \vec{v}_1 - \vec{V} \text{ and } \vec{v}_2' = \vec{v}_2 - \vec{V}.$$

Since the centre of mass throughout remains at rest in this reference frame, the total momentum is always zero and hence the momentum of the two particles must always be equal and opposite, clearly implying that the velocities $\vec{v}_1'$ and of $\vec{v}_2'$ the two particles, after collision, must be oppositely directed and inclined at the same angle to the initial direction of motion of the particles, as shown in Fig. 6.8. We thus have

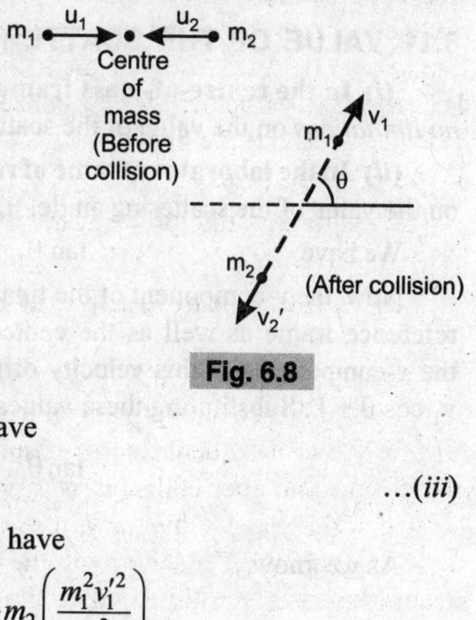

$$m_1\vec{u}_1' = -m_2\vec{u}_2' \qquad \ldots(i)$$

$$m_1\vec{v}_1' = --m_2\vec{v}_2'^{*} \qquad \ldots(ii)$$

Fig. 6.8

Whence, $\vec{v}_2' = \dfrac{m_1}{m_2}\vec{v}_1'$ and $\vec{u}_2' = \dfrac{m_1}{m_2}\vec{u}_1'$

Since total energy remains conserved on collision, we have

$$\frac{1}{2}m_1u_1'^2 + \frac{1}{2}m_2u_2'^2 = \frac{1}{2}m_1v_1'^2 + \frac{1}{2}m_2v_2'^2. \qquad \ldots(iii)$$

Substituting the values of $\mathbf{u}_2'$ and $\mathbf{v}_2'$, obtained above, we have

$$\frac{1}{2}m_1u_1'^2 + \frac{1}{2}m_2\left(\frac{m_1^2u_1'^2}{m_2^2}\right)\frac{1}{2}m_1v_1'^2 + \frac{1}{2}m_2\left(\frac{m_1^2v_1'^2}{m_2^2}\right)$$

Or, $$\frac{1}{2}m_1u_1'^2\left(1+\frac{m_1}{m_2}\right) = \frac{1}{2}m_1v_1'^2\left(1+\frac{m_1}{m_2}\right)$$

which gives $$\frac{1}{2}m_1u_1'^2 = \frac{1}{2}m_1v_1'^2. \quad \text{Or, } u_1' = v_1'.$$

---

* This may be easily shown by substituting the values of $\mathbf{u}'_1$ and $\mathbf{u}'_2$. Thus,

$$m_1\mathbf{u}_1' = m_1(\mathbf{u}_1 - \mathbf{V}) = m_1\left(\mathbf{u}_1 - \frac{m_1\mathbf{u}_1}{m_1+m_2}\right) = \frac{m_1m_2\mathbf{u}_1}{m_1+m_2}.$$

And $$-m_2u_2' = m_2\mathbf{V} = m_2\left(\frac{m_1\mathbf{u}_1}{m_1+m_2}\right) = \frac{m_1m_2\mathbf{u}_1}{m_1+m_2}$$

Similarly, it can be shown that $m_2\mathbf{v}_1' = -m_1\mathbf{v}_2'$

And, hence from energy relation (*iii*) above, $\vec{u'_2} = \vec{v'_2}$.

Thus, in the centre-of-mass frame of reference, the magnitudes of the velocities of the particles remain unaltered in an elastic collision.

Advantages of Studying Collision Process. Various types of interactions and forces are operating in nature at microscopic as well as macroscopic levels. A study of collision process *i.e.* relative motion between the two interacting particles helps us to understand the basic nature and characteristics of these interactions and forces. This is done by measuring the initial and final energy and linear as well as angular momentum of the participating particles in accordance with the laws of conservation of energy and momentum.

The deflection of the path of a comet passing near the solar system and the elliptic path of planets within the solar system helps us to understand the nature of gravitational forces.

Collision between molecules of gases according to Kinetic theory leads to understanding of inter-atomic and intermolecular forces.

Scattering of α-particles in Rutherford scattering, scattering of high energy photons in Compton scattering, nuclear reactions involving high energy electrons, protons, neutrons, deutrons and α-particles, scattering of slow neutrons by nuclei and emission of α and β particles from radioactive nuclei help us to understand the nature of nuclear forces, properties of the nucleus and atomic structure.

6.11 VALUE OF THE SCATTERING ANGLE

(*i*) In the centre-of-mass frame of reference. In this frame of reference, there are absolutely *no limitations* on the value of the scattering angle θ, so that it can have *all* possible values.

(*ii*) In the laboratory frame of reference. In this frame of reference, there are some restrictions on the value of the scattering angle, θ_1, (Fig. 6.7), as will be clear from the following:

We have $\tan\theta_1 = v_1 \sin\theta_1 / v_1 \cos\theta_1$.

Now, the *y*-component of the final velocity of the first particle being the same in the laboratory reference frame as well as the center-of-mass frame, we have $v_1 \sin\theta_1 = v'_1 \sin\theta$. And, since the *x*-components of this velocity differ by V in the two frames of reference, we have $v_1 \cos\theta_1 = v'_1 \cos\theta + V$. Substituting these values in the relation above, we, therefore, have

$$\tan\theta_1 = \frac{v'_1 \sin\theta}{v'_1 \cos\theta + V} = \frac{\sin\theta}{\cos\theta + (V/v'_1)} \qquad \ldots(i)$$

As we know,

$$V = \frac{m_1 u_1}{m_1 + m_2} = \frac{m_1(u'_1 + V)}{m_1 + m_2}$$

$$= \frac{m_1 u'_1}{m_1 + m_2} + \frac{m_1 V}{m_1 + m_2} \qquad [\because u_1 = u'_1 + V]$$

Or,

$$V\left(1 - \frac{m_1}{m_1 + m_2}\right) = \frac{m_1 u'_1}{m_1 + m_2}.$$

Or,

$$V\left(\frac{m_2}{m_1 + m_2}\right) = \frac{m_1 u'_1}{m_1 + m_2},$$

whence,

$$V = \frac{m_1}{m_2} u'_1 = \frac{m_1}{m_2} v'_1 \qquad [\because u'_1 = v'_1]$$

Substituting this value of V in relation (iv) above, we have

$$\tan\theta_1 = \frac{\sin\theta}{\cos\theta + (m_1/m_2)} \qquad \ldots(ii)$$

This shows that

(*a*) **If $m_1 > m_2$**, so that m_1/m_2 a little > 1, the denominator can never be zero and hence tan θ_1 can never be ∞. And, therefore, θ_1 must be less than 90°;

(*b*) **If $m_1 = m_2$**, so that $m_1/m_2 = 1$, the denominator can be zero for cos $\theta = -1$ and, therefore, tan θ_1 can be ∞. Thus, in this case, θ_1 can have any value up to the limiting value of 90°;

(*c*) **If $m_1 < m_2$**, so that $m_1/m_2 < 1$, the value of tan θ_1 can also be negative. In this case alone, therefore, **all values of θ_1 can be possible.**

If follows from case (*a*) that in an elastic collision, *if a massive particle collides against a lighter one at rest, it can never bounce back along its original path.* On the other hand, it follows from case (*c*) *that if a lighter particle collides against a massive one at rest, it may well bounce back along its original path.* And, it follows from case (*b*) that in an elastic collision between two particles of equal mass, one of which is initially at rest, the two particles move at right angles to each other after the collision, as mentioned already under 6.10(III) (*a*).

6.12. SYSTEMS OF VARIABLE MASS—THE ROCKET

In our discussion of the conservation of linear momentum, we have so far death with systems whose mass remains constant. We now propose to consider those whose mass is *variable, i.e.*, those in which mass enters or leaves the system. A typical case in that of a *rocket* from which hot gases keep on escaping, thereby continuously decreasing its mass.

Principle. Rocket propulsion is based on the principle of *conservation of linear momentum.* A rocket may use either a liquid or a solid fuel. In the former case the fuel (like liquid hydrogen or liquid paraffin) and a suitable oxidiser (like oxygen, hydrogen peroxide or nitric acid), stored up in separate chambers, are injected into a *combustion chamber* where the fuel is burnt (Fig. 6.9). In the latter case, the fuel itself carries its own oxidiser (as, for example, gun powder) and hence a separate chamber for it is not necessary. In either case, the large quantity of the heat of combustion produced greatly raises the pressure inside the chamber, resulting in the burnt up gases (like CO, steam etc.) issuing out of an orifice at the back or the tail end of the rocket in the form of a high velocity stream, called the jet, as indicated in the Figure. In consequence, the rocket is propelled forwards (*i.e.*, opposite to the direction of the jet), since the momentum lost by the jet of fuel gases must be equal to the momentum gained by the rocket.

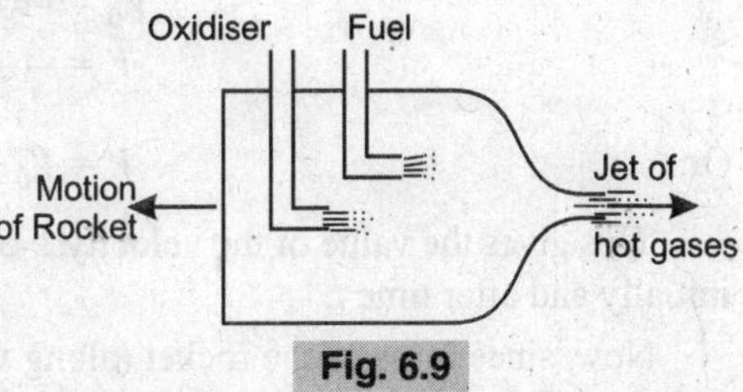

Fig. 6.9

Theory. Let M be the *mass* of the rocket (including that of its fuel and oxidiser) and V, its velocity at any given instant t in the inertial frame of the laboratory. Further, let α be the *rate of change of mass* of the rocket due to the escape of the hot gases through the orifice at its tail end with an *exhaust velocity* $-v$ relative to it. Them, clearly, *rate of change of mass of the rocket* = $dM/dt = -\alpha$, the negative sign indicating that the change of mass is a *decrease* in mass.

Assuming the forward velocity of the rocket to be along the same line with the oppositely directed velocity v of the hot gases or the jet, we have

velocity of the jet in the laboratory frame $= -v + V = (V - v)$

$\therefore$ *rate of change of momentum of the jet issuing out of the rocket,*

or $$\textit{force acting on it} = -\alpha(V - v) = \frac{dM}{dt}(V - v)$$

Hence, in accordance with Newton's third law of motion, this must also be equal to the force acting on the rocket, tending to move it forwards.

So that, *force acting on the rocket, propelling it forwards* $= \dfrac{dM}{dt}(V - v)$, neglecting the weight (Mg) of the rocket, or the force of attraction on it due to the earth, in comparison with it.

Since M is the mass and V, the *velocity* of the rocket at the instant considered, we have also, (in accordance with Newton's second law), force acting on the rocket given by $d(MV)/dt$. We therefore, have

$$\frac{d}{dt}(MV) = \frac{dM}{dt}(V-v). \qquad ...(i)$$

Or,
$$\frac{dM}{dt}V + M\frac{dV}{dt} = \frac{dM}{dt}V - \frac{dM}{dt}v$$

Or,
$$M\frac{dV}{dt} = -\frac{dM}{dt}v, \qquad ...(ii)$$

which gives the force (*i.e., mass × acceleration*) or the **thrust** on the rocket at the instant *t*, *i.e.*, **force or thrust** $F = -\frac{dM}{dt}v$.

We may re-write equation (*ii*) above as $dV = -\frac{dM}{M}v$,

when, on integrating it with respect to *t*, we have

$$\int\frac{dV}{dt}dt = -\frac{1}{M}\int\frac{dM}{dt}vdt. \text{ Or, } V = -v\log_e M + C,$$

where C is a constant of integration.

If M_0 be the mass of the rocket and V_0, its velocity at $t = 0$, (where V_0 would obviously be *zero* if the rocket just takes off from its launching pad), we have

$$V_0 = -v\log_e M_0 + C, \text{ whence, } C = V_0 + v\log_e M_0$$
$$V = -v\log_e M + V_0\log_e M_0.$$

Or,
$$V = V_0 + v\log_e\frac{M_0}{M}. \qquad ...(iii)$$

This gives the value of the velocity V of the rocket at instant t in terms of the mass of the rocket initially and after time t.

Now, since mass of the rocket (along with the fuel and the oxidiser left in it) is M after time t and since the mass decreases at the rate α, clearly, $M = (M_0 - \alpha t)$, *i.e.*,

$$M = M_0\left(1 - \frac{1}{M_0}\alpha t\right).$$

Denoting α/M_0, the *rate of change of mass in terms of the initial mass* M_0, by β, we have

$$M = M_0(1 - \beta t).$$

Substituting this value of M in relation (*iii*) above, we have

$$V = V_0 + v\log_e\left(\frac{M_0}{M_0(1-\beta t)}\right) = V_0 + v\log_e\left(\frac{1}{1-\beta t}\right)$$

Or,
$$V = V_0 - v\log_e(1 - \beta t), \qquad ...(iv)$$

which gives the velocity of the rocket at the instant t in terms of β (the rate of change of mass of the rocket in terms of its initial mass).

The distance covered by the rocket in time t can be easily obtained by integrating expression (*iii*) or (*iv*) with respect to t.

In case the weight of the rocket is taken into account, the equation of motion (*i*) for a rocket moving vertically upwards becomes

$$\frac{d}{dt}(MV) = \frac{dM}{dt}(V-v) - Mg.$$

Or,
$$\frac{dM}{dt}V + M\frac{dV}{dt} = \frac{dM}{dt}V - \frac{dM}{dt}v - Mg.$$

Or, $$M\frac{dV}{dt} = -\frac{dM}{dt}v - Mg, \text{ Whence, } \frac{dV}{dt} = -\frac{dM}{Mdt}v - g,$$

integrating which with respect to t, we have

$$\int\frac{dV}{dt}dt = -v\int\frac{dM}{Mdt}dt - \int g dt. \text{ Or, } V = -v\log_e M - gt + C.$$

Since at $t = 0$, $M = M_0$ and $V = V_0$, we have $V_0 = -v\log_e M_0 + C$. Or, $C = V_0 + v\log_e M_0$. So that,

$$V = -v\log_e M - gt + V_0 + v\log_e M_0.$$

Or, $$V = V_0 + v\log_e\frac{M_0}{M} - gt. \quad ...(v)$$

Again, since $M = M_0(1 - \beta t)$, we have

$$V = V_0 - v\log_e(1 - \beta t) - gt. \quad ...(vi)$$

It will be noted that both relation (*v*) and (*vi*) for the velocity of the rocket are essentially the same as (*iii*) and (*iv*) respectively, with the additional term $-gt$ (in view of the downward pull due to gravity), where t is the time of combustion of the fuel.

In case t be small, the addition of the term $-gt$ hardly makes any difference, *i.e.*, there is hardly any appreciable reduction in the value of V.

It t be large, however, *i.e.*, if the fuel is burnt at a slower rate, the term $-gt$ may become appreciably large and may slow down or even stop the ascent of the rocket. The rate of fuel combustion has, in fact, to be judiciously regulated, since both a slower and a more rapid rate of combustion are, for various reasons, equally undesirable.

A glance at the expressions for velocity (V) of the rocket will show that to obtain a higher value of the rocket velocity we must have (*i*) *a higher exhaust velocity* v and (*ii*) *a higher value of* M_0/M *(or of* β*) i.e., a higher loss of mass, so that the final mass of the rocket may be very much smaller than its initial mass.*

Now, the exhaust velocity depends upon the design for the nozzle as also upon the temperature and pressure developed inside the combustion chamber, the highest theoretical value possible being the *root mean square velocity* of the gas molecules at the temperature prevailing in the combustion chamber. Since, however, the temperature can hardly ever exceed 3000°C, the practical limit to the value of the exhaust velocity works out to 2 km/sec.

Then, again, the ratio M_0/M can at best be 10% of the initial value M_0, (even if the whole of the fuel is burnt, so that M is only the mass of the empty containers), but, its advantage is more than offset by a smaller exhaust velocity in this case.

As can be easily calculated from expression (*iii*) above, with an exhaust velocity of 2 km/sec, initial velocity (V_0) of the rocket *zero* and the ratio $M_0/M = 10$, the velocity (V) of the rocket works out to $0 + 2\log_e 10 = 2 \times 2.3026 = 4.6052$ km/sec.

This is less by far than the escape velocity 11.2 km/sec necessary to be able to escape from the gravitational field of the earth, or even the orbiting velocity 8 km/sec, necessary to be able to orbit around the earth close to its surface.

It can be easily seen that, with the exhaust velocity $v = 2$ km/sec, in order that a rocket may attain a velocity V equal to the escape velocity 11.2 km/sec, the mass ratio M_0/M must be 270 (see worked example (23) or even a bit more, actually, in view of the fact that the rocket will encounter, and will have to overcome, the resistance of the air. This means that a little more than 270 kg of the fuel will be consumed for every 1 kg mass of the rocket that leaves the earth. In the present stage of its development no single stage rocket is capable of such a performance and we have, therefore, to use a *multistage, i.e.,* a *two or three stage rocket* to achieve the purpose.

A multistage rocket is just a combination of rockets, either (*i*) joined consecutively, *i.e.*, in series, (*ii*) *one inside the other*, or (*iii*) with the rear part of one inside the nozzle of the other, as shown diagrammatically in Fig. 6.10. In all the three types, the first stage is the largest in dimensions as well as in weight, and the last stage the smallest and the lightest.

Naturally, the first stage rocket is used first and when its fuel is all burnt up and it has done its job it gets detached and is discarded, with the second stage taking over the task of producing further acceleration. This too, in its turn, is discarded when its fuel is burnt up the third stage rocket takes over. The velocity thus goes on increasing at each stage by the same amount as it does in a single stage rocket. The fuel consumption and the thrust for the first stage are about 100 times more than for the third stage and the fuel stock carried by it about 60 times that carried by the third stage.

Finally, a word may as well be said here as to the shape of the rocket. As can be readily seen, a rocket is subjected to intense air pressure during it upward flight through the atmosphere and a lot of heat is generated due to the viscous friction of the air. Both these factors are taken into account in designing it. Its frame is made of a heat-resisting material, with its velocity during its flight through the denser regions of the atmosphere kept sufficiently low and its body is given a cylindrical and *tapering, stream line* form to reduce the air pressure on each individual part of it to the very minimum, its overall shape resembling that of a cigar.

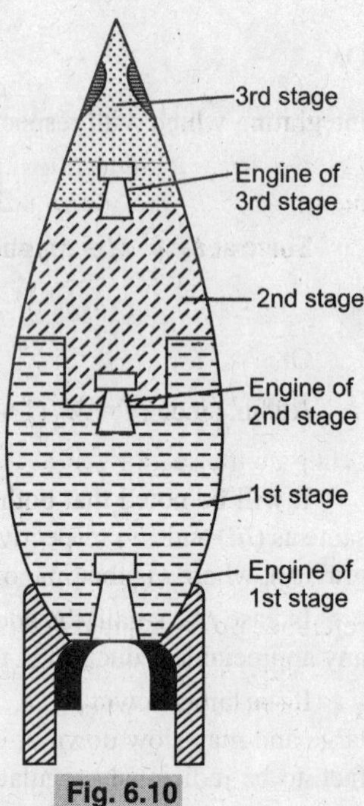

Fig. 6.10

6.13 ANGULAR MOMENTUM — TORQUE

The angular momentum of a particle about a point fixed in an intertial frame is *the moment of its linear momentum about that point*. That is why it is also called **moment of momentum**. It is usually denoted by the symbol $\vec{J}$ and is measured by the *product of the linear momentum* $\vec{p}(=m\vec{v})$ *of the particle and its vector distance* $\vec{r}$ *from the fixed or the reference point in the inertial frame.* Thus,

$$J = \vec{r} \times \vec{p} = m(\vec{r} \times \vec{v}) \qquad \text{...I [where } \vec{p} = m\vec{v}\text{]}$$

It is obviously a *vector quantity* and its direction, perpendicular to both $\vec{r}$ and $\vec{p}$(or $\vec{v}$), is given by the *right hand screw rule*. So that, in the case of a particle describing a circular motion its value is equal to $m\omega^2 r = mvr$ (where v is the linear velocity of the particle) and is perpendicular to the plane of the circle described, in the same direction with ω (fig. 6.11).

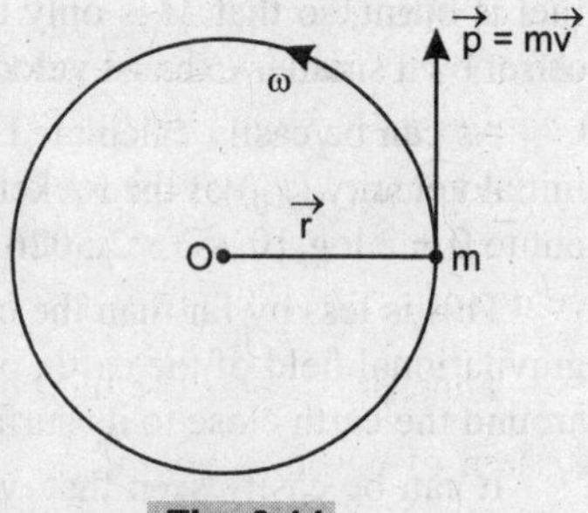

A component of the angular momentum about any axis (*i.e.*, a line) passing through the fixed or the reference point is referred to as the angular momentum of the particle about that axis (or line).

Fig. 6.11

The units of angular momentum in the *C.G.S.* and the *RMKS* (or *SI*) systems are respectively *gm-cm*^{2}*/sec* or *erg-sec* and *kg-m*^{2}*/sec* or *joule/sec*.

Relation I holds good even for a system of particles, each free to move independently of the other or compactly arranged to form a rigid body. Thus, if $\vec{J_1}, \vec{J_2}, \vec{J_3}$ *etc.* be the angular momenta of the different particles of the system about the fixed or the reference point, the angular momentum of the whole system about that point is given by

$$\vec{J} = \vec{J}_1 + \vec{J}_2 + \vec{J}_3 + \ldots = (\vec{r}_1 \times m\vec{v}_1) + (\vec{r}_2 \times m\vec{v}_2) + (\vec{r}_3 \times m\vec{v}_3) + \ldots$$

Or, $$\vec{J} = \Sigma(\vec{r} \times m\,\vec{v}) = \Sigma(\vec{r} \times \vec{p}),$$

i.e., the angular momentum of the whole system about the point is the vector sum of the angular momenta of the individual particles about that point.

Torque. Differentiating relation I above with respect to *t*, we have

$$\frac{d\vec{J}}{dt} = \frac{d}{dt}(\vec{r} \times \vec{p}) = \frac{d\vec{r}}{dt} \times \vec{p} + \vec{r} \times \frac{d\vec{p}}{dt}.$$

Now, $\frac{d\vec{r}}{dt} \times \vec{p} = \vec{v} \times m\,\vec{v} = 0$ and $d\vec{p}/dt$ = *rate of change of linear momentum* or the force $\vec{F}$ acting on the particle. So that,

$$\frac{d\vec{J}}{dt} = \vec{r} \times \frac{d\vec{p}}{dt} = \vec{r} \times \vec{F}.$$

The vector product $\vec{r} \times \vec{F}$ is called *torque** (or *moment of the force*) about the fixed or the reference point and is represented by the symbol τ.

Thus, the time rate of change of angular momentum of a particle about a point gives the torque τ about that point, where

$$\vec{\tau} = \vec{r} \times \vec{F} = d\vec{J}/dt. \qquad \ldots\text{II}$$

In the case of a system of particles, independent of each other or forming a rigid body, we have seen above how $\vec{J} = \Sigma(\vec{r} \times m\,\vec{v}) = \Sigma(\vec{r} \times \vec{p})$. It follows, therefore, that

$$\vec{\tau} = d\vec{J}/dt = \Sigma\,\vec{r} \times \frac{d}{dt}(m\,\vec{v}) = \Sigma(\vec{r} \times \vec{F}),$$

i.e., the torque or the time rate of change of angular momentum of the system about the fixed or the reference point is the sum of the torques of all the external forces acting on the system. The reason why we explicitly say *external* forces is that the internal forces all form collinear action-and-reaction pairs of equal and opposite forces, having equal and opposite moments about the given point and their sum is, therefore, *zero, i.e.*, they produce no effect.

As will be readily seen, *angular momentum is the rotational analogue of linear momentum.* Just as the rate of change of linear momentum of a particle gives the force acting upon it, so also the rate of change of angular momentum of the particle gives the torque acting upon it. And, as we shall shortly see, just as *linear momentum* = (*mass*) (*linear velocity*) or *mv*, we have, for a rigid body, *angular momentum* = (*moment of inertia*) (*angular velocity*) or *Iω*.

Another expression for angular momentum of a system. Sometimes it is found to be more convenient to express the angular momentum of a system of particles in terms of the velocity of the centre of mass and the velocities of the particles of the system relative to the centre of mass.

Thus, if $\vec{R}$ and $\vec{V}$ be the *position vector* and *velocity* respectively of the centre of mass of a system of particles relative to a fixed or a reference point, and $\vec{r}_c$ and $\vec{v}_c$, the *position vector* and *velocity* of a particle of mass *m* of the system, *relative to the centre of mass*, the position vector and velocity of the particle *relative to the fixed or reference point* will clearly be $\vec{r} = \vec{R} + \vec{r}_c$ and $\vec{v} = \vec{V} + \vec{v}_c$ respectively. Hence, the *angular momentum of the system about the fixed or the reference point* will, as just explained above, be given by

$$\vec{J} = \Sigma m(\vec{R} + \vec{r}_c) \times (\vec{V} \times \vec{v}_c) = \Sigma m(\vec{R} + \vec{V}) + \Sigma m(\vec{V} \times \vec{v}_c) + \Sigma m(\vec{R}_c \times \vec{V}) + \Sigma m(\vec{r}_c \times \vec{v}_c)$$

* From the Latin word '*torquere*' meaning '*to twist*'.

Now, $\quad \vec{r}_c = (\vec{r} - \vec{R})$ and $\because m\vec{r}_c = m\vec{r} - m\vec{R}$

Or, $\quad \Sigma m\vec{r}_c = \Sigma m\vec{r} - \Sigma m\vec{R} = \Sigma m\vec{r} - M\vec{R} \qquad [\because \Sigma m = M$, mass of the system.]

But, as we know, the inherent property of the centre of mass demands that

$$M\vec{R} = m_1\vec{r}_1 + m_2\vec{r}_2 + \ldots = \Sigma m\vec{r}$$

We, therefore, have $\Sigma m\vec{r} - M\vec{R} = 0$ or $\Sigma m\vec{r}_c = 0$.

Similarly, $\quad \Sigma m\vec{v}_c = 0$.

So that, the above relation for $\vec{J}$ simplifies to

$$\vec{J} = \vec{R} \times M\vec{V} + \Sigma(\vec{r}_c \times m\vec{v}_c).$$

Here, clearly, $\Sigma(\vec{r}_c \times m\vec{v}_c)$ is the angular momentum of the system about the centre of mass, say $\vec{J}_{c.m}$ and $M\vec{V} = \vec{p}$, the momentum of the centre of mass or the total linear momentum of the system. We, therefore, have

$$\vec{J} = \vec{R} \times p + \vec{J}_{C.M.} \qquad \ldots\text{III}$$

i.e., the total angular momentum of the system about the fixed or the reference point is the vector sum of the angular momentum of the centre of mass about that point and the angular momentum of the system about the centre of mass. The former depends upon the fixed or the reference point chosen and is referred to as the *orbital angular momentum* and the latter, which is independent of the fixed or the reference point, is called the *spin angular momentum.* So that, the *total angular momentum of the system is the vector sum of its orbital and spin angular momenta.*

Differentiating expression III above with respect to *t*, we have

torque acting on the system, $\vec{\tau} = \dfrac{d\vec{J}}{dt} = \dfrac{d\vec{J}_{c.m}}{dt} + \dfrac{d}{dt}(\vec{R} \times \vec{p}).$

If the centre of mass be chosen as the origin, so that it remains stationary, we have $\vec{p} = M\vec{V} = 0$ (since $\vec{V} = 0$). The second term in the expression for $\vec{\tau}$ above, therefore, vanishes and we have torque $\vec{\tau} = d\vec{J}_{c.m.}/dt$ and the body is said to be in a *state of spinning.*

Thus, each planet in the solar system possesses both an orbital and a spin angular momentum and its total angular momentum about the sun is the vector sum of the two. In the case of our own planet, *Earth*, the two momenta are inclined to each other at an angle of 23.5°. The sun alone in the solar system (considered in isolation from the rest of the universe) possess *zero orbital angular momentum* (because $\vec{V} = 0$) and it, therefore, has only spin angular momentum.

The total angular momentum of the solar system is thus the vector sum of all these orbital and spin angular momenta of the various planets, the contribution of the spin angular momentum of the sun itself being just 2%.

If, however, we consider the universe, as a whole with the centre of the galaxy as the origin, or the reference point, the sun too has an orbital angular momentum about the origin and thus possesses both types of angular momenta.

6.14 CONSERVATION OF ANGULAR MOMENTUM

We know that the external torque applied to a system of particles is given by the relation $\vec{\tau} = d\vec{J}/dt = \vec{r} \times \vec{F}$. If, therefore, the external torque be *zero*, we have $d\vec{J}/dt = 0$, *i.e.,* $\vec{J} = constant.$ This is the **principle or the law of conservation of angular momentum** and may be formally stated thus:

When the external torque (or the sum of external torques) applied to a system of particles is zero, the total angular momentum of the system remains conserved.

The law is not restricted to only closed orbits but applies equally well to open orbits as well as collisions.

Thus, if $\vec{J}_1, \vec{J}_2, \vec{J}_3$, etc. be the angular momenta of the different particles of a system, their sum total $\vec{J} = \vec{J}_1 + \vec{J}_2 = \vec{J}_3 + \ldots$ remains constant in the absence of any external torque applied to the system, though the particles may exchange momenta among themselves.

Similarly, in the case where the centre of mass is taken to be the origin, we have $\vec{\tau} = d\vec{J}_{c.m}/dt$. If, therefore, the external torque $\vec{\tau}$ be *zero*, we have $\vec{J}_{c.m.} =$ *constant*. This may be called the *law of conservation of spin angular momentum.*

It will be seen at once that just as the external force applied determines the motion of the centre of mass of a system; the external torque applied determines the rotation of the system about the centre of mass.

Now, from the relation for τ, mentioned above, *viz*, $\vec{\tau} = d\vec{J}/dt = \vec{r} \times \vec{F}$, it is abundantly clear that *the torque acting on a particle will be zero, and hence its angular momentum conserved, when (i) its position vector $\vec{r}$ is zero or (ii) the force $\vec{F}$ applied to it is zero or (iii) the direction of both $\vec{r}$ and $\vec{F}$ is the same, i.e.,* the line of action of force $\vec{F}$ passes through the fixed or the reference point.

The first two conditions are obvious by themselves and the third condition is satisfied in the case of *central forces, i.e.,* forces which are always directed towards (or away from) a fixed reference point. This will be seen from the following:

The magnitude of a central force on a particle depending only on the distance from the fixed or the reference point, we may represent it by $\vec{F} = \hat{r}f(r)$, where $\hat{r}$ is the *unit vector* along the direction of $\vec{r}$ and is equal to $\vec{r}/r$ and $f(r)$, a *scalar function* of distance $\vec{r}$.

$\therefore$ *torque acting on a particle under the action of a central force* is given by

$$\vec{\tau} = \frac{d\vec{J}}{dt} = \vec{r} \times \vec{F} = \vec{r} \times \hat{r}\, f(r) \;=\; f(r)(\vec{r} \times \vec{r}/r) = 0, \qquad [\because\ \vec{r} \times \vec{r} = 0]$$

showing that $\vec{J} = \vec{r} \times m\,\vec{v} =$ *constant.*

***i.e.*, the angular momentum of a particle moving under the influence of a central force always remains conserved.**

It follows, therefore, that $\vec{J}$ being constant, must be perpendicular to the plane containing $\vec{r}$ and $\vec{v}$ *i.e., the path of a particle under the influence of a central force must lie in a plane.*

Thus, since electrostatic forces are central forces, the angular momentum of the electron moving in its orbit around the proton in a hydrogen atom remains conserved.

Again, since gravitational forces too are central forces, the angular momenta of planets orbiting around the sun remain conserved (although they move in elliptical orbits) and so also of the satellites moving around a planet.

Let us examine the case of a planet moving around the sun *in an elliptical orbit* in a little more detail.

6.15 MOTION OF A PLANET IN AN ELLIPTICAL ORBIT AROUND THE SUN

The planets, as we know, move in elliptical orbits around the sun, with the sun at one of one foci. In fact, it is the centre of mass of the sun and the planet which should lie at this focus but, in view of the enormously greater mass of the sun compared with that of the planet, the centre of mass of the system (*i.e.*, of the sun and the planet) lies close to the centre of the sun itself which may, therefore, be assumed to lie there.

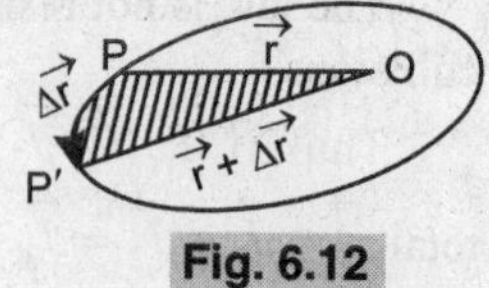

Fig. 6.12

Thus, let O be the centre of the sun lying at one focus of the ellipse and P and P', the two positions of the planet at instants t and $t + \Delta t$, given by the position vectors $\vec{r}$ and $\vec{r} + \Delta\vec{r}$ respectively, with the gravitational force on it due to the sun always directed towards the latter, (Fig. 6.12).

In this interval of time Δt the planet sweeps out, on account of its displacement $\Delta\vec{r}$, a vector areas $\Delta\vec{S}$ (shown shaded) $= \frac{1}{2}\vec{r}\times\Delta\vec{r}$.

$\therefore$ *Rate at which the radius vector sweeps out the area* $= \Delta\vec{S}/\Delta t = \frac{1}{2}\vec{r}\times\Delta\vec{r}/\Delta t$.

Or, in the limit $\Delta t \to 0$, we have $d\vec{S}/dt = \frac{1}{2}\vec{r}\times d\vec{r}/dt = \frac{1}{2}\vec{r}\times\vec{v}$

where $d\vec{S}/dt$ may be called the *areal velocity of the radius vector*.

Now, *angular momentum* $\vec{J} = \vec{r}\times m\vec{v}$; so that, $\vec{r}\times\vec{v} = \vec{J}/m$, and, therefore, *areal velocity of the radius vector,* $d\vec{S}/dt = \vec{J}/2m$.

Since $\vec{J}/2m$ is a constant, it follows that *the areal velocity of the radius vector remains constant under the influence of the central gravitational force.*

This is really **Kepler's second law** which states that *the radius vector from the sun to any planet sweeps out equal areas in equal time.*

A consequence of this is that *a planet moves faster at the point of its closet, than that of its farthest, approach to the sun.* This is obviously so because at these points the vector $\vec{r}$ is perpendicular to $\vec{v}$ (Fig. 6.13) and the angular momentum is thus equal to mvr. For the conservation of momentum, therefore, the angular momentum mv_2r_2 at the point of nearest approach must be equal to the angular momentum mv_1r_1 at the point farthest approach. We, therefore, have $mv_1r_1 = mv_2r_2$. Or $v_1r_1 = v_2r_2$, showing that *the larger velocity of the planet is associated with its shorter distance from the sun and vice versa.*

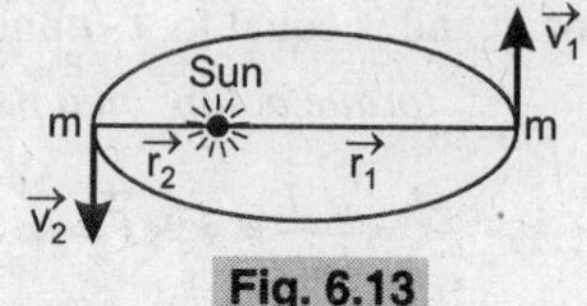

Fig. 6.13

An since the angular momentum $(\vec{J})$ remains constant, $\vec{J}/2m$ or the areal velocity of the radius vector too remains constant.

In the case of the earth, its orbital velocity is 30.26 km/sec when it is nearest the sun and 29.29 km/sec when it is farthest from it.

This result, arrived at by *Kepler* from his long and laborious calculations and most careful observations, is thus just a natural consequence of the law of conservation of angular momentum.

Interestingly enough, *Newton* used the reverse argument, half a century later, to show that the areal velocity $d\vec{S}/dt$ of the radius vector joining a planet and the sun being constant, the gravitational force is a central force.

6.16 CONSERVATION OF ANGULAR MOMENTUM OF A SYSTEM, A CONSEQUENCE OF ROTATIONAL INVARIANCE OF POTENTIAL ENERGY OF THE SYSTEM

Just as the conservation of linear momentum of a system of particles is a consequence of translational invariance of the potential energy of the system (§6.17), so also the conservation of angular momentum of a system of particles is a consequence of rotational invariance of the potential energy of the system, *i.e.*, *the angular momentum of the system remains conserved if its rotation does not bring about any change in its potential energy.*

This follows from the fact that the rotation of a system would normally require work to be done against any external torque that may be acting on the system; thus necessarily resulting in some change in its potential energy. In case, therefore, the rotation of the system brings about no change in its potential energy, the obvious inference is that no work is being done against any external torque or that, in other words, no external torque is acting on the system. And, as we know so well, in the absence of an external torque, the angular momentum of the system must remain conserved.

Analytically, we may proceed it a manner similar to that adopted in § 6.17, in the case of linear momentum.

Thus, let us consider first, for the sake of simplicity, a system consisting of only two particles having position vectors $\vec{r_1}$ and $\vec{r_2}$. Let these be rotated through any arbitrary angle about any arbitrary axis and let the rotated vectors be represented by $\Omega\vec{r_1}$ and $\Omega\vec{r_2}$ (where Ω is an operator and not a mere number), such that their lengths are the same as those of $\vec{r_1}$ and $\vec{r_2}$ respectively, indicating that, on rotation, the vectors $\vec{r_1}$ and $\vec{r_2}$ undergo no change in magnitude but only a change in direction.

Now, the rotational invariance of potential energy demands that the potential energy $U(\vec{r_1}, \vec{r_2})$ *before rotation* = the potential energy $U(\Omega\vec{r_1}, \Omega\vec{r_2})$ *after rotation*. This can obviously be possible only if $U(\vec{r_1}, \vec{r_2}) = U(\vec{r_1} - \vec{r_2})$ *and* $U(\Omega\vec{r_1}, \Omega\vec{r_2}) = U(\Omega\vec{r_1} - \Omega\vec{r_2})$, *i.e.*, if the potential energy depends only on the magnitude of the distance between the two particles, this magnitude being the *same* before and after the motion. In order that this be so, the force acting on the particles must be directed along the line $(\vec{r_2} - \vec{r_1})$, *i.e.*, it must be a *central force*. And since a central force gives rise to no torque on the system, its angular momentum remains conserved.

What is true for a system of two particles is equally true for a system consisting of any number of them, provided the potential energy depends on the magnitude of the distance between the various particles.

The conservation of angular momentum of a system is thus a natural corollary of the rotational invariance of its potential energy.

6.17 SOME ILLUSTRATIVE EXAMPLES OF CONSERVATION OF ANGULAR MOMENTUM

***(i)* Motion of a planet or a satellite in it orbit.** This has already been dealt with under § 6.15, where it has been shown (*a*) how to be able to conserve its angular momentum, a planet must move faster at its point of nearest approach to the sun than at the point of its farthest approach and also (*b*)how the principle of conservation of angular momentum has led to the deduction of Kepler's second law.

***(ii)* Scattering of a positive particle by a massive nucleus.** Suppose a positive particle, like a *proton* or an *alpha particle,* approaches a massive nucleus *N* of an atom, (Fig. 6.11), and that its velocity is not appreciably affected due to its passage into the atom. Then, clearly, as it approaches the (positive) nucleus of the atom, it experiences an electrostatic force of repulsion, varying inversely as the square of its distance from the nucleus. So that as it gets closer to the nucleus, this repulsive force on it goes on increasing. As a result, it gets deflected or scattered from its straight path (towards the nucleus) into a hyperbolic path, *PAP*′, as shown, with the nucleus *N* at its external focus.

Let the particle in question be a *proton*, of mass *m* and carrying a charge +*e*, and let the atomic number of the nucleus be *Z*, so that the charge on it is +*Ze*.

Suppose at an infinite distance from the nucleus where the repulsive force on it is zero*, the particle travels with velocity v_0 and enters the atom (with no appreciable change in its velocity)

* The nucleus may be supposed to have *infinite* mass, *so that its velocity of recoil may be negligibly small or zero and hence also its energy of recoil and the angular momentum imparted to it equal to zero.*

along the direction PO and that, on reaching the point A, the apse of the hyperbola, it proceeds along AP' such that PA and AP' make equal angles with the straight line from N passing through A.

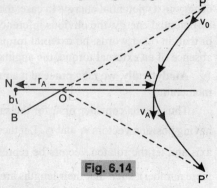

The perpendicular distance $NB = b$ between the nucleus and the initial direction PO of the particle is called the **impact parameter** or the **collision parameter** and distance $NA = r_s$ is called the **distance of closest approach** of the particle to the nucleus.

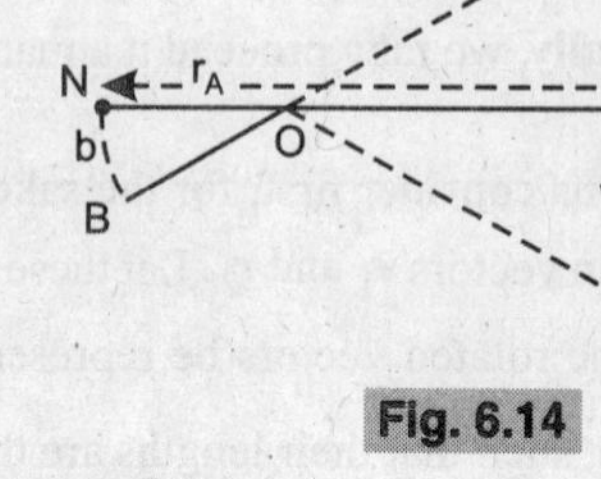

Fig. 6.14

Since electrostatic forces (like gravitational ones) are central forces, the angular momentum of the particle must remain conserved and we, therefore, have

$$mv_0 b = mv_A r_A,$$

whence, $$v_A = v_0 b/r_A$$

where v_A is the velocity of the particle at the point of closest approach, *i.e.*, at A. Also, since the energy of the particle must also remain conserved, we have

$$\frac{1}{2}mv_A^2 + Ze^2/r_A = \frac{1}{2}mv_0^2,$$

$$= \frac{1}{2}mv_0^2 + 0,$$

where $\frac{1}{2}mv_A^2$ is the *kinetic*, and Ze^2/r_A, the *potential* energy of the particle at A and $\frac{1}{2}mv_0^2$, its *initial kinetic energy, when its potential energy is zero* (*its distance from the nucleus being infinite*).

Or, substituting the value of v_A, obtained above, we have

$$Ze^2/r_A = \frac{1}{2}mv_0^2 - \frac{1}{2}m(v_0 b/r_A)^2.$$

Or, $$Ze^2/r_A = \frac{1}{2}mv_0^2\left[1 - \left(\frac{b}{r_A}\right)^2\right].$$

So that, knowing the *impact parameter b*, the *distance of closest approach of the particle* (r_A) can be easily obtained.

(*iii*) Effect on linear and angular speeds of a particle on contraction of its orbit. Let a particle of mass m be carried at one end of a light string such that it can be rotated in a horizontal circle, *i.e.*, made to move in circular orbit. Let the free end of the string pass through a small hollow tube, as shown in Fig. 6.15, so that the radius of the orbit of the particle can be decreased by simply applying a downward pull F on the free end of the string.

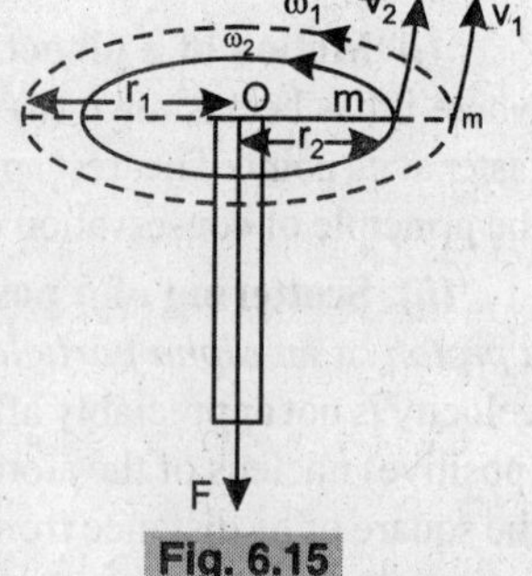

Fig. 6.15

Let the *initial radius* of the circular orbit described by the particle be r_1, its *linear speed* v_1 and angular speed $\omega_1 = v_1/r_1$, so that its *angular momentum* about the centre O of the orbit $= mv_1r_1$ and its *kinetic energy* $= \frac{1}{2}m_1v_1^2$.

And, when the free end of the string is pulled down a little by a force F, so that the radius of the circular orbit of the particle is reduced to r_2, let the *linear and angular speeds* of the particle be v_2 and ω_2 respectively and hence its *angular momentum about* $O = mv_2r_2$ and its kinetic energy = $\frac{1}{2}mv_2^2$.

Clearly, the downward pull on the free end of the string is transmitted to the particle as a *radial force* (*vis,* the centripetal force), directed towards the centre O of its orbit. As a radial force, therefore, it exerts no torque on the particle (its line of action passing through O) and its angular momentum thus remains conserved, so that we have

$$mv_1r_1 = mv_2r_2, \text{ whence } v_2 = v_1r_1/r_2.$$

Since, $r_2 < r_1$, it follows that $v_2 > v_1$ and hence the *K.E. of the particle in the second case, i.e.,* $\frac{1}{2}mv_2^2 = \frac{1}{2}m(v_1r_1/r_2)^2 = \frac{1}{2}mv_1^2(r_1/r_2)^2$ *is greater than its kinetic energy* $\frac{1}{2}mv_1^2$ *in the first case.*

Thus, by shortening the radius of the orbit of the particle from r_1 to r_2, its K.E. has increased by $\frac{1}{2}mv_2^2 - \frac{1}{2}mv_1^2$

$$= \frac{1}{2}mv_1^2(r_1/r_2)^2 - \frac{1}{2}mv_1^2 = \frac{1}{2}mv_1^2\left(\frac{r_1^2}{r_2^2} - 1\right) \quad \text{...I}$$

This additional energy must obviously be supplied by the work done on the particle against the centrifugal force in pulling it inwards towards O. Let us see if this is so.

Since angular momentum of the particle remains conserved, we have

$$mv_1r_1 = mv_2r_2 \quad \text{Or,} \quad v_1r_1 = v_2r_2 = k, \text{ say.}$$

This means that the linear speed of the particle, $v = k/r$. And, therefore, centrifugal force $F = mv^2/r = (m/r)(k^2/r^2) = mk^2r^3$.

∴ *work done against the centrifugal force in decreasing the orbit radius from* r_1 *to* r_2 *is given by*

$$W = \int_{r_1}^{r_2} -F dr = \int_{r_1}^{r_2} -\frac{mk^2}{r^3} dr = \left[\frac{mk^2}{2r^2}\right]_{r_1}^{r_2} = \frac{mk^2}{2}\left[\frac{1}{r^2}\right]_{r_1}^{r_2} = mk^2\left[\frac{1}{r_2^2} - \frac{1}{r_1^2}\right]$$

Or, Substituting v_1r_1 for k, we have

$$W = \frac{mv_1^2r_1^2}{2}\left(\frac{1}{r_2^2} - \frac{1}{r_1^2}\right) = \frac{1}{2}mv_1^2\left(\frac{r_1^2}{r_2^2} - 1\right) \quad \text{...II}$$

which is the same as expression I for gain in *K.E.*, above, *showing that the gain in K.E., of the particle on shortening its orbit, is indeed supplied by the work done against the centrifugal force acting on the particle.*

Obviously enough, in the absence of any such supply of energy to the particle, it would not be possible for it to conserve its angular momentum.

This may be easily seen if we simply attach the end of the string to a fixed vertical stick and set the particle in rotation, as before, at the end of the string (6.16). It will be found that as the particle moves in its circular orbit, the radius of the orbit goes on progressively decreasing and the string goes on winding itself around the stick in the form of a spiral.

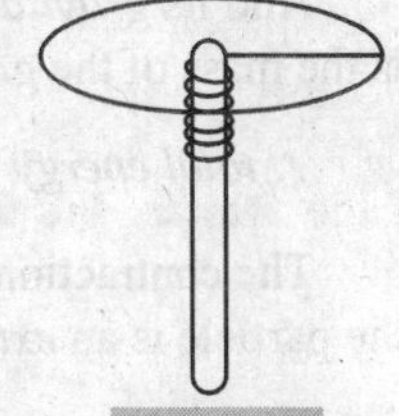

Fig. 6.16

Clearly, no work is done here against the centripetal force, as in the first case, and hence no energy is supplied to the particle. As a result, despite the continuous decrease in the radius of the orbit, there cannot be any increase in the kinetic energy, and hence, in the linear speed of the particle which therefore continues to remain the same throughout, although the angular speed $\omega = v/r$ goes on increasing with decrease in the value of r. The constancy of the linear speed indicates that the tension in the string is always perpendicular to the direction of v at any point in the spiral path of the particle and is no longer directed towards the centre of its initial circular path. This is so because, in the absence of energy supplied to the particle, its angular momentum mvr cannot possibly remain conserved, but must go on decreasing along with the radius r of the orbit.

(iv) The shape of the galaxy. Galaxies are physical systems, containing anything from 10^9 to 10^{12} stars with a lot of free gas, bound by gravitational attraction, and free to rotate about their own axes of symmetry. One galaxy is separated from another by a huge distance of about 3×10^{24} *cm*. The galaxy which contains our own sun is referred to *as the galaxy* and has a radius of about 10^{23} *cm*.

A conjecture as to the formation of galaxies, which some regard to be oversimplified, is due to *Hubble*, according to which there was, to start with, just a gaseous mass spread throughout space, some portion of which acquired angular momentum due to gravitational interaction within itself and the rest, free from angular momentum, condensed in the form of spheres to ultimately form stars.

A galaxy is supposed to have come to acquire its more or less lens-like or pancake shape due to the condensation of a great mass of the gas inside it under gravitational interaction. This may be explained somewhat in the following manner.

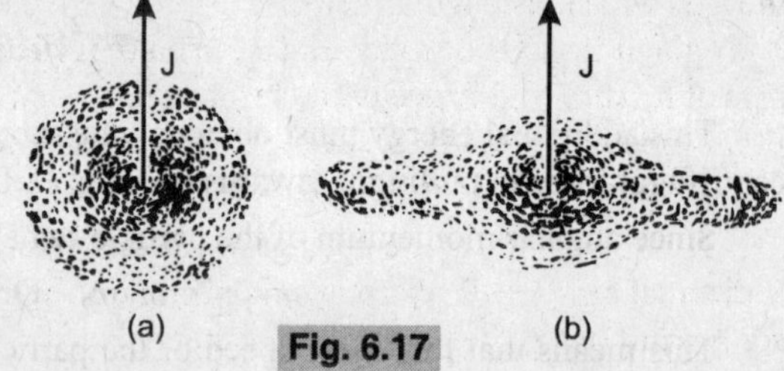

Fig. 6.17

Suppose there is a large mass of gas in a more or less spherical form, having an initial angular momentum $\vec{J}$ about any axis, as shown in Fig. 6.17(*a*). As the gas contracts under gravitational interaction, the forces of interaction being pairs of equal and opposite forces, there is no external torque acting on the system and its angular momentum, therefore, remains conserved. Since however, its volume is greatly reduced, energy has to be supplied to it to enable it to conserve its angular momentum, as we have seen under (*iii*) above. This energy can obviously come only from the gravitational potential energy of the gas itself.

Thus, if m be the mass of a particle of the gas in the outer regions of the galaxy, initially at a distance r_0 from its centre and rotating with velocity v_0 about it, its $K.E. = \frac{1}{2}mv_0^2$.

After gravitational interaction, if the particle lies at a distance r from the centre of the galaxy and if its velocity be v, its $K.E. = \frac{1}{2}mv^2$.

Since the angular momentum remains conserved, we have

$$mv_0r_0 = mvr,$$

whence, $v = v_0r_0/r$ and $\therefore$ $K.E.$ of the particle $= \frac{1}{2}mv_0^2\left(\frac{r_0}{r}\right)^2$.

And its *gravitational P.E.* at this distance r from the centre of the galaxy $= -GMm/r$, where M is the mass of the *galaxy*.

$$\therefore \textit{ total energy of the particle} = \frac{1}{2}mv_0^2\left(\frac{r_0}{r}\right)^2 - \frac{GMm}{r}.$$

The contraction of the gas will stop, or equilibrium attained, when the total energy of the gas or the particle is an *extremum* (*i.e.* either a maximum or a minimum), *i.e.*, when

$$\frac{d}{dr}\left[\frac{1}{2}mv_0^2\left(\frac{r_0}{r}\right)^2 - \frac{GMm}{r}\right] = 0$$

or, $$-mv_0^2\frac{r_0^2}{r^3} + \frac{GMm}{r} = 0$$

or, $$\frac{GMm}{r^2} = \frac{mv_0^2r_0^2}{r^3} = \frac{mv^2}{r}. \qquad \left[\text{Substituting } \frac{vr}{r_0} \text{ for } v_0\right]$$

Thus, the contraction of the gas continues, with its angular momentum conserved, until *equilibrium is attained when the inward pull due to gravitational force on it is just balanced by the outward pull due to centrifugal force,* the value of r, then being $v_0^2 r^2/GM$.

Any further reduction in the value of r beyond this is not possible, because the rapidly increasing centrifugal force opposes any further contraction of the gas.

There is, however, no such limitation to the contraction of the gas with its angular momentum conserved *along the direction of the axis of rotation,* any *K.E.* acquired during contraction being dissipated presumably in the form of radiation. As a result, the shape ultimately acquired by the galaxy is that of a *pancake*, with a small spherical, or nearly spherical, protion at the centre, as shown in Fig. 6.17 (*b*).

(*v*) Diving, skating, ballet-dancing etc. In all these processes, the performer utilises the principle of conservation of angular momentum. For, as mentioned earlier, the angular momentum of a body free to rotate about an axis is equal to $I\omega$ where I is the *moment of inertia* of the body about the axis and ω, its angular velocity. Now, I depends upon the square of the *radius of gyration* of the body about the axis of rotation, *i.e.*, upon the *effective distance* of the particles of the body from the axis of rotation and hence upon the *distribution of mass* about the axis. A large variation in the value of the moment of inertia (I) of the performer and hence a corresponding variation in the value of his angular velocity ω is, therefore, possible on his stretching his limbs out or pulling them in.

Thus, a **diver**, as he springs from the diving board, has a certain angular velocity about a horizontal axis passing through his centre of mass to enable him to spin about the axis or to make a somersault or two before striking water.

Let his initial *M.I.* about the axis be I_0 and his angular velocity about it, ω_0, so that his initial angular momentum about the axis $I_0\omega_0$. The only external force acting on the diver is the gravitations force due to the attraction of the earth, but since it is a *central force* it produces no torque about his centre of mass and his angular momentum thus remains conserved. He can, therefore, double of triple his angular velocity and thus increase the number of his somersaults before touching water by correspondingly reducing his *M.I.* about the axis of rotation to, say, I, by simply pulling in his hands and feet towards the centre of his body. If ω be his angular velocity corresponding to the value I of his moment of inertia, we have

$$I_0\omega_0 = I\omega$$

Since $I < I_0$, we have $\omega > \omega_0$ and $\therefore \ \frac{1}{2}I\omega^2 > \frac{1}{2}I_0\omega_0^2$, *i.e.*, the rotational *K.E.* of the diver increases in the process.

The source of this additional K.E. acquired by the diver is obviously the work done by him in pulling in his limbs towards the centre of his body.

In a similar manner, a skater or a bullet dancer, (Fig. 6.18), can increase or decrease his or her angular velocity and thus skin faster or slower about a vertical axis through the centre of mass by pulling in the hands and the feet or by extending them as far out as possible, thereby decreasing or increasing the *M.I.* about the axis of rotation, as desired.

Fig. 6.18

6.18. ANGULAR MOMENTUM OF ELEMENTARY PARTICLES—ITS QUANTISATION

We have seen under § 6.15 how a planet moving in its elliptical orbit around the sun possesses (*i*) an *orbital angular momentum* due to its motion around the sun and (*ii*) a *spin angular momentum* due to its rotating or spinning about an axis passing through its own centre of mass. The same is true for almost all the fundamental or elementary particles, including the *photon*, which may possess one or both these types of angular momenta. Thus, for example, the electron in a hydrogen atom possesses orbital angular momentum on account of its motion in its orbit around the proton and also spin angular momentum on account of spinning about its own axis (passing through its centre of mass).

Now, the student is, in all probability, already aware that in *Bohr's* atomic model, an electron can revolve round the nucleus, without emitting any radiant energy, in only certain specified or permissible orbits for which its orbital angular momentum is an integral multiple of $h/2\pi$, *i.e.*, $nh/2\pi$, where n is an integer, 1, 2, 3, etc. and h, the *Planck's constant* (6.25×10^{-27} *erg-sec*), these orbits are, for this reason, referred to as stationary orbits or Bohr's orbits.

The orbital angular momentum of the revolving electron is thus restricted to certain fixed or discrete values (*viz*., integral multiples of $h/2\pi$) and is, therefore, said to be *quantised.*

Bohr, of course, had no theoretical basis for making this assumption except that it could satisfactorily explain the various spectral series of hydrogen.

A mathematical basis for this hypothesis was, however, provided later by *De Broglie* who suggested that every particle has a *wave* associated with it and that the smaller the particle, the longer this wave. Thus, the wave associated with an electron is longer than that associated with a proton. The wavelength of this associated wave, called *wa Broglie wavelength*, may be easily obtained. For, in accordance with *Einstein's mass-energy equation* $E = mc^2$ and from *Planck's equation* $E = h\nu$, coupled with the fact that $c = \nu\lambda$ and, therefore, $\nu = c/\lambda$, (where ν is the frequency of the wave), we have $hc/\lambda = mc^2$, whence, $\lambda = h/mc$.

If, therefore, v be the velocity of an electron, the De Broglie wavelength associated with it may be obtained by substituting v for c in the above relation, when we have $\lambda = h/mv$, a fact rested experimentally by *Davisson* and *Germer*.

So that, instead of an electron moving in a stationary orbit, we must now consider a series of waves moving in the orbit and, in order that they may not cancel each other due to interference they must move in such a manner as to produce a stationary or standing wave in the orbit. The necessary condition for this is that the length of the path, *i.e.*, the circumference of the orbit, must be equal to an integral multiple of the wave length. Thus, if r be the radius of a stationary orbit, we must have $2\pi r = n\lambda = nh/mv$, whence, the *orbital angular momentum* of the electron, $mvr = n\lambda/2\pi$, as assumed by *Bohr*.

Now, the *centripetal force acting on the electron* moving with speed v in an orbital of radius r around the nucleus is clearly $-mv^2/r$, the $-ve$ sign indicating that it is directed inwards towards the centre of the orbit or the nucleus.

Since the charge on the nucleus is Ze, where Z is its atomic number and e, a charge equal in magnitude to that on an electron, the force acting on the electron inwards, towards the nucleus, is also $-Ze.e/r^2$, (the charge on the electron being negative).

In the case of hydrogen, $Z = 1$ and, therefore,

$\therefore$ *force acting on the electron, inwards* $= e^2/r^2$.

We, therefore, have $\dfrac{e^2}{r^2} = \dfrac{mv^2}{r}$, whence, $mv^2 = \dfrac{e^2}{r}$ ...(*i*)

And, since angular momentum of the electron, *i.e.*, $mvr = nh/2\pi$, we have

$$m^2v^2r^2 = n^2h^2/4\pi^2 \qquad ...(ii)$$

$\therefore$ dividing relation (*ii*) by (*i*), we have $\dfrac{m^2v^2r^2}{mv^2} = \dfrac{n^2h^2r}{4\pi^2e^2}$.

whence, $r = \dfrac{h^2}{4\pi^2me^2}n^2$. Or, $r \propto n^2$.

Thus, *the radii of the stationary or permissible orbits are proportional to* n^2.

Further, *potential at a distance r from the charge Ze on the nucleus* = Ze/r. We, therefore, have

$$P.E. \text{ of the electron} = (Ze)(-e)/r = -Ze^2/r = -e^2/r \qquad [\because Z = 1]$$

And, since *K.E. of the electron* = $\frac{1}{2}mv^2$, we have

total energy of the electron, $E = K.E. + P.E. = \frac{1}{2}mv^2 - e^2/r$

$$= \frac{1}{2}\frac{e^2}{r} - \frac{e^2}{r} = -\frac{1}{2}\frac{e^2}{r}.$$

Or, Substituting the value of r from above, we have

$$E = -\frac{1}{2}\frac{e^2 4\pi^2 me^2}{n^2h^2} = -\frac{2\pi^2 me^4}{n^2h^2}. \qquad \ldots(iii)$$

It may be pointed out that *Bohr* had originally taken the electron orbit to be circular. Later, *Sommerfield* extended the theory to include also elliptical orbits but showed that the value of $E = K.E. + P.E.$ for the electron orbit is still given by relation (*iii*) above, deduced for circular orbits.

Here, obviously, the motion of the nucleus (or the proton) has been ignored. More correctly, we can imagine the proton (of mass M, say) to be stationary and obtain *relative motion* of the electron about it if we replace the mass m of the electron by the reduced mass $\mu = mM/(m + M)$ of the electron and the proton. In that, case, clearly,

$$r = \frac{h^2}{4\pi^2 \mu e^2}n^2 \text{ and } E = -\frac{2\pi^2 \mu e^4}{n^2h^2}$$

Correct value of orbital angular momentum of an electron and other fundamental particles. A full fledged *quantum theory of the atom*, based on wave mechanics, was developed in the year 1925, thanks in main to the efforts of *Heisenberg*, *Schrodinger*, *Born* and others, according to which the correct value of the orbital angular momentum of an electron or, in fact, any elementary particle, is given not by $nh/2\pi$ but by $\sqrt{l(l+1)}\frac{h}{2\pi}$, where l is called the **orbital or Azimuthal quantum number** and may have values 0, 1, 2, 3, ...($n - 1$), where n is the **principal quantum number.**

A significant departure from Bohr's theory is at once noticeable in that here, with $l = 0$, we can have angular momentum $(\vec{J}) = 0$ which is surely not consistent with Bohr's theory which demands that an electron moving in its orbit around the nucleus must necessarily possess angular momentum.

Now, angular momentum is a vector quantity and is represented by a vector along the axis of rotation (or perpendicular to the plane of rotation). If, therefore, we express it in units of $h/2\pi$, *i.e.*, if $h/2\pi$ be taken as *unit angular momentum*, the orbital angular momentum may be represented by a vector $\vec{l}$ whose magnitude is not l but $\sqrt{l(l+1)}$ units, where 1 unit = $h/2\pi = 1.0542 \times 10^{-7}$ erg-sec or $\approx 10^{-34}$ kg-m²/sec, usually denoted by the symbol $\hbar$ (read as h bar).

In a complex atom, where there may be more orbiting electrons than one, the total orbital angular momentum $(\vec{L})$ is the vector sum of the orbital angular momenta of the individual electrons and will always have an integral value.

It may also be mentioned here that any *observable component* of the orbital angular momentum, such, for example, as the one in the direction of a magnetic field, is also *quantised* and is given by $\frac{h}{2\pi}m_l$ where m_l is called the *magnetic orbital quantum number* and may have any of its $(2l + 1)$ possible values, l, $(l - 1)$, $(l - 2)$, 0, –1, –2, –l.

Spin angular momentum. In order to explain the *fine structure* of the spectral lines of hydrogen and some other elements (*i.e.*, the splitting up of their spectral lines, when examined by an instrument of high resolving power), as also to explain *anomalous Zeeman effect*, *Uhlenbeck* and *Gondsmit* and also *Dirac* suggested, in the year 1925, that an electron, whether in an orbit or free, spins about an axis just like a top and has, therefore, also a *spin angular momentum*, whose magnitude is $sh/2\pi$, where s is called the *spin quantum number*. The same is true for all other elementary particles except π or *K*-mesons.

The spin angular momentum too is thus *quantised* and expressed in $h/2\pi$ or $\hbar$ units. Its correct value, however, based on wave mechanics (when measured in terms of $h/2\pi$ as the unit) is represented by the vector $\vec{s}$, whose magnitude is not s but $\sqrt{s(s+1)}$ units.

The value of the spin quantum number is not the same for all elementary particles. Thus, while it is $\frac{1}{2}$ for the the electron and for most of the other elementary particles, it is 1 for the *photon* and 0 for π and *K*-mesons. So that for the electron, proton and neutron etc., the vector $\vec{S}$ (*i.e., the spin angular momentum vector*) has the magnitude $\sqrt{\frac{1}{2}\left(\frac{1}{2}+1\right)} = \sqrt{3/2}$ units, where of course, 1 unit = $h/2\pi$ or $\hbar$.

Since a free and independent electron too spins about its axis, and so do most of the other elementary particles, they all possess spin angular momentum. For this reason, the spin angular momentum of an electron or an elementary particle is also referred to as its *intrinsic angular momentum*, which it preserves under all circumstances.

The vector sum $\vec{S}$ of the spin angular momenta of more than one electron must thus be an odd multiple of $\frac{1}{2}$ if the number of electrons be odd and must be an even integer, or an even multiple of $\frac{1}{2}$, if the number of electrons be even, *i.e.*, being quantised, it must always be a multiple of $\frac{1}{2}\hbar$ or $\frac{1}{2}h/2\pi$. It also follows that the values of spin angular momenta for different directions of spin must differ from each other by a whole unit h or $h/2\pi$. This means, in other words, that the vectors representing the spin angular momentum vectors (or the spin, for short) must always be *either parallel* (*i.e.*, similarly directed), as shown in Fig. 6.19 (*i*) *or anti parallel* (*i.e.*, oppositely directed), as shown in Fig. 6.19 (*ii*).

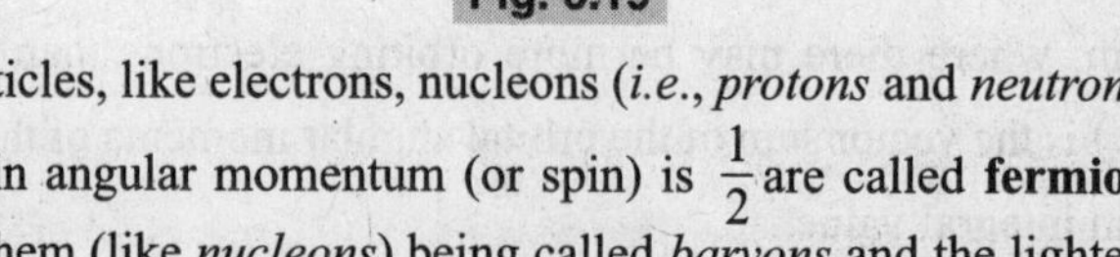

$s = \frac{1}{2}$, $s = \frac{1}{2}$, $s = \frac{1}{2}$ — $S = s + s + s = \frac{3}{2}$ (i)

$s = \frac{1}{2}$, $s = \frac{1}{2}$, $s = \frac{1}{2}$ — $S = s + s - s = \frac{1}{2}$ (ii)

Fig. 6.19

Fundamental particles, like electrons, nucleons (*i.e.*, *protons* and *neutrons*), *nutrions* μ*-mesons* etc. for which the spin angular momentum (or spin) is $\frac{1}{2}$ are called **fermions**, after *Fermi*,—the heavier ones among them (like *nucleons*) being called *baryons* and the lighter ones (like *electrons*, μ*-mesons* or *muons*), *leptons*.

A very important and far-reaching property of fermions is that *no two fermions inhabiting the same region, can possess identical properties,* thus *no two electrons in an atom can exist in the same state.* This was first stated by *Pauli*, in the year 1925, and is known as *Pauli's exclusion principle.* As can be easily understood, it is this principle which accounts for the arrangement of electrons in an atom.

Particles for which the spin is *zero* or an integral multiple of $\hbar$ (or $h/2\pi$) are called **Bosons** (after *Bose*), as for example, *α-particles, spin zero, photons, spin* 1, *deuteron* (nucleus of deuterium), *spin* 2.

Example of conservation of spin angular momentum. Such an example is furnished by a positron slowing down in a material and capturing an electron to form an '*atom*' of **positronium**, for a brief period, with the positron as nucleus. Since both positron and electron have the same mass, the two are really distributed about their centre of mass. So that, when they capture each other, the only angular momentum involved is the spin angular momentum of $\frac{1}{2}\hbar$ of each. If their spins be opposed to each other, *i.e.*, if their spin vectors be anti-parallel, we have what is called **para positronium** whose total spin is $\frac{1}{2}\hbar - \frac{1}{2}\hbar = 0$. On decay, therefore, the annihilated mass appears as electromagnetic energy in the form of two *photons*, with their spins of 1 each in opposite directions, so that the spin angular momentum carried off is zero. The spin angular momentum thus remains conserved, being zero both before and after decay of the 'parapositronium atom.' Obviously, we cannot have only one photon produced during annihilation, for it would mean the carrying off of an angular momentum of $1\hbar$ from where it is zero.

If, on the other hand, the spin of the positron and the electron be aligned, *i.e.*, be in the same direction (or their spin vectors parallel), we obtain what is called **ortho positronium** whose total angular momentum is $\frac{1}{2}\hbar + \frac{1}{2}\hbar = 1\hbar$. In order that the angular momentum may remain conserved, therefore, it must decay into three photons, with two of them having opposite spins, so that the total angular momentum carried off is $1\hbar + 1\hbar - 1\hbar = 1\hbar$, the same as that of the 'ortho positronium atom'.

It need hardly be pointed out that we can observe the quantum nature of angular momentum only in the interaction of small entities like the fundamental particles because its unit $\hbar$ or $h/2\pi$ is much too small (equal to 1.0542×10^{-7} *erg-sec*). It, God forbid, we were living in a world in which $\hbar$ or $h/2\pi$ were equal to 1, large objects of human size would start behaving the way these small particles do and very strange things will happen to us. Thus, for example, a 1 kg mass whirled at the end of a metre long string would revolve only at frequencies 0, $1/2\pi$, $2/2\pi$, $3/2\pi$, etc. and the swing would occur in directions such that the change in angular momentum from one direction to the next is equal to $1\hbar$. And, our bicycles would then pick up speeds which are integral multiples of some basic speed (depending upon their size and weight), their wheels and handles; would turn only through certain discrete angles, and so on.

Total angular momentum. The total angular momentum of a revolving electron would obviously be equal to the sum of its orbital angular momentum and its spin angular momentum and would be given by $j(h/2\pi)$, where j is the *total angular momentum quantum number.* So that, if $\vec{j}$ be the *total angular momentum vector,* we have $\vec{j} = \vec{l} + \vec{s}$, such that the vector sum has always a half odd integral value, *i.e.*, it is always an odd multiple of $\frac{1}{2}$. Since s in always equal to $\frac{1}{2}$, it means that j can have only two values for a given value of l, *viz.*, $l + \frac{1}{2}$ and $l - \frac{1}{2}$, except, of course, when $l = 0$, in which case it will have only the value $\frac{1}{2}$.

Again, on the basis of wave mechanics, the magnitude of **j** must be $\sqrt{j(j+1)}$, that of **l** must be $\sqrt{l(l+1)}$ and that of **s** must be $\sqrt{s(s+1)}$, all in units $\hbar$ or $h/2\pi$.

In the event of there being two or more electrons in an atom, it is found that in an overwhelming number of cases we have what is called an **L—S** coupling (or *Russel-Saunders* coupling) in which all orbital angular momenta combine to give a resultant orbital angular momentum vector $\vec{L}$, irrespective of the spin angular momenta, and, similarly, all spin angular momenta combine to give a resultant spin angular momentum vector $\vec{S}$, irrespective of the orbital angular momenta. The **total angular momentum of the atom** is thus represented by vector $\vec{J} = \vec{L} + \vec{S}$, such that $\vec{J}$ must be an integer or an odd multiple of according as $\vec{S}$ is an integer or an odd multiple of $\frac{1}{2}$. So that, the possible number of values that $\vec{J}$ can have if $\vec{L} > \vec{S}$ is $(2\vec{S}+1)$ and the number of values that it can have when $\vec{L} < \vec{S}$ is $(2\vec{L}+1)$. Of course, in case $\vec{L} = 0$, $\vec{J}$ can have only a single value, *viz.* $\vec{S}$.

N.B. For worked examples on quantisation of angular momentum, see chapter 7.

WORKED EXAMPLES

I—Conservation of linear momentum

Example 1. A hunter has a rifle that can fire 0.06 kg bullets with a muzzle velocity of 900 m/sec. A 40 kg leopard springs at him at a speed of 10 m/sec. How many bullets must the hunter fire into the leopard in order to stop it in its tracks?

Solution. Here, clearly, *momentum of the leopard* = (*mass*) (*velocity*) = (40)(10) *kg-m/sec*. The momentum of the bullets too that must be fired into the leopard must be at least this much in order to stop it in its tracks. Let this number of bullets be *n*. Then, *momentum of the bullets* (*in the opposite direction to that of the leopard* = *n*(0.06)(900) *kg-m/sec*. Equating the two, therefore, we have

$$n(0.06)(900) = (40)/(10), \text{ whence, } n = \frac{40 \times 10}{0.06 \times 900} = \frac{400}{54} \approx 8.$$

Thus, *the hunter must fire 8 bullets into the leopard in order to stop it.*

Example 2. (*a*) What is the momentum of an electron of *a* kinetic energy 100 electron volts? (mass of the electron may be taken to be 9 × 10^{-28} gm).

(*b*) At what velocity will a 10,000 kg truck have (*i*) the same momentum, (*ii*) the same kinetic energy as a 4,000 kg car at 30 m/sec?

Solution. (*a*) We have K.E. of the electron $= \frac{1}{2}mv^2 = 100 \text{ eV} = 100 \times 1.6 \times 10^{-12}$ ergs.

$$\therefore \quad \textit{momentum of the electron} = mv = \sqrt{m^2v^2} = \sqrt{2m \times \frac{1}{2}mv^2}$$

$$= \sqrt{2 \times 9 \times 10^{-28} \times 100 \times 1.6 \times 10^{-12}}$$

$$= \sqrt{18 \times 1.6 \times 10^{-38}} = 5.37 \times 10^{-19} \text{ gm-cm/sec.}$$

(*b*) (*i*) Let the truck have the same momentum as the car at a velocity of *v m/sec*. Then, clearly, 10,000 *v* = 4,000 × 30, whence, *v* = 4,000 × 30/10,000 = 12 m/sec.

(*ii*) If the truck has the same *K.E.* as the car at velocity *v*′, we have

$$\frac{1}{2} \times 10{,}000 \times v'^2 = \frac{1}{2} \times 4{,}000 \times 30^2, \text{ whence, } v' = \sqrt{360} = 18.97 \text{m/sec.}$$

Thus, the truck will have the same momentum as the car at a velocity of 12 m/sec *and the same K.E. as the car at a velocity of 18.97* m/sec.

Example 3. A vessel at rest explodes, breaking into three pieces. Two pieces, having equal masses, fly off perpendicular to one another with the same speed of 30 m/sec. The third piece has three times the mass of each other piece. What is the direction and magnitude of its velocity immediately after the explosion?

Solution. Here, the masses of the three pieces of the vessel are given to be as 1 : 1 : 3.

Let one of the smaller pieces move along the axis of x and the other, along the axis of y then clearly *momentum of the first small piece* = (1)(30**i**) = $30\hat{i}$

and *momentum of the second small pieces* = (1)(30**j**) = $30\hat{j}$.

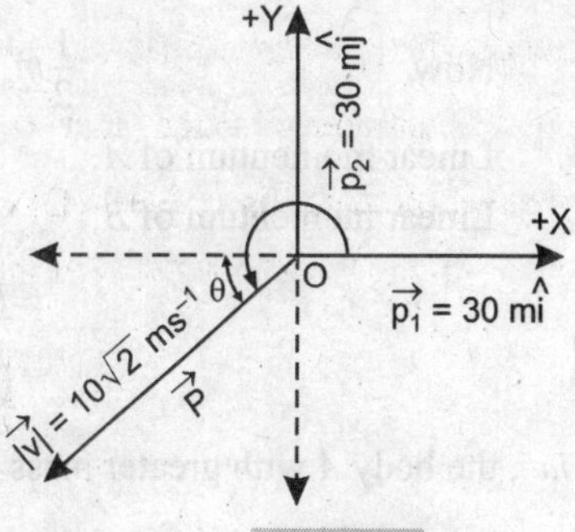

Fig. 6.20

If the speed of the third, bigger piece be $\vec{v}$ *m/sec*, we have

momentum of the bigger piece = $(3)(\vec{v}) = 3\vec{v}$.

Since initially the vessel was at rest and hence its linear momentum, zero, the total momentum of the three pieces, after explosion, should, in accordance with the law of conservation of momentum, be also *zero*, since no external force is acting on the vessel. We, therefore, have

$$30\hat{i} + 30\hat{j} + 3\hat{v} = 0,$$

whence, $3\vec{v} = -30\hat{i} - 30\hat{j}$ or, $\vec{v} = -(10\hat{i} \times 10\hat{j})$.

Thus, the magnitude of the velocity of the bigger piece, *i.e.*, $v = \sqrt{10^2 + 10^2} = \sqrt{200} = 10\sqrt{2}$ *m/sec*. And its direction with the axis of x or the direction of motion of the first piece, say, $\theta = \tan^{-1}(-1/1)$, *i.e.*, $\tan^{-1}(-1) = 135°$, the same as the angle that its direction makes with the axis of y or the direction of motion of the second piece.

Thus, *the velocity of bigger piece immediately after the explosion is* $10\sqrt{2}$ m/sec, *inclined at an angle of* 135° *to the direction of motion of either small piece.*

Example 4. Radioactive $_8O^{15}$ decays into $_7N^{15}$ by emitting a positron and neutrino. The positron and the neutrino are observed to move at right angles to each other and carry momenta 2×10^{-22} and 5×10^{-23} kg m sec^{-1} respectively. Find the momentum of the recoiling nucleus.

Solution. Let the positron move along the $+X$ direction and the neutrino along $+Y$ direction with momenta $\vec{p_1} = 2 \times 10^{-22} = 20 \times 10^{-23}$ kg m sec^{-1} and $\vec{P_2} = 5 \times 10^{-23}$ kgm sec^{-1} respectively. If $\vec{p}$ is the momentum of the recoiling nucleus, then according to the principle of conservation of linear momentum.

$$\vec{p_1} + \vec{p_2} + \vec{P} = 0$$

or $$\vec{P} = -(\vec{p_1} + \vec{p_2})$$

Now $$|\vec{p_1} + \vec{p_2}| = \sqrt{(20 \times 10^{-23})^2 + (5 \times 10^{-23})^2}$$

$$= 5\sqrt{17} \times 10^{-23} \text{ kg m sec}^{-1}.$$

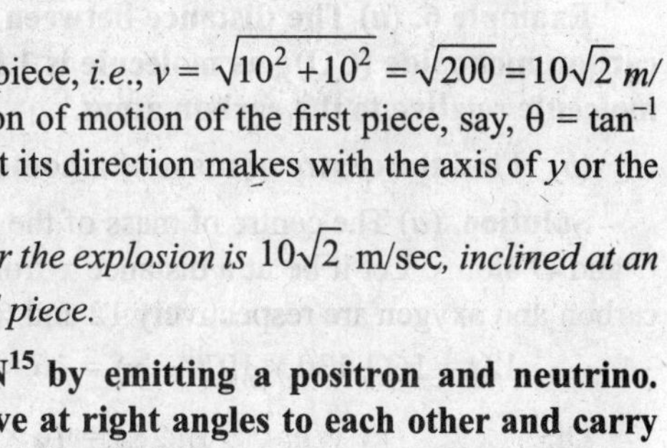

and its direction is given by

$$\tan\theta = \frac{5 \times 10^{-23}}{20 \times 10^{-23}} = \frac{1}{4} = 0.25$$

or, $\theta = 14°2'$

Fig. 6.21

$\therefore\ \vec{P} = 5\sqrt{17} \times 10^{-23}$ kg m sec^{-1} and it makes an angle 14°2′ with $-X$ direction or (180° + 14°2′) = 194°2′ with $+X$ direction.

Example 5. Two bodies of different masses are moving with the same kinetic energy of translation. Which has greater momentum?

Solution. Let m_a and v_a be the mass and velocity of mass A and m_b, v_b that of mass B with $m_a > m_b$, then

$$\text{K.E. of mass } A = \frac{1}{2}m_a v_a^2 \text{ and K.E. of mass } B = \frac{1}{2}m_b v_b^2$$

Now, $$\frac{1}{2}m_a v_a^2 = \frac{1}{2}m_b v_b^2 \quad \therefore \quad \frac{m_a}{m_b} = \frac{v_b^2}{v_a^2} \text{ or } \sqrt{\frac{m_a}{m_b}} = \frac{v_b}{v_a}$$

Linear momentum of A, $\quad p_a = m_a v_a$

Linear momentum of B, $\quad p_b = m_b v_b$

$$\therefore \quad \frac{p_a}{p_b} = \frac{m_a}{m_b}\frac{v_a}{v_b} = \frac{m_a}{m_b}\sqrt{\frac{m_b}{m_a}} = \sqrt{\frac{m_a}{m_b}} \text{ but } m_a > m_b$$

$$p_a > p_b$$

i.e., the body A with greater mass has greater momentum.

II—Centre of mass

Example 6. (*a*) The distance between the centres of the carbon and oxygen atoms in the carbon monoxide (CO)g as molecule is 1.130 × 10^{-10} metres. Locate the centre of mass of the molecule relative to the carbon atom.

(*b*) Find the centre of mass of a homogeneous semicircular plate of radius *a*.

Solution. (*a*) The centre of mass of the *CO* molecule will obviously lie on the line joining the *C* and *O* atoms. Let it be at a distance *x* from the carbon atom. Then, since the atomic weights of carbon and oxygen are respectively 12 and 6, we have

$$12x = 16(1.130 \times 10^{-10} - x) = 16 \times 1.130 \times 10^{-10} - 16x.$$

Or, $$28x = 16 \times 1.130 \times 10^{-10}, \quad \text{whence,} \quad x = 16 \times 1.130 \times 10^{-10}/28$$
$$= 6.457 \times 10^{-11} \text{ m.}$$

Hence, *the centre of mass of the CO molecule lies at a distance of* 6.457×10^{-11} *m from the centre of the carbon atom on the line joining the carbon and oxygen atoms.*

(*b*) Here, too, the centre of mass obviously lies on the line of symmetry *OA* (Fig. 6.22) passing through the mid-point *O* of the base and perpendicular to it.

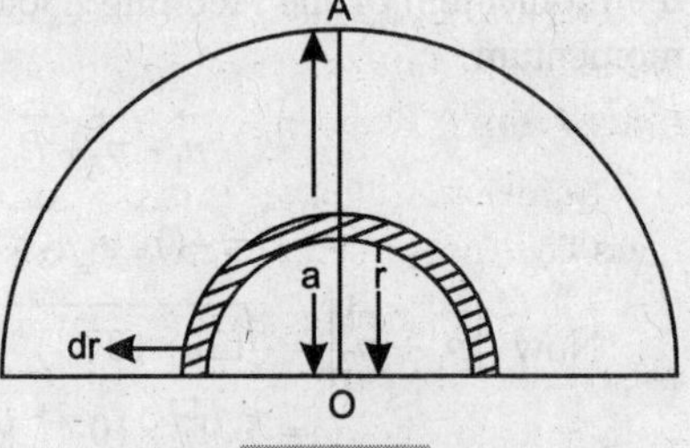

Fig. 6.22

Since it is a homogeneous plate, the centre of mass will be at a distance *R* and *O*, given by the relation $R = \frac{1}{M}\int_0^a r \cdot dm$, where *dm* is the mass of an element of it of radius *r* and *M*, the *mass* of the whole plate.

Clearly, *area* of the semicircular plate = $\pi a^2/2$. We therefore, have

$$\textit{mass per unit area of the plate} = M/\frac{\pi a^2}{2} = 2M/\pi a^2.$$

And, area of the element of the plate, of radius *r* = (length of shaded strip) × *i* (*its width dr*) = $\pi r dr$.

$\therefore$ *mass of the strip, i.e., dm* = $(\pi r dr)(2M/\pi a^2)$

$\therefore$ *distance of centre of mass of the semicircular plate from* 0, *i.e.*,

$$R = \frac{1}{M}\int_0^a r\pi r dr 2M/\pi a^2 = \frac{2}{a^2}\int r^2 dr = \frac{2}{a^2}\left[\frac{r^3}{3}\right]_0^a = \frac{2}{a^2}\left(\frac{a^3}{3}\right) = \frac{2a}{3}.$$

Thus, *the centre of mass of the semicircular plate lies on the right bisector OA of its base at a distance of 2a/3 from its mid-point O.*

Example 7. Two particles, of masses 100 and 300 gm, have at a given time positions $2\hat{i}+5\hat{j}+13\hat{k}$ and $-6\hat{i}+4\hat{j}-2\hat{k}$ cm respectively and velocities $10\hat{i}-7\hat{j}-3\hat{k}$ and $7\hat{i}-9\hat{j}+6\hat{k}$ cm/sec respectively. Deduce (*i*) the instantaneous position of the centre of mass, (*ii*) the velocity of the second particle in a frame of reference travelling with the centre of mass.

(Nagpur 2005)

Solution. (*i*) We know that the distance of the centre of mass from the chosen origin is given by

$$\vec{R} = \frac{m_1\vec{r_1}+m_2\vec{r_2}}{m_1+m_2}$$

∴ Substituting the given values of m_1, m_2, r_1 and r_2, we have

$$\vec{R} = \frac{100(2\hat{i}+5\hat{j}+13\hat{k})+300(-6\hat{i}+4\hat{j}-2\hat{k})}{100+300} = \frac{-16\hat{i}+17\hat{j}+7\hat{k}}{4}\text{ cm.}$$

Thus, the centre of mass lies at a distance of $(-16\hat{i}+17\hat{j}+7\hat{k})/4$ cm from the origin.

(*ii*) The *velocity of the centre of mass* is given by

$$\vec{V} = \frac{m_1\vec{v_1}+m_2\vec{v_2}}{m_1+m_2} = \frac{100(10\hat{i}-7\hat{j}-3\hat{k})+300(7\hat{i}-9\hat{j}+6\hat{k})}{100+300}$$

$$= \frac{31\hat{i}-34\hat{j}+15\hat{k}}{4}\text{ cm/sec.}$$

∴ *velocity of the second particle in the frame of reference travelling with the centre of mass*

$$= \vec{v_2}-\vec{V} = (7\hat{i}-9\hat{j}+6\hat{k})-\frac{31\hat{i}-34\hat{j}+15\hat{k}}{4}$$

$$= \frac{-3\hat{i}-2\hat{j}+9\hat{k}}{4}\text{ cm/sec.}$$

Example 8. Two particles *P* and *Q* are initially at rest, 1.0 metre apart. *P* has a mass of 0.10 kg and *Q*, a mass of 0.30 kg. *P* and *Q* attract each other with a constant force of 1.0×10^{-2} N. No external forces act on the system. Describe the motion of the centre of mass. At what distance from P's original position do the particles collide?

Solution. Since no external forces act on the system, the question of motion of the centre of mass does not arise. It, therefore, continues to be at rest.

Let the distance at which the two particles collide be *x metres* from *P*'s original position. Then, clearly, the two particles cover distances *x metes* and $(1-x)$ metres respectively, in the same interval of time *t*, say, that they take to come into contact with each other.

Now, acceleration of particle $P = \frac{force}{mass} = \frac{1\times10^{-2}}{0.1} = 10^{-1}$ m/sec^2 and that of particle

$$Q = \frac{1\times10^{-2}}{0.3} = \frac{1}{3}\times10^{-1}\text{ m/sec}^2.$$

∴ distance *x* covered by particle *P* in time $t = \frac{1}{2}\times10^{-1}\times t^2 = \frac{1}{20}t^2$ metres.

and *distance* $(1-x)$ *covered by particle Q in the same time* $t = \frac{1}{2}\times\frac{1}{3}\times10^{-1}\times t^2 = \frac{1}{60}t^2$ meters.

Clearly, therefore, $\frac{1}{20}t^2\ \frac{1}{60}t^2 = (x)+(1-x) = 1$, *whence*, $t^2 = 15$.

Hence $$x = \frac{1}{20}t^2 = \frac{1}{20} \times 15 = \frac{3}{4} = 0.75 \text{ metres.}$$

Thus, *the two particles collide at a distance of* 0.75 *m from the initial position of particle P*.

Example 9. A bomb in flight explodes into two fragments when its velocity is $10\hat{i} + 2\hat{j}$. If the smaller mass M flies with velocity $20\hat{i} + 50\hat{j}$, deduce the velocity of the larger mass 3 M. Deduce also the velocities of the fragments in the centre of mass reference frame and show these in a diagram.

Solution. Here, clearly, *initial momentum of the unexploded bomb* = *(total mass)* × *(velocity)*

$$= (M + 3M)(10\hat{i} + 2\hat{j}) = 4M(10\hat{i} + 2\hat{j})$$

After *explosion, momentum of the smaller fragment* = $M\vec{v}_1 = M(20\hat{i} + 50\hat{j})$

and *momentum of the larger fragment* = $3M\vec{v}_2$,

where $\vec{v}_1$ and $\vec{v}_2$ are the velocities of the two fragment respectively.

Since, *no external force acts on the system, its momentum must remain conserved.* We, therefore, have *total momentum after explosion* = *total momentum before explosion.* Or,

$$M(20\hat{i} + 50\hat{j}) + 3M\vec{v}_2 = 4M(10\hat{i} + 2\hat{j}). \text{ Or, } 3M\vec{v}_2 = 4M(10\hat{i} + 2\hat{j}) - M(20\hat{i} + 50\hat{j}),$$

whence, $$\vec{v}_2 = \frac{1}{3}(20\hat{i} + 42\hat{j}).$$

Thus, *the velocity of the larger mass* $3M$ is $\frac{1}{3}(20\hat{i} - 42\hat{j})$.

Now, in the absence of any external force, the centre of mass continues to move with the same velocity as that of the unexploded bomb, *viz.*,

$$\vec{V} = (10\hat{i} + 2\hat{j}).$$

∴ *velocity of the smaller mass in the centre of mass reference frame* = $\vec{v}_1 - \vec{V} = (20\hat{i} + 50\hat{j}) - (10\hat{i} + 2\hat{j}) = 10\hat{i} + 48\hat{j}$

and *velocity of the larger mass in the centre of mass reference frame* = $\vec{v}_2 - \vec{V} = \frac{1}{2}(20\hat{i} - 42\hat{j}) - (10\hat{i} + 2\hat{j}) = \frac{1}{3}(-10\hat{i} - 48\hat{j})$

$= -\frac{1}{3}(10\hat{i} + 48\hat{j})$

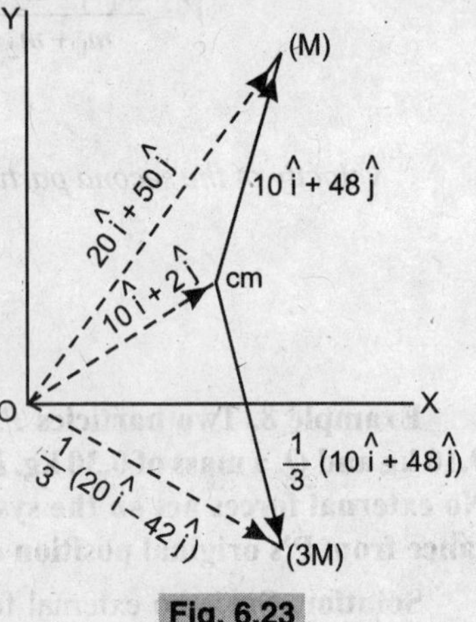

Fig. 6.23

All these velocities are shown in Fig. 6.23, both relative to the origin O and the centre of mass (*c.m.*), the former in dotted, and the latter, in full lines.

Example 10. If the centre of mass of three particles of masses 1, 2 and 3 kg be at the point 3, 3, 3, where should a fourth mass of 4 kg be placed so that the centre of mass of the four particles be at the point 1, 1, 1?

Solution. Let $x_1, y_1, z_1, x_2, y_2, z_2$ and x_3, y_3, z_3 be the positions of the three particles respectively.

Then, for the *x*-coordiante, $X = \dfrac{m_1x_1 + m_2x_2 + m_3x_3}{m_1 + m_2 + m_3}$

Or, $$3 = \frac{x_1 + 2x_2 + 3x_3}{1+2+3} = \frac{x_1 + 2x_2 + 3x_3}{6}.$$

Or, $$x_1 + 2x_2 + 3x_3 = 18 \quad \ldots(i)$$

Now, suppose the fourth particle of mass 4 kg must be placed at the point x_4, y_4, z_4 so that the centre of mass of the combination of all the four particles lies at 1, 1, 1. Then, again, for the x-coordinate, we have

Or, $$1 = \frac{x_1+2x_2+3x_3+4x_4}{1+2+3+4} = \frac{x_1+2x_2+3x_3+4x_4}{10}$$

Or, $$x_1 + 2x_2 + 3x_3 + 4x_4 = 10 \qquad ...(ii)$$

Subtracting relation (*i*) from (*ii*), we have $4x_4 = 10 - 18 = -8$, whence, $x_4 = -2$.

Proceeding in the same manner for the y and z coordinates also, we obtain $y_4 = -2$ and $z_4 = -2$.

Thus, *the fourth mass of the 4 kg must be placed at the point* –2, –2, –2, *in order that the centre of mass of the combination of all the four particles may be at the point* 1, 1, 1.

Example 11. Centre of mass is at *P*(1, 1, 1) when system consists of particles of masses 2, 3, 4 and 5 kg. If the centre of mass shifts to *Q*(2, 2, 2) on removing 5 kg, what was its position?

Solution. The position vector of centre of mass is given by

$$\vec{R} = \frac{m_1\vec{r_1}+m_2\vec{r_2}+m_3\vec{r_3}+m_4\vec{r_4}+...}{m_1+m_2+m_3+m_4+...}$$

Ist case $$\vec{R_1} = (\hat{i}+\hat{j}+\hat{k}) = \frac{2\vec{r_1}+3\vec{r_2}+4\vec{r_3}+5\vec{r_4}}{2+3+4+5} \qquad ...(i)$$

2nd case $$\vec{R_2} = (2\hat{i}+2\hat{j}+2\hat{k}) = \frac{2\vec{r_1}+3\vec{r_2}+4\vec{r_3}}{2+3+4} \qquad ...(ii)$$

From (*i*) we have $14\hat{i}+14\hat{j}+14\hat{k} = 2\vec{r_1}+3\vec{r_2}+4\vec{r_3}=5\vec{r_4}$ ...(*iii*)

From (*ii*) we have $18\hat{i}+18\hat{j}+18\hat{k} = 2\vec{r_1}+3\vec{r_2}+4\vec{r_3}$

Subtracting (*iv*) from (*iii*), we get $-4\hat{i}-4\hat{j}-4\hat{k} = 5\vec{r_4}$ ...(*iv*)

$$\therefore \quad \vec{r_4} = -\frac{4}{5}\hat{i}-\frac{4}{5}\hat{j}-\frac{4}{5}\hat{k}$$

∴ Co-ordinates of the mass of 5 kg are $\left(-\frac{4}{5}, -\frac{4}{5}, -\frac{4}{5}\right)$.

Example 12. Two bodies of masses 2 g and 10 g have position vectors $(3\hat{i}+2\hat{j}-\hat{k})$ and $(\hat{i}-\hat{j}+3\hat{k})$ respectively. Find the position vectors and the distance of centre of mass from the origin.

Solution. The position of centre of mass of two particles is given by $\vec{R} = \frac{m_1\vec{r_1}+m_2\vec{r_2}}{m_1+m_2}$

$$\therefore \quad \vec{R} = \frac{2(3\hat{i}+2\hat{j}-\hat{k})+10(\hat{i}-\hat{j}+3\hat{k})}{2+10}$$

$$= \frac{16\hat{i}-6\hat{j}+28\hat{k}}{12} = \frac{4}{3}\hat{i}-\frac{1}{2}\hat{j}+\frac{7}{3}\hat{k}$$

Distance of centre of mass from the origin.

$$|\vec{R}| = \sqrt{\left(\frac{4}{3}\right)^2+\left(\frac{1}{2}\right)^2+\left(\frac{7}{3}\right)^2} = \sqrt{\frac{16}{9}+\frac{1}{4}+\frac{49}{9}} = 2.73 \text{ units}$$

Example 13. The distance between Carbon and Oxygen atom in '*CO*' molecule is 1.12 Å. Find the centre of mass of '*CO*' molecule with respect to '*C*' atom.

Solution. Let us take the centre of mass as the origin of the co-ordinate system and axis of '*CO*' molecule along *X*-axis, then

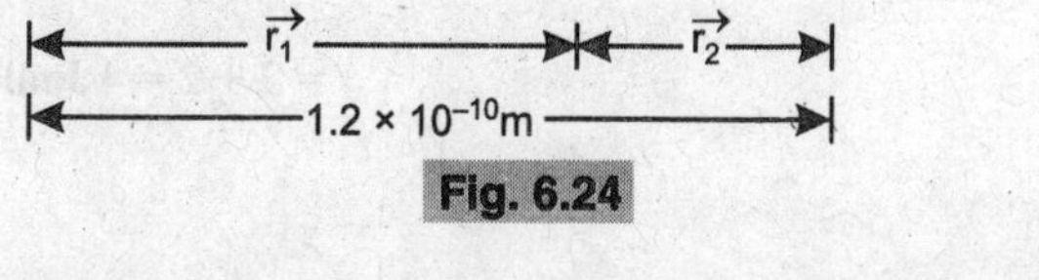

Position of Carbon atom of mass 12

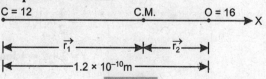

Fig. 6.24

$$= \vec{r_1} = -r_1\hat{i}$$

Position of Oxygen atom of mass 16

$$= \vec{r_2} = +(1.12\times10^{-10} - r_1)\hat{i}$$

As the centre of mass is taken as the origin of the co-ordinate system

$$\vec{R} = \frac{m_1\vec{r_1} + m_2\vec{r_2}}{m_1 + m_2} = 0$$

or $$m_1\vec{r_1} + m_2\vec{r_2} = 0$$

$$\therefore\ -12r_1\hat{i} + 16(1.12\times10^{-10} - r_1)\hat{i} = 0$$

or $$28r_1\hat{i} = 16\times1.12\times10^{-10}\hat{i}$$

$$\therefore\quad r_1 = \frac{16\times1.12\times10^{-10}}{28} = 0.64\times10^{-10}\,\text{m} = 0.64\ \text{Å}$$

As the position of Carbon atom with respect to centre of mass = $-r_1\hat{i}$, the position of centre of mass with respect to 'C' atom = $+r_1 i$ = + 0.64 × 10^{-10} m.

Example 14. Two masses constrained to move in a horizontal plane collide. Given initially m_1 = 85 gms, m_2 = 200 gms; u_1 = 6.48 cms/sec and u_2 = –6.78 cms/sec, find the velocity of centre of mass.

Solution. The velocity of centre of mass is given by $\vec{V}_{cm} = \dfrac{m_1\vec{u_1} + m_2\vec{u_2}}{m_1 + m_2}$

$$\therefore\quad \vec{V}_{cm} = \frac{85\times6.48 + 200\times(-6.78)}{85 + 200} = 2.82\ \text{cm/sec in the direction of motion of } m_2.$$

Example 15. Two particles each of mass 2 kg are moving with velocities $2\hat{i} + 4\hat{j}$ m/s and $5\hat{i} + 6\hat{j}$ m/s respectively. Find the kinetic energy of the system relative to centre of mass.

Solution. Given $m_1 = m_2 = 2$ kg.; $u_1 = 3\hat{i} + 4\hat{j}$; $u_2 = 5\hat{i} + 6\hat{j}$

$$\text{Velocity of centre of mass } \vec{V}_{\text{cm}} = \frac{m_1\vec{u_1} + m_2\vec{u_2}}{m_1 + m_2} = \frac{2(3\hat{i} + 4\hat{j}) + 2(5\hat{i} + 6\hat{j})}{2+2} = 4\hat{i} + 5\hat{j}$$

Velocity of m_1 in centre of mass frame $\vec{u_1'} = \vec{u_1} - \vec{V}_{\text{cm}}$

or $$\vec{u_1'} = 3\hat{i} + 4\hat{j} - 4\hat{i} - 5\hat{j} = -\hat{i} - \hat{j}$$

Velocity of m_2 in centre of mass $\vec{u_2'} = \vec{u_2} - \vec{V}_{\text{cm}}$

or $$\vec{u_2'} = 5\hat{i} + 6\hat{j} - 4\hat{i} - 5\hat{j} = \hat{i} + \hat{j}$$

Kinetic energy relative to centre of mass before collision = $\dfrac{1}{2}m_1u_1'^2 + \dfrac{1}{2}m_2u_2'^2$

$$= \frac{1}{2}m_1\left|\sqrt{(-1)^2 + (-1)^2}\right|^2 + \frac{1}{2}m_2\left|\sqrt{(+1)^2 + (+1)^2}\right|^2$$

$$= 2 + 2 = 4\ \text{Joule.}$$

III—Collisions

Example 16. (*a*) A particle of mass m_1, moving with a velocity u_1, collides head-on with a particle of mass m_2 at rest, such that, after collision, they travel with velocities v_1 and v_2 respectively. If the collision be an elastic one, show that $v_2 = 2u_1\left(1+\frac{m_2}{m_1}\right)$.

(*b*) If the collision in (a) be assumed to be an inelastic one, calculate the common velocity of the two particles after collision and the loss of kinetic energy due to collision.

Solution. (*a*) A '*head-on*' collision means that, after the collision, the two particles travel along the same line.

Now, in accordance with the law of conservation of momentum, we have

$$m_1u_1 + m_2 \times 0 = m_1v_1 + m_2v_2. \quad \text{Or,} \quad m_1u_1 = m_1v_1 + m_2v_2, \qquad \ldots(i)$$

whence,

$$v_1 = (m_1u_1 - m_2v_2)/m_1 = u_1 - \frac{m_2}{m_1}v_2. \qquad \ldots(ii)$$

And, in accordance with the law of conservation of energy, we have

$$\frac{1}{2}m_1u_1^2 + 0 = \frac{1}{2}m_1v_1^2 + \frac{1}{2}m_2v_2^2. \quad \text{Or,} \quad \frac{1}{2}m_1u_4^2 = \frac{1}{2}m_1v_1^2 + \frac{1}{2}m_2v_2^2 \qquad \ldots(iii)$$

This gives

$$u_1^2 = v_1^2 + \frac{m_2}{m_1}v_2^2 \qquad \ldots(iv)$$

Or, substituting the value of v_1 from relation (*ii*) above, we have

$$u_1^2 = u_1^2 + \frac{m_2^2}{m_1^2}v_2^2 - \frac{2m_2u_1v_2}{m_1} + \left(\frac{m_2}{m_1}v_2\right)^2$$

Or,

$$0 = \frac{m_2}{m_1}\left(v_2^2 + \frac{m_2}{m_1}v_2^2 - 2u_1v_2\right)$$

Or,

$$0 = \frac{m_2}{m_1}\left(v_2 + \frac{m_2}{m_1}v_2 - 2u_1\right) \quad \text{Or,} \quad v_2 + \frac{m_2}{m_1}v_2 - 2u_1 = 0.$$

Or,

$$v_2\left(1+\frac{m_2}{m_1}\right) = 2u_1, \quad \text{whence,} \quad v_2 = \frac{2u_1}{1+\dfrac{m_2}{m_1}}$$

(*b*) Here, the collision **being** *inelastic*, the two particles stick together on collision and move with a common velocity *v*, say.

Then, *for conservation of momentum*, we have

$$m_1u_1 + 0 = (m_1 + m_2)v, \quad \text{whence,} \quad v = m_1u_1/(m_1 + m_2).$$

And, clearly, *loss of kinetic energy due to collision* $= \frac{1}{2}m_1u_1^2 - \frac{1}{2}(m_1 + m_2)v^2$.

Or, substituting the value of v_1, we have

$$\textit{loss of kinetic energy} = \frac{1}{2}m_1u_1^2 - \frac{1}{2}(m_1 + m_2)\left(\frac{m_1u_1}{m_1 + m_2}\right)^2 = \frac{1}{2}m_1u_1^2 - \frac{1}{2}\frac{m_1^2u_1^2}{m_1 + m_2}$$

$$= \frac{1}{2}m_1u_1^2\left(1 - \frac{m_1}{m_1 + m_2}\right) = \frac{1}{2}m_1u_1^2\left(\frac{m_2}{m_1 + m_2}\right).$$

Example 17. A steel ball weighing 1 lb is fastened to a cord 27 inches long and is released when the cord is horizontal. At the bottom of its path the ball strikes a 5.0 lb block initially

at rest on a frictionless surface (Fig. 6.25). The collision is elastic. Find the speed of the ball and the speed of the block just after collision.

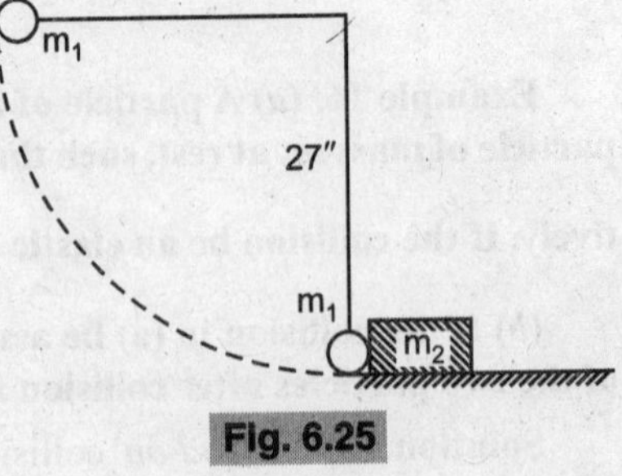

Fig. 6.25

Solution. As the ball comes down and hits the block, it is clearly a head-on collision. If, therefore, m_1 and m_2 be the masses of the ball and the block respectively, u_1, the velocity acquired by the ball on falling through 27", with which it hits the block, v_1, the *velocity of recoil of the ball* and v_2, the *forward velocity of the block*, we have, for conservation of momentum,

$$m_1u_1 + 0 = -m_1v_1 + m_2v_2 \quad \ldots(i)$$

K.E. acquired by the ball on falling through 27" or 9/4 ft $= \frac{1}{2}m_1u_1^2 = m_1gh$,

whence, $u_1^2 = 2gh = 2 \times 32 \times 9/4 = 144$. Or, $u_1 = \sqrt{144} = 12$ *ft/sec.*

Now, proceeding as in example 16 above, we have

$$v_2 = \frac{2u_1}{1 + m_2/m_1} = \frac{2 \times 12}{1 + 5/1} = \frac{24}{6} = 4 \text{ ft/sec.}$$

Substituting $v_2 = 4$ ft/sec in the momentum relation (*i*) above, we have

$$1 \times 12 = -1 \times v_1 + 5 \times 4, \quad \text{Or,} \quad v_1 = 20 - 12 = 8 \text{ ft/sec.}$$

Thus, *the ball recoils with a velocity of* 8 ft/sec *and the block moves forward with a velocity of* 4 ft/sec.

Example 18. A sand bag of mass 10 kg is suspended with a 3 metre long weightless string. A bullet of mass 200 gm is fired with a speed 20 m/sec into the bag and stays in the bag. Calculate (*i*) the speed acquired by the bag, (*ii*) the maximum displacement of the bag, (*iii*) energy converted to heat in the collision.

Solution. (*i*) This is obviously a case of an inelastic collision between the bullet and the bag, where $m_1 = 200$ *gm* $= 0.2$ *kg*, $m_2 = 10$ *kg*, $u_1 = 20$ *m/sec* and v, the common speed of the bullet and the bag is to be determined.

In accordance with the law of conservation of momentum, we have

$$m_1u_1 = (m_1 + m_2)v, \text{ whence,}$$

$$v = \frac{m_1u_1}{m_1 + m_2} = \frac{0.2 \times 20}{0.2 + 10} = \frac{4}{10.2} = 0.3922 \ m/sec.$$

(*ii*) The bag will oscillate like a simple pendulum of length 3 metres about its point of suspension under a *restoring force* $F = -mg \sin\theta = -Cx$, say (Fig. 6.26), where x is the *amplitude* or the *maximum displacement* of the bag and the bullet lodged into it.

If l be the length of the pendulum, we have $-mg \sin\theta = -mgx/l = -Cx$, where $C = mg/l$. Since m (the mass of the bag and the bullet) $= 10.2$ kg, $g = 9.8$ m/sec^2, we have $C = 10.2 \times 9.8/3$.

The *total work done in this displacement of the bag and the bullet* $= \int_0^x Cxdx = \frac{1}{2}Cx^2$. This work is obviously done at the expense of the *K.E.* acquired by the bag and the bullet, equal to $\frac{1}{2}mv^2$. We, therefore, have $\frac{1}{2}Cx^2 = \frac{1}{2}mv^2 = \frac{1}{2}(10.2)(0.3922)^2$.

Or, $$Cx^2 = (10.2)(0.3922)^2.$$

Or, $$x^2 = \frac{(10.2)(0.3922)^2(3)}{(10.2)(9.8)},$$

whence, $$x = \sqrt{\frac{(0.3922)^2 \times 3}{9.8}} = 0.217 \textit{ metre.}$$

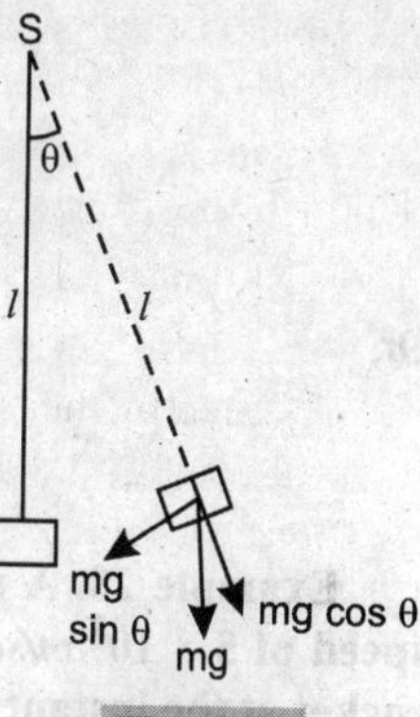

Fig. 6.26

The maximum displacement of the bag is thus 0.217 *metre.*

(*iii*) The *energy converted into heat* is obviously equal to the difference between the initial *K.E.* of the bullet and the final *K.E.* of the bullet and the bag, *i.e.*,

$$= \frac{1}{2}m_1u_1^2 - \frac{1}{2}(m_1 + m_2)v^2$$

$$= \frac{1}{2}(0.2)(20)^2 - \frac{1}{2}(10.2)(0.3922)^2$$

$$= 40 - 0.7845 = 39.2 \text{ joules.}$$

Example 19. Show that in the case of an elastic and glancing collision between two particles of masses m_1 and m_2 respectively, the maximum value of the scattering angle θ_1 in the laboratory frame corresponds to the scattering angle θ in the centre of mass reference frame, where $\theta = \cos^{-1}(-m_2/m_1)$. Also show that this maximum value of the scattering angle $\theta_1 = \tan^{-1}\left(\frac{m_1^2}{m_2^2} - 1\right)^{-\frac{1}{2}}$.

Solution. We know that the scattering angle θ_1 in the laboratory reference frame is related to the scattering angle θ in the centre of mass reference frame by the relation

$$\tan \theta_1 = \frac{\sin \theta}{\cos\theta + (m_1/m_2)} \qquad \text{...}(i)$$

(§ fig. 6.11(*ii*))

Differentiating with respect to θ, therefore, we have

$$\sec^2 \theta_1 \frac{d\theta_1}{d\theta} = \frac{\cos\theta\left(\cos\theta + \frac{m_1}{m_2}\right) - \sin\theta(-\sin\theta)}{(\cos\theta + m_1/m_2)^2}$$

$$= \frac{\cos^2\theta + \sin^2\theta + \frac{m_1}{m_2}\cos\theta}{(\cos\theta + m_1/m_2)^2} = \frac{1 + \frac{m_1}{m_2}\cos\theta}{(\cos\theta + m_1/m_2)^2}.$$

For maximum value of θ_1, $d\theta_1/d\theta$ must be equal to *zero*. This means, in other words, that $1 + \frac{m_1}{m_2}\cos\theta = 0$, or that $\cos\theta = -\frac{m_2}{m_1}$, whence, $\theta = \cos^{-1}\left(-\frac{m_2}{m_1}\right)$

Now, $\sin\theta = (1 - \cos^2\theta)^{\frac{1}{2}} = (1 - m_2^2/m_1^2)^{\frac{1}{2}}$. So that, substituting the values of $\sin\theta$ and $\cos\theta$ in relation (*i*) above, we have $\tan\theta_1 = \dfrac{(1 - m_2^2/m_1^2)^{\frac{1}{2}}}{-\frac{m_2}{m_1} + \frac{m_1}{m_2}}$

$$= \frac{(m_1^2 - m_2^2)^{\frac{1}{2}}/m_1}{(m_1^2 - m_2^2)/m_1m_2} = \frac{m_2}{(m_1^2 - m_2^2)^{\frac{1}{2}}}$$

$$= \left(\frac{m_2^2}{(m_1^2 - m_2^2)}\right)^{\frac{1}{2}} = \left(\frac{m_1^2 - m_2^2}{m_2^2}\right)^{-\frac{1}{2}}$$

Or, $$\theta_1 = \tan^{-1}\left(\frac{m_1^2}{m_2^2} - 1\right)^{-\frac{1}{2}}$$

IV–Rocket

Example 20. A rocket motor consumes 100 kg of fuel per second, exhausting it with a speed of 5 × 10^3 *m/sec*. What force is exerted on the rocket? What will be the velocity of the rocket at the instant that its mass is reduced to 1/20th of its initial mass, its initial velocity being zero? (Neglect gravitational and visicous forces etc.)

Solution. We have *force or thrust on the rocket* given by $F = -\frac{dM}{dt}v$. [§ 6.12]

Here, *rate of consumption of fuel, dM/dt* = 100 kg/sec and exhaust velocity $v = 5 \times 10^3$ m/sec. So that, *thrust on the rocket* $= -100 \times 5 \times 10^3 = -5 \times 10^5$ *newtons.*

Now, as we know, (§ 6.12), *velocity of the rocket at an instant t* is given by

$$V = V_0 + v\log_e\left(\frac{M_0}{M}\right),$$

where V_0 is its initial velocity at $t = 0$, M_0, its *initial mass* and M, its *mass at instant t.*

Here, initial velocity V_0, is given be be *zero*. So that, $V = v\log_e\frac{M_0}{M}$.

Since the mass of the rocket is reduced to 1/20*th* of its initial mass, $M_0/M = 20$. We therefore, have

$$V = v\log_e 20 = v \times 2.3026 \log_{10} 20 = v \times 2.3026 \times 1.3010$$
$$= 2.995\, v \approx 3v,$$

i.e., very nearly 3 times the exhaust velocity.

Since the exhaust velocity $v = 5 \times 10^3$ m/sec, we have

velocity of the rocket at the instant its mass is reduced to 1/20th *of its initial mass* $= 3 \times 5 \times 10^3 = 15 \times 10^3$ *metres per second* very nearly.

Example 21. If the maximum possible exhaust velocity of a rocket be 2 *km/sec*, calculate the ratio M_0/M for it if it is to attain the escape velocity 11.2 *km/sec*. How long will it take the rocket (starting from rest) to attain this velocity if its rate of change of mass in terms of its initial mass, i.e., β = 1/10?

Solution. We have velocity of the rocket, starting from rest (*i.e.*, $V_0 = 0$), given by

$$V = v\log_e\frac{M_0}{M} \text{ So that, } \log_e\frac{M_0}{M} = \frac{V}{v} = \frac{11.2}{2} = 5.6.$$

Or, $$2.3026\log_{10}\frac{M_0}{M} = 5.6, \quad \text{Or, } \log_{10}\frac{M_0}{M} = \frac{5.6}{2.3026} = 2.432,$$

whence, $$M_0/M = 270.$$

Thus, *the ratio M_0/M for the rocket must be* 270.

Now, as we know, $M = M_0(1 - \beta t)$. So that, $M/M_0 = 1 - \beta t$. Or, $\beta t = (1 - M/M_0)$,

whence, $$t = \frac{1}{\beta}\left(1 - \frac{M_0}{M}\right) = 10\left(1 - \frac{1}{270}\right) = \frac{10 \times 269}{270} = 9.96 \text{ sec.}$$

Thus, *the rocket will, in this case, attain the escape velocity in* 9.96 sec.

Example 22. A rocket starts vertically upward with speed v_0. Show that its speed v at a height h is given by $v_0^2 - v^2 = 2gh/(1 + h/R)$, where R is the radius of the earth and g the acceleration due to gravity at the earth's surface. Hence deduce an expression for the maximum height reached by a rocket fired with a speed 90% of the escape velocity.

Solution. For the velocity of a body going vertically upward with an initial velocity u, we have the relation $v^2 = u^2 - 2gh$, where v is the velocity acquired by it on covering a height h and g, the acceleration due to gravity, assumed to be constant over comparatively small heights above the surface of the earth.

In the case of a rocket, large heights being involved, g cannot be presumed to remain constant throughout. So that, at the surface of the earth g being equal to MG/R^2 (where M is the mass and R, the radius of the earth, and G the gravitational constant), we have at height h above the surface of the earth, the value of acceleration due to gravity given by

$$g' = MG/(R+h)^2 = MG/R^2(1+h/R)^2 = g/(1+h/R)^2$$

$$[\because MG/R^2 = g.]$$

So that,
$$v^2 = v_0^2 - 2\int_0^h \frac{g}{(1+h/R)^2}dh = v_0^2 - 2g\left[-\frac{R}{1+h/R}\right]_0^h$$
$$= v_0 + 2g\left[\frac{R}{1+h/R} - R\right]$$

Or,
$$v^2 = v_0^2 - \frac{2gh}{1+h/R}. \quad \text{Or,} \quad v_0^2 - v^2 = \frac{2gh}{1+h/R}.$$

Now, as we know, the *escape velocity* is equal to $\sqrt{2gR}$ and, therefore, 90% of this velocity is $0.9\sqrt{2gR}$. Hence, the *initial velocity of the rocket in the second case* is $v_0 = 0.9\sqrt{2gR}$. And, at the maximum height h_m, obviously, $v = 0$. So that, substituting these values in the expression above, we have

$$(0.9\sqrt{2gR})^2 - 0 = \frac{2gh_m}{1+h_m/R}. \quad \text{Or,} \quad 0.81 \times 2gR = \frac{2gh_mR}{R+h_m}.$$

Or,
$$0.81 = \frac{h_m}{R+h_m}, \text{ whence, } h_m = \frac{0.81}{0.19}R = 4.263\,R.$$

Thus, *the maximum height attained by the rocket in this case is* 4.26 R.

Example 23. (*a*) A rocket, set for vertical firing, weighs 50 kg and contains 450 kg of fuel. It can have a maximum exhaust velocity of 2 km/sec. What should be its minimum rate of fuel consumption (*i*) to just lift it off the launching pad, (*ii*) to give it an acceleration of 20 m/sec^2?

(*b*) What will be the speed of the rocket when the rate of consumption of fuel is (*i*) 10 kg/sec (*ii*) 50 kg/sec?

Solution. (*a*) We know that, at any instant, the *thrust* on the rocket is given by

$$F = M\frac{dV}{dt} = -\frac{dM}{dt}v - Mg.$$

(*i*) When the rocket is still on the launching pad, $M = M_0 = 50 + 450 = 500$ kg and *to just lift it off the pad with minimum fuel consumption*, therefore,

$$-\frac{dM_0}{dt}v = M_0g.$$

So that,
$$-\frac{dM_0}{dt} = \frac{M_0g}{v} = \frac{500\times9.8}{2\times10^3} = 2.45 \text{ kg/sec.}$$

$[\because M_0 = 500$ kg and $v = 2$ km/sec $= 2 \times 10^3$ m/sec.$]$

Or, the *minimum rate of consumption of fuel to just lift the rocket off the launching pad* should be 2.45 kg/sec.

(*ii*) Again, $F = MdV/dt = Ma = -vdM/dt - Mg$, where a is the *acceleration* of the rocket.

Since the rocket is still on the launching pad, $M = M_0 = 500\ kg$. We, therefore, have

$$M_0 a = -\frac{dM_0}{dt}v - M_0 g, \text{ whence, } -\frac{dM_0}{dt} = \frac{M_0(g+a)}{v}.$$

Or, $$-\frac{dM_0}{dt} = \frac{500(9.8+20)}{2\times10^3} = 7.45 \text{ kg/sec.}$$

Or, *the rate of the fuel consumption, in the case, should be* 7.45 kg/sec.

(*b*) Obviously, the rocket will acquire its maximum speed when its entire fuel has been consumed.

(*i*) Here, the rate of fuel consumption is 10 kg/sec. So that the time for the consumption of the entire fuel = 450/10 = 45 sec.

Now, velocity acquired by the rocket, starting from rest, in time t, is given by

$$V = v\log_e(M_0/M) - gt \text{ (§ 6.12, relation } V)$$

Here, $M_0 = 500$ kg and $M = 50$ kg (the entire fuel (450 kg) being burnt up)

$$\therefore \quad V = 2\times10^3 \log_e(500/50) - 9.8\times45$$
$$= 2\times10^3\times2.3026\log_{10}10 - 9.8\times45$$
$$= 2\times10^3\times2.3026 - 9.8\times45 = 4.164 \text{ km/sec.}$$

Thus, *the speed of the rocket, in the case, will be* 4.164 km/sec.

(*ii*) Here, the entire fuel is burnt up in 450/50 = 9 *sec*. And, therefore, *velocity of the rocket*,

$$V = 2\times10^3\log_e(500/50) - 9.8\times9 = 2\times10^3\times2.3026 - 9.8\times9$$
$$= 4517 \text{ m/sec} = 4.517 \text{ km/sec.}$$

Thus, *the maximum speed of the rocket here will be* 4.517 *km/sec.*

Example 24. Show that the rocket speed is twice the exhaust speed when $\frac{M_0}{M} = e^2$.

Solution. If V_0 is the speed of the rocket and V_e the exhaust speed, then $\frac{V_0}{V_e} = \log_e\frac{M_0}{M}$.

Now, $$\frac{M_0}{M} = e^2 \quad \therefore \frac{V_0}{V_e} = \log_e e^2 = 2$$

i.e. the rocket speed is twice the exhaust speed.

Example 25. A 6000 kg rocket is set for vertical firing. If the gas exhaust speed is 1000 ms^{-1}, how much gas must be ejected each second to supply the thrust needed (*i*) to overcome the weight of the rocket and (*ii*) to give the rocket an initial upward acceleration of 20 ms^{-2}?

Solution. (*i*) Here mass of the rocket and fuel $M = 6000$ kg

Exhaust velocity $V_e = -1000$ ms^{-1}. Acceleration due to gravity $g = -9.8$ ms^{-2}.

Net force on the rocket $M\frac{dV}{dt} = V_e\frac{dM}{dt} + Mg$

To overcome the weight of the rocket, the resultant force acting on it $M\frac{dV}{dt} = 0$

$$\therefore \quad 0 = -1000\frac{dM}{dt} - 6000\times9.8$$

Or $$\frac{dM}{dt} = -6\times9.8 = -58.8 \text{ kg s}^{-1}$$

(*ii*) To give the rocket an initial upward acceleration of 20 ms^{-2}, the resultant force

$$M\frac{dV}{dt} = Ma = 20 \times M$$

$\therefore$
$$20 \times 6000 = -1000 \times \frac{dM}{dt} - 6000 \times 9.8$$

or
$$\frac{dM}{dt} = -\frac{6000(20+9.8)}{1000} = -178.8 \text{ kg s}^{-1}.$$

Example 26. A rocket of mass 20 kg has 180 kg of fuel. The exhaust velocity of fuel is 1.60 km s^{-1}. Calculate the ultimate vertical speed gained by the rocket when the rate of consumption of fuel is 2 kg s^{-1}.

Solution. If V_f is the final velocity of the rocket when the entire fuel has been exhausted, V_e the exhaust velocity, and rocket starts from rest, then $V_f = -V_e \log_e \frac{M_0}{M_f}$

where M_0 is the initial mass of rocket and fuel and M_f the mass of the empty rocket.

Now $\quad M_0 = 20 + 180 = 200$ kg

Consumption of fuel = 2 kg s^{-1}

Time to consume whole of fuel = $\frac{180}{2} = 90$s

Exhaust velocity $V_e = -1.6$ kms^{-1} = -1.6×10^3 ms^{-1}

$\therefore$
$$V_f = 1.6 \times 10^3 \times 2.3026 \log_{10}\frac{200}{20} = 3.684 \times 10^3 \text{ ms}^{-1}$$

$$= 3.684 \text{ km s}^{-1}$$

V–Conservation of angular momentum

Example 27. A torque of 1 Nm is applied to a wheel of mass 10 kg and radius of gyration 50 cm. What is the resulting acceleration?

Solution. Here mass of the wheel, $M = 10$ kg

Radius of gyration, $\quad K = 50$ cm = 0.5 m

Moment of inertia of the wheel, $I = MK^2$

$$= 10 \times 0.5 \times 0.5 = 2.5 \text{ kg m}^2$$

Torque, $\quad \tau = 1$ Nm

Now, $\tau = I\alpha$, where α is the angular acceleration

$\therefore$
$$\alpha = \frac{\tau}{I} = \frac{1}{2.5} = 0.4 \text{ rad s}^{-2}$$

Example 28. A particle of mass *m* moving in a circular orbit of radius *r* has angular momentum *J* about its centre. Calculate the kinetic energy of the particle in terms of *J*, *m* and *r*.

Solution. The angular momentum of a particle of mass *m* moving in a circular orbit of radius *r* is given by

$$J = mvr \qquad \ldots(i)$$

If *E* is the kinetic energy of the particle, then $E = \frac{1}{2}mv^2$.

From equation (i), we get $\quad v = \frac{J}{mr}$ or $v^2 = \frac{J^2}{m^2r^2}$

$\therefore$
$$\text{K.E.} = \frac{1}{2}mv^2 = \frac{1}{2}m\frac{J^2}{m^2r^2} = \frac{J^2}{2mr^2}$$

Example 29. A particle of mass M travels with velocity $\vec{v} = v\hat{i}$ along the axis of y. At $t = 0$, the particle is at the point $(0, y_1)$. Calculate (*a*) the angular momentum of the particle about the origin, (*b*) the total angular momentum about the point $(0, y_2)$ where $y_2 > 0$.

Solution. (*a*) Here, clearly, the *position vector* of the particle, *i.e.*, $\vec{r} = y_1\hat{j}$ and its velocity vector $\vec{v} = v\hat{i}$. Therefore, its *angular momentum about the origin, i.e.*, $\vec{J} = \vec{r} \times m\,\vec{v}$.

Or,
$$\vec{J} = y_1\hat{j} + Mv\hat{i} = -Mvy_1\hat{k}$$

(*b*) In this case, the *position vector* of the particle, $\vec{r} = (y_2 - y_1)\hat{j}$ and its *velocity vector*, the *same as before, i.e.*, $\vec{v} = v\hat{i}$.

$\therefore$ *total angular momentum about the point* $0, y_2$, *i.e.*, $\vec{J} = \vec{r} \times M\,\vec{v}$.

$$= (y_2 - y_1)\hat{j} \times Mv\hat{i} = -Mv(y_2 - y_1)\hat{k}.$$

Example 30. (*a*) A satellite of mass M_S is going round the earth in a circular orbit of radius R_S. Obtain an expression for its angular momentum about the centre of its orbit (i.e., the centre of the earth).

(*b*) Express the total energy of the satellite in terms of its angular momentum.

Solution. (*a*) Let $\vec{v}$ be the speed of the satellite in its circular orbit around the earth. Then, *its angular momentum about the centre of its orbit, i.e., about the centre of the earth* is given by $\vec{J} = \vec{R}_S \times M_S\,\vec{v}$. And its magnitude is

$$J = R_S\, M_S\, v \sin\theta, \qquad \text{...I}$$

in a direction perpendicular to the plane of its motion.

Since the orbit is a circular one, $\theta = \pi/2$ and, therefore, $\sin\theta = 1$. So that,

angular momentum of the satellite about the centre of its orbit $= R_S M_S v$ ...II

To obtain the value of v we note that as the satellite goes round the earth, the outward pull on it due to centrifugal force, $M_S v^2/R_S$ is just balanced by the inward gravitational pull $M_E M_S G/R_S{}^2$ due to the earth (where M_E is the mass of the earth).

We, therefore, have $M_S v^2/RS = M_E M_S G/R_S^2$, whence, $v = (M_E G/R_S)^{1/2}$.

Substituting this value of v in expression II above, we have

angular momentum of the satellite about the centre of its orbit, i.e.,

$$J = (R_S M_S^2 M_E G)^{1/2} \qquad \text{...III}$$

(*b*) The *kinetic energy of the satellite* is given by $T = \frac{1}{2}M_S v^2 = \frac{1}{2}M_S M_E G/R_S$

From relation III above, $M_E = J^2/R_S M_S^2 G$. So that

$$T = \frac{1}{2}M_S \cdot \frac{J^2}{R_S M_S^2 G}\frac{G}{R_S} = \frac{J^2}{2R_S^2 M_S}.$$

And, *potential energy of the satellite* is given by $U = -\,M_S M_E G/R_S$

Again, *substituting the value of* M_E, we have $U = -\dfrac{M_S G}{R_S}\left(\dfrac{J^2}{R_S M_S^2 G}\right)$

$$= -\frac{J^2}{R_S^2 M_S}.$$

$\therefore$ *Total energy of the satellite,* $E = T + U = \frac{J^2}{2R_S^2 M_S} - \frac{J^2}{R_S^2 M_S} = \frac{\Omega}{2R_S^2 M_S}.$

Example 31. The moon revolves about the earth so we always see the same face of the moon. (*a*) How are spin and orbital parts of the angular momentum of the moon with respect to the earth related? (*b*) By how much would its spin angular momentum have to change if we were to be able to see all the moon's surface during the course of a month? (Mass of the moon, $M_m = 7.35 \times 10^{25}$ *gm*, radius of the moon, $R_m = 1.74 \times 10^8$ cm, radius of moon's orbit around the earth, $R_E = 3.84 \times 10^{10}$ cm and time of one revolution of the moon round the earth, $T = 2.36 \times 10^6$ sec.

Solution. (*a*) As we know (see next chapter), the angular momentum of a body rotating about an axis is given by $J = I\omega$, where I, is the *moment of inertia* and ω, the angular velocity of the body about that axis.

For a sphere *M.I.* about its diameter = $(2/5)MR^2$. Therefore, *spin angular momentum of the moon, due to rotation about its own axis, i.e., about its own diameter, say,*

$$S = I\omega = (2/5)\ M_m\ R_{m^2}.$$

Now, the moon revolves around the earth so as to always present the same face towards it, showing clearly that its rate of rotation about its own axis is the same as its rate of revolution about the earth, so that $\omega = 2\pi/2.36 \times 10^6$.

We, therefore, have
$$S = \frac{2}{5} M_m R_{m^2} \times \frac{2\pi}{2.36 \times 10^6}$$
$$= \frac{2}{5} \times 7.35 \times 10^{25} \times (1.74 \times 10^8)^2 \times \frac{2\pi}{2.36 \times 10^6}$$
$$= 2.369 \times 10^{36} \text{ erg-sec.}$$

And, *orbital angular momentum of the moon about the earth,* say, $L = R_E M_m v$, where v is the speed of the moon in its orbit around the earth.

Since $v = R_E \omega$, we have $L = R_{E^2} M_m \omega$.

$$= (3.84 \times 10^{10})^2 \times 7.35 \times 10^{25} \times 2\pi/2.36 \times 10^6$$
$$= 2.885 \times 10^{41} \text{ erg-sec.}$$

$\therefore$ *Ratio of the orbital to spin angular momentum of the moon, i.e., L/S*

$$= 2.885 \times 10^{41}/2.369 \times 10^{36} = 1.217 \times 10^5.$$

(*b*) obviously, the moon must spin about its axis half as fast or half as slow as it actually does now, in order that both faces of it may be visible on the earth during the course of a month. *There should thus be an increase or a decrease in its spin angular momentum of half its present value.*

Example 32. (*a*) The maximum and minimum distances of a comet from the sun are 1.4×10^{12} m and 7×10^{10} m. If its velocity nearest to the sun is 6×10^4 m/sec, what is its velocity when farthest? Assume in both positions that the comet is moving in a circular orbit.

(*b*) A wheel is rotating with an angular speed of 500 rev/min on a shaft whose rotational inertia is negligible. A second identical wheel, initially at rest, is suddenly coupled to the same shaft. What is the angular speed of the resultant combination of the shaft and the two wheels?

Solution. (*a*) Let m be the mass of the comet, r_1, r_2, v_1 and v_2, the radii of its orbits and its velocities when nearest to the sun and farthest from it respectively.

The law of conservation of angular momentum demands that $m\vec{v_1}\vec{r_1} = m\vec{v_2}\vec{r_2}$.

Since $\mathbf{r}_1$ and $\mathbf{r}_2$ are always perpendicular to the velocity vectors $\mathbf{v}_1$ and $\mathbf{v}_2$ respectively (the orbits being circular), we have $mv_1r_1 = mv_2r_2$.

Or, $v_2 = v_1r_1/r_2 = 6 \times 10^4 \times 7 \times 10^{10}/1.4 \times 10^{12} = 3 \times 10^3 = 3000$ *m/sec*.

Thus, *the speed of the comet when farthest from the sun* = 3000 *m/sec*.

(*b*) If I be the *M.I.* of the wheel and ω, its angular velocity about the shaft, we have *angular momentum of the wheel about the shaft* = $I\omega$.

When a second identical wheel is coupled with the first, the *M.I.* of the combination of the two wheels about the shaft = $2I$.

If ω' be the angular velocity of the combination about the shaft, we have *its angular momentum about the shaft* = $2I\omega'$.

Since no external torque has been applied to the system, its angular momentum must remain conserved. And we, therefore, have

$$2I\omega' = I\omega, \text{ whence, } \omega' = \omega/2.$$

Since $\omega = 500$ *rev/min*, we have $\omega' = 500/2 = 250$ *rev/min*,

i.e., the angular speed of the resultant combination is 250 *rev/min*.

Example 33. A 500 gm mass is whirled round in a circle at the end of a string 40 cm. long, other end of which is held in the hand. If the mass makes 5 rev/sec, what is its angular momentum? If the number of revolutions is reduced to just one, after 20 seconds, calculate the mean value of the torque acting on the mass.

Solution. Here, angular momentum of the mass is given by $\vec{J} = \vec{r} \times m\vec{v}$, in a direction perpendicular to the plane of the circle.

Or, $$J = r \times mv \sin\theta$$

Since $\mathbf{r}$ is at any instant perpendicular to $\mathbf{v}$ (Fig. 6.27),

$$\theta = 90° \text{ and } \therefore \sin\theta = 1.$$

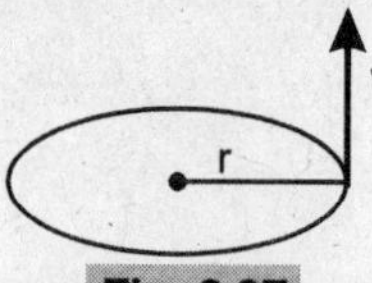

Fig. 6.27

we, therefore, have $J = rmv = rm\,(r\omega) = mr^2\omega$,

where ω is *the angular velocity of the mass* = $5 \times 2\pi$/sec. So that, substituting the values of m, r and ω, we have

$$\textit{angular momentum, } J = 500\,(40)^2\,(5 \times 2\pi) = 8 \times 10^6\pi = 2.5 \times 10^7 \text{ erg-sec.}$$

Now, torque $\tau = dJ/dt = mr^2 d\omega/dt = 500\,(40)^2\,(2\pi/20) = 2.5 \times 10^5$ dyne-cm.

Example 34. A string of length *l*, tied to the top of a pole, carries a ball at its other end, as shown in Fig. 6.28. On giving the ball a single hard blow, it acquires an initial velocity v_0 in the horizontal plane and moves in a spiral of decreasing radius, with the sting winding itself around the pole whose radius to negligible compared with the length of the string. (*i*) What is the instantaneous centre of revolution? (*ii*) Is the angular momentum conserved? (*iii*) Assuming the kinetic energy to be conserved, calculate the angular velocity of the all after it has made five complete revolutions.

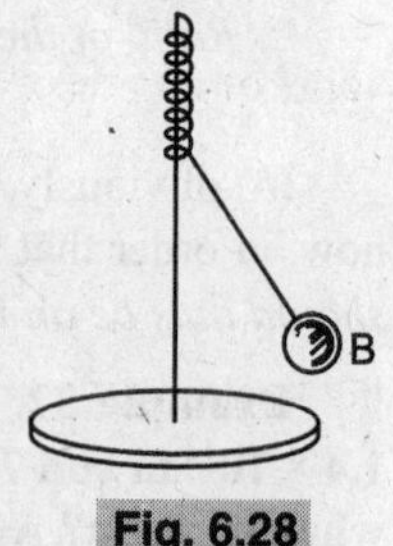

Fig. 6.28

Solution. (*i*) The instantaneous centre of the ball is obviously the point of contact of the string with the circumference of the pole at the instant considered.

(*ii*) Let $\vec{r}$ be the position vector of the ball, measured by the axis of the pole passing through O to the centre B of the ball (Fig. 6.29) and let $\vec{F}$ be the force applied to the ball, directed towards the point P on the circumference of the pole, which is the centre of revolution at

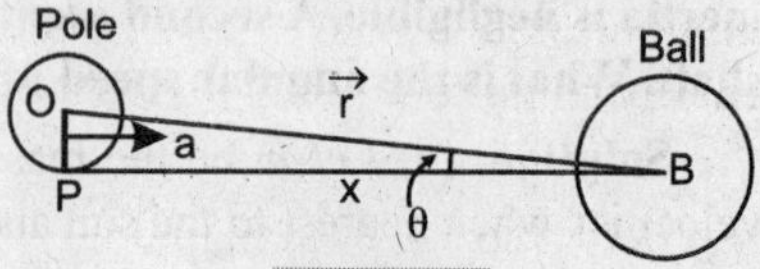

Fig. 6.29

the instant, and not towards O. So that $\vec{F}$ is not parallel to $\vec{r}$ and *the torque on the ball is not, therefore, zero.* It thus follows as a natural consequence that the *angular momentum of the system is not conserved.*

(*iii*) Since the *K.E.* of the system is assumed to be conserved, it is clear that the velocity of the ball remains constant at its initial value v_0. The component of the velocity perpendicular to the radius vector OB is $v_0 \cos\theta = v_0 x/r$ and the angular velocity of the ball about the axis of the pole is thus $\omega = \dfrac{v_0 x/r}{r} = v_0 x/r^2$.

After 5 revolutions, the length of the string will decrease to $l - 5(2\pi a) = l - 10\pi a$, where a is the radius of the pole. So that, the length of the string will now be $(l - 10\pi a)$. And, since $r^2 = OP^2 + PB^2 = a^2 + x^2 = a^2 + (l - 10\pi a)^2$, the angular velocity will now be given by $\omega' = v_0 \dfrac{l - 10\pi a}{a^2 + (l - 10\pi a)^2}$.

Or, Since $a << l$, we have $\omega' = \dfrac{v_0}{l - 10\pi a}$.

This will then be the angular velocity of the ball about the point on the circumference of the pole after five complete revolutions of the ball.

Example 35. A neutron of energy 1 MeV passes a proton at such a distance that the angular momentum of the neutron relative to the proton approximately equals 10^{-26} erg-sec. What is the distance of closest approach? (Neglect energy of interaction between the two particles).

Solution. As we know, the angular momentum of the neutron is given by $\vec{J} = \vec{r} \times m\vec{v}$, where m is the mass of the neutron, $\vec{v}$, its velocity and $\vec{r}$, its position vector relative to the proton.

If $\vec{r}$ be equal to the distance of closest approach, $\vec{r_A}$, we have $\vec{J} = \vec{r_A} \times m\vec{v}$.

And, therefore, $\quad J = r_A mv \sin\theta$.

Since at the distance of closest approach, the velocity vector is perpendicular to the position vector, $\theta = 90°$ and, therefore, $\sin\theta = 1$.

Hence, $\quad J = r_A mv$. Or, $r_A = J/mv$.

Now, *K.E. of the neutron*, $T = \dfrac{1}{2} mv^2$, whence, $v^2 = 2T/m$ and $\therefore\ v = \sqrt{2T/m}$. Substituting this value of v in the expression for r_A above, we have

$$r_A = \frac{J}{m\sqrt{2T/m}} = \frac{J}{\sqrt{2Tm}}.$$

Since $J = 10^{-26}$ erg-sec and $T = 1$ MeV $= 1.6 \times 10^{-12} \times 10^6 = 1.6 \times 10^{-6}$ *erg* and m, the mass of the neutron may be taken to be 1.67×10^{-24} *gm*, we have

$$\textit{distance of closest approach, } r_A = \frac{10^{-26}}{(2 \times 1.6 \times 10^{-6} \times 1.67 \times 10^{-24})^{1/2}} = 4.326 \times 10^{-12} \text{ cm}$$

Example 36. The distance of closest approach of a positive particle to a nucleus of atomic number 80 is 2×10^{-11} cm. If the charge on the particle be equal to e and its initial kinetic energy equal to 2 MeV, obtain the value of the impact parameter for it.

Solution. We have relation $\dfrac{Ze^2}{r_A} = \dfrac{1}{2} mv_0^2 \left[1 - \left(\dfrac{b}{r_A}\right)^2\right]$, [See § 6.17(*ii*)] where r_A is the *distance of closest approach* of the particle, b, the *impact parameter* for it and $\frac{1}{2}mv_0^2$, its *initial K.E.*

Since *initial K.E.* of the particle is given to be 2 *MeV*, we have

$$\frac{1}{2}Mv_0^2 = 2 \times 1.6 \times 10^{-12} \times 10^{-6} = 3.2 \times 10^{-6} \text{ ergs.}$$

So that,
$$\frac{Ze^2}{r_A} = 3.2\times10^{-6}\left[1-\left(\frac{b}{r_A}\right)^2\right], \text{ whence, } 1-\left(\frac{b}{r_A}\right)^2 = \frac{Ze^2}{3.2\times10^{-6}r_A}.$$

Or,
$$\left(\frac{b}{r_A}\right)^2 = 1-\frac{Ze^2}{3.2\times10^{-6}\times r_A} = 1-\frac{80(4.8\times10^{-10})^2}{3.2\times10^{-6}\times2\times10^{-11}}$$
$$= 1 - 0.288 = 0.712$$

$$\therefore \quad b^2 = 0.712 \times (r_A)^2, \quad \text{Or, } b = r_A\sqrt{0.712} = 2\times10^{-11}\times0.8437$$
$$= 1.6874 \times 10^{-11} \approx 1.7 \times10^{-11} \text{ cm.}$$

Thus, the *impact parameter for the particle* = 1.7×10^{-11} cm.

Example 37. Given that the orbital velocity of the sun about the centre of our galaxy is 3×10^7 cm/sec and its distance nearly equal to 3×10^{22} cm from the axis of the galaxy, estimate the mass of the galaxy ($G = 6.67 \times 10^{-8}$ C.G.S. units)

Solution. Obviously, the inward pull on the sun due to gravitational attraction between it and the galaxy just balances the outward pull on it due to centrifugal force. If, therefore, M_S and M be the masses of the sun and the galaxy respectively, we have

$$\frac{MM_S}{r^2}G = \frac{M_S v^2}{r}, \quad \text{whence,} \quad M = \frac{v^2 r}{G}.$$

Substituting the values of v, r and G, therefore, we have

$$\textit{mass of the galaxy, } M = \frac{(3\times10^7)^2\times3\times10^{22}}{6.67\times10^{-8}} = \frac{27\times10^{44}}{6.67} = 4.05 \times 10^{44} \text{ gm.}$$

EXERCISE

I–Conservation of Linear Momentum

1. (*a*) What is linear momentum? State and explain the principle of conservation of linear momentum with examples. (*Nagpur U. 2009, 2007*)
   (*b*) Derive the law of conservation of linear momentum from Newton's laws of motion.
2. (*a*) State and explain principle of conservation of linear momentum. Show that in the absence of any external force acting on it, the linear momentum of a system of particles remains constant.
   (*b*) A light and a heavy body have equal kinetic energies of translation. Which one has the larger momentum?
3. Explain whether (*a*) it is possible for a body to have energy without having momentum and vice versa, (*b*) a sail boat can be propelled by air blown at the sails from a fan attached to the boat itself.
4. Write a short note on the law of conservation of momentum and its importance in Physics. Does the law also hold good in nuclear and relativistic physics?
5. (*a*) A 27 kg and a 40 kg boy are at rest on frictionless roller skates. The larger boy pushes the other so that the latter rolls away at a speed of 8 km/hr. What is the effect of this action on the larger boy himself? [**Ans.** *He rolls away in the opposite direction with a speed of* 5.35 km/hr]

(*b*) A 200 kg bomb falling freely explodes and splits into two fragments, a larger one of 160 *kg* and a smaller one of 40 *kg*. The former moves away with a speed $\vec{v} = \hat{i} + 2\hat{j} + 3\hat{k}$. What is the speed of the latter? **[Ans.** $-4(\hat{i} + 2\hat{j} + 3\hat{k})$]

6. Show that when the vector sum of the external forces acting upon a system of particles equals zero, the total linear momentum of the system remains constant.

7. Show that the law of conservation of linear momentum of a system is a direct consequence of the translational invariance of the potential energy of the system.

8. A radioactive nucleus, initially at rest, decays by emitting an electron and a neutrino at right angles to one another. The momentum of the electron is 1.2×10^{-22} kg-m/sec and that of the neutrino is 6.4×10^{-23} kg-m/sec. (*a*) Find the direction and magnitude of the momentum of the recoiling nucleus. (*b*) The mass of the residual nucleus is 5.8×10^{-26} *kg*. What is the kinetic energy of recoil?

[Ans. (*a*) 1.36×10^{-22} kg-m/sec at $\angle$ 28°4′ *with the direction of the electron.*
(*b*) 1.595×10^{-19} *joule* or 1 eV.]

[Hint. Assuming the direction of motion of the electron to be along the axis of *x*, *momentum of the electron* = $1.2 \times 10^{-22}\ \hat{i}$ kg-m/sec and *momentum of nutrino* = $6.4 \times 10^{-23}\ \hat{j} = 0.64 \times 10^{-22}\ \hat{j}$ kg-m/sec.]

And, *momentum of the residual nucleus* = $n\vec{v}$, where *m* is its mass and $\vec{v}$, its *velocity*. Since, initially, the undecayed nucleus was at rest, its momentum was zero. Hence, in accordance with the law of conservation of momentum,

$1.2 \times 10^{-22}\,\hat{i} + 0.64 \times 10^{-22}\ \hat{j} + m\vec{v} = 0$, whence, $m\vec{v} = -(1.2 \times 10^{-22}\hat{i} + 0.64 \times 10^{-22}\,\hat{j})$

Hence, *magnitude of momentum of recoiling nucleus, mv*

$$= \sqrt{(1.2 \times 10^{-22})^2 + (0.64 \times 10^{-22})^2} = 1.36 \times 10^{-22} \text{ kg-m/sec.}$$

If its direction of motion be inclined at $< \theta$ with the *x*-axis or direction of motion of the electron, we have $\tan\theta = 0.64/1.2 = 0.5333$, whence, $\theta = \tan^{-1}(0.5333) \approx 28°4'$.

And, *velocity of the recoiling nucleus* $= \dfrac{momentum\ (mv)}{mass\ (m)} = \dfrac{1.36 \times 10^{-22}}{5.8 \times 10^{-26}}\ m/sec.$

$$\therefore \quad K.E.\ of\ recoil = \frac{1}{2}mv^2 = \frac{1}{2} \times 5.8 \times 10^{-26} \times \left(\frac{1.36 \times 10^{-22}}{5.8 \times 10^{-26}}\right)^2$$

$$= 1.595 \times 10^{-19}\ joule$$

$$= \frac{1.595 \times 10^{-4}}{1.60 \times 10^{-19}} \approx 1\text{eV.}]$$

9. A railroad flat car of weight *W* can roll without friction along a straight horizontal track. Initially, a man of weight ω is standing on the car which is moving to the right with speed v_0. What is the change in velocity of the car if the man runs to the *left* so that his speed relative to the car is *v* just before he jumps off *at the left end*? **[Ans.** $wv/(W + w)$]

10. A bomb of mass 40.0 kg explodes in flight at the instant when its velocity is $\vec{v_0} = 10\hat{i} + 5\hat{j}\ m/sec.$ It splits in two fragments of mass ratio 1 : 3 and the larger mass is observed to have velocity $\vec{v_2} = 100\hat{i} + 50\hat{j} + 10\hat{k}\ m/sec$ just after explosion. Deduce (*i*) velocity $\vec{v_1}$ of the smallest fragment just after explosion, (*ii*) kinetic energy produced in the explosion.

[Ans. (*i*) $-(260\hat{i} + 130\hat{j} + 30\hat{k})\ m/sec.$ (*ii*) 6.135×10^2 *joules.*]

[Hint. If *M* be the mass of the unexploded bomb, *its momentum before explosion* = $M\mathbf{v}_0$. And if m_1 and m_2 be the masses of the two fragments after explosion and $\mathbf{v}_1$ and $\mathbf{v}_2$, their respective velocities, we have $M\mathbf{v}_0 = m_1\mathbf{v}_1 + m_2\mathbf{v}_2$.

Or, $\quad 40(10\hat{i} + 5\hat{j}) = 10\vec{v_1} + 30(100\hat{i} + 50\hat{j} + 10\hat{k})$

whence, $\quad \vec{v_1} = -(260\hat{i} + 130\hat{j} + 30\hat{k})\ m/sec.$

And *K.E. produced in the explosion* $= \frac{1}{2}m_1v_1^2 + \frac{1}{2}m_2v_2^2 - \frac{1}{2}Mv_0^2 = \frac{1}{2} \times 10(260^2 + 130^2 + 30^2) + \frac{1}{2} \times 30(100^2 + 50^2 + 10^2) - \frac{1}{2} \times 40(10^2 + 5^2) = 6.135 \times 10^2$ joules].

11. Three particles of masses 20 *gm*, 30 *gm* and 40 *gm* are initially moving along the positive direction of the three coordinate axes respectively with the same velocity of 20 *cm/sec*, when due to their mutual interaction, the first particle comes to rest, the second acquires a velocity $10\hat{j} + 20\hat{k}$. What is then the velocity of the third particle? **[Ans.** $10\hat{i} + 7.5\hat{j} + 5\hat{k}$.]

[Hint. *Initial momentum of the system* $= 20(20\hat{i}) + 30(20\hat{j}) + 40(20\hat{k})$ and *final momentum of the system* $= 20(0) + 30(10\hat{j} + 20\hat{k}) + 40\vec{v}$, where $\vec{v}$ is the velocity of the third particle. Equating the two, $\vec{v}$ can be evaluated.]

12. Two blocks A and B of mass m_A and m_B are connected together by means of a spring and are resting on a horizontal frictionless table. The blocks are then pulled apart so as to stretch the spring and then released. Show that the kinetic energies of the blocks are, at any instant, inversely proportional to their respective masses.

13. A projectile is fired from a gun at an angle of 45° with the horizontal and with a muzzle speed of 1500 ft/sec. At the highest point in its flight the projectile explodes into two fragments of equal mass. One fragment; whose initial speed is zero, falls vertically. How far from the gun does the other fragment land, assuming a level terrain? **[Ans.** 1.1×10^5 ft.]

14. The wire cage of a bird is suspended from a spring balance. How does the reading on the balance differ when the bird flies about firm that when it just sits quietly?

15. Define centre of mass. Show that when no external force acts on a body the acceleration of the centre of mass is zero and its velocity is a constant.

(G.N.D.U. 2002; Indore U.2001; Nagpur U.2007; D.A.U. Agra 2006)

16. What is centre of mass? Find the total linear momentum of a system of particles about the centre of mass and show that it is zero. ***(Nag. U. 2009, 2007; Gharwal U. 2000)***

17. (*a*) What is reduced mass? Reduce two body problem to one body problem and obtain equation of motion for equivalent one body problem for two masses.

(H.P.U. 2001, 2000; Luck. U. 2001; P.U. 2000; Gharwal U. 2000; Purvanchal U. 2005; Nagpur U. 2007)

(*b*) Discuss the motion of reduced mass under the influence of inverse square force. ***(H.P.U. 2000)***

(*c*) Distinguish between centre of mass and reduced mass. What is their importance in Physics?

II–Centre of mass

18. Show that the position of the centre of mass of a system of particles is quite independent of the frame of reference used.

19. Show that the centre of mass of two particles is on the line joining them at a point whose distance from each particle is inversely proportional to the mass of that particle.

20. (*a*) What is meant by a centre of mass frame of reference? What is its particular advantage?

(*b*) Must there necessarily be any mass at the centre of mass in the case of a solid body and must it always lie within the body?

21. If only an external force can change the state of motion of the centre of mass of a body, how does it happen that the internal force of the brakes can bring a car to rest?

22. (*a*) Locate the centre of mass of three particles of 2 kg, 3 kg and 4 kg placed at the three corners of an equilateral triangle of 1 metre side. [**Ans.** $x = 0.56\ m$, $y = 0.385\ m$.]

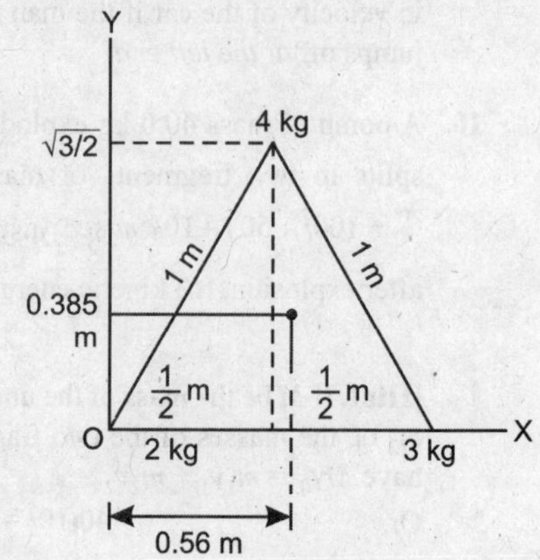

Fig. 6.30

[**Hint.** Imagine the triangle to lie in *X–Y plane*, with one side along the axis of x, as shown in Fig. 6.30. Then, we have

$$x = \frac{\Sigma m_k x_k}{\Sigma m_k} = \frac{2(0)+3(1)+4\left(\frac{1}{2}\right)}{2+3+4} = \frac{5}{9} = 0.56\ m \text{ and}$$

$$y = \frac{\Sigma m_k y_k}{\Sigma m_k} = \frac{2(0)+3(0)+4(\sqrt{3}/2)}{2+3+4}$$

$$= \frac{2\sqrt{3}}{9} = 0.385\ m.]$$

(*b*) Where does the centre of mass of a triangular plate lie?

[**Ans.** *At the point of intersection of the three medians.*]

23. Find the centre of mass (*i*) a solid hemisphere (*ii*) a thin hemispherical shell, of radius r.

[**Ans.** (*i*) $\frac{3}{8}r$ *above the centre of the plane face* (*ii*) $\frac{1}{2}r$ *above the mid-point of open face.*]

24. The centre of mass of three particles of masses 4 gm, 5 gm and 6 gm respectively lies at the point (2, 2, 2). Where should a fourth particle of mass 12 gm be placed so that the centre of mass of the system of four particles lies at (0, 0, 0)? [**Ans.** At the point (–2.5, –2.5, –2.5)]

25. In a given inertial frame, three particles of masses 10 gm, 30 gm and 20 gm are moving with velocities $6\hat{i}, 4\hat{j}$ and $9\hat{k}$ respectively. Calculate the velocity of the centre of mass of the system. What will be the velocities of the three particles in the centre-of-mass frame of reference whose coordinate axes are parallel to those of the inertial frame?

[**Ans.** $\vec{V} = \hat{i}+2\hat{j}+3\hat{k}, \vec{v_1} = 5\hat{i}-2\hat{j}-3\hat{k}, \vec{v_2} = -\hat{i}+2\hat{j}-3\hat{k}, \vec{v_3} = -\hat{i}-2\hat{j}+6\hat{k}.$]

[**Hint.** $\vec{V} = \frac{\Sigma m_k \vec{V_k}}{\Sigma m_k} = \frac{10(6\hat{i})+30(4\hat{j})+20(9\hat{k})}{10+30+20} = \hat{i}+2\hat{j}+3\hat{k}.$

And, velocities in the centre-of-mass frame of reference, are

$$\vec{v_1} = (6\hat{i})-\vec{V}, \vec{v_2} = (4\hat{j})-\vec{V} \text{ and } \vec{v_3} = (9\hat{k})-\vec{V}.]$$

26. The respective positions of three particles A, B and C, of masses 10 kg, 5 kg and 5 kg are given by $(4\hat{i}+2\hat{j})$, $(-2\hat{i}+2\hat{j})$ and $(2\hat{i}-4\hat{j})$ metres. If forces $20\hat{j}, -10\hat{i}$ and $25\hat{i}$ newtons act on them respectively, calculate the acceleration of the centre of mass of the system. Illustrate your answer by means of a proper diagram. [**Ans.** 1.25 *m/sec*^{2} *at an angle* 53° *with the axis of x.*]

[**Hint.** Here, the *x-component* of the resultant force $\vec{F}$ acting on the centre of mass is $\vec{F_x} = 25\hat{i} - 10\hat{i} = 15\hat{i}$ and its *y-component*, $\vec{F_y} = 20\hat{j}$.]

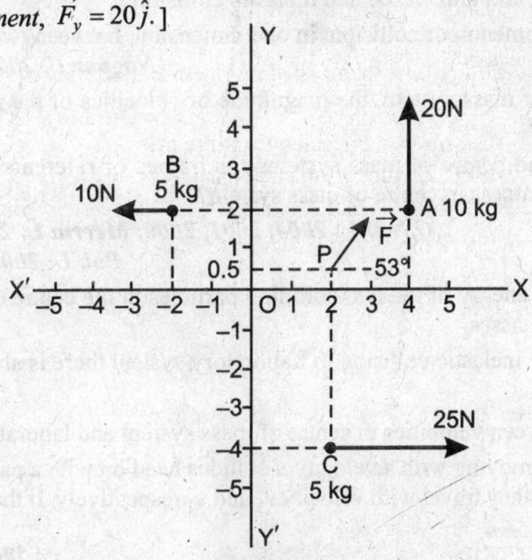

Fig. 6.31

$\therefore$ *magnitude of the resultant force acting at the centre of mass* $= \sqrt{15^2 + 20^2} = \sqrt{625} = 25N$. If θ be the angle that this force makes with the x-axis, we have $\theta = \tan^{-1}(20/15) = \tan^{-1}(4/3) = 53°$.

Hence, *acceleration of the centre of mass* $= \frac{force}{total\ mass} = \frac{25}{10+5+5} = \frac{25}{20} = 1.25\ m/sec^2$ at an angle of 53° with the x-axis.

To illustrate this by means of a diagram, we must first indicate the positions of the particles A, B and C, as shown in Fig. 6.31. Then, the x and y coordinates of the centre of mass are obtained as usual, *i.e.*,

$$x = \frac{10(4)+5(-2)+5(2)}{10+5+5} = 2m \text{ and}$$

$$y = \frac{10(2)+5(2)+5(-4)}{10+5+5} = 0.5\ m$$

Or, the position of the centre of mass P is ($2\mathbf{i} + 0.5\mathbf{j}$).

Thus, the *c.m.*, lies at the point P, as shown, and the force $F = 25N$ acts at this point P at an angle of 53° with the x-axis.

The acceleration of the centre of mas, $F/M = 25/20 = 1.25$ m/sec^2 is thus naturally *directed along F*, *i.e.*, at an angle of 53° with the x-axis.]

27. Calculate the changes in the values of energy and angular momentum when a two body system interacting through gravitational force is reduced to an equivalent one body problem.

28. (*a*) (*i*) what is the position vector of centre of mass?

(*ii*) What is the velocity and acceleration of centre of mass?

(*b*) Show that the linear momentum of the system of two particles is equal to the linear momentum of the centre of mass. ***(Gharwal U. 2000; P.U. 2004; Pbi. U. 2003)***

29. A bomb weighing 50 kg explodes into three pieces in flight when its velocity is $20\hat{i} + 22\hat{j} + 10\hat{k}$ ms^{-1}. Two fragments of the bomb weighing 10 and 20 *kg*, are found to have velocities $100\hat{i} + 50\hat{j} + 20\hat{k}$ and $30\hat{i} + 20\hat{j} + 10\hat{k}$ ms^{-1}. Find the third piece.

[**Hint.** The mass of third piece =20 kg. Let its velocity be $(x\hat{i} + y\hat{j} + z\hat{k})\ ms^{-1}$, then $50\ (20\hat{i} + 22\hat{j} + 10\hat{k}) = 10\ (100\hat{i} + 50\hat{j} + 20\hat{k}) + 20\ (30\hat{i} - 20\hat{j} - 10\hat{k}) + 20\ (x\hat{i} + y\hat{j} + z\hat{k})$] [**Ans.** $(-30\hat{i} + 50\hat{j} - 25\hat{k})$ ms^{-1}]

30. Deduce the equation of motion of the centre of mass. ***(Nagpur U. 2007)***

III–Collision

31. (*i*) What is collision? Explain elastic and inelastic collision.

(*ii*) Discuss the phenomenon of collision, in one dimension, between two particles, when collision is perfectly elastic. ***(Nagpur U. 2009, M.S.U. Tirunelveli 2007)***

32. Prove that in centre of mass system, the magnitude of velocities of the particles remain unaltered in elastic collision. ***(Pbi. U. 2001, P.U. 2000)***

33. Explain laboratory and centre of mass systems (or frames of reference). What is the advantage of studying a collision process in centre of mass system?

(G.N.D.U. 2004, 2001, 2000; Meerut U. 2003; P.U. 2004, 2001, 2000; Pbi. U. 2001, 2000; Guwahati U. 2000)

34. Prove that the kinetic energy of the two colliding particles in the centre of mass system are inversely proportional to their masses.

35. Show that in perfectly inelastic collision in Laboratory system there is always loss of kinetic energy. ***(G.N.D.U. 2004)***

36. State the relation between velocities in centre of mass system and laboratory system. ***(Pbi. U. 2001)***

37. A particle of mass m_1 moving with a velocity u collides head on with a particle of mass m_2 at rest such that after the collision they travel with velocity v_1 and v_2 respectively. If the collision is perfectly elastic one, show that $v_2 = \frac{2m_1u_1}{m_1 + m_2}$. ***(Agra U. 2007; G.N.D.U. 2003)***

38. What precisely is meant by the term 'collision'? Show that in an elastic one-dimensional collision, the relative velocity with which the two particles approach each other before collision is equal to the relative velocity with which they recede from each other after collision. ***(Nagpur U. 2008)***

39. Discuss the following special cases in an elastic collision:

(*i*) when the colliding particles have the same mass, (*ii*) when one of the colliding particles is also initially at rest, (*iii*) when the particle at rest is much more massive than the other, (*iv*) when the particle at rest is much lighter than the other. ***(Nagpur U. 2007)***

40. Show that in a head-on elastic collision between two particles, the transference of energy is the maximum when their mass ratio is unity.

41. A neutron of mass 1.67×10^{-27} kg and speed 10^5 m/sec collides with a stationary deuteron of mass 3.34×10^{-27} kg. The particles do not stick together and no kinetic energy is lost in collision. What is the subsequent speed of each particle. ***(Nagpur Uni. 2009, 2006)***

Ans. Speed of neutron = 3.33×10^4 m/sec; Speed of deuteron = 6.67×10^4 m/sec in opposite direction.

42. Obtain an expression for the fractional decrease in kinetic energy of a neutron of mass m_1 when it makes a head-on collision with an atomic nucleus of mass m_2 initially at rest and calculate the percentage decrease when the nucleus concerned is the one of (*i*) lead, (*ii*) carbon, (*iii*) hydrogen.

[Ans. $\dfrac{4m_1m_2}{(m_1+m_2)^2}$, (*i*) 2%, (*ii*) 28%, (*iii*) 100%.]

[Hint. If u_1 and v_1 be the velocities of the neutron before and after collision respectively, we have *K.E. of the neutron before collision*, $T_1 = \frac{1}{2}m_1u_1^2$ and its *K.E. after collision*, $T_2 = \frac{1}{2}m_1v_1^2$.

$$\therefore \text{ fractional loss of energy on collision} = \frac{T_1 - T_2}{T_1} = \frac{\frac{1}{2}m_1u_1^2 - \frac{1}{2}m_1v_1^2}{\frac{1}{2}m_1u_1^2} = \frac{u_1^2 - v_1^2}{u_1^2} = 1 - \frac{v_1^2}{u_1^2}. \quad \text{...I}$$

But, as we have seen in § 6.10 (*ii*) (*b*) above, in a collision of this type,

$$v_1 = \left(\frac{m_1 - m_2}{m_1 + m_2}\right)u_1.$$

Substituting this value of v_1 in relation I above, we have

$$\frac{T_1 - T_2}{T_1} = 1 - \left(\frac{m_1 - m_2}{m_1 + m_2}\right)^2 u_1^2/u_1^2 = 1 - \left(\frac{m_1 - m_2}{m_1 + m_2}\right)^2 = \frac{4m_1m_2}{(m_1 + m_3)^2}.$$

$\therefore$ (*i*) For lead, $m_2/m_1 = 206$ and $\therefore$ $m_2 = 206\, m_1$. So that,

$$\frac{T_1 - T_2}{T_1} = \frac{4 \times 206}{(1+206)^2} = 0.01912 \text{ or } 1.91\% \approx 2\%$$

(*ii*) For *cabon*, $m_2/m_1 = 12$, or, $m_2 = 12\, m_1$, and

$$\therefore \quad \frac{T_1 - T_2}{T_1} = \frac{4 \times 12}{(1+12)^2} = 0.2841 \text{ or } 28\%.$$

And (*iii*) for hydrogen, $m_2/m_1 = 1$ or, $m_2 = m_1$, and

$$\therefore \quad \frac{T_1 - T_2}{T_1} = \frac{4 \times 1}{(1+1)^2} = 1 \text{ or } 100\%.]$$

43. Show that in a one-dimensional elastic collision the speed of the centre of mass of two particles, m_1 moving with initial speed u_1, and m_2 moving with initial speed u_2 is given by $V = \left(\dfrac{m_1}{m_1+m_2}\right)u_1 + \left(\dfrac{m_2}{m_1+m_2}\right)u_2$ both before and after collision.

[Hint. *Before collision*, $(m_1 + m_2)V = m_1u_1 + m_2u_2$, whence, $V = \left(\dfrac{m_1}{m_1+m_2}\right)u_1 + \left(\dfrac{m_2}{m_1+m_2}\right)u_2$. After collision, using the values of v_1 and v_2, as given under \$6.10 and substituting in the relation $(m_1 + m_2)$ $V = m_1v_1 + m_2v_2$ we obtain the same value of V as before collision.]

44. Two objects of masses $m_1 = 2$ gm and $m_2 = 5$ gm possess velocities $\vec{u_1} = 10\hat{i}$ cm/sec and $\vec{u_2} = 3\hat{i} + 5\hat{j}$ *cm/sec* just prior to a collision during which they become permanently attached to each other. Obtain the values of (*i*) the velocity of the centre of mass of the system, (*ii*) final momentum of the system in (*a*) the laboratory (*b*) the centre-of-mass reference frame, (*iii*) the fraction of the initial total kinetic energy associated with the motion after collision.

[**Ans.** (*i*) $5\hat{i} + \frac{25}{7}\hat{j}$ *cm/sec*, (*ii*) (*a*) $35\hat{i} + 25\hat{j}$ *gm-cm/sec*, (*b*) 0, (*iii*) 0.72.]

[**Hint.** (*i*) $(m_1 + m_2)V = m_1u_1 + m_2u_2$. (*ii*) (*a*) Since momentum is conserved in both elastic and inelastic collisions, the final momentum is equal to the initial momentum $m_1u_1 + m_2u_2$ or equal to $(m_1 + m_2)V$. (*b*) since in the centre-of-mass reference frame, the centre of mass remains at rest, $V = 0$ and hence the momentum of the system $= (m_1 + m_2)\ V = 0$. (*iii*) *Initial K.E.*, $T_1 = \frac{1}{2}m_1u_1^2 + \frac{1}{2}m_2u_2^2$ and *final K.E.*, $T_2 = \frac{1}{2}(m_1 + m_2)v^2$, where v is the velocity of the combination after collision, equal to $(m_1u_1 + m_2u_2)/(m_1 + m_2)$, *i.e.*, the same as the velocity of the centre of mass. The fraction of the total K.E. associated with the motion after collision is thus T_2/T_1.]

45. The amount of energy transferred to a stationary body of mass m_2 by a collision with a moving body of mass m_1 can be increased by interposing another body of mass m_3 between them, so that m_1 strikes m_3 which, in turn, strikes m_2. Show that the energy transferred to m_2 is a maximum when $m_3 = \sqrt{m_1m_2}$.

46. A bullet of mass 20 gm and moving with a speed of 20 m/sec hits the bob of a simple pendulum of mass 0.5 kg and lodges into it. If the length of the pendulum be 100 cm and $g = 980$ cm/sec^2, find the angular amplitude of the swing of the pendulum. [**Ans.** 14°15′.]

[**Hint.** See worked example 12. *Angular amplitude* $\theta = \sin\theta = x/l$, where l is the length of the pendulum.]

47. A bullet of mass 10 gm strikes a ballistic pendulum of mass 2.0 kg. The centre of masses of the pendulum rises a vertical distance 12 cm. Assuming the bullet remains embedded in the pendulum, calculate its initial speed. [**Ans.** 310 m/sec.]

N.B. A ballistic pendulum is just a large wooden block suspended vertically by a pair of cords. The time of impact of the bullet with the pendulum is much smaller than the time-period o the pendulum, so that the cords remain vertical during the collision. No external force thus acts on the system (bullet + pendulum) and the horizontal component of the momentum remains conserved.

48. Calculate the percentage of the initial kinetic energy lost by a neutron colliding head-on with (*a*) a stationary deuterium nucleus, (*b*) a stationary carbon nucleus. [**Ans.** (*a*) 67% (*b*) 28%]

49. Show that the relative velocity between the particles after an elastic head-on collision is equal and opposite to the relative velocity before the collision. ***(Agra U. 2003)***

50. A body of mass 100 gms moving with a velocity $(8\hat{i} - 6\hat{j} - 10\hat{k})$ cm s^{-1} collides with a body of mass 200 gm moving with velocity $(-10\hat{i} + 6\hat{j} - 8\hat{k})$ cm s^{-1} and attain velocities $(3\hat{i} - 4\hat{j} - 5\hat{k})$ and $(-4\hat{i} + 5\hat{j} - 6\hat{k})$ cm s^{-1} respectively. Find kinetic energy before and after collision in the Lab system. Is the collision elastic?

[**Hint.** Energy before collision $= \frac{1}{2}\times 100(8\hat{i} - 6\hat{j} - 10\hat{k})^2 + \frac{1}{2}\times 100(-10\hat{i} + 6\hat{j} - 8\hat{k})^2 = 30{,}000$ *erg*

Energy after collision $= \frac{1}{2}\times 100(3\hat{i} - 4\hat{j} - 5\hat{k})^2 + \frac{1}{2}\times 100(-4\hat{i} + 5\hat{j} - 6\hat{k})^2 = 10{,}200$ *erg*

The collision is inelastic as the kinetic energy is not conserved.]

51. In a head-on collision, a particle with an initial speed V_0 strikes a stationary particle of the same mass. Find the velocies v_1 and v_2 of the two particles respectively after collisions if half of the original K.E. is lost. ***(D.A.U. Agra 2006)***

52. Two particles of masses 100 and 300 gm have at a given time positions $2\hat{i} + 5\hat{j} + 13\hat{k}$ and $-6\hat{i} + 4\hat{j} - 2\hat{k}$ cm respectively and velocities $10\hat{i} - 7\hat{j} - 3\hat{k}$ and $7\hat{i} - 9\hat{j} + 6\hat{k}$ *cm/s* respectively. Find (*a*) the instantaneous position and (*b*) velocity of centre of mass. ***(Nagpur U. 2007)***

[**Ans.** (*a*) $\frac{-16\hat{i} + 17\hat{j} + 7\hat{k}}{4}$ *m* and (*b*) $\frac{31\hat{i} - 34\hat{j} + 15\hat{k}}{4}$ *m/s*]

IV–Rocket

53. Explain the principle underlying a *rocket*. What is meant by the *thrust* of a rocket and on what factors does it depend?

Establish the relation for the velocity of a rocket both when its weight is ignored and when it is taken into account.

54. What is a two-stage rocket? What is the advantage of a two-stage rocket over a single stage rocket?

55. The final velocity of the final stage of a multistage rocket is much greater than the final velocity of a single stage rocket of the *same* total weight and fuel supply. Why is this so? Explain.

56. Show that the speed of a rocket is (*i*) equal to the exhaust speed, (*ii*) twice the exhaust speed, when the ratio M_0/M is very nearly (*i*) e (about 2.7), (*ii*) e^2 (about 7.4).

57. A rocket of mass 20 kg has 180 kg fuel. The exhaust velocity of the fuel is 1.6 km/sec. Calculate the minimum rate of consumption of fuel so that the rocket may rise from the ground. Also calculate the ultimate vertical speed gained by the rocket when the rate of consumption of fuel is (*i*) 2 kg/sec, (*ii*) 20 kg/sec. [**Ans.** 1.225 kg/sec (*i*) 2.8 km/sec, (*ii*) 3.6 km/sec.]

[**Hint.** See worked example 16.]

58. If an ion engine with an exhaust velocity of 108 m/sec could be constructed, what percentage of the initial mass must be fuel if the engine is used to power a rocket that can attain the escape velocity of 11.2 km/sec? Neglect gravity and air resistance. **Ans.** 0.011%.

59. An empty rocket weighs 5000 kg and contains 40,000 kg fuel. If exhaust velocity of the fuel is 2.0 km/sec, calculate the maximum velocity gained by the rocket. Deduce the formula used.

Ans. 4.29 km/s

60. What is a rocket? Describe the principle of a rocket? Why multistage rocket is necessary? Establish the following relation for a rocket

$$V = V_0 + v\log_e\left(\frac{M_0}{M}\right)$$

Calculate the burnt out velocity when rocket starts from rest.

(Nagpur U. 2009, 2007, 2003; Cal. U. 2003; Meerut U. 2001, 2000; Agra U. 2007, 2003)

V–Angular momentum

61. Define angular momentum of a particle. Show that the time rate change of angular momentum of a particle is equal to the torque acting on it.

62. (*a*) Define angular momentum $\vec{J}$ and torque $\vec{\tau}$. What are their units? Show that torque is given by the time rate of change of angular momentum.

(Meerut U. 2002; M.D.U. 2000; Kerala U. 2001; Agra U. 2007, 2005; Nagpur U. 2009)

(*b*) If no torque acts on a body will its angular velocity remain conserved? ***(Nagpur U. 2008)***

63. (*a*) Establish the vector relation between the force and the torque.

(*b*) Establish the relation between torque applied and angular acceleration.

64. (*a*) State and explain the law of conservation of angular momentum. Illustrate with examples. What are the consequences of the law of conservation of angular momentum?

(G.N.D.U. 2001; Luck. U. 2001; Meerut U. 2001; Guwahati U. 2000; Bang. U. 2000; Nagpur U. 2008)

(*b*) Explain why an ice skater always utilises the principle of conservation of angular momentum.

(M.D.U. 2000)

65. Discuss the motion of the top. Calculate the precessional velocity of a top and also show that $\vec{\tau} = \vec{\omega}_p \times \vec{L}$ where $\vec{\tau}$ is torque, $\vec{\omega}_p$ is precessional velocity and $\vec{L}$ is angular momentum.

(Meerut 2005)

66. Show that the total angular momentum of a system of particles about a fixed or a reference point is given by the relation $\vec{J} = \vec{R} \times \vec{P} + \vec{J}_{c.m.}$, where $(\vec{R} \times \vec{P})$ is the angular momentum of the centre of mass about that point and $\vec{J}_{c.m.}$, the angular momentum of the system about the centre of mass. What are spin and orbital angular momenta?

67. (*a*) State the law of conservation of angular momentum. Give one example of its application.
(*b*) Show that for a central force, the angular momentum is conserved. ***(Nagpur U. 2005)***

68. (*a*) Define angular momentum $\vec{J}$ and torque $\vec{\tau}$. Using Newton's second law in an inertial frame of reference, show that $d\vec{J}/dt = \vec{\tau}$
(*b*) Show that for a particle subjected to a central force, the angular momentum is a constant of motion ***(G.N.D.U. 2001)***

69. (*a*) A man turns on a rotating table with an angular speed ω. He is holding two equal masses at arm's length. Without moving his arms, he drops the two masses. What change, if any, is there in his angular speed? Is the angular momentum conserved? Explain.
(*b*) Show that the conservation of the angular momentum of a system is a consequence of the rotational invariance of its potential energy. ***(MDU 2003; Pbi U. 2001, P.U. 2000; HPU 2003)***

70. Show that the conservation of angular momentum applied to planetary motion leads to the law of constant areal velocity.

71. Why is the velocity of a satellite the *maximum* when it is *closest* to the sun and the *minimum* when it is farthest from it in its orbit around it?

72. State the law of conservation of angular momentum. Show that the sum of all internal torques is zero. Derive an expression for the distance of closest approach of a proton projected into the Coulomb field of a heavy nucleus. ***[Delhi (Hons), 1971]***

73. A proton of speed *u* travels towards an atomic nucleus such that if it is undeflected, the nearest approach would be *b*. Show that the actual nearest approach *b*′ is given by $Ze^2/b' = \frac{1}{2}mv^2[1-(b/b')^2]$, where *Z* is the atomic number of the nucleus and *m* is the mass of the proton.

74. (*a*) For a particle of mass $m = 10.0$ *gm*, position $r = 10\mathbf{i} + 6\mathbf{j}$ cm and velocity $v = 5\mathbf{i}$ *cm/sec*, calculate the angular momentum about the origin. ***[Agra (Supp), 1970]***
[**Ans.** –300 k.]
(*b*) Show that the angular momentum of a particle about a fixed point is equal to the product of its mass and double the area $\left(\frac{1}{2}r^2\omega\right)$ described by the rotating line in unit time and has a direction perpendicular to this area.

75. What is the angular momentum of a neutron of kinetic energy 1 MeV about a nucleus if the impact parameter be 1 A.U. (mass of neutron may be taken to be 1.67×10^{-24} gm; 1 *A.U.* = 10^{-8} cm.
[**Ans.** 2.31×10^{-23} gm-cm²/sec.]

76. Explain why due to atmospheric friction, the velocity of a satellite in its circular (or nearly circular) orbit around the earth increases. Does it not violate the law of conservation of energy? What happens to its angular momentum?
[**Hint.** Due to atmospheric friction, the satellite certainly loses some energy in the form of heat. Since, however, its *total energy E = its kinetic energy T + its potential energy U* we have

$$E = T + U = \frac{1}{2}mv^2 - MmG/r,$$

where *M* is the *mass of the earth, m,* the *mass of the satellite, r,* the *radius of its orbit* and *v,* its *velocity in the orbit.*

Now, for a circular motion around the earth, $mv^2/r = MmG/r$, whence, $v^2 = MG/r$.

$$\therefore \qquad E = \frac{1}{2}m\frac{MG}{r} - \frac{MmG}{r} = -\frac{1}{2}\frac{MmG}{r}.$$

Thus, a reduction in the value of *E* (due to friction) means that it should become less positive or more negative, *i.e., r,* the radius of the orbit of the satellite should become smaller.

Since, as we know, $v \propto 1/\sqrt{r}$ [see worked example 33(*a*)], a reduction in the value of *r*, the radius of the orbit of the satellite, must result in an increase in the value of *v*, the velocity of the satellite in the orbit.

Apparently, this increase in the K.E. of the satellite may look like a violation of the law of conservation of energy but a little reflection will show that the P.E. of the satellite decreases to an even greater extent, so that *there is an over all reduction in the energy of the satellite* on account of its conversion into heat due to atmospheric friction just in accordance with the law of conservation of energy.

And, since angular momentum **J** is also proportional to $1/\sqrt{r}$ [see worked example 30(*a*)], *the angular momentum of the satellite decreases with decrease in the radius of its orbit* (due to frictional effects). It may be noted, however, that the atmosphere gains an equal amount of angular momentum, so that *the angular momentum of the system, as a whole, remains conserved.*]

77. A flywheel of mass 100 kg and radius of gyration 0.5 m is rotating with a speed of 90 revolutions per minute. Calculate the torque required to bring it to rest in 4 minutes. [**Ans.** 0.98 Nm]

78. A massive ball comes moving and collides elastically with a comparatively very light stationary ball. Immediately after the collision, what is the approximate ratio of speeds of lighter and massive ball? (***Luck. U. 2001***).

[**Hint.** The velocity of heavy particle remains almost the same after collision and the light particle acquires nearly twice the velocity of heavy particle.

$$\frac{\text{Speed of lighter particle}}{\text{Speed of heavy (massive) particle}} = 2]$$

79. The earth is moving around the Sun under gravitational force and its orbit has semi-major axis of 1.495×10^8 km. When the earth passes closest to the Sun (*i.e.*, at its perhilion) its distance is 1.47×10^8 km and its orbital velocity is 0.303 km s^{-1}. Find earth's velocity at the apehilion and also its angular velocities at the two positions.

[**Hint.** Angular momentum $\vec{J} = \vec{r} \times m\vec{v}$ is conserved.]

[**Ans.** $V_a = 293$ km s^{-1}; $\omega_p = 0.206 \times 10^{-8}$ rad s^{-1}; $\omega_a = 0.193 \times 10^{-9}$ rad s^{-1}]

80. A grind stone weighing 40 kg has a radius of 1.2 m. Starting from rest it acquires a speed of 150 r.p.m. in 12 sec. Calculate the torque acting on it.

[**Hint.** $$I = \frac{1}{2}MR^2 = \frac{1}{2} \times 40 \times 1.2 \times 1.2 = 28.8 \text{ Kg m}^2$$

$$\alpha = \frac{2\pi \times 150}{60 \times 12} = \frac{5\pi}{12} \text{ rad s}^{-2} \quad \tau = I\alpha = \frac{28.8 \times 5\pi}{12} = 37.7\text{Nm}]$$

7 SIMPLE HARMONIC MOTION

Chapter

Brief Contents

INTRODUCTION

Every oscillatory motion is simple harmonic in character and continues due to the interaction of *inertia* and *elasticity*. Motion of a clock pendulum, balance wheel of a clock, mass attached to a suspended spring, vibrations of prongs of tunning fork, up and down motion of needle of sewing machine, a bar magnet suspended in uniform magnetic field are some of the familiar examples of simple harmonic motion. When an oscillator is displaced from its position of equilibrium by application of a force and thus doing work on it, a restoring force comes into play tending to bring it back to its equilibrium position. According to Hook's law, this restoring force is proportional to the displacement and depends upon the *elastic properties* or *elasticity* of the system. As soon as the restoring force tries to bring the system back to its equilibrium position, the property of *inertia* opposes this change in velocity. Further, when the system reaches the equilibrium position, it overshoots the mark and moves beyond the mean position again due to inertia of motion. The motion continues till the deforming force due to inertia develops, bring the system to rest. The restoring force again then sets the oscillator into motion back towards the equilibrium position. Throughout the process, the total energy remains conserved, only the conversion of P.E. and K.E. and vice-versa takes place within a limit set by the *potential well.*

7.1 PERIODIC AND HARMONIC MOTION

A motion which repeats itself over and over again after regularly recurring intervals of time, called as *time-period*, is referred to as a periodic motion.

If a particle, undergoing periodic motion, covers the same path *back and forth* about a mean position, it is said to be executing an *oscillatory* (or *vibratory*) motion or an *oscillation* (or a *vibration*). Such a motion is not only periodic but also bounded, *i.e.*, the displacement of the particle on either side of its mean position remains confined within a well defined limit. Such oscillations are termed as *simple harmonic*. It should be noted that all the peridic motions are not simple harmonic motions (S.H.M.). For example: the motion of earth around the sun and the motion of moon around the earth are periodic but not simple harmonic.

Further, since all of the trigonometrical ratios, the *sines* and the *cosines* alone are periodic as well as bounded, the displacement of a particle executing an oscillatory motion is usually expressed in terms of sines or cosines or a combination of both. Thus, coupled with the fact that this type of motion is, in general, associated with *musical instruments*, (particularly wire instruments whose complexity is solved by Fourier's series), is probably the reason why it is also spoken of as *harmonic motion.*

The term oscillatory motion is not restricted only to 'displacement' of a mechanical oscillator, but it may be any physical quantity. For example, in an electrical system an oscillatory vibration of charge, current or voltage may take place.

7.2 HARMONIC OSCILLATOR

We have seen already, under § 5.8*, how the position of minimum potential energy of a particle is its position of stable equilibrium and how its displacement remains confined to a little distance on either side of this equilibrium or mean position, within what is called a *potential well* and also, how a restoring force $F = -dU/dx$ acts upon it at every point of its displacement except at the mean position (where it is *zero*), tending to bring it back to its mean or equilibrium position. It has also been shown there how the energy function $U = F(x)$ may, in general, be expanded about the position x_0 of stable equilibrium by means of Taylor's theorem. which then gives $U = U_0 + \frac{Cx^2}{2!} + \frac{C_1x^3}{3!} + ...$

and, therefore, force acting on the particle is given by

$$F = -\frac{dU}{dx} = -Cx - \frac{C_1}{2}x^2 - \frac{C_2}{6}x^3 + ...$$

So that, if the displacement be small and C_1, C_2 etc ae negligible, we have $U = U_0 + \frac{1}{2}Cx^2$ and, therefore, force acting on the particle, $F = -(x$, where C is a *positive constant*, called the force constant. This relation indicates that a restoring force acts on the particle, tending to bring it back to its mean or equilibrium position and that the potential energy curve is parabolic in form, as shown in Fig. 5.11.

Such an oscillating particle is called a **harmonic oscillator** and in case the limits (x_1 and x_2) are equally spaced about the equilibrium position, it is called a *simple harmonic oscillator* and its motion, a *simple harmonic motion*, (*S.H.M.*, for short).

Thus, in the case of a simple harmonic motion, the *P.E. curve* varies as the square of the displacement and *the force acting on the particle, and hence its acceleration, is proportional to displacement but is directed oppositely to it* (*towards the mean or equilibrium position*), *the maximum displacement* (*or amplitude*) *of the particle being the same on either side of the mean or equilibrium position.*

In case the displacement is not the same on either side of the equilibrium position, the motion is harmonic all right but not simple harmonic. And, if the values of C_1, C_2 etc. in the relation for U above, cannot be neglected, the P.E. curve would no longer be parabolic but will assume the form shown dotted in Fig. 5.11. Even so, it will be parabolic in form at the bottom of the curve, implying that whatever be the nature of the potential function $U = U_{(x)}$, *small oscillations may always be regarded as simple harmonic.*

Common in nature, the *S.H.M.* is, in fact, the most fundamental type of periodic motion and *all* other periodic motions (*harmonic as well as non-harmonic*) can be obtained by a suitable combination of two or more simple harmonic motions. Let us, therefore, study this motion in some detail.

7.3 SIMPLE HARMONIC MOTION : DIFFERENTIAL EQUATION OF S.H.M.

From what we have just seen in § 7.2 above, we may give a clear-cut definition to S.H.M. as follows:

A particle may be said to execute a simple harmonic motion if its acceleration is proportional to its displacement from its equilibrium position, or any other fixed point in its path, and is always directed towards it.

Thus, if F be the force acting on the particle and x, its displacement from its mean or equilibrium position, we have $F = -Cx$.

Now, in accordance with Newton's second law of motion, $F = ma$. So that, substituting $-Cx$ for F and d^2x/dt^2 for acceleration a, we have

$$-Cx = m\frac{d^2x}{dt^2}. \quad \text{Or,} \quad \frac{d^2x}{dt^2} + \frac{C}{m}x = 0,$$

This equation is called the **differential equation of motion** of a simple harmonic oscillator or a siınple harmonic motion, because by solving it we can find out how the displacement of the particle depends upon time and thus know the correct nature of the motion of the particle.

Solution of differential Equation

To solve the equation, we may put it in the form $d^2x/dt^2 = -(C/m)x$, the negative sign, as we know, indicating that the acceleration is directed oppositely to displacement x.

---

* Students are adviced to go through this article again at this stage in order to understand what follows more thoroughly.

Or, putting $(C/m) = \omega^2$, where ω is the *angular velocity* of the particle, the equation takes the form

$$\frac{d^2x}{dt^2} = -\omega^2 x = -\mu x, \quad ...(i)$$

where μ is a constant, equal to ω^2. Or, since $d^2x/dt^2 = -\mu$ if $x = 1$, we may define μ as the *acceleration per unit displacement of the particle.*

Multiplying both sides of the equation by 2 dx/dt, we have

$$2\frac{dx}{dt}\frac{d^2x}{dt^2} = -\omega^2 . 2x\frac{dx}{dt},$$

integrating which with respect to t, we have

$$\left(\frac{dx}{dt}\right)^2 = -\omega^2 x^2 + A, \quad ...(ii)$$

where A is a constant of integration.

Since at the *maximum displacement* (or *amplitude*) a of the oscillator (or the oscillation), the velocity $dx/dt = 0$, we have

$$0 = \omega^2 a^2 + A, \text{ whence, } A = \omega^2 a^2.$$

Substituting this value of A in relation (*ii*), therefore, we have

$$\left(\frac{dx}{dt}\right)^2 = -\omega^2 x^2 + \omega^2 a^2 = \omega^2(a^2 - x^2),$$

whence, the *velocity of the particle at an instant t,* is given by

$$dx/dt = \omega\sqrt{a^2 - x^2}. \quad ...(iii)$$

Putting equation (*iii*) as $dx/\sqrt{a^2 - x^2} = \omega dt$ and integrating again with respect to t, we have

$$\sin^{-1}\frac{x}{a} = \omega t + \phi. \quad \text{Or,} \quad x = a\sin(\omega t + \phi). \quad ...(iv)$$

This gives the displacement of the particle at an instant t in terms of its amplitude (a) and its total phase $(\omega t + \phi)$, made up of the *phase* angle ωt and what is called the **initial phase, phase constant** or the **epoch** ϕ of the particle, usually denoted by the letter e. This *initial phase* or *epoch* arises because of our starting to count time, not from the instant that the particle is in some standard position, like its mean position or one of its extreme positions, but from the instant when it is anywhere else in between.

Other Solution:

Thus, if we start counting time *when the particle is in its mean position, i.e.,* when $x = 0$ at $t = 0$, we have $\phi = 0$ and, therefore,

$$x = a\sin\omega t.$$

And, if we start counting time *when the particle is in one of its extreme positions, i.e.,* when $x = a$ at $t = 0$, we have $a = a\sin(0 + \phi) = a\sin\phi$, *i.e.*, $\sin\phi = a/a = 1$ or $\phi = \pi/2$. So that, $x = a\sin(\omega t + \pi/2) = a\cos\omega t$.

If, on the other hand, we start counting time from an instant t', *before the particle has passed through its mean position,* we have $x = 0$ when $t = t'$, so that, $0 = a\sin(\omega t' + \phi)$. Or, $\omega t' + \phi = 0$, whence, $\phi = -\omega t' = -e$, say. And, therefore, $x = a\sin(\omega t - e)$.

Similarly, if we start counting time from an instant t', *after the particle has passed througn its mean position,* we have $x = a\sin(\omega t + e)$.

In all these cases, however, the particle executes an oscillation or vibration such that its displacement varies cyclically with time and it is said to execute a simple harmonic motion.

It will be readily seen that if we put $\phi = \phi' + \pi/2$, we shall have

$$x = a\sin(\omega t + \phi' + \pi/2). \quad \text{Or,} \quad x = a\cos(\omega t + \phi').$$

Thus, a simple harmonic motion may be expressed either in terms of a sine or a cosine function. Only, the initial phase or the phase constant will have different values in the two cases.

In fact, the general solution of equation *I*, *viz.*, $d^2x/dt^2 = -\omega^2 x$, is of the form $x = a \sin \omega t + b \cos \omega t$, which is a combination of both the sine and the cosine terms.

Coming back to our relation $x = a \sin(\omega t + \phi)$, we find that if we increase the time t by $2\pi/\omega$, we have $x = a \sin\left[\omega\left(t + \frac{2\pi}{\omega}\right) + \phi\right]$.

Or, $x = a \sin(\omega t + 2\pi + \phi) = a \sin(\omega t + \phi)$, the same, as before, thus indicating that *the particle repeats its movements after every* $2\pi/\omega$ sec, or that, in other words, the time-period of the particle,

$$T = 2\pi/\omega = 2\pi\sqrt{1/\omega^2} = 2\pi\sqrt{1/\mu}$$

Or,
$$T = 2\pi\sqrt{\frac{1}{\text{acceleration per unit displacement.}}}$$

Or,
$$T = 2\pi\sqrt{\frac{\text{displacement}}{\text{acceleration}}}.$$

Or, since $\omega^2 = C/m$, we also have $T = 2\pi\sqrt{m/C}$.

Since T is quite independent of both a and ϕ (or e), it is clear that the oscillations of the particle are *isochronous,* (*i.e.*, take the same time irrespective of the values of a and e).

The number of oscillations (or vibrations) made by the particle per second is called its *frequency of oscillation* or, simply, its *frequency,* usually denoted by the letter n. Thus, *frequency is the reciprocal of the time-period, i.e.,*

$$n = 1/T = \text{w}/2\text{p} = \frac{1}{2\pi}\sqrt{C/m}, \quad \text{whence, w} = 2\text{p}n = 2\text{p}/T.$$

Since ω is the angle described by the particle per second, it is also referred to as the **angular frequency** of the particle.

All these results are equally true for *angular simple harmonic motion,* if we consider angular velocity, displacement, acceleration etc, instead of the linear ones.

Alternatively, we may obtain the same results, perhaps a trifle more neatly, by solving the differential equation of motion of the particle with the help of *complex numbers.* Thus, taking the solution of the equation to be $x = Ae^{ipt}$, where A and p are arbitrary constants and $i = \sqrt{-1}$, we have

$$dx/dt = ipAe^{ipt} \quad \text{and} \quad d^2x/dt^2 = -p^2Ae^{ipt}.$$

Substituting these values in the differential equation $d^2x/dt^2 = -\omega^2 x$, we have

$$-p^2Ae^{ipt} = -\omega^2Ae^{ipt}, \text{ whence, } p^2 = \omega^2 \text{ and, therefore, } p = \pm\,\omega.$$

There are thus *two* solutions to the equation, *viz.*, $x = A_1e^{iwt}$ and $x = A_2e^{-iwt}$.

The *most general solution,* therefore, is $x = A_1e^{iwt} + A_2e^{-iwt}$, where the constants A_1 and A_2 can be determined from the initial conditions.

Now, as we know, $e\theta^i = (\cos\theta + i\sin\theta)$. We, therefore, have

$$x = A_1(\cos\omega t + i\sin\omega t) + A_2(\cos\omega t - i\sin\omega t)$$
$$= (A_1 + A_2)\cos\omega t + i(A_1 - A_2)\sin\omega t.$$

Or, putting $(A_1 + A_2) = a \sin \phi$ and $i(A_1 - A_2) = a \cos \phi$, we have

$$x = a \sin \phi \cos \omega t + a \cos \phi \sin \omega t,$$

i.e., $x = a \sin(\omega t + \phi)$, *the same relation as obtained above.*

Here, obviously, $a = \sqrt{(a \sin \phi)^2 + (a \cos \phi)^2}$

$$= \sqrt{(A_1 + A_2)^2 + [i(A_1 - A_2)^2]} = \sqrt{(A_1 + A_2)^2 - (A_1 - A_2)^2}$$

and $$\phi = \tan^{-1} \frac{A_1 + A_2}{i(A_1 - A_2)}.$$

7.4 PHASE RELATIONSHIP BETWEEN DISPLACEMENT, VELOCITY AND ACCELERATION OF S.H. OSCILLATOR

Displacement. The displacement of a simple harmonic oscillator at any instant of time t is given by $x = a \sin(\omega t + \phi)$. ...(*i*)

Velocity. The velocity is defined as the time rate of change of displacement.

$$\therefore \quad \text{Velocity } v = \frac{dx}{dt} = \dot{x} = a\,\omega \cos(\omega t + \phi)$$

$$= a\,\omega \sin\left(\omega t + \phi + \frac{\pi}{2}\right) \qquad ...(ii)$$

As $\sin(\omega t + \phi) = \frac{x}{a}$, $\cos(\omega t + \phi) = \sqrt{1 - \frac{x^2}{a^2}} = \sqrt{\frac{a^2 - x^2}{a}}$

Or $$v = \omega\sqrt{a^2 - x^2}$$

Maximum velocity. The velocity of the oscillator is maximum when $\sin\left(\omega t + \phi + \frac{\pi}{2}\right) = 1$.

Hence, $V_{max} = a\omega$

The value of $v = V_{max}$ when $x = 0$ *i.e.*, the particle executing S.H.M. is in its mean position.

Comparing equations (*i*) and (*ii*), we find that the velocity of simple harmonic oscillator at any instant of time t *leads* the displacement by a phase difference $\frac{\pi}{2}$ radian (or 90°) *i.e.*, the two are in *quadrature*. The velocity varies harmonically with the same frequency ω.

Acceleration. *Acceleration is defined as the time rate of change of velocity.* Now velocity

$$V = a\,\omega \cos(\omega t + \phi) = a\,\omega \sin\left(\omega t + \phi + \frac{\pi}{2}\right)$$

$$\therefore \quad \text{Acceleration} = \frac{dv}{dt} = \frac{d^2x}{dt^2} = \ddot{x} = -a\,\omega^2 \sin(\omega t + \phi)$$

$$= a\,\omega^2 \sin(\omega t + \phi + \pi) \qquad ...(iii)$$

Maximum acceleration. The acceleration of the oscillator is maximum when $\sin(\omega t + \phi + \pi) = 1$ and is given by $\left(\frac{d^2x}{dt^2}\right)_{max} = a\omega^2$.

Phase relationship between displacement, velocity and acceleration. The displacement of a particle executing S.H.M. is $x = a \sin \omega t$, the velocity $v = a\,\omega \cos(\omega t + \phi) = a\,\omega \sin\left(\omega t + \phi + \frac{\pi}{2}\right)$

and the acceleration = $a\omega^2 \sin(\omega t + \phi + \pi)$. From this we conclude that the acceleration of a simple harmonic oscillator leads the displacement by π radian (or 180°) in phase *i.e.*, the acceleration and displacement are *out of phase i.e., antiphase*.

Graphical representation. The displacement of a particle executing S.H.M. is

$$x = a \sin(\omega t + \phi)$$

$$\therefore \quad \text{Velocity, } V = \frac{dx}{dt} = a\omega \cos(\omega t + \phi)$$

$$\text{and} \quad \text{acceleration} = \frac{d^2x}{dt^2} = -a\omega^2 \sin(\omega t + \phi)$$

Hence, for $y = o, \quad v = +a\omega, \quad a = o$

$y = +a, \quad v = o, \quad a = -\omega^2 a$

$y = -a, \quad v = o, \quad a = +\omega^2 a$

The same is shown graphically in Fig. 7.1

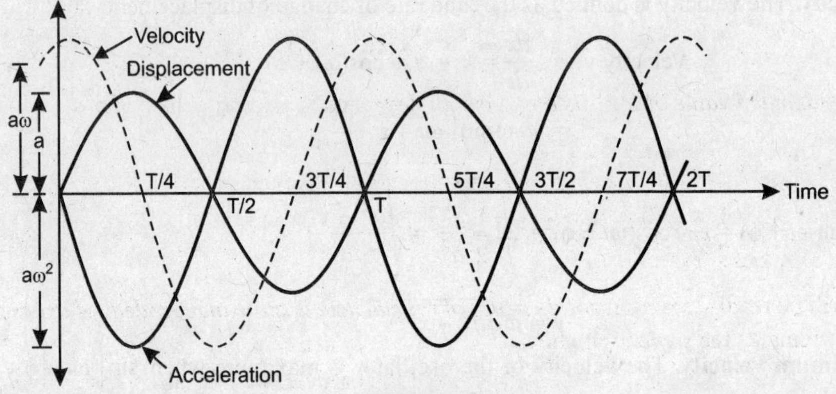

Fig. 7.1

7.5 ENERGY OF A HARMONIC OSCILLATOR

The acceleration of a harmonic oscillator, *i.e.*, of a particle executing a simple harmonic motion, is, as we know, directed towards its mean or equilibrium position, *i.e.*, opposite to the direction in which its displacement x increases. Work is, therefore, done during the displacement of the particle and it thus possesses *potential energy*. Also, the particle has velocity and, therefore, it possesses kinetic energy. Thus, a particle executing simple harmonic motion has, in general, both kinetic and potential energies. And if there be no dissipative forces (like friction etc.) at work, the sum total of the two remains constant, *i.e., the mechanical energy of the oscillator* (*or the particle*) *remains conserved* though, as the displacement increases, the *P.E.* increases and the *K.E.* decreases. Thus, at its maximum displacement (a), when it is momentarily at rest, the whole of its energy is present in the potential form, the kinetic energy being *zero*, and at its mean position, where its velocity is the maximum, the whole of the energy is present in the kinetic form, its potential energy now being *zero*. In between these two extreme positions, the energy of the oscillator or the particle is partly kinetic and partly potential, the sum total of the two remaining constant throughout. This may be seen from the following:

Since the acceleration of the particle, $d^2x/dt^2 = -\omega^2 x$, the force F required to maintain the displacement x is $m\omega^2 x$, where m is the mass of the particle.

$\therefore$ work done for a small displacement dx of the particle

$$= F dx = m\omega^2 x dx.$$

This work is obviously a measure of the *P.E.* of the particle at this displacement, so that *P.E. of the particle at displacement* $dx = m\omega^2 x dx$.

∴ work done for the whole displacement x of the particle or its *P.E. at displacement* x, say,

$$U = \int_0^x m\omega^2 \, x dx$$

$$= \frac{1}{2} m\omega^2 x^2 = \frac{1}{2} m\left(\frac{C}{m}\right) x^2 = \frac{1}{2} Cx^2, \qquad [\because \omega^2 = c/m]$$

i.e., P.E. of the particle $\alpha \; x^2$.

The maximum value of the potential energy is thus at $x = a$ and is, obviously, $\frac{1}{2} m\omega^2 a^2 = \frac{1}{2} C a^2$.

Now, *velocity of the particle at displacement x is* $v = \frac{dx}{dt} = \frac{d}{dt} \; a \sin(\omega t + \phi) = \omega\sqrt{a^2 - x^2}$.

(see equation (*iii*) under § 7.3 above).

∴ K.E. *of the particle at displacement* $x = \frac{1}{2} m\omega^2 (a^2 - x^2)$

$$= \frac{1}{2} C(a^2 - x^2)$$

The maximum value of K.E. lis obviously at $x = 0$ and is also equal to $\frac{1}{2} m\omega^2 a^2 = \frac{1}{2} Ca^2$.

Hence. *total energy of the particle at displacement x, i.e., E = K.E. + P.E.=* $\frac{1}{2} m\omega^2 (a^2 - x^2) + \frac{1}{2} m\omega^2 x^2 = \frac{1}{2} m\omega^2 a^2 = \frac{1}{2} Ca^2$.

As will be readily seen, *the total energy of the particle is quite independent of its displacement* x and thus remains the *same* throughout.

Since $\omega = 2\pi/T$, where T is the *time-period* of the particle, we may also express *total energy of the particle* as

$$E = \frac{1}{2} m(2\pi/T)^2 a^2 = 2\pi^2 ma^2/T^2.$$

Or, since $1/T = n$, the *frequency* of the particle, we also have

$$E = 2\pi^2 n^2 ma^2.$$

Now, since in a conservative system, such as this, the sum total of the kinetic and potential energies of the system remains a constant, it follows that any one of them can increase only t the expense of the other and thus attains its maximum value when that of the other is the minimum or zero.

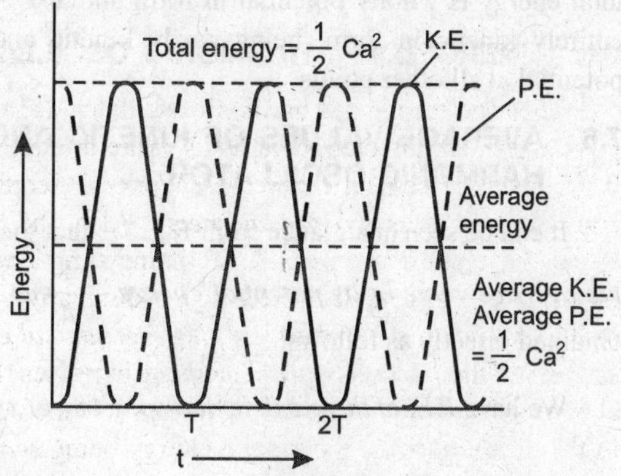

Fig. 7.2

This means, in other words, that *the maximum value of any one of the two forms of energy is the same as the total energy of the system.*

Thus, *maximum value of K.E. = maximum value of P.E. = total energy E* $= \frac{1}{2} m\omega^2 a^2 = \frac{1}{2} C a^2$.

And, since during motion of the particle, the kinetic energy varies from 0 to the maximum, the graph showing the relation between *K.E.* and time (t) is as shown in full line in Fig. 7.2.

Similarly, during motion of the particle, the *P.E.* of the particle varies between 0 and the same maximum $\frac{1}{2}m\omega^2a^2$ or $\frac{1}{2}Ca^2$, but reciprocally with *K.E.*, *i.e.*, when *K.E.* is the maximum, *P.E.* is zero and vice versa. Hence the graph between *P.E* and *t*, shown 7.2, is the reciprocal of that for *K.E.*

The total energy is represented by the upper horizontal line parallel to the time axis and touching the two curves at points representing the maximum values of kinetic and potential energies respectively.

If, on the other hand, we plot the potential energy (*U*) of the particle against its displacement (*x*), the relation between which is given by $U = \frac{1}{2}Cx^2$, we obtain a *parabola* with its vertex at $x = 0$, as shown in full line in Fig. 7.3.

The maximum displacement of the particle on either side of its mean position is the *same*, $+a$, and $-a$ respectively. The value of the *P.E.* is, therefore, the maximum at these points and equal to the total energy of the particle. The upper horizontal line passing through these points of maximum potential energy and parallel to the displacement axis thus represents the total energy curve of the particle.

A graph between *K.E.* and displacement (*x*) of the particle will obviously be the reciprocal of the *P.E.* curve, as shown dotted in the figure, with the vertex of the parabola touching the upper horizontal line or the total energy curve at $x = 0$.

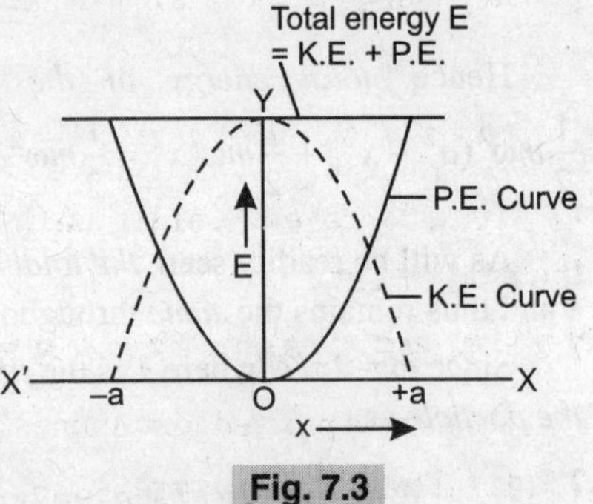

Fig. 7.3

Since the total energy curve is a horizontal line in either case (Fig. 7.2 and 7.3), being parallel to the time-axis in the former and to the displacement axis in the latter case, it follows that *the total energy of the particle remains constant throughout and is independent of both time and displacement,* (being equal to the sum of the *K.E.* and the P.E. of the particle at any given instant).

It is also clear from Fig. 7.3 that at $x = a$ or $-a$, the total energy is wholly potential in form and at $x = 0$, it is entirely kinetic in form, being partly kinetic and partly potential at all other points.

7.6 AVERAGE VALUES OF KINETIC AND POTENTIAL ENERGIES OF A HARMONIC OSCILLATOR

It can be seen at a glance from Fig. 7.2 that the *average value of K.E. of the particle is equal to the average value of its potential energy* $= \frac{1}{4}m\omega^2a^2 = \frac{1}{4}Ca^2$. The same result may, however, be obtained directly as follows:

We have *P.E. of the particle at displacement* $x = \frac{1}{2}m\omega^2x^2$

$$= \frac{1}{2}m\omega^2a^2\sin^2(\omega t + \phi)$$

$\therefore$ *Average P.E. of the particle over a complete cycle or a whole time-period*

$$T = \frac{1}{T}\int_0^T \frac{1}{2}m\omega^2a^2\sin^2(\omega t + \phi)dt.$$

$$= \frac{m\omega^2a^2}{4T}\int_0^T 2\sin^2(\omega t + \phi)\,dt = \frac{m\omega^2a^2}{4T}\int_0^T 1 - \cos 2(\omega t + \phi)\,dt.$$

Since the average value of both a sine and a cosine function for a complete cycle or a whole time-period T is 0, we have *average P.E. of the particle* $= \dfrac{1}{4T}m\omega^2a^2\left[t\right]_0^T - 0 = \dfrac{1}{4T}m\omega^2a^2T$

$$= \frac{1}{4}m\omega^2a^2 = \frac{1}{4}Ca^2.$$

And, since *K.E. of the particle at displacement* $x = \dfrac{1}{2}m\left(\dfrac{dx}{dt}\right)^2 = \dfrac{1}{2}m\left[\dfrac{d}{dt}(a\sin(\omega t+\phi))\right]^2$

$$= \frac{1}{2}m\omega^2a^2\cos^2(\omega t+\phi),$$

we have *average K.E. of the particle over a complete cycle or a whole* time-period

$$T = \frac{1}{T}\int_0^T \frac{1}{2}m\omega^2a^2\cos^2(\omega t+\phi)dt$$

$$= \frac{m\omega^2a^2}{4T}\int_0^T\left[1+\cos 2((\omega t+\phi))\right]dt.$$

Again, the average value of a sine or a cosine function over a complete cycle or a whole time-period T being zero, we have average *K.E. of the particle* $= \dfrac{m\omega^2a^2}{4T}\left[t\right]_0^T = \dfrac{m\omega^2a^2}{4T}T.$

$$= \frac{1}{4}m\omega^2a^2 = \frac{1}{4}Ca^2.$$

Thus, **Average P.E. of the particle = Average K.E. of the particle** $= \dfrac{1}{4}m\omega^2a^2 = \dfrac{1}{4}Ca^2$ **= Half the total energy.**

7.7 SOME EXAMPLES OF S.H.M.

Let us now proceed to examine some important examples of simple harmonic motion.

7.7.1 The simple pendulum

A simple (or a mathematical) pendulum is just a heavy particle (ideally, a *point-mass*) suspended from one end of an *inextensible, weightless* string whose other end in fixed in a rigid support, —this point being referred to as the *point of suspension* of the pendulum.

Obviously, it is simply impossible to obtain such an idealises simple pendulum. In actual practice, therefore, we take a small and heavy spherical bob tied to a long and fine silk thread, the other end of which passes through a split cork securely clamped in a suitable stand, the length (l) of the pendulum being measured from the point of suspension to the centre of mass of the bob.

In Fig. 7.4, let S be the point of suspension of the pendulum and O, the mean or equilibrium position of the bob. On taking the bob a little to one side and then gently releasing it, the pendulum starts oscillating about its mean position, as indicated by the dotted lines. At any given instant, let the displacement of the pendulum from its mean position SO into the position SA be θ. Then, the weight mg of the bob, acting vertically downwards, exerts a torque or a moment $-mg\,l\sin\theta$ about the point of suspension, tending to bring it back to its mean position, the negative sign of the torque indicating that it is oppositely directed to the displacement (θ).

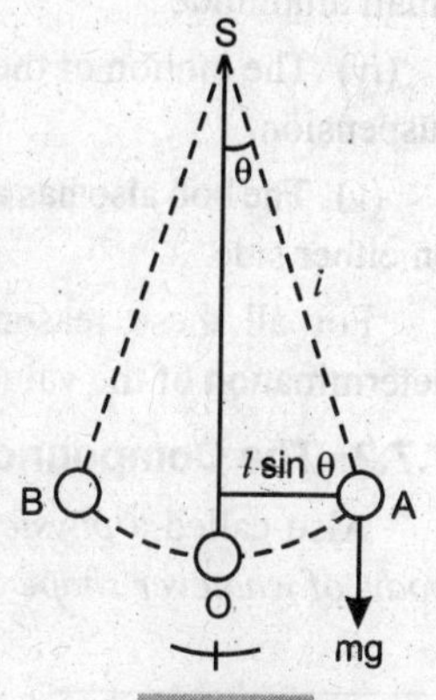

Fig 7.4

If $d^2\theta/dt^2$ be the acceleration of the bob, towards O, and I, its *M.I.* about the point of suspension (S), the moment of the force or the torque acting on the bob is also equal to $I.d^2\theta/dt^2$. We, therefore, have

$$I\frac{d^2\theta}{dt^2} = mg\, l \sin\theta.$$

Now, expanding *sin* θ into a power series, in accordance with *Maclaurin's theorem*, we have $\sin\theta = \theta - \frac{\theta^3}{3!} + \frac{\theta^5}{5!} - \ldots$ If, therefore, θ be small, *i.e.* if the amplitude of oscillation be small, we may neglect all other terms except the first and take *sin* θ = 0. So that,

$$I\frac{d^2\theta}{dt^2} = -mgl\theta, \text{ whence, } \frac{d^2\theta}{dt^2} = -\frac{mgl}{I}\theta$$

Or, since *M.I.* of the bob (or the point mass) about the point of suspension (S) is ml^2, we have $\frac{d^2\theta}{dt^2} = \frac{mgl}{ml^2}\theta = \frac{g}{l}\theta = \mu\theta$

where $g/l = \mu$, the *acceleration per unit displacement.*

The acceleration of the bob is thus proportional to its angular displacement θ and is directed towards its mean position O. The pendulum thus executes a simple harmonic motion and its time-period is, therefore, given by

$$T = 2\pi\sqrt{\frac{1}{\mu}} = 2\pi\sqrt{\frac{1}{g/l}} = 2\pi\sqrt{\frac{l}{g}}$$

it being clearly understood that the amplitude of the pendulum is small.*

The displacement here being angular, instead of linear, it is obviously an example of an angular simple harmonic motion.

Drawbacks of a simple pendulum. Although one of the simplest methods for determining the value of *g* at a place a simple pendulum suffers from a number of drawbacks, the more important of which are the following:

(*i*) It is just an ideal conception, not realisable in actual practice, since it is impossible to have both a point-mass and a weightless string. So that, the string too has a moment of inertia about the axis of suspension.

(*ii*) The resistance and the buoyancy of the air appreciably affect the motion of the bob.

(*iii*) The expression for the time-period ($T = 2\pi\sqrt{(l/g)}$) is true only for oscillations of infinitely small amplitude.

(*iv*) The motion of the bob is not strictly linear. It has also rotatory motion about the axis the of suspension.

(*v*) The bob also has a relative motion with respect to the string at the extremities of its amplitude on either side.

For all these reasons, a *compound pendulum* is preferred to a simple pendulum for the determination of the value of *g*.

7.7.2 The Compound Pendulum

Also called a *physical pendulum or a rigid pendulum, a compound pendulum is just a rigid body, of whatever shape capable of oscillating about a horizontal axis passing through it.*

* For correction for the finite amplitude of the pendulum, see §7.12

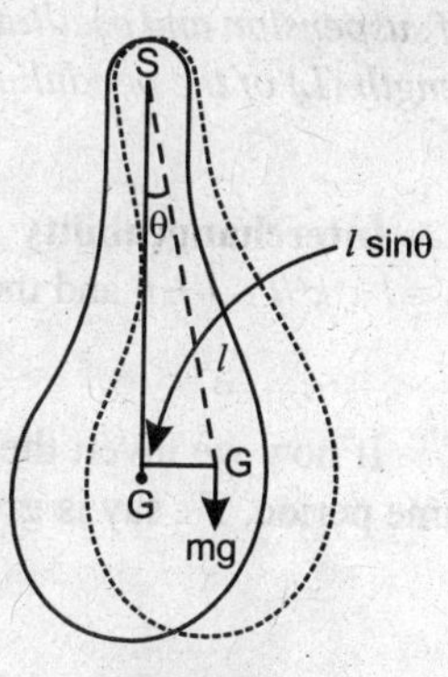

Fig. 7.5

The point in which the vertical plane passing through the *c.g.* of the pendulum meets the axis of rotation is called *its point or centre of suspension* and the distance between the point of suspension and the *c.g.* of the pendulum measures the *length* of the pendulum.

Thus, Fig. 7.5 shows a vertical section of a rigid body or a compound pendulum, free to rotate about a horizontal axis passing through the point or centre of suspension *S*. In its normal position of rest, its *c.g.*, *G*, naturally lies vertically below *S*, the distance between *S* and *G* giving the length *l* of the pendulum.

Let the pendulum be given a small angular displacement θ into the dotted position shown, so that its *c.g.* takes up the new position *G'* where, of course, *SG'* = *l*. The weight of the pendulum, *mg*, acting vertically downwards at *G'* and its reaction at the point of suspension *S* constitute a couple (*or a torque*), tending to bring the pendulum back into its original position.

Obviously, *moment of this restoring couple* = $-mg\, l \sin\theta$, the negative sign indicating that the couple is oppositely directed to the displacement θ.

If *I* be the *moment of inertia* of the pendulum about the axis of suspension (through *S*) and $d^2\theta/dt^2$, its angular acceleration, the couple is also equal to $I.\, d^2\theta/dt^2$. So that, we have

$$I.d^2\theta/dt^2 = -mgl \sin\theta.$$

Again, $\sin\theta = \theta - \theta^3/3! + \theta^5/5!....$, so that, if θ be small, $\sin \approx \theta$ and, therefore, $I.d^2\theta/dt^2 = -mgl\theta$, whence, $d^2\theta/dt^2 = -(mgl/I)\theta = -\mu\theta$, whence $mgl/I = \mu$, the *acceleration per unit displacement*.

The pendulum thus executes a simple harmonic motion and its *time-period* is given by

$$T = 2\pi\sqrt{\frac{1}{\mu}} = 2\pi\sqrt{\frac{1}{mgl/I}} = 2\pi\sqrt{\frac{I}{mgl}}$$

Now, if I_0 be the moment of inertia of the pendulum about an axis through its *c.g.*, *G*, parallel to the axis through *S*, we have, from the theorem of parallel axes, $I = I_0 + ml^2$. And if *k* be the radius of gyration of the pendulum about this axis through *G*, we have $I_\theta = mk^2$. So that, $I = mk^2 + ml^2 = m(k^2 + l^2)$.

$$\therefore \quad T = 2\pi\sqrt{\frac{m(k^2+l^2)}{mgl}} = 2\pi\sqrt{\frac{k^2+l^2}{gl}} = 2\pi\sqrt{\frac{k^2/I+l}{g}}$$

Thus, *the time-period* of the pendulum is the same as that of a simple pendulum of length* $L = (k^2/l + l)$ or $(k^2 + l^2)/l$. This length *L* is, therefore, called the **length of an equivalent simple pendulum** or the **reduced length** of the compound pendulum. Since k^2 is always greater than zero, *the length of the equivalent simple pendulum (L) is always greater than l, the length of the compound pendulum.*

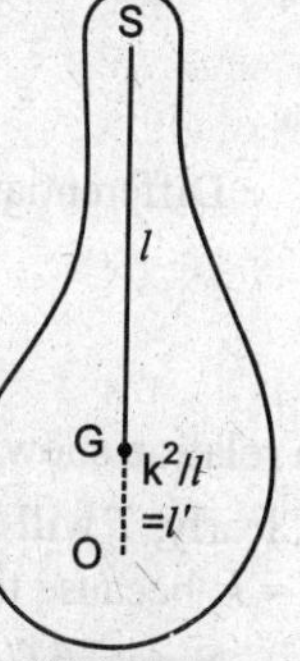

Fig. 7.6

Centre of oscillation. A point *O* on the other side of the *c.g.* (*G*) of the pendulum in a line with *SG* and at a distance k^2/l from *G* is called the *centre of oscillation* of the pendulum (Fig. 7.6) and a horizontal axis passing through it, parallel to the axis of suspension (through *S*) is called the axis of oscillation of the pendulum.

Now, clearly $GO = k^2/l$ and $SG = l$. So that, $SO = SG + GO = l + k^2/l = L$, the length of the equivalent simple pendulum, *i.e., the distance between the centers*

* Here, the amplitude of the pendulum has been supposed to be infinitely small. Since it is almost always finite, a proper correction has to be applied, as explained under § 7.12.

of suspension and oscillation is equal to the length of the equivalent simple pendulum or the reduced length (L) of the pendulum and we, therefore, have

$$T = 2\pi\sqrt{L/g}$$

Interchangeability of centers of suspension and oscillation. If we put $k^2/l = l'$, we have $L = l + k^2/l = l + l'$ and therefore,

$$T = 2\pi\sqrt{(l+l')/g}$$

If now we invert the pendulum, so that it oscillates about the axis of oscillation through O, its time period, T', say is given by

$$T' = 2\pi\sqrt{(k^2 + l'^2)/l'g}$$

Since $k^2/l = l'$, we have $k^2 = ll'$,

Substituting ll' for k^2 in the expression for T', therefore, we have

$$T' = 2\pi\sqrt{(ll' + l'^2)/l'g} = 2\pi\sqrt{(l+l')/g} = T$$

i.e., the same as the time-period about the axis of suspension

Thus, *the centers of suspension and oscillation are interchangeable or reciprocal to each other, i.e. the time-period of the pendulum is the same about either.*

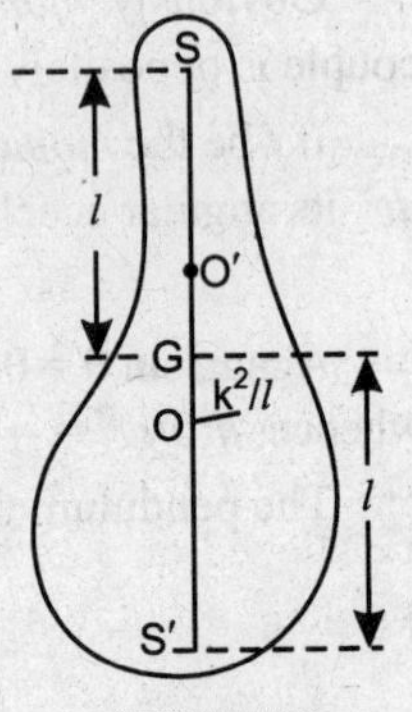

Fig. 7.7

In fact, there are two other points on either side of G, about which the time-period of the pendulum is the same as about S and O. For, if with G as centre and radii equal to l and k^2/l respectively, we draw two circles, so as to cut SG produced in S and O' above, and at O and S' below G, as shown in Fig. 7.7 we have $SG = GS' = l$ and $GO = GO = k^2/l = l'$

$$\therefore \quad O'S' = GS' + GO = l + k^2/l = l + l' = SO.$$

Thus, *there are four points in all, viz., S, O, S' and O', collinear with the c.g. of the pendulum (G) about which its time-period is the same.*

Maximum and minimum time-periods of a compound pendulum. For the time-period of a compound pendulum, we have the relation.

$$T = 2\pi\sqrt{(k^2 + l^2)/lg}$$

squaring which, we have

$$T^2 = \frac{4\pi^2(k^2 + l^2)}{lg} = \frac{4\pi^2}{g}\left(\frac{k^2 + l^2}{l}\right) = \frac{4\pi^2}{g}\left(\frac{k^2}{l} + l\right)$$

Differentiating with respect to l, we have

$$2T\frac{dT}{dl} = \frac{4\pi^2}{g}\left(-\frac{k^2}{l^2} + 1\right)$$

a relation showing the variation of T with length (l) of the pendulum.

Clearly, T will be a maximum or a minimum when $dT/dl = 0$, *i.e.*, when $l^2 = k^2$ or $l = \pm k$ or when $l = k$, because the negative value of k is simply meaningless.

Since d^2T/dl^2 comes out to be *positive* it is clear that T is a *minimum when $l = k$, i.e., the time-period of compound pendulum is the minimum when its length is equal to its radius of gyration about the axis through its c.g.* And the value of this minimum time-period will obviously be

$$T_{min} = 2\pi\sqrt{(k^2 + k^2)/kg} = 2\pi\sqrt{2k/g}$$

On the other hand, we see from the expression for T above that if $l = 0$ or ∞, $T = \infty$ or a *maximum*.'

Ignoring $l = \infty$ as absurd, we thus find that *the time-period of a compound pendulum is the maximum when its length is zero, i.e., when the axis of suspension passes through its c.g. or the c.g. itself is the point of suspension.*

This is obviously so because the pendulum is then in a state of neutral equilibrium, with no restoring action due to gravity on it.

Determination of the value of g. From the interchangeability of the points of suspension and oscillation it would appear that the easiest method of determining the value of g at a place would be to locate two points on either side of the *c.g.* of the pendulum about which the time-period of the pendulums is the same. These points would then correspond to the centres of suspension and oscillation of the pendulum and the distance between them would give L, *the length of the equivalent simple pendulum*. So that, if T be the time-period of the pendulum about either of these, we shall have $T = 2\pi\sqrt{L/g}$ and, therefore, $g = 4\pi^2 L/T^2$.

This is however, easier said than done, for it is extremely difficult if not impossible, to locate two such points in the pendulum. We, therefore, take recourse to one of the following two methods, using special forms of the pendulum.

(*i*) **By means of a bar pendulum.** A bar pendulum is the simplest form of a compound pendulum and consists of a uniform metal bar AB (7.8) having equally spaced holes drilled along its length on either side of its *c.g.*, G, so that any one of them may be slipped on to a horizontal knife-edge K and the bar made to oscillate about it in the vertical plane.

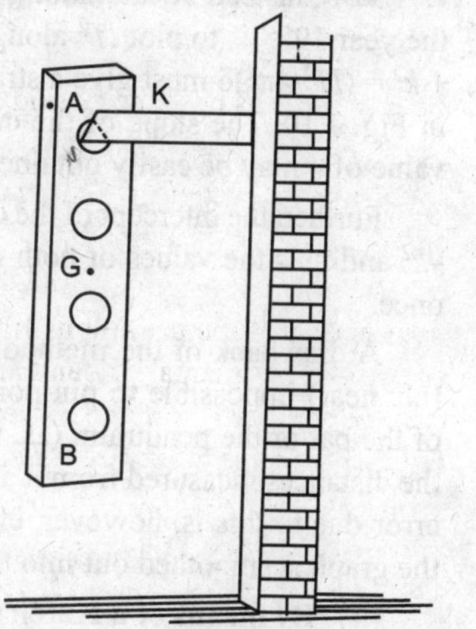

Fig. 7.8

First, the time-periods of different lengths of the pendulum are determined by slipping on to the knife-edge one hole after another from A to G and each length (*i.e.*, the distance between the point of suspension and the *c.g.*) carefully noted.

A graph ABD is then plotted between distances of the holes from the *c.g.* (or the lengths of the pendulum) along the x-axis and the time-periods (T) along the *y-axis*, and the time periods (T) along the *y-axis*, as shown in Fig. 7.9.

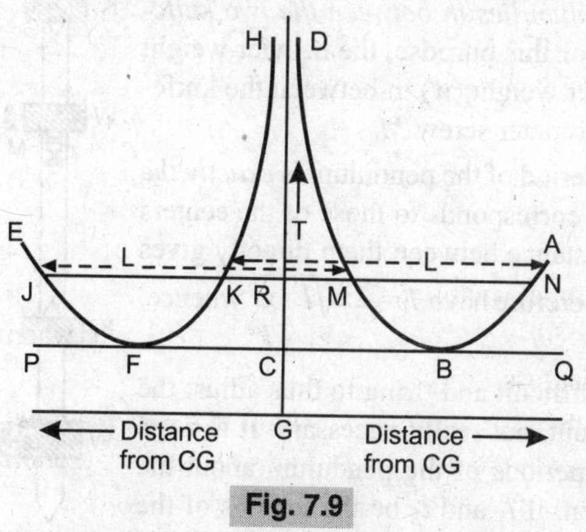

Fig. 7.9

The experiment is next repeated with the holes on the other side of the *c.g.* of the pendulum and a similar graph EFH drawn alongside the first on the same graph paper, using the same scale, or, this graph may be drawn symmetrically with the first without actually repeating the experiment with the holes on the other side of the *c.g.* This graph (EFH) will be a mirror image of the first (ABD), as is clear from the figure.

It will be seen at once that as the *c.g.* of the bar (G) is approached (*i.e.*, as the centre of suspension comes closer to the *c.g.*), the time-period first decreases, acquires minimum value and then increases until it becomes infinite at the *c.g.* itself.

Let a horizontal line JN be drawn, parallel to the x-axis so as to cut the two curves in points J, K, M and N. Then, clearly, the time period of the pendulum for lengths corresponding to all these points is the *same*. They thus correspond to the four points S, O', O and S', collinear with the *c.g.* G

in Fig 7.7 above about which the period of the pendulum is the same. Clearly, therefore, $JM = KN = L$, *the length of the equivalent simple pendulum*, for JR here corresponds to l and RM, to k^2/l; so that $JM = JR + RM = l + k^2/l = L$. And, similarly, $KN = KR + RN = k^2/l + l = L$.

Thus, knowing the value of T corresponding to these points (J, K, M and N) from the graph, we easily obtain the value of g at the place from the relation $T = 2\pi\sqrt{L/g}$, which gives $g = 4\pi^2 L/T^2$.

It will also be seen that if we draw a tangential line PQ, touching the two curves at B and F, then B and F represent the points where the centers of suspension and oscillation coincide with each other in the two cases respectively. The time-period of the pendulum corresponding to these points is therefore, the minimum. In other words, at these points $k^2/l = l$ or $k^2 = l^2$ and, therefore, $k = l$. So that, each of the distance (or lengths of the pendulum) CB and CF is equal to k, or $BF = 2k$, whence, the value of the radius of gyration (k) of the pendulum about the axis through its *c.g.* can also be easily obtained.

Now, instead of calculating the value of g as above, a better method, suggested by *Ferguson* in the year 1928 is to plot lT^2 along the axis of x and l^2 along the axis of y, which from the relation $l^2 + k^2 = (lT^2/4\pi^2)\delta$ must give a straight line graph, as shown in Fig. 7.10. The slope of the curve is $g/4\pi^2$, whence the value of g may be easily obtained.

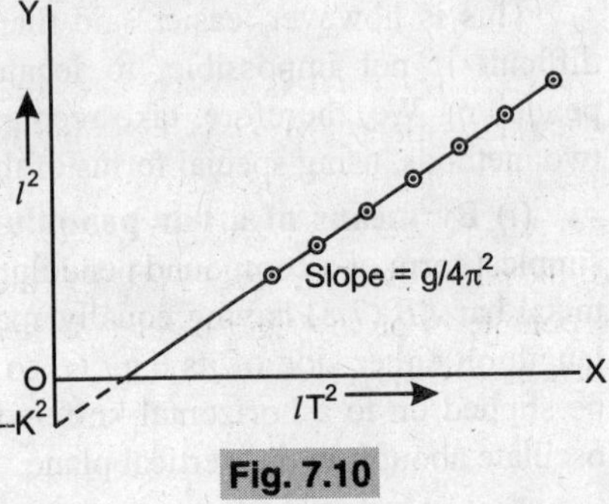

Fig. 7.10

Further, the intercept of the curve on the axis of y gives $-k^2$ and thus the values of both g and k can be obtained at once.

A drawback of the method is that it being well nigh (*i.e.* near) impossible to pin-point the position of the *c.g.* of the bar or the pendulum (as, infect, of any other body), the distances measured from it are not really accurate. Any error due to this is, however, eliminated automatically as the graph is smoothed out into the form of a straight line.

(*ii*) **By means of a Kater's pendulum.** A Kater's pendulum is a rigid bar AB of brass or steel, fitted with adjustable and mutually facing knife-edges K_1, and K_2, near its two ends, as shown in Fig. 7.11, so that it may be made to oscillate about any one of them, as desired-hence the name *reversible pendulum* given to it.

Two cylindrical weights w and W, sliding along the bar, can be clamped in any desired position, on it such that the *c.g. of the pendulum lies in between the two knife-edges and nearer to one of them than to the other*. For this purpose, the heavier weight (W) is clamped near one end of the bar and the lighter weight (w) in between the knife-edges, its position being adjusted by means of a micrometer screw M.

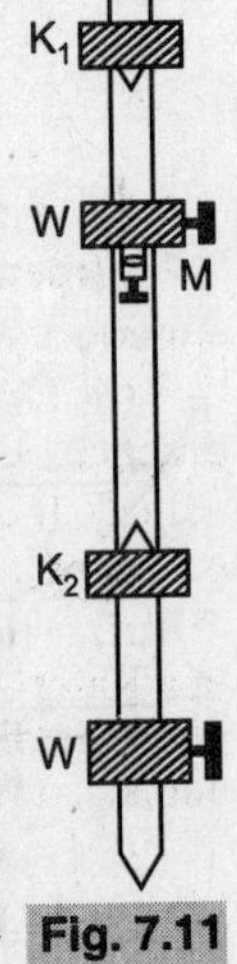

Fig. 7.11

In case the weights be so arranged that the time-period of the pendulum is *exactly the same* about either knife-edge, clearly, their positions corresponds to those of the centers of suspension and oscillation respectively and the distance between them directly gives the length L of the equivalent simple pendulum. We therefore have $T = 2\pi\sqrt{L/g}$ whence, $g = 4\pi^2 L/T^2$.

As mentioned earlier, however, it is extremely difficult and tiring to thus adjust the positions of the two weights and as *Bessel pointed* out, not really necessary. It is quite enough to adjust their positions such that the time-periods of the pendulum about the two knife edges are only very nearly equal. For, then, if l_1 and l_2 be the lengths of the pendulum (*i.e.* distances of knife-edges K_1 and K_2 respectively from the *c.g.*) and T_1 and T_2 (very nearly equal), their respective time periods, we have

$$T_1 = 2\pi\sqrt{\frac{k^2 + l_1^2}{l_1 g}} \text{ and } T_2 = 2\pi\sqrt{\frac{k^2 + l_2^2}{l_2 g}}$$

Squaring and rearranging, we have $T_1^2 l_1 g = 4\pi^2 (k^2 + l_1^2)$ and $T_2^2 l_{2g} = 4\pi^2 (k^2 + l_2^2)$. Subtracting the second relation from the first we have

$$g(T_1^2 l_2 - T_2^2 l_2) = 4\pi^2(k^2 + l_1^2) - 4\pi^2 (k^2 + l_2^2)$$

$$= 4\pi^2 (l_1^2 + l_2^2) = 4\pi^2 (l_1 + l_2)(l_1 - l_2).$$

Or,

$$\frac{4\pi^2}{g}(l_1 + l_2) = \frac{T_1^2 l_1 - T_2^2 l_2}{l_1 - l_2} = \frac{2(T_1^2 l_1 - T_3^2 l_2)}{2(l_1 - l_2)}$$

$$= \frac{\left(T_1^2 + T_2^2\right)(l_1 - l_2) + \left(T_1^2 + T_2^2\right)(l_1 - l_2)}{2(l_1 - l_2)}$$

Whence,

$$\frac{4\pi^2}{g}(l_1 + l_2) = \left(\frac{T_1^2 + T_2^2}{2}\right) + \left(\frac{T_1^2 - T_2^2}{2}\right)\left(\frac{l_1 + l_1}{l_1 - l_2}\right)$$

Here $(l_1 + l_2)$ is clearly the distance between the two-knife-edges and can, therefore, be accurately measured, $(l_1 - l_2)$ being the difference between the distances of the two knife-edges from the the *c.g.* of the between the distance of the two knife-edges from the *c.g.* of the pendulum can not, of course, be measured accurately on account of the difficulty in locating the exact position of the *c.g.* However, since T_1 and T_2 are are very nearly equal $(T_1^2 - T_2^2)$ is much two small and the second term on the right hand side, involving $(l_1 - l_2)$ becomes negligible compared with the first term. We, therefore, have

$$\frac{4\pi^2}{g}(l_1 + l_2) = \frac{T_1^2 + T_2^2}{2} \quad ...(ii)$$

Whence,

$$g = \frac{8\pi^2 (l_1 + l_2)}{T_1^2 + T_2^2}$$

The accurate value of g at the place can thus be obtained.

N.B. Comparing expression (*ii*) above with that for a simple pendulum, *viz.*, $4\pi^2 g/l = T^2$, we find that if T be the time period for a length $(l_1 + l_2)$ of the pendulum, we have

$$T^2 = \left(\frac{T_1^2 + T_2^2}{2}\right) + \left(\frac{T_1^2 - T_2^2}{2}\right)\left(\frac{l_1 + l_1}{l_1 - l_2}\right)$$

Here T is called the **computed time** of the pendulum.

Superiority of a compound pendulum over a simple pendulum. The main points of the superiority of a compound pendulum over a simple pendulum are the following:

(*i*) Unlike the ideal simple pendulum, a compound pendulum is easily realisable in actual practice.

(*ii*) It oscillates as a whole and there is no lag like that between the bob and the string in the case of a simple pendulum.

(*iii*) The length to be measured is clearly defined (*viz.*, the distance between the two knife-edges in a Kater's pendulum). In the case of a simple pendulum, the point of suspension and the *c.g.* of the bob, the distance between which gives the length to the pendulum, are both more or less indefinite points, so that the distance between them, *i.e.*, l, cannot be measured accurately.

(*vi*) On account of its large mass, and hence a large moment of inertia, it continues to oscillate for a longer time, thus enabling the time for a large number of oscillations to be noted and its time-period calculated more accurately. The time-period must, however, be corrected in the manner explained under § 7.12.

7.7.3 Loaded Spring

We have seen earlier under § 5.9 how when a particle is displaced from its mean or equilibrium position, a *linear restoring* force acts upon it, tending to bring it back into its original position.

Thus, suppose we have a mass *m* attached to the free end of a massless flat spiral spring*, with its other end fixed to a rigid support, like a wall etc. (Fig. 7.12). If the mass be displaced through a distance x, as shown, a *linear restoring force* $F = -Cx$ at once starts acting on the spring, tending to bring it back into its original condition, where C is the *force constant* of the spring. The –ve sign of the force simply indicates that it is directed oppositely to the displacement of the mass.

Fig. 7.12

Imagining the system to lie on a smooth horizontal surface, if the mass be released, it starts oscillating back and forth due to the spring getting alternately compressed and extended under the action of this force.

If d^2x/dt^2 be the acceleration set up in the spring, the force acting on the mass is also equal to $m.d^2x/dt^2$. We therefore, have

$$m\frac{d^2x}{dt^2} = -Cx \quad \text{or,} \quad \frac{d^2x}{dt^2} = -\frac{C}{m}x = -\mu x, \qquad ...(i)$$

Where $C/m = \mu$, the acceleration per unit displacement.

Thus, $d^2x/dt^2 \propto x$ and is directed oppositely to it.

The mass m thus executes a *simple harmonic motion* and its *time-period* is given by

$$T = 2\pi\sqrt{\frac{1}{\mu}} = 2\pi\sqrt{1\Big/\frac{C}{m}} = 2\pi\sqrt{\frac{m}{C}} \qquad ...(ii)$$

The solution of equation of motion I above is also of the form $x = a \sin(\omega t + \phi)$, where $\sqrt{C/m} = \omega$.

Or, if as is usually the case, the time is counted from the moment that the mass just crosses its mean or equilibrium position towards the positive direction of x, *i.e.*, if $x = 0$, at $t = 0$ we have $\phi = 0$ and

$$\therefore \quad x = a \sin \omega t.$$

In actual practice, the spiral spring is arranged vertically with either its lower end fixed and the mass m place on its upper end or with its upper end fixed and the mass suspended from its lower end (particularly if the wire of the spring be thin), as shown in figs. 7.13 (*a*) and (*b*) respectively.

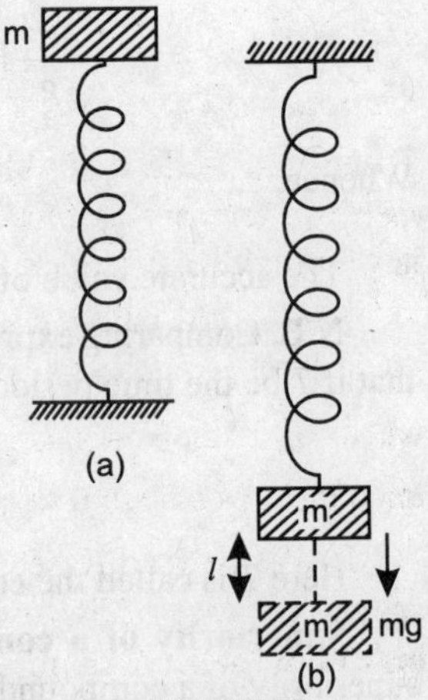

Fig. 7.13

Taking the more usual case (*b*), if the spring be extended through a distance l, say, due to the weight mg of the mass, as linear restoring force Cl at once comes into play in the opposite direction, so that the equilibrium position is attained when the two forces just balance each other, *i.e.*, when $mg = Cl$. Whence, $C = mg/l$.

If the mass be now pulled down through a distance x from this equilibrium position, the linear restoring force $F = mg - C(l + x) = mg - (mg/l)(l + x) = mg - mg - (mg/l)x = -(mg/l)x = -Cx$, *i.e.*, we have $md^2x/dt^2 = -Cx$, as before, clearly showing that *there is no effect of gravity on the force constant C and hence on the period of oscillation of the mass*, given by $T = 2\pi\sqrt{m/C}$.

---

* Spring is a uniform wire or ribbon which, in its normal unstrained condition, has the form of a helix such as the one obtained by closely and uniformly winding a wire around a cylinder of a radius much larger than that of the wire. If the plane of each coil of the spiral be/perpendicular to the axis of the cylinder, it is called a *flat spiral*.

7.7.4 Torsion Pendulum

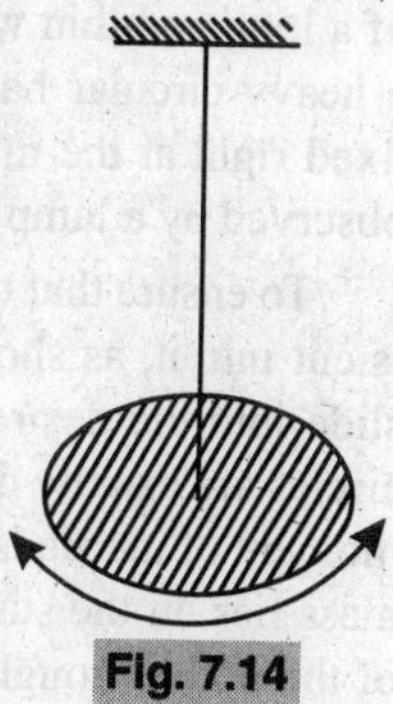

Fig. 7.14

A heavy body, like a cylinder or a cylinder or a disc, fastened at its mid-point to a fairly long and thin wire, suspended form a rigid support, constitutes a *torsional pendulum*, (Fig. 7.14). It is so called because, if the cylinder or the disc be turned in its own (*i.e.*, the horizontal) plane to twist the wire a little and then released, it executes torsional vibrations or oscillations about the wire as axis.

Thus, if the disc (or cylinder) be turned through an angle θ, say, the suspension wire too gets twisted through the same angle θ and this gives rise to a restoring torsional couple $C\theta$ in it, tending to bring it back into its original condition. Here, C is the *torsional couple per unit twist* of the wire, equal to $\pi nR^4/2L$, where R is the radius and L, the length of the wire and n, the modulus of rigidity of its material (see chapter on Elasticity).

It I be the *moment of inertia* of the disc (or cylinder) about the wire as axis, passing through its centre, and $d^2\theta/dt^2$. its angular acceleration, the couple acting on it is also equal to $I.d^2\theta/dt^2$. We, therefore, have $Id^2\theta/dt^2 = -C\theta$, the –ve sign indicating that the restoring couple or torque is oppositely directed to the angular displace ment. So that.

$$d^2\theta/dt^2 = -(C/I)\theta = \mu\theta. \qquad \text{...}(i)$$

where $C/I = \mu$, the acceleration per unit angular displacement.

Or, $d^2\theta/dt^2 \, \alpha\theta$ and is directed oppositely to it.

The disc (or the cylinder) thus executes an *angular simple harmonic motion* and its time-period is given by

$$T = 2\pi\sqrt{\frac{1}{\mu}} = 2\pi\sqrt{\frac{1}{C/I}} = 2\pi\sqrt{\frac{I}{C}} \qquad \text{...}(ii)$$

It may be noted that no approximations whatever have been used in arriving at this relation for T, unlike in the case of a simple or a compound pendulum. *The time-period of a torsional pendulum, therefore, remain unaffected (i.e. the oscillations remain isochronous)* even if the amplitude be large, provided, of course, the elastic limit of the suspension wire is not exceeded.

Further, the solution of relation I above is also of the form

$$\theta = \theta_m(\omega t + \phi),$$

where θ_m is the *maximum angular displacement* or *amplitude* of the disc (or the cylinder), ω, its *angular velocity* equal to $\sqrt{C/I}$ and ϕ, *the initial phase* or *phase constant*.

It will be readily seen that the angular *S.H.M.* is analogous to linear *S.H.M.* Only, we take angular in place of linear displacement, moment of inertia instead of mass and torsional constant instead of force constant.

N.B. It need hardly be pointed out that a torsion pendulum entirely different from simple or a compound pendulum. For, here, the *c.g.* of the suspended body, Instead of moving in an arc, remains fixed in its position, the body merely rotating about axis through it and, unlike there, the time-period of the pendulum is quite independent of the value of *g*.

Inertia table. A simple application of the torsional pendulum is what is called the Inertia table which is just a device to determine the moments of inertia of bodies of both regular geometrical shapes and irregular shapes.

It is merely a large disc D of aluminum, about 15 *cm* in diameter, fitted with two small vertical pillars P, P at the extremity of one diameter and connected at the top by a cross bar as shown in Fig. 7.15.

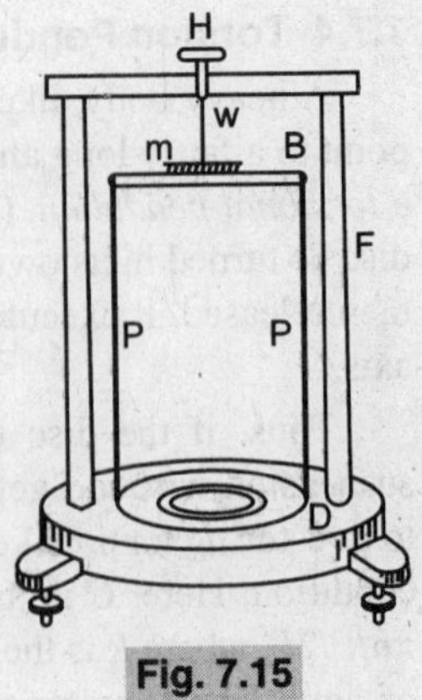

Fig. 7.15

The disc, along with the pillars and the cross bar, is suspended by means of a long and thin wire from the top of a large frame-work F, mounted on a heavy circular base, provided with levelling screws. A small mirror is fixed right at the mid-point of the cross bar enables the oscillations to be observed by a lamp and scale arrangement.

To ensure that the disc remains horizontal, a concentric circular groove is cut into it, as shown, such that three *balancing weights* can be made to slide into the desired positions inside it. Further, a number of concentric circles are usually drawn on the dise-or the table to enable the body, whose moment of inertia is to be determined, to be so placed on it that its centre of mass lies on the suspension wire, which thus becomes the axis of rotation of the body through its centre of mass and perpendicular to its plane. The whole apparatus is enclosed in a glass envelope as a safeguard against disturbance due to air draughts.

Procedure. First, the inertia table is made perfectly horizontal by means of the levelling screws and the sliding balancing weights, as indicated. It is than set into torsional vibration all by itself alone and its time-period T_0 determined. If L_0 is the moment of inertia of the *Inertia table* about the suspension wire as axis, we have

$$T_0 = 2\pi\sqrt{l_0 / C} \qquad ...(i)$$

where C is the torsional couple per unit twist of the wire.

The body whose moment of inertia l is to be determined is now placed centrally on the Inertia table in the manner explained (*i.e.*, with its centre of mass lying on the suspension wire), taking care to see that the table remains horizontal, so that its moment of inertia (I_o) about the suspension wire does not get altered. If T_1 be the time-period of the Inertia table, thus loaded, we have

$$T_1 = 2\pi\sqrt{(l_0 + l) / C} \qquad ...(ii)$$

Finally, the given body is replaced by another of a known moment of inertia I_1 (about the axis passing through its centre of mass and perpendicular to its plane) and, again taking care to keep the table horizontal (by changing the positions of the balancing weights, if necessary), the time-period of the loaded table determined. Let it be T_2. Then, we have

$$T_2 = 2\pi\sqrt{(l_0 + l_1) / C} \qquad ...(iii)$$

Now, squaring and dividing relation (*ii*) by (*i*) we have

$$T_1^2/T_0^2 = (I_o + I)/I_o. \text{ Or, } I/I_o = (T_1^2 - T_0^2)/T_0^2. \qquad ...(iv)$$

Similarly, squaring and dividing relation (*iii*) by (*i*), we have

$$T_2^2/T_0^2 = (I_o + I_1)/I_o. \text{ Or, } I_1/I_o = (T_1^2 - T_0^2)/T_0^2. \qquad ...(v)$$

So that, dividing relation (*iv*) by (*v*), we have $I/I_1 = (T_1^2 - T_0^2)/(T_2^2 - T_0^2)$.

Or, $$I = \left(\frac{T_1^2 - T_0^2}{T_2^2 - T_0^2}\right) I_1{}^*$$

whence, the moment of inertia (I) of the given body about the wire as axis can be easily obtained,

The amplitude (θ) here need not be small since the restoring couple, as pointed out above, is found to be proportional to θ even if θ be large. The assumption, however, that even with different loads suspended from the wire and with different longitudinal tensions in it, the value of C remains unaffected is not strictly true.

---

* Although we could the value of I from expression (*i*) and (*ii*), we adopt this procedure to eliminate I_0. which may not always be accurately known.

An obvious disadvantage of the method is that it can be used to determine the moment of inertia of a body only about one particular axis, *viz.*, the axis perpendicular to its plane and passing through its centre of mass.

7.7.5 Helmholtz Resonator

A resonator is a device to analyse a complex note of sound *i.e.*, to find out what particular frequencies are present in the given note. For this purpose it is necessary that the resonator should exhibit a sharp resonance, *i.e.* it should resound with a note of *only one particular frequency*, namely, its own natural frequency.

Thus, resonator of different natural frequencies are used to detect the different frequencies comprising the given note.

Helmholtz showed that sharpness of resonance in what is called a *volume resonator* is ensured if the resonator is a large vessel, spherical or cylindrical, of glass of metal, containing air, with a narrow neck *N*, through which it communicates with the outside air and receives the complex note to be analysed, and a narrow aperture *O* at the opposite end, to be plugged into the ear, [Figs. 7.16 (*a*) and (*b*)]. Whereas the *spherical type of resonator* (*a*) can be used to detect *just one frequency equal to its own, the cylindrical type* (*b*), being made up of two parts, one sliding over the other, can have its frequency altered at will and can thus be used to detect the different frequencies of the given note.

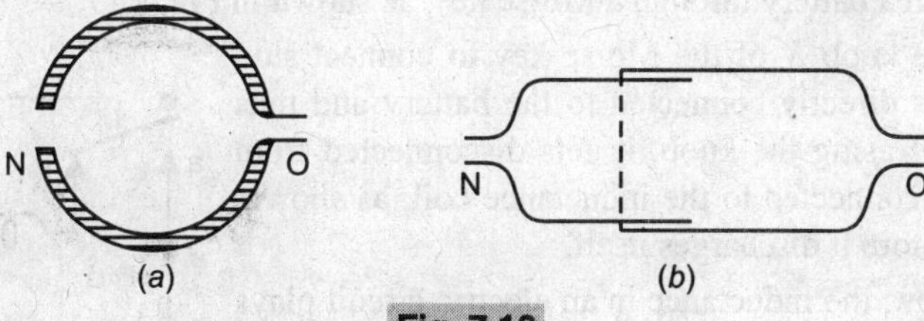

Fig. 7.16

The principle underlying the working of the resonator is that the *air in its neck serves as an air plug, as it were, and performs an oscillatory motion like a piston in a cylinder containing air, or a mass suspended form a spring.*

Thus, if l be the *length of the neck* and α, its *area of cross section*, the *mass of the air plug* or *the air piston in the neck* = $l\alpha\rho$, where ρ is the *density of the air* in the vessel.

If, therefore, this air plug be forced *inwards* through a small distance x, the decrease in the volume of air inside the vessel is, say, $-\delta V = -\alpha x$ (the $-$ *ve* sign indicating a decrease), resulting in a slight increase in pressure δp on the air inside the vessel. So that, if K be the *volume elasticity of the air and V*, the total volume of the vessel (or the initial volume of the air in it), we have

$$K = -\frac{\delta p}{\delta V / V} = -\delta p \frac{V}{\delta V}, \quad \text{whence, } \delta p = -K\frac{\delta V}{V}$$

$\therefore$ *Force acting on the air plug outwards* $= \delta p\alpha = -K\dfrac{\delta V}{V}\alpha = \dfrac{K\alpha^2 x}{V}$

If d^2x/dt^2 be the acceleration of the air plug, the force acting on it is also = $(l\alpha\rho)\, d^2x/dt^2$. We, therefore, have

$$l\alpha\rho\frac{d^2x}{dt^2} = -\frac{K\alpha^2 x}{V}, \quad \text{whence, } \frac{d^2x}{dt^2} = -\frac{K\alpha^2 x}{V} \times \frac{1}{l\alpha\rho} = \frac{K\alpha}{Vl\rho}x = -\mu x$$

where $K\alpha/Vl\rho = \mu$ = acceleration per unit displacement.

Thus, $d^2x/dt^2 \alpha\, x$ and is directed oppositely to it.

The *air plug* or the *air piston*, therefore, executes a *S.H.M.* and *its time-period* is given by

$$T = 2\pi\sqrt{\frac{1}{\mu}} = 2\pi\sqrt{\frac{1}{Ka/Vl\rho}} = 2\pi\sqrt{\frac{Vl\rho}{K\alpha}}$$

Now, the velocity of sound in air is given by the relation $v = \sqrt{K/\rho}$. So that, substituting v for $\sqrt{K/\rho}$ in the expression for T, we have

$T = \frac{2\pi}{v}\sqrt{\frac{Vl}{\alpha}}$ and the frequency of oscillation $n = 1/T = \frac{v}{2\pi}\sqrt{\frac{\alpha}{Vl}}$

Thus, *the frequency of the resonator depends upon the total volume of the vessel and the length and area of cross section of its neck*. By suitably adjusting these therefore, resonators of any desired frequencies may be constructed.

7.7.6 Inductance-Capacitance or L–C Circuit

Just as we have harmonic oscillators in mechanical systems performing *S.H.M.*, so also we come across harmonic oscillators in electrical systems where change, current or voltage executes *S.H.M.* under suitable conditions. As an example we shall take up here an inductance-capacitance circuit, written for short as an *L–C* circuit.

Let a *capacitor* of capacitance *C*, an inductance coil of inductance *L*, (with negligible resistance) be connected up with a battery through a Morse key, as shown in Fig. 7.17.

On pressing the knob *K* of the Morse key to connect stud *a*, the capacitor gets directly connected to the battery and thus gets charged. On releasing the knob, it gets disconnected from the battery but acts connected to the inductance coil, as shown, through which therefore it discharges itself.

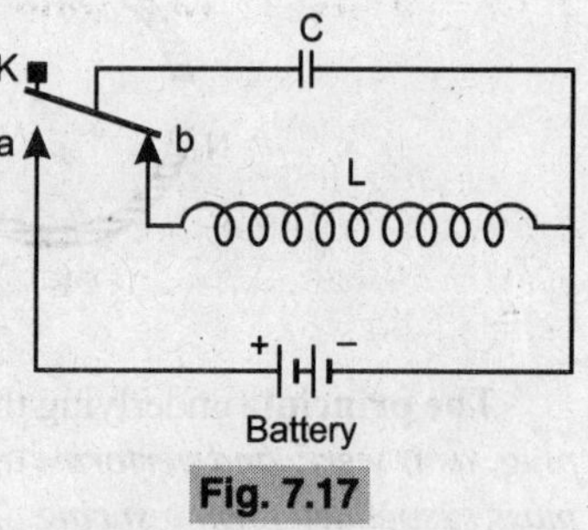

Fig. 7.17

Now, as we know, the inductance in an electric circuit plays the same part as mass and moment of inertia do in translatory and rotatory motion respectively and thus *opposes both growth and decay of current in the circuit*. So that, as the capacitor discharges itself through the inductance coil and the current in the latter grows, the increasing magnetic flux due to it gives rise to an induced *emf* in the circuit opposing the growth of the current in it. Thus, if *I* be the instantaneous value of the current in the coil (or the circuit) at any given instant, the opposing *emf* set up across the coil is $-LdI/dt$, where dI/dt is the rate of change of current through the coil or the circuit.

And, if Q be the charge on the capacitor at the instant considered, the voltage across it tending to drive the current through the coil (or the circuit) is Q/C. Since the external *emf* is now zero (the battery being cut off), we have net *emf in the circuit* $= Q/C + L\,dI/dt = 0$ ...(*i*)

A current being just the *rate of flow of charge*, we have $I = dQ/dt$.

The above relation thus takes the form $Q/C + Ld^2Q/dt^2 = 0$.

Or, $$Q/LC + d^2Q/dt^2 = 0.$$

Or, $$\frac{d^2Q}{dt^2} = -\left(\frac{1}{LC}\right)Q = -\mu Q, \quad \text{...(ii)}$$

where $1/LC = \mu$, a constant for the circuit.

This is clearly an equation similar to the one for simple harmonic motion of a mechanical system, with x replaced by Q, mass (m) *by inductance L* and the *force constant by reciprocal capacitance* $1/C$.

Thus, the charge on the capacitor oscillates simple harmonically with time, *i.e.*, *the discharge of the capacitor is oscillatory in character, its time-period* being

$$T = 2\pi\sqrt{1/\mu} = 2\pi\sqrt{LC}$$

And, therefore, its frequency $n = 1/T = 1/2\pi\sqrt{LC}$

As will be readily seen, the solution of relation (*ii*) above is

$$Q = Q_0 \sin(\omega t + \phi), \quad ...(iii)$$

where Q_0 is the *maximum value* or the *amplitude of* the charge, $\omega = 1/\sqrt{LC}$, the angular frequency (of the variation of charge) and ϕ, *the phase constant* which depends, as usual, on the initial conditions.

The charge in the circuit thus oscillates between $+Q_0$, and $-Q_0$, with a frequency $n = 1/2\pi\sqrt{LC}$.

Differentiating equation (*iii*) with respect to *t*, we have

Instantaneous value of the current, $I = dQ/dt = Q_0\omega \cos(\omega t + \phi)$,

where the maximum value or the amplitude of the current $= Q_0\omega$, *i.e.*, when $\cos(\omega t + \phi) = 1$. Denoting this by I_0, we have

$$I = I_0 \cos(\omega t + \phi)$$

Showing that the current in the circuit too is oscillatory in character and has same frequency as the charge, *viz.*, $\quad n = 1/2\,\pi\; 1/2\pi\sqrt{LC}$

7.7.7 Vibration of Magnet

Let *NS* be magnet of *pole-strength m* and *magnetic moment M*, suspended at an angle θ with the earth's field *H*, as shown in Fig. 7.18.

Clearly, forces *mH* and *mH* acting on the two poles of the magnet, being *equal*, *opposite* and *parallel*, constitute a *couple of moment* $mH \times ST = mHNS \sin\theta = MH\sin\theta$, tending to rotate the magnet back so as to lie parallel to the earth's field (*H*).

Since θ is small, we may take $\sin\theta = \theta$ and, therefore

couple acting on the magnet $= MH\theta$.

If *I* be the *moment of inertia* of the magnet about the suspension thread and $d^2\theta/dt^2$, its *angular acceleration*, the couple on it is also equal to $Id^2\theta/dt^2$.

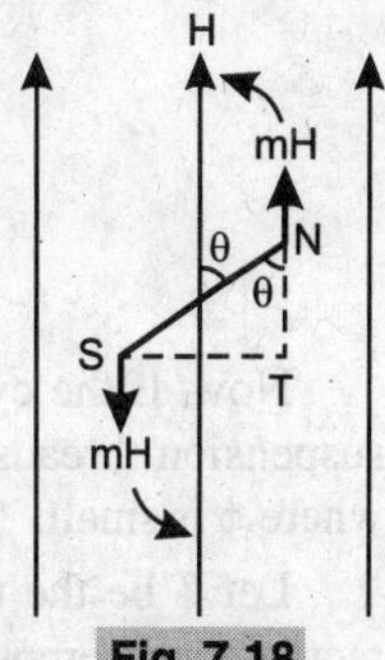

Fig. 7.18

So that, we have $Id^2\theta/dt^2 = MH\theta$, whence $d^2\theta/dt^2 = -(MH/I)\theta = -\mu\theta$, the *–ve* sign indicating that the acceleration is directed oppositely to the angular displacement θ from its equilibrium position parallel to the field.

The angular acceleration of the magnet is thus proportional to its angular displacement from its mean of equilibrium position and is directed oppositely to displacement. It, therefore, executes a S.H.M. and its time period is given by

$$T = 2\pi\sqrt{\frac{1}{\mu}} = 2\pi\sqrt{\frac{1}{MH/I}}$$

$$T = 2\pi\sqrt{\frac{I}{MH}}$$

7.7.8 Bifilar Oscillations

Bifilar Oscillations (with parallel threads): If a heavy and uniform bar or cylinder (or any rigid body), be suspended horizontally by means of two equal, vertical, flexible and inelastic thread, equidistant from its center of gravity, the arrangement constitutes bifilar suspension.

On being displaced a little in its own plane *i.e*, horizontal plane and then released, the bar or cylinder executes S.H.M. about the vertical axis through its centre of gravity.

Let *AB* [fig. 7.19(*a*)] represents the equilibrium position of a cylinder of mass *m* with its *c.g.* at 0 where its weight *mg* acts vertically downwards. Let the two suspension threads *PA* and *QB* be parallel to each other, and distance 2*d* apart and let the length of each thread be *l*.

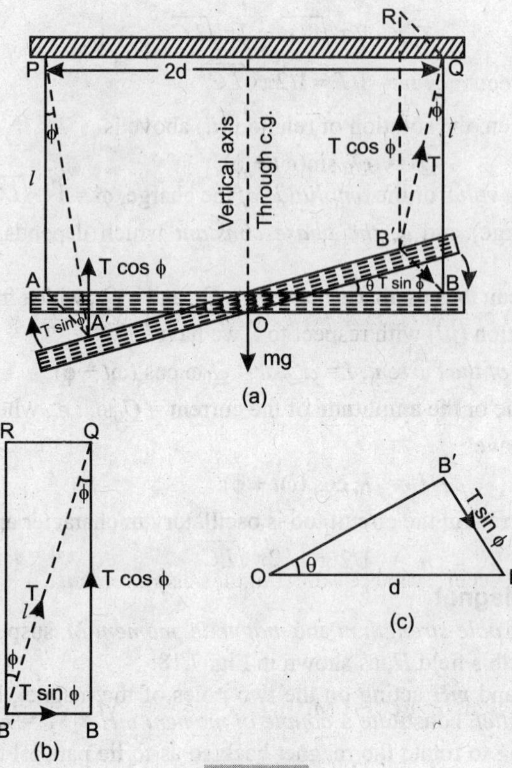

Fig. 7.19

Now, If the cylinder by displaced a little into the position $A'B'$ through a small angle ϕ, the suspension threads take up the positions PA' and QB' at an angle θ with their original positions, where ϕ is small.

Let T be the tension in each thread acting upwards along it. Then, resolving it into its two rectangular components, we have (*i*) component $T\cos\phi$, acting vertically upwards and (*ii*) component $T\sin\phi$, acting horizontally along $B'B$ or $A'A$.

Vertical components support the weight of the cylinder Hence,

$$2\,T\cos\phi = mg$$

$$T\cos\phi = mg/2$$

And since ϕ is small, $\cos\phi = 1$

So that $$T = \frac{mg}{2}$$

The components $T\sin\phi$ acting at A' and B' being equal, opposite and parallel constituent a couple, tending to bring the cylinder back to its original position. Since $A'A$ and B'B are practically at right angles to AB, we have

Moment of the restoring couple $= T\sin\phi\ 2d$

$$= T\phi\ 2d$$

Now, $$\phi = \frac{BB'}{OB} = \frac{BB'}{d}$$

$\therefore$ $$BB' = \theta\, d$$

And $$= \frac{BB'}{QB'} = \frac{BB'}{l} = \frac{\theta d}{l}$$

$\therefore$ Moment of the restoring couple $= T \cdot \dfrac{\theta d}{l} 2d$

$$= \frac{mg}{2} \cdot \frac{\theta d}{l} \cdot 2d$$

$$= \frac{mgd^2}{2} \cdot \theta$$

But, the moment of the restoring couple $= I \cdot \dfrac{d^2\theta}{dt^2}$

where I is M.I. of the cylinder about the vertical axis through its *c.g.* and $\dfrac{d^2\theta}{dt^2}$ is its angular acceleration

$$\therefore \qquad I \cdot \frac{d^2\theta}{dt^2} = -\frac{mgd^2}{l} \cdot \theta$$

$$\therefore \qquad \frac{d^2\theta}{dt^2} = -\frac{mgd^2}{Il} \cdot \theta = -\mu\theta$$

where $\dfrac{mgd^2}{I \cdot l} = \mu$, angular acceleration per unit angular displacement.

$$\therefore \qquad \frac{d^2\theta}{dt^2} \alpha - \theta$$

Hence, the bifilar oscillations are S.H.M. and its, time period is given by

$$T = 2\pi\sqrt{\frac{1}{\mu}} = 2\pi\sqrt{\frac{I \cdot l}{mgd^2}}$$

$$\therefore \qquad T = 2\pi\frac{1}{d} \cdot \sqrt{\frac{Il}{mg}}$$

Or, if we put $I = mk^2$, where k is radius of gyration of the cylinder about the vertical axis through O, we have

$$\therefore \qquad T = 2\pi\frac{1}{d} \cdot \sqrt{\frac{mk^2 \cdot l}{mg}} = 2\pi\frac{1}{d} \cdot \sqrt{\frac{k^2 \cdot l}{mg}}$$

$$T = 2\pi\frac{k}{d} \cdot \sqrt{\frac{l}{g}}$$

This equation gives the time period of the bifilar oscillator having parallel threads.

7.8 TWO-BODY HARMONIC OSCILLATOR

A system of two bodies connected by a spring so that both are free to oscillate simple harmonically along the length of the spring constitutes a *two-body harmonic oscillator or a coupled oscillator*.

Now, we have seen under §7.7.3 that a mass m, attached to the free end of a spring whose other end is fixed to a rigid support like a wall, constitutes a harmonic oscillator. This too is in fact a two-body oscillator, only one of the bodies, *viz.* the wall, is rigidly connected to the earth and has thus effectively an infinite mass and is there, immovable. Since the end of the spring connected to the wall does not move, the change in the length of the spring is given by the displacement of mass m itself. In short, the extension of the spring is determined by the motion of mass m alone, the infinite mass at its other end remaining fixed in its position.

In general, however, we seldom come across such infinite and immovable masses and have, therefore, to consider the motion of both the masses connected to the two ends of the spring. Among example of such two-body oscillators may be cited the diatomic molecules like those of hydrogen, carbon monoxide, *HCI* etc which can oscillate along their respective axes of symmetry. Although, of course, the two atoms in their molecules are coupled by electromagnetic forces, we may, for all practical purposes, imagine them to be connected together by means of tiny, massless springs.

Let us, however, consider the general case of a two-body oscillator consisting of two masses m_1 and m_2 (Fig. 7.20), connected by a horizontal massless spring of force constant C, so as to be free to oscillate along length of the spring on a frictionless horizontal surface.

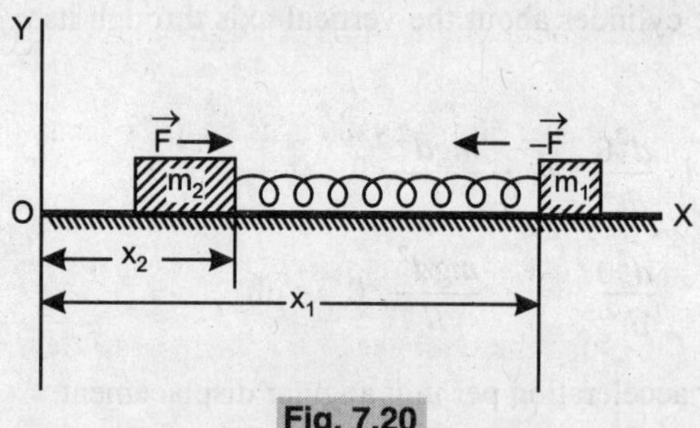

Fig. 7.20

Let the normal length of the spring be l and let, at any given instant, the coordinates of the two ends of the spring be x_1 and x_2, as shown. Then,clearly,

Extension of the spring, $x = (x_1 - x_2) - l$,

where x is positive if the spring is stretched, zero, if the spring has its *normal length and negative* if it be *compressed.* Here, we assume it to be positive. The forces (F) exerted by the spring on the two masses are obviously equal in magnitude but opposite in sign, as indicate in the figure, the magnitude of each being Cx.

If, therefore, d^2x_1/dt^2 be the acceleration of mass m_1 and d^2x_2/dt^2, that of mass m_2, we have

$$m_1 d^2x_1/dt^2 = -Cx \quad \ldots(i) \qquad \text{and} \qquad m_2 d^2x_2 dt^2 = Cx. \quad \ldots(ii)$$

Multiplying relation (*i*) by m_2 and relation (*ii*) by m_1 and subtracting the latter form the former, we have

$$m_1 m_2 \frac{d^2x_1}{dt^2} - m_1 m_2 \frac{d^2x_2}{dt^2} = -m_2 Cx - m_1 Cx$$

Or, $$m_1 m_2 \frac{d^2}{dt^2}(x_1 - x_2) = -Cx(m_1 + m_2)$$

Or, $$\left(\frac{m_1 m_2}{m_1 + m_2}\right)\frac{d^2}{dt^2}(x_1 - x_2) = -Cx$$

Now, l being a constant, $d^2(x_1 - x_2)/dt^2 = d^2x/dt^2$. So that,

$$\left(\frac{m_1 m_2}{m_1 + m_2}\right)\frac{d^2x}{dt^2} = -Cx$$

Or, putting $m_1 m_2/(m_1 + m_2) = \mu$, called the reduced mass of the system (being smaller than either of the two masses m_1 and m_2), we have

$$\frac{dx^2}{dt^2} = -\frac{C}{\mu}x$$

This is identical in form with the equation of motion obtained for a singly-body oscillator under §7.7.3, with the difference that μ here is the *reduced mass of the system instead of mass m* of the single-body there and x here is the *relative displacement of the two masses from their equilibrium positions instead of the displacement of mass m alone from its equilibrium position there.*

The system thus oscillates simple harmonically with a timed-period

$$T = 2\pi\sqrt{\frac{1}{C/\mu}} = 2\pi\sqrt{\frac{\mu}{C}} \quad \text{and} \quad \textit{frequency},\ n = \frac{1}{T} = \frac{1}{2\pi}\sqrt{\frac{C}{\mu}} \quad ...(iv)$$

This mean that *the two-body system oscillates along the axis of the spring with the same time-period and frequency as a one-body oscillator of mass* μ *and force constant C.*

Each of the two masses oscillates relatively to the other as though the latter were fixed and its own mass were reduced to μ but, since their directions of motions are opposite to each other (both moving inwards during compression and outwards during extension of the spring), they differ in phase by π.

Also, since no *external* force acts on the system, its centre of mass remains stationary and the amplitudes of masses m_1 and m_2, therefore, are respectively $m_2/(m_1 + m_2)$ and $m_1/(m_1 + m_2)$ times the extension x of the spring.

Further, as in the case of a singe-body oscillator, so also here, the *P. E. of the system* is given by $U = \frac{1}{2}Cx^2$ and hence the *P.E.* curve here too is *parabolic* in form. Here, x, however, depends upon the relative positions of the two masses and is equal to $(r - r_0)$ where r_0 is the distance between the two masses when they are at rest and r, the distance between them when the spring has been extended by a length x. So that,

$$U = \frac{1}{2}C(r - r_0)^2$$

Obviously, therefore, the *curve between U and r* (*i.e.* the *P.E. curve*) is parabolic in form as in form as in the case of a single-body system. *The potential energy here, however, the a characteristic of the system as a whole and no of the individual masses constituting it.*

7.9 OSCILLATION OF A DIATOMIC MOLECULE

As mentioned earlier, under §7.8 above, a diatomic molecule behaves as a two-body oscillator, with its two atoms connected by a small, massless spring, as it were.

The potential energy U of the system or the molecule change with distance r between the atoms or rather between their nuclei. Thus, putting $r - r_0 = x$, where r_0 is the distance between the atoms, when they are in their normal positions, or stationary, (and hence a constant), we have

force acting on the atoms, i.e., $F = dU/dr = -dU/dx$,

whence $dU = -Fdx$.

$$\therefore \quad U = \int F dx = \int Cx dx = \frac{1}{2}Cx^2 + A$$

where A is a constant of integration.

Now, assuming the *P.E.* to be *zero* at infinite separating of the atoms, it will be negative for ordinary finite distance (as measured on the atomic scale) and will have its *minimum value*, $-U_0$, say, at $x = 0$, *i.e.*, when $r = r_0$ or the atoms are in their normal, stationary state.

We, therefore, have $-U_0 = 0 + A$, Or, $A = -U_0$.

Substituting the value of A in the expression for U above, we have

$$U = -U_0 + \frac{1}{2}Cx^2 = -U_0 + \frac{1}{2}C(r - r_0)^2$$

indicating that $U - r$ or the potential energy curve for the diatomic molecule should also be parabolic in form like that of a two-body or a one-body harmonic oscillator.

The actual *P.E.* curve of a diatomic molecule, however, comes out to be of the form shown in Fig. 7.21, which departs somewhat from the true parabolic form (shown dotted) near the top of the potential well, where it more or less spreads out. This departure from the true parabolic form is due to two reasons: (*i*) *a rather large amplitude of the oscillations* and (*ii*) *the rotation of the molecule about its centre of mass*. Nevertheless, the bottom of the potential well is almost truly parabolic in form, indicating that for amplitudes about the equilibrium position (r_0), the system oscillates like a two-body harmonic oscillator, with its natural frequency $\nu_0 = \frac{1}{2\pi}\sqrt{\frac{C}{\mu}}$, where μ is its *reduced mass*.

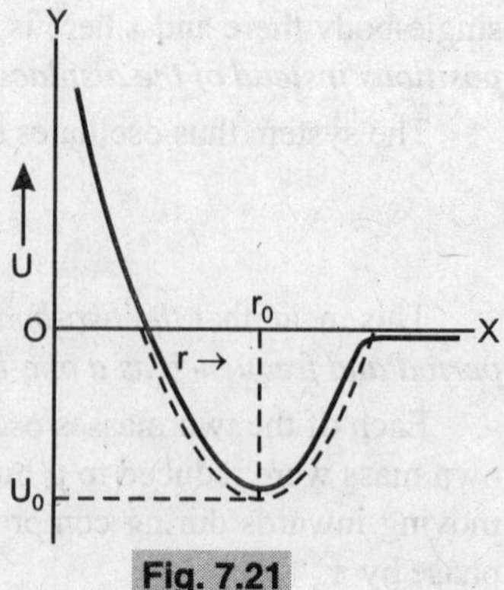

Fig. 7.21

Energy-level diagram of a diatomic molecule. Classical mechanics, as we know, puts no limit to the energy of vibration possessed by a harmonic oscillator which must go on increasing continuously with its amplitude. But quantum–and this assertion is borne out by experiment –that the oscillator can possess only certain discrete values of energy and no others. These discrete or permissible values of vibrational energy (E_V) are given by the relation,

$$E_V = \left(n + \frac{1}{2}\right)h\nu_0$$

where *n* can be either zero or a positive integer and is called the *vibrational quantum number; h is the familiar planck's constant* (6.62×10^{-27} erg-sec.) and ν_0, the *natural frequency of oscillation* of the molecule, equal to $\frac{1}{2\pi}\sqrt{C/\mu}$

This vibrational energy (E_V) of the molecule is of course relative to the vibrational energy *zero* that it possesses when at rest in its position of equilibrium, (*i.e.*, when $r = r_0$).

Now, the *total energy of molecule*, which, as we have seen above, is normally always negative, is given by $E = (-U_0 + Ev)$.

Or, $$E = -U_0 + \left(n + \frac{1}{2}\right)h\nu_0$$

which gives a various permissible discrete values of energy the molecule may possess if *n* be given the values 0,1,2,3, etc.

The vibrational energy E_{V0}, corresponding to $n = 0$, being obviously the lowest, is referred to as the **zero-point energy** and is clearly equal to $\left(0 + \frac{1}{2}\right)h\nu_0 = \frac{1}{2}h\nu_0$. The *minimum total energy* of the molecule (corresponding to $n = 0$) is thus $E_0 = \left(-U_0 + \frac{1}{2}h\nu_0\right)$. And the **dissociation energy** (*i.e.*, the energy needed to completely separate the atoms) and hence also, the **binding energy** (or the energy necessary to bind the atoms together) of the molecule is thus $-\left(-U_0 + \frac{1}{2}h\nu_0\right) = U_0 - \frac{1}{2}h\nu_0$.

It will also be easily seen that the vibrational energy of the molecule, and hence also its total energy, will go on increasing in equal steps of $h_{\nu 0}$ as n takes on the successive value 1, 2, 3 etc., for

$$E_{Vn} - E_{V(n-1)} = \left(n + \frac{1}{2}\right)h\nu_0 - \left(n - 1 + \frac{1}{2}\right)h\nu_0 = h\nu_0.$$

Thus, if we take $E = 0$, in the equilibrium position of the molecule, as its *upper limit* of energy (the energy in all other positions being energy, we can build up an *energy-level diagram*, consisting of a set of parallel straight lines representing energies of the molecule corresponding to $n = 0$, 1, 2, 3 etc, as shown in Fig. 7.22, such that the distance of any particular line form the reference line $E = 0$ is proportional to the energy represented by that line.

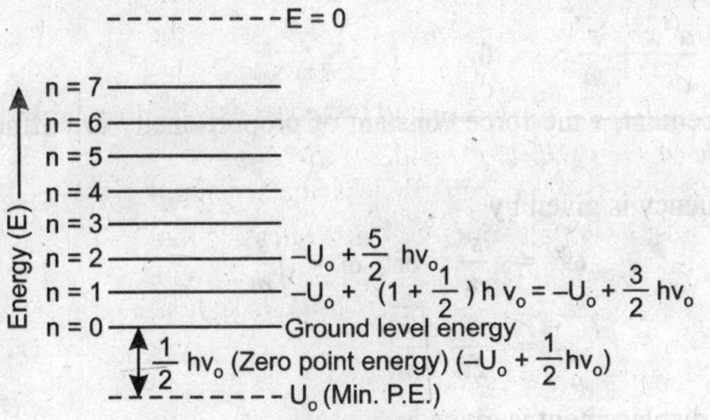

- - - - - - - - - E = 0

n = 7

n = 6

n = 5

n = 4

n = 3

n = 2 —— $-U_o + \frac{5}{2}\, hv_o$

n = 1 —— $-U_o + \left(1 + \frac{1}{2}\right) h\, v_o = -U_o + \frac{3}{2}\, hv_o$

n = 0 —— Ground level energy

$\frac{1}{2}\, hv_o$ (Zero point energy) $(-U_o + \frac{1}{2} hv_o)$

- - - - - - - - - U_o (Min. P.E.)

Energy (E)

Fig. 7.22

Thus, proceeding from the ground level upward, for *quite some distance the lines are all equally spaced* since an upper level differs from the one immediately below it by $h_{\nu 0}$. Only at the levels higher up, which correspond to the top of the potential well of fig. 7.21, above, where the *P.E.* curve departs from the parabolic form and spreads out sideways and where, therefore, the frequency is less than its value $\frac{1}{2\pi}\sqrt{C/\mu}$ in the lower parts, do the lines get closer togather, as shown.

Now, it may as well be mentioned here that just as a molecule, when it rises from a lower to a higher energy level, absorbs energy which is an integral multiple of $h_{\nu 0}$, so also when it falls from a higher to a lower energy level, it parts with energy which too, naturally, is an integral multiple of $h_{\nu 0}$. This energy is usually given out in the form of a *photon* or electromagnetic radiations, which are a direct consequence of the oscillations of electric charges in the molecule. Such radiations, however, are given out by what are called *polar molecules* (*i.e.*, molecules in which there are free electric poles or charges that can oscillate) like those of *HCI*, for example, but not by symmetrical molecules like those of hydrogen (because of the absence of electrical poles or charges). Here too, there are permissible and forbidden transitions, the permissible ones that occur most frequently are those in which the value of *n* change by 1. So that, if *v* be the frequency of the radiation emitted, we have *energy given out, i.e.*,

$$hv = Ev_n - E_{v_{(n-1)}} = \left(n + \frac{1}{2}\right) hv_0 - \left(n - 1 + \frac{1}{2}\right) hv_0 = hv_0$$

i.e., the frequency *v* of the radiation emitted is equal to the classical frequency $v_0 = \frac{1}{2\pi}\sqrt{C/\mu}$

And, therefore, the corresponding *wave number v* (*i.e.*, number of wave contained in a length of 1 cm) $= \frac{1}{\lambda} = \frac{v}{c} = \frac{v_0}{c}$

$$= \frac{1}{2\pi c}\sqrt{\frac{C}{\mu}}$$

where *c* is the velocity of light in free space (equal to 3×10^{10} cm/sec).

Some of the *forbidden transitions*, *i.e.*, those corresponding to the changes of more than 1 in the value of *n*, also occur quite often, giving electromagnetic radiations in the form of faint spectral lines.

It may also happen sometimes that the molecule oscillates and rotates simultaneously. In such cases, obviously, many more of the spectral lines are emitted.

7.10 SIMILARITY BETWEEN MECHANICAL AND ELECTRICAL OSCILLATIONS

There is a similarity between mechanical and electrical oscillations as discussed below:

The equation of motion of a simple harmonic mechanical oscillator is given by

$$\frac{d^2x}{dt^2} + \frac{s}{m}x = 0 \qquad ...(i)$$

where x is the displacement, s the force constant of proportionally or stiffness and m the mass of oscillator.

The angular frequency is given by

$$\omega^2 = \frac{s}{m} \quad \text{or} \quad \omega = \sqrt{\frac{s}{m}}$$

or frequency
$$n = \frac{1}{2\pi}\sqrt{\frac{s}{m}}$$

The equation for displacement is given by

$$x = a \sin(\omega t + \phi)$$

where a and ϕ are constants, known as amplitude and initial phase angle.

The total energy of the mechanical oscillator

$$E = \frac{1}{2}mv^2 + \frac{1}{2}sx^2 = \frac{1}{2}m\dot{x}^2 + \frac{1}{2}sx^2$$

where
$$= \frac{1}{2}m\dot{x}^2 \text{ is the } K.E. \text{ and } \frac{1}{2}sx^2 \text{ the } P.E.$$

The equation of motion of a simple harmonic electrical oscillator is given by

$$\frac{d^2Q}{dt^2} + \frac{1}{LC}Q = 0$$

where Q is the change, L the inductance and C the capacitance of the electrical circuit.

The angular frequency is given by

$$\omega = \sqrt{\frac{1}{LC}}$$

or frequency
$$n = \frac{1}{2\pi\sqrt{LC}}$$

The charge on the capacitance varies harmonically and is represented by an equation similar to displacement equation *i.e.*

$$Q = Q_0 \sin(\omega t + \phi)$$

where Q_0 is the amplitude of charge and ϕ the phase difference.

The current $I = \frac{dQ}{dt}$ corresponds to velocity $v = \frac{dx}{dt}$ and is given by

$$I = \omega Q_0 \cos(\omega t + \phi).$$

The voltage across the capacitor $V = \frac{Q}{C} = \frac{Q_0}{C}\sin(\omega t + \phi)$

Both I and V, therefore vary harmonically with the same angular velocity ω.

The total energy of an electrical oscillator is the sum of the magnetic energy and electric energy.

The magnetic energy can be calculated from the current I and potential $V = L\frac{dl}{dt}$ across the inductance and is given by

$$\int VI\,dt = \int L\frac{dI}{dt}I\,dt = \int LIdI\,\frac{1}{2}LI^2 = \frac{1}{2}L\dot{Q}^2$$

Compare it with kinetic energy in a mechanical oscillator given by $\frac{1}{2}mx^2$. Thus mass in a mechanical circuit corresponds to inductance in an electrical circuit and velocity to electric current.

The electrostatic energy can be calculated from the voltage across the capacitor and is given by

$$\frac{1}{2}CV^2 = \frac{1}{2}C\left(\frac{Q}{C}\right)^2 = \frac{1}{2}\frac{Q^2}{C}$$

Compare it with potential energy in a mechanical oscillator given $\frac{1}{2}sx^2$. Thus stiffness s in a mechanical circuit corresponds to $\frac{1}{C}$ in an electrical circuit.

7.11 ROLE OF L AND C IN ELECTRICAL OSCILLATOR

An oscillating electrical circuit consists of an inductance L and a capacitance C. In the electrical oscillator it is the charge on the capacitance that oscillates. In other words, *the charge on the capacitor is the harmonically varying quantity which gives rise to electrical oscillations*. In an electrical oscillator charge corresponds to displacement in a mechanical oscillator. The inductance L is the electrical counterparts of mass m (inertia) and the reciprocal of capacitance ($1/C$) is the counter part of stiffness s. The frequency is given by

$$n = \frac{1}{2\pi\sqrt{LC}}$$

We can realise an LC circuit in practice and obtain simple harmonic oscillations if the circuit has zero (ohmic) resistance and there is no loss of energy. In practice, however, it is not possible to have a circuit with zero resistance. Hence energy is supplied to the LC circuit to make up for this small inevitable loss by electronic devices like thermionic valves or transistors.

7.12 AN HARMONIC OSCILLATOR

An harmonic oscillator is one in which the relationship between *force* and *displacement is linear*. The harmonic oscillator is a highly idealized system that oscillates with a single frequency, irrespective of the amount of pumping or energy injected into the system Consequently, the fundamental frequency of vibration of an harmonic oscillator is *independent of the amplitudes* of the vibrations. Most commonly studied is the mass-spring system obeying Hook's law, as seen in detail.

However, in a mechanical anharmonic oscillator, the relationship between force and *displacement* is *not linear*, but *depends upon the amplitude* to the displacement. The non-linearity arises from the fact that the spring is not capable of exerting a restoring force that is proportional to its displacement because of, for example, stretching in the material comprising the spring. As a result of non-linearity, the vibration frequency can change, depending upon the system's displacement.

These changes in the vibration frequency result in energy being coupled from the fundamental vibration frequency to other frequencies through a process known as *parametric coupling*.

There are many systems throughout the physical world exhibiting an anharmonic oscillations in addition to the non-linear mass-spring system. For example, an atom, which consists of a positively charged nucleus surrounded by a negatively charged electronic cloud, experiences a displacement between the centre of mass of the nucleus and the electronic cloud when an electric field is present. The amount of that displacement, called the electric dipole moment, is related linearly to the applied field for small fields, but as the magnitude of the field is increased, the field-dipole moment relationship becomes non-linear, just as in the mechanical system.

Further example of anharmonic oscillator include the large-angle pendulum, which exhibits chaotic behaviour as a result of its anharmonicity non-equilibrium semiconductor, that possess a large not carrier population, which exhibit nonlinear behaviour of various types related to the effective mass, of the carriers; and ionosphere plasmas, which also exhibit nonlinear behaviour based on the an harmonicity of the plasma. Anharmonicity played a rôle in *lattice and molecular vibrations*, in *quantum oscillations* and in acoustics.

In fact, virtually all oscillators becomes anharmonic when their pump amplitude increases beyond some threshold and as a result, it is necessary to use non-linear equations of motion to describe their behaviour.

Analytical Treatment

We have seen under §5.9 how that *P.E.* of a particle at a distance *x* from its position of stable equilibrium is given by

$$U = U_0 + \frac{Cx^2}{2!} + \frac{C_1x^3}{3!} + \frac{C_2x^4}{4!} + \ldots \quad \ldots(i)$$

and the force acting on the particle by $F = -Cx - \frac{C_1x^2}{2!} - \frac{C_2x^3}{3!} \ldots$ ...(*ii*)

It will also be recalled that in the case of a harmonic oscillator, the terms containing C_1, C_2, etc., *viz.*, $C_1x^3/3!$, $C_2x^4/4!$ etc., are all equal to *zero*, so that $U = \frac{1}{2}Cx^2$ and hence the *P.E.* curve is a *parabola*, And the force $F = -Cx$ and hence proportional to displacement of the particle or the oscillator.

In case any of the terms containing C_1, C_2 etc is not equal to zero, the motion of the particle or the system no longer remain harmonic and it is, therefore, called an *anharmonic oscillator*. And since it is the presence of the terms containing C_1, C_2 etc that really makes it so, they are referred to as *anharmonic terms*.

Let us study the anharmonic oscillator in some detail.

With the forces acting on an anharmonic oscillator given by relation (*ii*) above, its equation of motion is

$$m\frac{d^2x}{dt^2} = -Cx - \frac{C_1x^2}{2!} - \frac{C_2x^3}{3!}$$

which may be put as $\frac{d^2x}{dt^2} + \frac{C}{m}x = -\frac{C_1x^2}{(2\times 1)m} - \frac{C_2x^3}{(3\times 2\times 1)m} - \ldots$

Or, putting $C/m = \omega_0^2$, $C_1/2m = \alpha$, $C_2/6m = \beta$ ..., we have

$$\frac{d^2x}{dt^2} + \omega_0^2 x = -\alpha x^2 - \beta x^3 - \ldots \quad \ldots(iii)$$

There is really no general solution to this equation. Approximate solution may however be obtained in specific cases if , as is usually the case, the anharmonic terms are small and, in particular, if the terms are small and, in particular, if the terms containing the 4*th* and the higher powers of *X* are negligible.

Now, as mentioned earlier (under §7.2), any complex periodic motion is really made up of a number of simple harmonic motions (called *harmonics*) whose frequencies are integral multiples of the lowest or the fundamental frequency. This means, in other words, that the displacement *x* is a *periodic function of t* and can as such, be expressed as a *Fourier series* as follows:

$$x = A_0 + A_1 \sin \omega t + A_2 \sin 2\omega t + \ldots A_n \sin (n\,\omega t) + B_1 \cos \omega t$$
$$+ B_2 \cos 2\omega t + \ldots B_n \cos (n\,\omega t). \quad \ldots(iv)$$

As will be easily seen, many of the coefficients in this equation will be equal to *zero* in view of the sheer symmetry of the motion. Thus, for example, if we start counting time from an instant such that the motion is an *even* functions of time, *i.e.*, when x has equal values at times t and $-t$ and, therefore, its maximum or minimum value at $t = 0$, all sine terms will be absent from the equation because the general *sine term*, sin ($n\,\omega t$), being an odd function of time t, its value changes sign with that of t. We, therefore, take as a possible solution the expression.

$$x = A_0 + B_1 \cos \omega t + B_2 \cos 2\omega t + B_3 \cos 3\,\omega t + \ldots, \qquad \ldots(v)$$

where the values of ω and the coefficients A_0, B_1, B_3, etc. are to be determined.

As we know, in the event of α and β etc being each equal to zero, we have (from relation (*iii*) above) a harmonic oscillator, with the solution $x = B_1 \cos \omega_0 t$.

Here, although α and β etc are not equal to *zero*, they are nevertheless supposed to be small, so that all coefficients other than B_1, *viz.*, A_0, B_2, B_3 etc. must also be small and hence the products and squares of α, β, A_0, B_2, B_3 etc must be negligibly small. Keeping this in mind and taking value of x as given by relation (*iv*) above, we have

$$\frac{d^2x}{dt^2} + \omega_0^2 x = -\omega^2 (B_1 \cos \omega t + 4B_2 \cos 2\omega t + 9\,B_3 \cos 3\,\omega t + \ldots)$$
$$+\,\omega_0^2 (A_0 + B_1 \cos \omega t + B_2 \cos 2\omega t + B_3 \cos 3\,\omega t + \ldots)$$
$$= \omega_0^2 A_0 + (\omega_0^2 - \omega^2)\, B_1 \cos \omega t + (\omega_0^2 - 4\omega^2)\, B_2 \cos 2\,\omega t$$
$$+\,(\omega_0^2 - 9\omega^2)\, B_3 \cos 3\omega t + \ldots$$

and
$$-\alpha x^2 - \beta x^2 = \alpha(A_0 + B_1 \cos \omega t + B_2 \cos 2\,\omega t + B_3 \cos 3\omega t + \ldots)^2$$
$$-\beta\,(A_0 + B_1 \cos \omega t + B_2 \cos 2\,\omega t + B_3 \cos 3\,\omega t + \ldots)^2$$
$$= -\alpha\, B_1^2 \cos^2 \omega t - \beta B_1^3 \cos^3 \omega t - \alpha \frac{L_1^2}{2}\,(1 + \cos 2\omega t)$$
$$-\beta \frac{B_1^3}{4}(3 \cos \omega t + \cos 3\,\omega t)$$
$$= -\alpha \frac{B_1^2}{2} - 3\beta \frac{B_1^3}{4} \cos \omega t - \alpha \frac{B_1^2}{2} \cos 2\omega t - \beta \frac{B_1^3}{4} \cos 3\,\omega t$$

Substituting these values in expression (*iii*) above, we have

$$\omega_0^2 A_0 - (\omega_0^2 - \omega^2)\, B_1 \cos \omega t + (\omega_0^2 + 4\omega^2)\, B_2 \cos 2\,\omega t + (\omega_0^2 + 9\omega t)\, B_3 \cos 3\,\omega t + \ldots$$
$$= -\alpha \frac{B_1^2}{2} - 3\beta \frac{B_1^2}{4} \cos \omega t - \frac{\alpha B_1^2}{2} \cos 2\omega t - \frac{\alpha B_1^2}{4} \cos 3\,\omega t \qquad \ldots(vi)$$

Clearly, in order that relation (*iii*) may hold good, relation (*v*) must be satisfied for all values of t. This will obviously happen when the coefficients of the respective cosine functions on both sides of equation (*vi*) are equal, *i.e.*, when

$$\omega_0^2 A_0 = -\alpha B_1^2/2 \quad \ldots(a), \quad (\omega_0^2 - \omega^2)\, B_1 = 3\,\beta\, B_1^2/4 \quad \ldots(b),$$
$$(\omega_0^2 - 4\omega^2)\, B_2 = -\,\alpha\, B_1^2/2 \ldots (c) \text{ and } (\omega_0^2 - 9\omega^2)\, B_3 = -\alpha B_1^2/4 \quad \ldots(d)$$

The terms containing the 4th and higher powers of x being assumed to be negligible, the coefficients B_4, B_5, B_6, etc. are all equal to zero.

Now, relation (*b*) above gives $\omega^2 = \omega_0^2 + \frac{3}{4}\beta B_1^2$

$$\omega = \left(\omega_0^2 + \frac{3}{4}\beta B_1^2\right)^{1/2}$$

Or,
$$\omega = \omega_0 \left(1 + \frac{3}{4}\frac{\beta B_1^2}{\omega_0^2}\right)^{\frac{1}{2}} = \omega_0 \left(1 + \frac{1}{2}, \frac{3}{4}\frac{\beta B_1^2}{\omega_0^2}\right)$$

Or, $$\omega = \omega_0 \frac{3}{8}\frac{\beta B_1^2}{\omega_0} \qquad ...(vii)$$

Assuming ω to be very nearly equal to ω_0, we have from relation (*c*),

$$-3\,\omega_0^2 B_2 = -\alpha B_1^2/2, \text{ whence, } B_2 = \alpha B_1^2/6\omega_0^2.$$

Similarly, from relation (*d*), we have $B_3 = \beta B_1^2/32\omega_0^2$,
and from relation (*a*), we have $A_0 = \alpha B_1^2/2\omega_0^2$.
Substituting these values of the coefficients in relation (*v*) above, we have

$$x = -\frac{\alpha B_1^2}{2\,\omega_0^2} + B_1 \cos \omega t + \frac{\alpha\, B_1^2}{6\,\omega_0^2} \cos 2\,\omega t + \frac{\beta\, B_1^2}{32\,\omega_0^2} \cos 3\,\omega t + ... \qquad ...(viii)$$

where the value of ω is as given by relation (*vii*) above.

Here, the term B_1 cos ω*t* is referred to as the **fundamental component of oscillation** of the particle or the system and B_1 as its *amplitude* and the terms in cos 2ω*t* and cos 3ω*t* as the second and third harmonics, with frequencies *twice* and *thrice* respectively of the fundamental.

As mentioned earlier also, if α = β = 0, we have the case of a *harmonic* oscillator, with $x = B_1 \cos \omega_0 t$, for then $\omega = \omega_0$ [from relation (*vii*) above].

The same happens when B_1 is small so that terms containing B_1^2 may be neglected. Relation (*viii*) then reduces again to $x = B_4 \cos \omega_0 t$ [because $\omega = \omega_0$ from relation (*vii*)].

This shown that *provided the amplitude be small, the oscillations even in the case of an arharmonic potential well are simple harmonic in character**, as already mentioned in §7.2.

If, however, the amplitude increases, the following changes occur:

(*i*) As can be seen from relation (*vii*) above, if the amplitude (B_1) be large, ω will no longer be equal to ω_0 and hence the *time-period* and, therefore, also the frequency, of the oscillation, will charge. Thus, if *T* be the *time-period* of the oscillations, we shall have

$$T = \frac{2\pi}{\omega} = \frac{2\pi}{\omega_0\,(1 + 3\beta B_1^2/8\omega_0^2)} = \frac{2\pi}{\omega_0}\left(1 + \frac{3\,\beta B_1^2}{8\omega_0^2}\right)^{-1}$$

$$= \frac{2\pi}{\omega_0}\left(1 - \frac{3\,\beta B_1^2}{8\,\omega_0^2}\right)$$

Since $2\pi/\omega_0 = T_0$, the time-period of the small amplitude (or simple harmonic) oscillations, we have

$$T = T_0\left(1 - \frac{3\,\beta B_1^2}{8\,\omega_0^2}\right)$$

(*ii*) The amplitudes of the second, third and higher harmonics, having twice, thrice etc frequencies of the fundamental, will increase still more rapidly, being proportional to B_1^2, B_1^3 etc.

(*iii*) The amplitude of the particle will clearly not be equal to B_1, the amplitude of the fundamental component of the oscillation, nor will move equally on either side of its equilibrium position, (see (*iv*) below).

(*iv*) Since the average values of the cosine functions (cos ω*t*, cos 2 ω*t* etc) over a time-period $T = 2\pi/\omega$ are zero, the average value of the displacement *x* will become

---

This is actually *not so universally true.* For, there are cases where, despite small amplitudes, the oscillations are not simple harmonic; for example, (*i*) when the potential well, instead being parabolic in its lower parts, is *V-shaped* with a well- marked cusp at the bottom. For, in such a case, *du*/*dx* and other derivatives simply, do not exist at the bottom of the well and *U* can not, therefore, be expanded in a Taylor's series (*ii*) Or, again, if the value of *U*, be given by some such relation as $U = -U_0 e^{-ax^4}$, with $F = -dU/dx = -4\,aU_0x^3$, so that the equation of motion turns out to be $md^2x/dt^2 + 4aU_0x^3 = 0$, clearly showing that the oscillations, although periodic in the range $-U_0 << E < 0$ are by no means simple harmonic despite a small amplitude.

$$< x > = -\alpha\, B_1^2/2\omega_0^2, \text{ with } \alpha, \text{ of course, not being } zero.$$

Thus, there will be a shift in the mean position of the particle, proportional to B_1^2, indicating a greater restoring force acting on one side of its equilibrium position than on the other. This means, in other words, that *the potential energy curve or the potential well no longer remain symmetrical and the particle, in consequence, will move more to one side of its equilibrium position than to the other. Its oscillation will thus no longer be simple harmonic.*

An interesting example of the shift in the mean position of a particle is provided by the oscillating atoms in a solid material. The atoms experience a considerable repulsive force when they are closer together, so that they can move apart move easily than they can come nearer to each other. When the solid is heated, therefore, the amplitude of their oscillation increases and their mean position shifts *outwards*, resulting in the linear expansion of the solid, –the greater the shift in the mean position of the atoms, the greater the linear expansion of the solid. Thus, *linear expansion of the solid* α *shift in the mean position of the atoms*.

Now, as we have just seen above, this shift in the mean position is proportional to the square of the amplitude of the oscillating atom which, in its turn, is proportional to the energy of the atom. And, since the average energy of the atom depends upon the temperature of the solid, it follows that the *linear expansion of a solid is proportional to its temperation*.

7.13 TIME-PERIOD OF A PENDULUM FOR LARGE AMPLITUDE OSCILLATION

A simple or a compound pendulum oscillating with a large amplitude a is familiar example of an anharmonic oscillator. The oscillation are simple harmonic only if the angular amplitude θ be infinitely small, *i.e.*, when in the expansion of *sin*θ into a power series (*viz*., $\sin\theta = \theta - \theta^3/3! + \theta^5/5!$ ...) all other terms except the first are negligibly small. So that, as shown in §7.71, the equation of motion of a *simple pendulum* comes out to be $d^2\theta/dt^2 = -(g/l)\theta$ and of a *compound pendulum*, $d^2\theta/dt^2 = -(mgl/I)\theta = -[mgl/(I_0 + ml^2)]\theta$

$$= -[mgl/(mk^2 + ml^2)]\theta = [mgl/m(k^2 + l^2)]\theta = \left[g\left(\frac{k^2}{k} + l\right)\right]0.$$

Or, putting $(k^2/l) + l = L$, *the length of the equivalent simple pendulum*, we have

$$d^2\theta/dt^2 = -(g/L)\theta,$$

the two cases being thus identical except that we have L in place of l in the case of a compound pendulum.

If θ be appreciable large, so that the second term $(\theta^3/3!)$ in the power series can not be neglected*, we have (taking the case of a simple pendulum),

$$\frac{d^2\theta}{dt^2} = -\frac{g}{l}\theta + \frac{g}{(3\times 2\times 1)l}\theta^2$$

Now, referring back to equation (*iii*) of §7.12 above, and taking θ in place of x we see that $\omega_0^2 = g/l$, $\alpha = 0$, $\beta = -g/6l = -\omega_0^2/6$.

$\therefore$ From relation (*viii*) of §7.9, taking amplitude θ_1 in place of B_1, we have

$$\theta = \theta_1 \cos\omega t + \frac{\theta_1^3\beta}{32\,\omega_0^2}\cos 3\omega t = \theta_1\cos\omega t - \frac{\theta_1^3\omega_0^2}{6\times 32\omega_0^2}\cos 3\omega t$$

$$= \theta_1\cos\omega t - \frac{\theta_1^3}{192}\cos 3\omega t,$$

where (as given by relation (*viii*) of §7.12) $\omega = \omega_0\left(1 - \frac{3}{8}\frac{\omega_0^2}{6}\cdot\frac{\theta_1^2}{\omega_0^2}\right)$

Thus, for example, if $\theta = 60°$ or $\pi/3$ radian, we have $\theta^3/3! = \theta^3/3 \times 2 \times 1 = 0.19$ which cannot be neglected, although $\theta^5/5! = 0.001$ may easily be ignored.

$$= \omega_0\left(1-\frac{\theta_1^2}{16}\right) = \sqrt{\frac{g}{l}}\left(1-\frac{\theta_1^2}{16}\right)$$

Hence, *time-period of the simple pendulum, i.e.,*

$$T = \frac{2\pi}{\omega} = 2\pi/\sqrt{g/l}\left(1-\frac{\theta_1^2}{16}\right) = 2\pi\sqrt{\frac{l}{g}}\left(1+\frac{\theta_1^2}{16}\right)$$

Putting $2\pi\sqrt{l/g}$, *the time-period when the amplitude* small, equal to T_0, we have

$$T = T_0(1 + \theta_1^2/16).$$

Similarly, for a compound pendulum, we shall obtain

$$T = 2\pi\sqrt{\frac{L}{g}}\left(1+\frac{\theta_1^2}{16}\right)$$

Or $$T = 2\pi\sqrt{\frac{(k^2/l^2)+l}{g}}\left(1+\frac{\theta_1^2}{16}\right)$$

Since $2\pi\sqrt{\frac{(k^2/l^2)+l}{g}}$ is the time-period T_0 for oscillations of small amplitude, we have

$$T = T_0\,(1 + \theta_1^2/16),$$

Indicating that the *time-period increases with amplitude.*

Since the amplitude of the pendulum in both cases does not remain constant but goes on progressively decreasing from θ_1 in the beginning to, say, θ_2, at the end, we may take $\theta_1\theta_2$ in place of θ_1^2. So that, in either case, $T = T_0\,(1 + \theta_1\theta_2/16)$

Now, what we actually observe is T. The correct value of the time-period (*i.e.*, if the amplitude be small) is, therefore, given by

$$T_0 = T\Big/\left(1+\frac{\theta_1\theta_2}{16}\right) = T\left(1-\frac{\theta_1\theta_2}{16}\right)$$

WORKED EXAMPLE

I–General–simple harmonic Motion

Example 7.1. A particle of mass 100 gm is placed in a field of potential $U = 5x^2 + 10$ ergs/gm. Find the frequency. ***(Meerut U. 2001)***

Solution. Here potential energy $U = 5x^2 + 10$ ergs/gm; $m = 100$ gm

Now $$F = -\frac{dU}{dx} \quad \therefore \quad F = -\frac{d}{dx}(5x^2+10) = -10x$$

Taking x as the displacement, we have $F = m\dfrac{d^2x}{dt^2}$

$$\therefore \quad m\frac{d^2x}{dt^2} = -10x \quad \text{or} \quad \frac{d^2x}{dt^2} = -\frac{10}{m}x$$

This is the equation of a simple harmonic motion with force constant $s = 10$ dyne/cm.

$\therefore$ Frequency $$n = \frac{1}{2\pi}\sqrt{\frac{s}{m}} = \frac{1}{2\pi}\sqrt{\frac{10}{100}} = \frac{1}{2\pi\sqrt{10}} = 0.05 \text{ Hz}$$

Example 7.2. (*a*) An oscilatory motion of a body is represented by $y = ae^{i\omega t}$ where symbols have usual meaning. Show that the motion is simple harmonic.

(*b*) The displacement of a moving particle at any time *t* is given by $y = a \cos \omega t + b \sin \omega t$ show that the motion is simple harmonic.

Solution. (*a*) Given $y = ae^{i\omega t}$

Differentiating with respect to '*t*' we get

$$\frac{dy}{dt} = ae^{i\omega t} \times i\omega = ia\,\omega e^{i\omega t}$$

Differentiating again, we get

$$\frac{d^2y}{dt^2} = ia\omega e^{i\omega t} \times i\omega = -a\,\omega^2 e^{i\omega t} = -\omega^2 y$$

Or
$$\frac{d^2y}{dt^2} + \omega^2 y = 0$$

This is differential equation of *S.H.M.* Hence $y = ae^{i\omega t}$ represents a *S.H.M.*

(*b*) $y = a \cos \omega t + b \sin \omega t$

$$\therefore \quad \frac{dy}{dt} = -a\,\omega \sin \omega t + b\omega \cos \omega t$$

and
$$\frac{dy}{dt} = -a\omega^2 \cos \omega t - b\omega^2 \sin \omega t$$

$$= -\omega^2 (a \cos \omega t + b \sin \omega t)$$

$$= -\omega^2 y$$

Or
$$\frac{d^2y}{dt^2} + \omega^2 y = 0$$

Hence $y = a \cos \omega t + b \sin \omega t$ is the equation of simple harmonic motion.

Example 7.3. A particle executes S.H.M. of period 10 sec. and amplitude 5 cm. calculate the maximum amplitude of velocity. ***(Guhati U. 2002)***

Solution. Here displacement amplitude $a = 5$ cm; Time period $T = 10$ sec.

$$\therefore \text{ Angular frequency} \quad \omega = \frac{2\pi}{T} = \frac{2\pi}{10} s^{-1}$$

$$\text{Maximum velocity} = a\omega = \frac{5 \times 2\pi}{10} \text{ cm/s}$$

$$= \pi \text{ cm/sec or } 3.14 \text{ cm/sec.}$$

Example 7.4. Calculate the displacement to amplitude ratio for a S.H.M when K.E. is 90% of total energy.

Solution. If *m* is the mass of the particle executing *S.H.M.* *a* the amplitude and ω the angular velocity, then

$$\text{Total energy} = \frac{1}{2} \omega a^2 \omega^2$$

Let *y* be the displacement when K.E.= 90% of total energy.

As K.E. is 90% of total energy.

Potential energy = Total energy – Kinetic energy = 10% of total energy

Now potential energy $= \frac{1}{2} m\omega^2 y^2$

$$\therefore \qquad \frac{\frac{1}{2}m\omega^2 y^2}{\frac{1}{2}m\omega^2 a^2} = \frac{y^2}{a^2} = \frac{10}{100} = 0.1$$

Or $$\frac{\text{Displacement}}{\text{Amplitude}} = \frac{y}{a} = \sqrt{0.1} = 0.316$$

Example 7.5. What is the ratio of kinetic energy at displacement one fourth to one third of the amplitude in case is simple harmonic motion?

Solution. If m is the mass of the particle executing S.H.M., a the amplitude and ω the angular velocity, then

$$\text{Total energy} = \frac{1}{2}m\omega^2 y^2$$

When the displacement is y, potential energy $= \frac{1}{2}m\omega^2 y^2$

$\therefore$ Kinetic energy = Total energy – Potential energy $= \frac{1}{2}m\omega^2(a^2 - y^2)$

At displacement $y = \frac{a}{4}$, kinetic energy $E_1 = \frac{1}{2}m\omega^2\left(a^2 - \frac{a^2}{16}\right) = \frac{15}{32}m\omega^2 a^2$

At displacement $y = \frac{a}{3}$, kinetic energy $E_2 = \frac{1}{2}m\omega^2\left(a^2 - \frac{a^2}{9}\right) = \frac{8}{18}m\omega^2 a^2$

$$\therefore \qquad \frac{E_1}{E_2} = \frac{15}{32} \times \frac{18}{8} \times \frac{135}{128} = 1.055$$

Example 7.6. A simple harmonic oscillator is characterised by $y = a \cos \omega t$. calculate the displacement at which kinetic energy is equal to its potential energy.

(*Nagpur U. 2003; Pbi.U, 2000*)

Or

At what displacement from the mean position the total energy of a simple harmonic oscillator is half kinetic and half potential. **(*G.N.D.U. 2001*)**

Solution. Let y be the displacement at which kinetic energy of the simple harmonic oscillator is equal to its potential energy.

Now $$y = a \cos \omega t \qquad \therefore \frac{dy}{dt} = -a\,\omega \sin \omega t$$

The kinetic energy of a simple harmonic oscillator is given by

$$\text{K.E.} = \frac{1}{2}mv^2 = \frac{1}{2}m\left(\frac{dy}{dt}\right)^2 = \frac{1}{2}m(-a\,\omega \sin \omega t)^2$$

$$= \frac{1}{2}ma^2\,\omega^2 \sin^2 \omega t = \frac{1}{2}ma^2\omega^2(1 - \cos^2 \omega t)$$

$$= \frac{1}{2}m\omega^2(a^2 - a^2\cos^2 \omega t) = \frac{1}{2}m\omega^2(a^2 - y^2)$$

$$\text{P.E.} = \frac{1}{2}sy^2 \text{ where s = stiffness and } \frac{s}{m} = \omega^2 \text{ or } s = m\omega^2$$

$$\therefore \qquad \text{P.E.} = \frac{1}{2}m\omega^2 y^2$$

when $$\text{K.E.} = \text{P.E.}$$

$$\frac{1}{2}m\omega^2(a^2-y^2) = \frac{1}{2}m\omega^2 y^2$$

or $$a^2 - y^2 = y^2 \quad \text{or} \quad a^2 = 2y^2$$

∴ Displacement $$y = \pm\frac{a}{\sqrt{2}}$$

In other words, for a displacement $y = \pm\dfrac{a}{\sqrt{2}}$ from the mean position P.E. = $\dfrac{1}{4}m^2\omega^2 a^2$, K.E. $\dfrac{1}{4}ma^2\omega^2$ and energy = $\dfrac{1}{2}m\omega^2 a^2$

i.e., half of the total energy is kinetic and half potential.

Example 7.7. The amplitude of a simple harmonic oscillator is doubled. How does this effect the time period, total energy and maximum velocity of the oscillator.

(P.U., 2003; Pbi, U. 2000)

Solution. When the displacement y of a simple harmonic oscillator is given by $y = A \sin(\omega t + \phi)$

velocity $v = \dfrac{dy}{dt} = A\omega\cos(\omega t + \phi)$

and acceleration $a = \dfrac{d^2y}{dt^2} = -A\omega^2 \sin(\omega t + \phi) = -\omega^2 y$

Now time period $T = 2\pi\sqrt{\dfrac{\text{Displacement}}{\text{Acceleration}}} = 2\pi\sqrt{\dfrac{y}{\omega^2 y}} = \dfrac{2\pi}{\omega}$ (ignoring the negative sign)

As $\dfrac{2\pi}{\omega}$ is a constant, the time period does no depend upon amplitude but remains constant.

Maximum velocity $v_{max} = A\,\omega$ when $\cos(\omega\, t + \phi) = 1$

When amplitude A is doubled, the maximum velocity is also doubled.

Total energy = $\dfrac{1}{2}mA^2\omega^2$

When the amplitude A is doubled, the total energy becomes four times, because energy $\propto A^2$.

Example 7.8. Show that for a particle executing S.H.M. average value of kinetic and potential energy is the same and each is equal to half the total energy.

(Nagpur U., 2009; Pbi. U., 2003; Luck. U., 2002)

Solution. Average kinetic energy. Kinetic energy at any instant

$$= \frac{1}{2}mv^2 = \frac{1}{2}m\dot{y}^2 = \frac{1}{2}m\left(\frac{dy}{dt}\right)^2$$

For a S.H.M $$y = a\sin(\omega\, t + \phi)$$

and $$\frac{dy}{dt} = a\omega\cos(\omega t + \phi)$$

∴ Instantaneous $$K.E. = \frac{1}{2}ma^2\omega^2\cos^2(\omega t + \theta)$$

If T is the time period, then

$$\text{Average } K.E. = \langle K.E.\rangle = \frac{1}{T}\int_0^{T_1}\frac{1}{2}ma^2\omega^2\cos^2(\omega t + \phi)\,dt$$

$$= \frac{ma^2\omega^2}{2T}\int_0^T \cos^2(\omega t + \phi)dt$$

$$= \frac{ma^2\omega^2}{2T}\int_0^T \frac{1}{2}[1 + \cos 2(\omega t + \phi)]dt$$

$$= \frac{ma^2\omega^2}{4T}\left[\int_0^T dt + \int_0^T \cos 2(\omega t + \phi)dt\right]$$

$$= \frac{ma^2\omega^2}{4T}T \qquad \left[\because \int_0^T \cos(2\omega t + \phi)dt = 0\right]$$

$$= \frac{1}{4}ma^2\omega^2$$

Average potential energy. Instantaneous potential energy is given by

$$P.E. = \frac{1}{2}sy^2 = \frac{1}{2}sa^2\sin^2(\omega t + \phi)$$

$\therefore$ Average

$$P.E. = \frac{1}{T}\int_0^T \frac{1}{2}sa^2\sin^2(\omega t + \phi)\,dt$$

$$= \frac{sa^2}{2T}\int_0^T \frac{1}{2}[1 - \cos 2(\omega t + \phi)dt$$

$$= \frac{sa^2}{4T}\left[\int_0^T dt - \int_0^T \cos 2(\omega t + \phi)dt\right]$$

$$= \frac{sa^2}{4T}T = \frac{1}{4}sa^2 \qquad \left[\because \int_0^T \cos 2(\omega t + \phi)\,dt = 0\right]$$

But $\omega^2 = \frac{s}{m} \quad \therefore s = m\omega^2$

$\therefore$ Average $P.E. = \frac{1}{4}ma^2\omega^2$

Total Energy. The total energy $= \frac{1}{2}ma^2\omega^2$

Thus it is clear from equations (*i*), (*ii*), and (*iii*) that the average kinetic energy of a harmonic oscillator is equal to the average potential energy and is equal to half the total energy *i.e.*,

$$<K.E.> = <P.E.> = \frac{1}{2}E_{total}$$

Example 7.9. The displacement of a simple harmonic oscillator is given by

$$x = a\sin(\omega t + \phi)$$

If the oscillations started at time $t = 0$ from a position x_0 with velocity $x = v_0$ show that

$$\tan\phi = \frac{\omega x_0}{v_0} \text{ and } a = \left[x_0^2 \frac{v_0^2}{\omega^2}\right]^{\frac{1}{2}}$$

Solution. Given $x = a\sin(\omega t + \phi)$; at $t = 0$, $x = x_0$

$\therefore$ $x_0 = a\sin\phi$

Also $\dot{x} = a\,\omega\cos(\omega t + \phi)$; at $t = 0$, $\dot{x} = v_0$

$\therefore$ $v_0 = a\,\omega\cos\phi$

Hence $\tan\phi = \frac{\sin\phi}{\cos\phi} = \frac{x_0}{a} \times \frac{a\omega}{v_0} = \frac{\omega x_0}{v_0}$

and $a^2\sin^2\phi + a^2\cos^2\phi = x_0^2 + \frac{v_0^2}{\omega^2}$

or $$a = \left[x_0^2 + \frac{v_0^2}{\omega^2}\right]^{\frac{1}{2}}$$

Example 7.10. A man stands on a platform which vibrates simple harmonically in a vertical direction at a frequency of 5 Hertz. Show that the mass loses contact with the platform when the displacement 10^{-2} metres.

Solution. The mass contact with the platform when the upward force acting on it exceeds its weight *mg*.

The mass vibrates simple harmonically given by

$$x = a \sin(\omega t + \phi)$$

$\therefore$ Acceleration $$\ddot{x} = a\,\omega^2 \sin(\omega t + \phi) = -\omega^2 x$$

Upward force $$= -m\omega^2 x$$

In the limiting case $mg = m\omega^2 x$

or $$x = \frac{g}{\omega^2} = \frac{9.81}{4\pi^2 5^2} = 0.1 \text{ m} = 10^{-2} \text{ metre}$$

Example 7.11. A body executing S.H.M. has velocities 80 cm/s and 60 cm/s when displacements are 3 cm and 4 cm respectively. Calculate the amplitude of vibration and the time taken to travel 2.5 cm from positive extremity of the oscillation.

Solution. Velocity $$v = \omega\sqrt{a^2 - y^2}$$

where ω = angular velocity; a = amplitude and y = displacement from the mean position

$$80 \text{ cm s}^{-1} = \omega\sqrt{a^2 - 3^2} \qquad ...(i)$$

$$60 \text{ cm s}^{-1} = \omega\sqrt{a^2 - 4^2} \qquad ...(ii)$$

$\therefore$ $$\frac{80}{60} = \frac{4}{3} = \frac{\sqrt{a^2 - 3^2}}{\sqrt{a^2 - 4^2}} \quad \text{or} \quad \frac{16}{9} = \frac{a^2 - 9}{a^2 - 16}$$

or $$a = 5 \text{ cm}$$

Substituting $a = 5$ cm in (*i*) we get

$$80 = \omega\sqrt{5^2 - 3^2}$$

$$\omega = 20 \text{ rad. s}^{-1}$$

or $$y = a \sin \omega t$$

$\therefore$ Time taken to reach the positive extremity is given by

$$5 = 5 \sin \omega t$$

or $$\sin \omega t = 1$$

or $$\omega t = \pi/2$$

$\therefore$ $$t = \frac{\pi}{2\omega} = \frac{\pi}{40} s$$

Distance of the point 2.5 cm from positive extremity, from the mean position = 5 – 2.5 = 2.5 cm

Time taken to reach a point 2.5 cm from the mean position is given by

$$2.5 = 5 \sin \omega t$$

or $$\sin \omega t = \frac{1}{2}$$

or $$\omega t = \pi/6$$

$$\therefore \qquad t = \frac{\pi}{6\omega} = \frac{\pi}{120} \text{ sec}$$

Time taken to travel from a point 2.5 cm from the positive extremity to the positive extremity

$$= \frac{\pi}{40} - \frac{\pi}{120} = \frac{\pi}{60} = 0.052 \text{ sec}$$

Hence time taken to travel from positive extremity a point 2.5 cm away = 0.052 sec.

Example 7.12. If a particle moves in a potential energy field $U = U_0 - ax + bx^2$, where *a* and *b* are positive constants, obtain an expression for the force acting on it as a function of position. At what point does the force vanish? Is this a point of stable equilibrium?

Calculate the force constant, time-period and frequency of the particle.

Soultion. As we know, *force acting on the particle* is given by

$$F = -\frac{dU}{dx} = -\frac{d}{dx}\left(U_0 - ax + bx^2\right), \qquad \text{whence, } F = a - 2bx$$

(*ii*) The force vanishes at the points where $dU/dx = 0$, *i.e.*, where $a - 2bx = 0$. So that, $2bx = a$

Or, $\qquad x = a/2b,$

which gives the position of the point where the force vanishes.

(*iii*) We have $d^2U/dx^2 = 2b$ So that, *b* being positive, the point $x = a/2b$ represents the points of *minimum potential energy* on the energy curve of the particle. *It is, therefore, a point of stable equilibrium.*

(*iv*) From the expression for force *F* in (*i*) above, it is clear that it is a *linear restoring force* and the force constant *C* is therefore equal to 2*b*.

(*v*) The time-period of the particle, $T = 2\pi\sqrt{1/\mu}$

where, as we know, $\mu = C/m = 2b/m$.

So that, $$T = 2\pi\sqrt{1\Big/\frac{2b}{m}} = 2\pi\sqrt{\frac{m}{2b}}$$

And, therefore, frequency of the particle, $n = 1/T = = \frac{1}{2\pi}\sqrt{2b/m}$

Example 7.13. (*a*) The potential energy of a harmonic oscillator of mass 2 kg in its resting position is 5 joules, its energy is 9 joules and its amplitude, 1 cm. Calculate its time-period.

(*b*) A particle of mass 5 gm lies in a potential field $V = (8x^2 + 200)$ ergs/gm. Calculate its time-period.

Solution. (*a*) Clearly, the energy gained by the oscillator in moving from its resting position to its extreme position, *i.e.*, in moving through a distance equal to its amplitude *a*, is equal to (9 – 5) = 4 joules.

Since, energy gained = $\frac{1}{2}Cx^2$, where *x* is the displacement of the particle and *C*, the force constant, we have $\frac{1}{2}C(1)^2$, whence, $C = 4 \times 2 = 8$ *joules/gm.*

$\therefore$ *Time-period of the oscillator,* $T = 2\pi\sqrt{m/C} = 2\pi\sqrt{2/8} = 2\pi\sqrt{1/4} = 2\pi \times 1/2 = \pi = 3.142$ sec.

(*b*) Here, *P.E.* of the particle, *i.e.*, $U = mV = 5(8x^2 + 200)$ *ergs.*

$\therefore$ *Force acting on the particle,* $F = -dU/dx = -5 \times 16x = 80x$ *dynes.*

So that, its equation of motion is $m\, d^2x/dt^2 = -80x$.

whence, $d^2x/dt^2 = -80x/m = -80x/5 = -16x = -\mu x$. Or, $d^2x/dt^2 \propto x$.

The particle thus executes a simple harmonic motion and its time-period is given by

$$T = 2\pi\sqrt{1/\mu} = 2\pi\sqrt{1/16} = 2\pi\sqrt{1/4} = \pi/2 = 1.571 \text{ sec.}$$

Example 7.14. A particle of mass 10 gm moves under a potential V_x given by $V_{(x)} = 8 \times 10^5 x^2$ ergs/gm, where x is in centimeters. Deduce the time-displacement relation when the total energy is 8×10^5 ergs. ***(Agra (supp), 2001)***

Solution. *Clearly, maximum energy acquired by the particle* $= mV_{(x)} = 10 \times 8 \times 10^5 x^2 = 8 \times 10^6 x^2$ ergs. The whole of this must be present in the form of potential energy (U) at the end of its maximum displacement and must be equal to the total energy of the particle, given to be 8×10^5 *ergs*. Thus, $8 \times 10^6 x^2 = 8 \times 10^5$, where x is the *maximum displacement.*

Since the *maximum displacement is the amplitude a* of the particle, we may replace x by a. So that, $8 \times 10^6\, a^2 = 8 \times 10^5$, whence, $a^2 = 8 \times 10^5/8 \times 10^6 = 1/10$.

Or, $$a = 1/\sqrt{10}$$

Now, force acting on the particle, $F = -dU/dx = -d(8 \times 10^6 x^2)/dx = -2 \times 8 \times 10^6 x = -16 \times 10^6 x$.

$\therefore$ the equation of motion of the particle is $md^2x/dt^2 = -16 \times 10^6\, x$,

whence, $$d^2x/dt^2 = -16 \times 10^6 x/m = -16 \times 10^6\, x/10 = -16 \times 10^5 x = -\omega^2 x. \quad ...(A)$$

So that, $$\omega^2 = 16 \times 10^5 \quad \text{and} \quad \therefore \omega = \sqrt{16 \times 10^5} = 400\sqrt{10}$$

If, therefore, the solution of the differential equation of motion of the particle, (which is clearly a simple harmonic motion) be $x = a \sin(\omega t + \phi)$, we have

$$x = \frac{1}{\sqrt{10}} \sin(400\sqrt{10}t + \phi)$$

Example 7.15. Show that if the displacement of a moving point at any time is given by an equation of the form $x = a \cos \omega t + b \sin \omega t$, the motion is simple harmonic. If $a = 3$, $b = 4$ and $\omega = 2$, determine the period, amplitude, maximum velocity and maximum acceleration of the motion. ***(Madras 2004)***

Solution. Since the *displacement of the particle or the point* is given by $x = a \cos \omega t + b \sin \omega t$, its velocity, $v = dx/dt = -a\,\omega \sin \omega t - b\,\omega \cos \omega t$ and its acceleration, $a = d^2x/dt^2 = \omega^2 (a \cos \omega t + b \sin \omega t) = -\omega^2 x$.

The particle, therefore, executes a *simple harmonic motion of amplitude* $\sqrt{a^2 + b^2} = \sqrt{3^2 + 4^2} = 5$ cm

The *time-period of the particle,* $T = 2\pi/\omega = 2\pi/2 = \pi = 3.142$ *sec.*,

Maximum velocity of the particle $= \omega a = 2 \times 5 = 10$ cm/sec.

and its maximum acceleration $= \omega^2 a = (2)^2 \times 5 = 20$ *cm/sec*^{2}.

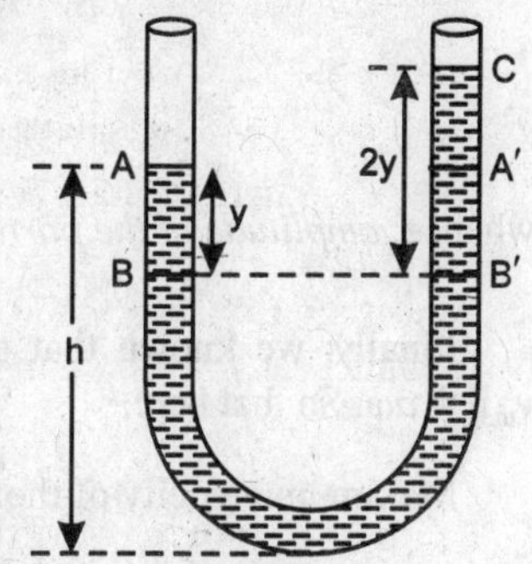

Fig. 7.22

Example 7.16. A vertical U-tube of uniform cross section contains water to a height of 30 cm. Show that if the water on one side is depressed and then released, its motion up and down the two sides of the tube is simple harmonic, and calculate its time-period.

Solution. Let AA' be the initial level of water in the U-tube and let the column on the left be depressed through distance y to B, (Fig. 7.22). Then, obviously, the column on the right will rise will rise up through the same distance y (liquids being incompressible) to the level C, so that the difference of level between the two columns $= B'C = 2y$, where B' is in a level with B.

The weight of this column of water $= 2y \times a \times \rho \times g$, where a is internal area of cross section of the tube (or of the water colum), ρ, the density of water and g, the acceleration due to gravity at the place.

This is then the force acting on the *total mass of water, m,* say, $= 2ha\rho = 2 \times 30 \times a \times \rho = 60\, a\rho$ gm in the two limbs of the U-tube.

$\therefore$ acceleration of the mass of water = force/mass = $-2\ ya\ \rho g/60\ a\rho = -(g/30)\ y = \mu y$, the negative sign indicating that it is directed opposite to the direction of displacement. Thus, the acceleration of the mass of water is proportional to its displacement and is directed opposite to it. It, therefore, executes a S.H.M. and its time-period is given by

$$T = 2\pi\sqrt{1/\mu} = 2\pi\sqrt{1\Big/\frac{g}{30}} = 2\pi\sqrt{30/g} = 2\pi\sqrt{30/981} = 1.098 \text{ sec.}$$

Example 7.17. A particle is moving with S.H.M. in a straight line. When the distance of the particle from the equilibrium position has the values x_1 and x_2, the corresponding values of the velocity are u_1 and u_2. Show that the period is $2\pi[(x_2^2 - x_1^2)/(u_1^2 - u_2^2)]^{1/2}$.

Find also the maximum velocity and amplitude of the particle.

Solution. As we know, the velocity of a particle, executing *S.H.M.*, at a distance x from its equilibrium position is given by $u = \omega\sqrt{a^2 - x^2}$, where ω is its *angular velocity* and a, its amplitude (§7.3). So that, we have here

$$u_1 = \omega\sqrt{a^2 - x_1^2} \quad \text{and} \quad u_2 = \omega\sqrt{a^2 - x_2^2}$$

$$\therefore \quad u_1^2 - u_2^2 = \omega^2\,(x_2^2 - x_1^2). \quad \text{Or} \quad \omega = [(u_1^2 - u_2^2)/(x_2^2 - x_1^2)]^{1/2} \quad \ldots(i)$$

And, therefore, time-period of the particle, $T = 2\pi/\omega$

$$= 2\pi\,[(x_2^2 - x_1^2)/(u_1^2 - u_2^2)]^{1/2}.$$

Now, we have, from above, $u_1^2 = \omega^2\,(a^2 - x_1^2)$, Or, $\omega^2 = u_1^2/(a^2 - x_1^2)$ ...(*ii*)

From relations (*i*) and (*ii*), therefore, we have

$$\frac{u_1^2 - u_2^2}{x_2^2 - x_1^2} = \frac{u_1^2}{(a^2 - x_1^2)}. \quad \text{Or} \quad a^2 - x_1^2 = u_1^2\left(\frac{x_2^2 - x_1^2}{u_1^2 - u_2^2}\right)$$

And $\therefore$

$$a^2 = \frac{u_1^2x_2^2 - u_1^2x_1^2}{u_1^2 - u_2^2} + x_1^2 = \frac{u_1^2x_2^2 - u_1^2x_1^2 + u_1^2x_1^2 - u_2^2x_1^2}{u_1^2 - u_2^2}$$

$$= \frac{u_1^2x_2^2 - u_2^2x_1^2}{u_1^2 - u_2^2}$$

whence, *amplitude of the particle*, $a = \left(\dfrac{u_1^2x_2^2 - u_1^2x_1^2}{u_1^2 - u_2^2}\right)^{1/2}$

Finally, we known that the maximum velocity of a particle executing S.H.M. is given by $v_{max} = a\omega$. So that here,

Maximum velocity of the particle, $v_{max} = \left(\dfrac{u_1^2x_2^2 - u_2^2x_1^2}{u_1^2 - u_2^2}\right)^{\frac{1}{2}}\left(\dfrac{u_1^2 - u_2^2}{x_2^2 - x_1^2}\right)^{\frac{1}{2}}$

$$= \left(\frac{u_1^2x_2^2 - u_2^2x_1^2}{x_2^2 - x_1^2}\right)^{1/2}$$

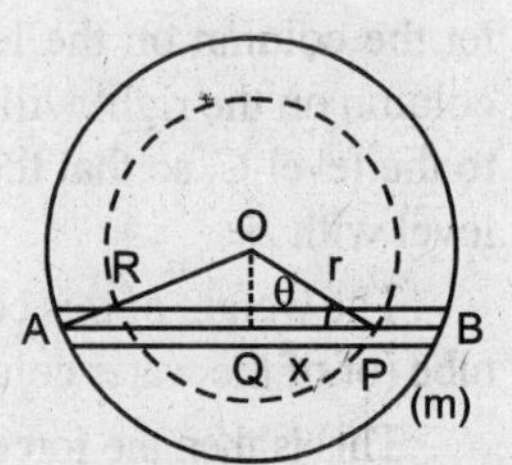

Fig. 7.23

Example 7.18. Two cities on the surface of the earth are joined by a straight, smooth underground tunnel of length 640 km. A body is released into the tunnel from one city. How much time will it take to reach the other city? Derive the formula used $G = 6.67 \times 10^{-8}$ *c.g.s* units and $\rho = 5.52$ gm/c.c. Calculate the velocity when the body would be nearest to the centre of the earth in its journey.

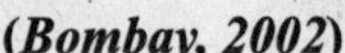

(Bombay, 2002)

Solution. Taking the earth to be a *solid and homogeneous sphere* of centre O, radius R and density ρ, let A and B be the two cities on its surface, joined by a straight, smooth underground tunnel AB, 640 km long, as shown in Fig. 7.23. Then, a perpendicular dropped from O on to AB meets it in Q where Q is the midpoint of AB.

Let the body of mass m, released at city A be at a point P inside the tunnel at a given instant such that it is at a distance x from Q (the mid-point of the tunnel) and $OP = r$.

Then, clearly, the body at P lies on the surface of a solid sphere, concentric with the earth, of radius r and density ρ, as shown dotted in the Figure It, therefore experiences a gravitational force of attraction towards the centre O, given by F = (mass of the sphere) $\times m \times G/r^2$. Since the mass of the sphere $= 4\pi r^3\rho/3$, we have

$$F = \frac{(4/3)\pi r^3 \rho \times m}{r^2}\cdot G = \frac{4}{3}\pi r\rho m G$$

Multiplying and dividing by R^3, we have $F = (4/3)\pi r\rho mG\, R^3/R^3$.

Clearly $(4/3)\pi R^3\rho = M$, the mass of the earth. So that,

force acting on the mass, $F = MmrG/R^3$, directed along PO.

The *component of this force along the tunnel* $= \dfrac{Mmr}{R^3} G\cos\theta$, where $\theta = \angle OPQ$

Or, since $\cos\theta = x/r$, we have

force acting on the mass, along the tunnel, towards $Q = \dfrac{-MmrG}{R^3}\dfrac{x}{r}$

the –*ve* sign indicating that its direction is opposite to that of displacement x.

$\therefore$ *Acceleration of the body towards* $Q = \dfrac{MmG}{R^3 m}x = \dfrac{-MG}{R^3}x = -\omega^2 x = -\mu x$

where $MG/R^3 = \omega^2 = \mu$, a constant.

The acceleration of the body is thus proportional to its displacement and is directed oppositely to it. It, therefore, executes a simple harmonic motion along AB about the point Q and its time-period is given by

$$T = 2\pi\sqrt{\frac{1}{\mu}} = 2\pi\sqrt{1\bigg/\frac{MG}{R^3}} = 2\pi\sqrt{\frac{R^3}{MG}}$$

Since the body is released at the end A, it will take time T to reach B and come back to A, completing one full oscillation.

$\therefore$ time taken in reaching from A to B $= T/2 = \pi\sqrt{R^3/MG} = \sqrt{R^3\bigg/\frac{4}{3}\pi R^3\rho G}$

$$= \sqrt{\pi^2 R^3\bigg/\frac{4}{3}\pi R^3\rho G} = \sqrt{3\pi/4\rho G} = \sqrt{3\pi/4\times 5.52\times 6.67\times 10^{-8}}$$

$= 2529$ sec.

$= 42$ min 29 sec.

Now, it is obvious that the body would be nearest to the centre of the earth (O) in its Journey at the point Q, OQ being the perpendicular from O on to AB. Its velocity here will clearly be the maximum, this being its mean its mean position or its position of equilibrium.

So that, *velocity of the body at Q* (*nearest to the of the earth*), say, $v = \omega a$, where a is its amplitude equal to $OA = OB = AB/2$.

Now, $\mu = \omega^2 = MG/R^3$ and, therefore, $\omega = \sqrt{MG/R^3}$.

So that, *velocity of the body at Q, nearest to the centre of the earth, i.e.,*

$$v = \sqrt{MG/R^3}\ a = \sqrt{\frac{4\pi R^3 \rho g}{3R^3}} \cdot a = \sqrt{\frac{4}{3}\pi\rho G} \times \frac{AB}{2}$$

$$= \sqrt{\frac{4}{3}\pi \times 5.52 \times 6.67 \times 10^{-8}} \times \frac{640}{2} \times 10^5 = 3.973 \times 10^4 \text{ cm/sec.}$$

Example 7.19. (*a*) A hydrogen atoms has a mass of 1.68×10^{-24} gm. When attached to a certain massive molecule, it oscillates a classical oscillator with a frequency of 10^{14} cycles per second and with an amplitude of 10^{-9} cm. Calculate the force acting on the hydrogen atom.

(Delhi, 2002)

(*b*) A test tube of weight 6 gm and of external diameter 2 cm is floated vertical in water by placing 10 gm of mercury at the bottom of the tube. The tube is depressed by a small amount and then released. Find the time of oscillation.

Solution. (*a*) We know that the frequency of a particle executing *S.H.M.* is given by $n = \omega/2\pi$. Here, $n = 10^{14}$ /sec. So that, $10^{14} = \omega/2\pi$, whence, $\omega = 2\pi \times 10^{14}$.

Now, acceleration of the particle $= -\omega^2 x$, where x is its displacement from its mean or equilibrium position, the *–ve* sing indicating that it is directed towards that position, *i.e.* opposite to displacement.

Here, since displacement = amplitude *a*, we have acceleration of the particle, or the hydrogen atom $= -\omega^2 a = -(2\pi \times 10^{14})^2 \times 10^{-9}$ cm/sec^2

$\therefore$ force acting on the hydrogen atom = mass × acceleration

$$= 1.68 \times 10^{-24} \times (2\pi \times 10^{14})^2 \times 10^{-9} = 6.63 \times 10^{-4} \text{ dynes.}$$

(*b*) Here *mass of the* tube + mercury = 6 + 10 = 16 *gm*, *external radius of the tube* = 2/2 = 1 *cm* and, therefore, its area of cross section $= \pi r^2 = \pi (1)^2 = \pi$ *sq* cm.

If the tube be depressed into water through a distance *y* cm, clearly, volume of water displaced $= y \times \pi$.*c.c.* Hence *upthrust on the tube due to displaced water*

$$= y \times \pi \times \rho \times g = y\pi g \ (\because \rho \text{ for water} = 1 \text{ gm/c.c.}).$$

$$\therefore \quad \textit{Acceleration of the tube} = \frac{\text{Force}}{\text{mass}} = -\frac{\pi g}{16} y = \mu y \quad \text{where } \pi g/16 = \mu.$$

The *–ve* sign, as usual, indicates that the acceleration is directed oppositely to displacement. Thus, the acceleration $\propto$ *displacement* and is directed oppositely to it. The tube, therefore, executes a *S.H.M.* and its time-period is given by

$$T = 2\pi\sqrt{1/\mu} = 2\pi\sqrt{1\Big/\frac{\pi g}{16}} = 2\pi\sqrt{16/\pi g}$$

$$= \sqrt{4\pi \times 16/g} = 0.4527 \text{ sec.}$$

Example 7.20. If the earth were a homogeneous sphere of radius R and a straight hole were bored in it through its centre, show that a particle dropped into the hole will excite a simple harmonic motion and find its time-period, ***(Jodhpur)***

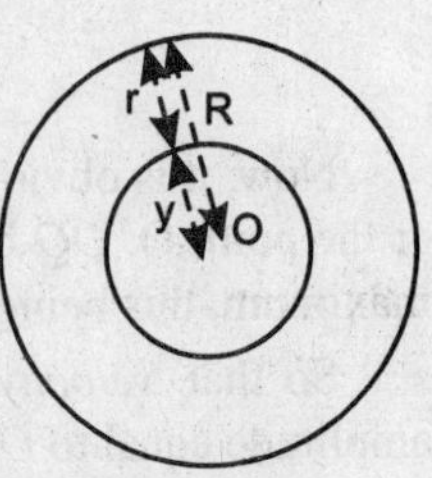

Fig. 7.24

Solution. We know that acceleration due to gravity on the surface of the earth is given by $g = MG/R^2$ where *M* is the mass of the earth, *R*, its radius and *G*, the gravitational constant.

If ρ be the density of the earth (assumed to be a homogeneous solid sphere), we have

$$M = \frac{4}{3}\pi R^3 \rho$$

So that,
$$g = \frac{4}{3}\pi R^3 \rho G / R^2 = \frac{4}{3}\pi R \rho G$$

At a depth r below surface of the earth, (Fig. 7.24), similarly, the acceleration due to gravity will be, say, $g' = \frac{4}{3}\pi [(R-r)\rho J g$

$$\therefore \quad g'/g = (R-r)/R.$$

Or,
$$g' = [(R-r)/R]g = (g/R)(R-r)$$

If we but $(R-r) = y =$ distance from the centre of the earth, we have

$$g' = -\frac{g}{R}y = -\mu y,$$

the $-ve$ sign indicating its opposite direction to y.

Thus, the *acceleration* α *displacement* from the centre of the earth and is directed towards it, *i.e.*, opposite to displacement.

The particle, therefore, executes a S.H.M. about the centre of the earth.

And, its time-period is given by $T = 2\pi\sqrt{\frac{1}{\mu}} = 2\pi\sqrt{1\Big/\frac{g}{R}} = 2\pi\sqrt{\frac{R}{g}}$

Example 7.21 The total energy of a particle executing a simple harmonic motion of period 2π sec is 10240 ergs. π/4 sec after the particle passes mid-point of the swing, its displacement is $8\sqrt{2}$ cm. Calculate the amplitude of the motion and the mass of the particle.

Solution. We know that the *total energy of a particle executing S.H.M.* $= 2\pi^2 ma^2/T^2$, where the symbols have their usual meanings.

Here, $T = 2\pi$ *sec* and, therefore, *total energy of the particle* $= 2\pi^2 ma^2/(2\pi)^2$

$$= 10240,$$

whence,
$$\frac{1}{2}ma^2 = 10240. \text{ Or, } ma^2 = 20480. \qquad ...(i)$$

Since the time here is counted from the instant the particle passes through its mean or equilibrium position, we have $\phi = 0$. Hence its *displacement* is given by the relation $x = a \sin \omega t$.

Now, $T = 2\pi/\omega = 2\pi$ (given). So that, $\omega = 1$ radian/sec, $x = 8\sqrt{2}$ cm and $t = \pi/4$.

$$8\sqrt{2} = a\,sin\,(1 \times \pi/4) = a \sin \pi/4 = a \times 1/\sqrt{2},$$

whence
$$a = 8\sqrt{2} \times \sqrt{2} = 8 \times 2 = 16 \text{ cm}.$$

i.e., the amplitude of the particle is 16 cm.

Substituting this value of a in expression (i) above, we have

$$m \times (16)^2 = 20480. \text{ whence, m} = 20480/16 \times 16 = 80 \text{ gm}.$$

Thus, the *mass of the particle* is 80 gm.

Example 7.22. The particle performing S.H.M. has a mass 2.5 gm and frequency of vibration 10 Hz. It is oscillation with an amplitude of 2 cm. Calculate the total energy of the particle. ***(Nagpur U. 2009, s/2007)***

Solution. Total energy,
$$E_T = \frac{1}{2}m\omega^2\alpha^2$$

$$\omega = 2\pi n = 2\pi \times 10 = 20\,\pi\text{ s}^{-1}$$

$$a = 2 \text{ cm} = 0.02 \text{ m}$$
$$m = 2.5 \text{ gm} = 2.5 \times 10^{-3} \text{ kg.}$$
$$E_T = \frac{1}{2} \times (20\pi)^2 \times (2.5 \times 10^{-3}) \times (0.02)^2$$
$$= \frac{1}{2} 400 (3.14)^2 \times 6.25 \times 10^{-6}$$
$$= 200 \times 9.86 \times 6.25 \times 10^{-6}$$
$$= 12324.5 \times 10^{-6}$$
$$= 12.3245 \times 10^{-3} \text{ J}$$

II – PENDULUMS

Type-I Simple Pendulum

Example 7.23. (*a*) what is the frequency of a simple pendulum 2.0 metres long?

(*b*) Assuming small amplitude, what would its frequency be in an elevator accelerating upwards at a rate of 2.0 metres/sec^2?

(*c*) What would its frequency be in free fall?

Solution. (*a*) We know that the time-period of a simple pendulum is given by

$$T = 2\pi\sqrt{l/g}\text{. Hence, its } \textit{frequency } n = 1/T = \frac{1}{2\pi}\sqrt{g/l}$$

Here, $l = 2.0$ metres. Therefore, taking $g = 9.8$ m/sec^2, we have frequency of the pendulum,

$$n = \frac{1}{2\pi}\sqrt{9.8/2} = \frac{1}{2\pi}\sqrt{4.9} = 0.3524/\text{sec}$$

(*b*) In the elevator going up with an acceleration *a*, the effective weight of the pendulum is $mg(1 + a/g) = m(g + a)$. So that, here the effective value of *g* is, say, $g' = (g + a) = (9.8 + 2.0) = 11.8$ m/sec^2.

∴ *Frequency of the pendulum in the elevator*, say, $n' = \frac{1}{2\pi}\sqrt{g'/l}$

$$= \frac{1}{2\pi}\sqrt{11.8/2} = \frac{1}{2\pi}\sqrt{5.9} = 0.3867/\text{sec}$$

(*c*) In free fall of the pendulum, the effective weight of the pendulum is $mg(1 - g/g) = 0$, *i.e.*, the effective value of *g*, *i.e.*, $g' = 0$.

∴ time-period of the pendulum $= 2\pi\sqrt{l/g'}$ = infinite, *i.e.* there is no oscillation of the pendulum at all. Its frequency (*n*) is, therefore, zero.

Example 7.24. A simple pendulum of length *l* and mass *m* is suspended in a car that is travelling with a constant speed *v* around a circle of radius *R*. If the pendulum undergoes small oscillations about its equilibrium position, what will its frequency of oscillation be?

Solution. Here, in addition to *g*, the acceleration due to gravity, the pendulum will also be subject to the centripetal acceleration v^2/R in a direction perpendicular to that of *g* on account of the car going round with speed *v* in a circle of radius *R*. Thus, resultant acceleration to which the pendulum is subjected $= [g^2 + (v^2/R)^2]^{1/2}$

$$= (g^2 + v^4/R^2)^{1/2}.$$

On a small angular displacement θ from its mean or equilibrium position, therefore, the restoring couple acting on the pendulum $= m(g^2 \times v^2/R^2)^{1/2}\, l \sin\theta$.

$$= m(g^2 \times v^2/R^2)^{1/2}\, l.\theta \qquad [\because \theta \text{ is small}].$$

If $d^2\theta/dt^2$ be the acceleration of the pendulum and I, its moment of inertia about the suspension thread, we have the couple on the pendulum also equal to $I.\ d^2\theta/dt^2$. or equal to $ml^2\ d^2\theta/dt^2$, because $I = ml^2$.

We, therefore, have $ml^2 d^2\theta/dt^2 = -m\ (g^2 + v^4/R^2)^{1/2}\ l\theta$,

whence, $$d^2\theta/dt^2 = -\frac{(g^2 + v^4/R^2)^{1/2}\theta}{l} = -\mu\theta,$$

where $$\mu = \frac{(g^2 + v^4/R^2)^{1/2}}{l}$$

The pendulum thus executes a *S.H.M.* and therefore,

$$\textit{frequency of the pendulum} = n = 1/T = \frac{1}{2\pi}\sqrt{\mu} = \frac{1}{2\pi}\sqrt{\frac{(g^2 + v^4/R)^{2,1/2}}{l}}$$

Example 7.25. (*a*) Show that the maximum tension in the string of a simple pendulum, when the amplitude θ_m is small, is $mg\ (1 + \theta_m^2)$. At what position of the pendulum is the tension a maximum?

(*b*) Using conservation of energy, show that the angular speed of a simple pendulum is given by $d\theta/dt = \left[\frac{2}{ml^2}\{E - mgl(1-\cos\theta)\}\right]^{1/2}$ where E is the total energy of oscillations, l and m are length and mass of the pendulum and θ is angular displacement from the vertical.

Solution. (*a*) Let *SO* be a simple pendulum of length l, with *S*, as its point of suspension and *O*, its mean or equilibrium position, (Fig. 7.25). If its angular amplitude be θ_m so that it is in the position *SP*, the whole of its energy is present in the potential form and is equal to $mg \times OP'$ where OP' is the vertical distance through which the bob rises with respect to its mean position *O*.

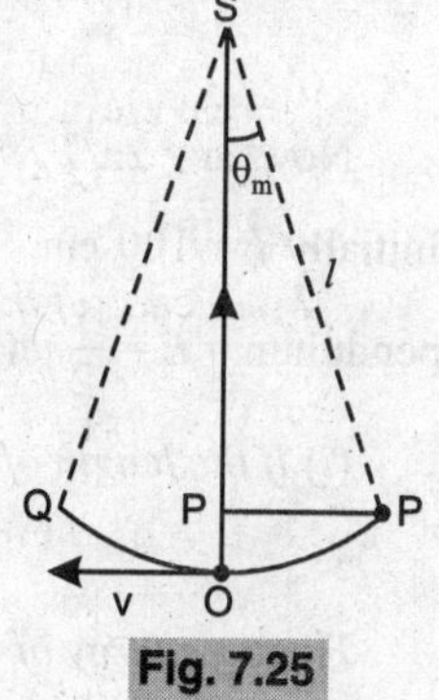

Fig. 7.25

Or, since $OP' = SO - SP' = l - l\cos\theta_m = l\ (1 - \cos\theta_m)$, we have total energy of the pendulum $= mgl\ (1 - \cos\theta_m)$.

Or, because θ_m is small, we may take $\cos\theta_m = 1 - \frac{1}{2}\theta_m^2$.

So that, *total energy of the pendulum*

$$= mgl\left[1 - \left(1 - \frac{1}{2}\theta m_2\right)\right] = \frac{1}{2}mg/\theta m^2$$

When the bob arrives at *O*, the whole of the energy of the pendulum is converted into the kinetic form, so that if v be its velocity at *O* tangential to the arc *PO*, its *K.E.* $= \frac{1}{2}mv^2$. Thus, $\frac{1}{2}mv^2 = \frac{1}{2}mg/\theta m^2$ whence, $v^2 = g/\theta\ m^2$, Or, $v = (gl\theta m^2)^{1/2}$.

Now, the *centripetal force necessary* to keep the bob moving in an are of radii $l = mv^2/l$ towards *S* and it must obviously be equal to $T - mg$, where T is the tension in the string along *OS* and *mg*, the weight of the bob, *i.e.*, $T - mg = mv^2/l$.

Or, substituting the value of v from above, we have

$$T - mg = mgl\theta m^2/l = mg\theta m^2, \text{ whence, } T = mg + mg\theta_m^2 = mg(1 + \theta_m^2).$$

The tension is clearly the maximum when the bob passes through its mean or equilibrium position, because only in this position is the velocity of the bob, and hence the centripetal force acting upon it, the maximum, as also the entire weight of the bob effective.

(*b*) If the angular displacement of the pendulum bob be θ, its *potential energy in its displaced position* = *mgl* (1 – cos θ), where, as we have just seen in part (*a*) above, *l*(1 – cos θ) is the vertical distance through which the bob rises relative to its mean position.

Since θ is less than the amplitude of the pendulum, the bob in this position possesses also kinetic energy = $\frac{1}{2}mv^2$, where *v* is the velocity of the bob in the displaced position. Therefore,

Total energy of the pendulum, $E = \frac{1}{2}mv^2 + mgl(1 - \cos\theta)$

which through remains constant in accordance with the *law of conservation* of *energy*.

We thus, have $\frac{1}{2}mv^2 = E - mgl\,(1 - \cos\theta)$. Or, $mv^2 = 2E - 2\,mgl\,(1 - \cos\theta)$

Now, $v = l\omega = l\,d\theta/dt$, where $\omega = d\theta/dt$ is the angular velocity of the bob.

So that, $ml^2(d\theta/dt)^2 = 2\,E - 2\,mgl\,(1 - \cos\theta)$

Or, $(d\theta/4t)^2 = (2/ml^2)[E - mgl(1 - \cos\theta)]$.

And, therefore, $\frac{d\theta}{dt} = \left[\frac{2}{ml^2}\{E - mgl(1 - \cos\theta)\}\right]^{1/2}$

Example 7.26. A simple pendulum of length 100 cm has an energy equal to 2 × 10⁶ ergs when its, amplitude is 4 cm. Calculate its energy when (*i*) its length is doubled (*ii*) its amplitude is doubled.

Solution: We have *energy of a simple pendulum* = its max. *P.E.* = its max.

$$K.E. = \frac{1}{2}mv^2 = \frac{1}{2}m\omega^2a^2$$

Now, $\omega = 2\pi/T$, where *T* is the time-period of the pendulum = $2\pi\sqrt{l/g}$, Or, $\omega = \sqrt{g/l}$.

Initially $l = 100$ cm. ∴ $\omega = \sqrt{g/100}$. So that, initially, with amplitude 4 cm, the energy of the pendulum = $E = \frac{1}{2}m(g/100)(4)^2 = 8$ mg/100 = 100 × 10^6 ergs.

(*i*) *If the length of the pendulum is doubled*, we have $l = 200$ cm and

$$\therefore \quad \omega = \sqrt{g/200}$$

Hence, *energy of the pendulum*, $E' = \frac{1}{2}m\,(g/200)(4)^2 = \text{mg}/200$

So that, $E'/E = \frac{8mg}{200}\bigg/\frac{8mg}{100} = \frac{1}{2}$, Or $E' = \frac{1}{2}E$

Since the *initial energy of the pendulum*, $E = 2 \times 10^6$ ergs (*given*), we have

energy of the pendulum now $= \frac{1}{2} \times 2 \times 10^6 = 10^6 = 10^6$ ergs

(*ii*) *If the amplitude of the pendulum be doubled*, *a* = *8 cm*, its length remaining 100 cm; we have energy of the pendulum, $E'' = \frac{1}{2}m\,(g/100)\,(8)^2 = 32\,mg/100$.

$$\therefore \quad E''/E = \frac{32mg}{100}\bigg/\frac{8mg}{100} = 4 \quad \text{Or,} \quad E'' = 4E.$$

Or, $E'' = 4 \times 2 \times 10^6$ *ergs*. = 8×10^6 ergs.

Thus, the energy of the pendulum is now 8×10^6 ergs.

Example 7.27. A hollow sphere is filled with water, used as pendulum bob. If water trickles out slowly through a hole made at the bottom, how will the time period be effected?

Solution. The time period of a simple pendulum given by

$$T = 2\pi\sqrt{\frac{l}{g}}$$

where l is the length of the pendulum and g the acceleration due to gravity.

When the water trickles out slowly through a hole made at the bottom of the hollow sphere used as bob of the pendulum, the mass of the bob goes on slowly decreasing. As time period does not depend upon the mass of the bob, there is no change in time period.

Example 7.28. A lift is ascending at acceleration of 3 m/s^2. What is the period of oscillation of a simple pendulum of length one metre suspended in the lift?

Solution. The time period of a simple pendulum is given by

$$T = 2\pi\sqrt{\frac{l}{g}}$$

where l is the length of a simple pendulum and g acceleration due to gravity.

As the lift is ascending with an acceleration of 3ms^{-2}, acceleration due to gravity

$g' = 9.8 + 3 = 12.8$ ms^{-2}.

Given: length of pendulum, $l = 1$ m.

∴ Time period of the simple pendulum suspended in the lift

$$T' = 2\pi\sqrt{\frac{l}{g'}} = 2\pi\sqrt{\frac{1}{12.8}} = 1.756 \text{ sec.}$$

Example 7.29: A uniform circular disc of radius R oscillates in a vertical plane about a horizontal axis. Find the distance of the axis of rotation from the centre for which the period is minimum. What is the value of this period? ***(Bombay, 2002; sagar, 2004)***

Solution. The circular disc here oscillates as a compound or a physical pendulum of length l, whose time-period is given by $T = 2\pi\sqrt{\frac{(k^2/l) + l}{g}}$

where k its radius of gyration about an axis through its *c.g.*, parallel to the axis of suspension.

Now, as we know, the time-period of compound pendulum is the minimum, *when its length is equal to its radius of gyration about its c.g., i.e.,* when $l = k$.

So that, $$T_{min.} = 2\pi\sqrt{\frac{(k^2/k) + k}{g}} = 2\pi\sqrt{\frac{2k}{g}}$$

Since the moment of inertia of a disc about an axis perpendicular to its plane and passing through its centre is equal to $I = Mk^2 = \frac{1}{2}MR^2$, where M is the mass of the disc and R, its radius, we have $k^2 = R^2/2$ and ∴ $k = R/\sqrt{2}$.

Thus, the disc will oscillate with the minimum time-period when the distance of the axis of rotation from the centre is $R/\sqrt{2}$.

The axis of rotation from the centre is $R/\sqrt{2}$.

And the value of this minimum time-period will be

$$T_{\min} = 2\pi\sqrt{\frac{2R/\sqrt{2}}{g}} = 2\pi\sqrt{\frac{\sqrt{2}R}{g}} = 2\pi\sqrt{\frac{1.414R}{g}}.$$

Example 7.30. There particles of the same mass *m* are fixed to a uniform circular hoop of mass *M* and radius *a* at the corners of an equilateral triangle. The hoop is free to move in a vertical plane about the point on the circumference opposite to one of the masses *m*. prove that the equivalent simple pendulum is equal in length to the diameter of the hoop.

Solution. Let the three equal masses (m) be fixed to the hoop of mass M and radius a, as shown in Fig 7.26, so as to lie at the corners of an equilateral triangle. Since all of them are equidistance from the centre, the *c.g.*, of the triangle lies at O, the centre of the hoop. *The whole arrangement is thus equivalent to a hoop of mass* $(M + 3m)$ *and radius a, with its centre of gravity at its centre O.*

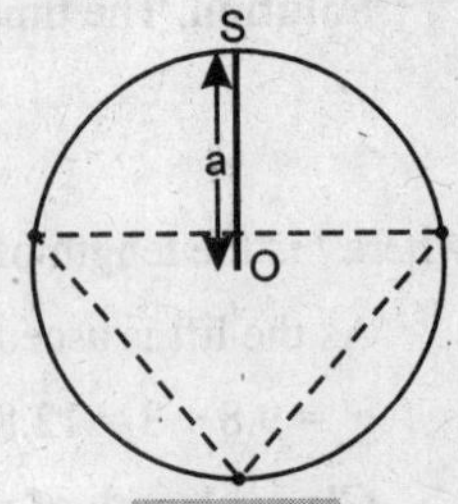

Fig. 7.26

∴ *M.I.* of this loaded hoop about an axis passing through its centre and perpendicular to its plane = $(M + 3m)a^2$ and hence, by the principle of parallel axes, its *M.I.* about a parallel axis through its point of suspension $S = (M + 3m)a^2 + (M + 3m)a^2 = 2(M + 3m)a^2$.

∴ Its time-period about S, *i.e.*,

$$T = 2\pi\sqrt{\frac{1}{(M + 3m)\,ga}}$$

Because, here mass of the pendulum = $(M + 3m)$ and its length $l = a$.

(See §7.7.2) where it is shown that $T = 2\pi\sqrt{I/mgl}$

Or, $T = 2\pi\sqrt{\dfrac{2(M + 3m)a^2}{(M + 3m)\,ga}} = \sqrt{\dfrac{2a}{g}}$, the same as that of a simple pendulum of length $2a$.

So that, the length of the equivalent simple pendulum is equal to 2a or the diameter of the hoop.

III–Torsional pendulum

Example 7.31 A solid sphere of radius 0.3 metre executes torsional oscillations of time-period $2\pi\sqrt{12}$ sec at the end of a suspension wire whose upper end is fixed in a rigid support. If the torque constant of the wire be 6×10^{-3} N-m/radian, calculate the mass of the sphere.

Solution. We know the *M.I.* of a solid sphere about any diameter, *i.e.*, about any axis passing through its centre is $\frac{2}{5}MR^2$, where M is its mass and R, its radius. We, therefore, have

$I = \frac{2}{5}MR^2$, *torque constant or torque per unit twist of the suspension* wire. *i.e.*,

$$C = 6 \times 10^{-3}\text{ N-m/radian and } T = 2\pi\sqrt{12}\text{ sec.}$$

Subsutituting these values in the relation $T = 2\pi\sqrt{I/C}$ for the time-period of a torsional oscillation, we have

$$2\pi\sqrt{12} = 2\pi\sqrt{I/C}\text{, whence } \sqrt{12} = \sqrt{I/C}\text{ or, } I/C = 12.\text{ Or, } I = 12C,$$

i.e.,
$$\frac{2}{5}MR^2 = 12 \times 6 \times 10^{-3} = 72 \times 10^{-3}$$

Or,
$$MR^2 = 72 \times 10^{-3} \times 5/2 = 180 \times 10^{-3} = 18 \times 10^{-2}.$$

$$\therefore \quad M = \frac{18\times10^{-2}}{R^2} = \frac{18\times10^{-2}}{(0.3)^2} = \frac{18\times10^{-2}}{9\times10^{-2}} = 2 \text{ kg}$$

Thus, *the mass of the sphere is* 2 kg.

Example 7.32. The time-period of a rod of mass 120 gm and length 10 cm, executing torsional vibration about a suspension wire passing through its centre and perpendicular to its length is 2 sec. The period of a flat plate of the shape of an equilateral triangle suspended from the suspension wire, passing through its centre of mass and perpendicular to its plane is fond to be 4 sec. What is the moment of inertia of the triangular plate about the suspension wire as axis?

Solution. Let I_1 be the *M.I.* of the rod about the suspension wire as axis and I_2, that of the triangular plate about the *same* axis. Then, if T_1 and T_2 be the respective time-periods of the two torsional oscillations, we have

$T_1 = 2\pi\sqrt{I_1/C}$ and $T_2 = 2\pi\sqrt{I_2/C}$ So that, $T_2/T_1 = \sqrt{I_2/I_1}$ Or $I_2/I_1 = T_2^2/T_1^2$

whence, $\quad I_2 = (T_2^2/T_1^2)\, I_1 = (T_2/T_1)^2\, I_1.$

Now, *M.I.* of the rod about the suspension wire *i.e.*, $I_1 = Ml^2/12 = 120 \times (10)^2/12 = 10^3$ gm-cm^2, $T_1 = 2$ sec and $T_2 = 4$ sec.

$\therefore$ *M.I.* of the triangular plate about the suspension wire, $I_2 = (4/2)^2 \times 10^3 = 4 \times 10^3 =$ gm-cm^2.

Example 7.33. The balance wheel of a watch vibrates with an angular amplitude of π radians and a period of 0.5 sec. Find (*a*) the maximum angular speed of the wheel, (*b*) the angular speed of the wheel when its displacement is π/2 radians and (*c*) the angular acceleration of the wheel when its displacement is π/4 radians.

Solution (*a*) Just as in linear *S.H.M.*, so also, here in torsional vibration, we have

$$\theta = \theta_0 \sin(\omega t + \phi),$$

where θ is the angular displacement at the given instant and θ_0, the *maximum angular displacement* or *amplitude*.

$\therefore$ *angular speed*, $d\theta/dt = \theta_0\, \omega \cos(\omega t + \phi)$, the maximum value of which will clearly be $\theta_0\omega$, *i.e.*, when $\cos(\omega t + \phi) = 1$.

Here, $\theta_o = \pi$ radians and $\omega = 2\pi n = 2\pi \times 1/T = 2\pi \times 1/0.5 = 4\pi$.

$\therefore$ *maximum angular speed of the balance wheel* $= \theta_o\omega = \pi \times 4\pi = 4\pi^2 = 39.48$ radians/sec.

(*b*) Again, as in linear *S.H.M.*, so also here, angular speed at angular displacement $\theta = \omega\sqrt{\theta_0^2 - \theta^2}$. So that,

Angular speed of the wheel at displacement $\pi/2$ radian $= 4\pi\sqrt{\pi^2 - (\pi/2)^2} = 4\pi\sqrt{3\pi^2/4}$

$$= 2\pi^2\sqrt{3} = 34.18 \text{ radians/sec.}$$

(*c*) Again, acceleration of the balance wheel at displacement θ is given by $d^2\theta/dt^2 = -\omega^2\theta$. Therefore,

acceleration of the balance wheel at displacement $\theta = \pi/4$ radian is clearly equal to $-(4\pi)^2(\pi/4) = -4\pi^3 = -124$ radians/sec^2.

Example 7.34. A mass of 1 kg is attached to a spring of stiffness constant 16 Nm^{-1}. Find its natural frequency. ***(Nagpur U. 2008; H.P.U. 2001)***

Solution. Here stiffness constant $e = 16\ Nm^{-1}$, mass $m = 1$ kg

$$\therefore \quad \text{Frequency } n = \frac{1}{2\pi}\sqrt{\frac{e}{m}} = \frac{1}{2\pi}\sqrt{\frac{16}{1}} = \frac{2}{\pi} = 0.64 \text{ Hz.}$$

Example. 7.35 A spring whose force constant is 80 N/m. hangs vertically supporting a 1 kg mass at rest. Find the distance by which the mass should be pulled down so that on being released it may pass the equilibrium position with a velocity of 1 m/s.

Solution. For a loaded spring.

$$\omega = \sqrt{\frac{c}{m}}$$

Here, $c = 80\ N/m,\ m = 1$ kg

$$\therefore \quad \omega = \sqrt{\frac{80}{1}} = 8.944$$

Let a be the distance by which the mass has to be pulled down (amplitude of vibration)

$$v = a\omega$$

or
$$a = \frac{v}{\omega}$$

Here $v = 1\ m/s$ and $\omega = 8.944$

$$\therefore \quad a = \frac{1}{8.944} = 0.118 \text{ m}$$

Example 7.36. A uniform spring of force constant S is cut into two pieces whose lengths are in the ratio of 1:3. Calculate the force constant of each piece.

Solution. Here force = F

Increase in length = l

$$s = \frac{F}{l}$$

When the springs are cut in the ratio 1 : 3, increase in length for the first piece for force will be $\frac{l}{4}$, and increase in length for the second piece will be $\frac{3l}{4}$.

$$s_1 = \frac{F}{l/4} = 4\left[\frac{F}{l}\right]$$

$$s_1 = 4\,s \qquad \text{...(i)}$$

$$s_2 = \frac{F}{3l/4} = \frac{4}{3}\left[\frac{F}{l}\right]$$

$$s_2 = \frac{4}{3}s \qquad \text{...(ii)}$$

Example 7.37. A spring when compressed by 10 cm developed a restoring force of 10 N. A body of mass 4 kg is attached to it. Calculate the compression of the spring due to the weight of the body and calculate the period of oscillation.

Solution. Here restoring force $F = 10$ N; displacement $y = 10$ cm = 0.1 m

$\therefore$ Force constant
$$s = \frac{F}{y} = \frac{10}{0.1} = 100 \text{ Nm}^{-1}$$

Mass attached $m = 4$ kg

Force applied $F = 4$ kg $\omega t = 4 \times 9.8 = 38.2$ N

Displacement
$$y' = \frac{F'}{s} = \frac{39.2}{100} m = 39.2 \times 10^{-2} = 39.2 \text{ cm}$$

Time period
$$T = 2\pi\sqrt{\frac{m}{s}} = 2\pi\sqrt{\frac{4}{100}} = \frac{2}{5}\pi = 1.26 \text{ sec.}$$

Example 7.38. A spring of force constant 1200 N/m is mounted on a horizontal table. A mass of 3 kg is attached to the free end of the spring which is pulled sideways to a distance of 2 cm and released. What is (*a*) the frequency of oscillation of the mass, and (*b*) the max. acceleration of the mass.

Solution. (*a*) period $\quad T = 2\pi\sqrt{\dfrac{m}{s}} = 2\pi\sqrt{\dfrac{3}{1200}} = 2\pi\sqrt{\dfrac{1}{400}}$

$\therefore$ Frequency $\quad n = \dfrac{1}{T} = \dfrac{1}{2\pi}\sqrt{400} = \dfrac{20}{2\times 3.14} = 3.185$ Hz.

(*b*) Acceleration $\quad \dfrac{d^2x}{dt^2} = -\dfrac{c}{m}x = -\dfrac{1200}{3}\times 0.02 \quad (\because x = 0.02\ m)$

$$= -8 \text{ m/s}$$

Example 7.39. The scale of a spring balance reading from 0 to 14.5 kg is 10.25 cm long. A package suspended from the balance is found to oscillate vertically with a frequency of 2.0 oscillations per second. How much does the package weigh?

Solution. Here, clearly, a mass of 14.5 kg suspended from the spring balance extends the spring by 10.25 cm = 0.1025 m.

$\therefore$ Force constant of the spring, *i.e.*, $C = \dfrac{\text{forced applied}}{\text{extension produce}} = \dfrac{14.5\times 9.81}{0.1025} = 1387.75\ Nm^{-1}$.

Now, *time-period of oscillation of the spring*, $T = 2\pi\sqrt{m/C}$

$\therefore \quad T^2 = 4\pi^2\, m/C$, whence, $m = CT^2/4\pi^2$.

Since $C = 1387.75$ Nm^2 and $T = 1/2$ sec, we have

$$m = \frac{1387.75\times 1/4}{4\pi^2} = \frac{86.73}{\pi^2}$$

The package thus weighs 8.796 kg.

Example 7.40. Two springs S_1 and S_2 are connected to a mass *M*, as shown in Figs. 7.27 (*a*) and (*b*), with the mass lying on a frictions surface. If the respective force constants of the springs be C_1 and C_2. obtain expression for the time-periods of the mass in the two cases. What are their electrical analogues?

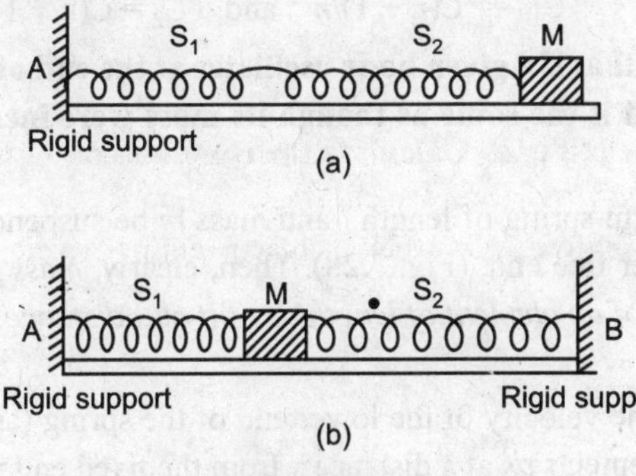

(a)

(b)

Fig. 7.27

Solution. (*a*) If x_1 and x_2 the extensions produced in the two springs respectively as the mass (*M*) is displaced outwards, the total extension $x = x_1 + x_2$. Since the restoring force due to each spring is the same, *F*, say, we have $F = -C_1x_1 = -C_2x_2$; so that, $x_1 = -F/C_1$ and $x_3 = -F/C_2$.

$$\therefore x = x_1 + x_2 = -F\left(\frac{1}{C_1} + \frac{1}{C_2}\right) = -F\left(\frac{C_1 + C_2}{C_1C_2}\right) \text{ whence } F = -\left(\frac{C_1C_2}{C_1 + C_2}\right)x$$

indicating that the effective force constant of the combination of the two springs, say, $C = \left(\dfrac{C_1C_2}{C_1 + C_2}\right)$.

$$\therefore \quad \textit{Time-period of the oscillating mass, } T = 2\pi\sqrt{\frac{M}{C}} = 2\pi\sqrt{\frac{M}{(C_1C_2)(C_1 + C_2)}}$$

$$= 2\pi\sqrt{\frac{(C_1 + C_2)M}{C_1C_2}}$$

(*b*) In this case, if the mass (M) be displaced to one side or the other, through a distance x, say, one springs gets extended and the other compressed, both exerting a restoring force on the mass in the same direction, tending to bring it back to its original position. Thus, if F_1 and F_2 be the restoring forces due to the two springs respectively, we have resulting restoring force $F = F_1 + F_2 = -C_1x - C_2x = -(C_1 + C_2)x = Cx$, indicating that the effective force constant C of the combination of the two springs is now equal to $(C_1 + C_2)$, the sum of their individual force constants.

The time-period of the oscillating mass is, therefore, $T = 2\pi\sqrt{M/C} = 2\pi\sqrt{M/(C_1 + C_2)}$.

The electrical analogues of the two systems are a parallel and a series arrangement of two capacitors respectively.

Example 7.41. A uniform spring of normal length l has a force constant C. It is cut into two pieces of lengths l_1 and l_2. such that $l_1 = nl_2$ where n is an integer. What are the force constants C_1 and C_2 of the two pieces respectively in terms of n and C?

Solution. Here, clearly, $l = l_1 + l_2$. Or, since $l_1 = nl_2$ and, therefore, $l_2 = l_1/n$, we have

$l = l_1 + l_1/n = l_1(1 + l/n) = l_1(n + 1)/n$ ...(*i*) Also, $l = nl_2 + l_2 = l_2(n + 1)$ ...(*i*)

Now, for a given spring, its force constant is inversely proportional to its length, *i.e.*, C α $1/l$ or Cl = *a* constant. We, therefore, have

$C_1l_1 = Cl = Cl_1(n + 1)/n$, whence, $C_1 = C(n + 1)/n$,

Similarly $C_2l_2 = Cl = Cl_2(n + 1)$, whence, $C_2 = C(n + 1)$.

Thus, the force constants of the two pieces of the spring are respectively

$$C_1 = C(n + 1)/n \quad \text{and} \quad C_2 = C(n + 1).$$

Example 7.42. Show that if a given body oscillates at the end of a spring whose mass is not negligible, its time-period is the same as though its mass were increased by one-third of that of the spring.

Solution. Let a uniform spring of length l and mass m be suspended from a rigid support and carry a mass M at its lower free end, (Fig. 7.28). Then, clearly, *mass per unit length of the spring* = m/l, and therefore *mass of an element of length ds of it at a distance s form the upper fixed end* = $(m/l)\,ds$.

If at a given instant, the velocity of the lower end of the spring (and therefore also of mass M) be v, the velocity of the elements ds at a distance s from the fixed end = $(v/l)s$.

$$\therefore \quad \textit{K.E. of the element} = \frac{1}{2}\left(\frac{m}{l}ds\right)\left(\frac{vs}{l}\right)^2 = \frac{1}{2}\frac{mv^2}{l^3}s^2\,ds$$

Hence *K.E.* of the whole spring at the given instant.

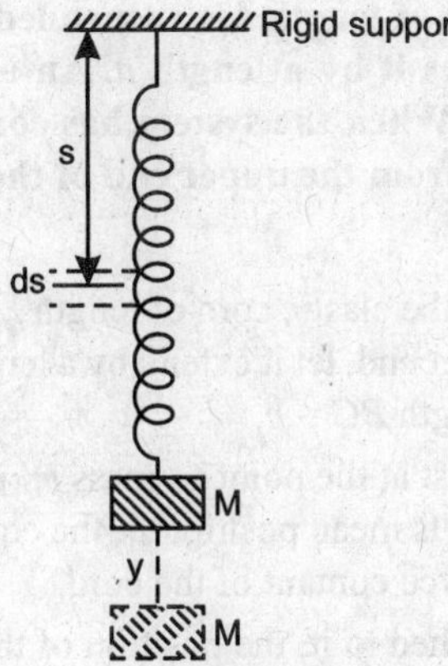

Fig. 7.28

$$= \int_0^l \frac{1}{2}\frac{mv^2}{l^3}s^2 ds = \frac{1}{2}\frac{mv^2}{l^3}\cdot\frac{l^3}{3} = \frac{mv^2}{6}$$

And *K.E.* of the suspended mass $(M) = \frac{1}{2}Mv^2$.

$$\therefore \text{ K.E. of the system, as a whole } = \frac{1}{2}Mv^2 + \frac{mv^2}{6} = \frac{1}{2}\left(M + \frac{m}{3}\right)v^3$$

If at the instant considered, y be the displacement of mass M from its mean or equilibrium position, we have, substituting dy/dt for v.

$$\text{K.E. of the system, as a whole} = \frac{1}{2}(M + m/3)(dv/dt)^2 \qquad ...(i)$$

If C be the force constant of the spring, we have restoring force set up in the spring $= - Cy$ and, therefore,

$$\text{P.E. of the system} = \int_0^y Cy\,dy = \frac{1}{2}Cy^2 \qquad ...(ii)$$

$$\therefore \text{ Total energy of the system, } E = K.E. + P.E. = \frac{1}{2}\left(M + \frac{m}{3}\right)\left(\frac{dy}{dt}\right)^2 + \frac{1}{2}Cy^2.$$

Since the total energy of the system must remain conserved, we have

$$\frac{dE}{dy} = 0, \text{ i.e., } \frac{d}{dy}\left[\frac{1}{2}\left(M + \frac{m}{3}\right)\left(\frac{dy}{dt}\right)^2 + \frac{1}{2}Cy^2\right] = 0$$

$$\text{i.e., } \left(M + \frac{m}{3}\right)\frac{d^2y}{dt^2} + Cy = 0. \text{ Or, } \frac{d^2y}{dt^2} = -\frac{C}{(M + m/3)}y,$$

Indicating that the spring executes a *S.H.M.* of time-period

$$T = 2\pi\sqrt{1\Big/\frac{C}{M + m/3}} = 2\pi\sqrt{\frac{M + m/3}{C}}$$

which is clearly the same as though the value of the suspended mass has been increased by one-thired of the mass of the spring.

Example 7.43. An elastic cord of length l is suspended from a rigid support, A mass m, attached to its lower end, stretches it by a length a. An additional mass m', attached to it, stretches it further by a length b. When the system has come to rest, mass m' gets detached. Show that the distance of mass m from the upper end of the cord is, at any instant t, given by $l + a + b \cos \sqrt{g/a}.t$.

Solution. In Fig. 7.29 let SA be the elastic cord of length l, suspended from a rigid support at S. When a mass m is attached to its lower end, let it extend by a length $AB = a$ and, on attaching another mass m' to it, further extend by a length $BC = b$.

When the system has come to rest at the point C, mass m' is suddenly detached, so that mass m starts oscillating up and down about its mean position B, the equitation of motion of the mass being $d^2y/dt^2 = -(C/m)y$, where C is the force contant of the cord.

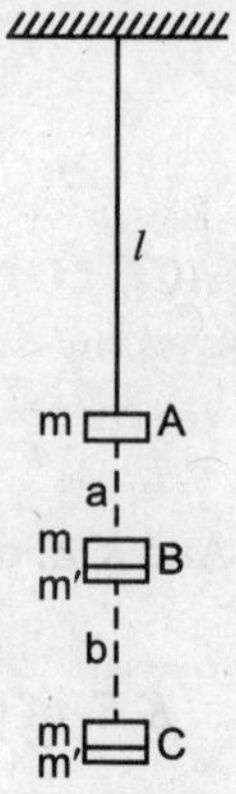

Clearly, before the mass m was attached to it, the position of the lower end of the cord was at A. The addition of mass m, *i.e.*, the application of a force mg to it, brought it down to B or produced in it an extension $AB = a$. So that, $mg = Ca$, whence, $C = mg/a$. And, therefore, $d^2y/dt^2 = -(g/a)y$, *i.e.* mass m executes a *S.H.M.* about B as its mean or equilibrium position, its displacement at any instant t being given by $y = a \sin(\omega t + \phi)$, where a is the *amplitude* of the oscillation and $\omega^2 = g/a$ or $\omega = \sqrt{g/a}$.

Fig. 7.29

$\therefore$ velocity of the mass at the given instant $= dy/dt = \omega\sqrt{a^2 - y^2}$.

At $t = 0$, *i.e.*, at the instant that the mass m' just gets detached, $y = b$ and $dy/dt = 0$. So that,

$$0 = \omega\sqrt{a^2 - b^2}. \text{ Or, } a^2 - b^2 = 0 \text{ Or, } a = b$$

Substituting these values in the expression for y above we, have

$$b = b \sin\phi, \text{ whence, } \sin\phi = 1 \text{ or } \phi = \pi/2.$$

We therefore have $y = b \sin(\omega t + \pi/2) = b \cos \omega t = b \cos \sqrt{g/a}\, t$

$\therefore$ *Distance of mass m from the point of suspension (or the upper end of the cord) at instant*

$$t = l + a + y = l + a + b \cos \sqrt{g/a}\, t$$

IV–Hemholtz resonator—L-C Circuit

Example 7.44. A spherical Helmholtz resonator of capacity 10 litres has a narrow neck of length 1 cm and radius 1 cm. If the velocity of sound in air be 340 m/sec, calculate the frequency and the wavelength of the note to which it will sharply respond.

Solution. We know that the frequency of the note to which a spherical resonator responds is given by $n = (v/2\pi)\sqrt{\alpha/Vl}$ [(§ 7.6 (5)], where v is the velocity of sound in air, l, the *length* and α, the area of cross-section of the neck and V, the volume (or capacity) of the resonator.

Here, $v = 340$ *m/sec* = 34000 cm/sec, $\alpha = \pi(1)^2 = \pi$ sq cm, $l = 1$ cm and $V = 10$ litres = 10000 *c.c.*

$$\therefore \quad \text{frequency of the note,} \quad n = \frac{34000}{2\pi}\sqrt{\frac{\pi}{10000 \times 1}} = 170/\sqrt{\pi} = 95.92/\text{sec}$$

And, wavelength of the note, $\lambda = v/n = 34000/95.92 = 345.5$ cm.

Example 7.45. Calculate the frequency of an L-C circuit in which the inductance and capacitance are respectively 5 millihenry and 2μF. If the maximum potential difference across the capacitor be 10 volts, what is the energy of the system?

Solution. For the frequency of the oscillations in an *L-C* circuits, we have the relation

$$n = \frac{1}{2\pi\sqrt{LC}}$$

where *L* and *C* are the inductance and capacitance in the circuit respectively.

Here, $L = 5$ milli henry $= 5 \times 10^{-3}$ henry and $C = 2\mu F = 2 \times 10^{-6}$ farad.

$\therefore$ *Frequency of the L-C circuit,* $n = \dfrac{1}{2\pi\sqrt{5\times10^{-3}\times2\times10^{-6}}} = \dfrac{10^4}{2\pi} = 1592/\text{sec}$

And, with $V = 10$ volts, *energy of the system* $= \dfrac{1}{2}CV^2 = \dfrac{1}{2}\times2\times10^{-6}\times(10)^2 = 10^{-4}$ Joule

V–Two-body harmonic oscillator

Example 7. 46. (*a*) What is the reduced mass of each of the following diatomic molecules: O_2, HCI, CO? Express your answers in atomic mass units, the mass of a hydrogen atom being approximately 1.00 amu.

(*b*) An HCI molecule is known to vibrate at a fundamental frequency of 8.7×10^{13} cycles/sec. What is the effective ' force constant' *C* for the coupling forces between the atoms?

Solution. (*a*) We know that a diatomic molecule behaves like a system of two masses connected by a small massless spring. So that, its reduced mass is given by

$$m = \frac{m_1 \times m_2}{m_1 + m_2}$$

Now, in the case of O_2, $m_1 = 16$ *amu* and $m_2 = 16$ amu

$$\therefore \quad \mu = \frac{16\times16}{16+16} = \frac{256}{32} = 8 \text{ amu}$$

In the case of HCl, $m_1 = 1amu$ and $m_2 = 35.5$ *amu.*

$$\mu = \frac{1\times35.5}{1+35.5} = \frac{35.5}{36.5} = 0.97 \text{ amu.}$$

And, *in the case of CO,* $m_1 = 12$ amu and $m_2 = 16$ amu

$$\therefore \quad \mu = \frac{12\times16}{12+16} = \frac{192}{28} = 6.857 \text{ amu}$$

(*b*) The frequency of a two-body harmonic oscillator, as we know, is given by $n = \dfrac{1}{2\pi}\sqrt{\dfrac{C}{\mu}}$

where *C* is the '*force constant*' for the coupling forces and μ, the reduced mass of the system.

Here, the reduced mass μ for the HCI molecule = 0.97 amu [sec above under (*a*)], *i.e.*, equal to 0.97 × *mass of a hydrogen atom* = $0.97 \times 1.67 \times 10^{-24}$ gm and $n = 8.7 \times 10^{13}$ cycles/sec So that,

$$8.7\times10^{13} = \frac{1}{2\pi}\sqrt{\frac{C}{0.97\times1.67\times10^{-24}}}, \text{ whence, } C = 4\pi^2(8.7\times10^{13})^2\times0.97\times1.67\times10^{-24}$$

$$= 485200 \text{ dyne/cm} = 485 \text{ N/m.}$$

Example 7.47. Two dises D_1 and D_2 of masses 1 kg and 2 kg respectively are connected to the two ends of a massless spring and placed on a table, as shown in Fig. 7.30, with the spring vertical and the heavier disc (D_2) resting on the table. Calculate the frequency of oscillation of the system, if the force constant of the spring be 10^6 dynes/cm.

(*b*) After the system has come to rest, the table is suddenly removed from under disc D_2. Calculate (*i*) the frequency of the system, (*ii*) the instantaneous acceleration of the two discs of the centre of mass of the system.

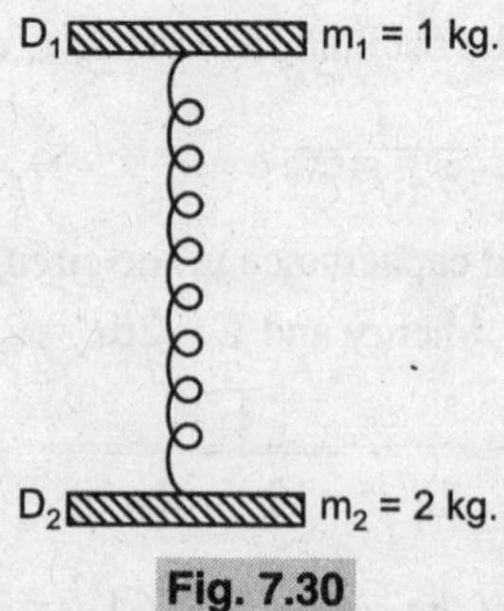

Fig. 7.30

Solution. (*a*) Obviously, here, the system functions as an ordinary one-body harmonic oscillator, with the lower end of the spring fixed and the upper on carrying disc D_1 of mass $m_1 = 1$ kg.

If, therefore, n_1 be the *frequency of the system*, we have

$$n_1 = \frac{1}{2\pi}\sqrt{\frac{C}{m_1}} = \frac{1}{2\pi}\sqrt{\frac{10^6}{1000}} = 5.025 \text{ or } 5.0/\text{sec.}$$

(*b*) (*i*) When the table is suddenly removed from under disc D_2, the system oscillates as a two-body harmonic oscillator, with both the discs oscillation simultaneously,

If n_2 = be the frequency of the system, we have $n_2 = \frac{1}{2\pi}\sqrt{\frac{C}{\mu}}$

Where μ is the reduced mass of the system , equal to $\frac{m_1 m_2}{m_1 + m_2} = \frac{1 \times 2}{1+2} = \frac{2}{3}$ kg

$$\therefore \quad n_2 = \frac{1}{2\pi}\sqrt{\frac{10^6}{(2/3)\times 1000}} = \frac{1}{2\pi}\sqrt{\frac{3\times 10^6}{2000}} = \frac{1}{2\pi}\sqrt{\frac{3\times 10^3}{2}} = 6.165 \text{ sec.}$$

(*ii*) Clearly, with the sudden removal of the table from under disc D_2. the latter is subjected to an instantaneous force equal to (1 *kg* + 2 *kg*) = 3 *kg wt* = $3 \times 10^3 \times g$ dynes.

If its acceleration be *a*, the force on it is clearly $m_2 a = 2 \times 10^3 a = 3 \times 10^3 \times g$, whence, $a = 3g/2$.

Thus, the *instantaneous acceleration of disc* $D_2 = \frac{3}{2}$ g cm / sec^2

As to acceleration of disc D_1, we note that the system was at rest before removal of the table from under disc D_2. Since disc D_1 was at rest on top of the spring, its weight was being supported by the elastic reaction of the spring and it continues to be so supported at the instant the table is just removed. So that, *the instantaneous acceleration of disc* D_1 *is zero.*

The acceleration of the centre of mass of the system will naturally be the same as the of a body falling freely under the action of gravity, *viz*., *g*. This may be shown as follows:

If *y* be the instantaneous displacement of the centre of mass (taking *y*-direction along the vertical) and y_1 and y_2, the corresponding displacements of the two discs of masses m_1 and m_2 respectively, we have $(m_1 + m_2)y = m_1 y_1 + m_2 y_2$. Differentiating with respect to *t*, we have $(m_1 + m_2)\, d^2y/dt^2 = m_1 d^2y_1/dt^2 + m_2 d^2y_2/dt^2$, where, as we known, $d^2y_1/dt^2 = 0$ and $d^2y_2/dt^2 = 3g/2$.

If, therefore, the acceleration of the centre of mass, *i.e.*, d^2y/dt^2 be *a′ cm/sec*^{2}, we have

$$(1+2)\,a' = 0 + 2 \times \frac{3}{2} g \text{ . Or, } 3a' = 3g \text{, whence, } a' = g,$$

i.e., the acceleration of the centre of mass is g.

Example. 7.48. The angular vibration frequency of the carbon monoxide molecule (CO) is 0.6 × 10^{15}/sec. Calculate (*i*) the reduced mass of the molecule in gms, (*ii*) the reduced mass of the molecule in gms, (*ii*) the force constant for stretching the molecule and (*iii*) the work done in stretching the molecule by 0.5 Angstrom unit.

Solution. (*i*) Clearly, *reduced mass of the CO molecule, i.e.*, $\mu = \dfrac{m_1 m_2}{m_1 + m_2} = \dfrac{12 \times 16}{12 + 16}$

$= \dfrac{192}{28}$ amu $= \dfrac{192}{28} \times$ mass of hydrogen atom $= \dfrac{192}{28} \times 1.67 \times 10^{-24}$

$$= 1.145 \times 10^{-23} \text{ gm.}$$

(*ii*)As we know, the vibrational frequency of the molecule is given by

$$n = (1/2\pi)\sqrt{C/\mu} \quad \text{Or} \quad 2\pi n = \sqrt{C/\mu}$$

Now, $\sqrt{C/\mu} = \omega$, whence, $C = \mu\omega^2$, where, $\mu = 1.145 \times 10^{-23}$ gm and $\omega = 0.6 \times 10^{15}$(given).

∴ *Force constant* $C = (1.145 \times 10^{-23})(0.6 \times 10^{15})^2 = 1.145 \times 0.36 \times 10^7 = 4.122 \times 10^6$ dynes/cm.

(*iii*) Work done in stretching the molecule by $(r - r_0)$ is given by $\frac{1}{2}C(r - r_0)^2$ [§7.9]

Here, $C = 4.122 \times 10^6$ dynes/cm and $(r - r_0) = 0.5$ A $= 0.5 \times 10^{-8}$ *cm*.

∴ work done in stretching the molecule through 0.5 *A* $= \frac{1}{2} \times 4.122 \times 10^6\ (0.5 \times 10^{-8})^2 = 2.061 \times 10^6 \times 0.25 \times 10^{-16} = 5.15 \times 10^{-11}$ erg.

Example 7.49. HCI gas absorbs light of wave length λ, thereby causing the transition in the vibrational energy level from *n* = 0 to *n* = 1. Calculate the force constant of the HCI molecule and the wavelength of the light absorbed if the vibrational energy levels be separated by 0.36 eV.

Solution. Here transition in the energy level occurring from $n = 0$ to $n = 1$, *i.e.*, with *n* changing by 1, the energy absorbed $= hv = hv_0$, where *h* is the planck's constant $= 6.6 \times 10^{-27}$ erg-sec and v = frequency of the light absorbed.

Since $hv = 0.36$ eV $= 0.36 \times 1.6 \times 10^{-12}$ ergs, we have

$v = v_0 = 0.36 \times 1.6 \times 10^{-12}/6.6 \times 10^{-27} = 8.728 \times 10^{13}$/sec.

Now, $v = v_0 = (1/2\pi)\sqrt{C/\mu}$, where *C* is the *force constant* and μ, the *reduced mass of the* molecule.

Clearly, $\mu = \dfrac{1 \times 35.5}{1 + 35.5} \times 1.67 \times 10^{-24} = 0.97 \times 1.67 \times 10^{-24}$ gm. We, therefore, have

$$8.728 \times 10^{13} = \frac{1}{2\pi}\sqrt{\frac{C}{0.97 \times 1.67 \times 10^{-24}}}$$

whence, $\quad C = (8.728 \times 10^{13})^2 \times 4\pi^2 \times 0.97 \times 1.67 \times 10^{-24}$.

Or, force constant $C = (8.728)^2 \times 0.97 \times 1.67 \times 4\pi^2 \times 10^2 \times 4.87 \times 10^5$ dynes/ cm.

And, *wavelength of light absorbed*, $\lambda = \dfrac{\text{velocity of light } (c)}{\text{frequency } (v)} = \dfrac{3 \times 10^{10}}{8.728 \times 10^{13}}$

$$= 3.438 \times 10^{-4} \text{ cm} = 34380 \text{ A.}$$

Example 7.50. (*a*) If the transition form one energy level to an adjacent on involves an energy change of 0.5 eV in the case of hydrogen, calculate the energy change involved in a similar transition in the case of HCI.

(*b*) While comparing the potential energy curve of two diatomic molecules *A* and B, it is observed that the potential well of the latter is narrower. What conclusions can be drawn from this? Can an estimate of the binding energies of the two molecules be made form these curves?

Solution. (*a*) The energy, change involved in transition between adjacent energy levels is, as we know, *hv*, where $hv = hv_0 = (h/2\pi)\sqrt{C/\mu}$, with *C* as the force constant of the molecule and μ, its reduced mass.

Now, in the case of hydrogen, $hv = 0.5$ eV, and, taking the mass of an atom of hydrogen to be m *amu*, $\mu = m \times m/(m + m) = m/2$ *amu*. And, therefore,

$$\therefore \qquad 0.5 = \frac{h}{2\pi}\sqrt{\frac{C}{m/2}} = \frac{h}{2\pi}\sqrt{\frac{2C}{m}}.$$

In the case of *HCl*, $$\mu = \frac{m \times 35.5\,\text{m}}{m + 35.5\,\text{m}} = \frac{35.5\text{m}^2}{36.5\text{m}} = 0.97 \text{ amu.}$$

If, therefore the energy change involved in transition between adjacent energy levels be E, we have

$$E = \frac{h}{2\pi}\sqrt{\frac{C}{0.97\,m}}$$

$\therefore$ dividing relation (*ii*) by (*i*), we have

$$\frac{E}{0.5} = \sqrt{\frac{C}{0.97m} \times \frac{m}{2C}} = \sqrt{\frac{1}{2 \times 0.97}} \text{ or, } E = \sqrt{\frac{1}{2 \times 0.97}} \times 0.5 = 0.359$$

Thus, *the energy change involved in transition between adjacent energy levels in the case of HCl is* 0.36 *electron volts*.

(*b*) A narrower potential well in the case of molecule *B* signifies a higher value of d^2U/dr^2 and, in consequence, a larger value of the force content *C*. So that, for the same value of the reduced mass (μ) in the two cases the vibrational frequency n [equal to $(1/2\mu)\sqrt{C/\mu}$] will be higher in the case of molecule *B*.

An estimate of the binding energies of the two molecules can be made by observing the minima of the potential energies in the two cases. For, *if we ignore the zero-point energy, the numerical values of the minimum potential energy and the binding energy of a molecule are the same.*

Example 7.51. The vibrational frequency of H^1Cl^{35} molecule is 8990 × 10^{10} cycles/sec. Deduce the vibrational frequency of H^2Cl^{35} molecule, assuming the force constant to be the same in the two cases. ***(Agru (supp), 2002)***

Solution. Since the vibrational frequency of a diatomic molecule is given by $(1/2\pi)\sqrt{C/\mu}$, it is clear that for the same value of the force constant (*C*), $n \propto \sqrt{1/\mu}$.

If therefore, μ_1 and μ_2, be the reduced masses of the HCl molecule in the two cases, and n_1 and n_2, their vibrational frequencies respectively, we have

$$\frac{n_2}{n_1} = \sqrt{\frac{\mu_1}{\mu_2}}, \text{ whence, } n_2 = \sqrt{\frac{\mu_1}{\mu_2}}n_1 \qquad [C \text{ being the same for both.}]$$

Now, $\mu_1 = 1 \times 35/(1 + 35) = 35/36$, $\mu_2 = 2 \times 35/(2 + 35) = 70/37$ and

$$n_1 = 8990 \times 10^{10} \text{ c.p.s. (given)}$$

$$\therefore \qquad n_2 = \sqrt{\frac{35}{36} \times \frac{37}{70}} \times 8990 \times 10^{10} = \sqrt{\frac{37}{72}} \times 8990 \times 10^{10} = 6445 \times 10 \text{ c.p.s.}$$

Thus, *the vibrational frequency of the* H^2C^{35} *molecule* = 6445 × 10^{10} *cycles*/sec.

VI—Anharmonic Oscillator

Example 7.52. Calculate the percentage change in the time-period of a simple pendulum if the angular amplitude of the pendulum be (*i*) 30°, (*ii*) 60°.

Solution. Let the length of the simple pendulum be l. Then, its true time-period (for infinitely small amplitudes) is $T_o = 2\pi\sqrt{l/g}$

If its amplitude be θ_1, the time-period $T = T_0\,(1 + \theta_1^2/16)$ ...[see 7.13]

$\therefore$ *Percentage change in the time-period* $= \left(\dfrac{T - T_0}{T}\right) \times 100 = \dfrac{\theta_1^2}{16} \times 100$

Now, in case (*i*) $\theta_1 = 30° = \pi/6$ radian. So that, we have

percentage change in the time-period $= \dfrac{(\pi/6)^2}{16} \times 100 = \dfrac{25\pi^2}{144} = 1.7$

And, in case (*ii*) $\theta_2 = 60° = \pi/3$ radian and we, therefore, have

Percentage change in the time-period $= \dfrac{(\pi/3)^2}{16} \times 100 = \dfrac{25\pi^2}{36} = 6.85$

Example 7.53. An oscillating particle of mass 1 gm has potential to $500x^2 + 200x^4$ ergs what is its frequency for small oscillations? What will be its frequency if the amplitude of its fundamental component be 3 cm? Also calculate the frequency and the amplitude of the first overtone in the latter case.

We have here $U = 5000x^2 + 200x^4$ ergs $\therefore F = -dU/dx = -10{,}000x - 800x^3$ dynes.

For small oscillations, the second term in x^3 may be neglected. So that,

$$F = -10{,}000x \text{ dynes.}$$

And $\therefore$ *acceleration*, $d^2x/dt^2 = -10{,}000x/1 = -10{,}000x = -(C/m)x = -\omega_0^2 x$,

i.e., $\omega_0^2 = 10{,}000$ and therefore, $\omega_0 = \sqrt{10{,}000} = 100$

$\therefore$ frequency for small oscillations, $n_o = \omega_o/2\pi = 100/2\pi = 15.92$/sec

Now, $\omega = \omega_0 + \dfrac{3}{8}\beta\dfrac{B_1^2}{\omega_0}$ (Equation VII, §7.12). And here, $\beta = 800$, $B_1 = 3$ cm.

So that,

$$\omega_0 = 100 + \frac{3}{8} \times 800 \times \frac{(3)^2}{100} = 127$$

$\therefore$ frequency, *when amplitude of fundamental component* is 3 cm is $n = \omega/2\pi$,

Whence, $n = 127/2\pi = 20.21$/sec.

Clearly, the first overtone here has thrice the frequency of the fundamental component, *i.e.*, a frequency n', say, $= 3\omega/2\,\pi = 20.21 \times 3 = 60.63$/sec.

and its amplitude is $\dfrac{\beta B_1^3}{32\,\omega_0^2} = \dfrac{800 \times (3)^2}{32 \times (100)^2} = \dfrac{27}{400} = 0.0675$ cm.

EXERCISE

1. Differentiate between simple harmonic motion and oscillatory motion. Define simple harmonic motion. Discuss potential well. ***(Nagpur U. 2009, H.P.U. 2001, Bang. U.2000, Gauhati. U.2000)***
2. Explain how interaction of inertia and elasticity account for simple harmonic motion ***(P.U. 2002)***
3. Enumerate the characteristics of simple harmonic motion. ***(Purvanchal U. 2005)***
4. Derive a general differential equation of motion of a simple harmonic oscillator and obtain its various solutions. ***(Nagpur U. 2006)***
5. (*a*) Find an expression for the velocity of a simple harmonic oscillator. ***(Nagpur U. 2008, 2003, Bang. U. 2000)***

   (*b*) Velocity of simple harmonic oscillator at any time t leads the displacement by an angle $\pi/2$ radium. Explain why? ***(Nagpur U. 2003)***
6. (*a*) Find an expression for the acceleration of a simple harmonic oscillator. ***(Nagpur U. 2008)***

   (*b*) Show that for the body executing simple harmonic motion, the acceleration leads the velocity by $\pi/2$ and displacement by π.

7. Show that the phase relation between the displacement, velocity and acceleration diagrammatically, given displacement $y = A \sin(\omega t + \phi)$.

8. What is meant by a harmonic oscillator? Obtain expressions for (*i*) its displacement and velocity at a given instant, (*ii*) time-period and frequency.

9. What are the important properties of a simple harmonic oscillator? Why is a simple harmonic motion considered to be a fundamental periodic motion? Show that the time-period of a simple harmonic oscillation is given by

$$T = 2\pi\sqrt{\frac{\text{displacement}}{\text{acceleration}}}$$

10. Explain the vibration of the kinetic and potential energies of a simple harmonic oscillator. Illustrate your answer with suitable graphs.

11. Show that for a simple harmonic oscillator, mechanical energy remains conserved and that its energy is, on and average, half kinetic and half potential in form. At what particular displacement is this exactly so? And what is the ratio between its kinetic and potential energies at a displacement equal to half its amplitude?

[**Ans.** *At displacement* $a\sqrt{2}$, *where a is the amplitude.* 3:1.]

12. It is said that all oscillations, if their amplitudes be infinitely small, may be regarded as simple harmonic. Do you agree? If so, explain why. Is it possible to have an oscillator for which even with small amplitudes, the oscillations are not simple harmonic?

13. Solve the differential equation $d^2x/dt^2 + \omega^2 x = 0$ to obtain the expression $x = a \sin(\omega t + \phi)$ for the displacement of a particle executing *S.H.M.*

14. Show that a simple harmonic motion may be expressed as either a since or a cosine function, there being only a difference of initial phase in the two cases.

15. (*a*) A particle of mass 10 *gm* lies in a potential field $V = 32x^2 + 200$ *ergs/gm*. What is its frequency of oscillation.

[**Ans.** 1.27 sec^{-1}.]

(*b*) A block executes a *S.H.M.* on a horizontal surface. If its frequency be 2 oscillations per second and the coefficient of static friction between the block and the surface, 0.50, how great can the amplitude be if the block does not slip on the surface?

16. A quantity of gas is enclosed in a cylinder, fitted with a smooth, heavy piston. The axis of the cylinder is vertical. The piston is thrust downwards to compress the gas and then let go. Is the ensuing motion of the piston a simple harmonic motion? If so, what is its time-period?

Ans. Yes; $T = \dfrac{2\pi}{a}\sqrt{\dfrac{Vm}{P}}$, where V and P are the *initial volume* and *pressure* of the gas respectively, a, the area of cross-section of the piston and m, its mass.

17. Prove that in a simple harmonic motion, the average potential energy equals the average kinetic energy $= \frac{1}{4}Ca^2$ *when the average is taken with respect to time over one period of the motion, and that, if the average is taken with respect to position over one cycle,* it is equal to $\frac{1}{2}Ca^2$. Explain why.

18. (*a*). A particle executing a *S.H.M.* has a maximum displacement of 4 cm and its acceleration at a acceleration at a distance of 1cm from its mean position is 3 cm/ sec^2. What will its velocity be when it is at a distance of 2 cm from its mean position?

[**Ans.** 6 cm/ sec.]

(*b*) A particle, moving in a straight line with *S.H.M.* of period $2\pi/\omega$ about a fixed point O, has a velocity $\sqrt{3}b\omega$ when at a distance b from O. shown that its amplitude is $2b$ and that it will cover that rest of its distance in time $\pi/3\omega$.

19. A particle executes linear harmonic motion about the point $x = 0$; at $t = 0$, it has displacement $x = 0.37$ cm and zero velocity. If the frequency of the motion is 0.25/sec, determine (*a*) the period, (*b*) the amplitude, (*c*) the maximum speed and (*d*) the maximum acceleration.

[**Ans.** (*a*) 4.0 sec, (*b*) 0.37 cm, (*c*) 0.58 cm/sec, (*d*) 0.91 cm/sec^2.]

20. A light string is suspended vertically from a point and carries a heavy mass at its lower free end which stretches it through distance l cm. Show that the vertical oscillations of the system are simple harmonic in nature and of a time-period equal to that of a simple pendulum of length l cm.

21. Two particles execute *S.H.M.* of the same amplitude and frequency along adjacent straight lines. They pass one another when going in opposite directions each time their displacement is half their amplitude. What is the phase difference between them? **[Ans.** $2\pi/3$]

22. Are all periodic motions simple harmonic? Is the reverse true? Explain. ***(P.U. 2004 pbi. 2003)***

23. A particle is dropped down in a deep hole which extends to the centre of the earth. Calculate its velocity at a depth of 1 kilometer from the surface of the earth. Assume that g = 1000 *cm/sec*^{2} and radian of the earth = 6400 kilometers. ***(Gorakpur, 2005)***

[Ans. 1.414×10^4 cm/sec.]

24. The displacement of an oscillating particle at an instant t is given by $x = a \cos \omega t + b \sin \omega t$. Show that it is executing a *S.H.M.*

If a = 5 *cm*, b = 12 *cm* and ω = 4 radians/sec, calculate (*i*) the amplitude, (*ii*) the time-period, (*iii*) the maximum velocity and (*iv*) the maximum acceleration of the particle.

[Ans. (*i*) 13 cm, (*ii*) 1.57 cm (*iii*) 52 cm/sec and (*iv*) 208 cm/sec^2.]

25. A smooth, straight tunnel is bored through the moon along any line takes at random. Show that if a smooth ball is dropped inside the tunnel, it excutes *S.H.M.* In how, much time will it reach one end of the tunnel from the other ened? Given: mass of the moon = 7.35×10^{25} gm, radius of the moon = 1.75×10^8 cm and $G = 6.67 \times 10^{-8}$ dynes-cm^2 gm^{-2}. **[Ans.** 54 min. 44 sec.]

[Hint. Sec worked example 7.]

26. The position of a particle executing *S.H.M.* along the x = *axis* are $x = A$ $x = B$ *at time* t and time $2t$ respectively. Show that its period of oscillation is given by $T = 2\,\pi t/\cos^{-1}(B/2A)$.

[Hint. Here, A = a sin ωt and $B = a \sin 2\omega t = 2$ a sin ωt cos ωt. If at $t = 0, x = 0$, we have $\cos \omega t = B/24$, *i.e.*, $\omega = \cos^{-1}(B/2A)/t$. $\therefore$ $T = 2\pi/\omega = 2\pi t/\cos^{-1}(B/2A)$.]

27. If the potential energy curve is $U = -A/x + B/x^2$, where A and B are positive constants, obtain the position of stable equilibrium and the force constant for small oscillations. What is the time-period for such oscillations?

[Ans. $2\,B/A$; $A^4/8\,B^3$; $4\pi B\sqrt{2mB/A^2}$]

28. The ends of one of the prongs of a tuning fork, which executes *S.H.M.* of frequency 1000/sec, has an amplitude of 0.40 nm. Calculate (*a*) its maximum acceleration and maximum speed (*b*) its acceleration and its speed when it has a displacement equal to half its amplitude.

[Ans. (*a*) 1.6×10^4 m/sec^2; 2.5 m/sec. (*b*) 7.9×10^3 m/sec^2; 2.2 m/sec.]

II–Pendulums—(*i*)–Simple pendulum

29. Show that a simple pendulum executes simple harmonic motion find its period.

30. Is it really possible to construct a truly simple pendulum ? show that as the angular amplitude of the pendulum approaches 180°, its time-period approaches infinity.

31. What are the drawbacks of a simple pendulum? The time-period of a simple pendulum for infinitely small amplitudes is given by $T = 2\pi\sqrt{l/g}$. What will it be for a infinite amplitude?

32. A simple pendulum of length 100 cm has energy equal to 0.3 joule when its amplitude is 2 cm. what will be its energy if (*i*) its length is increased to 150 cm, (*ii*) its amplitude is increased to 3 cm?

[Ans. (*i*) 0.2 joule, (*ii*) 0.675 joule]

33. A hollow sphere is filled with water through a small hole in it. It is hung by a long thread and, as the water slowly flows out of the hole at the bottom, the period of oscillations first increases and then decreases. Why is it so?

34. Show that the time-period of a simple pendulum at depth h below the earths' surface is inversely proportional to $\sqrt{R-h}$, where R is the radius of the earth. Calculate its time-period when $h = R/2$.

[Ans. 28 sec.]

35. What is a compound pendulum? How does a compound pendulum differ from a simple pendulum? Obtain an expression for its time-period and mention its pints of superiority over a simple pendulum.
(Nagpur U. 2009, 2005, 2006; P.U. 2004, 2003)

36. How is the time period of a pendulum affected when its points of suspension is (*a*) moved horizontally with acceleration *a*, (*b*) moved vertically upwards with acceleration *a*, (*c*) moved vertically downward with acceleration $a < g$? which case, if any, applies to a pendulum mounted on a cart rolling down an inclined plane?

37. Define centres of suspension and oscillation of a compound pendulum and show that they are interchangeable. What length of the pendulum has its minimum ime-period?

38. Show that if a uniform stick of length *l* is mounted so to rotate about a horizontal axis perpendicular to the stick and at a distance *d* from its centre of mass, the period has the minimum value when $d = l\sqrt{12} = 0.289l$.

39. Give the theory of kater's pendulum and find and find an expression for acceleration due to gravity terms of two nearly equal periods of oscillation about the two parallel knife-edges.
(Bombay; punjab)

40. A thin uniform bar of length 120 cm is made to oscillate about an axis through its end. Find the period of oscillation and other points about which it can oscillate with the same time-period.
(Punjab; Poona Raipur)
[**Ans.** 1.795 sec; at 40 cm, 80 *cm* and 120 cm from either end.]

41. In a reversible pendulum, the periods about the two knife-edges are *t* and $(t + T)$, where *T* is a small quantity. The knife-edges are distance *l* and *l*′ from the centre of gravity of the pendulum. Prove that $l + l' = \frac{gl}{4\pi^2}\left(t + \frac{2l'}{l' - l}T\right)$.
(Madras; Agra)

42. Obtain an expression for the time-period of a compound pendulum and show that (*i*) there are four points collinear with the *c.g.* about which the time-period is the same, (*iii*) its time-period remains unaffected by the fixing of a small additional mass to it at its centre of suspension.

43. What is meant by an equivalent simple pendulum? If the periods of a kårter's pendulum in the erect and inverted positions are equal, prove that the distance between the knife-edges is equal to the length of the equivalent simple pendulum.

44. A body of mass 200 gm oscillates about a horizontal axis at a distance of 20 cm from its centre of gravity. If the length of the equivalent simple pendulum be 35 cm, find its moment of inertia about the axis of suspension.
(Patna)
[**Ans.** 1.4×10^6 gm/cm^2]

45. A uniform rod *AB* of mass 100 gm and length 120 cm can swing in a vertical plane about *A* as a pendulum. A particle of mass 200 gm is attached to the rod at a distance *x* from *A*. Find *x* such that the period of vibration is a minimum.
(Gorakhpur, Madras)
[**Ans.** $x = 2.748$ cm.]

46. A uniform circular disc of radius 25 cm oscillates in a vertical plane about a horizontal axis. Find the distance of the axis of rotation from the centre for which the period is the minimum. What is the value of this period?
(Nagpur U. 2009)
[**Ans.** $25\sqrt{2}$ cm; $2\pi\sqrt{1.44 \times 25 / g}$]

47. A uniform cube is free to turn about one edge which is horizontal. Find in terms of a seconds pendulum the length of the edge, so that it may exeute a complete oscillation in 2 sec. [**Ans.** $3\sqrt{2l}$]

48. At a certain place the value of *g* is 980 cm/sec^2 and the length of the pendulum is so adjusted that period is 1 *sec.* When the period of the pendulum is measured on an elevator, undergoing uniform acceleration, it is found to be 1.025 *sec.* (*i*) For an acceleration $a \ll g$ of the elevator, show that the period measured on the elevator is given by $T = T_0\,(1 - a/2g)$, where T_0 is the period measured on the elevator is given by $T = T_0\,(1 - a/2g)$, where T_0 is the period of the unaccelerated pendulum and upward acceleration is assumed to be positive. (*ii*) What is the acceleration of the elevator?
[**Ans.** 49 cm/sec^2 *downward.*]

49. An annular ring of internal and outer radii *r* and *R* respectively oscillates in the vertical plane about a horizontal axis perpendicular to its plane and passing through a point on its outer edge. Calculate its time-period and show that the length of an equivalent simple pendulum is 2 *R* as $r \to 0$ and 3 *R* as $r \to R$.

[Ans. $T = 2\pi\sqrt{r^2 + 2R^2/Rg}$]

(iii) Torsional Pendulum

50. what is torsion pendulum? Show that oscillations of torsion pendulum are *S.H.M.* find its period. What are the merits of torsion pendulum. ***(Nagpur U. 2009, 2006, 2007)***

51. What is a torsional pendulum? Obtain an expression for its time-period. Explain why, unlike a simple or a compound pendulum, the time-period in this case remains unaffected even if the amplitude be large.

52. A disc of 10 cm radius and mass 1 kg is suspended in a horizontal plane by a vertical wire attached to its centre. If the diameter of the wire is 1 mm and its length is 1.5 metres and period of torsional vibration of the disc is 5 sec, find the rigidity (*n*) of material of the wire. ***(Madras)***

[Ans. 1.206×10^{12} dynes-cm^2.]

53. A solid cylinder of 2 cm radius weighing 200 gm is rigidly connected, with its axis vertical, to the lower end of a fine wire. The period of oscillation of the cylinder under the influence of the torsion wire is 2 seconds. Calculate the couple necessary to twist it through four complete turns. ***(Alahebed)***

[Ans. 9.9×10^4 dyne km^{-1}]

54. A body suspended by means of a wire, executes torsional vibrations about the wire as axis, of time-period 5.0 sec. If the moment of inertia of the body about the suspension wire as axis be 7.5×13^3 gm-cm^2, calculate the maximum angular velocity of the body if its amplitude be $\pi/2$ radian. What would then be its average kinetic energy? **[Ans.** 1.973 radian/sec. 7.30×10^3 ergs.]

[Hint. Since $\theta = \theta_0 \sin(\omega t + \phi)$, we have angular velocity $d\theta/dt = \omega\theta_0 \cos(\omega t + \phi)$,
Where θ_0 is the amplitude. $\therefore$ maximum value of $d\theta/dt = \omega\theta_0 = 2\pi n\theta_0$ ($\because \omega = 2\pi n$).
Here, $n = 1/T = 1/5$ *per sec* and $\theta_0 = \pi/2$ *radian*. Hence *maximum angular velocity of the body* $= 2\pi \times (1/5) \times (\pi/2) = \pi^2/5 = 1.973$ radian/sec.

And, average *K.E.* $= \frac{1}{2}$ total energy total energy $= \frac{1}{2}\left(\frac{1}{2}C\theta_0^2\right) = \frac{1}{2}C\theta_0^2$

Since $T = 2\pi\sqrt{1/C}$ and $\therefore C = 4\pi^2 I/T^2$, we have

$$\textit{average K.E.} = \frac{1}{4} \times \frac{4\pi^2 I}{T^2}\left(\frac{\pi}{2}\right)^2\Bigg]$$

III–Loaded spring (Mass on spring)

55. An unstressed spring has a force constant *C*. It is stretched by a weight hung from it to an equilibrium length well within the elastic limit. Does the spring have the same force constant C for displacements from this new equilibrium position?

56. Show that an oscillating loaded exhibits S.H.M. find its time period ***(Nagpur U. 2006)***

57. Show that the time period of oscillations of a loaded spring is

$$T = 2\pi\sqrt{\frac{Mx}{mg}}$$

58. Derive an expression for time period of oscillations of a loaded spring. ***(Nagpur U. 2009)***

59. What are the dimensions of force constant of vibrating spring? ***(Pbi. U. 2002, H.PU. 2000)***

60. Explain the terms: restoring force and force constant.

61. Explain how we can determine the period of oscillation of a spring-mass system from the extension produced in the spring on suspending the mass from it, even though we neither know the magnitude of the mass nor the force constant of the spring.

62. A spring has a force constant C. it be cut two pieces whose lengths are in the ratio 1:2, will the force constant continue to be the same (C) for each piece? If not, obtain the value of the force constant of each piece of C. **[Ans.** 3C, 3C/2]

[**Hint.** See worked example 7.41]

63. A massless spring, as we know, is purely a myth. Any real spring must have some mass. If this fact be taken into account, explain what change, if any, will it bring about in the expression for the time-period of a spring-mass system.

[**Hint.** See worked example 7.42]

64. A spring of force constant 19.6 N/m hangs vertically. A body of mass 0.20 kg. is attached to its free end and then released. Assume that the spring was unstretched before the body was released and find how far below the initial position the body descends. Find also the frequency and amplitude of the resulting S.H.M. [**Ans.** 0.1 m; 1.576/ sec; 0.1 m.]

65. A 2 kg mass hangs from a spring. A 300 gm body hung below the mass stretches the spring 2 cm further. If the 3000 gm body is removed and the mass set into oscillation, find the period of motion.

[**Ans.** 0.73 sec.]

66. (*a*) show that 'gravity' has no effect upon the force constant or the period of oscillation of a spring-mass system.

(*b*) Calculate the ratio of *K.E.* to P.E. when a mass oscillating at the lower end of a spring has covered half its amplitude. [**Ans.** 3:1]

67. An 8 *lb* block is suspended from a spring with a force constant of 3.0*lb*/*in*. An bullet weighing 0.10 *lb* is fired into the black from below with a velocity of the 500 ft/sec and comes to rest in the block. (*a*) Find the amplitude of the resulting S.H.M. (*b*) What fraction of the original K.E. of the bullet is stored in the harmonic oscillator? [**Ans.** (*a*) 6.2 in., (*b*) 1.2 %]

68. Fig. (7.27) show a mass M resting on a smooth table between two firm supports A and B and controlled by two massless springs. If the mass M is 30 gm and the force constants of the two springs are 2000 and 3000 dynes/cm, deduce (*i*) the frequency of small oscillations of M, (*ii*) the energy of oscillations for amplitude 0.5 cm. ***(Agra, 1969)***

[**Ans.** (*i*) 1.592*l* sec., (*ii*) 375 ergs.]

[**Hint.** See worked example 7.40 (*b*): $n = 1/T$; Energy of oscillations $= \frac{1}{2}Ca^2$]

69. (*a*) Calculate the frequency for small oscillations of mass M in problem 53 above, if it were connected to the two spring as shown in Fig 7.27 (*a*). [**Ans.** 0.75/sec.]

[**Hint.** See worked example 7.40 (*a*); $n = 1/T$]

(*b*) A car may be considered to be mounted on a stout vertical spring so far as its vertical oscillations are concerned. Thus, if the frequency of such vertical oscillations of a car weighing 1700 kg be 4 when unoccupied, what would be the frequency if it were occupied by five persons, each weighing 60 *kg* on an average? [**Ans.** 3.4/sec.]

70. The scale of a spring balance reading 0–5 kg is 12.5 cm. A body suspended from the balance oscillates with a frequency 5/π Hertz. Calculate the mass of the body attached to the spring. [**Ans.** $m = 3.92$ kg]

71. A spring hung vertically and loaded with a mass of 400 gm made to oscillate. Caulate (*i*) the time period, and (*ii*) the frequency of oscillation. When the spring is loaded with 100 gm, it extends by 5 cm.

[**Ans.** (*i*) 0.8985 (*ii*) 1.11 Hz]

72. A spherical vessel of capacity 500 *c.c.* is fitted with a tube of 5 cm. length and $\sqrt{\pi}$ cm radius. Calculate the wavelength of sound for which of will serve as a resonator. If the velocity of sound be 340 m/sec, what will be the frequency of the sound to which it will respond? [**Ans.** $\lambda = 100$ cm; $n = 340$ Hz.]

$$\left[\textbf{Hint. } n = \frac{v}{2\pi}\sqrt{\frac{\alpha}{Vl}} \quad \therefore \lambda = \frac{v}{n} = 2\pi\sqrt{\frac{Vl}{\alpha}}\right]$$

73. A spherical resonator with a neck of length 4 cm and area of cross section $4\pi^2$ sq cm responds sharply to a note of frequency 112. If the velocity of sound in air be 336 m/sec, what is the capacity of the resonator? [**Ans.** 10 litres.]

74. What is helmholtz resonator? Show that the oscillations are simple harmonic. Find its frequency. ***(Nagpur U. 2007, 2008, meerut 2005)***

75. A spherical Helmoltz resonator of capacity 10 liters has a narrow neck of length 0.01 m and and radius 0.01 m. If the velocity of sound in air is 340 m/sec, calculate the frequency of the note to which shorply responds. ***(Nagpur U. 2008) (Ans. 95.92 Hz)***

76. Discuss the *LC* circuit and show that the change on capacitor oscillates simple harmonically. Find the frequency of oscillations. Can it be realized in practice? ***(Agra U. 2007, 2004)***

77. What oscillates in a simple harmonic electrical oscillator? Can we realize in practice?

78. Derive the differential equation of S.H.M. for an electrical circuit. Can it be realized in practice?

79. It is desired to have an *L–C* circuit of frequency 10 kilocycles/sec. Calculate the capacitance that must be put in series with an inductance of 1 millihenry to achieve the purpose. [**Ans.** 0.2533 μF.]

80. An L–C circuit oscillates with a frequency of 20 cps. The capacitance in the circuit is 5 μF. Calculate the value of inductance in the circuit. [**Ans.** 12.67 henry.]

81. Show that the time period of the swing of a magnet in the earth's field is given by $t = 2\pi\sqrt{I / MH}$, where M is the magnetic moment, I its moment of inertia about the axis of suspension and H, the earth's field. ***(Sagar 2005)***

V–Two-body harmonic oscillator

82. What is meant by a two-body harmonic oscillator? Obtain an expression for the time-period of its oscillation and point out its similarities with a one-body oscillator. What is meant by reduced mass? Why is it so called. ***(Nagpur U. 2006, 2007, 2008)***

83. Show that the *K.E.* of a two-body oscillator (*i.e.*, two bodies connected by a spring) is given by $\frac{1}{2}\mu v^2$, where μ is the reduced mass and $v(= v_1 - v_2)$ the relative velocity.

[**Hint.** Linear momentum remains conserved during oscillations of the system.]

84. Is there any connection between the F versus x relation at the molecular level and the macroscopic relation between F and x in a spring? Explain briefly.

85. Draw a typical potential energy curve for a diatomic molecule, clearly pointing out and explaining its peculiarities, if any show that, for small amplitudes, its oscillations are simple harmonic and deduce their time-period.

86. (*a*) Two masses m_1 and m_2 of 1.0kg and 3.0 kg respectively are connected by a spring of force constant 250 *N*/*M* and are placed on a smooth table. They are slightly pulled apart and released. What is the frequency of the two-body system? [**Ans.** 2.90/sec.]

(*b*) What is the ratio between the kinetic energies of the two masses of the system? [**Ans.** 3:1.]

[**Hint.** Since linear momentum remains conserved during the oscillations, we have $m_1v_1 = m_2v_2$, or $m_1/m_2 = v_2/v_1$] Hence *K.E.* of mass m_1/*K.E.* of mass $m_2 = \frac{1}{2}n_1v_1^2 / \frac{1}{2}n_2v_2^2 = (m_1/m_2)(v_1^2/v_2^2) = (m_1/m_2)$, $(m_2^2/m_1^2) = m_2/m_1 = 3/1$.]

87. Draw characteristic potential energy diagram of a diatomic molecule and mark on it (*i*) the binding energy, (*ii*) equilibrium internuclear distance.

88. Draw the energy-level diagram of a diatomic molecule and explain its salient points. What is meant by the terms: vibrational quantum and zero-point energy?

89. In an HCl molecule, the force required to alter the distance between the atoms from its equilibrium value is 5.4×10^5 dynes *per* cm. what is the fundamental frequency of the vibration of the molecule, assuming the vibration to be simple harmonic and the mass of the *Cl* atom to be infinite compared to that of the H atom, which is 1.66×10^{-24} gm? [**Ans.** 9.078×10^{13}]

90. The separation of energy levels in *HCl* molecules made from H^1 and Cl^{35} isotopes of atomic weights 1 and 35 is 0.36 eV. What will be the value of the separation levels is *HCl* molecules made from D^2 and Cl^{37} isotopes. [**Ans.** 0.258 eV.]

VI–Bifilar oscillations

91. Show that bifilar oscillations are *S.H.M* Derive the expression for periodic time of a bifilar oscillator with parallel threads. ***(Nagpur U. s/2003, 2007, 2008).***

92. Describe bifilar oscillations and bifilar suspension. ***(Nagpur U. 2009)***

VII–Anharmonic oscillator

93. Discuss a large amplitude pendulum as an anharmonic oscillator.

94. Assuming the solution of the differential equation $md^2x/dt^2 = -Cx + C_1x^2$ for an anharmonic oscillator to be $x = A\cos\omega t + B\cos^2\omega t + x_1$, and neglecting all terms involving products of A and B and the second and higher powers of *B*, show that the average value of *x* is $x_1 = \alpha A^2/z\omega_0^2$, where $\omega^2 = \omega_0^2 = C/m$ and $\alpha = C_1/m$.

95. A particle oscillates in a potential field $U = \frac{1}{2}Cx - \frac{1}{2}C_1x^2$, where C_1 is positive and very much smaller them *C*. Will its potential well be symmetrical? If not, how not, how will it affect the mean position of the particle?

8

Chapter

DAMPED AND DRIVEN HARMONIC OSCILLATORS

Brief Contents

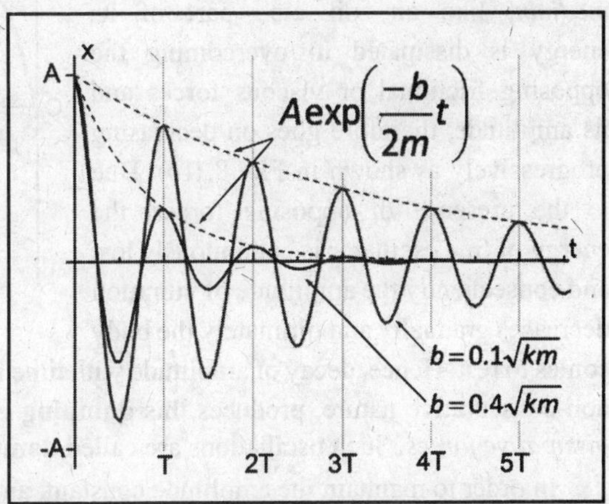

INTRODUCTION

In an ideal simple harmonic motion (S.H.M.), the displacement follows a sinusoidal curve as shown in Fig. 8.1(a). The amplitude (a) of oscillations remain constant for an *infinite time*. This is because there is no loss of energy and total energy remains constant. Such oscillations are called **'Free oscillations'**. However, in actual practice, the situation is different. In our discussion in the last chapter, on harmonic oscillator, we completely ignored the effect of frictional forces on it. Since, however, an oscillator, in actual practice, always experiences *frictional* or *resistive medium*, like air, oil etc., part of its energy is dissipated in overcoming the opposing frictional or viscous forces and its amplitude, therefore goes on decreasing progressively as shown in Fig. 8.1(b). Due to the presence of opposing forces, the energy of free oscillator is continuously lost and consequently the amplitude of vibration decreases gradually and ultimately the body comes to rest. Hence, decay of amplitude with time is called **damping**. These opposing forces, being non-conservative nature, produces this **damping effect** are also referred as *damping*, *resistive* or *dissipative forces*. Such oscillations are called **damped harmonic oscillations.**

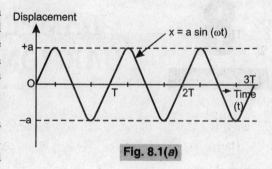

Fig. 8.1(*a*)

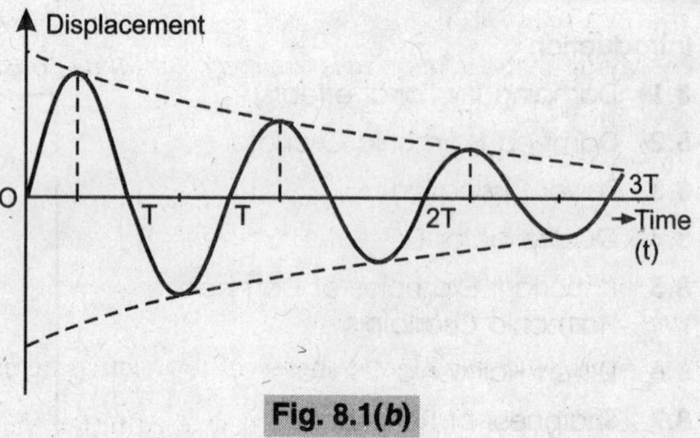

Fig. 8.1(*b*)

In order to maintain the amplitude constant, an *external periodic force* is applied. These forced vibrations initially gains the frequency equal to its natural frequency and then after short time, the oscillator acquires the frequency of the impressed periodic force. The externally applied periodic force is, hence, known as *driven force* and the oscillator is named as *driven harmonic oscillator* or *forced harmonic oscillator.* In this chapter, we will discuss amplitude resonance, quality factor and energy considerations of both damped and driven harmonic oscillators in detail.

8.1 DAMPING (FRICTIONAL EFFECTS)

Let us discuss the damping effect on the oscillations of a harmonic oscillator in detail. It has been shown by Mayevski that at ordinary velocities—and most cases of interest to us fall in this category—the opposing, resistive or damping force is, to a first approximation, proportional to velocity and may thus be represented by

$$F = -\gamma v = -\gamma dx/dt, \qquad ...(i)$$

where γ is a *positive constant*, called **damping coefficient** of the medium and may be looked upon as the *resistive force per unit velocity*.

So that, if there is no other force, other than this resistive or damping force, acting on the oscillating body or particle, of mass m, we have, in accordance with Newton's second law of motion,

$$F = m\frac{d^2x}{dt^2} = m\frac{dv}{dt} = -\gamma v, \quad \text{Or,} \quad \frac{dv}{dt} + \frac{\gamma}{m}v = 0. \qquad ...(ii)$$

Here, m/γ is usually denoted by τ, a constant, having the dimensions of time and called **relaxation time**,

We, therefore, have $\frac{dv}{dt} + \frac{1}{\tau} v = 0$ ...(*iii*)

The constant $1/\tau = \gamma/m$, or *the resistive force per unit mass per unit velocity*, is often denoted by $2k$, where k is called the **damping constant** of the medium.

Now, rewriting differential equation (*iii*) in the form $dv/v = -dt/\tau$, we have

$$\int \frac{dv}{v} = -\frac{1}{\tau}\int dt, \text{ which gives } \log_e v = -\frac{t}{\tau} + C,$$

where C is a constant of integration to be determined from the initial conditions.

Thus, if at $t = 0$, $v = v_0$, we have $\log_e v_0 = C$. And, therefore,

$$\log_e v - \log_e v_0 = -t/\tau, \quad \text{Or,} \quad v = v_0 e^{-t/\tau}, \qquad ...(iv)$$

clearly showing that *the velocity decreases exponentially with time*, as shown by the curve in Fig. 8.2 between the function $e^{-t/\tau}$ and t. We express this by saying that *the velocity is damped, with time constant* τ.

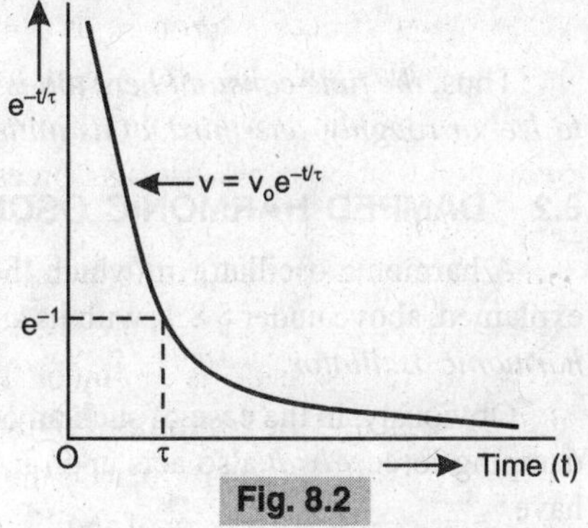

Fig. 8.2

As will be readily seen, at $t = \tau$, $v = v_0 e^{-1} = v_0/e = v_0/2.718 = 0.368\, v_0$.

This enables us to define the *time constant* (or the *relaxation time*) τ *as the time in which the velocity of the oscillating particle falls to* $1/eth$ (*i.e.*, 0.368 *or, roughly, one-third*) *of its initial value.*

And, since the kinetic energy of the oscillating particle is given by $T = \frac{1}{2} mv^2$, we have, on substituting the value of v from relation (iv) above, $T = \frac{1}{2} mv_0^2 e^{-2t/\tau}$. Or, representing the initial kinetic energy $\frac{1}{2} mv_0^2$ by T_0, we have $T = T_0 e^{-2t/\tau}$ indicating that *the kinetic energy of the oscillating particle too falls exponentially with time, with a relaxation time half that for velocity, i.e.*, $\tau/2$, which is only to be expected since $K.E. \propto (\text{velocity})^2$.

Putting dx/dt for v in relation (*iv*) above, we have $dx/dt = v_0 e^{-t}/\tau$, which, on integration, gives $x = -v_0 \tau e^{-t/v} + C$, where C is a constant of integration.

At $t = 0$, $x = 0$, so that $C = v_0 t$. And, therefore, $x = v_0 \tau (1 - e^{-t}/\tau)$.

Now, as $t \to \infty$, $e^{-t/v} \to 0$ and, therefore, $x \to v_0 \tau$.

Thus, *the maximum value of x is the distance that would be covered by the particle in time* τ *if its velocity remained constant at its initial value* v_0.

Examples. (*i*) As an example of the resistive or damping force of the type represented by relation (*i*) above may be cited the force experienced by a flat disc moving normally to its plane through a gas (or air), at very low pressure, at a speed very much smaller than that of its molecules.

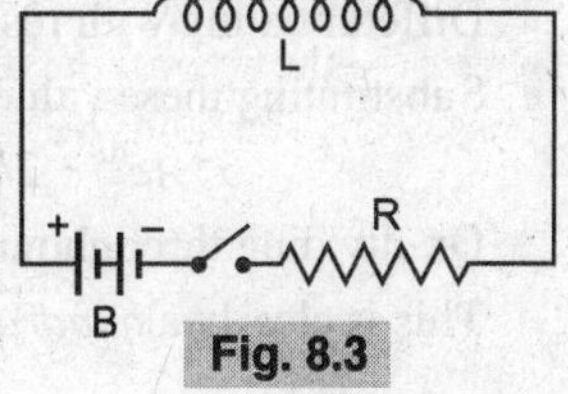

Fig. 8.3

(*ii*) Or, perhaps a more familiar example is that furnished by the ohmic resistance in an electrical circuit containing an inductance, such as the one shown in Fig. 8.3. On suddenly breaking the circuit, an induced *emf*, $-LdI/dt$, is set up across the inductance L, where I is the value of the current flowing through the circuit at the instant it is broken. Since there is now no external *emf* operative, we have

$$RI = -LdI/dt. \quad \text{Or,} \quad LdI/dt + RI = 0 \qquad ....(v)$$

where RI is the potential drop across the resistance R.

This is a relation, identical in form with relations (*ii*) and (*iii*) above, with the time constant $\tau = L/R$, clearly indicating that the ohmic resistance plays the same part here as the damping force there, so that *the current in the circuit falls exponentially with time*. For, putting relation (*v*) in the form $dI/I = -(R/L)\,dt$ and integrating, we have

$$\log_e I = -\frac{R}{L}t + C\text{, where } C \text{ is a constant of integration.}$$

Since at $t = 0$, $I = I_0$, its initial (or maximum) value, we have $C = \log_e I_0$. And, therefore,

$$\log_e I = -\frac{R}{L}t + \log_e I_0.$$

Or,
$$\log_e \frac{I}{I_0} = -\frac{R}{L}t,\ \text{whence, } I = I_0\, e^{-(R/L)t}.$$

It will be seen at once that if t = *time constant L/R*, we have

$$I = I_0 e^{-1} = I_0/e.$$

Thus, *the time constant here too is the time in which the value of the current in the circuit falls, to 1/e, or roughly, one-third, of its initial or maximum value.*

8.2 DAMPED HARMONIC OSCILLATOR

A harmonic oscillator in which the oscillations are damped on account of resistive forces, as explained, above under § 8.1, with its amplitude progressively decreasing to zero, is called a *damped harmonic oscillator.*

Obviously, in the case of such an oscillator, in addition to the restoring force $-Cx$, a resistive or damping force $\gamma dx/dt$ also acts upon it, where dx/dt is its velocity at displacement x. We, therefore, have

$$m\frac{d^2x}{dt^2} = -\gamma\frac{dx}{dt} - Cx. \quad \text{Or,} \quad \frac{d^2x}{dt^2} + \frac{\gamma dx}{mdt} + \frac{C}{m}x = 0.$$

Or, since $\gamma/m = 2k$ (where k is the *damping constant* of the resistive medium) and $\sqrt{C/m} = \omega_0$, the *natural angular frequency of the oscillating particle, i.e.*, its frequency in the absence of damping, we have

$$\frac{d^2x}{dt^2} + 2k\frac{dx}{dt} + \omega_0^2 x = 0, \qquad ...(vi)$$

which is called the **differential equation of a damped harmonic oscillator**.

Solution of the equation. The differential equation, which is a *homogeneous linear type, of the second order*, has at least one solution of the form $x = Ae^{\alpha t}$, where A and α are both *arbitrary constants*. We shall, therefore, use this as a trial solution.

Differentiating with respect to t, we have $dx/dt = \alpha Ae^{\alpha t}$ and $d^2x/dt^2 = \alpha^2 Ae^{\alpha t}$.

Substituting these values in the differential equation (*vi*) above, we have

$$\alpha^2 Ae^{\alpha t} + 2k\alpha Ae^{\alpha t} + \omega_0^2 Ae^{\alpha t} = 0.$$

Or, dividing throughout by $Ae^{\alpha t}$, we have $\alpha^2 + 2k\alpha + \omega_0^2 = 0$. ...(*vii*)

This is clearly a *quadratic equation* in α and, therefore,

$$\alpha = -k + \sqrt{k^2 - \omega_0^2}$$

The differential equation (*vi*) is thus satisfied by two values of x, *viz.*,

$$x = Ae^{(-k+\sqrt{k^2-\omega_0^2})t} \quad \text{and} \quad x = Ae^{(-k-\sqrt{k^2-\omega_0^2})t}.$$

The equation being a linear one, the linear sum of the two linearly independent solutions of the equation is also a — and, indeed, the most — general solution. Thus, the general solution is

$$x = A_1 e^{(-k+\sqrt{k^2-\omega_0^2})t} + A_2 e^{(-k-\sqrt{k^2-\omega_0^2})t} \qquad ...(viii)$$

Now, $k = 1/2\tau$ and if we put $\sqrt{k^2 - \omega_0^2} = \beta$, we may also put the solution in the form

$$x = A_1 e^{-\frac{t}{2\tau}+\beta t} + A_2 e^{-\frac{t}{2\tau}-\beta t}$$

where the values of the *arbitrary constants* A_1 and A_2 may be determined as follows:

Differentiating expression (*viii*) with respect to *t*, we have

$$\frac{dx}{dt} = (-k+\sqrt{k^2-\omega_0^2})A_1 e^{(-k+\sqrt{k^2-\omega_0^2})t} + (-k-\sqrt{k^2-\omega_0^2})A_2 e^{(-k-\sqrt{k^2-\omega_0^2})t} \qquad ...(ix)$$

So that, if the displacement *x* be the *maximum*, equal to $x_{max} = a_0$, say, at $t = 0$ and, therefore, the velocity $dx/dt = 0$, we have from relation (*viii*) above,

$$x_{max} = a_0 = (A_1 + A_2) \qquad ...(A)$$

and from relation (*ix*).

$$(-k+\sqrt{k^2-\omega_0^2})A_1 + (-k-\sqrt{k^2-\omega_0^2})A_2 = 0.$$

Or, $$-k(A_1+A_2) + \sqrt{k^2-\omega_0^2}\,(A_1 - A_2) = 0.$$

Or, $$\sqrt{k^2-\omega_0^2}\,(A_1 - A_2) = k(A_1+A_2) = k\,a_0,$$

whence, $$(A_1 - A_2) = ka_0 \Big/ \sqrt{k^2-\omega_0^2} \qquad ...(B)$$

Adding relations *A* and *B*, therefore, we have

$$2A_1 = a_0 + ka_0 \Big/ \sqrt{k^2-\omega_0^2}$$

And $\therefore$ $$A_1 = \frac{1}{2}\left(a_0 + \frac{ka_0}{\sqrt{k^2-\omega_0^2}}\right) = \frac{1}{2}a_0\left(1+\frac{k}{\sqrt{k^2-\omega_0^2}}\right)$$

$$= \frac{1}{2}a_0\left(1+\frac{1}{2\beta\tau}\right)$$

and $$A_2 = (A_1+A_2) - A_1 = a_0 - \frac{1}{2}a_0\left(1+\frac{k}{\sqrt{k^2-\omega_0^2}}\right)$$

$$= \frac{1}{2}a_0\left(1-\frac{k}{\sqrt{k^2-\omega_0^2}}\right) = \frac{1}{2}a_0\left(1-\frac{1}{2\beta\tau}\right)$$

Substituting these values in expression (*viii*) above, we have

$$x = \frac{1}{2}a_0 e^{-kt}\left[\left(1+\frac{k}{\sqrt{k^2-\omega_0^2}}\right)e^{\sqrt{(k^2-\omega_0^2)}t} + \left(1+\frac{k}{\sqrt{k^2-\omega_0^2}}\right)e^{-\sqrt{(k^2-\omega_0^2)}t}\right] \qquad ...(x)$$

Or, since $k = 1/2\tau$ and $\sqrt{k^2 - \omega_0^2} = \beta$, we have

$$x = \frac{1}{2}a_0 e^{-t/2\tau}\left[\left(1+\frac{1}{2\beta\tau}\right)e^{\beta t} + \left(1-\frac{1}{2\beta t}\right)e^{-\beta t}\right] \quad ...(xi)$$

Now, *three important cases arise*:

1. When k (or 1/2τ) > ω_0 — (Case of overdamping). In case of high damping such as this, clearly, $\sqrt{k^2 - \omega_0^2}$ (or $\sqrt{1/4\tau^2 - \omega_0^2}$) is a *real quantity* with a *positive value, less than k*. So that, each of the two terms on the right hand side of equation (*x*) or (*xi*) has an exponential term with a negative power. The displacement, after attaining its maximum value, therefore, dies off exponentially with time, without changing direction. There is thus no oscillation and the motion is, therefore, called **overdamped**, **aperiodic** or **dead beat**, as we have in the case of a *dead beat galvanometer* (§ 8.7, I) or that of a pendulum oscillating in a viscous fluid like oil.

2. When k (or 1/2τ) = ω_0 — (Case of critical damping). In this case, obviously, $\sqrt{k^2 - \omega_0^2}$ (or $\sqrt{1/4\tau^2 - \omega_0^2}$) = 0, so that each of the two terms on the right hand side of equation (*x*) or (*xi*) above, becomes infinite and the solution breaks down.

Let us, however, consider the case when $\sqrt{k^2 - \omega_0^2} = h$, *a very small quantity but not zero*. We shall then have, from relation (*viii*) above,

$$x = A_1 e^{(-k+h)t} + A_2 e^{(-k-h)t} = e^{-kt}(A_1 e^{ht} + A_2 e^{-ht}).$$

Or,
$$x = e^{-kt}\left[A_1\left(1 + ht + \frac{h^2t^2}{2!} + \frac{h^3t^3}{3!} + ...\right) + A_2\left(1 - ht + \frac{h^2t^2}{2!} - \frac{h^3t^3}{3!}\right)\right]$$

Or, neglecting terms containing the second and higher powers of *h*, we have

$$x = e^{-kt}[A_1(1+ht) + A_2(1-ht)] = e^{-kt}[(A_1+A_2) + (A_1-A_2)ht]$$

Or, putting $(A_1 + A_2) = M$ and $(A_1 - A_2)h = N$, we have

$$x = e^{-kt}(M + Nt).$$

Now, taking $x = x_{max} = a_0$ and $dy/dt = 0$ at $t = 0$, we have

$$M = x_{max} = a_0 \quad \text{and} \quad N = ka_0.$$

So that,
$$x = e^{-kt}(a_0 + ka_0 t) = a_0 e^{-kt}(1 + kt) = a_0 e^{-t/2\tau}\left(1 + \frac{t}{2\tau}\right).$$

Here, the second term $a_0 + kte^{-kt}$ [or $(a_0 t/2\pi)e^{-t/2\tau}$] decays less rapidly than the first term $a_0 e^{-kt}$ (or $a_0 e^{-t/2\tau}$) and the displacement of the oscillator first increases but it then returns back quickly to its equilibrium position. The motion of the oscillator thus becomes *just aperiodic or non-oscillatory, i.e., it just ceases to oscillate*. This is called the case of **critical damping**, the necessary condition for which, as we have just seen, is the $k \to \omega_0$. It finds an application in many pointer-type instruments like galvanometers where the pointer moves at once to, and stays at, the correct position, without any annoying oscillations.

3. When *k* (or 1/2τ) < ω_0 — (Case of underdamping). Here, clearly, the quantity $\sqrt{k^2 - \omega_0^2}$ will be an *imaginary* one, say, equal to $i\omega$, where $i = \sqrt{-1}$ and $\omega = \sqrt{\omega_0^2 - k^2}$, a *real quantity*. Expression (*viii*) above thus becomes $x = A_1 e^{(-k+i\omega)t} + A_2 e^{(-k-i\omega)t}$

Or, $$x = e^{-kt}\left[A_1(\cos \omega t + i \sin \omega t) + A_2(\cos \omega t - i \sin \omega t)\right]$$
$$= e^{-kt}\left[(A_1 + A_2)\cos \omega t + i(A_1 - A_2)\sin \omega t\right]$$

Or, putting $(A_1 + A_2) = A$ and $i(A_1 - A_2) = B$, we have

$$x = e^{-kt}(A \cos \omega t + B \sin \omega t)$$

If A, B and a_0 be related as shown in Fig. 8.4, we have

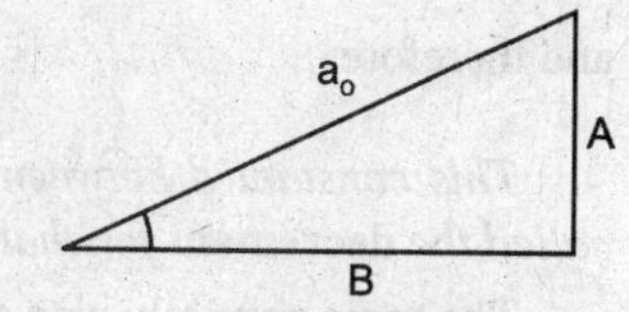

$$x = e^{-kt}\left(a_0 \cos \omega t \frac{A}{a_0} + a \sin \omega t \frac{R}{a_0}\right)$$
$$= e^{-kt}(a_0 \cos \omega t \sin \phi + a_0 \sin \omega t \cos \phi)$$

Fig. 8.4

Or, $$x = a_0 e^{-kt} \sin(\omega t + \phi)$$
$$= a_0 e^{-t/2\tau} \sin(\omega t + \phi) \quad \text{...(xii)}$$

This is the equation of a damped harmonic oscillator, with amplitude $a_0 e^{-kt}$ (or $a_0 e^{-t/2\tau}$) and *frequency* $\omega/2\pi = \sqrt{\omega_0^2 - k^2}/2\pi$. It is so called because the sine term in the equation suggests the oscillatory character of the motion and the exponential term, the gradual damping out of the oscillations.

Damping thus clearly produces two effects:

(*i*) *The frequency of the damped harmonic oscillator,* $\omega/2\pi$ *is smaller than its undamped or natural frequency* $\omega_0/2\pi$, *i.e.*, damping somewhat decreases the frequency or increases the time-period of the oscillator. In actual practice, in a majority of cases, particularly in the case of musical instruments, the damping is small and its effect on the frequency or the time-period of the oscillator, therefore, quite negligible.

(*ii*) *The amplitude of the oscillator does not remain constant at* a_0, *which represents the amplitude in the absence of damping, but decays exponentially with time, to zero, in accordance with the term* e^{-kt}, *called the damping factor.*

This is illustrated by the time-displacement curve of the damped harmonic oscillator, shown in Fig. 8.5.

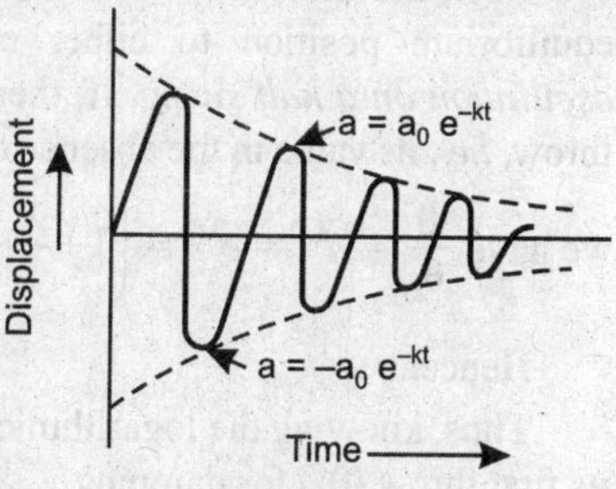

Fig. 8.5

Since the maximum values of $\sin(\omega t + \phi)$ are +1 and −1 alternately, the time-displacement graph of the oscillating particle is bounded by the dotted curves

$a = a_0 e^{-kt}$ (or $a = a_0 e^{-t/2\tau}$) and $a = -a_0 e^{-kt}$ (or $a = -a_0 e^{-t/2\tau}$).

Thus, although its amplitude decreases exponentially with time, the underdamped harmonic oscillator does perform a sort of oscillatory motion. *The motion does not, of course, repeat itself and is thus not periodic in the usual sense of the term.* However, it has still a time-period $= 2\pi/\omega = 2\pi\Big/\sqrt{\omega_0^2 - k^2}$, which is the time-interval between its successive passages in the same direction past the equilibrium point. It is obviously also the time-interval between successive maximum displacements on the same side of the equilibrium point.

N.B. Actually, as we shall see later, a damped oscillation may, in terms of *Fourier's theorem*, be imagined to result from the superposition of a very large number (*i.e.*, an infinite series) of undamped oscillations, with their frequencies varying continuously on either side of the main or principal frequency $\omega/2\pi$ and with their amplitudes diminishing in proportion to the departure of their frequencies from the principal one.

Logarithmic decrement. As we have just seen above, the amplitude in the case of a damped harmonic motion goes on decreasing progressively. So that, if a_n and $a_{(n+1)}$ be the successive amplitudes of the oscillating particle on the two sides of the equilibrium position respectively, the time-interval between them is clearly half the time-period (T) of oscillation and is thus $T/2$. We thus have

$$a_n = a_0\, e^{-kt} \quad \text{and} \quad a_{(n+1)} = a_0\, e^{-k(t+T/2)}$$

and therefore,

$$\frac{a_n}{a_{(n+1)}} = \frac{e^{-kt}}{e^{-k(t+T/2)}} = e^{kT/2} = d, \text{ a constant.}$$

This constant d between two successive amplitudes of a given damped harmonic motion is called the **decrement** *for that motion.*

The same naturally also applies to angular amplitudes, where we have

$$\frac{\theta_n}{\theta_{(n+1)}} = d.$$

The logarithm of the decrement, *i.e.*, $\log_e d = kT/2 = \lambda$. Or, $d = e^{\lambda}$.

This constant, λ, which is obviously the *natural logarithm of the decrement or the ratio between two successive amplitudes of the oscillation* is referred to as the **logarithmic decrement** for that motion or oscillation.

Use is made of this in applying the necessary correction for damping to the *first deflection or* the *first 'throw'* θ_1 of a ballistic galvanometer as follows:

Each half oscillation, as we know, comprises one swing from θ_1 to θ_2 or from θ_2 to θ_3, *i.e.*, from the extreme position on one-side to the extreme position on the other, as shown in Fig. 8.6.

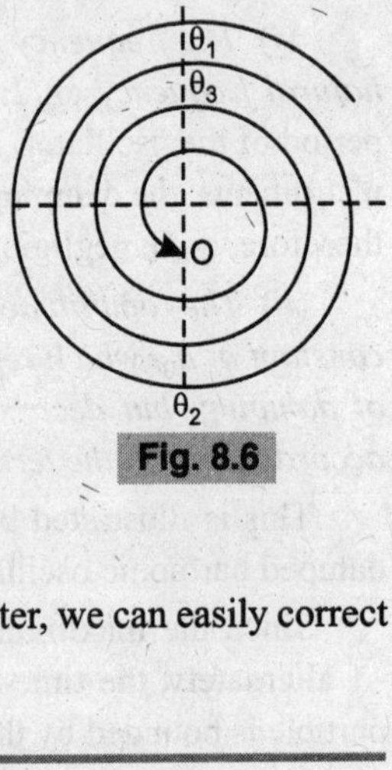

So that, $\theta_1/\theta_2 = \theta_2/\theta_3 = d = e^{\lambda}$.

Now, the first throw of a ballistic galvanometer, from the mean or equilibrium position to either extreme, constitutes only a *quarter oscillation on a half swing*. If, therefore, θ be the *true* value of this first throw, *i.e.*, its value in the absence of damping, and θ_1, its observed value, we have

$$\frac{\theta}{\theta_1} = d^{1/2} = e^{\lambda/2} = \left(1 + \frac{\lambda}{2} + \frac{(\lambda/2)^2}{2!} + \ldots\right) = 1 + \frac{\lambda}{2} \text{ very nearly.}$$

Fig. 8.6

Hence, $0 = \theta_1 (1 + \lambda/2)$.

Thus, knowing the logarithmic decrement (λ) for the given galvanometer, we can easily correct its first throw (θ_1) for damping.

8.3 POWER DISSIPATION

Since the amplitude of a damped harmonic oscillator goes on falling exponentially with time, on account of the resistive or damping forces it has to overcome, it is clear that its energy gets continuously dissipated during its oscillation. Let us calculate its *rate of dissipation of energy* or *its power dissipation*, as it is more commonly called (because *energy or work/time = power*).

Since the displacement of the oscillator is given by

$$x = a_0\, e^{-kt} \sin(\omega t + \phi),$$

we have, *velocity of the particle at a given instant t, i.e.,*

$$dx/dt = a_0\, e^{-kt} [-k \sin(\omega t + \phi) + \omega \cos(\omega t + \phi)]$$

$\therefore$ *K.E. of oscillation of the particle at the given instant t*

$$= \frac{1}{2} m \left(\frac{dx}{dt}\right)^2 = \frac{1}{2} m a_0^{\,2}\, e^{-2kt} [-k \sin(\omega t + \phi) + \omega \cos(\omega t + \phi)]^2$$

$$= \frac{1}{2} m a_0^{\,2}\, e^{-2kt} [k^2 \sin^2(\omega t + \phi) + \omega^2 \cos^2(\omega t + \phi) - 2k\omega \sin(\omega t + \phi) \cos(\omega t + \phi)]$$

If the damping be small (as it usually is), the amplitude does not change appreciably over a time-period, so that the factor e^{-2kt} may be taken to be constant over the period. Further, since the average value over a time-period of both $\sin^2(\omega t+\phi)$ and $\cos^2(\omega t+\phi)$ is 1/2 and that of $2\omega\sin(\omega t+\phi)\cos(\omega t+\phi)=\sin 2(\omega t+\phi)=0$, we have *average K.E. of the particle or the oscillator over one cycle at the given instant* $t=\frac{1}{2}ma_0^2e^{-2kt}\left(\frac{1}{2}k^2+\frac{1}{2}\omega^2-0\right)=\frac{1}{4}ma_0^2\omega^2e^{-2kt}$, neglecting k^2 in comparison with ω^2, in view of its very small value.

And, *P.E. of the particle or the oscillator at the given instant t (when the displacement is x)* = $\frac{1}{2}Cx^2=\frac{1}{2}m\omega_0^2x^2$, where ω_0 is the natural (undamped) angular frequency of the particle.

$$\left[\because P.E.=\int_0^x Cx\,dx=\frac{1}{2}Cx^2 \text{ and } \frac{C}{m}=\omega_0\right]$$

Or, substituting the value of x, we have

$$P.E. \textit{ of the oscillating particle}=\frac{1}{2}m\omega_0^2[a_0\,e^{-kt}\sin(\omega t+\phi)]^2$$

$$=\frac{1}{2}ma_0^2\,e^{-2kt}\,[\omega_0^2\sin^2(\omega t+\phi)]$$

Again, since the average value of $\sin^2(\omega t+\phi)$ over a time-period is 1/2, we have *average P.E. of the particle or the oscillator over one cycle, at the given instant* $t=\frac{1}{4}ma_0^2\omega_0^2e^{-kt}$ $=\frac{1}{4}ma_0^2\omega^2e^{-2kt}$, because, damping being small, $\omega_0\approx\omega$.

Hence, *average total energy of the oscillator at the given instant = (average K.E. + average P.E.) at the instant* $=\frac{1}{4}ma_0^2\omega^2e^{-2kt}+\frac{1}{4}ma_0^2\omega^2e^{-2kt}=\frac{1}{2}ma_0^2\omega^2e^{-2kt}=E=E_0e^{-2kt}=E_0\,e^{-t/\tau}$, where $\frac{1}{2}ma_0^2\omega^2=E_0$, *the average total energy of the undamped oscillator*.

$\therefore$ *average power dissipation* (P) = *rate of loss of energy*

$$=-dE/dt=ma_0^2\,\omega^2\,ke^{-2kt}=2kE=E/\tau. \qquad (\because 2k=1/\tau)$$

This loss of energy is obviously due to the work done against the damping or dissipative force $-\gamma\,dx/dt$ and usually appears in the form of heat.

Alternatively, we could obtain the same result as follows:

As in the case of a harmonic oscillator, so also here, the energy of an oscillator must be proportional to the square of its amplitude, *i.e.*,

$$E\propto(a_0e^{-kt})^2, \quad \text{Or,} \quad E=Ca_0^2e^{-2kt},$$

where C is a constant of proportionality.

After one full cycle (*i.e.*, one full time-period T), the energy is, say.

$$E_T=Ca_0{}^2e^{-2k(t+T)}=Ee^{-2kT}$$

$\therefore$ *loss of energy in one time-period* $T=E-Ee^{-2kT}=E-E\left(1-2kT+\frac{4k^2T^2}{2!}\ldots\right)$

$$=E-E(1-2kT)=2kET,$$

neglecting higher terms in k, since k is small.

And $\therefore$ *rate of loss of energy over a time-period, i.e.,* $P=2kET/T=2kE=E/\tau$.

8.4 QUALITY FACTOR Q

As its very name indicates, it is a factor which measures the quality of a harmonic oscillator in so far as damping is concerned. *The less the damping, the better the quality of the harmonic oscillator as an oscillator and, therefore, the higher its quality factor Q.*

It is also referred to as the figure of merit of a harmonic oscillator and is defined as 2π *times the ratio between the energy stored and the energy lost per period.* Being thus a mere number, it is a *dimensionless quantity.*

Thus, $$Q = 2\pi \frac{\text{Energy stored}}{\text{Energy lost per period}} = \frac{2\pi E}{PT},$$

where P is the *average loss of energy over a period* $= E/\tau$. (See § 8.3 above)

And, since $2\pi/T = \omega$, we have $Q = \dfrac{E_\omega}{P} = \dfrac{E_\omega}{E/\tau} = \omega\tau$.

In the case of low damping, $\omega = \omega_0$ and, therefore, $Q = \omega_0\tau$.

But, as we know, $$\omega_0 = \sqrt{\frac{C}{m}} \quad \text{and} \quad \tau = \frac{m}{\gamma}. \text{ So that,}$$

$$Q = \sqrt{\frac{C}{m}} \cdot \frac{m}{\gamma} = \frac{\sqrt{Cm}}{\gamma}.$$

clearly indicating that the lower the value of γ, *i.e.*, the lower the damping, the higher the value of Q, *i.e.*, as $\gamma \to 0, Q \to \infty$.

Again; we know that the energy of a damped harmonic oscillator is given by $E = E_0 e^{-t/\tau}$. Hence, if $t = \tau$, we have $E = E_0 e^{-1} = E_0/e$, *i.e.*, the energy of the oscillator falls to $1/e$*th* of its initial value in time $t = \tau$. In this interval of time, the oscillator executes $(\omega_0/2\pi)\tau$ or $Q/2\pi$ oscillations, so that *the phase of the oscillator changes by Q.*

This gives us another method of defining Q, *viz. as the phase change brought about in the oscillator in the time taken by its energy to fall to 1/eth of its initial value.*

8.5 IMPORTANT EXAMPLES OF DAMPED HARMONIC OSCILLATORS

I. Dead beat and ballistic galvanometers. In the case of a moving coil galvanometer, the turning of the coil under the *deflecting couple* is opposed, as we know, by a *restoring couple* $C\theta$, where C is the torsional couple per unit twist in the suspension fibre (equal to $\pi n r^4/2l$) and θ, the deflection of the coil at the given instant t. In addition to this, there are two other damping couples acting on the coil, *viz.*, (*i*) a couple $-\gamma\, d\theta/dt$ due to the *mechanical damping* on account of viscosity of air and the elastic hysteresis of the suspension fibre, where γ is the damping coefficient for this type of damping and (*ii*) a couple $-(\wedge/R)\, d\theta/dt$ due to *electromagnetic damping, i.e.*, damping on account of the induced current set up in the coil, which apart from being directly proportional to its velocity $d\theta/dt$, is also inversely proportional to its resistance and directly proportional to the magnetic flux generated through it and its area etc., all included in the constant $\wedge$.

If, therefore, I be the moment of inertia of the coil or the suspended system about the suspension fibre, the *equation of motion* of the system is

$$I\frac{d^2\theta}{dt^2} = -\gamma\frac{d\theta}{dt} - \frac{\wedge}{R}\frac{d\theta}{dt} - C\theta.$$

Or, $$\frac{d^2\theta}{dt^2} + \left(\frac{\gamma + \wedge/R}{I}\right)\frac{d\theta}{dt} + \frac{C\theta}{I} = 0.$$

Now, $(\gamma + \wedge/R)I = 2k = 1/\tau$ and $C/I = \omega_0^2$, where ω_0 is the undamped angular frequency of the system.

So that, $$\frac{d^2\theta}{dt^2} + 2k\frac{d\theta}{dt} + \omega_0^2\theta = 0.$$

on, $$\frac{d^2\theta}{dt^2} + \frac{1}{\tau}\frac{d\theta}{dt} + \omega_0^2\theta, = 0.$$

This differential equation of motion of the coil, it will be readily seen, is the same as that of a damped harmonic oscillator, discussed under § 8.2, except that we have here an angular, instead of a linear, displacement. And, therefore, its solution, as explained there, is given by

$$\theta = A_1 e^{\left(-k+\sqrt{k^2-\omega_0^2}\right)t} + A_2 e^{\left(-k-\sqrt{k^2-\omega_0^2}\right)t}$$

where the values of the arbitrary constants A_1 and A_2, obtained in the same manner, are

$$\frac{1}{2}\theta_0\left(1+\frac{k}{\sqrt{k^2-\omega_0^2}}\right) \text{ and } \frac{1}{2}\theta_0\left(1-\frac{k}{\sqrt{k^2-\omega_0^2}}\right)$$

respectively, with θ_0 as the initial or maximum deflection.

So that, $$\theta = \frac{1}{2}\theta_0 e^{-kt}\left[\left(1+\frac{k}{\sqrt{k^2-\omega_0^2}}\right)e^{(\sqrt{k^2-\omega_0^2})t} + \left(1-\frac{k}{\sqrt{k^2-\omega_0^2}}\right)e^{(-\sqrt{k^2-\omega_0^2})t}\right]$$

As before, *three cases* arise:

(*i*) **When** $k > \omega_0$. This is the case of overdamping or heavy damping and $k^2 > \omega_0^2$ or $\left(\frac{\gamma+\wedge/R}{4I^2}\right)^2 > \frac{C}{I}$. So that, both the terms in the expression for θ above have an exponential term with a negative power and θ, therefore, decays exponentially without changing sign. *The motion is thus non-oscillatory, aperiodic or dead beat.*

Hence, **for a galvanometer to be dead beat,** $k = 1/2\tau = (\gamma + \wedge/R)/2I$ *must be large, i.e.,* (*a*) *I, the M.I. of the coil or the suspended system must be small,* (*b*) *R, the resistance of the coil should be small,* (*c*) *∧ should be large,* indicating that *the induced currents set up in the coil and hence the magnetic flux through it should be large, i.e., the coil must be wound on a conducting frame* and (*d*) *the damping coefficient γ for mechanical damping must be large.*

(*ii*) When $k = \omega_0$, or $(\gamma + \wedge/R)^2/4I^2 = C/I$. In this case, the damping is critical (See § 8.2, above) and the coil comes back to its original position quickly.

(*iii*) When $k < \omega_0$ or $(\gamma + \wedge/R)^2/4I^2 < C/I$. This is *the case of underdamping* when, as explained under § 8.2, (3), the solution of the differential equation of motion of the coil is of the form $\theta = \theta_0 e^{-kt}\sin(\omega t + \phi)$, where $\omega = \sqrt{\omega_0^2 - k^2} = \sqrt{C/I - (\gamma+\wedge/R)^2/4I^2}$ and, therefore, frequency $n = \omega/2\pi$.

The amplitude here goes on decreasing exponentially with time.

A galvanometer used for measuring charges must have the minimum damping and is called a **ballistic galvanometer**. Thus, in a ballistic galvanometer, $k = 1/2\tau = (\gamma + \wedge/R)/2I$ must be as small as possible and, therefore, the conditions for it are just the opposite of those for a dead beat galvanometer, *i.e.,* (*a*) *I must be large,* (*b*) *R must be large,* (*c*) *the mechanical damping coefficient γ must be small* and (*d*) *∧ should be small, i.e., the magnetic flux through the coil should be small and* *it should, therefore, be wound on a non-conducting frame of ebonite, ivory, bamboo etc.*—all these conditions being the very opposite of those required for a dead beat type of galvanometer.

The first throw of the ballistic galvanometer is corrected for any damping that may still be present, with the help of the logarithmic decrement of the instrument.

II—The L-C-R circuit. Any electrical circuit containing inductance (L), capacitance (C) and resistance (R) is an excellent example of a damped harmonic oscillation, with the resistance, by itself alone, playing the part of a resistive or dissipative force analogous to that of friction or viscosity in the case of mechanical oscillations.

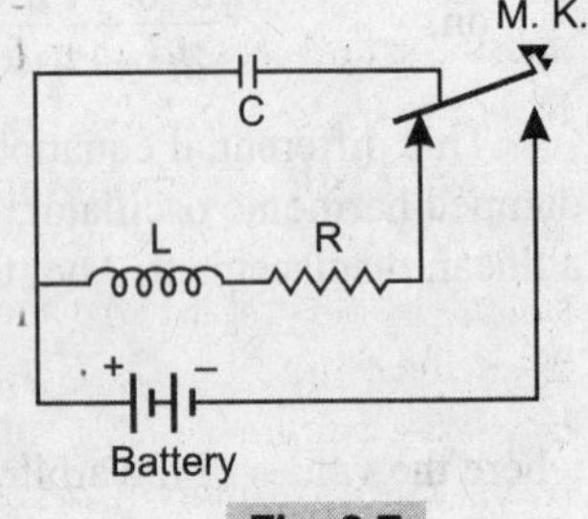

Fig. 8.7

Thus, suppose we have such an electrical circuit, connected up as shown in Fig. 8.7, such that on pressing the knob of the Morse Key, *M.K.*, the capacitor gets charged by the battery and on releasing it, the battery is thrown out of the circuit and the capacitor (C) connected in series with the inductance (L) and the resistance (R) through which it then discharges itself.

Suppose further that at a given instant t, the charge on the capacitor is Q, the current flowing through the circuit (consisting of capacitor, inductance and resistance, with the battery thrown out) is I, so that the *induced emf* across the inductance is LdI/dt and the potential difference across the resistance is RI. Then, since there is now no external *emf* in the circuit (the battery being out), we have, in accordance with Kirchoff's law,

$$RI+\frac{Q}{C} = -L\frac{dI}{dt}. \quad \text{Or,} \quad L\frac{dI}{dt}+RI+\frac{Q}{C}=0,$$

But $I = dQ/dt$ and, therefore, $L\dfrac{d^2Q}{dt^2}+R\dfrac{dQ}{dt}+\dfrac{Q}{C}=0.$

Or, $$\frac{d^2Q}{dt^2}+\frac{R}{L}\frac{dQ}{dt}+\frac{Q}{LC} = 0. \qquad \text{...I}$$

This equation is of the same form as that for a damped harmonic oscillator (equation (*vi*), page 378), with the difference that displacement x there is replaced by charge Q here, $2k$ (or $1/\tau$) by R/L and ω_0^2 by $1/LC$.

Proceeding in the same manner, therefore, we find the solution of the equation to be

$$Q = A_1e^{(-k+\sqrt{k^2-\omega_0^2})t} + A_2e^{(-k-\sqrt{k^2-\omega_0^2})t},$$

where the values of the arbitrary constants A_1 and A_2 respectively are

$$\frac{1}{2}Q_0\left(1+\frac{k}{\sqrt{k^2-\omega_0^2}}\right) \text{ and } \frac{1}{2}Q_0\left(1-\frac{k}{\sqrt{k^2-\omega_0^2}}\right).$$

Thus, $$Q = \frac{1}{2}Q_0e^{-kt}\left[\left(1+\frac{k}{\sqrt{k^2-\omega_0^2}}\right)e^{(\sqrt{k^2-\omega_0^2})t} + \left(1-\frac{k}{\sqrt{k^2-\omega_0^2}}\right)e^{(-\sqrt{k^2-\omega_0^2})t}\right] \qquad \text{...II}$$

Again, the following three cases arise:

(*i*) **When the damping is large,** *i.e.*, when $k^2 > \omega_0^2$ or $(R^2/4L^2) > 1/LC$ or $R^2 > 4L/C$. In this case, both the terms in expression II for Q above have exponential terms with a negative power, so that the charge decays exponentially with time, without changing sign, as shown by curve (*i*) in

Fig. 8.8, and there is thus no oscillation, *i.e., the discharge of the capacitor is non-oscillatory or aperiodic.*

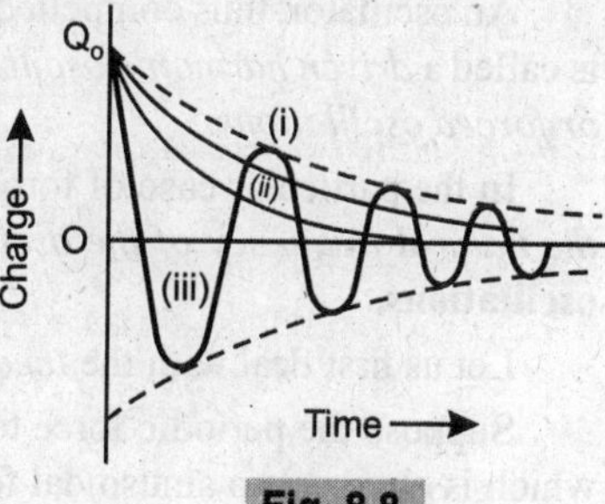

Fig. 8.8

(*ii*) **When the damping is critical,** *i.e.*, when $k^2 = \omega_0^2$ or $R^2/4L^2 = 1/LC$ or $R^2 = 4L/C$. Here, the discharge becomes just aperiodic and dies down in the shortest possible time, as shown by curve (*ii*) in Fig. 8.8.

(*iii*) **With the damping is small,** *i.e.*, when $k^2 < \omega_0^2$ or $R^2/4L^2 < 1/LC$ or $R^2 < 4L/C$. This is the case of interest to us, since here the solution of the equation of motion of the charge takes the form $Q = Q_0\, e^{-kt} \sin(\omega t + \phi)$, *viz*, that of a *damped harmonic oscillator. The charge on the capacitor thus repeatedly acquires positive and negative values before ultimately decaying to zero. The discharge curve* of the capacitor is of the from shown by curve (*iii*) in Fig. 8.8 above, which it will be recalled, is identical in form with the displacement curve of a damped harmonic oscillator, shown in Fig. 8.5 and is similarly bound by the curves $Q = Q_0\, e^{-kt}$ and $Q = -Q_0 e^{-kt}$.

Thus, *the discharge of the capacitor is oscillatory in character, the oscillations being damped as in the case of a damped harmonic oscillator.*

Differentiating the expression for Q with respect to t, we have

$$\frac{dQ}{dt} = \frac{dQ_0}{dt} e^{-kt} \sin(\omega t + \phi).$$

Or, since $dQ/dt = I$ and $dQ_0/dt = I_0$, the *maximum value* or the *amplitude* of the current, we have

$$I = I_0 e^{-kt} \sin(\omega t + \phi)$$

The frequency of the oscillations is $n = \dfrac{\omega}{2\pi} = \dfrac{\sqrt{\omega_0^2 - k^2}}{2\pi}$

$$= \frac{1}{2\pi}\sqrt{\frac{1}{LC} - \frac{R^2}{4L^2}}.$$

That the resistance R alone is responsible for the damping of the oscillations in this case (the energy dissipated appearing as heat) is clear from the fact that in the absence of R, *i.e.*, if $R = 0$, we shall have $n = \dfrac{1}{2\pi}\sqrt{\dfrac{1}{LC}}$, the same as that of an L–C circuit, with no damping of the oscillations.

The *quality factor of the circuit,* $Q = \omega\tau = \omega/2k = L\omega/R$, where $\omega = \sqrt{\omega_0^2 - k^2} = \sqrt{\omega_0^2 - R/4l^2}$.

Since R is small, $\omega \approx \omega_0$ and, therefore, quality factor $Q = L\omega_0/R$.

It will be readily seen that *in a purely inductive circuit, i.e., with R = 0, the quality factor Q will be infinite.*

8.6 DRIVEN HARMONIC OSCILLATOR

When a harmonic oscillator oscillates in a medium like air, its oscillations, as we know, get damped, *i.e.*, its amplitude falls exponentially with time to *zero*.

If, however, we apply an *external periodic force* to the oscillator, of a frequency *not necessarily the same as its own natural frequency,* a sort of tussle ensues between the damping force tending to retard its motion and the applied force tending to continue it. So that, after some initial erratic movements, it ultimately succumbs to the applied or the driving force and *settles down to oscillating with the forcing or the driving frequency* (*i.e., the frequency of the applied or the driving force*) *and a constant amplitude and phase so long as the applied force remains operative.*

An oscillator, thus compelled to oscillate with a frequency other than its own natural frequency, is called a *driven harmonic oscillator* and the oscillations executed by it are, therefore, called *driven or forced oscillations.*

In the particular case of forced oscillations *when the frequency of applied force is the same as the natural frequency of the oscillator itself, we have the phenomenon of* **resonance** *or* **resonant oscillations.**

Let us first deal with the *theory of a forced or driven oscillator*, in general.

Suppose the periodic force to which a damped harmonic oscillator is subjected is $F = F_0 \sin pt$ which is obviously a sinusoidal force, of *amplitude* (or *maximum value*). F_0 and frequency $p/2\pi$.

Since the damping and the restoring forces acting on the oscillator are respectively $-\gamma\, dx/dt$ and $-Cx$, its *equation of motion* becomes

$$m\frac{d^2x}{dt^2} = -\gamma\frac{dx}{dt} - Cx + F. \text{ Or, } \frac{d^2x}{dt^2} + \frac{\gamma}{m}\frac{dx}{dt} + \frac{C}{m}x = \frac{F_0}{m}\sin pt.$$

Now, $\gamma/m = 2k$ and $C/m = \omega_0^2$, where ω_0 is the *natural angular frequency* of the oscillator. So that, putting $\frac{F_0}{m}\sin pt = f_0 \sin pt$, representing the *applied force per unit mass*, we have

$$\frac{d^2x}{dt^2} + 2k\frac{dx}{dt} + \omega_0^2 x = f_0 \sin pt. \qquad \text{...I}$$

When the *steady state* has been attained, *i.e.*, when, after the tussle between the damping and the applied forces, the oscillator has settled down to oscillate with the forcing frequency $p/2\pi$ and a constant amplitude, let us try $x = A \sin (pt - \theta)$ as a particular solution of its equation of motion (*I*, above), where θ is the possible phase difference between the applied force and the displacement of the oscillator.

Then, clearly, $dx/dt = A\,p \cos (pt - \theta)$ and $\frac{d^2x}{dt^2} = -A\,p^2 \sin (pt - \theta)$.

Substituting these values in equation *I*, we have

$$-Ap^2 \sin (pt - \theta) + 2k\,Ap \cos (pt - \theta) + \omega_0^2 A \sin (pt - \theta)$$
$$= f_0 \sin [(pt - \theta) + \theta]$$
$$= f_0 \sin (pt - \theta) \cos \theta + f_0 \cos (pt - \theta) \sin \theta$$

Or, $A(\omega_0^2 - p^2) \sin (pt - \theta) + 2k\,Ap \cos (pt - \theta)$

$$= f_0 \cos \theta \sin (pt - \theta) + f_0 \sin \theta \cos (pt - \theta) \qquad \text{...II}$$

If this solution is to hold good for all values of t, the coefficients of $\sin (pt - \theta)$ on either side of equation II must respectively be equal, *i.e.*, we must have

$$A\,(\omega_0^2 - p^2) = f_9 \cos \theta \qquad \text{...}(i)$$

and

$$2k\,Ap = f_0 \sin \theta. \qquad \text{...}(ii)$$

Squaring and adding relations (*i*) and (*ii*), we have

$$A^2(\omega_0^2 - p^2)^2 + 4k^2p^2 = f_0^2 \cos^2 \theta + f_0^2 \sin^2 \theta.$$

Or, $$A^2[(\omega_0^2 - p^2)^2 + 4k^2p^2] = f_0^2,$$

whence, $$A^2 = \frac{f_0^2}{(\omega_0^2 - p^2)^2 + 4k^2p^2}$$

$\therefore$ *amplitude of the driven or forced oscillator,*

$$A = \frac{f_0}{\sqrt{(\omega_0^2 - p^2)^2 + 4k^2p^2}}, \qquad \text{...}(III)$$

taking only the positive value of the square root. Its negative value will mean opposite phase but then θ too will change by π and there would, therefore, be no effect on the value of A.

And, $\tan\theta = \dfrac{f_0 \sin\theta}{f_0 \cos\theta} = \dfrac{2kp}{(\omega_0^2 - p^2)}$. Or, the *phase difference* between the driven or forced oscillator and the applied force is

$$\theta = \tan^{-1}\frac{2kp}{(\omega_0^2 - p^2)} \qquad ...(IV)$$

Since $\sin\theta$ is positive, it follows that θ *lies within the range 0 to* π. Substituting these values in the relation $x = A\sin(pt - \theta)$, we have

$$x = \frac{f_0}{\sqrt{(\omega_0^2 - p^2)^2 + 4k^2p^2}}\sin\left(pt - \tan^{-1}\frac{2kp}{\omega_0^2 - p^2}\right) \qquad ...(V)$$

which represents a *S.H.M.* of frequency $p/2\pi$, *i.e.*, the same as that of the driving force, but lagging behind it in phase by $\theta = \tan^{-1}[2kp/(\omega_0^2 - p^2)]$, where Q lies between 0 and π ($\because \sin\theta$ is positive).

Now, $x = A\sin(pt - \theta)$ is not really the complete solution of equation (*I*), which is an *inhomogeneous differential equation* because of the presence of the term $f_0 \sin pt$ which contains neither the variable (x) nor its derivative. The solution will, therefore, be complete only if we add to it a complementary function which is a solution of the related homogeneous equation $d^2x/dt^2 + 2k\,dx/dt + \omega^2 x = 0$.

One such solution, as we know, is $x = a_0 e^{-kt}\sin(\omega t + \phi)$, representing a damped harmonic oscillation, where $\omega = \sqrt{\omega_0^2 - k^2}$. The addition of this term $[x = a_0 e^{-kt}\sin(\omega t + \phi)]$ to the solution $x = A\sin(pt - \theta)$ does not in any way impair the validity of the latter, since the term, taken by itself, reduces the left hand side of equation (*I*) to zero.

The *complete solution of equation* (*I*) is thus $x = a_0 e^{-kt}\sin(\omega t + \phi) + A\sin(pt - \theta)$, where, obviously, the first term on the right hand side represents an initial damped oscillation of frequency $\omega/2\pi$, with its amplitude decaying *exponentially* to zero, and the second represents a forced or driven oscillation of the forcing (or driving) frequency $p/2\pi$ and a *constant amplitude A*. The former oscillation dies out quickly and the latter alone then remains effective, so that we are left with $x = A\sin(pt - \theta)$ as the *equation of motion of the forced or driven oscillation*, with its *amplitude A* and phase angle θ given by relations (*III*) and (*IV*) above respectively.

Now, when k has a finite value, greater than zero, the value of A will obviously be the maximum when the denominator in expression (*III*) (for A) has its minimum value,

i.e., when $\dfrac{d}{dp}[(\omega_0^2 - p^2)^2 + 4k^2p^2] = 0$,

Or, $\qquad -4(\omega_0^2 - p^2)p + 8k^2p = 0$,

i.e., when $p^2 = \omega_0^2 - 2k^2$ and, therefore, $p = \sqrt{\omega_0^2 - 2k^2}$.

Alternatively, we can obtain the same result by putting expression (*III*) for A in the form

$$A = \frac{f_0}{\sqrt{(p^2 + 2k^2 - \omega_0^2)^2 + 4k^2\omega_0^2 - 4k^4}}$$

from which also, A will be maximum when $p^2 + 2k^2 - \omega_0^2 = 0$, or when

$$p^2 = \omega_0^2 - 2k^2, \text{ or } p = \sqrt{\omega_0^2 - 2k^2}.$$

Thus, the amplitude of the driven oscillator will be the maximum when the driving frequency is $\sqrt{\omega_0^2 - 2k^2}/2\pi$, which we may denote by PR/π.

This phenomenon where for a particular driving frequency, the response or the amplitude of the driven oscillator is the maximum is called **amplitude resonance** and the particular driving frequency is referred to as the **resonant frequency.**

It may be noted that *this resonant frequency* $(p_R/2\pi = \sqrt{\omega_0^2 - 2k^2})/2\pi$ *is smaller than both the natural, undamped frequency* $\omega_0/2\pi$ *and the natural damped frequency* $\omega/2\pi = \sqrt{(\omega_0^2 - k^2)}/2\pi$ *of the oscillator.*

Substituting p_R for P in the relation for A above therefore, we have

$$\textit{maximum amplitude, } A_{max} = \frac{f_0}{2k(\omega_0^2 - k^2)^{1/2}} \qquad \text{... (i)}$$

Or, because $\omega_0^2 - 2k^2 = p^2$ or, $\omega_0^2 = p^2 + 2k^2$, we have

$$A_{max} = \frac{f_0}{2k(p^2 + k^2)^{1/2}}, \qquad \text{...(ii)}$$

showing that the smaller the value of k, the greater the value of A_{max}.

(*i*) It follows, therefore, that *in case the damping be low,* $p \approx \omega_0$ and the maximum amplitude in that case is $A_{max} = f_0/2k\,\omega_0 = f_0\tau/\omega_0$, ($\because \tau/2k = \tau$). Obviously then, *in the absence of damping* (*i.e.,* $k = 0$), the amplitude should become *infinite*. Since, however, damping is never actually zero, this never happens.

(*ii*) Again, if *the driving frequency be negligibly small or zero and the damping low,* we have

$$A = f_0/\omega_0^2.$$

Thus, the ratio of the response (or amplitude) of the oscillator when the driving frequency is zero or negligible is clearly

$$\frac{f_0\tau/\omega_0}{f_0/\omega_0^2} = \omega_0\tau = Q, \text{ the } \textit{quality factor of the oscillator,}$$

which thus actually controls its response or amplitude at this frequency.

It will also be easily seen that $f_0/\omega_0^2 = \dfrac{F_0/m}{C/m} = F_0/C$, showing that if *the driving frequency be negligible or zero and the damping low, the amplitude or the response of the oscillator is controlled neither by its mass nor any damping but simply by the force constant C.*

(*iii*) Finally, if *the damping be low and the driving frequency high,* so that ω_0 is negligible in comparison, the amplitude of the driven oscillator is given by

$$A = f_0/p^2,$$

indicating that *the response in this case falls as p increases.*

It is thus clear from the above discussion, as indeed from the expression for A itself, that the magnitude of A depends upon the relative values of p and ω_0 and that it is, infact, controlled by the factor $(\omega_0^2 - p^2)$. The natural consequence is that its value diminishes both when $p < \omega_0$ and when $p > \omega_0$. This will be amply clear from Fig. 8.9, where a number of curves are drawn showing the relation between p and the amplitude (A) of the driven oscillator for different cases of damping. It will be noted that

(*a*) *The peak value of amplitude,* $A_{max} = f_0/2k\,\omega_0 = f_0/2kp$ *occurs when* $(\omega_0^2 - p^2) = 0$, *i.e.,* when $P = \omega_0$, *which represents the condition for amplitude resonance.*

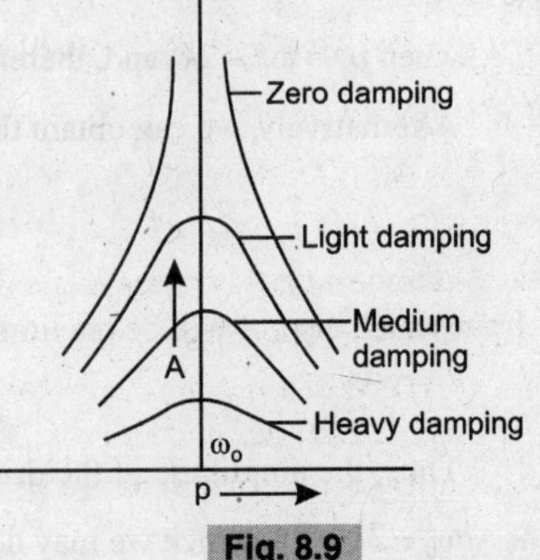

Fig. 8.9

And, if $k = 0$, *i.e.*, if there be no damping, A_{max} becomes infinite for this value of p, the curve being asymptotic to the y or the amplitude axis. Since damping is never zero, we do not obtain such a curve in actual practice but only those of the type shown for light and medium damping.

(*b*) *The peak value of A* (*i.e.*, A_{max}) *is naturally different for different cases of damping, becoming less and less as* ***damping increases,*** *but always occurs at, or very nearly at,* $(\omega_0^2 - p^2) = 0$ *provided the damping is* ***not too*** *large, i.e., the resonant frequency* (p_R) *in all these cases is equal to, or very nearly equal to,* ω_0.

Only in the case of heavy damping does the peak value occur at a frequency less than ω_0 *(being equal to* $\sqrt{\omega_0^2 - 2k^2}$ *).*

(*c*) *The fall in the curves on either side of* $(\omega_0^2 - p^2) = 0$ *is steeper in the case of smaller than in the case of heavier damping.*

8.7 SHARPNESS OF RESONANCE

We have just seen in Fig. 8.9 above how the curves between p and A fall more steeply on either side of the respective peak values of A when the damping is low than when it is high. *Thus, in the case of high damping, the amplitude remains more or less at its peak value over an appreciable range on either side of* $(\omega_0^2 - p^2) = 0$, *i.e.*, even when $p \neq \omega_0$. *The oscillator thus responds to a number of frequencies near about* ω_0 *on either side of it. The resonance in this case is, therefore, said to be* **flat**.

On the other hand, *if the damping be low,* the steep fall of curve on either side of the peak value of A shows that *the oscillator responds only to the frequency exactly equal to its natural frequency* ω_0 *and to none others. The resonance here is, therefore, said to be* **sharp**.

Thus, sharpness of resonance is, in a way, a measure of the rate of fall of amplitude from its maximum value at resonant frequency, on either side of it. *The sharper the fall in amplitude, the sharper the resonance.*

Familiar examples of *flat* and *sharp* resonance are the case of air column and the sonometer wire respectively. On account of the large value of k for air, the curve between p and A is comparatively flat at the peak value of A. The air column thus continues to respond to frequencies over an appreciable range on either side of its natural frequency ω_0, so much so that it becomes difficult to determine the correct length of the air column that *exactly* responds to the oscillator. This is, therefore, a case of *flat resonance.*

A sonometer wire, on the other hand, with little or no damping, responds only to one particular frequency, *viz.*, its own natural frequency ω_0 and to none others. *The resonance here is, therefore, sharp.*

Thus, *the smaller the damping, the sharper the resonance.* In fact, it can be shown that *sharpness of resonance is inversely proportional to the square of the damping constant k.*

8.8 PHASE OF THE DRIVEN OSCILLATOR

We have seen above (§ 8.6) how a forced or driven oscillation is represented by the equation $x = A \sin (pt - 0)$, indicating that it always lags a phase angle $\theta = \tan^{-1} [2kp/(\omega_0^2 - p^2)]$ behind the driving force $f_0 \sin pt$.

Obviously, this phase angle (θ) depends upon the damping and the relative values of ω_0 and p. *If the damping be negligible, the following three cases arise:*

(*i*) **When** $p < \omega_0$, *i.e., when the forcing or driving frequency is smaller than the natural, undamped frequency of the oscillator.* In this case, clearly, $\tan \theta = 2kp/(\omega_0^2 - p^2)$ will be a small positive quantity and *the driven oscillator will, therefore, very nearly be in phase with the driving force.*

(*ii*) **When** $p > \omega_0$, *i.e., when the driving frequency is greater than the natural, undamped frequency of the oscillator.* Here, obviously, tan θ will be a small negative quantity and *the driven oscillator will thus be out of phase with the driving force, i.e.,* the phase difference between the two will be π (or $T/2$).

(*ii*) **When** $p = \omega_0$, *i.e., when the driving frequency is equal to the natural, undamped frequency of the oscillator.* In this case, tan θ = ∞ and, therefore, θ = π/2, *i.e., the driven or forced oscillator will differ in phase from the driving force by* π/2 (or $T/4$). Thus, *its displacement will be the maximum when the driving force is zero and vice versa.*

It is clear from the above that *the phase angle θ changes from 0 to π but remains positive throughout.*

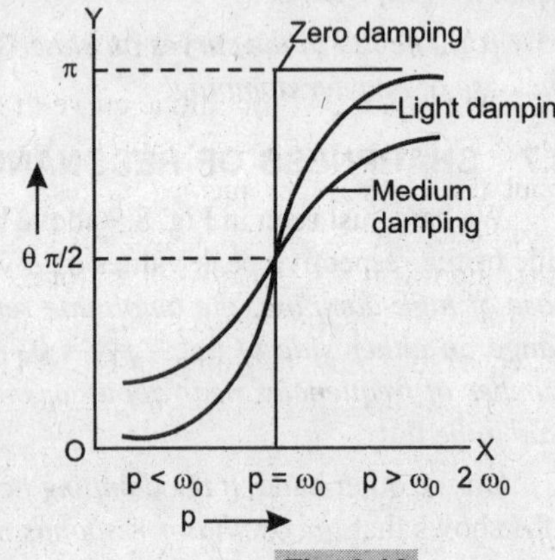

Fig. 8.10

The general nature of the phase lag of a driven oscillator as the driving frequency increases, passing through the value ω_0 (the natural or undamped frequency of the oscillator) will be clear from the curves in Fig. 8.10, drawn for different cases of damping. The following points emerge:

(*i*) When the damping is zero, the curve runs along the frequency axis from 0 to ω_0 and again parallel to it from ω_0 to $2\omega_0$ but removed from the first part by π. This means, in other words, that for $p << \omega_0$, θ = 0 but when $p >> \omega_0$, θ suddenly jumps to π.

(*ii*) With damping present, the phase lag (θ) increases from 0 to π/2 as the driving frequency p increases from 0 to ω_0 and then approaches π as p continues to increase beyond ω_0.

(*iii*) The rate of change of the phase angle is more rapid when the damping is low than when it is high.

(*iv*) Except at very high damping, all curves pass through π/2 when $p = \omega_0$, *i.e.,* amplitude resonance occurs when the driving frequency is equal to the natural, undamped frequency of the oscillator, or the resonance frequency in all these cases remains ω_0.

8.9 VELOCITY RESONANCE

The displacement of a driven oscillator at a given instant t, is, as we know, given by

$$x = A \sin(pt - \theta) = \frac{f_0}{\sqrt{(\omega_0^2 - p^2)^2 + 4k^2p^2}} \sin(pt - \theta) \qquad \text{...I[§ 8.6]}$$

∴ the *velocity of the driven oscillator at that instant* is $v = dx/dt = pA \cos(pt - \theta) = v_0 \cos(pt - \theta)$, because

$$pA = \frac{f_0}{\sqrt{(\omega_0^2 - p^2)^2 + 4k^2p^2}} = v_0.$$

Or, $$v = v_0 \sin(pt - \theta + \pi/2),$$
showing that *the velocity leads the displacement in phase by* π/2.

Clearly, the *velocity amplitude* $v_0 = pA = f_0 p/\sqrt{(\omega_0^2 - p^2)^2 + 4k^2p^2}$ and 0, as we know, equal to $\tan^{-1}[2kp/(\omega_0^2 - p^2)]$.

Thus, *the velocity amplitude* (v_0) *varies with p, being zero when p = 0 and the maximum when* $p = p_R = \omega_0$, this maximum value being $f_0/2k = f_6\tau$.

This acquiring of its maximum velocity by a driven oscillator is spoken of as velocity resonance and obviously occurs when the driving frequency (p) *is equal to the resonant frequency* (p_R), *equal to the natural, undamped frequency of the oscillator,* $\omega_0 = C/m$.

For all other values of p, greater or smaller than $p_R = \omega_0$, the velocity amplitude is naturally smaller, because the displacement amplitude (A) is then much smaller.

Now, as we know, the displacement at resonance lags in phase by $\pi/2$ behind the driving force and, as we have just seen, the velocity, then, leads the displacement in phase by $\pi/2$, *i.e.*, the displacement also lags in phase by $\pi/2$ behind the velocity. Obviously, therefore, *at resonance, the velocity of the driven oscillator is in phase with the driving force.* This is, therefore, the most favourable circumstance for the transference of energy from the driving force (F) to the driven oscillator, for both F and v being in the same phase, with v at its maximum, the rate of transference of energy, Fv, has its highest positive value.

8.10 HALF WIDTH OF RESONANCE CURVE

The frequency—amplitude curve of a driven oscillator, (Fig. 8.9), is, as we know, symmetrical (for small damping) about the resonant frequency $p_R = \omega_0$, indicating that its amplitude, which is the maximum (A_{max}) at p_R, falls on either side of it. There must, therefore, be a frequency p_H, say, for which the amplitude will be half of the maximum, *i.e.*, equal to $A_{max}/2$, as shown in Fig. 8.11.

The change Δp, (from pR to pH), in the value of the driving frequency p for which the amplitude of the driven harmonic oscillator falls from its maximum value A_{max} to half this maximum value $A_{max}/2$ is called the half width of the resonance curve.

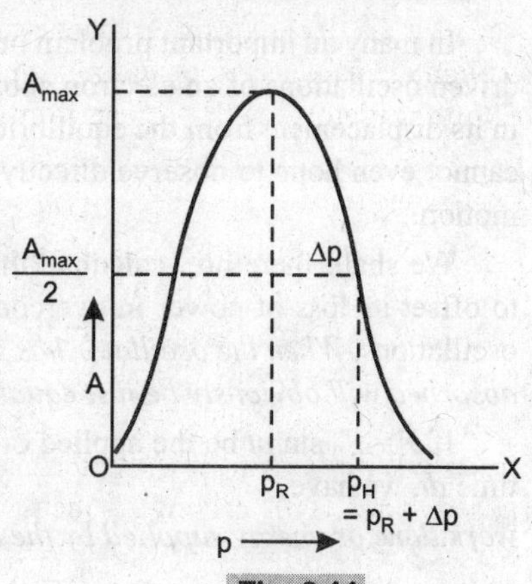

Fig. 8.11

Thus, *half width of the resonance curve*, $\Delta p = |p_H - p_R|$.

Now, as we know, (§ 8.6, Expression (*i*)),

$$A_{max} = \frac{f_0}{2k(\omega_0^2 - k^2)^{1/2}} = \frac{f_0}{\sqrt{4k^2\omega_0^2 - 4k^4}}.$$

$$\therefore \quad A_{max}/2 = \frac{f_0}{2\sqrt{4k^2\omega_0^2 - 4k^4}} \quad \ldots(i)$$

Now,

$$A = \frac{f_0}{\sqrt{(\omega_0^2 - p^2)^2 + 4k^2p^2}}$$

$$= \frac{f_0}{\sqrt{(\omega_0^2 - 2k^2 - p^2)^2 + 4k^2\omega_0^2 - 4k^4}} \quad \text{[§ 8.6, Exp. III.]}$$

So that, $A_{max}/2$ also $= \dfrac{f_0}{\sqrt{(\omega_0^2 - 2k^2 - p_{H^2})^2 + 4k^2\omega_0^2 - 4k^4}}$ [$\because p \neq pH$ when $A = A_{max}/2$.]...(*ii*)

From the two values of $A_{max}/2$, as given by relations (*i*) and (*ii*), we, therefore, have

$(\omega_0^2 - 2k^2 - p_H{}^2)^2 + 4k^2\omega_0^2 - 4k^4 = 4(4k^2\omega_0^2 - 4k^4)$

But, as we know, $(\omega_0^2 - 2k^2) = p_R{}^2$. And, therefore,

$$(p_R{}^2 - p_H{}^2)^2 = 3(4k^2\omega_0^2 - 4k^4) = 3(4k^2p_R{}^2 - 4k^4) \quad [\because \omega_0 = pR.]$$

Since with low damping, k is small and, therefore, $4k^4$ quite negligible, we have

$$(p_R{}^2 - p_H{}^2)^2 = 3(4k^2p_R{}^2), \text{ whence, } p_R{}^2 - p_H{}^2 = \pm\sqrt{3}(2kp_R).$$

Or, $$p_H^2 = p_R^2 \mp \sqrt{3}(2kp_R) = p_R^2\left(1 \mp \sqrt{3}\frac{2k}{p_R}\right).$$

Or, $$p_H = p_R\left(1 \mp \sqrt{3}\frac{2k}{p_R}\right)^{1/2} \approx p_R\left(1 \mp \frac{\sqrt{3}k}{p_R}\right) = p_R \mp \sqrt{3}k.$$

$\therefore$ *for low damping, half width of the resonance curve,* $\Delta p = (p_H - p_R) \approx \sqrt{3}k.$

It is thus possible to estimate the value of the damping constant, as also, of course, that of ω_0, from the frequency-amplitude curve of a driven harmonic oscillator.

8.11 POWER ABSORPTION

In many an important problem on driven harmonic oscillators, as for example, in discussing the driven oscillations of an electron about a point of stable equilibrium, we are interested not so much in its displacement from the equilibrium, position—which, in the case of an electron, at any rate, we cannot even hope to observe directly—as in the energy absorbed by the oscillator to keep itself in motion.

We shall, therefore, calculate the average power absorbed per cycle by the driven oscillator to offset its loss of power in overcoming the frictional or resistive forces and thus to maintain its oscillations. *When the oscillator has settled down to a steady state of oscillation, the average power absorbed will obviously be just equal to the average power dissipated.*

If $F = F_0 \sin pt$ be the applied or the driving force and dx, the displacement of the oscillator in time dt, we have

work done or energy supplied by the applied force to the oscillator, is given by

$$dE = Fdx = F\frac{dx}{dt}dt, \text{ whence, } \frac{dE}{dt} = F\frac{dx}{dt}. \quad \ldots(i)$$

Now, $F = F_0 \sin pt = mf_0 \sin pt$ and

$$\frac{dx}{dt} = \frac{pf_0}{\sqrt{(\omega_0^2 - p^2)^2 + 4k^2p^2}}\cos(pt - \theta) \quad \ldots(ii)$$

[From relation I, § 8.9]

Substituting these values in relation (*i*) above, we have

power absorbed by the oscillator, $P = \dfrac{dE}{dt} = F\dfrac{dx}{dt}$

$$= mf_0 \sin pt \frac{pf_0 \cos(pt - \theta)}{\sqrt{(\omega_0^2 - p^2)^2 + 4k^2p^2}}.$$

Or, $$P = F\frac{dx}{dt} = \frac{mf_0^2 p}{\sqrt{(\omega_0^2 - p^2)^2 + 4k^2p^2}}\sin pt \cos(pt - \theta).$$

To obtain the *average power,* $P_{(av)}$, *over a full cycle or time-period,* we note that the average value of $\sin pt \cos(pt - \theta)$

$= \frac{1}{2}[\sin(2pt - \theta) - \sin\theta]$ over a cycle or time-period T is

$$\frac{1}{T}\int_0^T \frac{1}{2}[\sin(2pt - \theta) - \sin\theta]dt = \frac{1}{2}\sin\theta.$$

And, since $2k\,Ap = f_0 \sin\theta$ and $A = \dfrac{f_6}{\sqrt{(\omega_0^2 - p^2)^2 + 4k^2p^2}}$, [See § 8.6 (*ii*) and III]

we have
$$\sin\theta = \frac{2kAp}{f_0} = \frac{2kp}{f_0}\cdot\frac{f_0}{\sqrt{(\omega_0^2-p^2)^2+4k^2p^2}}.$$
$$= \frac{2kp}{\sqrt{(\omega_0^2-p^2)^2+4k^2p^2}}.$$

So that, average value of sin pt cos $(pt-\theta)$ over a full cycle or time-period
$$= \frac{1}{2}\sin\theta = \frac{1}{2}\frac{2kp}{\sqrt{(\omega_0^2-p^2)^2+4k^2p^2}}.$$
$$= \frac{kp}{\sqrt{(\omega_0^2-p^2)^2+4k^2p^2}}$$

∴ *average power,*
$$P_{(av)} = \frac{mf_0^2\,p}{\sqrt{(\omega_0^2-p^2)^2+4k^2p^2}}\cdot\frac{kp}{\sqrt{(\omega_0^2-p^2)^2+4k^2p^2}}$$
$$= \frac{mkf_0^2\,p^2}{(\omega_0^2-p^2)+4k^2p^2} \quad ...(iii)$$

But $\frac{f_0^2 p^2}{(\omega_0^2-p^2)^2+4k^2p^2} = v_0^2$, where v_0 is the velocity amplitude (See § 8.9).

Therefore, *average power absorbed by the driven oscillator per cycle or time-period,*
$$P_{(av)} = mkv_0^2 = mv_0^2/2\tau = \gamma v_0^2/2 \quad [\because k = 1/2\tau \text{ and } m/\tau = \gamma.] \quad ...(iv)$$

It is clear from relation (*iii*) above that the average power absorbed will have its *maximum value*, P_{max}, when $p = \omega_2$. So that,

maximum power absorbed, $P_{max} = \frac{1}{4}\frac{mf_0^2}{k} = \frac{1}{2}mf_0^2\tau.$ ...(*v*)

Thus, $\omega_0 = p_R$, *the resonant frequency for velocity also turns out to be the resonant frequency for the average power absorbed.*

It may be noted that *the maximum power is absorbed at the frequency of velocity resonance,* $p_R = \omega_0$, *and not at the frequency of amplitude resonance,* $\sqrt{\omega_0^2 - 2k^2}$.

Half width of average power absorbed versus frequency curve. As we have just seen above (expression *v*), the maximum value of average power absorbed is $P_{max} = mf_0^2/4k$ at resonance frequency $p_R = \omega_0$. So that, half its maximum value of average power absorbed = $P_{max}/2 = mf_0^2/8k$. Let us calculate the frequency at which this is the average power of absorbed.

We have relation (*iii*) above for average power absorbed ($P_{(av)}$). So that, if $P_{(av)} = P_{max}/2 = mf_0{}^2/8k$, we have

$$P(av) = \frac{mkf_0^2\,p^2}{(\omega_0^2-p^2)^2+4k^2p^2} = \frac{mf_0^2}{8k},$$

whence, $\frac{kp^2}{(\omega_0^2-p^2)^2+4k^2p^2} = \frac{1}{8k}.$

Or, $(\omega_0^2-p^2)^2 + 4k^2p^2 = 8k^2p^2.$

Or, $(\omega_0^2-p^2)^2 = 4k^2p^2,$

whence, $\omega_0^2 - p_0^2 = \pm 2kp$

Or, $\omega_0 - p = \pm\frac{2kp}{\omega_0+p} = \frac{2k}{\omega_0/p+1}$

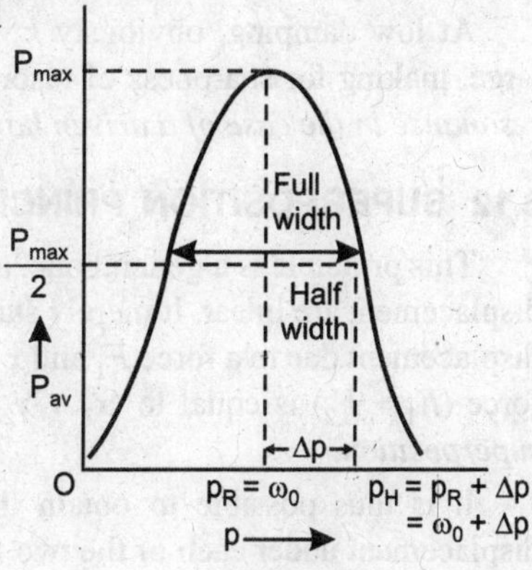

Fig. 8.12

$$= \pm\frac{2k}{2} = +k. \qquad [\because \omega_0 \approx p.]$$

Thus, $p = \omega_0 \mp k = p_H$, say.

Or, since $\omega_0 = p_R$, we have $|p_H - p_R| = \Delta p = k$.

This change Δp, (from p_R to p_H), in the value of the driving frequency p for which the average power absorbed by the driven oscillator falls from its maximum value P_{max} to half this value $P_{max}/2$ is called the half width of the average power absorbed versus driving frequency curve, shown in Fig. 8.12.

So that, *half width of the average power absorbed versus driving frequency curve*, $\Delta p = k = 1/2\tau$.

Quality factor Q of the driven oscillator. We know that $Q = \omega_0\tau$. (§8.4).

Here, $\Delta p = k = 1/2\tau$ and $\therefore\ \tau = 1/2\ \Delta p$.

So that, $Q = \omega_0\tau = \omega_6/2\Delta p = \dfrac{\textit{Resonance frequency}}{\textit{Full width of power-frequency curve at half maximum power}}$

It may, however, also be obtained directly as follows:

By definition, $$Q = 2\pi\frac{\textit{averge energy stored}}{\textit{energy dissipated per cycle or per time-period}}$$

$$= \frac{E_{(av)}}{P_{(av)} \times T}$$

Now, at any instant, $E = K.E. + P.E.$

$$= \frac{1}{2}mp^2A^2\cos^2(pt - \theta) + \frac{1}{2}m\omega_0^2A^2\sin^2(pt - \theta).$$

Since the average value of $\cos^2(pt - \theta)$ and $\sin^2(pt - \theta)$ over a whole time-period is $\frac{1}{2}$ each and the *average power absorbed*, $P_{(av)} = mv_0^2/2\tau = mA^2p^2/2\tau$, we have

$$Q = 2\pi\frac{\frac{1}{4}mp^2A^2 + \frac{1}{4}m\omega_0^2A^2}{(mA^2p^2/2\tau)\times T} = 2\pi\frac{\frac{1}{4}mA^2(p^2 + \omega_0^2)}{(mA^2p^2/2\tau)\times(2\pi/6)} = \frac{1}{2}\frac{(p^2 + \omega_0^2)}{p}\tau \qquad [\because T = 2\pi/p.]$$

Or, $$Q = \frac{1}{2}(p + \omega_0^2/p)\tau = \frac{1}{2}(1 + \omega_0^2/p^2)p\tau.$$

Since at, or near, resonance, $p = \omega_0$, we have

$$Q = \frac{1}{2}(2)p\tau = p\tau = \omega_0\tau = \omega_0/2\ \Delta p, \text{ as obtained above.}$$

At low damping, obviously $k = 1/2\tau$ will be small or τ large, so that $Q = \omega_0\tau$ will also be large, making for sharpness of resonance. Thus, the *quality factor Q is a measure of sharpness of resonance in the case of a driven harmonic oscillator.*

8.12 SUPERPOSITION PRINCIPLE

This principle is a general one, applicable to all cases where the equations governing motion or displacement are linear. It merely states that *solutions in all such cases are additive, i.e.,* if x_1 be the displacement due to a force F_1 and x_2 due to another force F_2, the displacement due to the combined force $(F_1 + F_2)$ is equal to $(x_1 + x_2)$. This process of vector addition of displacements is termed *superposition*.

It is thus possible to obtain the displacement under the combined force $(F_1 + F_2)$ if the displacement under each of the two forces individually be known.

The principle is also applicable to electromagnetic waves because the relationship between electrical and magnetic fields is linear. It, however, fails to apply the moment the displacements or disturbances are large and the ordinary linear laws of mechanical action cease to hold. Thus, in the case of sound, it certainly applies to ordinary sound waves but not to shock waves caused by violent explosions.

In our present case of harmonic oscillators it applies because of the linearity of their equations of motion. It ceases to apply when this linearity is lost. Thus, it does not apply in the case of an harmonic oscillators or even in the case of harmonic oscillators with large displacements when the linear relationship given by Hooke's law no longer holds.

In view of this principle, therefore, we can look upon the response of a harmonic oscillator to a sinusoidal force as being the sum of its responses to a number of components of various frequencies into which the given force may be imagined to be resolved.

8.13 DRIVEN L-C-R CIRCUIT

An *LCR* circuit, *i.e.*, a circuit containing an inductance (L), a capacitance (C) and a resistance (R) in series, (Fig. 8.13), functions as a driven oscillator if it be connected to an external source of alternating *emf* to supply the necessary energy to maintain the oscillations.

If I be the current in the circuit at a given instant, with Q as the charge on the capacitor at that instant, we have *potential difference across the inductance* $= -L dI/dt$, *potential difference across the capacitor* $= Q/C$ and *potential difference across the resistance* $= RI$.

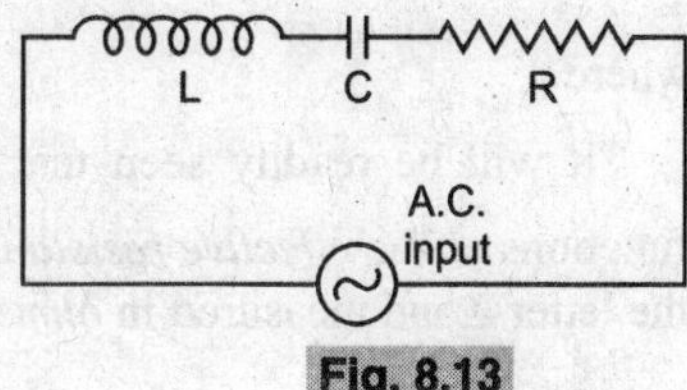

Fig. 8.13

If, therefore, $E = E_0 \sin pt$ be the external *emf* applied to the circuit, we have

$$E - L(dI/dt) = (Q/C) + RI.$$

Or, $$L(dI/dt) + RI + (Q/C) = E = E_0 \sin pt \qquad \ldots(i)$$

Or, $$dI/dt + (R/L)\, I + Q/LC = (E_0/L) \sin pt.$$

Or, since $I = dQ/dt$, we have

$$d^2Q/dt^2 + (R/L)\,(dQ/dt) + Q/LC = (E_0/L) \sin pt.$$

This is an equation of an identical form with that for a driven harmonic oscillator, discussed earlier (Equation I, §8.6), with Q replacing x and R/L, $1/LC$ and E_0/L replacing $2k$, ω_0^2 and f_0 respectively.

If steady state solution too is similarly

$$Q = \frac{E_0/L}{\sqrt{(1/LC - p^2) + (pR/L)^2}} \sin(pt - \theta), \qquad \ldots(ii)$$

where $$\theta = \tan^{-1} \frac{pR/L}{1/LC - p^2}.$$

We can easily obtain the value of the current flowing through the circuit by differentiating this expression for Q with respect to t, just as we can obtain the value of the velocity v of the oscillator by differentiating the earlier expression for x with respect to t.

Alternatively, we can proceed directly with a trial solution $I = I_0 \sin (pt - \phi)$

So that, $$dI/dt = I_0 p \cos (pt - \phi)$$

and $$Q = \int I dt = \int I_0 \sin (pt - \phi)\, dt = \frac{I_0}{p} \cos(pt - \phi).$$

Substituting these values in equation (i) above, we have

$$LpI_0 (\cos pt - \phi) + RI_0 \sin (pt - \phi) - \frac{I_0}{Cp} \cos (pt - \phi) = E_0 \sin pt.$$

Or, $I_0[R\sin(pt-\phi)+(Lp-1/Cp)\cos(pt-\phi)] = E_0 \sin pt$ ...(iii)

Now, putting $R = a\cos\phi$ and $(Lp - 1/Cp) = a\sin\phi$, we have

$$a = \sqrt{R^2+(Lp-1/Cp)^2} \text{ and } \tan\phi = (Lp-1/Cp)/R.$$

Substituting these values of R and $(Lp - 1/Cp)$ in relation (*iii*) above, we have $I_0 a[\cos\phi\sin(pt-\phi)+\sin\phi\cos(pt-\phi)] = E_0 \sin pt$.

Or, $I_0 a \sin[(pt-\phi)+\phi] = I_0 a \sin pt = E_0 \sin pt$.

Or, $I_0\sqrt{R^2+(Lp-1/Cp)^2}\sin pt = E_0 \sin pt$,

whence, $I_0\sqrt{R^2+(Lp-1/Cp)^2} = E_0$.

Or, $$I_0 = \frac{E_0}{\sqrt{R^2+(Lp-1/Cp)^2}} \quad ...(iv)$$

$\therefore$ $$I = I_0 \sin(pt-\phi) = \frac{E_0}{\sqrt{R^2+(Lp-1/Cp)^2}}\sin(pt-\phi), \quad ...(v)$$

where $\phi = \tan^{-1}(Lp-1/Cp)/R$.

It will be readily seen tnat in expression (*iv*) for I_0, the denominator $\sqrt{R^2+(Lp-1/Cp)^2}$ functions as the *effective resistance* in the circuit. It is called **impedance** of the circuit, denoted by the letter Z and measured in *ohms*.

Clearly, the impedance is made up of two parts, the *ohmic* resistance R and the quantity $(Lp - 1/Cp)$, called **reactance**, usually denoted by X and also measured in *ohms* (though L and C are individually measured in *henry* and *farad* respectively).

The relation between *resistance*, *reactance*, *impedance* and ϕ is best illustrated as in Fig. 8.14.

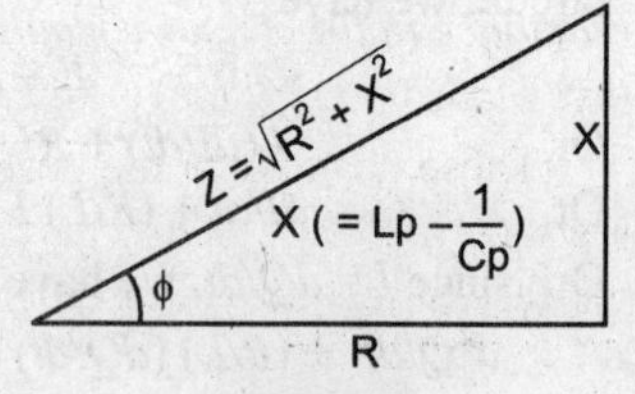

Fig. 8.14

The *reactance* too, as can readily be seen, is made up of two parts: Lp, the *reactance due to inductance*, usually denoted by X_L and $1/Cp$, the *reactance due to capacitance*, denoted by X_C; so that,

$$X = X_L + X_C.$$

We thus have $$Z = \sqrt{R^2+X^2}.$$

Or, $$\textbf{Impedance} = \sqrt{\textbf{Resistance}^2 + \textbf{Reactance}^2}.$$

And, clearly, *peak value or amplitude* of the current, *i.e.*,

$$I_0 = E_0/Z = E_0/\sqrt{R^2+X^2}.$$

And, therefore, $$I = \frac{E_0}{Z}\sin(pt-\phi) = I_0 \sin(pt-\phi).$$

Obviously, the *current* and *emf* in the circuit differ in phase by ϕ,

where $$\phi = \tan^{-1}\frac{Lp-1/Cp}{R} = \tan^{-1}\left(\frac{Reactance}{Resistance}\right)$$

$$= \tan^{-1}\left(\frac{X_L - X_C}{R}\right).$$

Now, whereas *the ohmic resistance (R) has no effect on the phase angle* (because it is quite independent of the frequency), *the inductance in a circuit makes the emf lead the current (in phase)*, and *the capacitance in a circuit makes the current lead the emf. When both are present in a circuit, therefore, the lead or lag of the emf or the current depends upon the relative values of X_L or Lp and X_C or 1/Cp and the following* **three cases** *arise:*

(*i*) **When the value of p is such that $X_L = X_C$.** In this case, obviously, *Lp* = 1/*Cp*, *i.e., the reactance in the circuit,* $X = X_L - X_C = 0$. So that,

impedance in the circuit = resistance R, and, therefore, *the least*.

∴ amplitude or peak value of the current, $I_0 = E_0/R$, the *maximum*, which approaches ∞ as $R \to 0$.

Obviously, here, $\tan \phi = \dfrac{X_L - X_C}{R}$ and ∴ $\phi = 0$, *i.e., the current in the circuit is in phase with the applied emf.*

This is, therefore, the *case of resonance*, with $p^2 = 1/LC$ and ∴ $p = 1/\sqrt{LC} = \omega_0$.

Thus, *resonance frequency* $= p/2\pi = \omega_0/2\pi = 1/2\pi\sqrt{LC}$.

The circuit is, therefore, called a **series resonance circuit.**

It may be noted that current resonance here is analogous to velocity resonance in the case of mechanical oscillators.

(*ii*) **When *p* has a value such that $X_L > X_C$.** Here, since $Lp > 1/Cp$, the *net reactance in the circuit is inductive*, tan ϕ, a *positive quantity* and, therefore, $\phi = \pi/2$. *The applied emf thus leads the current by π/2 and the value of p is greater than ω_0.*

(*iii*) **When the value of *p* is such that $X_L < X_C$.** In this case, *Lp* being less than 1/*Cp*, *the net reactance in the circuit is capacitive,* tan ϕ, a *negative quantity* and, therefore, $\phi = -\pi/2$. *The current thus leads the applied emf by π/2 and the value of p is less than ω_0.*

These changes in the peak value of the current I_0 and in the value of the phase angle ϕ with *p* are shown in Figs. 8.15(*a*) and (*b*) respectively, for different values of *R*, which corresponds to *k* in the case of mechanical oscillators.

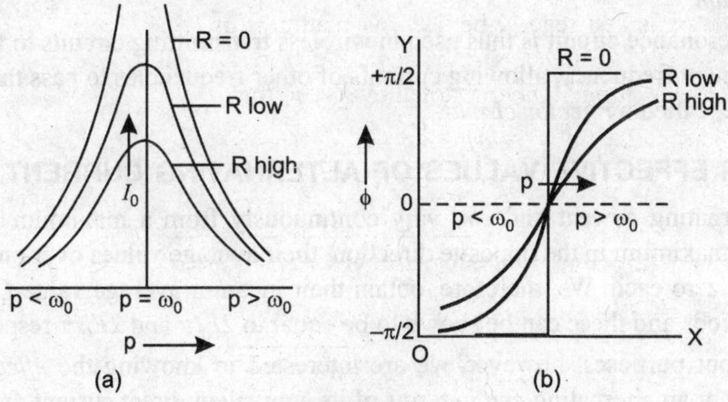

Fig. 8.15

It will be seen at once that *the lower the value of R, the sharper the resonance* and that *the current lags or leads the emf according as p is greater than or less than ω_0.*

8.15 PARALLEL RESONANCE CIRCUIT

When the *inductance* (*L*) and the *capacitance* (*C*) in a circuit are placed in parallel (instead of in series), as shown in Fig. 8.16, the applied voltage is the *same* across both inductance and capacitance.

Now, as we know, the current I_L through the inductance *lags*, and the current I_C through the capacitance *leads*, the *emf* the by $\pi/2$, *i.e.*,

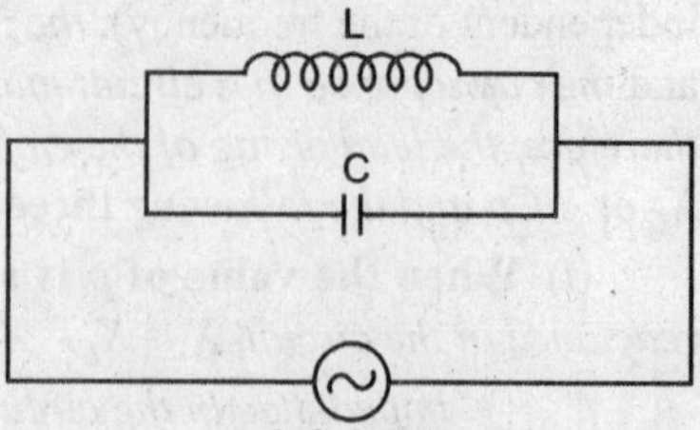

$$I_L = \frac{E_0}{Lp}\sin(pt - \pi/2)$$

and
$$I_C = \frac{E_0}{1/Cp}\sin(pt + \pi/2)$$

$\therefore$ *total current in the circuit,*
$$I = I_L + I_C$$
$$= \frac{E_0}{Lp}\sin(pt - \pi/2) + \frac{E_0}{1/Cp}\sin(pt + \pi/2)$$

Or,
$$I = E_0(Cp - 1/Lp)\cos pt.$$

L

C

A.C. input

Fig. 8.16

The current thus leads or lags the emf by a phase angle π.

For a particular value of p, we have $Cp = 1/Lp$, when $p^2 = 1/LC$ or $p = 1/\sqrt{LC}$. The current through the inductance is equal in magnitude to that through the capacitance, the two differing in phase by π. The net current through the circuit is thus *zero*.

This frequency p is called the *resonant frequency* of the circuit and the circuit itself is referred to as a *parallel resonance circuit*.

As in the series resonant circuit, therefore, we have $p = 2\pi n = 1/\sqrt{LC}$ or $n = 1/2\pi\sqrt{LC}$.

The circuit, under this condition, oscillates with its natural frequency, without requiring any supply of energy from an outside source. In actual practice, however, the inductance coil does possess some resistance and the oscillations of the circuit can be maintained only by some supply of energy from an external source.

It will be seen at once that *whereas in a series circuit, the current at resonance is the maximum and the impedance minimum* (*or zero*), *in a parallel circuit, the current at resonance is zero and the impedance maximum.*

The parallel resonance circuit is thus used in wireless transmitting circuits to filter or to cut out the current of resonant frequency, allowing currents of other frequencies to pass through the circuit. It is also, therefore, called a *rejector circuit.*

8.16 R.M.S. OR EFFECTIVE VALUES OF ALTERNATING CURRENT AND EMF

Since an alternating current and *emf* vary continuously from a maximum in one direction, through zero, to a maximum in the opposite direction, their average values over one complete cycle or time-period are zero each. We, therefore, obtain their mean or average value $I_{(av)}$ and $E_{(av)}$ over half their time-periods and these can be shown to be equal to $2I_0/\pi$ and $2E_0/\pi$ respectively.

For most of our purposes, however, we are interested in knowing the *effective value* of an alternating current or an alternating *emf* in terms of its equivalent direct current or *emf.*

This effective or virtual value of an alternating current is defined as that steady (*or direct*) *current which would produce the same heating effect as the alternating current in a given resistance in a given time.*

Thus, if I_v be the effective or virtual value of an alternating current $I = I_0 \sin \omega t$, clearly, *the heating effect produced by this steady or direct current in a resistance R in time t* $= I_v^2\, Rt$.

And *the heating effect produced by the alternating current in the same resistance in the same time t* = (*average value of* $I^2 = I_0^2 \sin^2\omega t$ *over a cycle or time-period T*) $\times R \times t = (I_0^2/2) \times R \times t$, (because the average value of $\sin^2 \omega t$ over a whole cycle or time-period is 1/2).

We, therefore, have $I_v^2 Rt = (I_0^2/2) Rt$. Or, $I_v^2 = I_0^2/2$, whence, $I_v = I_0/\sqrt{2}$, *i.e.*,**effective or virtual value of alternating current** = $I_0/\sqrt{2}$.

Since this is the square root of the mean square value $(I_0^2/2)$ of the current, it is also called the *root mean square* or the *r.m.s. value of* the alternating current.

Similarly, we have **effective, virtual** or **r.m.s value of alternating emf equal to** $E_0/\sqrt{2}$.

8.17 POWER IN AN ALTERNATING CURRENT CIRCUIT

The power (P) in an electrical circuit is the amount of energy delivered per second by the source to the circuit, and in a direct current (or *D.C*) circuit is measured by the product *EI*, where *E* is the *emf* in the circuit and *I*, the current.

Since in a *D.C.* circuit, we have only resistance and no inductance or capacitance, $E = IR$ and, therefore, power $P = I^2R$, appearing in the form of heat.

In an *alternating current* (or *A.C.*) *circuit*, say in an *LCR* circuit, the *emf* and *current* both vary continuously, *sinusoidally*, and are given by $E = E_0 \sin pt$ and $I = I_0 \sin (pt - \phi)$ respectively. We, therefore, have

$$\text{power } P = EI = (E_0 \sin pt)\,[I_0 \sin (pt - \phi)] = \frac{E_0 I_0}{2}[\cos \phi - \cos (2pt - \phi)]$$

Since the average value of $\cos (2pt - \phi)$ over a whole cycle or time-period is *zero*, we have

$$P = \frac{E_0 I_0}{2}\cos\phi = \frac{E_0}{\sqrt{2}}\frac{I_0}{\sqrt{2}}\cos\phi = E_v I_v \cos\phi, \quad [\because E_0/\sqrt{2} = E_v \text{ and } I_0/\sqrt{2} = I_v]$$

where $$\cos\phi = R/Z = R/\sqrt{R^2 + (Lp - 1/Cp)^2}. \qquad \text{[See Fig. 8.14.]}$$

The unit of power is the **watt** = 1 **joule/sec.**

Obviously, the maximum power will be $E_v I_v$ (when $\cos \phi = 1$) and, therefore,

$$\frac{\textit{True power expended}}{\textit{Maximum power}} = \frac{E_v I_v \cos\phi}{E_v I_v} = \cos\phi.$$

Thus, true *power expended* = *maximum power* × $\cos \phi$.

This is why $\cos \phi = R/Z$ is called the **power factor** *of the A.C. circuit.*

As we know, $\phi = 0$ and, therefore, $\cos \phi = 1$ *only in the case of resonance,* for *reactance* is then zero and *impedance* $Z = R$. So that, *in this case, true power* = *maximum power* = $E_v I_v = I_v^2 R$.

$[\because \; E_v = I_v R$ here.]

It may as well be pointed out that, even otherwise, *the power in an A.C. circuit, like that in a D.C. circuit, appears in the form of heat in the resistance alone, because the power expended in a pure inductance or a pure capacitance is always zero.* This may also be seen from the following:

We have $$P = E_v I_v \cos\phi. \text{ Or, since } E_v = I_v Z, \text{ we have}$$
$$P = (I_v Z)\, I_v \cos\phi.$$

Or, $$P = I_v^2 Z(R/Z) = I_v^2 R,$$

showing that *the power appears in the form of heat in the resistance R.*

Finally, as in the case of a mechanical oscillator, so also here, the *quality factor of the circuit,* $Q = Lp/R = L\omega_0/R$ ($\because p \approx \omega_0$ at or near resonance) $= \omega_0\tau = \omega_0/2\,\Delta p$ = *frequency at resonance/ full width of power frequency curve at half maximum power*, and is a *measure of the sharpness of resonance of the LCR circuit.* See § 8.11).

WORKED EXAMPLES

I–Damping force—Damped harmonic oscillator

Example 8.1. A particle of mass 5 kg lies in a potential field $V = 8x^2 + 200$ Joules/kg. Calculate its time period. ***(Nagpur U.2004)***

Solution. Potential energy (U) of a particle

$$U = mV$$
$$= m(8x^2 + 200)$$

Restoring force (F) acting is given by

$$F = -\frac{dU}{dx}$$
$$= -\frac{d}{dx}(8m^2 + 200) = -16mx$$
$$= -kx \qquad \text{(where } k = 16m\text{, a constant)}$$

As $f \propto -x$, the motion is S.H.M.

$\therefore$ Angular frequency, $\omega = \sqrt{\frac{k}{m}} = \sqrt{\frac{16m}{m}} = 4$

and Time period, $T = \frac{2\pi}{\omega} = \frac{2\pi}{4} = 1.57$ sec.

Example 8.2. A mass of 25×10^{-2} kg is suspended from the lower end of a vertical spring having a force constant 25 Nm^{-1}. What should be the damping constant of the system so that the motion is critically damped? ***(Nagpur U. 2004, 2001)***

Solution. Here $m = 25 \times 10^{-2}$ kg; Force (spring) constant, $s = 25$ Nm^{-1}

Damping constant r = ?

For critical damping $\frac{r^2}{4m^2} - \frac{s}{m} = 0$

or $r^2 = 4ms$ or $r = 2\sqrt{ms} = 2\sqrt{25 \times 10^{-2} \times 25}$

$$= 2 \times 25 \times 10^{-1} = 5 \text{ kg s}^{-1}$$

Example 8.3. A mass 25×10^{-3} kg is suspended from the lower end of a vertical spring having a force constant 25 N/m. The mechanical resistance of the system is 1.5 Ns/m. The mass is displaced vertically and released. Find whether the motion is oscillatory? If so, calculate its period of oscillation.

Solution. Given : $m = 25 \times 10^{-3}$ kg, $s = 25$ N/m, $r = 1.5$ Ns/m

$$b^2 = \frac{r^2}{4m^2} = \frac{(1.5)^2}{4 \times (25 \times 10^{-3})^2} = \frac{2.25}{25 \times 10^{-4}} = 900$$

and $\omega^2 = \frac{s}{m} = \frac{25}{25 \times 10^{-3}} = 10^3 = 1000$

Since, $b^2 < \omega^2$, the motion is oscillatory.

$\therefore$ Period, $T = \frac{2\pi}{\sqrt{\frac{s}{m} - \frac{r^2}{4m^2}}} = \frac{2 \times 3.14}{\sqrt{1000 - 900}} = \frac{6.28}{\sqrt{100}} = \frac{6.28}{10} = 0.628$ s.

Example 8.4. A mass of 1 kg is suspended from a spring of stiffness constant 25 N m^{-1}. If the undamped (or natural) frequency is $\frac{2}{\sqrt{3}}$ times the damped frequency, calculate the damping factor (or constant).

Solution. Damped frequency $f' = \frac{1}{2\pi}\sqrt{\frac{s}{m} - \frac{r^2}{4m^2}}$

and undamped frequency $f_0 = \frac{1}{2\pi}\sqrt{\frac{s}{m}}$

Now $\frac{f_0}{f'} = \frac{2}{\sqrt{3}}$

or $\frac{\sqrt{\frac{s}{m}}}{\sqrt{\frac{s}{m} - \frac{r^2}{4m^2}}} = \frac{2}{\sqrt{3}}$ or $\frac{\frac{s}{m}}{\frac{s}{m} - \frac{r^2}{4m^2}} = \frac{4}{3}$

or $\frac{3}{4}\frac{s}{m} = \frac{s}{m} - \frac{r^2}{4m^2}$

or $\frac{r^2}{4m^2} = \frac{1}{4}\frac{s}{m}$

$\therefore$ $r^2 = sm$

Given $s = 25 \text{ Nm}^{-1}$ and $m = 1\text{kg}$

$r^2 = 25 \text{ Nm}^{-1} \text{ kg} = 25 \text{ kg}^2 \text{ s}^{-2}$ $[\because N = \text{kg ms}^{-2}]$

$\therefore$ $r = 5 \text{ kg s}^{-1}$

Example 8.5. Show that the unit of damping term (or damping coefficient) *b* is s^{-1}. ***(G.N.D.U. 2001; H.P.U. 2002)***

Solution. For a damped harmonic oscillator the equation of motion is

$$m\frac{d^2y}{dt^2} + r\frac{dy}{dt} + sy = 0$$

or $$\frac{d^2y}{dt^2} + \frac{r}{m}\frac{dy}{dt} + \frac{s}{m}y = 0$$

Substituting $\frac{r}{m} = 2b$ and $\frac{s}{m} = \omega^2$, we get

$$\frac{d^2y}{dt^2} + 2b\frac{dy}{dt} + \omega^2 y = 0$$

$\therefore$ The unit of $r\frac{dy}{dt}$ is that of force, *i.e.*, Newton

$\therefore$ Unit of damping constant r is $\frac{\text{Force}}{\text{velocity}} = \text{Nm}^{-1}\text{ s} = \text{kg ms}^{-2}\text{ m}^{-1}\text{ s} = \text{kgs}^{-1}$

Hence unit of damping (coefficient) or term $b = \frac{r}{m} = \frac{\text{kg s}^{-1}}{\text{kg}} = \text{s}^{-1}$ *i.e.*, b has the dimensions of frequency.

Example 8.6. In an oscillatory circuit $L = 0.5$ H, C = 1.8 μfd what is the maximum value of resistance to be connected so that the circuit may produce oscillations. ***(Nagpur U., 2006)***

Solution. $L = 0.5\text{H}$ $C = 1.8 \ \mu\text{fd} = 1.8 \times 10^{-6}$ F.

Let R be the maximum resistance for which the discharge is oscillatory. For the circuit to produce oscillations,

$$\frac{R^2}{4L^2} = \frac{1}{LC}$$

or $$R = 2\sqrt{\frac{L}{C}} = 2\times\sqrt{\frac{0.5}{1.8\times10^{-6}}} = 1054 \text{ ohm}$$

Example. 8.7. The frequency of an underdamped harmonic oscillator is adjusted to be equal to half the frequency experienced by the oscillator without damping. Calculate the logarithmic decrement of the system.

Solution. Let the frequency of the harmonic oscillator without damping be ω_0 and the frequency of the underdamped harmonic oscillator be ω', then,

$$\omega' = \frac{1}{2}\omega_0$$

Now $$\omega' = \sqrt{\omega_0^2 - b^2}$$ where b is the *damping coefficient*.

$\therefore$ $$\frac{1}{2}\omega_0 = \sqrt{\omega_0^2 - b^2} \text{ or } \frac{\omega_0^2}{4} = \omega_0^2 - b^2$$

or $$b^2 = \omega_0^2 - \frac{\omega_0^2}{4} = \frac{3}{4}\omega_0^2$$

$$b = \frac{\sqrt{3}}{2}\omega_0 = \sqrt{3}\omega'$$

Now logarithmic decrement $\lambda = bT$ and $T = \frac{2\pi}{\omega'}$

$\therefore$ $$\lambda = \sqrt{3}\omega' \cdot \frac{2\pi}{\omega'} = 2\pi\sqrt{3}$$

Example 8.8. A damped vibrating system, starting from rest, reaches a first amplitude of 500 mm which reduces to 50 mm in that direction after 100 oscillations each of period 2.3 sec. Find the damping constant, relaxation time and the correction for the first displacement for damping [$\log_e^{10} = 2.3$]. ***(Indore U. 2001)***

Solution. The damping constant b is given by the relation

$$\log_e \frac{A_1}{A_2} = \log_e \frac{A_2}{A_3} = \ldots = b$$

where A_1, A_2, A_3 etc. are the successive amplitudes and T the time period. The amplitude n vibrations after the first i.e., $n + 1$ vibration is A_{n+1}, then

$$\log_e \frac{A_1}{A_{n+1}} = \log_e \frac{A_1}{A_2} \times \log_e \frac{A_2}{A_3} \times \ldots \log_e \frac{A_n}{A_{n+1}} = nkT$$

Now $A_1 = 500$ mm; $A_{101} = 50$ mm; $n = 100$; $T = 2.3$ sec

$\therefore$ $$\log_e \frac{500}{50} = 100\, b \times 2.3$$

or $$2.3 \log_{10} 10 = 2.3 \times 100\, b$$

or $$100\, b = 1$$

$\therefore$ Damping constant $$b = \frac{1}{100} = 0.01$$

Relaxation time $$t_r = \frac{1}{b} = \frac{1}{0.01} = 100 \text{ Sec.}$$

Logarithmic decrement $\lambda = bT = 0.01 \times 2.3 = 0.023$

The amplitude A_0 which could be obtained if the damping force were absent, is given by

$$A_0 = A_1\left(1+\frac{\lambda}{4}\right) = 500\left(1+\frac{1}{4}\times 0.01\times 2.3\right) = 502.875$$

$\therefore$ Correction for the first displacement = 2.875 mm.

Example 8.9. Deduce the frequency and quality factor of an LCR circuit with L = 2mH, C = 5μF and R = 0.2 ohm. ***(G.N.D.U. 2003; P.U. 2004, 2003)***

Solution. Here $L = 2mH = 20 \times 10^{-3}\ H$; $C = 5\mu F = 5 \times 10^{-6}$ F; $R = 0.2\ \Omega = 2 \times 10^{-1}\ \Omega$

Angular frequency $\omega' = \sqrt{\frac{1}{LC} - \frac{R^2}{4L^2}} = \sqrt{\frac{1}{2\times 10^{-3}\times 5\times 10^{-6}} - \frac{2\times 2\times 10^{-2}}{4\times 4\times 10^{-6}}}$

$$= \sqrt{10^8 - 25\times 10^2} = 10^4 \text{ rad s}^{-1} \quad \text{(approx)}$$

Frequency $\nu = \frac{\omega'}{2\pi} = \frac{10^4}{2\pi} = \frac{10}{2\pi}\times 10^3 = 1.59 \times 10^3 = 1590$ Hz

and Quality factor $Q = \frac{L\omega'}{R} = \frac{2\times 10^{-3}\times 10^4}{2\times 10^{-1}} = 10^2 = 100$

Example 8.10. A simple pendulum has a period of 1 sec. and an amplitude of 10°. After 10 complete oscillations its amplitude is reduced to 5°. What is the relaxation time of the pendulum and quality factor?

Solution. For a damped simple harmonic oscillator, the amplitude is given by

$$A = A_0 e^{-bt} = A_0 e^{-\frac{r}{2m}t} \qquad \ldots(i)$$

Here $A_0 = 10°$; $A = 5°$

after 10 complete oscillations *i.e.*, after a time = 10 × Time period = 10 × 1 = 10 sec. Substituting in (*i*)

$$5 = 10e^{-10b}$$

$\therefore$ $e^{-10b} = \frac{1}{2} \quad \therefore \quad e^{10b} = 2$

or $b = \frac{\log_e 2}{10} = \frac{0.6931}{10} = 0.06931$

The relaxation time $t_r = \frac{1}{b} = \frac{1}{0.06931} = 14.428$ sec

Quality factor $Q = \omega\frac{m}{r} = \frac{\omega}{2b}$ where $\omega = \frac{2\pi}{T} = 2\pi$ $\quad [\because T = 1s]$

$\therefore$ $Q = \frac{2\pi}{T\times 2b} = \frac{\pi}{bT} = \frac{\pi}{b} = \frac{\pi}{0.06931} = 45.33$

Example 8.11. A condenser of capacity 1 μF, an inductance of 0.2 Henry and a resistance of 800 ohm are connected in series. Is the circuit oscillatory? If yes, calculate the frequency and quality factor of the circuit. ***(G.N.D.U. 2002 ; H.P.U 2002)***

Solution. Here $C = 1\mu F = 10^{-6}$ F; $L = 0.2$ H; $R = 800\ \Omega$.

For the circuit to be oscillatory $\frac{R^2}{4L^2} < \frac{1}{LC}$

Now $\frac{R^2}{4L^2} = \frac{800\times 800}{4\times 0.2\times 0.2} = 4\times 10^6$

and $\frac{1}{LC} = \frac{1}{0.2\times 10^{-6}} = 5 \times 10^6$

As $\frac{R^2}{4L^2} < \frac{1}{LC}$, the circuit is oscillatory.

The angular frequency $\omega' = \sqrt{\frac{1}{LC} - \frac{R^2}{4L^2}} = \sqrt{5\times10^6 - 4\times10^6} = 10^3 \text{ rad s}^{-1}$

Hence frequency $f' = \frac{\omega'}{2\pi} = \frac{10^3}{2\pi} = 159 \text{ s}^{-1}$

and quality factor $Q = \frac{L\omega'}{R} = \frac{0.2\times10^3}{800} = 0.25$

Example 8.12. A damped oscillator consists of a mass 200 gm attached to a spring of constant 100 Nm^{-1} and damping constant 5 Nm^{-1} s. It is driven by a Force $F = 6 \cos \omega t$ Newton, where $\omega = 30\text{s}^1$. If displacement in steady state is $x = A \sin (wt - \phi)$ metre, find A and ϕ. Also calculate the power supplied to the oscillator. ***(Pbi. U., 2003; P.U., 2001, 2000)***

Solution. Amplitude of the driving force $F_0 = 6\text{N}$

Frequency of the driving force $\omega = 30 \text{ s}^{-1}$

Mass of damped oscillator $m = 200 \text{ gm} = 0.2 \text{ kg}$

Spring constant $s = 100 \text{ Nm}^{-1}$

Damping constant $r = 5 \text{ Nm}^{-1} \text{ s}$

When an external force $F = F_0 \cos \omega t$ acts on a damped oscillator the steady state is given by

$$x = A \sin (\omega t - \phi)$$

where $A = \frac{F_0}{\omega Z_m}$, Z_m being the 'impedance' of the mechanical system given by

$$Z_m = \sqrt{r^2 + \left(\omega m - \frac{s}{\omega}\right)^2}$$

and $$\tan \phi = \frac{\omega m - \frac{s}{\omega}}{r}$$

$\therefore$ $$\tan \phi = \frac{30\times0.2 - \frac{100}{30}}{5} = 0.534$$

$\therefore$ $$\phi = 28°6' \text{ and } \cos \phi = 0.8821$$

$$Z_m = \sqrt{(5\times5) + \left(30\times0.2 - \frac{100}{30}\right)^2} = 5.67 \text{ Nm}^{-1} \text{ s}$$

$$A = \frac{F_0}{\omega Z_m} = \frac{6}{30\times5.67} = 0.0352 \text{ m} = 3.52 \text{ mm}$$

Average power supplied $= \frac{F_0^2}{2Z_m}\cos\phi = \frac{6\cdot6}{2\times5.67}\times0.8821 = 2.8 \text{ watt}$

Example 8.13. If the resonant (angular) frequency of acoustic system is 280 Hz and half power frequencies are 200 Hz and 360 Hz respectively, calculate the quality factor. ***(Nagpur U., 2002)***

Solution. Here $\omega_0 = 280$ Hz, $\omega_1 = 200$ Hz, $\omega_2 = 360$ Hz

$\therefore$ Quality factor $Q = \frac{\omega_0}{\omega_2 - \omega_1} = \frac{280}{360-200} = \frac{280}{160} = 1.75$

Example 8.14. Light of wavelength 6 × 10^{-5} cm is emitted by an electron in an atom (a damped simple harmonic oscillator) with a quality factor 3 × 10^{6}. Find the width of the spectral line from such an atom from resonance bandwidth.

Solution. The quality factor Q is given by

$$Q = \frac{\omega_0}{\omega_2 - \omega_1}$$

where ω_0 is the angular frequency of maximum velocity response (resonance) and $\omega_2 - \omega_1$ is the bandwidth in terms of angular frequency at half maximum power.

Quality factor in terms of wavelength. The above relation can be put in terms of wavelength as under. Let ν_1, ν_2 and ν_0 be the frequencies and λ_1, λ_2 and λ_0 the wavelengths corresponding to angular frequencies ω_1, ω_2 and ω_0, then

$$\frac{\omega_0}{\omega_2 - \omega_1} = \frac{2\pi\nu_0}{2\pi\nu_2 - 2\pi\nu_1} = \frac{\nu_0}{\nu_2 - \nu_1}$$

$$= \frac{\dfrac{c}{\lambda_0}}{\dfrac{c}{\lambda_2} - \dfrac{c}{\lambda_1}} = \frac{\dfrac{1}{\lambda_0}}{\dfrac{1}{\lambda_2} - \dfrac{1}{\lambda_1}} \qquad \left[\because \nu = \frac{c}{\lambda}\right]$$

$$= \frac{1}{\lambda_0}\frac{\lambda_1\lambda_2}{\lambda_1 - \lambda_2} = \frac{\lambda_0}{\lambda_1 - \lambda_2}$$

since $\lambda_1\lambda_2 = \lambda_0^2$ (approx.). Hence $Q = \dfrac{\lambda_0}{\lambda_1 - \lambda_2}$

$\therefore$ Bandwidth $\lambda_1 - \lambda_2 = \dfrac{\lambda_0}{Q}$

Now $\lambda_0 = 6 \times 10^{-5}$ cm $= 6 \times 10^{7}$ m and $Q = 3 \times 10^{6}$

$\therefore$ Bandwidth $= \dfrac{\lambda_0}{Q} = \dfrac{6\times10^{-7}}{3\times10^{6}} = 2 \times 10^{-13}$ m $= 2 \times 10^{-3}$ Å

Example 8.15. A particle of mass 50 gm, moving with an initial velocity of 100 cm/sec, is acted upon by a damping force which brings it to rest in a distance of 10 metres. Assuming the damping force to be proportional to velocity, calculate *(i)* its relaxation time, *(ii)* the time in which *(a)* its velocity is halved *(b)* its kinetic energy is halved, *(iii)* the damping force on it when its velocity is 20 cm/sec. (Take log$_e$10 = 2.30).

Solution. We have the relation $x = \nu_0\tau\,(1 - e^{t/\tau})$ for the distance covered by a particle in time t, where ν_0 is its initial velocity and τ, its relaxation time. (See § 8.1)

(i) Clearly, x will have its maximum value as $t \to \infty$ and, therefore, the quantity $e^{-t/\tau} \to 0$. So that,

$$x_{max} = \nu_0\tau \text{ and } \therefore\ \tau = x_{max}/\nu_0.$$

Here, x_{max} = 10m = 1000 cm and ν_0 = 100 cm/sec. We, therefore, have

relaxation time τ = 1000/100 = 10 sec.

(ii) *(a)* The velocity of the particle after time t from the start is given by the relation $v = v_0e^{-t/\tau}$ (§ 8.1), whence $\log_e (v/v_0) = -t/\tau$. Or, $t = \tau \log_e(v_0/v)$.

$\therefore$ The velocity will be reduced to half, *i.e.*, 50 *cm/sec* in time t given by

$$t = 10 \times 2.30 \log_{10} (100/50) = 10 \times 2.30 \times \log_{10}2 = 10 \times 2.30 \times 0.3010 = 6.92 \textit{ sec.}$$

(*b*) We know that if T be the kinetic energy of the particle after time t and T_0, its initial kinetic energy, we have $T = T_0\, e^{-2t/\tau}$. [See § 8.1]

$\therefore$ $$\log_e(T/T_0) = -2t/\tau, \text{ whence, } 2t = t\log_e(T_0/T).$$

Or, $2t = 10 \times 2.30 \log_{10}(2/1)$. Or $t = 5 \times 2.30 \log_{10}2 = 5 \times 2.30 \times 0.3010 = 3.46$ *sec.*

Or, we could have obtained this result directly from (*a*) above, since, as we know, relaxation time for *K.E.* is half that for velocity. (See § 8.1).

Thus, *the K.E. of the particle will be reduced to half its initial value in* 3.46 *sec.*

(*iii*) The *damping force* $= \gamma v$, where $\gamma = m/\tau$.

$\therefore$ *damping force at velocity* 20 *cm/sec* $= mv/\tau = 50 \times 20/10 = 100$ *dynes.*

Example 8.16. A charged oil drop falls through air under the combined action of an electric field *E* and gravity *g*, both acting along the same direction. If *m* be the mass of the drop and *Q*, the charge on it, show that the terminal velocity attained by it (*i.e.*, when $t \to \infty$) is given by $v_{terminal} = (qE/m)\tau + g\tau$, assuming a solution of the form $v = A + Be^{-\alpha\tau}$. (Assume damping force to be proportional to velocity).

Solution. Since the electric field E and g are both similarly directed, they both act *downwards.* So that, the force acting on the drop is given by

$$F = m(dv/dt) = mg + qE - \gamma v,$$

where γv is the *damping force.*

Or, $$m(dv/dt) + \gamma v = mg + qE. \text{ Or, } (dv/dt) + (\gamma/m)v = g + (q/m)E.$$

Or, Since $\gamma/m = 1/\tau$, where τ is the *relaxation time*, the *equation of motion* of the drop is

$$\frac{dv}{dt} + \frac{v}{\tau} = g + \frac{qE}{m}. \qquad \text{...I}$$

Now, let us assume a solution of this equation to be $v = A + Be^{-\alpha t}$, where A and B are *arbitrary constants* to be determined from the initial conditions.

Since at $t = 0$, *i.e., when the drop just starts from rest*, $v_0 = 0$, we have

$0 = A + B$, whence, $B = -A$. And, therefore,

$$v = A + Ae^{-\alpha t} = A(1 - e^{-\alpha t}). \qquad \text{...II}$$

Hence, $$\frac{dv}{dt} = A\alpha e^{-\alpha t}$$

Substituting this value of dv/dt in the equation of motion (I) above, we have

$$A\alpha e^{-\alpha t} + \frac{1}{\tau}A\left(1 - e^{-\alpha t}\right) = g + \frac{qE}{m}.$$

Clearly, at $t \to \infty$, we have $A/\tau = g + qE/m$.

Or, $$A = \tau(g + qE/m) \qquad \text{...III}$$

And, at $t = 0$, we have $$A\alpha = g + qE/m. \qquad \text{...IV}$$

From relations III and IV, we thus have $\alpha = 1/\tau$.

Hence from equation II, we have

$$v = \tau(g + qE/m)(1 - e^{-\alpha t}) = \tau(g + qE/m)(1 - e^{-t/\tau}) \qquad \text{...V}$$

Clearly, therefore, when $t \to \infty$, we have

$$v_{terminal} = \tau(g + qE/m) = (qE/m)\tau + g\tau.$$

Example 8.17. A small ball bearing is falling freely through a viscous medium, of coefficient of viscosity η, under the action of gravity alone. The viscous drag on it due to the medium is $-6\pi\eta av$, where *a* is its radius and *v*, its velocity. Obtain (*i*) the relaxation time, (*ii*) the terminal velocity of the ball bearing. (*iii*) If the ball bearing has an initial horizontal velocity *u*, what will be the maximum horizontal distance covered by it? (*iv*) If the radius of the ball bearing be doubled, how will it affect its terminal velocity?

Solution. (*i*) Here, obviously, the *damping force* = $6\pi\eta av = \gamma_v$, where $\gamma = 6\pi\eta a$, and is thus *proportional to velocity*.

$\therefore$ *relaxation time* $\tau = m/\gamma = m/6\pi\eta a$.

(*ii*) Proceeding as in worked example 8.16 above and remembering that, here, the ball bearing (a tiny sphere) is falling only under the action of gravity, we have terminal velocity of the ball bearing given by

$$v_{terminal} = g\tau = g(m/6\pi\eta a) = mg/6\pi\eta a.$$

(*iii*) The *maximum horizontal distance covered by the ball bearing is*, as we know, equal to its *initial velocity* (*u*) × *relaxation time* (τ) = $u(m/6\pi\eta a) = mu/6\pi\eta a$.

(*iv*) We have seen under (ii) above that the *terminal velocity of the ball bearing* = $mg/6\pi\eta a$ = $\frac{4}{3}xa\rho g/6\pi\eta a = 2a^2\rho g/9\eta$, where $\frac{4}{3}\pi a^3$ is the volume and, therefore, $\frac{4}{3}\pi a^3\rho$, the mass (*m*) of the ball bearing.

Thus, *the terminal velocity* $\propto a^2$, (ρ and *g* being constants).

Hence, *if the radius of the ball bearing be doubled, its terminal velocity will be four times its previous value, i.e.*, equal to $4mg/6\pi\eta a = 2mg/3\pi\eta a$.

Example 8.18. An underdamped harmonic oscillator has its amplitude reduced to 1/10th of its initial value after 100 oscillations. If its time-period be 1.15 sec, calculate (*i*) the damping constant, (*ii*) the relaxation time.

If the observed value of the first amplitude of the oscillator be 2 cm. What would be its value in the absence of damping?

Solution. (*i*) The amplitude (*a*) of an underdamped oscillator is, as we know, given by the relation $a = a_0 e^{-kt}$, where a_0 is its amplitude in the absence of damping and *k*, the *damping constant*.

Now, for the first amplitude (a_1), obviously, $t = T/4$ where *T* is the *time-period* of the oscillator. So that, $a_1 = a_0\, e^{-kT/4}$.

Since successive amplitudes occur at intervals of *T*/2 *sec* each, the 201th amplitude after 100 oscillations occurs after $(200T/2 + T/4) = (100T + T/4)$ *sec*. And, therefore,

$$a_{201} = a_0 e^{-k(100T+T/4)}$$

Hence,
$$\frac{a_{201}}{a_1} = \frac{a_0 e^{-k(100T+T/4)}}{a_0 e^{-kT/4}} = e^{-100kT}.$$

But we are given that $a_{201}/a_1 = 1/10$ or 10^{-1} and $T = 1.15$ *sec*.

$\therefore$ $10^{-1} = e^{-100k(1.15)} = e^{-115k}$. Or, $\log_e 10 = 115\,k$.

Or, $2.30 \log_{10}10 = 115k$, *i.e.*, $2.30 = 115k$, whence, $k = 2.30/115 = 0.02$.

Thus, the *damping constant* = 0.02.

(*ii*) And, therefore, *relaxation time* $\tau = 1/2k = 1/2 \times 0.02 = 25$ *sec*.

Now, since the *first amplitude* $a_1 = a_0 e^{-kT/4} = 2$ *cm*, we have

$$2 = a_0 e^{(0.02 \times 1.15/4)} \text{ or, } a_0 = 2e^{0.023/4} \text{ or, } \log_{10}a_0 = \log_{10}2 + \frac{0.023}{4} \times \frac{1}{2.30}$$

Or, $\log_{10}a_0 = 0.3010 + 0.0025 = 0.3025$, whence, $a_0 = 2.011$ cm.

Thus, *the undamped amplitude of the oscillator would be* 2.011 *cm*.

Example 8.19. Write down the equation of motion of the damped harmonic oscillator ot example (8.18) above and calculate the time in which (*i*) its amplitude (*ii*) its energy falls to 1/e^th^ of its undamped value.

If the mass of oscillator be 1.127 gm, calculate its average rate of loss of energy.

Solution. The differential equation of a damped harmonic oscillator, as we know (§ See 8.2), is

$$\frac{d^2x}{dt^2} + 2k\frac{dx}{dt} + \omega_0^2 x = 0,$$

which, when the oscillator is underdamped, *i.e.*, when $k << \omega_0$, gives

$$x = a_0 e^{-kt} \sin(\omega t + \phi).$$

So that its amplitude is given by $a = a_0 e^{-kt} = a_0 e^{-t/2\tau}$, where a_0 is its amplitude in the absence of damping.

(*i*) Now, as we have seen under example 8.18 above, the damping constant k for the given oscillator works out to 0.02. If, therefore, its amplitude is reduced to $1/e^{th}$ of its undamped value, we have

$$a = a_0/e = a_0 e^{-1} \text{ and, therefore, } a_0 e^{-1} = a_0 e^{-kt}. \text{ Or, } kt = 1,$$

whence, $t = 1/k = 1/0.02 = 50$ *sec.*

Thus, *the amplitude of the oscillator falls to* $1/e^{th}$ *of its undamped value in* 50 sec.

(*ii*) Again, as we have seen in § 8.3, the energy of a damped harmonic oscillator at a given instant t is given by $E = E_0 e^{-2kt}$. So that, when its energy falls to $1/e^{th}$ of its value E_0 in the absence of damping, we have

$$E = E_0/e = E_0\, e^{-1}. \text{ And, therefore, } E_0 e^{-1} = E_0 e^{-2kt}. \text{ Or, } 2kt = 1,$$

whence, $t = 1/2k = 1/2 \times 0.02 = 25$ *sec.*

Thus, *the energy of the oscillator falls to* $1/e^{th}$ *of tis value in the absence of damping in* 25 *sec.*

And, as shown in § 8.3, *the rate of loss of energy* $= E/\tau = 2kE.$

Now, $E = \frac{1}{2} m a_0^2 \omega_0^2 e^{-2kt}$, where $m = 1.127$ *gm*, $a_0 = 2.011$ *cm*, $\omega_0 = 2\pi/T = 2\pi/1.15$, $k = 0.02$ and $t = 25$ *sec.* So that,

$$\textit{rate of loss of energy} = 2 \times 0.02 \times \frac{1}{2} \times 1.127 \times (2.011)^2 \times (2\pi/1.15)^2\, e^{-2(0.02 \times 25)}$$

$$= \frac{0.02 \times 1.127 \times (2.011)^2 \times 4\pi^2}{(1.15)^2 \times e} = \frac{0.02 \times 1.127 \times (2.011)^2 \times 4\pi^2}{(1.15)^2 \times 2.7183}$$

$$= 1 \textit{ erg/sec.}$$

Example 8.20. If the amplitude of a seconds pendulum, with a bob of mass 200 gm, is reduced to half its undamped value in 200 seconds, what is its quality factor Q? What should be the mass of the bob, its size and shape remaining unchanged, in order that the damping of the pendulum may become critical? (Take $\log_e 10 = 2.30$)

Solution. We know that the amplitude of the pendulum (a damped harmonic oscillator) at a given instant t is given by $a = a_0\, e^{-kt} = a_0 e^{-t/2\tau}$.

Here, $a = a_0/2$ and $t = 200$ sec. So that, $a_0/2 = a_0 e^{-200/2\tau} = a_0 e^{-100/\tau}$.

Or, $100/\tau = \log_e 2 = 2.30 \log_{10} 2 = 2.30 \times 0.3010$

whence, $\tau = 100/2.30 \times 0.3010 = 100/0.6923.$

And, since $\omega_0 = 2\pi/T = 2\pi/2 = \pi$ ($\because T = 2$ *sec*), we have

Quanlity factor of the pendulum, $Q = \omega_0 \tau = \pi)\ 100/0.6923 = 453.7.$

For *critical damping*, as we know, the condition is that $k = \omega_0$. So that, if τ' be the value of the *relaxation time* in this case, we have $1/2\tau' = \omega_0$

Or, since $\omega_0 = \pi$, we have $1/2\tau' = \pi$ and, therefore, $\tau' = 1/2\pi$.

If m and m' be the masses of the bob in the two cases respectively, we have $\gamma/m = 1/\tau$ and $\gamma/m' = 1/\tau'$ ($\because \gamma$ remains the same in either case).

$\therefore$ $\tau'/\tau = (\gamma/m)(\gamma/m') = m'/m$, whence, $m' = m \times \tau'/\tau$.

Substituting the values of m, τ' and τ, therefore, we have

$$m' = 200 \times \frac{1}{2\pi} \times \frac{0.6923}{100} = \frac{0.6923}{\pi} = 0.2204 \textit{ gm.}$$

Thus, *for the damping to be critical, the mass of the bob must be* 0.2204 gm.

Example 8.21. If the quality factor of an underdamped harmonic oscillator of frequency 512 be 8×10^4, calculate the time in which its energy is reduced to $1/e^{th}$ of its energy in the absence of damping. How many oscillations does the oscillator make in this time?

Calculate the percentage reduction in the frequency of the oscillator due to damping. What inference do you draw from it?

Solution. The energy of a damped harmonic oscillator at an instant t, as we know, is given by $E = E_0 e^{-2kt} = E_0 e^{-t/\tau}$, where E_0 is its energy in the absence of damping.

Since here $E = E_0/e = E_0 e^{-1}$, we have $E_0 e^{-1} = E_0 e^{-t/\tau}$, whence, $1 = t/\tau$ or, $t = \tau$. And since $Q = \omega_0 \tau$, we have

$$\tau = \frac{Q}{\omega_0} = \frac{Q}{2\pi n_0} = \frac{8 \times 10^4}{2\pi \times 512} = \frac{10^4}{2\pi \times 64} = \frac{10^4}{128\pi}.$$

And, therefore, *the time in which the energy of the oscillator falls to 1/e th of its energy in the absence of damping, i.e,* $t = \tau = 10^4/128\pi = 24.87$ *sec.*

And, clearly, *number of oscillations made by the oscillator in this time*

$$= nt = (\omega_0/2\pi)\tau = Q/2\pi = 8 \times 10^4/2\pi = 12740.$$

Now, in the case of an underdamped harmonic oscillator, we have

$$\omega = \sqrt{\omega_0^2 - k^2}\,. \text{Or, } \omega^2 = \omega_0^2 - k^2 = \omega_0^2 - (1/2\tau)^2 = \omega_0^2 - 1/4\tau^2.$$

So that, dividing by ω_0 throughout, we have

$$\frac{\omega^2}{\omega_0^2} = 1 - \frac{1}{4\omega_0^2\tau^2} = 1 - \frac{1}{4Q^2} \qquad [\because \omega_0\tau = Q]$$

And, therefore,
$$\frac{\omega}{\omega_0} = \left(1 - \frac{1}{4Q^2}\right)^{1/2} = \left(1 - \frac{1}{2} \times \frac{1}{4Q^2} + \ldots\right) = 1 - \frac{1}{8Q^2}.$$

Or,
$$\frac{2\pi n}{2\pi n_0} = \frac{n}{n_0} = 1 - \frac{1}{8Q^2},$$

where n_0 is the frequency of the undamped oscillator.

$\therefore$ *Percentage reduction in the frequency of the oscillator* $= \dfrac{n_0 - n}{n_0} \times 100$

$$= \left(1 - \frac{n}{n_0}\right) \times 100 = \left[1 - \left(1 - \frac{1}{8Q^2}\right)\right] \times 100 = \frac{100}{8Q^2} = \frac{12.5}{Q^2}$$

$$= \frac{12.5}{(8 \times 10^4)^2} = 1.953 \times 10^{-9}.$$

The obvious inference from the above result is that *for oscillators with large values of the quality factor Q (which is usually the case), the reduction in frequency due to damping is negligibly small.*

Example 8.22. A massless spring, suspended from a rigid support, carries a mass of 500 gm at its lower end and the system oscillates with a frequency of 5/sec, with the amplitude reduced to half its undamped value in 20 sec. Calculate (*i*) the force constant of the spring. (*ii*) the relaxation time of the system and (*iii*) its quality factor. (*iv*) What would be the quality factor of the system if the suspended mass be reduced to 150 gm?

Solution. (*i*) We have the relation $\omega_0 = \sqrt{C/m}$ or $C = m\omega_0^2$, where C is the *force constant* of the spring and m, the *mass* suspended from it.

Here, $\omega_0 = 2\pi n = 2\pi \times 5 = 10\pi$ *radian/sec* and $m = 500$ gm.

So that, *force constant of the spring*, $C = 500 \times (10\pi)^2 = 5\pi^2 \times 10^4$

$= 4.934 \times 10^5$ *dynes/cm.*

(*ii*) The amplitude at an instant t is given by $a = a_0 e^{-kt}$.

Since $a = a_0/2$ and $t = 20$ *sec*, we have $a_0/2 = a_0 e^{-20k}$. Or, $\log_e 2 = 20k$.

Or, $2.30/\log_{10}2 = 20k$. Or, $2.30 \times 0.3010 = 20k$, whence, $k = 2.30 \times 0.3010/20$.

$\therefore$ *relaxation time of the system*, $\tau = 1/2k = \dfrac{1 \times 20}{2 \times 2.30 \times 0.3010} = 14.44$ *sec.*

(*iii*) The *quality factor of the system*, $Q\tau = \omega_0 t = 10\pi \times 14.44 = 453.7$.

(*iv*) Since the force constant (C) of the spring remains the same irrespective of the mass suspended from it, and so does the damping factor $\gamma = 2\,km = 2 \times 2.30 \times 0.010 \times 500/20 = 115 \times 0.3010$, we have

$$\omega_0' = \sqrt{C/m'} = \sqrt{5\pi^2 \times 10^4/150} = 18.26\pi, \text{ since } m' = 150 \text{ gm.}$$

$\therefore$ τ', the relaxation time now $= 1/2k = m'/\gamma = 150/115 \times 0.3010$.

And, therefore, the *quality factor now*, $Q = \omega_0'\tau'$

$= 18.26\pi \times 150/115 \times 0.3010 = 248.5$.

Example 8.23. The restoring torque exerted by the suspension fibre of a ballistic galvanometer is 10^3 dyne-cm/radian. If the period of vibration of the coil be 2π seconds and its amplitude be reduced to $1/e^{th}$ of its undamped value in 100 seconds, calculate the values of (*i*) the moment of inertia of the suspended system, (*ii*) the damping factor γ and (*iii*) the quality factor Q of the system.

Solution. (*i*) The oscillating system in a ballistic galvanometer, as we know, is an underdamped one (§ 8.5 I (*ii*)) and, therefore, the angular frequency of the system is given by $\omega = \sqrt{{\omega_0}^2 - k^2}$,

where ω_0 is the undamped angular frequency of the system and k, the damping constant.

$\therefore$ *Time-period of the suspended system or the coil*, $T = 2\pi/\sqrt{\omega_0^2 - k^2}$.

Or, since $T = 2\pi$ *sec*, we have $2\pi = 2\pi/\sqrt{\omega_0^2 - k^2}$, whence, $\sqrt{\omega_0^2 - k^2} = 1$.

Or, $\omega_0^2 - k^2 = 1$.

Now, the amplitude of the coil at an instant t is given by $\theta = \theta_0 e^{-kt}$, where θ_0 is its undamped amplitude. And, since the amplitude is reduced to $\theta_0/e = \theta_0 e^{-1}$ in time $t = 100$ *sec*, we have

$$\theta_0 e^{-1} = \theta_0 e^{-100k} \quad \text{or,} \quad 100\,k = 1 \text{ or } k = 1/100 = 0.01.$$

$\therefore$ $\omega_0^2 - k^2 = \omega_0^2 - (0.01)^2 = 1$. Or, $\omega_0^2 \approx 1$ and $\therefore$ $\omega \approx 1$ *rad/sec.*

Hence $C/I = \omega_0^2 = 1$, where C is the torque exerted by the suspension fibre per radian twist of the fibre.

Since $C = 10^3$ *dyne-cm/radian* (given), we have $10^3/I = 1$. Or, $I = 10^3$ *dyne-cm*^{2}.

Thus, the *moment of inertia of the suspended system about the suspension fibre*,

i.e., $I = 10^3$ or 1000 *dyne-cm*^{2}.

(*ii*) Now $(\gamma \times N/R)/I = 2k$. Or, $\gamma/I = 2k$, (the electromagnetic damping being obviously ignored in the problem). So that,

damping factor $\gamma = I \times 2k$

$= 1000 \times 2 \times 0.01$

$= 20$ *dyne-cm/sec.*

(*iii*) The *quality factor of the system*, $Q = \omega_0\tau = \omega_0/2k = 1/2 \times 0.01 = 50$.

Example 8.24. Give the theory of oscillations in a series LCR circuit with small damping. Deduce the frequency and quality factor for a circuit with $L = 2$mH, C = 5μF and $R = 0.2$ ohm. (*Agra, 2001*)

Solution. For answer to the first part of the question, see § 8.5 II. The circuit being equivalent to an *underdamped harmonic oscillator,* we have $\omega = \sqrt{\omega_0^2 - k^2}$ and, therefore, *frequency of the oscillations,* $n = \omega/2\pi = \sqrt{\omega_0^2 - k^2}/2\pi$.

Or,
$$n = \frac{1}{2\pi}\sqrt{\frac{1}{LC} - \frac{R^2}{4L^2}}. \qquad [\S\ 8.5\ \text{II}, (iii)]$$

Here, $L = 2mH = 0.002$ *henry*, $C = 5\mu F = 5 \times 10^{-6}$ *farad* and $R = 0.2$ *Ohm*.

We, therefore, have *frequency of the circuit*.

$$n = \frac{1}{2\pi}\sqrt{\frac{1}{0.002 \times 5 \times 10^{-6}} - \frac{(0.02)^2}{4(0.002)^2}} = \frac{1}{2\pi}\sqrt{\frac{4 \times 10^8 - 10^4}{4}}$$

$$= \frac{10^2}{2\pi}\sqrt{10^4 - 1} = 10^4/2\pi = 1.592 \times 10^3 \text{ cps.}$$

Now, the resistance being small, *quality factor* $Q = L\omega_0/R = L\omega/R$, where $\omega = 2\pi n = 2\pi \times 10^4/2\pi = 10^4$ rad/sec.

∴ *Quality factor for the circuit,* $Q = 0.002 \times 10^4/0.2 = 0.01 \times 10^4 = 100$.

Example 8.25. The line width of orange line of Kr^{86} at $\lambda = 6058$ Å is found to be 5.50×10^{-3} Å. Calculate (*a*) line frequency (*ii*) line width in Hertz.

Solution. Line wavelength $\lambda_0 = 6058$ Å $= 6058 \times 10^{-10}$ m

∴ Line frequency $v_0 = \dfrac{c}{\lambda_0} = \dfrac{3 \times 10^8}{6058 \times 10^{-10}} = 4.95 \times 10^{14}$ Hertz

Line width in wavelength $\lambda_1 - \lambda_2 = 5.50 \times 10^{-3}$ Å $= 5.50 \times 10^{-13}$ m

∴ Line width in terms of frequency $= \dfrac{c}{\lambda_1 - \lambda_2} = \dfrac{3 \times 10^8}{5.50 \times 10^{-13}} = 5.45 \times 10^{20}$ Hz

Example 8.26. A root mean square voltage of 100 volts is applied to a series LCR circuit having $R = 10$ ohm, $L = 10$ mH and $C = 1\mu$F. Calculate

(*i*) The natural frequency

(*ii*) Current at resonance

(*iii*) Q value of the circuit at resonance

(*iv*) Bandwidth of the circuit.

Solution.

(*i*) Natural frequency $v = \dfrac{1}{2\pi\sqrt{LC}} = 1592$ Hz

(*ii*) Current at Resonance $I_{max} = \dfrac{V_{max}}{R} = \dfrac{\sqrt{2}V_{rms}}{R} = \dfrac{\sqrt{2} \times 100}{10} = 14.14$ A.

(*iii*) Q value $= \omega_0 \dfrac{L}{R} = \dfrac{1}{\sqrt{LC}}\dfrac{L}{R} = \sqrt{\dfrac{L}{C}}\dfrac{1}{R} = \sqrt{\dfrac{10 \times 10^{-3}}{1 \times 10^{-6}}} \times \dfrac{1}{10} = 10$

(*iv*) Bandwidth $\omega_2 - \omega_1$

$$Q = \frac{\omega_0}{\omega_2 - \omega_1}$$

∴
$$\omega_2 - \omega_1 = \frac{\omega_0}{Q} = \frac{1}{\sqrt{LC}} \cdot \frac{1}{Q} = \sqrt{\frac{1}{10 \times 10^{-3} \times 10^{-6}}} \times \frac{1}{10} = 1000 \text{ rad s}^{-1}$$

Example 8.27. The equation of motion is

$$2 \times 10^{-4} \frac{d^2x}{dt^2} + 4 \times 10^{-2} \frac{dx}{dt} + 5x = 0.124 \sin 100\, t,$$ **where all quantities are in S.I. units**

Find (*i*) Natural frequency of undamped oscillation.

(*ii*) Mechanical impedance. ***(Nagpur U.2009, 2004)***

Solution. Comparing with

$$m\frac{d^2x}{dt^2} + r\frac{dx}{dt} + sx = F_0 \sin \omega_0 t$$

we get, $m = 2 \times 10^{-4}$ kg, $r = 4 \times 10^{-2}$ Nsm^{-1}, $s = 5$ Nm^{-1}, $F_0 = 0.124$ N, and $\omega_0 = 100$ rad s^{-1}

(*i*) Natural frequency of undamped oscillation is

$$F_0 = \frac{\omega_0}{2\pi} = \frac{1}{2\pi}\sqrt{\frac{s}{m}}$$

$$= \frac{1}{2 \times 3.14}\sqrt{\frac{5}{2 \times 10^{-4}}} = \frac{10^2}{6.28}\sqrt{\frac{5}{2}} = 25.16 \text{ Hz.}$$

(*ii*) Mechanical impedance (z):

Amplitude, $$a = \frac{f_0}{\sqrt{4b^2\omega_0^2 + (\omega^2 - \omega_0^2)^2}} = \frac{F_0}{m\sqrt{4b^2\omega_0^2 + (\omega^2 - \omega_0^2)}} = \frac{F_0}{z}$$

$\therefore$ Mechanical impedance, $$z = m\sqrt{4b^2\omega_0^2 + (\omega^2 - \omega_0^2)^2}$$

Here $$\omega^2 - \omega_0^2 = \frac{s}{m} - \omega_0^2$$

$$= \frac{5}{2 \times 10^{-4}} - (10^2)^2 = 1.5 \times 10^4$$

and $$4b^2\omega_0^2 = (2b)^2\,\omega_0^2 = \left(\frac{r}{m}\right)^2 \omega_0^2 = \left(\frac{4 \times 10^{-2}}{4 \times 10^{-4}}\right) \times (10^2) = 4 \times 10^8$$

$\therefore$ $$z = 2 \times 10^{-4}\sqrt{4 \times 10^8 + 2.25 \times 10^8} = 2 \times 10^{-4}\sqrt{10^8(4 + 2.25)}$$

$$= 2 \times 10^{-4} \times 10^4 \times \sqrt{6.25} = 2 \times 2.25 = 5 \text{ Nsm}^{-1}$$

Example 8.28. A harmonic oscillator consisting of 50 gm mass attached to a mass less spring has a quality factor 200. If it oscillates with an amplitude of 2 cm in resonance with a periodic force of frequency 20 Hz. Calculate (*i*) the average energy stores in it and (*ii*) the rate of dissipation of energy. ***(Nagpur U. 2007)***

Solution. Here, the average energy stored in the oscillator is equal to its maximum potential energy $= \frac{1}{2}cx^2 = \frac{1}{2}m\omega_0^2 x_0^2$

Here, $m = 50$ gm, $\omega_0 = 2\pi n = 2\pi \times 20 = 40\pi$, and $x_0 = 2$ cm.

(*i*) The average energy stored or absorbed in the oscillator

$$= \frac{1}{2} \times 50 \times (40\pi)^2 \times (2)^2 = 1.58 \times 10^6 \text{ ergs.}$$

(*ii*) By definition, the quality factor

$$Q = 2\pi \times \frac{\text{Average energy stored}}{\text{Energy dissipated per cycle}}$$

$\therefore$ Energy dissipated per cycle $= 2\pi \times \dfrac{\text{Average energy stored}}{Q}$

$$= 2\pi\frac{1.58\times10^6}{200} = \pi \times 1.58 \times 10^4 \text{ ergs.}$$

Since there are 20 cycles per cycle, we have energy dissipated per second or rate of dissipated, of energy

$$= 20 \times \pi \times 1.58 \times 10^4 = 9.926 \times 10^5 \cong 10^6 \text{ erg/sec.}$$

II–Driven harmonic oscillator

Example 8.29. In an experiment on forced oscillations, the frequency of a sinusoidal driving force is changed while its amplitude is kept constant. It is found that the amplitude of vibrations is 0.01 mm at very low frequency of the driver and goes upto a maximum of 5.0 mm at driving frequency 200 sec^{-1}. Calculate (*i*) Q of the system, (*ii*) relaxation time τ and (*iii*) half width of resonance curve. ***(Agra (Supp.) 2005)***

Solution. We know that if the driving frequency be negligibly small and the damping be low, the *amplitude of the driven oscillator,* $A = f_0/\omega_0^2$ and that at low damping, the *maximum amplitude* (or *amplitude at resonance*) is $A_{max} = f_0\tau/\omega_0$, where ω_0 is the *natural frequency of the oscillator* (or the system) and τ, its *relaxation time*, (See § 8.6)

(*i*) We, therefore, have $\dfrac{A_{max}}{A} = \dfrac{f_0\tau/\omega_0}{f_0/\omega_0^2} = \omega_0\tau = Q.$

Since $A_{max} = 5.0$ *mm* and $A = 0.01$ *mm*, we have

quality factor of the system, $Q = 5/0.01 = 500$.

(*ii*) Since $Q = \omega_0\tau$, we have $\tau = Q/\omega_0$.

Here, $Q = 500$ and $\omega_0 = 2\pi n = 2\pi \times 200 = 400\pi$

$\therefore$ *relaxation time of the system*, $\tau = 5000/400\pi = 0.3971 \approx 0.40$ *sec.*

(*iii*) For *low damping, half width of the resonance curve,* $\Delta p = \sqrt{3}$ [§ 8.10]

Since $k = 1/2\tau = 1/2 \times 0.40 = 1.25$, we have

half width of the resonance curve, $\Delta p = \sqrt{3} \times 1.25 = 2.165$ *radian/sec*

$= 2.165/2\pi = 0.3445$ *c.p.s.*

Example 8.30. A harmonic oscillator of quality factor 10 is subjected to a sinusoidal applied force of frequency one and a half times the natural frequency of the oscillator. If the damping be small, obtain (*i*) the amplitude of the forced oscillation in terms of its maximum amplitude and (*ii*) the angle θ by which it will be out of phase with the driving force.

Solution. As we know, the *amplitude of the forced oscillation* is given by

$$A = \frac{f_0}{\sqrt{(\omega_0^2 - p^2)^2 + 4k^2p^2}} = \frac{f_0}{\omega_0^2\sqrt{\left(1-\dfrac{p^2}{\omega_0^2}\right)^2 + 4\dfrac{k^2p^2}{\omega_0^4}}},$$

where ω_0 is the *natural angular frequency of the oscillator and p, the angular frequency of the driving force.*

Now, the *quality factor* $Q = \omega_0\tau = \omega_0/2k = 10$. So that, $2k = \omega_0/10$ and $p/\omega_0 = 3/2$ (given). We therefore, have

$$A = \frac{f_0}{\omega_0^2\sqrt{\left(1-\dfrac{p^2}{\omega_0^2}\right)^2 + \dfrac{1}{100}\times\dfrac{p^2}{\omega^2}}} = \frac{f_0}{\omega_0^2\left(\dfrac{25}{16}+\dfrac{1}{100}\times\dfrac{9}{4}\right)^{1/2}}$$

$$= \frac{f_0}{\omega_0^2\left(\frac{634}{400}\right)^{1/2}} = \frac{20 f_0}{\omega_0^2\sqrt{634}}.$$

And, *for low damping,* amplitude is maximum when $P = \omega_0$. So that,

$$A_{max} = \frac{f_0}{\omega_0^2\sqrt{(1-1)^2 + \frac{1}{100}\times 1}} = \frac{f_0}{\omega_0^2\left(\frac{1}{100}\right)^{1/2}} = \frac{f_0}{\omega_0^2(1/10)} = \frac{10 f_0}{\omega_0^2}.$$

$$\therefore \quad \frac{A}{A_{max}} = \frac{20 f_0}{\omega_0^2\sqrt{634}} \times \frac{\omega_0^2}{10 f_0} = \frac{2}{\sqrt{634}} = 0.07943 \approx 0.08. \text{ Or, } A = 0.08\,A_{max}.$$

Thus, *the amplitude of the forced oscillation will be 0.08 of the maximum amplitude.*

Now, $$\tan\theta = \frac{2kp}{\omega_0^2 - p^2} = \frac{p\omega_0/10}{\omega_0^2 - p^2} = \frac{(3\omega_0/2)(\omega_0/10)}{\omega_0^2 - 9\omega_0^2/4}$$

$$= \frac{3\omega_0^2}{20} \times \frac{4}{5\omega_0^2} = \frac{3}{25} = 0.12.$$

Or, $$\theta = \tan^{-1}(0.12) = 6°51'$$

Therefore, *the forced oscillation is* $(180° - 6°51') = 173°9'$ *out of phase with the driving force.*

Example 8.31. A torison pendulum of moment of inertia 10^5 gm-cm^2 suffers an angular displacement of 4° under a constant torque of 2000 dynes-cm. What should be the frequency of the periodic torque that would set the pendulum in resonant vibration?

Solution. Here, *angular displacement* of the pendulum = 4° = 4 × π/180 *radian* and the *torque applied* = 2000 *dyne-cm.*

$$\therefore \quad \textit{Torque per unit angular displacment } (C) = \frac{\textit{Torque applied}}{\textit{Angular displacement}} = \frac{2000}{4\pi/180}$$

$$= \frac{2000\times 180}{4\pi} \textit{ dyne-cm/rad.}$$

Now, *for setting the pendulum into resonant vibration, the frequency of the applied torque must be the same, or very nearly the same, as the natural frequency of the pendulum,* $n = \frac{1}{2\pi}\sqrt{C/I}$.

Substituting the values of C and I, therefore, we have

$$\textit{required frequency of the periodic torque, } n = \frac{1}{2\pi}\sqrt{\frac{2000\times 180}{4\pi\times 10^5}} = 0.1704 \text{ or } 0.17 \text{ sec}^{-1}.$$

Example 8.32. A harmonic oscillator consisting of a 50 gm mass attached to a massless spring has a quality factor 200. If it oscillates with an amplitude of 2 cm in resonance with a periodic force of frequency 20 c.p.s., calculate (*i*) the average energy stored in it, (*ii*) the rate of dissipation of energy.

Solution. In the case of resonant vibration, *the average energy stored in the oscillator is equal to its maximum potential energy*

$$= \frac{1}{2}Cx_0^2 = \frac{1}{2}m\omega_0^2 x_0^2. \qquad [\because \quad C = m\omega_0^2]$$

Here, $m = 50$ *gm*, $\omega_0 = 2\pi n = 2\pi \times 20 = 40\pi$ and $x_0 = 2$ *cm*. So that,

$$\textit{average energy absorbed or stored up in the oscillator} = \frac{1}{2}\times 50\times(40\pi)^2\times(2)^2$$

$$= 16\times 10^4\,\pi^2 = 1.58\times 10^6 \textit{ ergs.}$$

Now, by its very definition, the quality factor

$$Q = 2\pi \frac{\textit{average energy stored}}{\textit{energy dissipated per cycle}}$$

$\therefore$ energy dissipated per cycle $= 2\pi \dfrac{\textit{average energy stored}}{Q}$

$$= 2\pi \frac{1.58 \times 10^6}{200} = \pi \times 1.58 \times 10^4 \textit{ ergs.}$$

Since there are 20 cycles to the second, we have

energy dissipated per second or *rate of dissipation of energy* $= 20\pi \times 1.58 \times 10^4$

$= 9.926 \times 10^5 \approx 10^6$ *erg/sec.*

Example 8.33. If in problem 8.32 above, the rate of dissipation of energy is desired to be halved, what should be (*i*) the amplitude of the applied periodic force, its frequency remaining unchanged, (*ii*) the frequency of the applied periodic force, its amplitude remaining unchanged?

Solution. (*i*) We know that the *rate of dissipation of energy* α(*amplitude of the force*)^2.

Thus, if R_1 and R_2 be the rate of dissipation of energy and f_{01} and f_{02} the amplitudes of the force in the two cases respectively, *the frequency of the force remaining the same in either case,* we have

$$R_1/R_2 = (f_{01}/f_{02})^2$$

Since, $R_2 = \dfrac{1}{2}R_1$, we have $R_1/\dfrac{1}{2}R_1 = f_{01}^2/f_{02}^2$, whence, $f_{01}^2/f_{02}^2 = 2$.

So that, $f_{02}^2 = f_{01}^2/2$ and, therefore, $f_{02} = f_{01}/\sqrt{2} = 0.7071 f_{01}$.

Thus, *the amplitude of the applied force n the second case must be* 0.7071 of its amplitude in the first case.

(*ii*) We have *quality factor of the oscillator*, $Q = \omega_0\tau = p_0\tau$, because at resonance, $\omega_0 = p_0$.

Since $\Delta p = k = 1/2\tau$, we have $\tau = 1/2\ \Delta p$.

$\therefore\ Q = p_0/2\ \Delta p$, whence, $\Delta p = p_0/2Q = 2\pi \times 20/2 \times 200 = \pi/10 = 0.3142$.

Or, angular frequency of the applied force must be $p = p_0 + \Delta p$.

And, therefore, *frequency of the applied force* $= \dfrac{p}{2\pi} = \dfrac{p_0}{2\pi} \pm \dfrac{\Delta p}{2\pi}$

$$= 20 \pm \frac{0.3142}{2\pi} = 20 \pm 0.05.$$

Example 8.34. A resistance of 10 ohms is joined in series with an inductance of 0.5 henry. What capacitance should be put in series with the combination to obtain maximum current? What will be the potential difference acros the resistance, inductance and capacitance? The current is being supplied by a 200 volts and 50 cycles A.C. mains. (*Agra, 2004*)

Solution. The impedance in an *LCR* circuit is, as we know, given by

$$Z = \sqrt{R^2 + (LP - 1/Cp)^2}$$

For resonance or maximum current, $Z = R$, *i.e.*, $(Lp - 1/Cp) = 0$. Or, $Lp = 1/Cp$, and, therefore, $C = 1/Lp^2$.

Here, $L = 0.5\ H$ and $p = 2\pi n = 2\pi \times 50 = 100\pi$. So that,

the required capacitance $C = \dfrac{1}{0.5 \times (100\pi)^2} = 20.27 \times 10^6$ *farad* $= 20.27\ \mu$F.

The *maximum current* will obviously be $I_0 = E_0/Z = 200/10 = 20$ *amp* $[\because Z = R = 10$ *ohms.*$]$

$\therefore$ *Potential difference across resistance* $R = I_0 \times R = 20 \times 10 = 200$ *volts.*

Since here reactance $X_L = Lp$ *due to inductance = reactance* $X_C = 1/Cp$ *due to capacitance*, we have *p.d. acorss* X_L = *p.d. across* $X_C = I_0\,Lp = I_0/Cp = 20 \times 0.5 \times 2\pi \times 50 = 3142$ *volts.*

Example 8.35. An *A.C.* potential of 1 × 10⁵ sec⁻¹ frequency and 1.0 volt amplitude is applied to a series *LCR* circuit. If *R* = 2.0 ohm, *L* = 0.50 millihenry, calculate the value of *C* to secure resonance. Also calculate the *rms* value of current and peak potential difference across the condenser.

Solution. As in problem 8.34 above, so also here, for resonance, $Z = R$, *i.e.*, $Lp = 1/Cp$, whence,

$$C = 1/Lp^2 = 1/L \times (2\pi n)^2 = 1/0.5 \times 10^{-3} \times (2\pi \times 10^5)^2$$
$$= 5.067 \times 10^{-9}\,F = 5.067 \times 10^{-3}\,\mu\text{F}.$$

Now, *rms or virtual value of current*, $I_v = E_v/Z = E_v/R$ [$\because$ at resonance $Z = R$.]

Since $E_v = E_0/\sqrt{2}$ and $R = 2$ *ohms*, we have

rms value of current, $I_v = E_0/2\sqrt{2} = 1/2\sqrt{2} = 0.3536$ *amp.* [$\because E_0 = 1$ *volt.*]

And, *peak p.d. across the condenser or capacitor = peak value of current × reactance* (X_C) *due to capacitor* $= (E_0/R) \times (1/Cp) = (1/2)\,(2 \times 10^7\pi^2/2\pi \times 10^5) = 157$ *volts.*

Example 8.36. A circuit contains a resistance of 4 ohms and an inductance of 0.68 henry, and an alternating effective emf of 500 volts at a frequency of 120 cps is applied to it. Find the value of the effective current in the circuit and the power factor.

Solution. We know that the *effective current in an LCR circuit*

$$= \frac{\textit{Effective emf}}{\textit{Impedance of the circuit}} = \frac{E}{Z}.$$

Here, *effective emf* $E = 500$ *volts* and *impedance* $Z = \sqrt{R^2 + L^2p^2} = \sqrt{R^2 + L^2(2\pi n)^2}$.

Or, $Z = \sqrt{(4)^2 + (0.68)^2(2\pi \times 120)^2} = \sqrt{16 + 262800} = 512.6$ ohms.

$\therefore$ *Effective current in the circuit*, $I = \dfrac{500}{512.6} = 0.9754$ amp.

And, power factor of the circuit $= R/Z = 4/512.6 = 0.0078$.

Example 8.37. An electric lamp which runs at 40 volts D.C. and consumes 10 amperes current is connected to A.C. mains at 100 volts, 50 cycles. Calculate the inductance of the choke.

Solution. Clearly, *resistance of the lamp*, $R = \dfrac{\textit{voltage}}{\textit{current}} = \dfrac{40}{10} = 4$ ohms.

And, *impedance of A.C. circuit*, $Z = \sqrt{R^2 + (Lp)^2}$, where L is the *inductance of the choke.*

Here, $R = 4$ *ohms*, $P = 2\pi n = 2\pi \times 50 = 100\,\pi$ and $I = 10$.

$$\therefore \quad I = \frac{E}{Z} = \frac{E}{\sqrt{R^2 + (Lp)^2}} = \frac{100}{\sqrt{4^2 + (L + 100\pi)^2}} = 10.$$

Or, $\dfrac{10^4}{16 + 10^4\pi^2L^2} = 100$. Or, $10^6\pi^2L^2 = 10^4 - 1600 = 8400$.

So that, $L^2 = 8400/10^6\pi^2$. Or, $L = \sqrt{84/10^4\pi^2} = \sqrt{84}/100\pi = 0.02917$.

Thus, the *inductance of the choke* = 0.02917 henry.

Example 8.38. An inductance coil of inductance 0.05 henry and resistance 12.4 ohms is connected to an A.C. supply at 200 volts and 50 cycles. Find (*a*) power factor, and (*b*) angle of lag. (*c*) Show that the power consumed in just equal to the rate of production of heat.

Solution. (*a*) We know that the *power factor*, $\cos\phi = R/Z = R/\sqrt{R^2+(Lp)^2}$.

Here, $R = 12.4$ *ohms*, $L = 0.05$ henry and $p = 2\pi n = 2\pi \times 50 = 100\,\pi$.

$\therefore$ *power factor*, $\cos\phi = \dfrac{12.4}{\sqrt{(12.4)^2+(0.05\times 100\pi)^2}} = \dfrac{12.4}{\sqrt{153.8+246.7}} = \dfrac{12.4}{20} = 0.62.$

(*b*) And, therefore, angle of lag, $\phi = \cos^{-1}(0.62) = 51°41'$.

(*c*) Clearly, power consumed, $E_v I_v \cos\phi$.

Now, $E_v = 100$ volts, $I_v = E_v/Z = 100/\sqrt{(12.4)^2+(0.05\times 100\pi)^2} = 100/20$

$= 5$ *ampere* and $\cos\phi = 0.62$.

$\therefore$ *power consumed* $= 100 \times 5 \times 0.62 = 310$ *watts*.

And, *rate of production of heat* $= I^2R = 25 \times 12.4 = 310$ *watts*.

Thus, *power consumed* = *rate of production of heat*.

EXERCISE

I–Damping force–Damped harmonic oscillator

1. What is meant by a damping or a dissipative force? What is its effect on a harmonic oscillator? Illustrate your answer by one or two homely examples. ***(Purvanchal 2004)***
2. Prove that the damping force is independent of acceleration or displacement and is proportional to velocity. ***(H.P.U. 2003, 2000; GNDU 2000)***
3. Obtain an expression for the velocity of a damped harmonic oscillator and deduce from it the definition of *relaxation time* (τ) of the oscillator.
4. Show that both velocity and kinetic energy of a damped harmonic oscillator fall exponentially with time, the relaxation time in the latter case being half that in the former. ***(Guhati 2004)***
5. (*a*) What are damped vibrations? Establish the differential equation of motion for a damped harmonic oscillator and obtain an expression for displacement. Discuss the case of heavy damping, and light damping. ***(P.U. 2003; Nagpur U. 2002, 2001, Kerala U.2001; Pbi. U. 2001; H.P.U. 2000; Purvanchal U. 2007, 2006, 2004)***

   (*b*) Using the general solution of equation of damped simple harmonic motion discuss the case of critical damping. ***(Nagpur U. 2001; P.U.)***
6. Write down the equation of damped simple harmonic oscillator. Find the expression for displacement and discuss when we get oscillatory damped simple harmonic motion. ***(P.U.2003; Luck. U. 2002; Nagpur U. 2001; Indore U. 2001; Purvanchal U. 2004; H.P.U. 2000)***
7. Deduce the differential equation of a damped harmonic oscillator and discuss in detail the case of critical and underdamping.
8. Write the differential equations for the following cases of damped harmonic oscillator: (*i*) mechanical (*ii*) electrical. ***(Kanpur 2004)***
9. What is meant by the terms (*i*) *logarithmic decrement* and (*ii*) quality factor (Q) of a damped harmonic oscillator? Obtain the usual expressions for them. ***(Bangalore 2006)***
10. Obtain the differential equation for the motion of the coil of a moving coil galvanometer and discuss the conditions under which its motion is (*i*) *dead beat*, (*ii*) *critical* and (*iii*) *ballistic*. Enumerate the essential requirements of a ballistic galvanometer. ***(Patna, 2006)***

11. Show that $x = (A+Bt)e^{\frac{-r}{2m}t}$ is the solution of the differential equation $\frac{d^2x}{dt^2}+\frac{r}{m}\frac{dx}{dt}+\frac{s}{m}x=0$ for the critically damped oscillations.

12. A charged capacitor discharges through an inductance and resistance in series. Discuss possible solutions and represent these by graphs. Deduce the condition under which the discharge is (*i*) critically damped and (*ii*) oscillatory. Obtain expression for the frequency. Does the presence of resistance effect the amplitude and frequency of damped oscillations? ***(P.U., 2003; H.P.U., 2002, 2000)***

13. Define logarithmic decrement and derive a relation for it for a mechanical oscillator and an electrical oscillator. How can you determine experimentally the value of logarithmic decrement and damping co-efficient? ***(P.U. 2003, 2002; Meerut U. 2001; G.N.D.U. 2004, 2000; Pbi. U., 2000)***

14. (*a*) In a ballistic galvanometer the coil is wound over a non-metallic frame, comment. ***(Pbi. U. 2002)***

    (*b*) Why the coil of a moving coil galvanometer, ammeter and voltmeter is wound over a metallic frame? ***(Pbi. U. 2001)***

15. Define relaxation time of damped oscillatory system. Show that it varies inversely as damping constant. Derive an expression for relaxation period of (*i*) a mechanical oscillator (*ii*) electrical oscillator. How is it useful in determining the logarithmic decrement of a system? ***(P.U., 2004; H.P.U., 2001; Pbi. U., 2000; G.N.D.U., 2001)***

16. (*a*) Define quality factor of a damped oscillator. Deduce an expression for it for a mechanical oscillator and an electrical oscillator.

    (*b*) Show that (*i*) lower the damping higher will be the quality factor. (*ii*) For large quality factor damping has little or no effect on the frequency. ***(G.N.D.U. 2002; H.P.U. 2001; Pbi. U. 2000)***

17. (*a*) What is damping? On what factors the damping depends?

    (*b*) What is the effect of damping on the natural frequency of an oscillator? ***(Pbi. U. 2003)***

    (*c*) Does viscous damping remain proportional to velocity under all conditions? ***(Pbi. U. 2000)***

    (*d*) Write unit of damping constant and damping coefficient for mechanical and electrical oscillator. ***(H.P.U. 2002)***

18. Distinguish between transient and steady state in a forced oscillator. Explain the transient and steady state behaviour of a mechanical oscillator driven by a force.

    $$F = F_0 e^{i\omega t}$$

    Discuss the case when $F = F_0 \cos \omega t$ and when $F = F_0 \sin \omega t$ and show that the driven oscillator is always behind the driving force in phase.

    (Nagpur U. 2003; H.P.U., 2003, 2002, 2000; P.U., 2004, 2003, 2002, 2000; G.N.D.U., 2003; Luck. U., 2001; Pbi. U., 2002, 2000; Meerut U., 2002)

19. Discuss the behaviour of displacement versus driving force frequency in case of a forced oscillator. Show that (*i*) The displacement at low frequency is independent of frequency (*ii*) The resonant frequency of driving force is slightly less than the natural frequency of the oscillator (*iii*) Maximum amplitude $A_{max} = \frac{F_0}{r\omega'}$ where r is damping constant and $\omega' = \sqrt{\frac{s}{m}-\frac{r^2}{4m^2}}$

    (H.P.U., 2003, 2001; P.U., 2002, 2000; G.N.D.U. 2001; Meerut U., 2000)

20. For a mechanical oscillator driven by a force $F = F_0 \cos \omega t$, discuss the variation of phase difference between displacement and driving force with driving force frequency. What is the phase difference between displacement and force at very high frequency? ***(G.N.D.U., 2002; H.P.U., 2001, 2000)***

21. (*a*) Draw a graph between velocity amplitude and driving force frequency of a forced oscillator. ***(H.P.U., 2001)***

    (*b*) Show that whereas at resonance displacement lags behind the driving force by $\pi/2$, the velocity is in phase with driving force. ***(G.N.D.U., 2002)***

22. Discuss the variation of acceleration amplitude with driving force frequency of a forced mechanical oscillator and show that

(*i*) Acceleration amplitude at high frequency is frequency independent and

(*ii*) When damping constant is very small the acceleration amplitude resonance frequency equals the natural frequency of the forced oscillator. **(*P.U., 2003; G.N.D.U., 2003*)**

23. (*a*) What is absorption resonance curve? Draw it for a forced oscillator. Draw is it so called? **(*P.U., 2001, 2000*)**

(*b*) What is meant by resonance absorption band width? Define it and show it on a $P - \omega$ graph. Explain how the damping of the medium effects the band width? **(*Pbi. U., 2003; Nagpur U., 2001; H.P.U., 2000*)**

24. Derive an expression for the *Q*-value of a forced oscillator in terms of resonance absorption band width. If the *Q*-value of an oscillator is increased how is band width of the absorption curve affected.

Prove that band width = $\frac{\omega_0}{Q}$ where the symbols have their usual meaning.

(*Pbi. U. 2001; P.U. 2004, 2001; Nagpur U. 2003, 2001; G.N.D.U., 2000*)

25. (*a*) Find the *Q*-value of an oscillator in terms of the energy decay.

(*b*) What is figure of merit of a vibration and how is it defined in terms of bandwidth? The quality factor *Q* is a measure of sharpness of resonance in case of a forced oscillator. Explain. **(*P.U., 2000*)**

26. An electric oscillator is driven by an *e.m.f.* $E = E_0 e^{i\omega t}$. Derive an expression for the current in the electric circuit in the steady state and find its value when the applied *e.m.f* is

(*i*) $E = E_0 \cos \omega t$. (*ii*) $E_0 \sin \omega t$ **(*P.U.2001, 2000*)**

27. (*i*) What are damped oscillations?

(*ii*) Obtain differential equation of motion of a damped harmonic oscillator.

(*iii*) Obtain general solution of differential equation of a damped harmonic oscillator.

(*iv*) In an oscillatory circuit, $L = 0.2$ Henry, $C = 0.0012$ μF. What is the maximum value of resistance for the circuit to be oscillatory? **(*Nagpur U. 2006*)**

28. Obtain an expression for the power dissipated in damped harmonic oscillator. **(*Nagpur U. 2007*)**

29. Discuss an LCR circuit as an example of a damped harmonic oscillator and show that it is the resistance alone which is responsible for the damping of the oscillations. Discuss the conditions under which the discharge of the capacitor is *aperiodic, critical* and *oscillatory.* What is the quality factor or such a circuit?

30. A body is propelled through a viscous medium with a speed of 300 *cm/sec*. On the propelling force being suddenly removed, it comes to rest after covering a distance of 45 metres. What is its relaxation time? How long would it be before its speed falls to 30 *cm/sec*? **[Ans.** 15 *sec*; 34.5 *sec*.]

31. Show that whereas the amplitude of a pendulum oscillating in a viscous medium like air is affected, its time-period remains practically unaffected.

[**Hint.** Damping force due to a viscous medium $= -6\pi\eta r v = -6\pi\eta r l\, d\theta/dt$, where *r* is the radius of the bob, *v*, its velocity and *l*, the length of the pendulum. The *equation* of motion of the pendulum is thus $ml d^2\theta/dt^2 + 6\pi\eta r l\, d\theta/dt + mg\theta = 0$, where *m* is the mass of the bob. This reduces to $d^2\theta/dt^2 + (6\pi\eta r/m)\, d\theta/dt + (g/l)\theta = 0$ which gives $k = 3\pi\eta r/m = 3\pi\eta r/\frac{4}{3}\pi r^3\rho = 9\eta/4r^2\rho$, (where ρ is the density of the material of the bob) and ω_0^2 is *g/l*.

Now, *time-period* $T = 2\pi/\omega = 2\pi/\sqrt{\omega_0^2 - k^2}$. Since *k* is small compared with ω_0, we have $T = 2\pi/\sqrt{\omega_0^2} = 2\pi/\omega_0 = 2\pi/\sqrt{g/l} = 2\pi\sqrt{l/g}$, the same as in the absence of damping.

And the *amplitude* is of course given by $a = a_0 e^{-kt}$, where a_0 is the amplitude in the absence of damping.]

32. If the damping in the case of a damped harmonic oscillator be very small, obtain expression for (*i*) average total energy of the oscillator and (*ii*) average rate of energy dissipation. (*iii*) Show that the latter is equal to the work done by the damping force per second.

[Ans. (*i*) $E = \frac{1}{2} m\omega^2 a_0^2 e^{-2kt}$, (*ii*) E/τ, (*iii*) $-\gamma dt/dt = P$.]

33. Show that the relaxation time of a damped harmonic oscillator has the dimensions of time. Also show that (*i*) in this time (τ) the amplitude of the oscillator falls to 0.6084 of its undamped value and that (*ii*) it is reduced to half its undamped value in time 1.3846 τ. ($e = 2.718$ and $\log_e 10 = 2.30$).

34. (*a*) Show that damping has little or no effect on the frequency of a harmonic oscillator if its quality factor (Q) be large.

[**Hint.** See worked example 7]

(*b*) If the quality factor of a sonometer wire of frequency 300 *cps* be 2×10^3, in what time will its energy be reduced to $1/e^{th}$ of its energy in the absence of damping. [**Ans.** In 1.061 *sec.*]

35. The amplitude of a simple pendulum, with a bob of mass 400 *gm* and oscillating in air, falls to half its undamped value on completion of 50 complete oscillations. (*i*) If its time-period be 2 sec, calculate its quality factor. (*ii*) What should be the mass of the bob, its size and shape remaining unchanged, so that the damping may become critical? [**Ans.** (*i*) 453.7, (*ii*) 0.44 *gm.*]

36. A capacitor of capacitance 1 μF is discharged through a resistance of 2 *ohms* and an inductance of 1 henry. Is the discharge of the capacitor oscillatory? If so, obtain its frequency and calculate the time in which the amplitude of the oscillations falls to 10% of its undamped value.

[**Ans.** *Discharge oscillatory*; $n = 159$; In 2.3 *sec.*]

37. (*a*) In an *LCR* circuit, $L = 0.2$ *henry* and $C = 2\mu F$. What should be the maximum resistance in the circuit for the discharge of the capacitor to be oscillatory in character?

(*b*) The quality factor of an oscillatory circuit is 100 and its frequency 8 kilo-cycles per second. How will its frequency change if the resistance in the circuit be reduced to zero?

[**Ans.** (*a*) *Less than* 20 *ohms*, (*b*) *The frequency will increase by* 1 *cycle per sec.*]

38. Find whether the discharge of a condenser for the following inductive circuit is oscillatory: $C = 0.1\ \mu F$, $L = 10\ mH$, $R = 200$ *ohms*. If the circuit is oscillatory, calculate its frequency. ***(Agra, 1963)***

[**Ans.** *Discharge oscillatory*; $n = 4772$ *cps*]

39. (*a*) What is physical significance of logarithmic decrement of a damped oscillatory system?

(*b*) Explain how the conditions of critical damping are used in designing of electrical instruments.

40. Express amplitude, energy, logarithmic decrement and relaxation time in terms of Q the quality factor. ***(Pbi. U. 2002; H.P.U. 2000)***

41. Discuss the methods (logarithmic decrement, relaxation time and quality factor) for quantitative measurement of damping effect in a damped simple harmonic oscillator.

42. Which is greater the natural frequency of damped oscillations or frequency of displacement resonance?

43. Why is there large amplitude, when frequency of external periodic force is same as natural frequency of the body.

44. Show that the displacement resonance occurs at a frequency slightly less than the frequency of velocity resonance. ***(P.U., 2002; H.P.U., 2001)***

45. What is sharpness of resonance? Explain the effect of damping on sharpness of resonance.

(Meerut U., 2005, 2003, 2001; Nagpur U., 2003, 2002; G.N.D.U., 2003; Luck., 2002)

II–Driven harmonic oscillator

46. Write down and solve the differential equation of a damped harmonic oscillator subjected to a sinusoidal force and obtain expressions for its maximum amplitude and quality factor.

47. For a driven harmonic oscillator of natural frequency $\omega/2\pi$, described by $mx + rx - kx = F \sin pt$, deduce an expression for velocity amplitude $\dot{x}_0$. Show that for the cases $p >> \omega$, $p = \omega$ and $p << \omega$, this amplitude is governed by the inertia factor, the resistance factor and the spring factor respectively.

48. Show that in the case of a system undergoing a forced oscillation, the response is (*i*) independent of its mass if $p << \omega_0$ and (*ii*) independent of the spring constant if $p >> \omega_0$.

49. Show that in a driven oscillator, the maximum power is absorbed at the frequency of velocity resonance and not at the frequency of amplitude resonance.

50. Assuming the results of forced oscillations, discuss the sharpness of resonance.
Explain the statement '*the quality factor (Q) is a measure of the sharpness of resonance in the case of a driven oscillator*'.

51. Show that the half width of the velocity versus driving frequency curve and that of the power absorbed versus driving frequency curve are $\sqrt{3k}$ and k respectively.

52. Why should two tuning forks be very accurately in unison to show resonance while a tuning fork and an air column require to be approximately turned. ***(Nagpur U. 2002)***

53. Derive the expression for the average power supplied to a forced (*i.e.*, driven) oscillator by an external driving force

$$F = F_0 \cos \omega t$$ ***(P.U. 2000)***

54. What is driven harmonic oscillator? How does it differ from simple and damped harmonic oscillator? ***(Nagpur U. 2009)***

55. (*a*) Explain the terms *reactance, impedance* and *power factor*. ***(Patna, 2001)***
(*b*) Define *virtual current* and *virtual potential* in an *A.C.* circuit. ***(Delhi (Subs.), 2000)***

56. Show that a driven oscillator is always behind the driving force in phase and that its displacement is maximum when the driving force is zero and vice versa.
Illustrate for zero, low and medium damping, the general nature of the phase lag of a driven oscillator as the driving frequency gradually increases and passes through the natural frequency of the oscillator.

57. Give the theory of oscillations in a *LCR* circuit with small resistance, deducing expressions for (*i*) frequency of oscillations, (*ii*) power dissipation and (*iii*) quality factor of the circuit. ***(Agra (Supp), 2001)***

58. Write explanatory notes on the terms: *reactance, impedance, rms value of current, rms value of emf* and *power factor* in a driven *LCR* circuit.
Show that the power in such a circuit, like that in a D.C. circuit, appears in the form of heat in the resistance alone.

59. Obtain an expression for the current in a driven *LCR* circuit and discuss how the current lags or leads the applied emf in phase (*a*) when the net reactance in the circuit is (*i*) capacitive, (*ii*) inductive and (*b*) when reactance in the circuit is equal to resistance. Illustrate your answer with the help of suitable graphs.

60. A damped harmonic oscillator is subjected to a sinusoidal driving force whose frequency is altered but amplitude kept constant. It is found that the amplitude of the oscillator increases from 0.02 *mm* at very low driving frequency to 8.0 *mm* at a frequency of 100 *cps*. Obtain the values of (*i*) the quality factor, (*ii*) the relaxation time, (*iii*) the damping factor and (*iv*) the half-width of the resonance curve.
[**Ans.** (*i*) $Q \cong 400$, (*ii*) $\tau = 0.4245$ *sec*, (*iii*) $k = 1.178$, (*iv*) 2.04 *rad/sec*.]

61. A damped harmonic oscillator of quality factor 20 is subjected to a sinusoidal driving force of frequency twice the natural frequency of the oscillator. If the damping be small, what fraction will the amplitude of the oscillator be of its maximum value and by what angle will it differ in phase from the driving force? [**Ans.** $a = 0.017\ a_{max}$; 178.5° *out of phase with the driving force*.]

62. Obtain the frequency of the periodic torque which, when applied to a torsion pendulum of moment of inertia 900 *gm-cm*^{2}, sets it into resonant oscillation. The torison constant of the suspension fibre may be taken to be 4×10^4 *dyne-cm/radian*. It is found that a small increase of 0.2% in the frequency of the periodic torque results in a fall of 80% in the amplitude of the pendulum. Calculate the quality factor of the pendulum. [**Ans.** $p = 1.06$ *cps*; $Q = 187$.]

63. An alternating sinusoidal emf is applied to a circuit containing an inductance L and a resistance R. Calculate the current at any instant in the circuit.

64. Find the natural frequency of a circuit containing inductance of 50 micro-henry and a capacitance of 0.0005 microfarad. Find the wavelength to which it corresponds. ***(Punjab, 2002)***
[**Ans.** 1.007 *cps*; 298.1 *metres*.]

[**Hint.** $c = n\lambda$, where c is the velocity of light (or electromagnetic radiation)]

65. An alternating potential of 110 volts and 50 cycles frequency is applied to a circuit containing a resistance of 200 *ohms*, inductance of 5 henry and a capacitance of 2 μF. Calculate the maximum current in the circuit. ***(Delhi (Subs.), 2003)***

[**Ans.** *peak value of current* = 0.78 *amp*.]

66. To a circuit containing an inductance of 10 millihenry, a capacitance of 1 μF and a resistance of 10 *ohms* in series, an *rms* voltage of 100 V is applied. Calculate the frequency at which the circuit will be in resonance with the current of the same frequency and find the value of the current.

[**Ans.** $n = 1592$ and $I_v = 10$ *amp*.]

67. Find the capacitance of the capacitor which must be placed in series with a resistance of 5 *ohms* and inductance of 200 millihenry to bring the current in phase with the voltage if the frequency be 60 cycles per sec. What current will flow if 100 volts be imposed on the circuit? ***(Delhi (Hons.), 1957)***

[**Ans.** 35.20 μF; 20 *amp*.]

68. Find the value of the inductance which should be connected in series with a capacitance of 0.5 μF, a resistance of 10 *ohms* and an *A.C.* source of frequency 50 *cps*, so that the power factor of the circuit be unity. [**Ans.** 20.29 *henry*.]

69. An alternating voltage of 4 *volts* is applied at the resonant frequency to a coil of inductance 0.004 H and resistance 20 ohms in series with a 0.001 μF capacitor. Find (*i*) the resonant frequency (*ii*) the current flowing, (*iii*) the voltage across the capacitor. [**Ans.** (*i*) 79600 *cps*; 0.2 *amp*; 400 *volts*.]

70. An alternating voltage of 100 *rms* is applied to a circuit of resistance 0.5 *ohm* and an inductance of 0.01 *henry*, the frequency being 50 *cycles/sec*. What is the current and the time lag?

(Patna (Supp.), 1963) **Ans.** 31 *amp*; 0.0045 *sec*.

71. (*a*) Find whether the discharge of a condenser through the following inductive circuit is oscillatory: $C = 0.1\ \mu F, L = 10$ *milli henry*, $R = 200$ *ohms*. If the circuit is oscillatory, calculate its frequency.

(Agra, 1963) **Ans.** *Oscillatory*; 4772 *cps*.

(*b*) In an oscillatory circuit, $L = 0.2$ *henry*, $C = 0.0012\ \mu F$. What is the maximum value of resistance for the circuit to be oscillatory? ***(Punjab, 1959)*** [**Ans.** Less than 2.582×10^4 *ohms*.]

72. A coil connected to a sinusoidal alternating supply of *emf* 240 *volts* (*rms*) and of frequency 50 *cps* takes a current of 5.0 *amp* (*rms*). A wattmeter in the circuit reads 1000 *watts*. Find (*a*) the power factor of the circuit, (*b*) the resistance of the coil, (*c*) the reactance of the coil, (*d*) the maximum stored energy. [**Ans.** (a) 0.8; (*b*) 40 *ohms*; (*c*) 27 *ohms very nearly*, (*d*) 21 *joules very nearly*.]

73. Calculate the band width of an acoustic system having $Q = 1.75$ and resonant frequency 280 Hz.

[**Ans.** 160 Hz] ***(Nagpur U., 2001, 2006)***

74. Find the resonant frequency of an acoustic system having Q equal to 1.60 and half power frequencies equal to 180 Hz and 380 Hz respectively. [**Ans.** 320 Hz]***(Nagpur U., 2008)***

75. Find the frequency of a circuit containing inductance of 1000 μH and capacity of 0.01 μF. To which wavelength (of radio wave) its response will be maximum? [**Ans.** 1890 m]***(P.U. 2001, 2000)***

76. A torsion pendulum of moment of inertia 10^5 *gm-cm*^{2} suffers an angular displacement of 4° under a constant torque of 2000 *dynes-cm*. What should be the frequency of the periodic torque that would set the pendulum in resonant vibration? [**Ans.** 9.926×10^5 *erg/sec*]

9

Chapter

COUPLED OSCILLATORS

Brief Contents

INTRODUCTION

In the previous chapter, we have studied damped and driven oscillators. The harmonic oscillator and the system it models have a *single degree of freedom*. More complicated systems have more degrees of freedom, for example two masses and three spring system. In such cases, the behaviour of each variable influences that of the others. This leads to a *coupling* of oscillations of the individual degrees of freedom. When the motion of one oscillating system influences another, the two are said to be *coupled.*

The two or more oscillators linked together in such a way that an exchange of energy transfer takes place between them are called coupled oscillators.

In a forced oscillator, it is assumed that the external driving force is practically not affected by the oscillations of the driven system, *i.e.,* the flow of energy between the driving agency and the driven system is only in one direction-from the driving agency to the driven system. However, in actual practice, there is always some feed back of energy, although small. In this chapter, let us study two coupled oscillators and their normal modes of vibration and extend the idea to N coupled oscillators.

9.1 SOME DEFINITIONS

Normal Coordinates: Normal co-ordinates are those co-ordinates which help us to express the equations of motion of the harmonic oscillators of a coupled system in the form of a set of *linear differential equations with constant co-efficients* and in which each equation contains only *one variable.*

Normal Modes of Vibration. *The manner in which a coupled system oscillates is called a mode.* The mode of a coupled system may be harmonic or non-harmonic.

The harmonic modes of a coupled system are called normal modes.

Normal modes have definite characteristics and are represented by linear differential equations with constant coefficients and only one dependent variable or normal co-ordinates. A normal mode has its own frequency known as *normal frequency*. In each normal mode all the components of the system vibrate with the same normal frequency. The normal modes of vibration are *entirely independent of each other*, since the energy associated with a normal mode is never exchanged with the energy associated with another normal mode. The total energy of the oscillator is equal to the sum of the energies of all the normal modes. If at any time only one mode is excited and vibrates the other modes will always be at rest and unexcited and these will acquire no energy from the vibrating mode.

Degrees of Freedom. A degree of freedom of a system is the *independent way* by which the system may *acquire energy*. A degree of freedom is assigned its own particular normal co-ordinates. The *number* of degrees of freedom and the number of normal co-ordinates of a system is the number of different ways in which the system can acquire energy. Each harmonic oscillator has two degrees of freedom as it may have *both kinetic* as well as *potential energy*.

The kinetic energy of a simple harmonic oscillator of mass m and having displacement co-ordinate x is given by $\frac{1}{2}m\dot{x}^2 = a\dot{x}^2$ where $a = \frac{1}{2}m$. The potential energy is given by $\frac{1}{2}sx^2 = bx^2$ where s is the stiffness constant.

It the normal modes of a harmonic oscillator are represented by normal co-ordinates X and Y, then the total energy corresponding to the two modes will be

$$E_X = a\dot{X}^2 + bX^2$$

and
$$E_Y = c\dot{Y}^2 + dY^2$$

where a, b, c and d are constants, $a\dot{X}^2$ and $c\dot{Y}^2$ give the kinetic energy and bX^2 and dY^2 the potential energy.

9.2 EQUATION OF MOTION OF STIFFNESS COUPLED SYSTEM OF TWO PENDULUMS

Consider a coupled system of two identical pendulums each having a pendulum bob of mass m suspended by a light weightless, rigid rod of length l. The bobs are connected by a light spring of stiffness s, whose normal length is equal to the distance between the bobs when none of the two pendulums is displaced from its equilibrium position. Such pendulums are known as **stiffness coupled**.

Let the two pendulums A and B be set into vibrations with a *small* amplitude in the plane of the paper and let x and y be the displacements (in the same direction) of the pendulums marked A and B respectively as shown in Fig. 9.1 and Fig. 9.2, then the spring is elongated by a length $(x-y)$ and the corresponding force comes into play is $s(x-y)$. The component of the force due to gravity tending to bring the bobs of the pendulums back to its mean position is

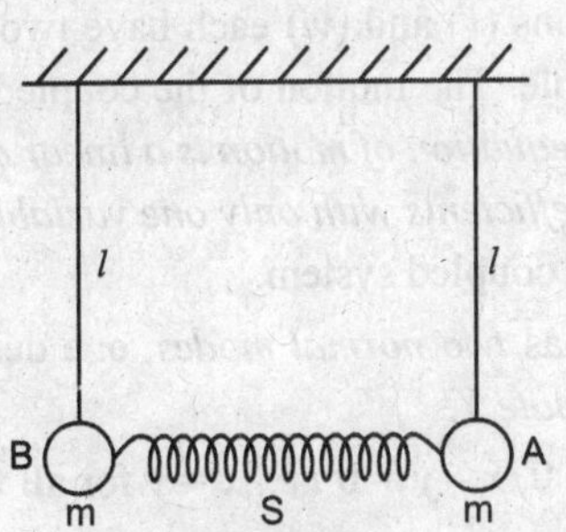

Fig. 9.1

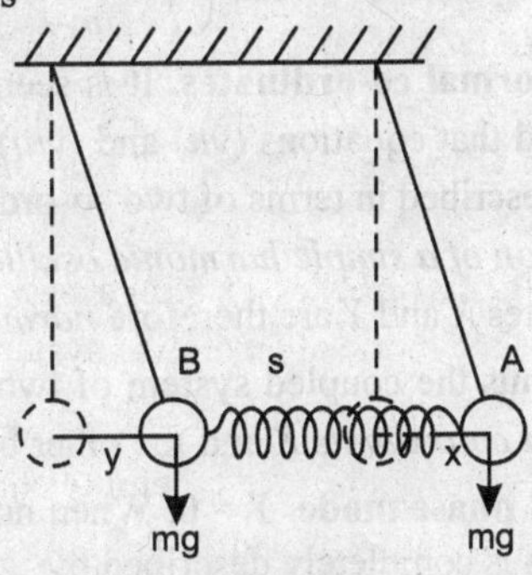

Fig. 9.2

$$= -\frac{mgx}{l} \text{ for the pendulum } A$$

and
$$= -\frac{mgy}{l} \text{ for the pendulum } B.$$

$\therefore$ The equations of motion for the pendulums A and B respectively, are

$$m\ddot{x} = -mg\frac{x}{l} - s(x-y) \quad ...(i)$$

and
$$m\ddot{y} = -mg\frac{y}{l} + s(x-y) \quad ...(ii)$$

The first term in each equation is the normal simple harmonic motion term and the second term is due to the *coupling of the spring*. If $x > y$ the spring is extended beyond its normal length and will, therefore, apply a force against the acceleration of x but in favour of the acceleration of y. Dividing equations (*i*) and (*ii*) by m and substituting $\frac{g}{l} = \omega_0^2$, we have

$$\ddot{x} + \frac{g}{l}x = \ddot{x} + \omega_0^2 x = -\frac{s}{m}(x-y) \quad ...(iii)$$

$$\ddot{Y} + \frac{g}{l}y = \ddot{Y} + \omega_0^2 y = -\frac{s}{m}(m - x) \quad \text{...(iv)}$$

Adding (*iii*) and (*iv*), we get

$$\ddot{x} + \ddot{Y} + \frac{g}{l}(x + y) = \ddot{x} + \ddot{Y} + \omega_0^2(x + y) = 0 \quad \text{...(v)}$$

Subtracting (*iv*) from (*iii*), we get

$$\ddot{x} - \ddot{Y} + \frac{g}{l}(x - y) = \ddot{x} - \ddot{y} + \left(\omega_0^2 + \frac{2s}{m}\right)(x - y) = 0 \quad \text{...(vi)}$$

Let us choose two new co-ordinates X and Y so that

$$X = x + y \quad \text{and} \quad Y = x - y$$

then $\dot{X} = \dot{x} + \dot{y}$ and $\dot{Y} = \dot{x} - \dot{y}$

and $\ddot{X} = \ddot{x} + \ddot{y}$ and $\ddot{Y} = \ddot{x} - \ddot{y}$

Substituting the values in (*v*) and (*vi*), we get

$$\ddot{X} + \frac{g}{l}X = \ddot{X} + \omega_0^2 X = 0 \quad \text{...(vii)}$$

and $$\ddot{Y} + \left(\frac{g}{l} + \frac{2s}{m}\right)Y = \ddot{Y} + \left(\omega_0^2 + \frac{2s}{m}\right)Y = 0 \quad \text{...(viii)}$$

Normal co-ordinates. It is seen that whereas equations (*v*) and (*vi*) each have two variables, we find that equations (*vii*) and (*viii*) have only one variable. The motion of the coupled system is thus described in terms of two co-ordinates X and Y. *Each equation of motion is a linear differential equation of a simple harmonic oscillator with constant coefficients with only one variable.* The co-ordinates X and Y are therefore *normal co-ordinates* of the coupled system.

Thus the coupled system of two simple pendulums has *two normal modes*, one described by *normal co-ordinate X* and the other by the *normal co-ordinate Y*.

In phase mode. $Y = 0$. When normal co-ordinate $Y = 0$, $x - y = 0$ *i.e.*, $x = y$ for all times. The motion is completely described by

$$\ddot{X} + \frac{g}{l}X = = \ddot{X} + \omega_0^2 X = 0$$

As the relative displacement of the two pendulum always remain the same ($\because$ $x = y$), *the stiffness of the coupling has no effect*. The spring always remains at its normal length. The frequency of oscillations is the same as that of either pendulum in isolation *i.e.*, $\omega_0^2 = \frac{g}{l}$. Both pendulums are always swinging in the same phase. Such vibrations are called *in-phase vibrations* and the corresponding mode is known as *in-phase mode*.

Out of phase mode: $X = 0$. When normal co-ordinate $X = 0$, $x + y = 0$ or $x = -y$ for all times. The motion is completely described by

$$\ddot{Y} + \left(\frac{g}{l} + \frac{2s}{m}\right)Y = \ddot{Y}\left(\omega_0^2 + \frac{2s}{m}\right)Y = 0$$

When the displacement (x) of the pendulum A is *positive* that of $B(y)$ is *negative* but equal to that of $A(x = -y)$. At zero displacement the two pendulums will be moving in opposite directions. Thus the periodic motion of the pendulums will be 180° out of phase. Such vibrations are called *out of phase vibrations* and the corresponding mode is known as *out of phase mode*.

9.3 TOTAL ENERGY OF TWO IDENTICAL STIFFNESS COUPLED PENDULUMS

The equation of motion of a stiffness coupled system of two identical pendulums A and B is given by

$$\ddot{X} + \omega_0^2 X = 0 \qquad ...(i)$$

$$\ddot{Y} + \left(\omega_0^2 + \frac{2s}{m}\right) Y = 0 \qquad ...(ii)$$

where $X = x + y$ and $Y = x - y$ are the *normal co-ordinates of the system* x and y are the displacement (in the same direction) of the pendulums A and B respectively as shown in Fig. 9.2 and $\omega_0^2 = \frac{g}{l}$ where l is the length of the pendulum and s is the stiffness constant. Solving equations (*i*) and (*ii*), we get

$$X = x + y = X_0 \cos(\omega_1 t - \phi_1) \qquad ...(iii)$$

and

$$Y = x - y = Y_0 \cos(\omega_2 t - \phi_2) \qquad ...(iv)$$

X_0 and Y_0 are the *normal mode amplitudes* and $\omega_1 = \omega_0 = \left(\frac{g}{l}\right)^{\frac{1}{2}}$ and

$$\omega_2 = \left(\omega_0^2 + \frac{2s}{m}\right)^{\frac{1}{2}} = \left(\frac{g}{l} + \frac{2s}{m}\right)^{\frac{1}{2}}$$ are *normal mode frequencies.*

To simplify further discussions, let

$$X_0 = Y_0 = 2a$$

and

$$\phi_1 = \phi_2 = 0$$

∴ Equations (*iii*) and (*iv*) give

$$X = x + y = 2a \cos \omega_1 t$$

and

$$Y = x - y = 2a \cos \omega_2 t$$

Adding (*v*) and (*vi*), we get

$$2x = X + Y = 2a \cos \omega_1 t + 2a \cos \omega_2 t$$

$$\therefore \quad x = \frac{1}{2}(X + Y) = a \cos \omega_1 t + a \cos \omega_2 t$$

Subtracting (*vi*) from (*v*), we get

$$y = \frac{1}{2}(X - Y) = a \cos \omega_1 t - a \cos \omega_2 t$$

The corresponding velocities are given by

$$\dot{x} = -a\omega_1 \sin \omega_1 t - a\omega_2 \sin \omega_2 t$$

and

$$\dot{y} = -a\omega_1 \sin \omega_1 t + a\omega_2 \sin \omega_2 t$$

Now let the system be set in motion by displacing the bob x to the right by a distance $x = 2a$ keeping $y = 0$ and both the bobs be released from rest so that $\dot{x} = \dot{y} = 0$ at a time $t = 0$. The motion of pendulum A is given by

$$x = a \cos \omega_1 t + a \cos \omega_2 t = 2a \cos \frac{(\omega_2 - \omega_1)t}{2} \cos \frac{(\omega_1 + \omega_2)t}{2}$$

and the motion of pendulum B is given by

$$y = a \cos \omega_1 t - a \cos \omega_2 t = -2a \sin \frac{(\omega_2 - \omega_1)t}{2} \sin \frac{(\omega_1 + \omega_2)t}{2}$$

$\left(\frac{\omega_2 - \omega_1}{2}\right) = \omega_m$ is called the *modulated* or beat frequency and $\frac{\omega_1 + \omega_2}{2} = \omega_a$ is called the *average frequency*.

Hence the modulated amplitude of pendulum $A = A = 2a \cos \omega_m t$

and $$x = A \cos \omega_a t$$

The modulated amplitude of pendulum $B = B = 2a \sin \omega_m t$

and $$y = -B \sin \omega_a t$$

If we assume that the spring is very weak and does not store any energy we can consider the modulated amplitude $2a \cos \omega_m t$ and $2a \sin \omega_m t$ to remain constant over one cycle of average frequency.

$\therefore$ Energy of pendulum A; $$E_A = \frac{1}{2}mv^2 = \frac{1}{2}m(A\omega_a)^2$$

$$= \frac{1}{2}m(2a\cos\omega_m t)^2\omega_a^2 = 2ma^2\omega_a^2\cos^2\omega_m t$$

Energy of pendulum B; $$E_B = \frac{1}{2}mv^2 = \frac{1}{2}m(B\omega_a)^2$$

$$= \frac{1}{2}m(2a\sin\omega_m t)^2\omega_a^2 = 2ma^2\omega_a^2\sin^2\omega_m t$$

Hence total energy $$E = E_A + E_B = 2\,ma^2\,\omega_a^2$$

Evidently, the total energy $E = E_A + E_B$ is constant as m, a and ω_a are constants.

Also $$E_A - E_B = 2ma^2\,\omega_a^2\,[\cos^2\omega_m t - \sin^2\omega_m t]$$

$$= E\cos 2\,\omega_m t = E\cos(\omega_2 - \omega_1)t$$

$\therefore$ $$E_A = \frac{1}{2}E[1 + \cos(\omega_2 - \omega_1)t]$$

and $$E_B = \frac{1}{2}E[1 - \cos(\omega_2 - \omega_1)t]$$

This shows that total energy is *constant* but *it flows back* and *forth between the pendulums at the modulated* (or beat) *frequency*.

Thus we see that after drawing aside the bob of the first pendulum by a distance $2a$ and releasing in the pendulum shows the cosine behaviour at a frequency ω_a which is the average of the two normal mode frequencies and its amplitude also varies according to the cosine law at a low frequency of half the difference between the normal mode frequencies. On the other hand pendulum 2 starts from zero and vibrates according to the sine law with the same average frequency and its amplitude builds up to $2a$ and then decays according to sine law at the same low frequency of half the difference between the normal mode frequencies.

The initial configuration $x = 2a$, $y = 0$ can be decomposed into X and Y modes as shown in Fig 9.3. The X mode *i.e.*, $x = y = a$ so that $X_0 = x + y = 2a$ is known as the '*in phase*' mode and the Y mode *i.e.*, $x = a$, $y = -a$ so that $Y_0 = x - y = 2a$ is known as the *out of phase* mode.

As the Y- mode has a higher frequency it will gain half a vibration (phase difference π radian) on the X-mode after a number of vibrations and the combination of X and Y mode then will give $x = 0$ and

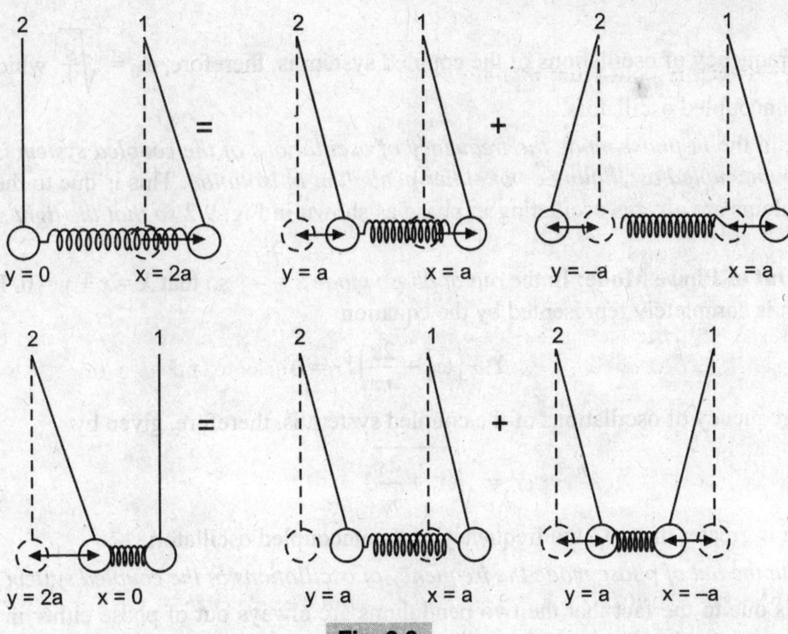

Fig. 9.3

$y = 2a$ as shown in the lower Fig. 9.3. After some time when Y gains another half a vibration $x = 2a$ and $y = 0$. Thus the pendulums only exchange energy the normal modes do not. The 'in phase' mode remains '*in phase*' mode and '*out of phase mode*' remains '*out of phase*' mode.

9.4 TYPES OF COUPLING

Two oscillators are coupled together to bring about an exchange of energy between them. The common coupling components for mechanical oscillators may be '*stiffness*' or '*mass*' and in case of electrical oscillators it may be '*capacitance*' or '*inductance*'. Capacitance and inductance are energy storing electrical components and coupling through them consumes no power, there by making it possible for the energy transfer to take place over a number of oscillations. Coupling may also be done through the '*resistance*' component but this causes an inevitable loss of energy that the amplitude goes on rapidly falling.

9.5 FREQUENCY OF OSCILLATION IN-PHASE AND OUT-OF-PHASE MODE

The differential equations of motion of coupled system of two identical (mechanical) oscillators say two simple pendulums in terms of normal co-ordinates X and Y are given by equations (*vii*) and (*viii*) of article 9.2 as

$$\ddot{X} + \frac{g}{l}X = \ddot{X} + \omega_0^2 X = 0$$

and $$\ddot{Y} + \left(\frac{g}{l} + \frac{2s}{m}\right)Y = \ddot{Y} + \left(\omega_0^2 + \frac{2s}{m}\right)Y = 0$$

where $X = x + y$ and $Y = x - y$; x and y being the displacements of the two (mechanical) oscillations, s the stiffness and m the mass.

(*i*) In Phase Mode: In the *in-phase* mode $x = y$ so that $Y = x - y = 0$. In such a case the motion is completely represented by the equation.

$$\ddot{X} + \frac{g}{l}X = \ddot{X} + \omega_0^2 X = 0$$

The frequency of oscillations of the coupled system is, therefore, $\omega_0 = \sqrt{\frac{g}{l}}$ which is the same as that of uncoupled oscillators.

Thus, in the *in-phase mode the frequency of oscillations of the coupled system is the same as that of the uncoupled oscillators or of either pendulum in isolation.* This is due to the fact that the two pendulums are always oscillating in phase as shown in Fig. 9.2 *so that the light spring always has its*

(*ii*) Out of Phase Mode: In the *out of phase mode* $x = -y$ so that $X = x + y = 0$. In such a case the motion is completely represented by the equation

$$\ddot{Y} + \left(\omega_0^2 + \frac{2s}{m}\right)Y = 0$$

The frequency of oscillations of the coupled system is, therefore, given by

$$\omega' = \sqrt{\omega_0^2 + \frac{2s}{m}}$$

which is greater than ω_0, the frequency of the uncoupled oscillators.

Thus in the out of phase mode the frequency of oscillations of the coupled system gets raised.

This is due to the fact that the two pendulums are always out of phase either in the *extended* or in the compressed position as shown in Fig. 9.3 *i.e., extreme positions and* hence the *coupling becomes*

9.6 CHARACTERISTICS OF IN-PHASE AND OUT-OF-PHASE MODES OF VIBRATION

Two oscillating, identical coupled simple pendulums have as we know, two normal modes of vibration.

(*i*) In-phase mode and (*ii*) Out of phase mode, each having its own characteristics.

(*a*) Characteristics of in phase mode. (*i*) The in-phase mode can be excited by displacing the bobs of the two pendulums to the same side by the same amount and then letting them oscillate purely on their own.

(*ii*) The equation of the in-phase mode is

$$\ddot{X} + \omega_0^2 X = 0 \qquad \text{...}(i)$$

It describes the oscillatory behaviour of the system when

$$Y = (x - y) = 0 \text{ or } x = y$$

(*iii*) The displacement of both the (bobs) or masses is the *same in magnitude* as well as in *direction* and both the masses continuously oscillate in the *same phase*. It means that both the pendulums pass through their mean position or through either of the extreme positions simultaneously.

(*iv*) The amplitude of the two simple pendulums is the same *i.e., a*.

(*v*) The shape or configuration of the mode is $\frac{x}{y} = +1$

(*vi*) Each pendulum executes simple harmonic oscillation at frequency $\omega_0 = \sqrt{g/l}$ which is the natural frequency of free oscillations of either pendulum in isolation.

(*vii*) In the in-phase mode there is no effect of the stiffness term s of the coupling on the motion of the two masses because the spring always has its natural length — it is neither stretched nor compressed.

(*viii*) A solution of Eq. (*i*) gives

$$X = X_0 \cos(\omega_0 t - \phi).$$

If the maximum value of x and y be a, then $X_0 = 2a$ is the *normal mode amplitude.*

(*b*) Characteristics of out of phase mode. (*i*) The out of phase mode can be excited by displacing the bobs of the two pendulums in opposite directions by the same amount and then let them oscillate freely on their own.

(*ii*) The equation of the out of phase mode is

$$\ddot{Y} + \left(\omega_0^2 + \frac{2s}{m}\right)Y = 0 \qquad ...(ii)$$

It describes the oscillatory behaviour of the system when

$$X = (x + y) = 0 \text{ or } x = -y$$

(*iii*) The displacement of either mass (bob) is equal in magnitude but opposite in direction to the other mass and the two masses continuously oscillate *out of phase* by an angle of 180° or π-radian with respect to each other.

It means that both the pendulums pass through their position (in opposite directions) or are at their (opposite) extreme positions simultaneously.

(*iv*) The amplitude of the two simple pendulums is the same *i.e.*, '*a*'.

(*v*) The shape or configuration of the mode is $\frac{x}{y} = -1$.

(*vi*) Each pendulum executes simple harmonic oscillations at a frequency

$$\omega' = \sqrt{\frac{g}{l} + \frac{2s}{m}} = \sqrt{\omega_0^2 + \frac{2s}{m}}$$

Which is higher than the natural frequency of the free oscillations of either pendulum.

(*vii*) In the out of phase mode the coupling term s dominates the motion of the two masses and raises the frequency of oscillation. It is because the coupling spring is either in the stretched or in the compressed state. Only once in one time period of oscillation the spring acquires its normal length when the masses pass through their mean positions.

(*viii*) A solution of Eq. (*ii*) gives

$$Y = Y_0 \cos(\omega' t - \phi')$$

If the maximum value of x and y be a, then $Y_0 = 2a$ is the normal mode amplitude.

Note. X_0 and Y_0 are purely mathematical quantities and do not represent the amplitude of the oscillation of either pendulum which has a value $a = \frac{X_0}{2}$ for the in-phase mode and $a = \frac{Y_0}{2}$ for the out of phase mode.

9.7 GENERAL METHOD OF FINDING NORMAL MODE FREQUENCIES

Consider a system of two coupled simple pendulums of the same length coupled by a spring of stiffness s, then their equations of motion are

$$m\ddot{x} + \frac{mg}{l}x + s(x - y) = 0 \qquad ...(i)$$

and

$$m\ddot{y} + \frac{mg}{l}y - s(x - y) = 0 \qquad ...(ii)$$

where x and y are the displacements of the bobs of the two pendulums respectively from their mean positions, l is the length of each pendulum, m the mass of each pendulum bob as proved in Eq.(*i*) and (*ii*) of article 9.2.

Now, when a coupled system oscillates in a *single normal mode* each component of the system vibrates with the frequency of that mode.

Therefore, supposing that the system of the coupled pendulums vibrate only in one of its normal modes, let the frequency be ω, then the solutions of the above equations are

$$x = A\cos\omega t$$

and

$$y = B\cos\omega t$$

where A and B are the displacement amplitudes of x and y at the frequency ω.

$$\ddot{x} = -A\omega^2\cos\omega t \text{ and } \ddot{y} = -B\omega^2\cos\omega t$$

Substituting in (*i*) and (*ii*), we have

$$\left[-m\omega^2 A + \frac{mg}{l}A + s(A-B)\right]\cos\omega t = 0 \qquad ...(iii)$$

and

$$\left[-m\omega^2 B + \frac{mg}{l}B - s(A-B)\right]\cos\omega t = 0 \qquad ...(iv)$$

First normal mode frequency. Adding (*iii*) and (*iv*), we get

$$(A+B)\left(-m\omega^2 + \frac{mg}{l}\right) = 0 \qquad ...(v)$$

This equation is satisfied when $\omega^2 = \frac{g}{l}$.

Thus this gives the *first normal mode frequency* (*or frequency of in-phase mode*) $\omega = \sqrt{\frac{g}{l}}$.

Second normal mode frequency. Subtracting (*iv*) from (*iii*), we get

$$(A-B)\left(-m\omega^2 + \frac{mg}{l} + 2s\right) = 0 \qquad ...(vi)$$

This equation is satisfied when

$$\omega^2 = \frac{g}{l} + \frac{2s}{m}$$

This gives the *second rorual mode. Frequency for frequency of out of phases mode.*

$$\omega = \sqrt{\frac{g}{l} + \frac{2s}{m}}$$

In phase conditions. Substituting $\omega^2 = \frac{g}{l}$ in (*vi*), we have

$$(A-B)\,2s = 0$$

on

$$A - B = 0$$

∴

$$A = B$$

which gives the *in phase* condition.

Out of phase condition. Substituting $\omega^2 = \frac{g}{l} + \frac{2s}{m}$ in (*v*), we have

$$(A+B)\,2s = 0$$

or

$$A + B = 0$$

∴

$$A = -B$$

which gives the *out of phase* or (antiphase) condition.

9.8 EXCHANGE OF ENERGY BETWEEN TWO NORMAL MODES

The equation of motion of a stiffness coupled system of two identical simple pendulums A and B is given by

$$\ddot{X} + \omega_0^2 X = 0 \qquad ...(i)$$

and $$\ddot{Y} + \left(\omega_0^2 + \frac{2s}{m}\right)Y = 0 \qquad ...(ii)$$

where $X = x + y$ and $Y = x - y$ are the normal co-ordinates of the system. x and y are the displacements (in the same direction) of the pendulums A and B respectively, $\omega_0^2 = \frac{g}{l}$ where l is the length of the pendulum and s the stiffness constant as given by eq. (*vii*) and (*viii*) of article 9.2.

Solving equation (*i*) and (*ii*), we get

$$X = x + y = X_0 \cos(\omega_1 t - \phi_1)$$

and $$Y = x - y = Y_0 \cos(\omega_2 t - \phi_2)$$

where X_0 and Y_0 are the normal mode amplitudes, $\omega_1 = \omega_0 = \left(\frac{g}{l}\right)^{\frac{1}{2}}$ and $\omega_2 = \left(\omega_0^2 + \frac{2s}{m}\right)^{\frac{1}{2}} = \left(\frac{g}{l} + \frac{2s}{m}\right)^{\frac{1}{2}}$ are normal mode frequencies.

Putting $X_0 = Y_0 = 2a$, we have

$$X = 2a \cos(\omega_1 t - \phi_1)$$

and $$Y = 2a \cos(\omega_2 t - \phi_2)$$

As $X = x + y$, X mode is known as *in-phase* mode. The total energy of the system in X-mode is given by

$$E_x = \frac{1}{2} m\omega_1^2 (2a)^2 = 2ma^2\omega_1^2$$

As $Y = x - y$, Y-mode is known as *out of phase* mode. The total energy of the system in Y-mode is given by

$$E_y = \frac{1}{2} m\omega_2^2 (2a)^2 = 2ma^2\omega_2^2$$

Both E_x and E_y do not vary with time. They are constant quantities. Therefore, *we conclude that no exchange of energy takes place from one normal mode to another.* In other words, *normal modes are independent of each other*.

When we say that normal co-ordinates are independent of each other, we mean that between the in phase mode represented by the normal co-ordinate X and the out of phase mode represented by the normal co-ordinate Y there is no exchange of energy and hence the two are independent of each other.

9.9 FREQUENCY OF A TWO BODY COUPLED OSCILLATOR

Consider two masses m_1 and m_2 connected by a spring of stiffness or force constant s. When the two masses are displaced from their equilibrium positions, the spring either contracts or extends, depending upon the displacement of the masses. This causes a linear restoring force to be produced in the spring and both masses begin to vibrate harmonically about their equilibrium position. Such a system is known as a *two body oscillator* or *coupled oscillator*. A familiar example is a diatomic molecule in which the two atoms are connected by some internal force known as '*bond*'.

As no external force acts on the system, the centre of mass either remains stationary or moves with constant velocity. The motion executed is simple harmonic. The system will oscillate with a frequency $\frac{1}{2\pi}\sqrt{\frac{s}{\mu}}$ where $\mu = \frac{m_1 m_2}{m_1 + m_2}$ [For proof refer 7.8 (*iv*)]

9.10 APPLICATIONS

Inductively coupled circuits. Two electrical circuits are said to be inductively coupled when the magnetic flux due to the current flowing in one circuit threads the second circuit. The two circuits are then said to have a *mutual inductance*. According to Faraday's law of electromagnetic induction, whenever the magnetic flux in one circuit changes an induced *e.m.f.* is set up in the other which is proportional to the time rate of change of magnetic flux and lasts only for the time the change is taking place. The most familiar example is that of a transformer whose working depends on the mutual induction between its primary and secondary coils.

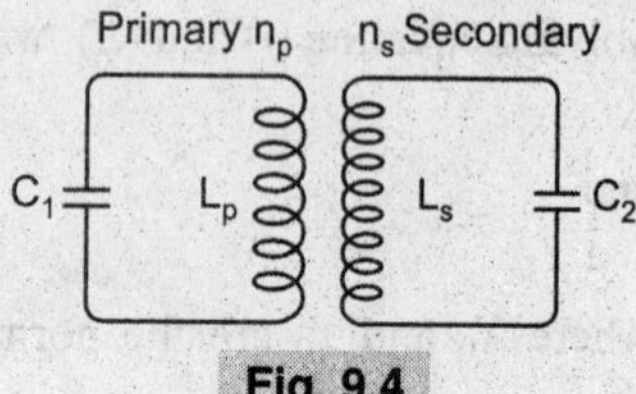

Fig. 9.4

The power source is connected to the primary and the secondary is wound over the primary in the *same sense*.

Two inductively coupled electrical circuits are shown in Fig. 9.4.

Let n_p represent the number of turns in the primary coil. If ϕ is the magnetic flux set up in the *primary* when a unit current flows through a single turn of the primary coil, then assuming that there is no leakage of flux outside the coil,

Flux linked with *each* primary turn $= n_p\phi$

$\therefore$ Total flux linked with primary coil $= n_p \,.\, n_p\phi$

or $$L_p = n_p^2\,\phi$$

where L_p is the co-efficient of self-induction of the primary. Similarly, if a unit current flowing through a single turn of the secondary coil also produces a magnetic flux ϕ, then

Flux linked with each secondary turn $= n_s\phi$

or $$L_s = n_s^2\phi$$

where L_s is the co-efficient of self-induction of the secondary.

If we suppose that all the lines of magnetic flux due to a unit current in the primary, thread all the turns of the secondary, then

Total flux lines linking the secondary $= n_s(n_p\phi)$

or $$M = n_s n_p \phi = \sqrt{L_p L_s}$$

where M is the co-efficient of mutual induction between the two coils.

Co-efficient of coupling. The above result is true only when there is no leakage of magnetic flux. In practice, however, some leakage of flux does take place and $M < \sqrt{L_p L_s}$.

The ratio $\dfrac{M}{\sqrt{L_p L_s}} = k$ is called the *co-efficient of coupling.*

For *small* value of k the two circuits have a *loose coupling* and are said to be *lightly coupled.*

9.11 ENERGY TRANSFER BETWEEN TWO ELECTRICALLY COUPLED CIRCUITS

To consider the *energy transfer* between the two inductively coupled circuits as shown in Fig. 9.4. let the two circuits be made to oscillate with a frequency ω and let $I_p = I_1 e^{i\omega t}$ and $I_s = I_2 e^{i\omega t}$ be the currents in the two circuits respectively, then

$$\text{Rate of change of primary current} = \frac{dI_p}{dt}$$

$$= \frac{d}{dt} I_1 e^{i\omega t} = i\omega I_1 e^{i\omega t} = i\omega I_p$$

$\therefore$ Induced *e.m.f.* in the primary coil $= -L_p \frac{dI_p}{dt} = -i\omega L_p I_p$

and Rate of change of secondary current $= \frac{dI_s}{dt}$

$$= \frac{d}{dt} I_2 e^{i\omega t} = i\omega I_2 e^{i\omega t} = i\omega I_s$$

$\therefore$ Induced *e.m.f* in the secondary coil $= -L_s \frac{dI_s}{dt} = -i\omega L_s I_s$

and Potential difference across the capacitor C_1 (Fig. 9.4) in the primary circuit $= \frac{\int I_p dt}{C_1}$

$$= \frac{\int I_1 e^{i\omega t} dt}{C_1} = \frac{I_1 e^{i\omega t}}{i\omega C_1} = -\frac{iI_p}{\omega C_1}$$

Potential difference across the capacitor C_2 (Fig. 9.4) in the secondary circuit $= \frac{\int I_s dt}{C_2}$

$$= \frac{\int I_2 e^{i\omega t} dt}{C_2} = \frac{I_2 e^{i\omega t}}{i\omega C_2} = \frac{iI_s}{\omega C_2}$$

If the two circuits are considered free from resistance and have inductance and capacitance only, then the *e.m.f.* equations for the primary and the secondary respectively are

$$-L_p \frac{dI_p}{dt} + \frac{\int I_p dt}{C_1} - M\frac{dI_s}{dt} = 0$$

and
$$-L_s \frac{dI_s}{dt} + \frac{\int I_s dt}{C_2} - M\frac{dI_p}{dt} = 0$$

Substituting the values of various quantities, we have

$$i\omega L_p I_p - \frac{i}{\omega C_1} I_p + i\omega M I_s = 0 \quad ...(i)$$

and
$$i\omega L_s I_s - \frac{i}{\omega C_2} I_s + i\omega M I_p = 0 \quad ...(ii)$$

Multiplying (*i*) by $\frac{\omega}{iL_p}$ and (*ii*) by $\frac{\omega}{iL_s}$, we have

$$\omega^2 I_p - \frac{I_p}{L_p C_1} + \frac{M}{L_p}\omega^2 I_s = 0$$

and
$$\omega^2 I_s - \frac{I_s}{L_s C_2} + \frac{M}{L_s}\omega^2 I_p = 0$$

Now $\frac{1}{L_p C_1} = \omega_1^2$ where ω_1 is the *natural frequency* of the *primary circuit* containing inductance L_p and capacitance C_1 and $\frac{1}{L_s C_2} = \omega_2^2$ where ω_2 is the *natural frequency* of the *secondary* circuit containing inductance L_s and capacitance C_2.

Substituting $\frac{1}{L_p C_1} = \omega_1^2$ and $\frac{1}{L_s C_2} = \omega_2^2$, we get

$$I_p(\omega_1^2 - \omega^2) = \frac{M}{L_p}\omega^2 I_s$$

and
$$I_p(\omega_2^2 - \omega^2) = \frac{M}{L_s}\omega^2 I_p$$

Multiplying we have

$$I_p I_s(\omega_1^2 - \omega^2)(\omega_2^2 - \omega^2) = \frac{M^2}{L_p L_s}\omega^4 I_s I_p$$

or
$$(\omega_1^2 - \omega^2)(\omega_2^2 - \omega^2) = \frac{M^2}{L_p L_s}\omega^4 = k^2\omega^4$$

where $k = \frac{M}{\sqrt{L_p L_s}}$ is the co-efficient of coupling.

To simplify put $\omega_1 = \omega_2 = \omega_0$, then

$$(\omega_0^2 - \omega^2)^2 = k^2\omega^4$$

or
$$\omega_0^2 - \omega^2 = \pm k\omega^2$$

$\therefore$
$$\omega = \pm\frac{\omega_0}{\sqrt{1 \pm k}}$$

The negative sign on the right hand side has no meaning as ω cannot be negative.
The positive sign gives two frequencies

$$\omega_a = \frac{\omega_0}{\sqrt{1+k}} \text{ and } \omega_b = \frac{\omega_0}{\sqrt{1-k}}.$$

These are the *normal mode frequencies*.

In phase and out of phase normal modes. From the relation

$$I_p(\omega_1^2 - \omega^2) = \frac{M}{L_p}\omega^2 I_s$$

We have
$$\frac{I_s}{I_p} = \frac{\omega_1^2 - \omega^2}{\omega^2}\frac{L_p}{M} = \frac{\omega_0^2 - \omega^2}{\omega^2}\frac{L_p}{M} \qquad [\because \omega_1 = \omega_0]$$

$$= \left(\frac{\omega_0^2}{\omega^2} - 1\right)\frac{L_p}{M} \qquad ...(iii)$$

Selecting the value of $\omega = \frac{\omega_0}{\sqrt{1+k}}$, we have

$$\frac{\omega_0^2}{\omega^2} = 1 + k \text{ or } \frac{\omega_0^2}{\omega^2} - 1 = +k$$

Substituting in Eq. (*iii*), we get

$$\frac{I_s}{I_p} = +k\frac{L_p}{M} \qquad ...(iv)$$

It is clear that the right hand side of the above equation is positive *i.e.,* I_s and I_p are *in phase.*

Hence $\omega = \dfrac{\omega_0}{\sqrt{1+k}} = \omega_a$ represents the frequency of the *in-phase mode.*

Similarly selecting $\omega = \dfrac{\omega_0}{\sqrt{1-k}}$, we find that

$$\frac{I_s}{I_p} = -k\frac{L_s}{M} \qquad ...(v)$$

i.e., I_s and I_p are *out of phase*. Hence $\omega = \dfrac{\omega_0}{\sqrt{1-k}} = \omega_s$ represents the frequency of *out of phase mode.*

Loose and tight coupling. In loose coupling k is small (<< l) and both the systems behave almost independently. In this case ω_a and ω_b are very nearly equal to ω_0. In tight coupling k is large (very nearly equal to unity) so that ω_a and ω_b differ from ω_0 by a large quantity, the peak values of current are displaced and the dip between the peaks is more pronounced. The variation of current amplitude with driving force frequency ω for different values of k is shown in Fig. 9.5. The three cases shown are

(1) for k small (2) for k having intermediate value and (3) for k large.

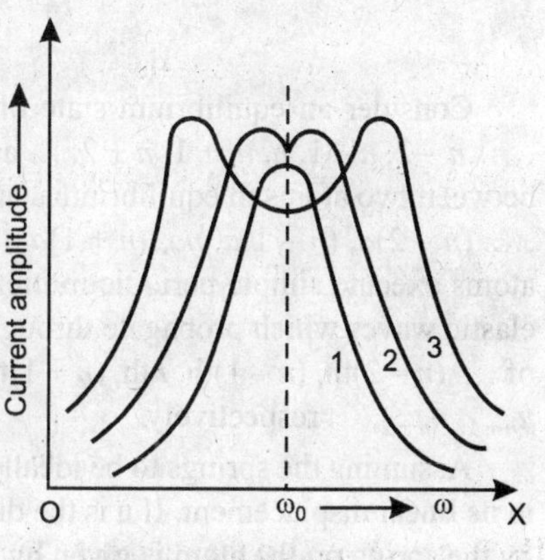

Fig. 9.5.

It may be noted that for k small (loose coupling) band width is negligible *i.e.,* resonance occurs at one frequency. For large k (tight coupling) bandwidth is large *i.e.,* resonance occurs at two widely apart frequencies.

9.12 N-COUPLED OSCILLATORS

We have seen so far a system in which two atoms coupled together by a massless spring, with an analogy of diatomic molecules like O_2, H_2, N_2 etc. However, in a solid, say in a crystal large number of molecules (*viz.* mono-, di-, poly-atomic) arranged in a particular regular manner depending upon its structure *i.e.,* simple cubic (s.c.), body-centred cubic (b.c.c.), or face-centred cubic (f.c.c). A lattice may be regarded as a regular arrangement of atoms which are joined together by elastic springs in three-dimension. At room temperature (or above), the connected atoms start oscillating about their mean position and thereby forms a case of N-coupled oscillator, in which N number of atoms coupled together by massless springs. The lattice may vibrate freely in its normal modes due to its internal energy or may experience forced vibrations under the action of external forces, which may be mechanical or electromagnetic in nature.

Simplest Case: One dimensional monoatomic lattice.

Consider a one-dimensional chain of atoms, each of mass m attached by massless springs as shown in Fig. 9.6. In figure both, the state of equilibrium and state of displacement (disturbed state) are shown.

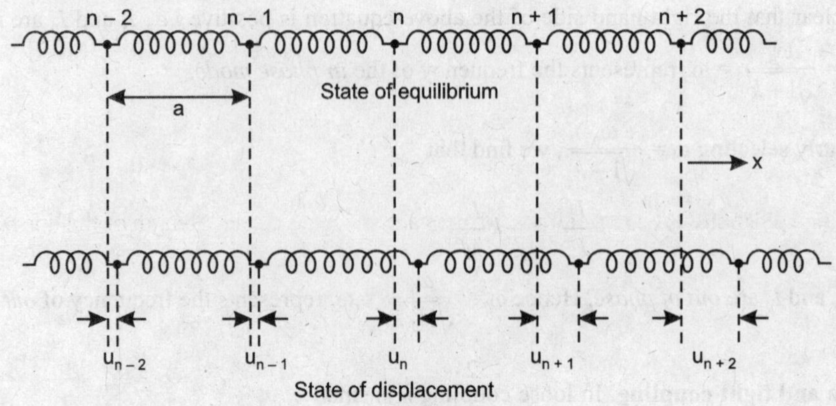

Fig. 9.6

Consider an equilibrium state of the atoms in which the atoms are equally spaced by sites, ...$n-2$, $n-1$, n, n, $+1$, $n+2$, ... as shown in figure. Let a be the lattice parameter, (the distance between two atoms in equilibrium state), the x-coordinates of the corresponding atoms are given by ..... $(n-2)a$, $(n-1)a$, na, $(n+1)a$, $(n+2)a$, ... In the state of vibratory motion along x-axis, the atoms execute simple periodic motion (S.H.M.) about their mean positions and become source of elastic waves which propagate through the medium. Let the displacements, at any instant of time t, of .... $(n-2)$th, $(n-1)$th, nth, $(n+1)$th, $(n+2)$th .... from their mean position be .... u_{n-2}, u_{n-1}, u_n, u_{n+1}, u_{n+2},.... respectively.

Assuming the springs to be ideally elastic, force between any two atoms is directly proportional to its linear displacement. If u is the displacement of spring with spring constant β, the force exerted by the spring on the atom is given by $F = \beta u$.

Since nth atom is connected to its neighbours $(n-1)$th and $(n+1)$th atoms by two springs, it experiences two opposite forces. The net force on the nth atom will be

$$F = \beta(u_{n+1} - u_n) - \beta(u_n - u_{n-1})$$

$$= \beta(u_{n+1} + u_{n-1} - 2u_n) \quad ...(i)$$

Using Newton's second law of motion, we write

$$m\frac{d^2u_n}{dt^2} = \beta(u_{n+1} + u_{n-1} - 2u_n) \quad ...(ii)$$

where $\frac{d^2u_n}{dt^2}$ represents the acceleration of the nth atom. Let the solution for this wave function be

$$u_n = u_0 e^{i(\omega t - Kna)} \quad ...(iii)$$

where na represents the x-coordinate of nth atom in equilibrium state, $K = 2\pi/\lambda$ is the wave vector or propagation vector and ω is the angular frequency of the wave. Similar quantities for $(n-1)$th and $(n+1)$th atoms are

$$u_{n-1} = u_0 e^{i[\omega t - K(n-1)a]} \quad ...(iv)$$

$$u_{n+1} = u_0 e^{i[\omega t - K(n+1)a]} \quad ...(v)$$

From eq. (*iii*), (*iv*) and (*v*), we obtain

$$-m\omega^2 = \beta[e^{iKa/2} - e^{-iKa/2}]^2 \quad ...(vi)$$

Since, $\sin x = \frac{e^{ix} - e^{-ix}}{2i}$ or $\sin^2 x = -\frac{1}{4}(e^{ix} - e^{-ix})^2$

Substituting in eq. (*vi*),

$$-m\omega^2 = -4\beta\sin^2\left(\frac{Ka}{2}\right)$$

or
$$\omega = \pm\sqrt{\frac{4\beta}{m}}\sin\left(\frac{Ka}{2}\right) \quad ...(vii)$$

If c and ρ denotes the longitudinal stiffness and the mass per unit length of the line respectively, then

$$c = \beta a \text{ and } \rho = \frac{m}{a}$$

$\therefore$
$$\omega = \pm\frac{2}{a}\sqrt{\frac{c}{\rho}}\sin\left(\frac{Ka}{2}\right)$$

or
$$\omega = \pm\frac{2}{a}v_s\sin\left(\frac{Ka}{2}\right) \quad ...(viii)$$

where $v_s = \sqrt{c/\rho}$ is a constant for a given lattice.

Eq. (*viii*) gives the angular frequency in terms of v_s, generally referred as velocity of sound waves in solids.

WORKED EXAMPLES

Example 9.1. One of the pendulums of a coupled oscillator is clamped while the other is free to oscillate. Show that the frequency of the single pendulum is given by

$$\nu = \frac{1}{2\pi}\sqrt{\frac{g}{l}+\frac{s}{m}}$$

Solution. Suppose the two pendulums A and B of length l and having bobs of mass m are coupled together by a light spring of stiffness constant s as shown in Fig. 8.1. Then, as proved in (article 9.2) the equations of motion of the pendulums A and B respectively, when the coupled system is set into oscillation are

$$m\frac{d^2x}{dt^2} = -mg\frac{x}{l} - s(x-y)$$

and
$$m\frac{d^2x}{dt^2} = -mg\frac{y}{l} + s(x-y)$$

When the pendulum B is clamped, $y = 0$ and the equation of motion of A is given by

$$m\frac{d^2x}{dt^2} = -mg\frac{x}{l} - sx$$

or
$$\frac{d^2x}{dt^2} = -\left(\frac{g}{l}+\frac{s}{m}\right)x$$

This is the equation of motion of a simple harmonic oscillator and the angular frequency of oscillation ω_1 is given by

$$\omega_1 = \sqrt{\frac{g}{l}+\frac{s}{m}}.$$

and frequency
$$\nu_1 = \frac{1}{2\pi}\sqrt{\frac{g}{l}+\frac{s}{m}}$$

When the pendulum A is clamped $x = 0$ and the equation of motion of B is given by

$$m\frac{d^2y}{dt^2} = -mg\frac{y}{l} + s(-y)$$

or

$$\frac{d^2y}{dt^2} = -\left(\frac{g}{l} + \frac{s}{m}\right)y$$

This is again the equation of motion of a simple harmonic oscillator and the angular frequency of oscillation ω_2 is given by $\omega_2 = \sqrt{\frac{g}{l} + \frac{s}{m}}$

and frequency

$$\nu_2 = \frac{1}{2\pi}\sqrt{\frac{g}{l} + \frac{s}{m}}$$

Thus whether the pendulum A is clamped or the pendulum B, the frequency of oscillation of the unclamped single pendulum is given by

$$\nu = \frac{1}{2\pi}\sqrt{\frac{g}{l} + \frac{s}{m}}$$

or

$$\omega = \sqrt{\frac{g}{l} + \frac{s}{m}}$$

Example 9.2. Two identical pendulums are connected by a light spring attached to their bobs. The mass of each bob is 10 gm and the stiffness constant of the spring is 8×10^{-3} Nm^{-1}. When one pendulum is clamped the period of the other is found to be 1.20 sec. Find the periods of the normal modes. ***(H.P.U., 2001)***

Solution. When one of the pendulums is clamped the angular frequency ω of the other is given by

$$\omega = \sqrt{\frac{g}{l} + \frac{s}{m}}$$

But $\frac{g}{l} = \omega_0^2$ where ω_0 is the normal mode frequency of the in-phase mode.

$$\therefore \quad \omega = \sqrt{\omega_0^2 + \frac{s}{m}}$$

or

$$\omega^2 = \omega_0^2 + \frac{s}{m} \qquad ...(i)$$

Here $T = 1.20$ sec. $\therefore$

$$\omega = \frac{2\pi}{T} = \frac{2\pi}{1.20} = 5.237\ s^{-1}$$

$$s = 8 \times 10^{-3}\ \text{Nm}^{-1};\ m = 109 = 10^{-2}\ \text{kg}$$

Substituting in Eq. (i), we have

$$(5.237)^2 = \omega_0^2 + \frac{8 \times 10^{-3}}{10^{-2}}$$

or

$$\omega_0^2 = (5.237)^2 - 0.8 = 26.626$$

$$\therefore \quad \omega_0 = 5.16\ \text{sec}^{-1}$$

and $T_0 = \frac{2\pi}{\omega_0} = 1.218 = 1.22$ sec.

This is the time period of the in-phase mode.

The normal mode frequency of the out of phase mode is given by

$$\omega_2 = \sqrt{\omega_0^2 + \frac{2s}{m}}$$

$$\therefore \qquad \omega_2^2 = 26.626 + \frac{2 \times 8 \times 10^{-3}}{10^{-2}} = 26.626 + 1.6$$

$$= 28.226$$

or $\qquad \omega_2 = 5.312$

Hence $T_2 = \dfrac{2\pi}{\omega_2} = 1.18$ sec.

This is the time period of the out of phase mode.

Example 9.3. The angular vibrational frequency of *CO* molecule is $0.6 \times 10^{15}\ s^{-1}$. Calculate the amount of work required for stretching it by 0.5 Å from the equilibrium position.

Solution. Reduced mass of *CO* molecule

$$\mu = \frac{m_1 \times m_2}{m_1 + m_2} = \frac{12 \times 16}{12 + 16} a.m.u = 6.85 \times 1.67 \times 10^{-27} \text{ kg}$$

(where 1 *a.m.u.* = 1.67×10^{-27} kg)

Angular vibration frequency $\omega = 2\pi n = 0.6 \times 10^{15}\ \text{s}^{-1}$

Now $\qquad \omega = \sqrt{\dfrac{s}{\mu}}$

$\therefore$ Inter-atomic force constant $\qquad s = \omega^2\mu$

$$= (0.6 \times 10^{15})^2 \times 6.85 \times 1.67 \times 10^{-27}$$

$$= 4.118 \times 10^3 \text{ Nm}^{-1}$$

Work done for stretching by $\qquad x = 0.5 \text{ Å} = 0.5 \times 10^{-10}$ m

$$W = \frac{1}{2}sx^2 = \frac{1}{2} \times 4.118 \times 10^3 \times 0.5 \times 0.5 \times 10^{-20} = 5.15 \times 10^{-18} \text{ J}$$

Example 9.4. Sodium chloride molecule vibrates with natural frequency 1.14×10^{13} Hz. Calculate the interatomic force constant for the molecule. Given mass of sodium atom = 23 a.m.u. and that of chlorine atom is 35 a.m.u. (1 a.m.u. = 1.67×10^{-27} kg).

Solution. The vibrations of sodium chloride molecule are similar to the vibrations of a mechanical system of two masses coupled by a spring of force constant *s*, the frequency of which is given by

$$n = \frac{1}{2\pi}\sqrt{\frac{s}{\mu}}$$

where μ is the reduced mass equal to $\dfrac{m_1 m_2}{m_1 + m_2}$.

$\therefore$ Reduced mass of sodium chloride molecule

$$\mu = \frac{23 \times 35}{23 + 35} = 13.88 \text{ a.m.u.} = 13.88 \times 1.67 \times 10^{-27} = 23.18 \times 10^{-27} \text{ kg}$$

Now frequency $n = \dfrac{1}{2\pi}\sqrt{\dfrac{s}{\mu}}$

$$\therefore \qquad n^2 = \frac{1}{4\pi^2}\frac{s}{\mu}$$

or $\qquad s = 4\pi^2 n^2 \mu = 4 \times \left(\dfrac{22}{7}\right)^2 \times (1.14 \times 10^{13})^2 \times 23.18 \times 10^{-27}$

$$= 118.9 \text{ Nm}^{-1}.$$

Example 9.5. In a transformer the mutual inductance of two coils is 0.3 H where as the self inductance of primary and secondary are 0.28 H and 0.36 H respectively. Is the transformer loose or tight coupled. ***(G.N.D.U. 2004, P.U., 2002, 2000; H.P.U., 2003)***

Solution. Co-efficient of coupling, $k = \frac{M}{\sqrt{L_p L_s}} = \frac{0.3}{\sqrt{0.28 \times 0.36}} = 0.95$

As the co-efficient of coupling k is nearly equal to unity, the transformer is almost *tight coupled.*

EXERCISE

1. (*a*) Explain the meaning of couple oscillator.

   (*b*) Define and explain normal co-ordinates, degrees of freedom and normal modes of vibration of an oscillatory system. ***(Pbi. U., 2002; H.P.U., 2000; P.U., 2000; G.N.D.U., 2000)***

2. What is ment by coupling of two oscillators? Discuss completely the oscillations of two identical stiffness coupled pendulums and write the equation of motion of the system in different cases in terms of normal co-ordinates, X and Y. ***(H.P.U., 2002, 2001; P.U., 2002)***

3. Derive an expression for the total energy of a stiffness coupled system of identical pendulums and show that the total energy of the system remains constant. ***(H.P.U., 2003, 2002)***

4. Which different types of coupling are used for coupling two oscillators? Show that in the in phase mode, the frequency of oscillations is the same as of uncoupled oscillators whereas in the out of phase mode, the frequency of oscillations gets raised.

5. Give a general method of finding normal mode frequencies and obtain expression for the normal mode frequencies of stiffness coupled pendulums. ***(G.N.D.U., 2002, P.U., 2000)***

6. (*a*) Do normal modes exchange energy with each other?

   (*b*) Show that normal modes are independent of each other and there is no exchange of energy between two coupled pendulums. What do you mean by the statement that normal co-ordinates are independent of each other? ***(P.U., 2003, 2000; Pbi., 2002, 2000; H.P.U., 2003, 2002, 2000)***

7. Explain transfer of energy between two resistance free electric circuits which are inductively coupled. When is the coupling loose or tight? Obtain an expression for the normal mode frequencies and show that they are almost equal for loose coupling.

   (P.U., 2004, 2003, 2002, 2001, 2000; Pbi. U., 2003, 2002; H.P.U., 2001, 2000)

8. Give the characteristics of the in-phase and out of phase mode of vibration of two identical coupled simple pendulums (oscillators).

   (G.N.D.U., 2003, 2002, 2001; Pbi.U., 2003; H.P.U., 2000; P.U., 2000,)

9. Explain the inductance coupling of two electrical oscillators and define co-efficient of coupling. ***(G. N. D.U., 2001; P.U., 2004, 2001; H.P.U., 2001)***

10. Discuss coupled oscillations using coupled system of two identical bodies. ***(Nagpur U. 2007)***

11. Obtain an expression for the time period of a two body harmonic oscillator.

    (Nagpur U. 2008, 2006)

12. Define and explain Normal co-ordinates, normal modes and degree of vibration of an oscillatory system.

13. Discuss exchange of energy between two normal modes of frequencies of two coupled pendulums.

14. What do you understand by degenerate (normal) modes of vibration? Writing down the equations of motion of two identical simple pendulums connected by light spring, find out the frequency of faster normal modes of vibration. ***(Purvanchal U. 2007)***

15. Explain the oscillations of two coupled oscillators. What are different modes of vibration? ***(Nagpur U. 2009)***

16. Two masses m_1 and m_2 are coupled by a spring of stiffness s. The masses are pulled apart and released. Show that their motion is simple harmonic. Prove that the system will oscillate with a frequency

$$\sqrt{\frac{s}{\mu}} \text{ where } \mu = \frac{m_1 m_2}{m_1 + m_2}.$$ ***(P.U., 2001, 2000; Nagpur U. 2007, 2008)***

[**Hint:** For proof Pl. refer article 5.9.8]

17. Find self inductance of secondary coil of a transformer having tight coupling with co-efficient of coupling 0.96. The self inductance of primary coil is 0.3 H and mutual inductance 0.2 H between the two coils. [**Ans.** $L_s = 0.1477$ H]

10 Chapter

WAVE MOTION

Brief Contents

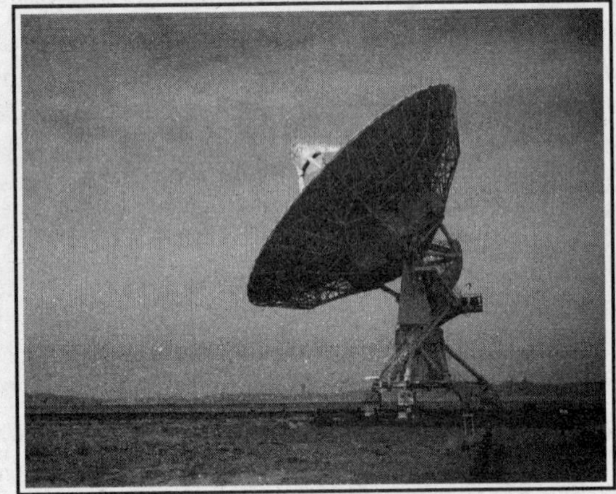

INTRODUCTION

More complicated systems possess more degrees of freedom. These compound oscillations (coupled) typically appears very complicated but can be simplified by *resolving the motion* into *normal modes*. As the number of degrees of freedom becomes arbitrarily large, the system approaches continuity. For example, a string or the surface of a body of water. In the classical limit, such systems have an infinite number of *normal modes* and their oscillations occur in the form of *waves* that can characteristically propagate.

10.1 WAVE MOTION - TYPES OF WAVES

One of the commonest modes of transfer of energy from one point to the another is in the form of *waves*. The waves propagates from the point of disturbance, as which they are generated. Thus, for example, we known that *water waves*, *sound waves*, *light waves* and *radio waves* all carry energy of one form or the other from one place to another, without any bulk motion of the interventing medium of the first two types of waves. For light and radio waves propagation, no medium is required at all. There is just propagation of energy takes place. Such a mode of transfer of energy is called **Wave motion**, and may be divided into two broad categories: (*i*) *mechanical* wave motion and (*ii*) *non-mechanical* or *electromagnetic wave motion*.

(*i*) **Mechanical wave motion** is possible only in material media (solids, liquids and gases) which possese inertia as well as elasticity; so that,water waves and sound waves are both example of this type of wave motion and are, therefore referred to as *mechanical waves*.

(*ii*) **Non mechanical or electromagnetic wave motion**, on the other hand, requires no material medium for its propagation; so that, light and radio waves, which can travel through empty space, belong to this category and are, therefore referred to *as non mechanical* or *electromagnetic waves*.

We are concerned here with only the mechanical type of wave motion and shall, for simplicity, refer to it merely as wave motion.

Since all material media posses elasticity as well as inertia, it is easy to see how a wave motion is produced and propagated through them. For, not particle of an elastic medium can be disturbed without affecting its immediate neighbour and, tending to recover its original position, it first stores up potential energy and then coverts it back into kinetic energy. The neighbouring particle which has thus been disturbed then performs a similar motion, so that each successive particle repeats, in turn, the movements of its predecessor a little later than it and hands the same on to its successor, resulting in the transference of energy from particle to particle all along the line. One complete oscillation of a particle of the medium obviously produces *one single wave* or a *pulse* and its repeated periodic motion, a succession of waves or a *wave train*.

We may thus define *a wave motion as a disturbance (or a condition) that travels onwards through a medium due to the repeated periodic motion of its particles about their mean or equilibrium position, each particles repeating the movements of its predecessor a little later than it and handing it on to its successor, so that there is a regular phase difference between one particle and the next.*

The simplest type of periodic motion performed by a particle is, of course, the simple harmonic motion and the corresponding wave motion is therefore called a *simple harmonic or a sinusoidal wave motion*, which alone is the most general type of wave motion and the one we shall deal with in the following discussion.

It may be emphasised again that, but for the properties of elasticity and inertia, no wave motion could be produced in, or propagated through , a medium. These two properties in fact determine the velocity of propagation of the wave motion through the medium, as we shall presently see. And, in order that a wave may travel through a medium over fairly large distances without attenuation (*i.e.*, without any decrease in its amplitude), a third property is also necessary, *viz.*, that the medium should offer the least frictional resistance so as not to unduly damp the periodic motion of the particles.

A wave motion which thus progresses onwards through a medium, with energy transferred across every section of it, is called a *travelling* or a *progressive wave motion* to distinguish it from what a called a *standing* or a *stationary wave motion*, which we shall study a little later and in which there is no onward movement of the wave motion through the medium and hence no transference of energy across any section of it.

10.2 TRANSVERSE AND LONGITUDINAL WAVE MOTION

There are two distinct class of wave motion: (*i*) *transverse* and (*ii*) *longitudinal*

(*i*) In a *transverse wave motion*, the particles of the medium oscillate up and down about their mean or equilibrium position, at *right angles to the direction of propagation of the waves itself.* This form of wave motion therefore travels in the form of *crests and troughs* (Fig. 10.1), as, for example, waves travelling along a stretched string. *A crest and an adjoining trough constitute one wave or pulse* and a succession of them, a *wave train.*

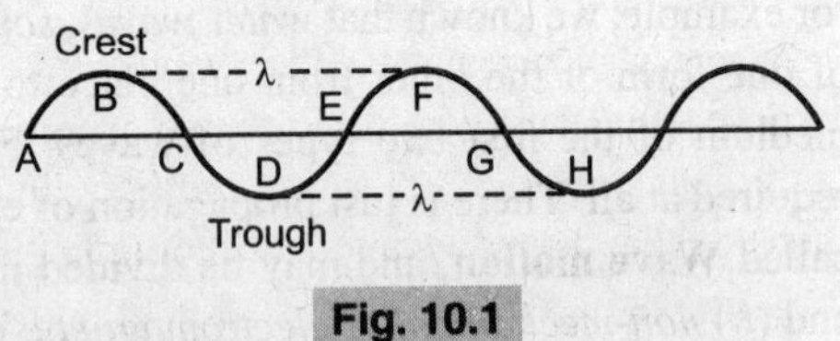

Fig. 10.1

This type of waves motion is possible in media which possess elasticity of shape or rigidity, *i.e.* in *solids*. But, as we know, they are also possible in water and liquids, in general, even though they do not possess the property of rigidity. This is because they possess another equally effective property of resisting any vertical displacement of their particles (or keeping their level). Gases, however, possess neither rigidity nor do they resist any vertical displacement of their particles (or keep their level). *A transverse wave motion is therefore, not possible in a gaseous medium.*

N.B. It may just be mentioned for the information of the student that an electromagnetic wave is necessarily a transverse wave because of the electric and magnetic fields being perpendicular to its direction of propagation.

(*ii*) In a *longitudinal wave motion*, the particles of the medium oscillate to and fro about their mean or equilibrium position, *along the direction of propagation of the wave motion itself.* This type of wave motion, therefore, travels in the form of *compressions* (or *condensations*) and *rarefactions*, *i.e.* in the particles of the medium getting closer together and further apart alternately, (Fig. 10.2), and is possible in media possessing elasticity of volume, *i.e.*, in solids, liquids as well as gases. As examples may be mentioned sound waves in air [Fig. 10.2 (*a*)] and waves in a spring or helix when one end of it is suddenly compressed or pulled out and then released [Fig. 10.2 (*b*)].

Here, *one compression and the adjoining rarefaction constitute one wave or pulse* and, as in case (*i*) a succession of them, a *wave train.*

In some cases, the waves are neither purely transverse nor purely longitudinal as, for example, *ripples* or *surface waves* on water (produced by dropping a stone in water), in which the particles of the medium (here, water) oscillate across as well as along the direction of propagation of the wave motion, describing elliptical) paths.

We need not, however, bother ourselves with any such types of waves here.

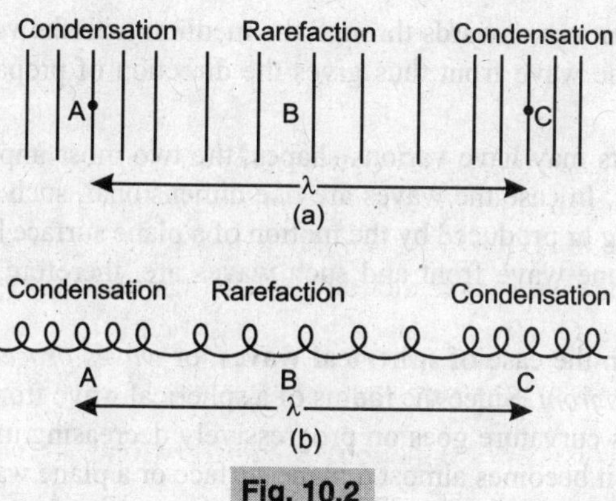

Fig. 10.2

Again, waves may be *one-dimensional*, *two dimensional* or *three dimensional* according as they propagate energy in just one, two or three dimensions. Thus, transverse wave along a string or longitudinal wave along a spring are one-dimensional, surface waves or ripples on water are two-dimensional and sound wave proceeding radially from a point-source are three dimensional.

Before proceeding further, we had better summarise here the important characteristics of a wave motion, in general, whether transverse or longitudinal, *viz.*, that

(*i*) It is simply a disturbance, a condition or a state of motion that travels through the medium and nothing material, *i.e., there is no transference of any part of the medium (or matter) from one point to another*. For, as we have seen, the particles of the medium simply oscillate up and down or to and fro about their mean position and do not move onwards with the wave motion itself.

(*ii*) Each particle of the medium receives the disturbance a little later than its predecessor, repeats its movements and hands it on to the next succeeding particle, *i.e., there is a regular phase lag between one particle and the next.*

(*iii*) *The velocity of the particles of the medium or the particles velocity, as it is referred to, is entirely different from the velocity of the wave motion or the wave velocity.*

Characteristics of wave motion. A progressive simple harmonic wave is that whose amplitude remains constant with time. Its characteristics are:

(*i*) A wave is a form of disturbance which propagates in a medium.

(*ii*) When the wave propagates the particles of the medium simply oscillate about their mean position.

(*iii*) There is a definite phase different between every two consecutive particles.

(*iv*) The velocity of the wave is different from the velocity of the particles. The velocity of the wave is a constant for a given medium but the velocity of the particle goes on changing, being maximum in the mean position and minimum in the extreme position.

(*v*) Wave motion is possible only in media which have the property of inertia and elasticity.

(*vi*) The energy of the vibrating particle at the extreme position is wholly potential and in the mean position wholly kinetic.

(*vii*) When a wave travels in a medium, there is a flow of energy without any transfer of matter.

10.3 WAVE FRONT

A plane or a surface on which all particles of the medium are in an identical state of motion at a given instant, *i.e.* in the same phase, is called a *wave front.*

In a homogeneous and isotropic medium, the wave front is always perpendicular to the direction of propagation of the wave motion and the position of a given wave front shifts onwards with the wave. In other words, it moves onwards through the medium with the velocity of the wave motion itself. A line normal to the wave front thus gives the direction of propagation of the wave and is called a *ray*.

Although wave fronts may have various shapes, the two most important types are plane and the spherical wave fronts. In case the waves are one dimensional, such as those travelling along a stretched string or a spring or produced by the motion of a plane surface back and forth in a gaseous medium, we obtain a plane wave front and such waves are, therefore, also referred to as **plane waves.**

On the other hand, in the case of **spherical waves**, or *waves proceeding from a point-source*, we obtain a *spherical was front*. Since the radius of a spherical wave front goes on increasing as the wave moves onwards, its curvature goes on progressively decreasing until at an infinite or a large distance from the source it becomes almost a plane surface or a plane wave front, implying thereby that *at large distances from the source, spherical waves–and, in fact, waves of all types-may be treated as plane waves.*

We shall therefore, restrict our discussion here to only plane or one-dimensional waves. For, this, without in any way detracting from the applicability of our result to waves in general, will greatly facilitate our task by doing away with undue mathematical complexities.

10.4 WAVE LENGTH, FREQUENCY AND WAVE NUMBER

It may be recalled that in § 10.2 above, a crest and an adjoining trough, in the case of a transverse wave, and a compression and an adjoining rarefaction, in the case of a longitudinal wave, have been said to constitute one wave. The distance between the particles at the two ends of the wave or the pulse, therefore, constitutes a *wave length*, usually denoted by the symbol λ. Since these two particles are in an identical state of motion or *in the same phase*, a more general definition of wavelength would be *the distance between any two nearest particles of the medium in the same phase*. Thus, in the case of a transverse wave (Fig. 10.1) the *distance between the centres of two nearest crests are two nearest troughs* (*i.e.* distance *BF* or *DH*) also constitutes one wave length. Similarly, in the case of longitudinal wave (Fig. 10.2) the *distance between the centres of two nearest compressions* or *two nearest rarefactions* (*e.g.* the distance *AC*) also constitutes one wavelength.

Again, since a wave or a pulse is produced in the time taken by a particle of the medium to compete its one full oscillation about its mean position, a *wavelength may also be defined as the distance covered by the disturbance during one full time-period (T) of a particle of the medium.*

The number of waves produced per second (which is obviously the same as the number of complete oscillations made by a particle of the medium per second) is called the **frequency** (*n*) of the wave motion or the wave, and is obviously the *reciprocal of the time-period T*, *i.e.*, $n = 1/T$.

The time rate of change of phase (*i.e.*, its rate of change with time) is called the **angular frequency** (ω) of the wave motion and is equal to $2\pi/T$ because a complete cycle of phase change 2π occurs in one full time-period T of a particle of the medium.

On the same analogy, we have a quantity, called the **wave number** k, representing the *space rate of change of phase* (*i.e.* its rate of change with distance) and since one complete cycle of phase change 2π occurs in a distance λ (the wave length), we have $k = 2\pi/\lambda$.

Quite often, however, the wave number is defined as the *number of waves is unit distance*, *i.e.*, equal to $1/\lambda$ and is denoted by the symbol ν. So that, $k = 2\pi/\lambda$ is, in this case, referred to as the propagation constant.

It will also be seen from the above that if the number of waves produced per second, *i.e.* the frequency of the wave motion, be n and the length of each wave (or wavelength) be λ, we have

$v = n\lambda$ or , since $n = 1/T$, we also have $v = \lambda/T$

where v is the *phase velocity*, usually referred to simply as the *velocity of the wave motion or of the wave.*

10.5 DISPLACEMENT, VELOCITY AND PRESSURE CURVES

(i) Displacement, curve. In the case of a transverse wave, as we know, the particles of the medium oscillate up and down about their mean position, at right angles to the direction of propagation of the wave. So that, if we plot the displacements of the various particles at a given instant against their respective distances from the origin or, in fact any fixed point, we obtain the *displacement curve* of the wave, which, for a sinusoidal wave, will be a series of sine curves, (Fig. 10.1), with one complete sine curve representing one full wave, as shown in Fig. 10.3. The displacement curve thus gives the form of the wave or the wave profile, as it were.

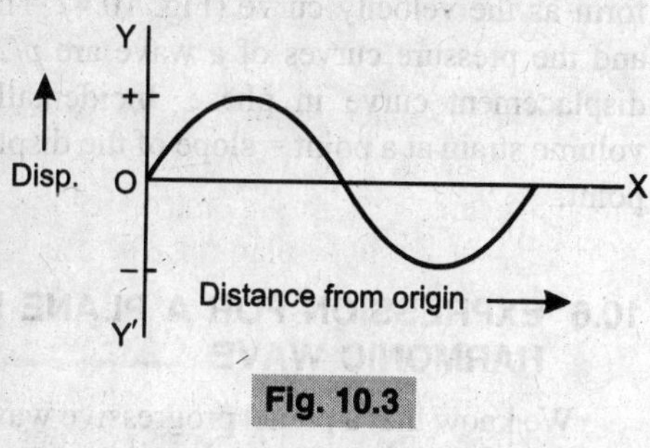

Fig. 10.3

In the case of a longitudinal wave, on the other hand, the particles oscillate to and fro about their mean position along the direction of the wave motion, so that the displacement curve would, in this case, be a straight line along the direction of wave propagation itself. For our convenience, however, we *conventionally* represent the displacement curve of a longitudinal wave motion too by a sine curve of the type shown in Fig. 10.1, the curve here being referred to as the *associated displacement curve* in and it is clearly understood that the displacements of the particles shown perpendicular to the direction of wave propagation are in fact along it.

(ii) Velocity curve. The graph between the velocity (U) of an oscillating particle of the medium and its distance from the origin or a fixed point is called the velocity curve of the wave motion. Using the same convention as in case (*i*) above, the velocity curve in the case of both a transverse and a longitudinal wave is of the form shown in Fig. 10.4, which is obviously also a *sine curve, a phase angle $\pi/2$ or a quarter period $T/4$ ahead of the displacement curve.*

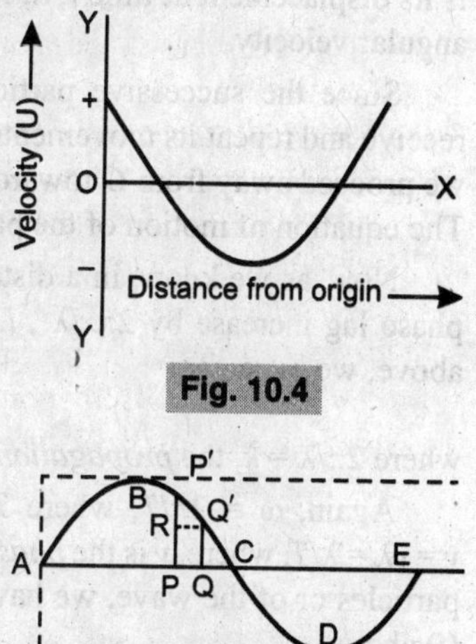

Fig. 10.4

Fig. 10.5

(iii) Pressure curve. Let $ABCDE$ (Fig. 10.5) be the associated displacement curve of a longitudinal wave travelling towards the right along the axis ACE of a cylinder of unit area of cross section (shown dotted).

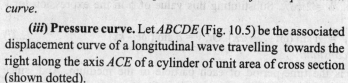

Consider two particles P and Q of the medium (*say, air*), a small distance δx apart. Before the wave is setup in the cylinder, *i.e.* when the air inside it is yet undisturbed, *the volume of the air enclosed between P and Q is obviously $PQ \times 1 = \delta x \times 1 = \delta x$* (the cross section of the cylinder being unity). After the wave is set up and takes the form shown in the figure, displacement at P is PP, and that at Q is QQ' and the change in displacement is, therefore, $PP' - QQ' = P'R = \delta y$, say, where $Q'R$ is the perpendicular from Q' on the PP'. So that, remembering that the displacements are in fact longitudinal, along the direction of wave propagation, *the change in volume between P and $Q = (PP' - QQ') \times 1 = P'R \times 1 = \delta y \times 1 = \delta y$.*

$\therefore$ *volume strain set up in the medium = change in volume/original volume* $= \delta y/\delta x = dy/dx$ if PQ be really small.

But *dy/dx is the slope of the displacement curve at P* and represents a compression or a rarefraction according as it has a negative or a positive sign. If, therefore, we plot dy/dx for the particles along the axis of y and their displacements from the origin along the axis of x, we obtain the *pressure curve* of the wave (Fig. 10.6) which is of the same form as the velocity curve (Fig. 10.4). Thus, both the velocity and the pressure curves of a wave are $p/2$ or $T/4$ ahead of the displacement curve in phase. Incidentally, we also see that volume strain at a point = slope of the displacement curve at that point.

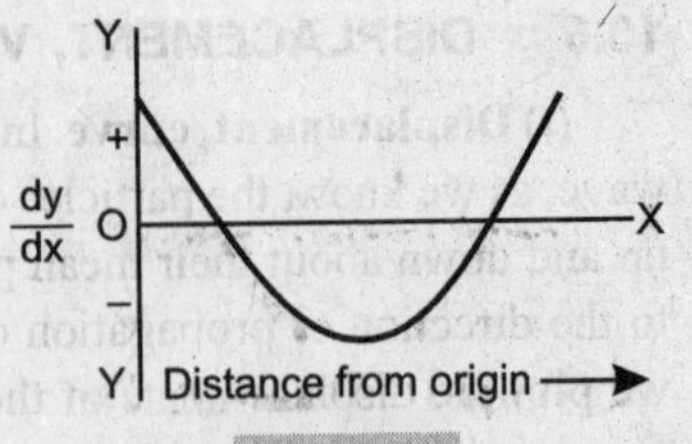

Fig. 10.6

10.6 EXPRESSION FOR A PLANE PROGRESSIVE HARMONIC WAVE

We know that a plane progressive wave is one which travels onwards through the medium in a given direction without attenuation, *i.e*, with its amplitude constant.

Now, a progressive wave may be transverse or longitudinal. In either case, however, there exists a regular phase difference between any two successive particles of the medium.

Thus, suppose a wave, originating at *O*, travels to the right along the axis of x (Fig. 10.7). Then, if we start counting time when the particle at *O* just passes through its mean position in the positive direction (*i.e.*, upwards in the case of a transverse wave and forwards in the case of a longitudinal wave) the equation of motion of this particle (at *O*) is obviously $y = a \sin \omega t$, where y is its displacement at time t, a, its amplitude and ω, its angular velocity.

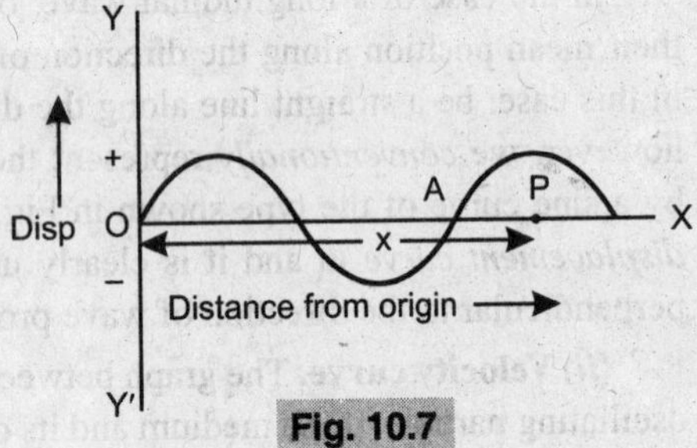

Fig. 10.7

Since the successive particles to the right of *O* receive and repeat its movements after definite intervals of time, the phase lag goes on increasing as we proceed away from *O* towards the right. So that, for a particle at *P*, *distant x from O*, it is ϕ, say. The equation of motion of the particle at *P* is thus $y = a \sin (\omega t - \phi)$.

Now, as we know, in a distance λ, the phase lag increases by 2π. In distance x, therefore, the phase lag increase by $2\pi x/\lambda$, *i.e.*, $\phi = 2\pi x/\lambda$. Substituting this value of ϕ in the expression for y above, we have

$$y = a \sin (\omega t - 2\pi x/\lambda). \text{ Or, } y = a \sin (\omega t - kx) \quad \text{...(i)}$$

where $2\pi/\lambda = k$, the *propagation constant*.

Again, $\omega = 2\pi/T$, where T is the time-period of each particle of the medium. And, since $v = v\lambda = \lambda/T$, where, v is the *phase velocity* or the *wave velocity* and n, the frequency of the oscillating particles or of the wave, we have $1/T = v/\lambda$ and, therefore, $\omega = 2\pi v/\lambda$. We thus have from relation (*i*) above,

$$y = a \sin\left(\frac{2\pi vt}{\lambda} - \frac{2\pi x}{\lambda}\right).$$

Or,
$$y = a \sin \frac{2\pi}{\lambda}(vt - x). \quad \text{Or,} \quad y = a \sin k(vt - x). \quad \text{...(ii)}$$

Any one of these expressions or any one of their variations, such as

$$v = a \sin \frac{2\pi v}{\lambda}\left(t - \frac{x}{v}\right) \quad \text{... (iii)} \quad y = a \sin 2\pi n\left(t - \frac{x}{v}\right) \quad \text{...(iv)}$$

Or
$$y = a \sin \frac{2\pi}{T}\left(t - \frac{x}{v}\right) \quad \text{... (v) [because } n = 1/T]$$

Or
$$y = a \sin 2\pi\left(\frac{t}{T} - \frac{x}{\lambda}\right) \quad \text{... (vi) [because } v = n\lambda = \lambda]$$

is referred to as the *equation of a plane, progressive harmonic or sinusoidal wave* – the one most commonly used being equation (*ii*).

Since $\lambda = v/T$, $\omega = 2\pi/T$ and $k = 2\pi/\lambda$, it will be esaily seen that

$$v = \lambda/T = \lambda\bigg/\frac{2\pi}{\omega} = \lambda\omega/2\pi = \omega\bigg/\frac{2\pi}{\lambda} = \omega/k$$

For a wave travelling *towards the left*, since x will be negative, we shall have

$$y = a\sin\frac{2\pi}{\lambda}(vt + x) \quad \text{or,} \quad y = a\sin(\omega t + kx)$$

Note. In deducing these equations, we have assumed that the particle at O just passes through its mean position, in the positive direction, at $t = 0$, *i.e.*, $y = 0$ at $t = 0$. If this be not so, the particle is said to have an *initial phase* θ, say, and the equation of the wave then becomes

$y = a\sin\frac{2\pi}{\lambda}(\omega t - x + \theta)$. Or, $y = a\sin(\omega t - kx + \theta)$,

where θ is referred to as the *phase constant.*

Thus, if $\theta = 90°$, we have $y = a$ at $x = 0$ and $t = 0$

The following points the emerge from the above discussion may be carefully noted.

(*i*) *At a given point x* (*i.e.*, for a constant value of x) the displacement (y) varies simple harmonically with time, completing one full cysle in time λ/v which, therefore, gives the periodic time T of the wave and hence also its frequency $n = 1/T = v/\lambda$.

(*ii*) *At a given instant t* (*i.e.*, for a constant value of t), the displacement (y) varies simple harmonically with distance from the origin and for $x = \lambda$, y is restored to its original value, so that the wave length = λ.

(*iii*) The phase lag for a distance x is $2\pi x/\lambda$ and hence for distance λ it is $2\pi\lambda/\lambda = 2\pi$ which is, in effect, the same thing as zero. So that, particles separated by a distance λ or an integral multiple of λ are in the same phase.

(*iv*) If we increase time t by δt, and distance x by $v\delta t$, the value of y remains the same, showing that a disturbance at one point is repeated an interval δt later at a point $v\delta t$ further away. This means, in other words, that the disturbance or the wave travels, without attention, with velocity v.

10.7 PARTICLE VELOCITY

We have the equation of plane progressive wave motion,

$$y = a\sin\frac{2\pi}{\lambda}(vt - x),$$

where y is the displacement of a particle of the medium at distance x from the origin at instant t, a its amplitude and v, the wave velocity (*i.e.*, the *phase velocity*).

∴ Differentiating the expression for y with respect to t, we have

particle velocity $$U = \frac{dy}{dt} = \frac{2\pi v}{\lambda}a\cos\frac{2\pi}{\lambda}(vt - x) \qquad ...(i)$$

Relation between particle velocity and wave velocity:

Differentiating the same expression for y with respect to x, we have

Slope of the displacement curve (or *strain or compression*)

$$\frac{dy}{dx} = -\frac{2\pi}{\lambda}a\cos\frac{2\pi}{\lambda}(vt - x) \qquad ...(ii)$$

From relations (*i*) and (*ii*) we thus obtain $U = \frac{dy}{dt} = -v\frac{dy}{dx}$ ...(*iii*)

i.e. **Particle velocity at a point = – (Wave velocity) × Slope of displacement curve at that point).**

10.8 DIFFERENTIAL EQUATION OF A WAVE MOTION

Differentiating equation (*i*), under § 10.7 above, for the particle velocity again with respect to *t*, we have

acceleration of the particle, $\dfrac{d^2y}{dt^2} = -\dfrac{4\pi^2v^2}{\lambda^2}a\sin\dfrac{2\pi}{\lambda}(vt-x)$

$$= -\frac{4\pi^2v^2}{\lambda^2}y. \quad \text{...}(iv)$$

And, similarly, differentiating equation (*ii*) under the same article, for strain or compression, again with respect to *x*, we have

rate of change of compensation with distance,

$$\frac{d^2y}{dx^2} = -\frac{4\pi^2}{\lambda^2}a\sin\frac{2\pi}{\lambda}(vt-x) = -\frac{4\pi^2}{\lambda^2}y \quad \text{...}(v)$$

From relations (*iv*) and (*v*) we thus obtain $\dfrac{d^2y}{dt^2} = v^2\dfrac{d^2y}{dx^2}$ ...(*vi*)

This is referred to as the differential equation of a plane or one dimensional progressive wave, in which *the coefficient of d^2y/dx^2 straightaway gives square of the wave velocity.*

Any equation of this form can unphesitatingly be declared to represent a plane progressive harmonic wave, the velocity of which is given by the square root of the coefficient of d^2y/dx^2.

Since d^2y/dx^2 also gives the curvature of the displacement curve, we may interpret the differential equation to mean that

Particle acceleration at a point

= (Wave velocity)² × (Curvature of displacement curve at that point)

It may once again be pointed out here that *the essential characteristics of a wave motion, in general, is the onward progression of a disturbance* with a velocity depending upon factors pertaining to the particular situation in question. It does not by any means imply that *y* in the wave equation must necessarily represent a physical displacement of particles as we have assumed here. In fact, for a wave, in general, we replace the symbol *y* in the differential equation of the wave by ψ(psi), referred to as the *wave function*. So that, for a one dimensional wave the differential equation takes the form

$$\frac{d^2\psi}{dt^2} = v^2\frac{d^2\psi}{dx^2}$$

where ψ may represent physical quantities as disparate as, for example, (*i*) pressure in a medium in the case of a sound wave travelling through it, (*ii*) the magnitude of the electric vector of a plane-polarised electromagnetic wave or (*iii*) even the probability amplitude of what is called a matter wave (from which the probability of finding a particle within a given volume of space may be determined).

10.9 DIFFERENTIAL EQUATION OF A THREE-DIMENSIONAL WAVE

A three-dimensional wave, as have seen, is one that travels out in all direction. For such a wave, the differential equation takes the form

$$\frac{d^2\psi}{dt^2} = v^2\nabla^2\psi$$

where $\nabla^2\psi = \dfrac{\delta^2\psi}{\delta x^2} + \dfrac{\delta^2\psi}{\delta y^2} + \dfrac{d^2\psi}{\delta z^2}$.

One possible solution of the equation is $\psi = a\sin(\omega t - \mathbf{kr} + \theta)$

where ψ is the displacement at a point **r** at an instant t and **k**, the *propagation vector* whose magnitude is equal to $k = 2\pi/\lambda$ (the propagation constant) and direction the same as that of the wave propagation.

10.10 ENERGY DENSITY OF A PLANE PROGRESSIVE WAVE

We have already seen how in a progressive wave motion, the energy derived from the source is passed on from particle to particle, so that *there is a regular transmission of energy across every section of the medium.*

By the energy density of a plane progressive wave we mean *the total energy (kinetic + potential) per unit volume of the medium through which the wave passing*. It is usually denoted by the letter E.

Let us proceed to obtain an expression for it

As we know, the displacement of a particle of the medium distant x from the origin or the source, at an instant t, is given by

$$y = a\sin\frac{2\pi}{\lambda}(vt - x)$$

where the symbols have their usual meanings.

$\therefore$ *the velocity of the particle,* $U = \dfrac{dy}{dt} = \dfrac{2\pi v}{\lambda}a\cos\dfrac{2\pi}{\lambda}(vt - x)$

and *acceleration of the particle* , $\dfrac{dU}{dt} = \dfrac{d^2y}{dt^2}$

$$= -\frac{4\pi^2v^2}{\lambda^2}a\sin\frac{2\pi}{\lambda}(vt - x) = -\frac{4\pi^2v^2}{\lambda^2}y$$

Now, if we consider *unit volume* of the medium in the form of an extremely thin element of the medium parallel to the wave front, we have

mass of the element = ρ, *its density* (because density is mass per unit volume).

And since the layer is very thin, the velocity of all the particles in it may be assumed to be the same. We therefore have

K.E. per unit volume of the medium $= \dfrac{1}{2}$ *(mass) (velocity)*$^2 = \dfrac{1}{2}\rho U^2$

$$= \frac{1}{2}\rho\frac{4\pi^2v^2}{\lambda^2}a^2\cos^2\frac{2\pi}{\lambda}(vt - x) = \frac{2\pi^2v^2\rho}{\lambda^2}a^2\cos^2\frac{2\pi}{\lambda}(vt - x) \qquad ...(i)$$

Clearly, *force acting on unit volume = mass × acceleration*

$$= \rho\frac{d^2y}{dt^2} = \frac{4\pi^2v^2\rho}{\lambda^2}y,$$

ignoring the – *ve* sign which merely indicates that the acceleration is directed oppositely to the displacement.

$\therefore$ *work done in a small displacement dy of the layer*

$$= \textit{force} \times \textit{displacement} = \frac{4\pi^2v^2\rho}{\lambda^2}y\,dy$$

Hence, *work done during the whole displacement from 0 to y*

$$= \int_0^y \frac{4\pi^2v^2\rho}{\lambda^2}y\,dy = \frac{4\pi^2v^2\rho}{\lambda^2}\int_0^y y\,dy$$

$$= \frac{4\pi^2v^2\rho}{\lambda^2}\cdot\frac{y^2}{2} = \frac{2\pi^2v^2\rho}{\lambda^2}y^2 = \frac{2\pi^2v^2\rho}{\lambda^2}a^2\sin^2\frac{2\pi}{\lambda}(vt - x)$$

This work done must obviously be stored up in the medium in the form of potential energy. So that,

P.E. per unit volume of the medium $= \dfrac{2\pi^2 v^2 \rho}{\lambda^2} a^2 \sin^2 \dfrac{2\pi}{\lambda}(vt - x).$

$\therefore$ *total energy per unit volume of the medium or energy density of the plane progressive wave, i.e.,*

$$E = K.E. + P.E.$$

or,

$$E = \frac{2\pi^2 v^2 \rho}{\lambda^2} a^2 \cos^2 \frac{2\pi}{\lambda}(vt - x) + \frac{2\pi^2 v^2 \rho}{\lambda^2} a^2 \sin^2 \frac{2\pi}{\lambda}(vt - x)$$

$$= \frac{2\pi^2 v^2 \rho}{\lambda^2} a^2 \qquad ...(ii)$$

$$= 2\pi^2 \left(\frac{v}{\lambda}\right)^2 \rho a^2 = 2\pi^2 n^2 a^2 \rho \qquad [\because v/\lambda = n] \; ...(iii)$$

where n is the frequency of the wave

In case the cross section of the beam be unity, expressions (*ii*) and (*iii*) give the *total energy of the beam or the wave per unit length.*

A point of interest that must clearly be noted here is that *although both kinetic and potential energies of the wave depend upon the values of x and t, its total energy or the energy density is quite independent of either.*

10.11 DISTRIBUTION OF ENERGY IN A PLANE PROGRESSIVE WAVE

Having calculated the total energy of a plane progressive wave in § 9.10 above, let us see how it is distributed over a complete wave length.

Clearly, average K.E. *over a complete wavelength*

$$= \frac{1}{\lambda}\int_0^{\lambda} \frac{2\pi^2 v^2 \rho}{\lambda^2} \cos^2 \frac{2\pi}{\lambda}(vt - x)dx$$

$$= \frac{2\pi^2 n^2 a^2 \rho}{\lambda} \int_0^{\lambda} \frac{1}{2}\left[1 + \cos\frac{4\pi}{\lambda}(vt - x)\right]dx \qquad [\because v^2/\lambda^2 = n^2]$$

Now,

$$\int_0^{\lambda} \cos\frac{4\pi}{\lambda}(vt - x)dx = -\frac{\lambda}{4\pi}\left[\sin\frac{4\pi}{\lambda}(vt - x)\right]_0^{\lambda}$$

$$= -\frac{\lambda}{4\pi}\sin\frac{4\pi}{\lambda}\left[(vt - x) - \sin\frac{4\pi}{\lambda}vt\right]$$

$$= -\frac{\lambda}{4\pi}\left[\sin\left(\frac{4\pi}{\lambda}vt - 4\pi\right) - \sin\frac{4\pi}{\lambda}vt\right] = 0$$

So that, average K.E. *of the wave over a complete wavelength* $= 2\pi^2 n^2 a^2 \rho\lambda/2\lambda$

$$= \pi^2 n^2 a^2 \rho = \frac{1}{2}\text{total energy}$$

Similarly, average P.E. of the wave over a complete wavelength

$$= \frac{1}{\lambda}\int_0^{\lambda} \frac{2\pi^2 v^2 a^2 \rho}{\lambda^2} \sin^2 \frac{2\pi}{\lambda}(vt - x)dx = \pi^2 n^2 a^2 \rho = \frac{1}{2}\text{ total energy}$$

Thus, *at any given instant, the energy of a plane progressive harmonic wave is, on an average, half kinetic and half potential form.*

10.12 ENERGY CURRENT—INTENSITY OF A WAVE

It has been pointed out earlier under § 10.10 above that if the cross section of the beam or the wave be taken to be unity, we may regard the total energy per unit volume or the energy density $E = 2\pi^2 n^2 a^2 \rho$ as the *total energy per unit length of the wave.* And, since in progressive wave train, a new length v of the medium is set into motion every second, the energy transferred per second must be the energy contained in a length v. *This rate of flow of energy per unit area of cross section of the wave front along the direction of wave propagation is called the* **energy current** *(C) or* **the energy flux** *of the wave and is obviously equal to* $E \times v$.

Thus, *energy current or energy flux of a plane progressive wave,*

$$C = 2\pi^2 n^2 a^2 \rho v \text{ erg/sec/cm}^2$$

Now, we define the intensity of the wave (I) as the *quantity of incident energy per unit area of the wave front per unit time.* It is thus the same thing as the energy current or the energy flux of the wave. So that, we have $I = 2\pi^2 n^2 a^2 \rho v$

indicating that in any given case it is *proportional to the square of the amplitude of the wave, i.e.,* $I \propto a^2$.

Since in a medium with little or no frictional resistance, a **plane or one-dimensional wave** travels without attenuation, *i.e.* with its amplitude undiminished, *the intensity of the wave remains the same throughout.*

In the case of a **three-dimensional or a spherical wave**, on the other hand, such as the one emanating from a point-source, the wave fronts are spherical shells of successively increasing radii and the intensity obey the well known *inverse square law, viz.,* $I \propto 1/r^2$ and thus goes on falling as the squre of the distance (r) from the source.

And, since $I \propto a^2$, we have $a^2 \propto 1/r^2$ or $a \propto 1/r$, *i.e. the amplitude in the case of a spherical wave goes on decreasing progressively with distance from the source.*

Thus, whereas *for a plane progressive wave*, we have

$$y = a \sin \frac{2\pi}{\lambda}(vt - x),$$

for a *spherical wave*, $y = \frac{A}{r} \sin \frac{2\pi}{\lambda}(vt - x)$, where A is a constant.

10.13 SUPERPOSITION OF WAVES

All types of waves, mechanical as well as electromagnetic, are, in general, subject to the **principle of superposition**, first enunciated by *Huyghens, according to which if two or more independent waves are propagated through a medium or space, all at the same time, the resultant physical quantity (i.e., displacement etc.) at any point is the vector sum of the quantities due to each individual wave, i.e.,*

$$\psi = \psi_1 + \psi_2 + \psi_3 + \ldots$$

Thus, *in the case of one dimensional or plane waves, the resultant displacement at any point is the linear sum of the displacements due to the individual waves.*

Or, $y = y_1 + y_2 + y_3 + \ldots$

This means in other words, the two or more waves can traverse the same medium or space independently of one another. This is amply borne out by the fact that we can hear the individual notes of the various instruments constituting an orchestra, even though the resultant sound wave reaching our ears is a complex one. Similarly, we can tune our radio receiver to a particular frequency or wavelength even though waves of several frequencies or wavelength may be simultaneously crossing the aerial.

The *only one condition* for the principle of superposition to apply is that *the equation of the waves in question must be a linear one.* Thus, it holds good for waves in an elastic medium because the relation between the deformation produced and the recovering force is linear; and for electromagnetic waves, because the mathematical linear; and for electromagnetic waves because the mathematical relationship between the electric and magnetic fields is also linear.

The principle fails in the cast of waves for which the equations governing their propagation are not linear as, for example, *shockwaves* produced by large explosions. Even though these waves too are longitudinal elastic waves in air, the equation governing their propagation is quadratic and not linear.

The importance of the principle of superposition lies in the fact that in the case where it holds good, it is possible to analyse a complicated wave motion into a set of simple waves. We shall revert back to it and discuss it more fully later in § 10.24.

Another important consequence of this principle is that it gives rise to the phenomenon referred to as *interference of waves*. (See next article)

10.14 INTERFERENCE–BEATS

Let two identical waves (*i.e.* waves having the *same amplitude and wavelength*) with a *path-difference* λ between them, travelling along the *same, or very nearly the same path and in the same direction*, be represented respectively by

$$y_1 = a\sin\frac{2\pi}{\lambda}(vt - x) \quad \text{and} \quad y_2 = a\sin\frac{2\pi}{\lambda}[vt - (x+\delta)]$$

Then, the resultant wave will, in accordance with the principle of superposition, be clearly represented by

$$y = y_1 + y_2 = a\sin\frac{2\pi}{\lambda}(vt - x) + a\sin\frac{2\pi}{\lambda}[vt - (x+\delta)]$$

$$= 2a\sin\frac{2\pi}{\lambda}\left[vt - \left(x + \frac{\delta}{2}\right)\right]\cos\frac{\pi\delta^*}{\lambda}$$

Or,

$$y = 2a\cos\frac{\pi\delta}{\lambda}\sin\frac{2\pi}{\lambda}\left[vt - \left(x + \frac{\delta}{2}\right)\right]$$

i.e., the resultant wave is also a simple harmonic wave, of the *same wavelength, frequency and velocity* as the two constituent waves but has an amplitude $2a\cos\pi\delta/\lambda$, indicating that the amplitude changes with the path difference δ (or the phase difference $2\pi\delta/\lambda^*$) between the two waves.

Constructive interference

The amplitude of the resultant wave will be the maximum ($+2a$ or $-2a$) when $\cos\pi\delta/\lambda = +1$ or -1, *i.e.*, when $\pi\delta/\lambda = 0, \pi, 2\pi, 3\pi$ etc. and, therefore, $\delta = 0, 1, 2\lambda, 3\lambda$ or $n\lambda$, where $n = 0, 1, 2, 3$ etc., or $2\pi\delta/\lambda = 0, 2\pi, 4\pi$ or $n(2\pi)$ where $n = 0, 1, 2, 3$ etc.

In other words, the amplitude, and also the intensity of the resultant wave (which is proportional to the square of the amplitude) will be the *maximum*, and equal to twice and four times respectively of the amplitude and intensity of one single wave when the two waves arrive at a point *in phase* (*i.e.*, with a path difference equal to an integral multiple of λ or a phase difference equal to an even multiple of 2π); for, then, the crest or the condensation of one wave falls on the crest or the condensation of the other and so also the trough or the rarefaction of one wave over the through or rarefaction of the other.

The two waves, in this case, thus *reinforce* each other and are said to interfere constructively.

Destructive interference

On the other hand, the amplitude, and hence the intensity, of the resultant wave will be the *minimum or zero* when $\cos\pi\delta/\lambda = 0$, *i.e.*, when $\pi\delta/\lambda = \pi/2, 3\pi/2, 5\pi/2$ etc. and therefore, $\delta = \lambda/2, 3\lambda/2, 5\lambda/2$ etc., or $(2n+1)\lambda/2$ or when $2\pi\delta/\lambda = \pi, 3\pi, 5\pi \ldots$ or $(2n+1)\pi$, where $n = 1, 2, 3$ etc.

Thus, the amplitude, and hence the intensity, will be the *minimum or zero* when the two waves arrive at a point *out of phase* (*i.e.*, with a path difference equal to an odd multiple of δ/2 or a phase difference equal to an odd multiple of π); for, then, the crest or the condensation of one wave falls

* Because, as we know, the phase changes by 2π in a distance λ, and, therefore, by 2πδ/λ in a distance δ.

on the trough or the rarefaction of the other. The two waves here thus *nullify* each other and are said to interfere destructively.

Because the energy of the resultant wave at the former points (of constructive interference) is *four times* that due to one single wave and at the latter points (of destructive interference), *zero*, we must not jump to the conclusion that energy has been created at the former and *destroyed* at the latter points *it has simply been redistributed in the medium or space, i.e.*, transformed from the points of minimum or zero intensity to those of maximum intensity, the total energy of the resultant wave being the same as the sum of the total energies of the two constituent waves.

This may be easily seen from the fact that energy being proportional to a^2, the total energy of the two waves before interference is proportional to $2a^2$ throughout the medium (or space). After interference, the energy of the resultant wave is proportional to $4a^2$ at some points and zero at others. The average energy of the wave is thus again proportional to $2a^2$.

The phenomenon of interference thus does not any means violate the law of conservation of energy. On the other hand, it is a direct consequence of this law, for we cannot possibly have points of increased intensity without there being also corresponding points of decreased intensity. In fact, *interference may more aptly be defined as the redistribution of energy due to superposition of waves.*

In case the two identical waves travel along the same path in *opposite directions*, (as, for example, an incident and a reflected wave), we have a new type of waves produced, called *standing or stationary waves* for the simple reason that they do not move onward into the medium or space but appear and disappear within the limited region in which they are produced. This is, therefore, referred to as *interference in space.*

The maxima and minima of displacement do not move forwards into the medium or space but throughout remain fixed in their respective positions alternating with each other and there is thus no transference of energy across any section of the medium or space. We shall deal fully with these in § 10.21.

Beats. If the two waves, travelling along the same path and in the same direction, have *slightly different frequencies or wavelengths* and also different amplitudes, they arrive in phase at some points and out of phase at others, thus producing maximum displacements, and hence also maximum intensity, at the former, and minimum (but *not zero*) displacements and hence minimum intensity at the latter points as they proceed along.

In view, however, of the frequencies of the two waves being slightly different, their relative phase at various points keeps on changing progressively. For, if at a particular instant the two waves arrive in *phase* at a given point, we have the maximum displacement or amplitude there and hence also the maximum intensity. But, as soon as the wave with the higher frequency has gained half a period or half a wavelength over the other, there is the minimum displacement and hence the minimum intensity at the point instead of the previous maximum which has shifted further on to the point where half a period before there was the minimum displacement and hence also minimum intensity. And, as the higher frequency wave gains one full time-period or wavelength over the other the two gain arrive *in phase* at the point in question, producing the maximum displacement and intensity there, with the condition of minimum displacement and intensity shifting further up to the point where half a period before there had been the maximum of displacements and intensity.

Thus, the condition of maximum and minimum displacement and intensity travels onwards through successive points as the two waves proceed forwards in the medium or space and we have, as it were, *an interference pattern travelling onwards with respect to the observer. This is referred to as interference in time, and these alternations of maxima and minima of intensity are called* ***beats****, one maximum and one succeeding minimum (or vice versa) constituting one beat. The number of beats produced per second is equal to the difference between the frequencies of the two waves.*

If the two waves be sound waves in air, the maxima and minim a of displacement and intensity manifest themselves as louder and fainter sounds alternating with each other as the two waves travel through the air, *one loudness and one succeeding faintness constituting one beat.* Due to the limitations of our car, we cannot, however, hear more than 16 beats per second. In point of fact, we can hardly ever hear more than 7 or 8 beats per second.

Theory of Beats

Let two sound waves, or plane harmonic waves, of *amplitudes* a_1 and a_2 (where $a_1 > a_2$) and of nearly equal *frequencies* n_1 and n_2 (where $n_1 > n_2$) be travelling along the *same path* and in the *same direction* through air.

Considering any one point in the medium (air) through which the waves are passing, the *displacements there* due to the two waves which, as we know, *very cyclically with time*, are given by $y_1 = a_1 \sin 2\pi n_1 t$ and $y_2 = a_2 \sin 2\pi n_2 t$.

In accordance with the *principle of superposition, therefore, the resultant displacement at the point will be* $y = y_1 + y_2 = a_1 \sin 2\pi n_1 t + a_2 \sin 2\pi n_2 t$.

Or, $y = a_1 \sin 2\pi n_1 t + a_2 \sin 2\pi(n_1 - (n_1 - n_2)$

$$= a_1 \sin 2\pi n_1 t + a_2 \sin 2\pi n_1 t \cos 2\pi (n_1 - n_2)t - a_2 \cos 2\pi n_1 t \sin 2\pi (n_1 - n_2)t$$

$$= \sin 2\pi n_1 t[a_1 + a_2 \cos 2\pi (n_1 - n_2)t] - \cos 2\pi n_1 t[a_2 \sin 2\pi(n_1 - n_2)t]$$

Or, putting $a_1 + a_2 \cos 2\pi (n_1 - n_2)t = a \cos\theta$ and $a_2 \sin 2\pi (n_1 - n_2)t = a \sin\theta$

we have $$y = a \sin 2\pi n_1 t \cos\theta - a \cos 2\pi n_1 t \sin\theta$$

Or, $$y = a \sin (2\pi n_1 t - \theta).$$

showing *the displacement at the point due to the resultant wave too varies cyclically with time, with an amplitude a but lags an angle θ behind the displacement due to the first wave, where,*

$$a = \sqrt{(a \cos\theta)^2 + (a \sin\theta)^2}$$

$$= \sqrt{a_1^2 + a_2^2 \cos^2 2\pi(n_1 - n_2)t + 2a_1 a_2 \cos 2\pi(n_1 - n_2)t + a_2^2 \sin^2 2\pi(n_1 - n_2)t}$$

Or $$a = \sqrt{a_1^2 + a_2^2 + 2a_1 a_2 \cos 2\pi (n_1 - n_2)t}$$

and $$\tan\theta = \frac{a \sin 2\pi (n_1 - n_2)t}{a_1 + a_2 \cos 2\pi (n_1 - n_2)t}$$

indicating that *the value of both a and θ keep on changing with time.*

Clearly, the amplitude at the point in question will have its *maximum* value $(a_1 + a_2)$ when $\cos 2\pi (n_1 - n_2)t = +1$,

i.e, when $2\pi (n_1 - n_2)t = 2r\pi$, where, r is an integer, 0, 1, 2, 3 etc. *i.e.*, at

$$t = \frac{r}{n_1 - n_2} = 0, \frac{1}{(n_1 - n_2)}, \frac{2}{(n_1 - n_2)}, \frac{3}{(n_1 - n_2)} \text{ etc.}$$

The *time-interval between two successive maxima is thus* $1/(n_1 - n_2)$.

And, the amplitude will have its minimum value $(a_1 - a_2)$, when $\cos 2\pi (n_1 - n_2)t = -1$; or, $2\pi(n_1 - n_2)\, t = (2r + 1)\pi$, where again, $r = 0, 1, 2, 3$ etc. *i.e.*, at

$$t = \frac{2r+1}{2(n_1 - n_2)} = \frac{r}{(n_1 - n_2)} + \frac{1}{2(n_1 - n_2)} = \frac{1}{2(n_1 - n_2)}, \frac{3}{2(n_1 - n_2)}, \frac{5}{2(n_1 - n_2)} \text{ etc.}$$

the *time-interval between two successive minima again being* $1(n_1 - n_2)$, *although they occur in between the maxima.*

Thus, maxima and minima of amplitude alternate at the point in question as the two waves travel onwards, producing alternate loudness and faintness of sound there. *These alternations of loudness and faintness constitute beats, one loudness and one succeeding faintness constituting one beat.*

And, clearly the *frequency of beats, i.e., the number of beats produced per second* = $(n_1 - n_2)$ = *the difference between the frequencies of the two sound waves.*

10.15 VIBRATIONS OF STRINGS

A string may be made to execute *longitudinal transverse* as well as torsional vibrations. We shall, however, concern ourselves here only with its transverse mode of vibration, this being the chief source of most musical sounds and hence the basis of a host of musical instruments.

Now, a transverse vibration in a string may be excited by *plucking, hammering* or *bowing* it, as in the cases of the *guitar*, the *pianoforte* and the *violin* respectively, all these different modes of excitation having their own subtle differences. Again, therefore, we shall restrict ourselves here to the transverse vibration in a string excited mainly by plucking it.

Before proceeding further, we may as well understand clearly that a **string**, for our purpose, may be defined as *a wire or a cord, homogeneous in composition and having a uniform area of cross section, so that its mass per unit length or its line density is the same all along it. Further, it should be perfectly flexible so as to be able to bend without giving rise to any viscous forces in its material, i.e.*, it should have no stiffness. And, *finally, it should not yield when under tension, so that there is no increase in its length.*

No actual wire or cord can, of course, satisfy these ideal conditions, at fully particularly that flexibility (or non-stiffness), but if its length be very much greater than its thickness or diameter, it approximates more or less to our definition of a string. *For all partial purposes. therefore, a a long, infinitely thin and flexible wire or cord of a uniform composition and area of cross section may be considered to be a string.*

10.16 PROPAGATION OF TRANSVERSE VIBRATION (OR A TRANSVERSE WAVE) ALONG A STRING

Consider a long string with its one end fixed and with its normal or equilibrium position along the axis of x, *i.e.*, with the tension in it sufficiently large so as to make the effects of gravity quite negligible. It will be found that on giving its free end a smart and quick up and down jerk, the hump thus produced travels along it towards the fixed end. Or, if the string under tension be fixed at both ends plucked at any point, a hump travels towards either fixed end.

In either case, the string is thrown into transverse vibration, with each successive portion of it executing an up and down motion perpendicular to its length, *i.e.*, a transverse vibration perpendicular to the direction of propagation of the wave (constituted by these vibrations) which obviously travels along the length of the string.

Now, as we know, the two essential conditions for the production and propagation of a wave in a medium are that (*i*) *it must possess inertia* and (*ii*) *a restoring force must be called into play, tending to restore the displaced particles back to their normal positions. The former is here supplied by the mass of the particles of the sting and the latter, by the transverse component of the tension along the string.*

It is thus clear that *in the absence of any tension, no transverse waves can possibly travel along a string.*

10.17 VELOCITY OF A TRANSVERSE WAVE ALONG A STRING

A string is cord whose length is very large as compared to its diameter and which is perfectly uniform and flexible. When a string is stretched between two points and is plucked in a direction at right angles to its length *transverse vibrations* are produced in it. The particle vibrate perpendicular to its length and movement is handed on from particle to particle. A transverse wave travels along the string with a velocity depending upon certain constants of the string.

Velocity of transverse waves. Consider a part of the wave AB travelling in the sting from left to right with a velocity v. If the string is pulled from right to left with the same velocity the wave AB will remain stationary with respect to the paper in space. A small part PQ of the wave AB can be considered to be the arc of a circle. As the string moves along the circular PQ a centripetal force acts on it along the radius towards the centre O [Fig. 10.8]

A uniform tension or stretching force T acts in the string throughout. This tension T acts along CP and at P and along CQ at Q, where CP and CQ are tangents to the arc PQ at P and Q respectively.

Draw PO and QO perpendiculars to the arc at P and Q meeting at O the centre of the circular arc having a radius r.

Let the angle POQ be denoted by $2\ \delta\theta$. Join OC; then OC is the bisector of the angle POQ.

$$\therefore \qquad \text{Arc } PQ = r \times 2\ \delta\theta$$

Let ρ be the mass per unit length of the string, then

Mass of the part $PQ = \rho \times PQ = 2\rho r\delta\theta$

The centripetal force actiing on

$$PQ = \frac{2\rho r\delta\theta v^2}{r} = 2\rho v^2 \delta\theta \qquad ...(i)$$

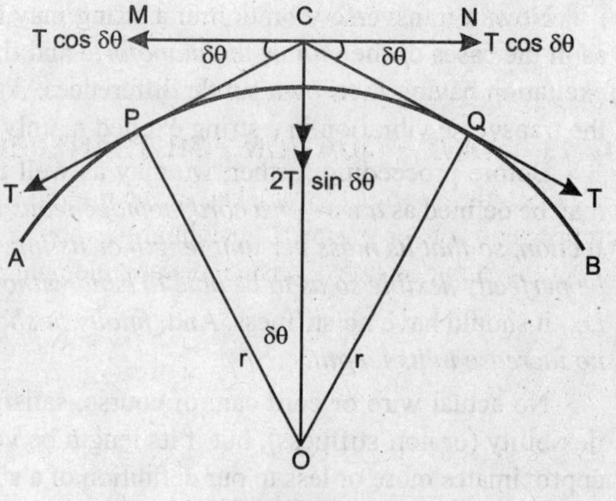

Fig. 10.8

The tension T can be resolved into two rectangular components. The horizontal component $T\cos\delta\theta$ along CM and $T\cos\delta\theta$ along CN, cancel each other being equal and opposite. The vertical components of tension act in the same direction and total force along CO.

$$= 2T\sin\delta\theta = 2\ T\delta\theta \qquad [\because \delta\theta \text{ is small}] \ ...(ii)]$$

This provides the necessary centripetal force. Equating (i) and (ii), we have

$$2T\ \delta\theta = 2\ \rho\ v^2\ \delta\theta$$

or

$$T = \rho\ v^2 \quad \text{or} \quad v^2 = \frac{T}{\rho}$$

$$\therefore \quad \text{Velocity of the transverse wave, } v = \sqrt{\frac{T}{\rho}}$$

Frequency of the fundamental note. When a string is fixed at both ends, it is said produce a *fundamental note*, if it vibrates as a whole in one segment. In such a case the length l of the string is equal to $\frac{\lambda}{2}$ where λ is the wavelength of the note.

$$\lambda = 2\ l$$

Now frequency

$$n = \frac{v}{\lambda} = \frac{l}{2l}\sqrt{\frac{T}{\rho}}$$

This is the frequency of the fundamental note.

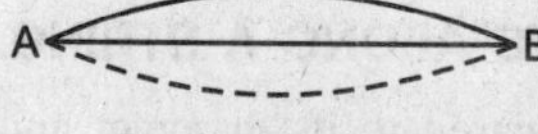

Fundamental note

First octave

Fig. 10.9

The two fixed ends A and B of the string act as nodes.

Frequency of first octave. When the string vibration in two segments, it is said to produce *first octave*. In such a case $\lambda = l$.

$$\therefore \quad \text{Frequency of the first octave} = n_1 = \frac{v}{\lambda} = \frac{1}{l}\sqrt{\frac{T}{\rho}}$$

In addition to the two ends A and B, there is a node at the mid point C.

Role of elasticity and inertia of a string

The wave velocity in a string is given by, $v = \sqrt{\frac{T}{\rho}}$ where ρ is the mass per unit length of the string. As ρ is the mass; it represents the property of *inertia*. Again T is the tension in the string due to its stretching. As the string is stretched a restoring force is called into play. This restoring force is due to the stress caused by the elastic properties of the string. Thus the wave velocity in a string is a function of elasticity and inertia of the medium or the string.

10.18 WAVE EQUATION FOR TRANSVERSE WAVE IN A STRING

Consider a string *AB* plucked in the middle so that when left to itself it begins to vibrate. The components of the tension *T* at right angles to the length of the string tend to bring the string back to equilibrium position. Consider a small element *PQ* of the string, as shown in fig. 10.10.

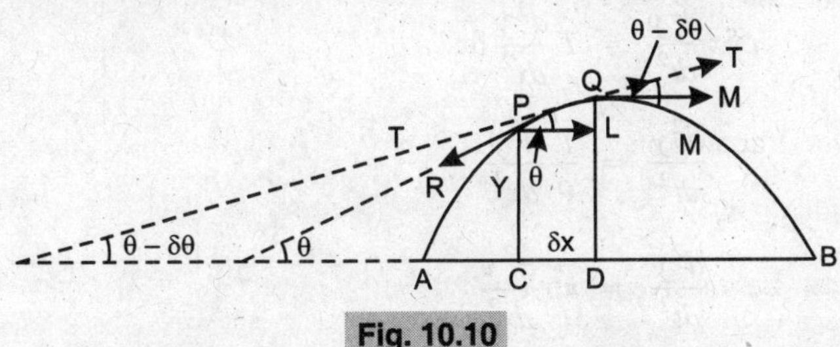

Fig. 10.10

The tension *T* at *P* acts along the tangent *PR* and at *Q* along the tangent *QT*. It is supposed that the gradient of the curve formed by the string in the displaced position is very small so that the tension *T* acts uniformly along the string and the normal position of the string coincides with the *X*-axis of the co-ordinate system.

The small element *PQ* of the string executes simple harmonic motion and undergoes a vertical displacement which varies with the position of the element as well as with time.

Form *P* and Q draw *PL* and *QM* respectively parallel to *AB*. The tangent at *P* is inclined to the X-axis and the line *PL* at an angle θ and the tangent at *Q* is inclined to X-axis and the line *QM* at an angle θ – δθ. The angle δθ is very small as the amplitudes of string is small.

The components of tension *T* acting at *P* are

$T \cos \theta$ in the horizontal direction

and $T \sin \theta$ in the vertically downward direction.

Similarly, the components of tension *T* acting at *P* are

$T \cos (\theta - \delta\theta)$ in the horizontal direction

and $T \sin (\theta - \delta\theta)$ in the vertically upward direction

As θ and (θ – δθ) differ by a very small value δθ

$$T \cos \theta = T \cos (\theta - \delta\theta)$$

Hence the two horizontal components cancel each other as they act almost in the same line in opposite directions. The resultant force *F* acting in the vertically downward direction.

$$= T \sin \theta - T \sin (\theta - \delta\theta)$$

$$= T \sin \theta - T \sin \theta \cos \delta\theta + T \cos \theta \sin \delta\theta$$

But δθ is very small.

$$\therefore \quad \cos \delta\theta = 1 \text{ and } \sin \delta\theta = \delta\theta$$

Hence, the resultant force $F = T \sin \theta - T \sin \theta + T \cos \theta \delta\theta = T\delta(\sin\theta)$

As θ is small, $\sin \theta = \tan \theta = \dfrac{dy}{dx}$

where $\dfrac{dy}{dx}$ is the slope of the curve

$$\therefore \quad F = T\delta\left(\frac{dy}{dx}\right) = T\left[\frac{d}{dx}\left(\frac{dy}{dx}\right)\right]\delta x$$

$$= T\frac{d^2 y}{dx^2}\delta x \qquad \text{...}(i)$$

If ρ is the mass per unit length of the string, then mass of the element PQ of length $\delta x = \rho \delta x$.

The acceleration of the elements in the direction of Y-axis $= \frac{d^2 y}{dt^2}$

If we neglect the effect of gravity, then

$$\text{Force on the element} = \rho \delta x \times \frac{d^2 y}{dt^2} \qquad ...(ii)$$

Comparing (*i*) and (*ii*), we have

$$\rho \delta x \frac{d^2 y}{dt^2} = T \frac{d^2 y}{dx^2} \delta x$$

or

$$\frac{d^2 y}{dt^2} = \frac{T}{\rho} \frac{d^2 y}{dx^2}$$

or

$$\frac{d^2 y}{dt^2} = v^2 \frac{d^2 y}{dx^2} \qquad ...(iii)$$

Where $\sqrt{\frac{T}{\rho}} = v$ = a constant. The dimensions of v are those of velocity $[L^1 T^{-1}]$.

The equation (*iii*) is the differential equation of wave motion and can be put in the form

$$\frac{d^2 y}{dx^2} = \frac{1}{v^2} \frac{d^2 y}{dt^2}$$

The wave equation $\frac{d^2 y}{dt^2} = v^2 \frac{d^2 y}{dx^2}$ has been derived by considering the vibrating string as a proto type. Any partial differential equation of the form

$$\frac{\partial^2 \psi}{\partial t^2} = v^2 \frac{\partial^2 \psi}{\partial x^2}$$

or

$$\frac{\partial^2 \psi}{\partial x^2} = \frac{1}{v^2} \frac{\partial^2 \psi}{\partial t^2}$$

represents a general wave equation where ψ is a function of space and time co-ordinates and v the velocity with which the wave travels without any change of form. The wave variable ψ represents the transverse displacement y in the case of a string, pressure in the case of sound waves in a gas and electric field vector $\vec{E}$ in the case of electromagnetic wave and so on. For plane waves in one dimension only it is a function of x but in the case of waves in two or three dimensions it is a function of two or three space co-ordinates.

Solution of the wave equation. We shall consider the wave equation in the form

$$\frac{d^2 y}{dt^2} = v^2 \frac{d^2 y}{dx^2}$$

It is clear from the form of the wave equation that the solution of this equation must be a linear function of the variable x and t. A function of the form

$$y = f_1(vt - x) \text{ or } y = f_2(vt + x)$$

is one of its solutions. Therefore, a general solution is given by

$$y = f_1(vt - x) + f_2(vt + x)$$

To show that $y = f_1(vt - x)$ is solution of the wave equation, we have

$$\frac{dy}{dt} = vf_1'(vt - x)$$

and

$$\frac{d^2y}{dt^2} = v^2 f_1''(vt - x)$$

where f_1' and f_1'' are the first and second derivatives of f_1 respectively with respect to $(vt - x)$

Similarly

$$\frac{dy}{dx} = -f_1'(vt - x)$$

and

$$\frac{d^2y}{dx^2} = f_1''(vt - x)$$

Hence

$$\frac{d^2y}{dt^2} = v^2\frac{d^2y}{dx^2}$$

Similarly it can be shown that $y = f_2(vt + x)$ as well as $y = f_1(vt - x) + f_2(vt + v)$ is a solution of the wave equation.

In a harmonic progressive wave each particle of the medium executes simple harmonic motion which may be represented by a sine or a cosine function.

For a wave travelling along the positive x direction, we have

For sine function $y = f(vt - x) = a \sin k(vt - x)$ ...(*i*)

where a is the amplitude and k a constant. The wave profile repeats itself regularly at a distance $\frac{2\pi}{k}$ because $a \sin k\left(vt - x + \frac{2\pi}{k}\right) = a \sin k(vt - x)$. The distance $2\pi/k$, therefore, gives the wavelength λ.

Hence,

$$\lambda = \frac{2\pi}{k} \quad \text{or} \quad k = \frac{2\pi}{\lambda}$$

Substituting in (*i*), we have

$$y = a\sin\frac{2\pi}{\lambda}(vt - x) = a\sin\left(\frac{2\pi vt}{\lambda} - \frac{2\pi}{\lambda}x\right)$$

$$= a\sin 2\pi\left(vt - \frac{x}{\lambda}\right) = a\sin(\omega t - kx)$$

where $\omega = 2\pi\nu$ (ν = frequency) and $k = \frac{2\pi}{\lambda} = 2\pi\bar{v}$ and $\bar{v}$ is the wave number *i.e.* the reciprocal of the wavelength or *the number of waves contained in a unit length.* The constant k is known as *propagation constant*.

For cosine function

$$y = a\cos\frac{2\pi}{\lambda}(vt - x) = a\cos 2\pi\left(vt - \frac{x}{\lambda}\right)$$

$$= a\cos(\omega t - kx)$$

Exponential form. The exponential form of the equation $y = ae^{i(\omega t - kx)}$ is equally valid solution of the differential equation as it contains both the sine and cosine function. The real part of the expression is the cosine function and the part multiple by $(i = \sqrt{-1})$ is the sine function.

$$y = a\sin\frac{2\pi}{\lambda}(vt - x) \text{ or } y = a\cos\frac{2\pi}{\lambda}(vt - x) \text{ or } y = ae^{i(\omega t - kx)}$$

represents a wave moving to the right whereas

$$y = a\sin\frac{2\pi}{\lambda}(vt + x) \text{ or } y = a\cos\frac{2\pi}{\lambda}(vt + x) \text{ or } y = ae^{i(\omega t + kx)}$$

represents a wave moving to the left in the negative $(-x)$ direction.

10.19 CHARACTERISTIC IMPEDANCE OF A STRING

A wave of any type-mechanical, electrical or electromagnetic experiences an impedance while propagating through a medium. When there is no resistive or dissipating mechanism, the impedance is determined by two energy string parameters *i.e.* inertia and elasticity for mechanical waves and inductance and capacitance in the case of electrical waves. The impedance in such a case is a real quantity. The presence of a loss mechanism introduces a complex term into the impedance.

Transverse impedance. *It is the impedance offered by a string to transverse, progressive waves and its defined as the ratio of transverse force to the transverse velocity.*

$$\text{Impedance, } Z = \frac{\text{Transverse force}}{\text{Transverse velocity}} = \frac{F}{v}$$

Suppose we have a continuous string stretching from left to right with the left end at $x = 0$. Consider a progressive wave on the string which is generated by an impressed oscillating force $F = F_0 e^{i\omega t}$ acting at this end (Fig. 10.11). The force acts only in the plane of the paper in a *transverse* direction *i.e.* perpendicular to the equilibrium position of the string.

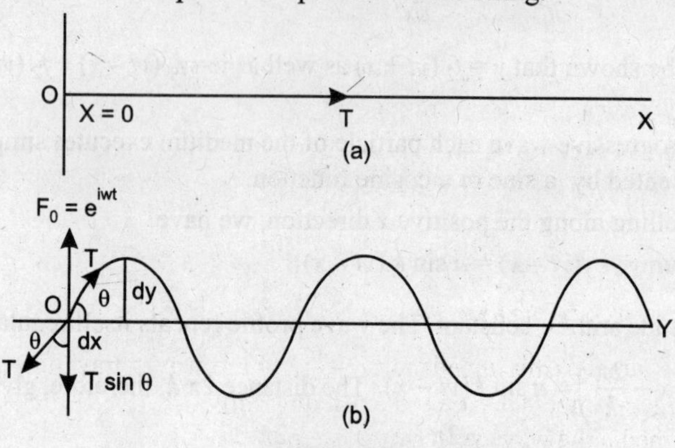

Fig. 10.11

If the string has a constant tension T, then at the end of the string ($x = 0$) the applied force $F_0 e^{i\omega t}$ and the $T \sin\theta$ component of T always balance each other.

$$\therefore \qquad F = F_0 e^{i\omega t} = -T\sin\theta$$

As θ is small, then as shown in Fig. 10.11 (*b*)

$$\sin\theta = \tan\theta = \frac{dy}{dx}$$

$$\therefore \qquad F_0 e^{i\omega t} = -T\left(\frac{dy}{dx}\right)_{x=0}$$

The displacement of the progressive wave is represented in the exponential form by the equation

$$\vec{y} = \vec{A}\, e^{i(\omega t - kx)}$$

where $\vec{A}$ is the amplitude and may be a *complex* quantity due to its phase relation with F and $k = \frac{2\pi}{\lambda} = \frac{\omega}{v}$, ω being the angular frequency of the applied periodic force and v the wave velocity.

Hence at the end of the string where $x = 0$

$$F_0 e^{i\omega t} = -T\left(\frac{dy}{dx}\right)_{x=0} = ik\,T\,\vec{A}\, e^{i\omega t}$$

$$\therefore \qquad \vec{A} = \frac{F_0}{ikT}$$

and $$\vec{y} = \frac{F_0}{iT} \times \frac{v}{\omega} e^{i(\omega t - kx)}$$

$\therefore$ Transverse velocity $$\vec{v} = \frac{d\vec{y}}{dt}$$

$$= F_0 \frac{v}{T} e^{i(\omega t - kx)} = ve^{i(\omega t - kx)}$$

where v is the velocity amplitude $$= \frac{F_0 v}{T}$$

According to definition, impedance $Z = \frac{F_0}{v}$

$\therefore$ $$Z = \frac{F_0}{v} = \frac{T}{v}$$

Now for the string velocity, $v = \sqrt{\frac{T}{\rho}}$ or $T = \rho v^2$

where ρ is the mass per unit length or the linear density of the string.

$\therefore$ Characteristic impedance $Z = \rho v$.

Factors on which characteristic impedance depends. The characteristic impedance depends upon ρ the mass power unit length of the string. It also depends upon the value of the velocity of the wave v. The value of velocity v depends upon inertia and elasticity of the medium. Therefore, the impedance also depends upon these two *energy storing* factors.

10.20 REFLECTION AND TRANSMISSION ON A STRING AT DISCONTINUITY

A string offers a characteristic impedance $Z = \rho v$ to the waves travelling along it. Whenever there is a *sudden* change in impedance due to a *discontinuity* at the junction of two media the wave suffers reflection at the boundary. This applies to all types of waves whether they are sound waves along a string, voltage or current waves along a transmission line or electromagnetic waves in a medium.

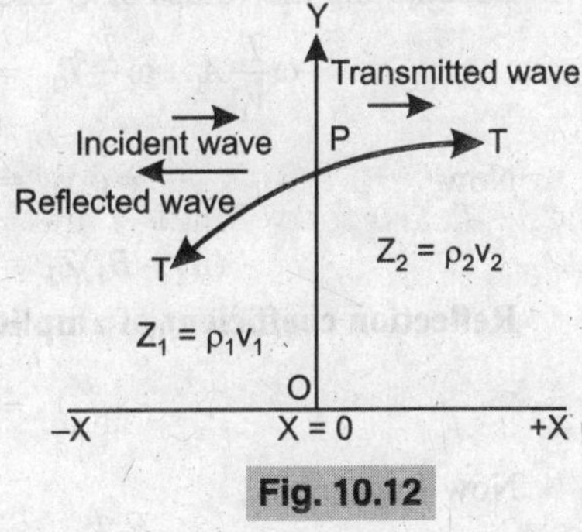

Fig. 10.12

Let us suppose that the string consists of two parts smoothly joined at the point P, $x = 0$ and has a constant tension T along the whole string. The two sections have different linear densities ρ_1 and ρ_2 and, therefore, different wave velocities v_1 and v_2 given by

$$v_1 = \sqrt{\frac{T}{\rho_1}} \text{ and } v_2 = \sqrt{\frac{T}{\rho_2}}$$

The specific or characteristic impedances respectively are $Z_1 = \rho_1 v_1$ and $Z_2 = \rho_2 v_2$. If the incident wave is represented by the real part of the displacement equation

$$y_1 = A_1 e^{i(\omega t - k_1 x)}$$

where A_1 is the amplitude of the incident wave travelling in the *positive X-direction* with velocity v_1 and $k_1 = \frac{\omega}{v_1}$, then the reflected and transmitted waves are represented by the real part of the equations

$$y_r = B_1 e^{i(\omega t + k_1 x)}$$

and $$y_t = A_2 e^{i(\omega t - k_2 x)}$$

where B_1 is the amplitude of the reflected wave travelling in the *negative X-direction* with velocity v_1 and A_2 is the amplitude of the transmitted wave travelling in the *positive X-direction* with velocity

v_2 and $k_2 = \frac{\omega}{v_2}$. The value of B_1 and A_2 can be determined with the help of two boundary conditions which must be satisfied at the point of impedance discontinuity at $x = 0$. The boundary conditions are:

(1) The displacement y is the same immediately to the left and to the right of $x = 0$ for all times so that there is *no discontinuity of displacement*. This is the *geometrical condition* and is stated as

$$y_i + y_r = y_t$$

or $$A_1 e^{i(\omega t - k_1 x)} + B_1 e^{i(\omega t + k_1 x)} = A_2 e^{i(\omega t - k_2 x)}$$

At $$x = 0$$

$$A_1 e^{i\omega t} + B_1 e^{i\omega t} = A_2 e^{i\omega t}$$

$$A_1 + B_1 = A_2 \quad \text{...}(i)$$

(2) The transverse force $T\left(\frac{dy}{dx}\right)$ at $x = 0$ is *continuous across the boundary*. This means that *the gradient* $\frac{dy}{dx}$ *must have the same value on both sides*. If it is not so a finite transverse force will act on an infinitesimally small mass of the string producing an infinite acceleration which is physically an absurd statement. This is the *dynamical condition* and is stated as

$$T\frac{dy_i}{dx} + T\frac{dy_r}{dx} = T\frac{dy_t}{dx}$$

or $$-Tk_1 A_1 e^{i(\omega t - k_1 x)} + Tk_1 B_1 e^{i(\omega t + k_1 x)} = -Tk_2 A_2 e^{i(\omega t - k_2 x)}$$

At $$x = 0$$

$$-Tk_1 A_1 e^{i\omega t} + Tk_1 B_1 e^{i\omega t} = -Tk_2 A_2 e^{i\omega t}$$

or $$-Tk_1 A_1 + Tk_1 B_1 = -Tk_2 A_2$$

Substituting the values of k_1 and k_2, we have

$$-\omega\frac{T}{v_1}A_1 + \omega\frac{T}{v_1}B_1 = -\omega\frac{T}{v_2}A_2$$

Now $$\frac{T}{v_1} = \rho_1 v_1 = Z_1 \text{ and } \frac{T}{v_2} = \rho_2 v_2 = Z_2$$

$\therefore$ $$(A_1 - B_1)Z_1 = A_2 Z_2 \quad \text{...}(ii)$$

Reflection coefficient of amplitude. The reflection coefficient

$$= \frac{\text{Amplitude of reflected wave}}{\text{Amplitude of incident wave}} = \frac{B_1}{A_1}$$

Now from (*ii*)

$$\frac{A_2}{A_1 - B_1} = \frac{A_1 + B_1}{A_1 - B_1} = \frac{Z_1}{Z_2}$$

$\therefore$ Reflection co-efficient $$\frac{B_1}{A_1} = \frac{Z_1 - Z_2}{Z_1 + Z_2}$$

Transmission coefficient of amplitude. The transmission coefficient

$$= \frac{\text{Amplitude of transmitted wave}}{\text{Amplitude of incident wave}} = \frac{A_2}{A_1}$$

Substituting $B_1 = A_2 - A_1$ in (*ii*), we have

$$(A_1 - A_2 + A_1)Z_1 = A_2 Z_2$$

or $$2A_1 Z_1 = A_2(Z_1 + Z_2)$$

$\therefore$ $$\frac{A_2}{A_1} = \frac{2Z_1}{Z_1 + Z_2}$$

It is clear from the above expression that both these coefficients are independent of ω *i.e.*, these hold for waves of all the frequencies. These are real quantities and, therefore, are free from phase changes except the phase change of π when reflection takes place at a fixed end.

Amplitude after reflection at dense medium ($Z_2 \cong \infty$)

If $Z_2 = \infty$ *i.e.*, $x = 0$ is a fixed end, then $A_2 = 0$ and there is no transmitted wave. This also gives

$$\frac{B_1}{A_1} = \frac{Z_1/Z_2 - 1}{Z_1/Z_2 + 1} = -1$$

so that the incident wave is completely reflected with a phase change of π *i.e.*, the phase is reversed. This condition is necessary for standing waves to exist. A group of waves having a number of component frequencies will *retain* its shape on reflection.

Amplitude after reflection at rarer medium ($Z_2 \cong 0$)

If $Z_2 = 0$, *i.e.*, $x = 0$ is a *free* end, then

$$\frac{B_1}{A_1} = 1 \text{ and } \frac{A_2}{A_1} = 2$$

i.e., the amplitude of the transmitted wave A_2 is twice that of the incident wave A_1. It is due to this reason that there is 'flick' at the end of a whip or the free end of a string when a wave reaches it.

As $B_1 = A_1$, the incident wave is completely reflected without any phase change.

Flick. There is a 'flick' at the end of a whip or the free end of a string because when a wave travelling through the string reaches the free end it meets a highly rare medium for which the characteristic impedance $Z_2 \cong 0$. The transmission coefficient of amplitude A_2 is given by

$$\frac{A_2}{A_1} = \frac{2Z_1}{Z_1 + Z_2}$$

when $\quad Z_2 = 0, \quad \frac{A_2}{A_1} = 2 \text{ or } A_2 = 2A_1$

The amplitude at the free end is thus doubled and hence the intensity of the wave becomes four times. The sound becomes very loud and is called 'flick'.

10.21 ENERGY ALONG A STRETCHED STRING

When a transverse wave is propagated through a string, the displacement of the particles of the string is given by $y = Ae^{i(\omega t - kx)}$.

We shall, however, assume that the displacement varies as a sine function and is given by the imaginary part of the above equation *i.e.*,

$$y = A \sin(\omega t - kx)$$

where $\omega = 2\pi v$, v being the frequency and $k = \frac{2\pi}{\lambda}$, λ being the wave length of the wave travelling through the string.

∴ Particle velocity $\quad v = \frac{dy}{dt} = A\omega \cos(\omega t - kx)$

and acceleration $\quad a = \frac{d^2y}{dt^2} = -A\omega^2 \sin(\omega t - kx) = -\omega^2 y$

Consider a very small element of length dx of the string of mass m, then

$$\text{Potential energy of the element } E_p = -\int_0^y m\frac{d^2y}{dt^2}\,dy$$

$$= m\omega^2 \int_0^y y\,dy = \frac{1}{2}m\omega^2 y^2 = \frac{1}{2}m\omega^2 A^2 \sin^2(\omega t - kx)$$

$$\text{and Kinetic energy of the element } E_k = \frac{1}{2}mv^2 = \frac{1}{2}m\left(\frac{dy}{dt}\right)^2$$

$$= \frac{1}{2}m\omega^2 A^2 \cos^2(\omega t - kx)$$

$$\therefore \quad \text{Total energy of the element } E = E_p + E_k$$

$$= \frac{1}{2}m\omega^2 A^2[\sin^2(\omega t - kx) + \cos^2(\omega t - kx)]$$

$$= \frac{1}{2}m\omega^2 A^2$$

If ρ is the mass per unit length (or linear density) of the string, then $m = \rho dx$.

$$\therefore \quad E = \frac{1}{2}\rho\omega^2 A^2 dx \qquad \ldots(i)$$

$$\text{Hence total energy per unit length } E_1 = \frac{1}{2}\rho\omega^2 A^2 \qquad \ldots(ii)$$

Rate of flow of energy. The rate of flow of energy across any cross-section of the string is given by

$$I = \frac{dE}{dt} = \frac{1}{2}\rho\omega^2 A^2 \frac{dx}{dt}$$

From Eq. (*i*).

But $\frac{dx}{dt} = v$, the velocity of propagation of the wave in the string.

$$\therefore \quad I = \frac{1}{2}\omega^2 A^2(\rho v) = \frac{1}{2}\omega^2 A^2 Z \qquad [\because Z = \rho v] \qquad \ldots(iii)$$

From relation (*iii*), we find that

(*i*) The rate of flow of energy through the string when a wave propagates through it is proportional to Z-the characteristic impedance of the string.

(*ii*) It is independent of x and t.

(*iii*) The rate of flow of energy is the same everywhere in the string and at all instants of time.

10.22 REFLECTION AND TRANSMISSION OF ENERGY

When a wave meets a boundary between two media having different impedance values a part of it is reflected and a part transmitted. If A_1 is the amplitude of the incident wave in the medium of impedance Z_1 (linear density ρ_1, wave velocity v_1), B_1 the amplitude of the transmitted wave A_2 the amplitude of the transmitted wave in the medium of impedance Z_2 (linear density ρ_2, wave velocity v_2), then

$$\text{The reflection coefficient } \frac{B_1}{A_1} = \frac{Z_1 - Z_2}{Z_1 + Z_2} \qquad \ldots(i)$$

$$\text{and transmission coefficient } \frac{A_2}{A_1} = \frac{2Z_1}{Z_1 + Z_2} \qquad \ldots(ii)$$

In a general case, the total energy per unit length of a string of linear density ρ, amplitude A and angular frequency ω is given by

$$E = \frac{1}{2}\rho\omega^2 A^2 \qquad \text{[Refer 10.21, Eq. (ii)]}$$

As the wave travels along the string with a velocity v each unit length of the string takes up its oscillation with the passage of the wave.

$$\therefore \quad \text{Rate of flow of energy along the string} = \text{Energy} \times \text{Velocity} = \frac{1}{2}\rho\omega^2 A^2 v$$

If the point at which reflection takes place is at $x = 0$, then the rate of energy arriving at the boundary $x = 0$, with the incident wave

$$= \frac{1}{2}\rho_1\omega^2 A_1^2 v_1 = \frac{1}{2}Z_1\omega^2 A_1^2 \qquad [\because\ \rho_1 v_1 = Z_1]$$

The energy leaves the boundary *via* the reflected and the transmitted waves.

$\therefore$ Rate at which energy leaves the boundary

$$= \frac{1}{2}\rho_1\omega^2 B_1^2 v_1 + \frac{1}{2}\rho_2\omega^2 A_2^2 v_2$$

$$= \frac{1}{2}Z_1\omega^2 B_1^2 + \frac{1}{2}Z_2\omega^2 A_2^2$$

Substituting the values of B_1 and A_2 from (*i*) and (*ii*) the above expression

$$= \frac{1}{2}\omega^2 A_1^2 \frac{Z_1(Z_1 - Z_2)^2 + 4Z_1^2 Z_2}{(Z_1 + Z_2)^2} = \frac{1}{2}Z_1\omega^2 A_1^2$$

which is equal to the energy arriving with the incident wave.

This shows that all the energy arriving at the boundary in the incident wave leaves the boundary in the reflected and transmitted wave.

Reflected and transmitted energy coefficients. The reflected and transmitted energy coefficients are defined as

$$\text{Reflected energy coefficient} = \frac{\text{Reflected energy}}{\text{Incident energy}}$$

$$= \frac{\frac{1}{2}Z_1\omega^2 B_1^2}{\frac{1}{2}Z_1\omega^2 A_1^2} = \frac{B_1^2}{A_1^2} = \left(\frac{Z_1 - Z_2}{Z_1 + Z_2}\right)^2 \qquad \ldots(iii)$$

$$\text{Transmitted energy coefficient} = \frac{\text{Transmitted energy}}{\text{Incident energy}}$$

$$= \frac{\frac{1}{2}Z_2\omega^2 A_2^2}{\frac{1}{2}Z_1\omega^2 A_1^2} = \frac{Z_2 A_2^2}{Z_1 A_1^2} = \frac{4Z_1 Z_2}{(Z_1 + Z_2)^2} \qquad \ldots(iv)$$

$\therefore$ Reflected energy co-efficient + Transmitted energy coefficient $= \left(\frac{Z_1 - Z_2}{Z_1 + Z_2}\right)^2 + \frac{4Z_1 Z_2}{(Z_1 + Z_2)^2} = 1$

10.23 IMPEDANCE MATCHING

When two electric transmission cables are joined at a point, proper transmission of power takes place only when the impedance of the two cables is the same *i.e.*, $Z_1 = Z_2$. If it is not so *i.e.*, the transmission lines are of different impedance, then the impedances are matched by inserting a *quarter wavelength* stub of the line between them such that the impedance of the stub Z is given by

$$Z = \sqrt{Z_1 Z_2}$$

When a wave meets a boundary between two media having different impedance values, a part of it is reflected and a part transmitted. The reflection energy coefficient is given by

$$\frac{\text{Reflected energy}}{\text{Incident energy}} = \left(\frac{Z_1 - Z_2}{Z_1 + Z_2}\right)^2$$

If $Z_1 = Z_2$, the reflected energy = 0

The transmitted coefficient of energy is given by

$$\frac{\text{Transmitted energy}}{\text{Incident energy}} = \frac{4Z_1 Z_2}{(Z_1 + Z_2)^2}$$

If $Z_1 = Z_2$, the transmitted coefficient of energy = 1. In such a case

Transmitted energy = Incident energy

This shows that when $Z_1 = Z_2$, no enegy is reflected and all energy is transmitted.

In such a case the impedances are said to be perfectly matched.

Conditions for impedance matching when $Z_1 \neq Z_2$. When the impedances of the two media are not equal. As for example, in the case of two strings of different characteristic impedance ($Z_1 \neq Z_2$), it can be shown that '*impedance matching*' can be brought about by 'coupling' a piece of string of impedance Z and length l between the two strings of impedance Z_1 and Z_2, such that

$$Z = \sqrt{Z_1 Z_2}$$

and

$$l = \lambda/4$$

where λ is the wavelength of the incident wave in the material of the coupling element.

Thus the conditions are

(*i*) The impedance of the coupling element is the geometric mean of the impedances of the media to be matched.

(*ii*) The coupling element has length $l = \frac{\lambda}{4}$ where λ is the wavelength of the incident wave in the medium of the coupling element.

Uses of impedance matching What has been stated above for matching of impedance of two strings is equally applicable to all types of waves travelling through two wave conducting media of different impedances. The principle of '*impedance matching*', therefore, finds wide application in many fields. Some of these are:

(*i*) The transfer of power from a generator to a load is maximum when the impedance of the generator and the load are matched.

(*ii*) In electronic appliances, like the power amplifier or the radio set the impedance of the output circuit is matched to the impedance of the loud speaker with the help of a suitable coupling transformer.

(*iii*) **Anti-reflection films.** Lenses of optical instruments are coated with a dielectric layer of thickness $\lambda/4$ (quarter wave layer) and refractive index $n = \sqrt{n_1 n_2}$ where n_1 is the refractive index of air and n_2 that of the material of the lens. The application of the anti-reflection coating is known as '*blooming*' and is brought about by evaporating a dielectric substance of suitable refractive index on the surface of the lens. For example, magnesium oxide ($n = 1.38$) is used for impedance matching between air ($n_1 = 1$) and glass $n_2 = (1.38)^2 = 1.9$. It is not possible to have an exact matching because a material of the required refractive index may not be available. Moreover, a quarter wave impedance may give a perfect match for waves of light of a particular wavelength say in the middle of the visible spectrum but may give appreciable reflection in the extreme blue and red regions. The coating, therefore, gives a '*purple*' appearances by reflected light.

(*iv*) Two transmission lines of different impedances are matched by inserting quarter wavelength stubs of the line between them.

10.24 IMPEDANCE OF THE COUPLING ELEMENT

Two media of characteristic impedance Z_1 and Z_2 ($Z_1 \neq Z_2$) coupled through an element of impedance Z and length l is shown in Fig. 10.13. The boundaries of the coupling element are located at $x = 0$ and $x = l$. The value of wave enters the coupling medium at $x = 0$ and leaves it at $x = l$. The value of wave numbers for the three media are k_1, k and k_2 respectively. The incident reflected and transmitted waves in all the three media are as shown in the figure.

For maximum transfer of power the two boundary conditions that must be satisfied are

(*i*) The displacement y is continuous at the interfaces $x = 0$ and $x = l$ and

(*ii*) The transverse force $T\frac{dy}{dx}$ is also continuous at these two points.

At $x = 0$ According to first condition at $x = 0$

$$y_{i1} + y_{r1} = y_i + y_r$$

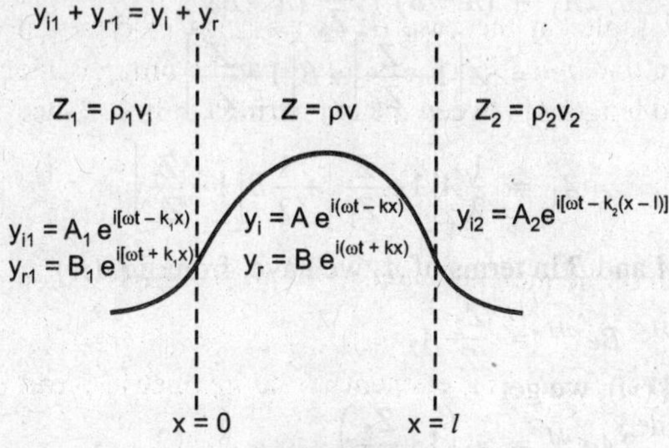

Fig. 10.13

or
$$A_1e^{i(\omega t - k_1x)} + B_1e^{i(\omega t + k_1x)} = Ae^{i(\omega t - kx)} + Be^{i(\omega t + kx)}$$

Putting $x = 0$, we get

$$A_1e^{i\omega t} + B_1e^{i\omega t} = Ae^{i\omega t} + Be^{i\omega t}$$

or
$$A_1 + B_1 = A + B \qquad \ldots(i)$$

According to the second condition at $x = 0$

$$T[-ik_1A_1 + ik_1B_1] = T[-ikA + ikB]$$

or
$$-i[A_1Tk_1 - B_1Tk_1] = -i[ATk - BTk]$$

Now
$$Tk = T\frac{2\pi}{\lambda} = T\frac{2\pi\nu}{v} = \frac{T}{v}\omega = Z\omega \quad \text{since } \frac{T}{v} = Z.$$

∴ Substituting $Tk_1 = Z_1\omega$ and $Tk = Z\omega$ in the above equation we get

$$Z_1\omega(A_1 - B_1) = Z\omega(A - B)$$

or
$$Z_1(A_1 - B_1) = Z(A - B) \qquad \ldots(ii)$$

At $x = l$ At the boundary of the coupling medium and the medium into which the wave is finally transmitted, we have, according to the first condition

$$y_i + y_r = y_{i2}$$

or
$$Ae^{i(\omega t - kx)} + Be^{i(\omega t + kx)} = A_2e^{i[\omega t - k_2(x - l)]}$$

At $x = l$, we have

$$Ae^{i(\omega t - kl)} + Be^{i(\omega t + kl)} = A_2e^{i\omega t}$$

or
$$e^{i\omega t}[Ae^{-ikl} + Be^{ikl}] = A_2e^{i\omega t}$$

or
$$Ae^{-ikl} + Be^{+ikl} = A_2 \qquad \ldots(iii)$$

Similarly according to second condition at $x = l$

$$-iATke^{i(\omega t - kl)} + iBTke^{i(\omega t + kl)} = -iA_2Tk_2e^{i\omega t}$$

or
$$-ATke^{-ikl} + BTke^{+ikl} = -A_2Tk_2$$

Substituting $Tk = Z\omega$ and $Tk_2 = Z_2\omega$, we get

$$\omega[AZe^{-ikl} - BZe^{+ikl}] = \omega A_2Z_2$$

or
$$Z[Ae^{-ikl} - Be^{+ikl}] = A_2Z_2 \qquad \ldots(iv)$$

To find the value of $\frac{\text{transmitted energy}}{\text{Incident energy}} = \frac{Z_2A_2^2}{Z_1A_1^2}$, we first find the value of $\frac{A_2}{A_1}$.

From Eq. (*i*) $B_1 = A + B - A_1.$

Substituting in Eq. (*ii*), we get

$$Z_1(A_1 - A - B + A_1) = Z(A - B)$$

or $$2Z_1A_1 = Z_1(A + B) + Z(A - B)$$

or $$2A_1 = (A + B) + \frac{Z}{Z_1}(A - B)$$

$$= A\left[1 + \frac{Z}{Z_1}\right] + B\left[1 - \frac{Z}{Z_1}\right]$$

or $$A_1 = \frac{1}{2}A\left[1 + \frac{Z}{Z_1}\right] + \frac{1}{2}B\left[1 - \frac{Z}{Z_1}\right] \qquad ...(v)$$

To find the value of A and B in terms of A_2 we have, from Eq. (*iv*)

$$Ae^{-ikl} - Be^{+ikl} = \frac{Z_2}{Z}A_2 \qquad ...(vi)$$

Adding Eqs. (*iii*) and (*vi*), we get

$$2Ae^{-ikl} = A_2\left(1 + \frac{Z_2}{Z}\right)$$

or $$A = \frac{A_2}{2}\left(1 + \frac{Z_2}{Z}\right)e^{+ikl}$$

Subtracting (*vi*) from (*iii*), we get

$$2Be^{+ikl} = A_2\left(1 - \frac{Z_2}{Z}\right)$$

or $$B = \frac{A_2}{2}\left(1 - \frac{Z_2}{Z}\right)e^{-ikl}$$

Substituting these values of A and B in eq. (*v*), we get

$$A_1 = \frac{A_2}{4}\left(1 + \frac{Z}{Z_1}\right)\left(1 + \frac{Z_2}{Z}\right)e^{+ikl} + \frac{A_2}{4}\left(1 - \frac{Z}{Z_1}\right)\left(1 - \frac{Z_2}{Z}\right)e^{-ikl}$$

or $$\frac{A_1}{A_2} = \frac{1}{4}\left(1 + \frac{Z}{Z_1} + \frac{Z_2}{Z} + \frac{Z_2}{Z_1}\right)e^{+ikl} + \frac{1}{4}\left(1 - \frac{Z}{Z_1} - \frac{Z_2}{Z} + \frac{Z_2}{Z_1}\right)e^{-ikl}$$

$$= \frac{1}{2}\left(1 + \frac{Z_2}{Z_1}\right)\frac{e^{ikl} + e^{-ikl}}{2} + \frac{1}{2}\left(\frac{Z_1}{Z_2} + \frac{Z_2}{Z}\right)\frac{e^{ikl} - e^{-ikl}}{2}$$

$$= \frac{1}{2}\left(1 + \frac{Z_2}{Z_1}\right)\cos kl + i\frac{1}{2}\left(\frac{Z}{Z_1} + \frac{Z_2}{Z}\right)\sin kl$$

$$\therefore \quad \frac{\text{Transmitted energy}}{\text{Incident energy}} = \frac{E_T}{E_i} = \frac{Z_2(A_2)^2}{Z_1(A_1)^2} = \frac{Z_2}{Z_1}\left(\frac{A_2}{A_1}\right)\left(\frac{A_2}{A_1}\right)$$

$$= \frac{Z_2}{Z_1}\frac{4}{\left(1 + \frac{Z_2}{Z_1}\right)^2\cos^2 kl + \left(\frac{Z}{Z_1} + \frac{Z_2}{Z}\right)^2\sin^2 kl}$$

If $l = \frac{\lambda}{4}$, then $\cos kl = \cos\frac{k\lambda}{4} = \cos\frac{2\pi}{\lambda}\cdot\frac{\lambda}{4} = \cos\frac{\pi}{4} = 0$ and $\sin kl = \sin\frac{\pi}{2} = 1.$

$$\therefore \quad \frac{E_T}{E_i} = \frac{Z_2}{Z_1}\frac{4}{\left(\frac{Z}{Z_1} + \frac{Z_2}{Z}\right)^2}$$

For maximum transfer of power $\frac{E_T}{E_i} = 1$

$$\therefore \quad \frac{Z_2}{Z_1} \times \frac{4}{\left(\frac{Z}{Z_1} + \frac{Z_2}{Z}\right)^2} = 1$$

or
$$4\frac{Z_2}{Z_1} = \left(\frac{Z}{Z_1} + \frac{Z_2}{Z}\right)^2 = \left(\frac{Z}{Z_1}\right)^2 + \left(\frac{Z_2^2}{Z}\right) + 2\frac{Z_2}{Z_1}$$

or
$$\left(\frac{Z}{Z_1}\right)^2 + \left(\frac{Z_2}{Z}\right)^2 - 2\frac{Z_2}{Z_1} = \left(\frac{Z}{Z_1} - \frac{Z_2}{Z}\right)^2 = 1$$

or
$$\frac{Z}{Z_1} - \frac{Z_2}{Z} = 1$$

or
$$Z^2 = Z_1 Z_2 \quad \text{or} \quad Z = \sqrt{Z_1 Z_2}$$

Thus perfect matching is achieved and all the incident energy is transmitted when the following two conditions are satisfied:

1. The impedance of the coupling element is given by $Z = \sqrt{Z_1 Z_2}$ *i.e.* it is the geometric mean of the impedance of the media to be matched.

2. The coupling element has a length $l = \frac{\lambda}{4}$ where λ is the wave length of the incident wave in the medium of the coupling element.

10.25 STANDING WAVES IN A STRING CLAMPED AT BOTH ENDS

Consider a string of fixed length l clamped rigidly at both ends fig. 10.14. Consider a monochromatic wave *i.e.*, a wave of only one (angular) frequency ω and amplitude a travelling in a positive X-direction, then the wave equation is given by

$$y_1 = ae^{i(\omega t - kx)}$$

where $k = \frac{2\pi}{\lambda} = \frac{\omega}{v}$

This wave is reflected from the fixed end and if the amplitude of the reflected wave travelling along the *negative* X-direction is b, then the equation of the reflected wave is given by

$$y_2 = b\, e^{i(\omega t + kx)}$$

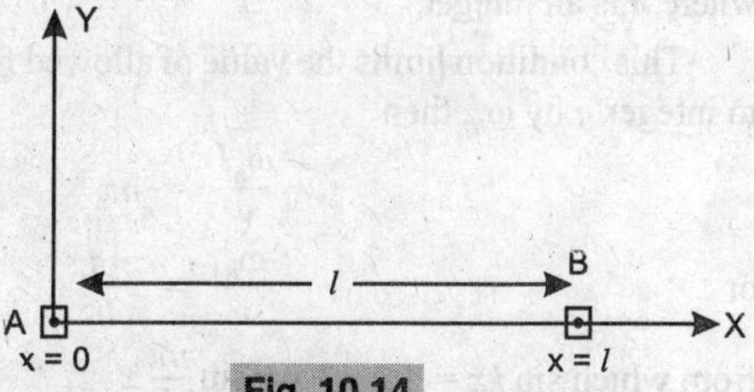

Fig. 10.14

This displacement of a point on the string due to both these waves is given by

$$y = y_1 + y_2 = a\, e^{i(\omega t - kx)} + b\, e^{i(\omega t + kx)} \qquad \ldots(i)$$

The boundary condition to be satisfied at all times are

(*a*) At $x = 0$, displacement $y = 0$

(*b*) At $x = l$, displacement $y = 0$

Applying the boundary condition (*a*) we have from (*i*)

$$0 = ae^{i\omega t} + be^{i\omega t}$$

or
$$a = -b$$

This condition implies that the wave is completely reflected at either end which offers infinite impedance with a *reversal of phase* or a phase change of π.

Substituting $b = -a$ in (*i*), we have

$$y = ae^{i\omega t}\,[e^{-ikx} - e^{+ikx}]$$

$$= (-2i)ae^{i\omega t}\,\frac{e^{-ikx} - e^{+ikx}}{-2i}$$

or

$$y = -2i\,a\,e^{i\omega t}\sin kx \qquad \ldots(ii)$$

This equation satisfies the *standing wave time independent* form of the wave equation

$$\frac{d^2y}{dt^2} + k^2y = 0, \text{ because from Eq. } (ii)$$

$$\frac{dy}{dt} = (-2i)\,a\,(i\omega)\,e^{i\omega t}\sin kx$$

and

$$\frac{d^2y}{dt^2} = (-2i)\,a\,(-\omega)^2\,e^{i\omega t}\sin kx = -\omega^2 y$$

$$\therefore \qquad \frac{1}{v^2}\cdot\frac{d^2y}{dt^2} = -\frac{\omega^2}{v^2}y = -k^2y$$

Substituting in the differential form of wave equation

$$\frac{d^2y}{dx^2} = \frac{1}{v^2}\frac{d^2y}{dt^2}, \text{ we have}$$

$$\frac{d^2y}{dx^2} + k^2y = 0$$

Thus equation (*ii*) gives a general result for all wave shapes and frequencies.

Applying the boundary condition (*b*), we have from (*ii*)

$$0 = -2i\,a\,e^{i\omega t}\sin kl$$

or

$$\sin kl = \sin\frac{\omega}{v}l = 0 \qquad \left[\because k = \frac{\omega}{v}\right]$$

or

$$\frac{\omega l}{v} = n\pi \qquad \ldots(iii)$$

where *n* is an integer.

This condition limits the value of allowed frequencies. If we denote the value of ω corresponding to integer *n* by ω_n, then

$$\frac{\omega_n l}{v} = n\pi$$

or

$$\frac{\omega_n}{v} = \frac{n\pi}{l} \qquad \ldots(iv)$$

from which $\sin kx = \sin\frac{\omega_n}{v}x = \sin\frac{n\pi}{l}x$ ...(*iv*)(*a*)

Substituting $\omega_n = 2\pi\nu_n$ in (*iv*), we have

$$\frac{2\pi\nu_n}{v} = \frac{n\pi}{l}$$

or

$$\nu_n = \frac{nv}{2l} \qquad \ldots(v)$$

If λ_n is the corresponding wavelength, then

$$\lambda_n = \frac{v}{\nu_n} = \frac{2l}{n}$$

or

$$l = \frac{n\lambda_n}{2} \qquad \ldots(vi)$$

Hence we find that *the allowed frequencies define the length of the string as an exact number of half wavelengths.*

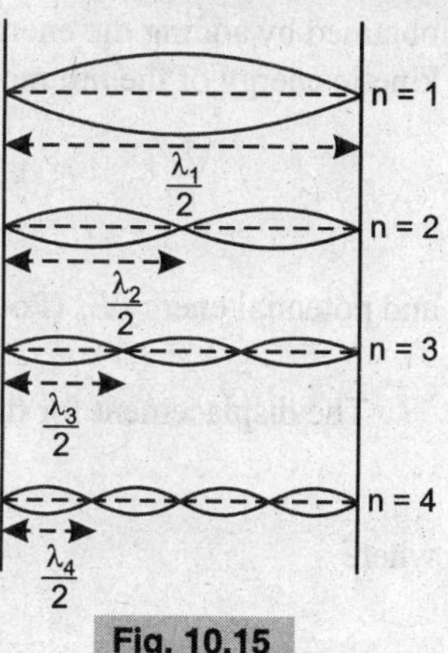

Fig. 10.15

Eigen frequencies. The frequencies given by equation (*v*) for various integral values of *n* are the *normal frequencies* or *normal modes of vibration* and are often called *Eigen frequencies*. The term Eigen frequencies is commonly used in *wave-mechanics*.

The lowest frequency corresponding to $n = 1$ is called the *fundamental* and those corresponding to $n > 1$ are known as *harmonics*. The first three harmonics for $n = 2, 3, 4$ are shown in Fig. 10.15. In general all normal modes may be present at the same time. The general displacement is the supervision of all the displacements due to different allowed frequencies.

Nodes and antinodes. From equation (*iv*)(*a*), we find that for values of *n* greater than 1, there are a number of positions along the string which are always at rest. These positions are given by

$$\sin\frac{\omega_n}{v}x = \sin\frac{n\pi}{l}x = 0$$

or

$$\frac{n\pi x}{l} = r\pi$$

where $r = 0, 1, 2, 3 \ldots n$

The position of the two fixed ends is given by $r = 0$ and $r = n$ because $r = 0$ gives $x = 0$ and $r = n$ gives $x = l$. Between these two positions there are $n - 1$ positions for the *n*th harmonic which are equally spaced along the string where the displacement is zero for all times. These positions are known as *nodes* or *nodal points* and give the positions of zero motion in a *system of standing waves*. These standing waves are produced by the superposition of the incident and the reflected waves travelling in the opposite direction. The nodal points will exist if the reflection is complete so that the amplitude of incident and the reflected progressive waves are equal and opposite. For $n = 4$, the number of nodes $= n - 1 = 3$. In between two consecutive nodes and equally spaced are the positions having maximum displacement. These points are known as *antinodes*.

Equations for standing waves. Equation (*ii*) for *n*th harmonic can be expressed as

$$y_n = -2aie^{i\omega_n t}\sin\frac{\omega_n}{v}x$$

$$= 2a(-i)(\cos\omega_n t + i\sin\omega_n t)\sin\frac{\omega_n}{v}x$$

$$= (A_n\cos\omega_n t + B_n\sin\omega_n t)\sin\frac{\omega_n}{v}x \qquad \ldots(vi)$$

where $A_n = -2\,ai$ and $B_n = 2\,a$.

Equation (v*iii*) gives the equation of standing wave, along the string.

as $$\left[1+\left(\frac{dy}{dx}\right)^2\right]^{\frac{1}{2}} = 1+\frac{1}{2}\left(\frac{dy}{dx}\right)^2$$

neglecting higher power of $\frac{dy}{dx}$ and also assuming *T* to be a constant.

$$\therefore \quad \text{Total } P.E. \text{ of the string} = \frac{1}{2}T\int_0^l\left(\frac{dy}{dx}\right)^2 dx$$

Energy in each normal mode. When a string vibrates in a pure normal mode, every point in the string vibrates with the same frequency and at any moment all parts move either in the same or in the opposite phase. In a normal mode the total displacement *y* in the string is the superposition of the displacements y_n of the individual harmonic and the total energy of the resultant vibration is obtained by adding the energy of each mode as if it existed independently of other modes. Thus the kinetic energy of the nth mode

$$E_n(\text{kinetic}) = \frac{1}{2}\int_0^l \rho \dot{y}_n^2 dx$$

and potential energy E_n (Potential) $= \frac{1}{2}T\int_0^l \left(\frac{dy_n}{dx}\right)^2 dx$

The displacement for the nth harmonic is given by

$$y_n = (A_n \cos\omega_n t + B_n \sin\omega_n t)\sin\frac{\omega n}{v}x \qquad \text{[Eq. (vii)]}$$

where $A_n = -2\,ai$ and $B_n = 2a$

$\therefore \quad \dot{y}_n = (-A_n\omega_n \sin\omega_n t + B_n\,\omega_n \cos\omega_n t)\sin\frac{\omega_n}{v}x$

and $\quad \frac{dv_n}{dx} = \frac{\omega_n}{v}(A_n \cos\omega_n t + B_n \sin\omega_n t)\cos\frac{\omega_n}{v}x$

$\therefore$ Total Energy $= E_n$ (Kinetic) $+ E_n$ (potential)

$$= \frac{1}{2}\rho\omega_n^2(-A_n \sin\omega_n t + B_n \cos\omega_n t)^2\int_0^l \sin^2\frac{\omega_n}{v}x dx$$

$$+\frac{1}{2}T\frac{\omega_n^2}{v^2}(A_n \cos\omega_n t + B_n \sin\omega_n t)^2\int_0^l \cos^2\frac{\omega_n}{v}x dx$$

Now $\quad \frac{T}{v^2} = \rho, \quad \int_0^l \sin^2\frac{\omega_n}{v}x dx = \frac{1}{2}l, \quad \int_0^l \cos^2\frac{\omega_n}{v}x dx = \frac{1}{2}l$

and $(-A_n \sin\omega_n t + B_n \cos\omega_n t)^2 + (A_n \cos\omega_n t + B_n \sin\omega_n t)^2 = (A_n{}^2 + B_n{}^2)$

$\therefore \quad$ Total energy $= \frac{1}{4}\rho l\omega_n^2(A_n^2 + B_n^2) = \frac{1}{4}m\omega_n^2(A_n^2 + B_n^2)$

where $m = \rho\, l$ = mass of the whole string.

As mass m, normal mode frequency ω_n, and normal mode amplitudes A_n and B_n are constants, the total energy in the normal mode vibration of the string remains constant.

10.26 LONGITUDINAL WAVES (OR SOUND WAVES) IN A GASEOUS (OR A FLUID) MEDIUM

In a gaseous medium, as we know, only a longitudinal wave motion is possible, with its particles executing a simple harmonic motion along the direction of propagation of the wave and that the wave thus travels in the from of *condensations* (*i.e.*, crowding together of the particles) and *rarefactions* (*i.e.*, the particles getting further apart); so that, *there is a continuous variation of pressure all along its direction of propagation.*

To obtain an expression for the velocity of such a wave in a gaseous (or a fluid) medium, let us imaging the wave to be traveling from left to right along the axis of x through a uniform cylindrical tube of area of cross section α and with its axis coinciding with the axis of x, (Fig. 10.16).

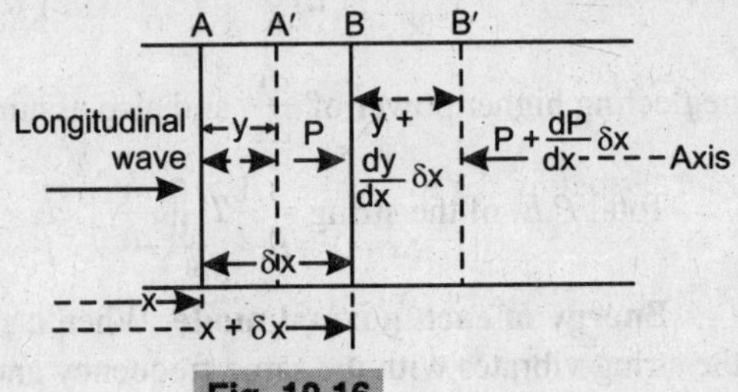

Fig. 10.16

Let A and B be two right plane sections of the tube (*i.e.*, planes perpendicular to the axis)whose positions *before the passage of the wave* are at distances x and $x + \delta x$ respectively from an arbitrary origin, so that they lie δx apart and the volume of the cylindrical slab or slice of the gas (or the fluid) enclosed in between them is $\delta x.\alpha$.

On the passage of the wave, let the two plane sections get displaced to positions A' and B' respectively. Then, if the displacement of section A be y, *i.e.*, if $AA' = y$, the displacement of section B, *i.e.*, $BB' = y + (dy/dx)\,\delta x$, where dy/dx is the *rate of change of displacement with distance.*

The two right sections thus get displacement further apart and the *increase in the distance between them* $= y + (dy/dx)\delta x - y = (dy/dx)\delta x$.

So that, *increase in volume of the cylindrical slab or slice of the gas (or fluid) in between them* $= (dy/dx)\delta x.\alpha$.

$$\therefore \qquad \textit{Volume strain} = \frac{\textit{Increase in volume}}{\textit{Original volume}} = \frac{(dy/dx)\,\delta x.\alpha}{\delta x.\alpha} = \frac{dy}{dx}.$$

If, therefore, K be the *volume elasticity* of the gas (or the fluid) and p, the *excess pressure* (*i.e.*, pressure over and above that of the atmosphere) at section A, now at A', we have

$$K = -\frac{p}{dy/dx}$$

The $-ve$ sign indicating that the excess pressure and the change in volume bear opposite signs, if p be $-ve$, the change in volume is $+ve$ or *an increase* and vice versa.

Thus, *excess pressure at section A, now at A'*, is given by

$$p = -K(dy/dx).$$

If *the pressure gradient*, or the rate of change of pressure with distance, along the axis of x be dp/dx, we have

excess pressure at section B, now at B' $= p + (dP/dx)\,\delta x$.

$$= p + \frac{d}{dx}\left(-K\frac{dy}{dx}\right)\delta x = p - K\frac{d^2y}{dx^2}\delta x.$$

$\therefore$ *resultant pressure on the slice of gas (or fluid)* enclosed between A' and $B' = p - K(d^2y/dx^2)\delta x - p = -K(d^2y/dx^2)\delta x$, the $-ve$ sign indicating that it is directed from B' to A', opposite to the direction of propagation of the wave.

$\therefore$ *force acting on this slice of gas (or fluid)*, say,

$$F = -K(d^2y/dx^2)\delta x.\alpha.$$

Now, force is also equal to *mass* × *acceleration*. So that, if $-d^2y/dt^2$ be the *acceleration* of the slice of gas (or fluid) enclosed by the two sections (in the direction B' to A'), the *force acting on it is also = mass of the slice* × $(-d^2y/dt^2)$.

If ρ be the density of the gas (or the fluid), we have *mass of the slice* $= \delta x.\alpha.\rho$. And, therefore acting on it, *i.e.*,

$$F = -\delta x.\alpha.\rho.\,(d^2y/dt^2)$$

Equating the two values of F, we have

$$-\delta x.\alpha.\rho(d^2y/dt^2) = -k(d^2y/dx^2).\delta.x.\alpha. \text{ Or, } d^2y/dt^2 = (K/\rho)d^2y/dx^2,$$

which is of the same form as the standard differential equation of a wave motion (equation (*vi*)) § 10.8. So that, *velocity of the longitudinal wave through the gas (or the fluid) is given by*

$$v = \sqrt{\frac{K}{\rho}},$$

$$i.e., \quad \textit{Velocity of the wave} = \sqrt{\frac{\textit{Volume elasticity of the gas (or fluid)}}{\textit{Density of the gas (or fluid)}}}$$

Now, Newton, who first deduced this relation for v assumed that during the passage of a sound wave through a gets (or air) the temperature of the gas (or air) remains unaffected, the heat passing from the hotter regions of condensations to the adjacent colder regions of rarefactions, thereby equalising the temperature. In other words, he assumed that a sound wave passes through a gas (or air) under *isothermal* conditions, and hence took K to be the *isothermal elasticity* of the gas (or air), which, as we know, is equal to its pressure (P). So that, *Newtons's formula for the velocity of a sound wave (or a longitudinal wave) in a gaseous medium* becomes

$$v = \sqrt{P/\rho}.$$

If, however, we calculate the velocity of sound in air at *N.T.P.* with the help of this formula, we have $P = 76 \times 13.6 \times 981$ dynes/cm^2 and $\rho = 0.001293$ gm/c.c. and, therefore,

$$v = \sqrt{\frac{76\times13.6\times981}{0.001293}}$$

$$= 280 \text{ metres/sec, very nearly.}$$

Actually, the velocity of sound in air at *N.T.P.*, as measured by *Newton* himself, is found to be 332 metres/sec.

Newton could offer no satisfactory explanation for this large discrepancy between his theoretical and experimental results. Strangely enough, the error in Newton's formula remained undetected for almost a century and a half (or 140 years, to be exact) until *La'place*, a French mathematician, pointed it out in the year 1816, (See next articale).

10.27 LA'PLACE'S CORRECTION OF NEWTON'S FORMULA-EFFECT OF PRESSURE AND TEMPERATURE ON THE VELOCITY OF SOUND IN A GAS (OR AIR)

La'place correctly argued that as a sound wave passes through a gas (or air) the condensations and rarefactions succeed each other much too rapidly. This coupled with the fact that a gas (or air) is a poor conductor of heat, does not make for any equalization of temperature due to passage of heat from the hotter regions of condensation to the colder ones of rarefaction. So that, although the total quantity of heat in the medium (gas or air) remains constant, *there are temperature variations throughout the medium and that, therefore, a sound wave passes through a gas (or air) under adiabatic, and not isothermal, conditions*. Newton should thus have used *the adiabatic*, and *not the isothermal*, elasticity of the gas (or air) in his formula.

Now, *adiabatic elasticity* = γ × isothermal elasticity = γP,

where γ is the ratio between the two principal specific heats of the gas (or air) *viz.*, the specific heats at constant pressure and at constant volume.

Thus, Newton's formula, *as corrected by La' place, becomes*

$$v = \sqrt{\gamma P/\rho}.$$

The value of γ is the highest, 1.67, for a monatomic gas, like helium or mercury vapour, 1.4 for a diatomic gas like hydrogen, oxygen etc. and 1.33 for a triatomic gas like ozone (O_3) or water vapour (H_2O), *i.e.*, its value goes on decreasing with increasing atomicity of the gas or vapour but is always greater than 1.

For *air*, which is a mixture of gases, $\gamma = 1.41$. So that, in air,

$$v = \sqrt{1.41P/\rho},$$

which gives 331.6 metres/ sec as the velocity of sound (in air) at *N.T.P.* in excellent agreement with Newton's own experimental result, *thus fully justifying La'places' correction of Newton's formula.*

Effect of pressure and temperature on the velocity of sound in a gas (or air). Considering a gram-molecule of a gas (or air), we have $PV = RT$, where V is the *volume of a gram-molecule of the gas (or air)*, T, its *absolute temperature* and R, the *gas constant.*

If M be the molecular weight of the gas (or air), we have $V = M/\rho$.

So that $P(M/\rho) = RT$, whence, $\rho = PM/RT$. And, therefore,

$$v = \sqrt{\frac{\gamma P}{\rho}} = \sqrt{\frac{\gamma P}{PM/RT}} = \sqrt{\gamma\frac{RT}{M}},$$

showing that the velocity of sound in a gas (or air) *is quite independent of its pressure and directly proportional to the square root of its absolute temperature.*

Thus, if the velocity of sound in a gas (or air) at t°C or $(t + 273)$ or T° *abs.* be v and its velocity at 0°C or $(0 + 273)$ or T_0° *abs.* be v_0, we

$$\frac{v}{v_0} = \sqrt{\frac{T}{T_0}}. \quad \text{Or, in general,} \quad \frac{v_1}{v_2} = \sqrt{\frac{T_1}{T_2}},$$

where v_1 and v_2 are the velocities of sound in a gas (or air) at absolute temperature T_1 and T_2 respectively.

10.28 LONGITUDINAL WAVES IN RODS

Newton's formula for the velocity of a longitudinal wave in a fluid (*viz.*, $v = K/\rho$) may also be extended to the case of an isotropic solid if it be in the form of a *thin rod* or wire, so that lateral contraction and expansion (in the regions of condensations and rarefactions) are permissible. Obviously, the elasticity involved here will be the *linear elasticity or Young's modulus Y.* So that, if a *thin rod or wire* (*i.e.*, one whose diameter is very much smaller than its length) be set into longitudinal vibration by rubbing it (in one direction only) with a chamois leather or a resined cloth, the velocity of the longitudinal wave, thus set up in it and travelling along its length, is given by $v = \sqrt{Y/\rho}$, where ρ is the *density* of the material of the rod or the wire.

This relation may, however, also be deduced **directly** in the same manner as used in § 10.18 in the case of a gas (or a fluid).

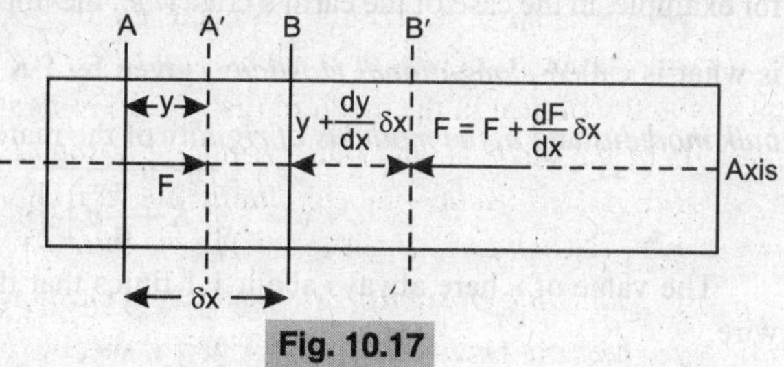

Fig. 10.17

Thus, consider two right plane sections A and B of a thin rod to be a distance δx apart before the passage of a longitudinal wave (or a sound wave) through it, (Fig. 10.17)

On the passage of the wave, let the two sections be displaced to positions A' and B' respectively, such that the displacement of section A, *i.e.*, $AA' = y$ and that of section B, *i.e.*, $BB' = y + (dy/dx)\delta x$, where dy/dx is the rate of change of displacement with distance.

Then, obviously, *increase the length of element* δx *of the rod*

$$= y + (dy/dx)\delta x - y = (dy/dx)\delta x.$$

$\therefore$ *Linear or tensile strain set up in the rod* $= \dfrac{\textit{Increase in length}}{\textit{Original length}}$

$$= \frac{(dy/dx)\delta x}{\delta x} = \frac{dy}{dx}.$$

This increase in the length of the element gives rise to restoring forces in the material of the rod, tending to bring it back to its original length. If F be force acting at section A, now at A', clearly, tensile stress = F/α, where α is the area of cross section of the rod.

$\therefore$ *Young's modulus for the material of the rod*, $Y = \dfrac{\textit{Tensile stress}}{\textit{Tensile strain}}$

Or,
$$Y = \frac{F/\alpha}{dy/dx}$$

whence,
$$F = Y.\alpha(dy/dx) \text{ in the direction } A' \text{ to } B'.$$

Force acting at section B, now at B', say, $F' = F + (dF/dx)\delta x$, *in the direction B'* to A', where dF/dx is the rate of change of force with distance.

Hence *resultant force acting on element* δx *of the rod*

$$= F + (dF/dx)\delta x - F = (dF/dx)\delta x$$

$$= \frac{d}{dx}\left(Y\alpha\frac{dy}{dx}\right)\delta x = Y\alpha\frac{d^2y}{dx^2}\delta x \textit{ in the direction } B' \text{ to } A'.$$

Also, if d^2y/dt^2 be the *instantaneous acceleration* produced in the element δx of the rod by this force, in the direction B' to A', we have

force acting on elements δx = *mass of element* $\times\, d^2y/dt^2$.

$= \delta x.\alpha.\rho.d^2y/dt^2$, where ρ is the density of the material of the rod.

Equating the two values of the force, therefore, we have

$$\delta x.\alpha.\rho.(d^2y/dt^2) = Y.\alpha.\,(d^2y/dx^2).\,\delta x, \text{ whence, } (d^2y/dt^2) = (Y/\rho)\,(d^2y/dx^2).$$

This equation being of the same form as the standard differential equation of a wave motion, we have

= *velocity of the longitudinal wave in the rod*,

i.e.,
$$v = \sqrt{Y/\rho}.$$

N.B. This relation, it may be emphasized once again, is valid only if the solid be *isotropic* and in the form of *thin rod* or wire.

In the case of an *extended solid*, where lateral contractions and extensions are not possible, as for example, in the case of the earth's crust (*i.e.*, the upper layers of the earth), the elasticity involved is what is called *elongational elasticity* given by $\left(K + \frac{4}{3}n\right)$, where K is the *volume elasticity* or *bulk modulus* and n, *the modulus of rigidity* of the material of the solid. So that, in such a case,

$$v = \sqrt{\left(K + \frac{4}{3}n\right)/\rho}.$$

The value of v here always about 1.1 times that if the material be in the form of a thin rod or wire.

For different modes of vibration of rods, see § 10.29 (I and II)

10.29 STATIONARY OF STANDING WAVES IN A LINEAR BOUNDED MEDIUM

A *linear medium* is one in which a wave is constrained to travel along a fixed linear path. Since *plane waves*, as we know, *being one-dimensional*, also travel along a fixed linear path, they too *may just as well be treated as waves in a linear medium, as*, for example, transverse waves along a string or a longitudinal wave along a thin rod or a pipe.

If the medium be of an infinite or unlimited length, the waves just continue to travel along or through it for an infinite time.

In case, however, the length of the medium be a limited or a finite one, it is spoken of as a *linear bounded medium* and if the waves travelling along it suffer normal reflection at the boundary, we have two *identical* waves (*i.e.*, having the *same wavelength, frequency and amplitude*) travelling along the same linear path in opposite directions. The superposition of such waves gives rise to a very special case of interference in which the positions of maxima and minima of displacement remain fixed throughout, so that the interference pattern or the resulting waves appear to remain stationary in space, with no onward or progressive movement. This is the reason why they are called *stationary or standing waves*.

Now, obviously, **two main cases** arise: (*i*) *when the boundary of the linear medium is fixed or rigid* and (*ii*) *when the boundary is free*.

A possible third case may be that of a boundary separating two media of different densities and hence of different velocities of the wave in them, so that the incident wave at the boundary is partly reflected and partly transmitted (or absorbed) into the second medium. We need, however concern ourselves here with only the former two, with which alone, therefore, we shall deal in proper detail.

It is pretty obvious that in *case* (*i*), the particle at the fixed or rigid boundary, like a wall, the fixed end of a string or the closed end of a pipe, for example, is not free to move and hence *the displacement* (y) *of the particle there will be zero at all times*. But equally obviously, dy/dx *must not simultaneously be zero* or else it would mean zero displacement at all points of the medium and hence no wave at all. Thus, *although the displacement at the fixed or rigid boundary is zero throughout, the strain* (dy/dx) *and the pressure variation there are not simultaneously zero* (since $p = -Kdy/dx$).

This means, in other words, that whereas the displacement of the particle at the fixed or rigid boundary is *exactly* cancelled by an equal and opposite displacement due to reflection, *i.e., the displacement, and hence also the particle velocity, undergoes a phase change of* π, *the strain and the pressure variation do not undergo any such phase change and are not, therefore, zero*. This is expressed by saying that *at a fixed or rigid boundary, a wave is reflected without change of type, i.e., a crest* (*or a condensation*) *as a crest* (*or a condensation*) *and a trough* (*or a rarefaction*), *as a trough* (*or a rarefaction*), *but with change of sign, i.e., with the direction of displacement of the particles reversed.*

On the other hand, in case (*ii*), there being no insurmountable opposing force or resistance encountered, the strain (dy/dx) and the excess pressure $p(= - Kdy/dx)$ becomes *zero*, *i.e., the phase of pressure variation gets reversed or undergoes a phase change of* π, but, obviously, y *is not zero* or else the displacement will be zero everywhere and there will be no wave at all. This means, in other words, that *the particles of the medium continue to have their displacements, and hence their velocities,* (*i.e., particle velocities*) *in the same direction as before, with no phase change and only the direction of strain and pressure variation gets reversed.* So that, a *crest* (*or a condensation*) *is reflected back as a trough* (*or a rarefaction*) *and vice versa, with the direction of displacement of the particles remaining the same.* This is expressed by saying that at a *free boundary, a wave is reflected with change of type but without change of sign.*

The difference between reflection at a fixed or rigid boundary and that at a free boundary may, for ready reference, be summarized as follows:

Reflection at a fixed or rigid boundary	Reflection at a free boundary
1. Displacement, and hence also particle velocity, undergoes a phase change of π, *i.e.*, gets reversed.	1. Displacement the particle velocity undergo no phase change and do not, therefore, get reversed.
2. Strain and pressure variation undergo no phase change and, therefore, reflection occurs without change of type but with change of sign.	2. Strain and pressure variation undergo a phase change of π and thus get reversed, so that reflection occurs with change of type but without change of sign.

We are now in a position to study the formation of stationary or standing waves in the two cases and, therefore, proceed on to it.

Case I—When reflection occurs at a fixed or rigid boundary. Let the equation of a simple harmonic wave of amplitude *a* and wave-length λ, travelling along the positive direction of the *x*-axis be $y_1 = a\sin\frac{2\pi}{\lambda}(vt - x)$, where *v* is the velocity of the wave in the medium.

Then, if it be incident *normally* on, and reflected from, a *fixed* or *rigid* boundary, the equation of the reflected wave will be $y_2 = -a\sin\frac{2\pi}{\lambda}(vt + x)$, since both, the direction of displacement of the particles and the direction of travel of the wave itself, get reversed.

Now, both the waves, travelling along the same linear path, get superposed and the equation of the resultant stationary or standing wave is, therefore,

$$y = y_1 + y_2 = a\sin\frac{2\pi}{\lambda}(vt - x) - a\sin\frac{2\pi}{\lambda}(vt + x)$$

Or, $$y = a\left[\sin\frac{2\pi}{\lambda}(vt - x) - \sin\frac{2\pi}{\lambda}(vt + x)\right] = -2a\cos\frac{2\pi vt}{\lambda}\sin\frac{2\pi x}{\lambda}$$

Or, $$y = -2a\sin\frac{2\pi x}{\lambda}\cos\frac{2\pi vt}{\lambda} = -2a\sin\frac{2\pi x}{\lambda}\cos\omega t, \quad ...(i)$$

$[\because v/\lambda = n \text{ and } 2\pi n = \omega.]$

showing that *the resulting wave is also a simple harmonic wave of the same time-period and wavelength as the two constituent waves but with an amplitude* = $-2a \sin 2\pi x/\lambda$.

Clearly, particle velocity, $$U = \frac{dy}{dt} = \frac{4\pi v}{\lambda}a\sin\frac{2\pi x}{\lambda}\sin\omega t, \quad ...(ii)$$

strain $$\frac{dy}{dx} = -\frac{4\pi}{\lambda}a\cos\frac{2\pi x}{\lambda}\cos\omega t \quad ...(iii)$$

and excess pressure, $$p = -K\frac{dy}{dx} = K\frac{4\pi}{\lambda}a\cos\frac{2\pi x}{\lambda}\cos\omega t$$

$$= v^2\rho\frac{4\pi}{\lambda}a\cos\frac{2\pi x}{\lambda}\cos\omega t, \quad ...(iv)$$

because $v = \sqrt{K/\rho}$ and, therefore, $K = v^2\rho$.

Let us now consider the changes that occur (*a*) with respect to position of a particle, (*b*) with respect to time.

(*a*) Changes with respect to position.

(*i*) **Displacement.** The displacement of a particle of the medium in the resulting wave is given by relation *I* above and, as can be seen at once, *varies simple harmonically with time.*

It is, however, zero at all times for points for which $\sin 2\pi x/\lambda = 0$ or $\cos 2\pi x/\lambda = \pm 1$, or $2\pi x/\lambda = m\pi$, where *m* is an integer, 0, 1, 2, 3, etc. and, therefore, 0, λ/2, 3λ/2, etc.

Thus, *the displacement is zero at points distant* 0, λ/2, 3λ/2 *etc from the fixed or the rigid boundary, irrespective of time. These points of permanent zero displacement are called* **nodal points** *or* **nodes**, *or, more correctly*, **displacement nodes**, *and obviously lie* λ/2 *apart.*

On the other hand, the displacement will be the maximum (positive or negative) or the amplitude ±2*a*, irrespective of the value of ω*t* and hence of time, for points for which $\sin 2\pi x/\lambda = \pm 1$ or $\cos 2\pi x/\lambda = 0$ or $2\pi x/\lambda = (2m + 1)\pi/2$, where *m* = 0, 1, 2, 3 *etc*., and, therefore, *x* = λ/4, 3λ/4, 5λ/4 etc.

Thus, *the displacement is the maximum at points distant* λ/4, 3λ/4, 5λ/4 *etc. from the fixed or the rigid boundary, irrespective of time. These points of maximum displacement (positive or negative)* are called **antipodal points** *or* **antinodes**, *or, more correctly*, **displacement antinodes**, *and also lie* λ/2 *apart.*

It may be noted that *the displacement at the antinodal points also varies simple harmonically with time but is always the maximum there at any given instant relative to that at all other points, where the displacement lies between the two extremes, decreasing from the maximum at an antinodal point to zero at the preceding or succeeding nodal point.*

Further, it will be easily seen that *no two nodes can exist without an antinode in between and vice versa*, so that *the distance between a node and a succeeding or preceding antinode is λ/4*.

(*ii*) **Particle velocity.** *At the nodal points or displacement nodes*, as we have seen under (*i*) above, sin $2\pi x/\lambda = 0$. So that, *the particle velocity U* (given by relation (*ii*)) *is zero there at all times.* These points, therefore, permanently remain at rest throughout the passage of the wave.

And, *at the antinodal points or displacement antinodes, since sin $2\pi x/\lambda = \pm 1$, the particle velocity (U) is the maximum* (positive or negative) *irrespective of time*. It may be noted that the particle velocity here too varies simple harmonically with time but is, at any given instant, maximum relative to that at all other points, where it lies between these two extremes, decreasing from the maximum at an antinodal point to zero at the preceding or succeeding nodal point, its amplitude being obviously $\frac{4\pi v}{\lambda} a \sin \frac{2\pi x}{\lambda}$.

(*iii*) **Strain.** Since sin $2\pi x/\lambda = 0$ and, therefore, cos $2\pi x/\lambda = \pm 1$ at the nodal points, the strain (dy/dx) *there*, (given by relation (*iii*) above), *is the maximum at all times, due*, obviously, to the condensations or the rarefactions of the oppositely travelling waves coming across each other, as show in Fig. 10.18 (*a*).

At the antinodal points, on the other hand, sin $2\pi x/\lambda = \pm 1$ and, therefore, cos $2\pi x/\lambda = 0$. So that, *the strain at these points is zero at all times*, no doubt, to the condensation of one wave coming across the rarefaction of the other, as shown in Fig. 10.18 (*b*).

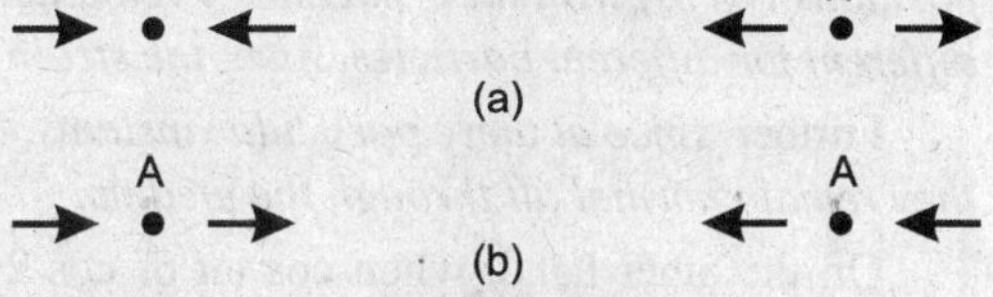

Fig. 10.18

(*iv*) **Pressure variation.** In equation *IV* above for excess pressure *p*, if we put $K.4\pi a/\lambda$ or ρv^2 $4\pi a/\lambda = P_m$, *the maximum value of pressure*, we have $p = P_m \cos \frac{2\pi x}{\lambda} \cos \omega t$, where, clearly, $P_m \cos \frac{2\pi x}{\lambda}$ is the *amplitude of pressure variation*. Denoting it by P_s, therefore, we have $p = P_x$ cos ωt, indicating that *the pressure at all points of the medium varies simple harmonically with time, except, of course, at the antinodal points or displacement antinodes,* for which cos $2\pi x/\lambda = 0$ and, therefore $p = 0$.

Thus, there being no excess pressure at the antinodal points, *there is no change of pressure and hence also of density at these points, which thus throughout remain normal.* For this reason these points are also referred to as **pressure nodes**.

At the nodal points or displacement nodes, cos $2\pi x/\lambda = \pm 1$ and hence *the excess pressure* (*p*) *is the maximum there* (Positive or negative). *The pressure and density changes are, therefore, the maximum at these points—higher and lower than the normal, alternately.* These points are, therefore, also referred to as **pressure antinodes**.

(*v*) **Phase.** Considering two points at distance x_1 and x_2, we have $y_1 = -2a \sin \frac{2\pi x_1}{\lambda} \cos \omega t$ and $y_2 = \frac{-2a \sin 2\pi x_2}{\lambda} \cos \omega t$.

Or, putting $-2a \sin 2\pi x_1/\lambda = A_1$ and $-2a \sin 2\pi x_2/\lambda = A_2$, where A_1 and A_2 are the amplitudes at distance x_1 and x_2 respectively, we have

$$y_1 = A_1 \cos \omega t \text{ and } y_2 = A_2 \cos \omega t.$$

Thus, although the *amplitudes* of the two particles are different, their *phases* are the *same*, indicating *that the phase of a particle is quite independent of its position.*

This means, in other words, that *all particles attain their respective maximum displacements (positive or negative) simultaneously* (though, of course, their maximum are all different, those of the antipodal points being the greatest).

Similarly, *all particles pass through their mean position simultaneously, though with their different maximum velocities.*

Further, since the displacement of the particles varies simple harmonically, with time, their phases get reversed every half a period.

It follows, therefore, that with the nodal points lying $\lambda/2$ apart, *the particles between one pair of nodal points are in opposite phase to those between the next succeeding (or preceding) pair.*

(*b*) **Changes with respect to time.** From equations *i, ii* and *iii* above, it is clear that when cos ωt or cos $2\pi vt/\lambda = 0$ and, therefore, sin $2\pi vt = \pm 1$, we have displacement $y = 0$; **particle velocity** $U = dy/dt = maximum$ (positive or neative), though this maximum is different for different points; strain $dy/dx = 0$ and hence also excess pressure $p = -K\, dy/dx = 0$. (From equation (*iv*))

This will obviously happen when $2\pi vt/\lambda = (2m + 1)\pi/2$ or $(2\pi/\lambda)\,(\lambda/T)$ $\because$ $t = (2m + 1)\pi/2$ ($V = n\lambda = \lambda/T$), *i.e.*, when $t = (2m + 1)T/4$, or $t = T/4$, $3T/4$, $5T/4$ etc., half a period apart from each other.

Thus, *at instants $T/4$, $3T/4$, $5T/4$, half a period apart, all particles pass through their mean positions ($y = 0$) with their maximum velocities ($U = dy/dt = maximum$), though these maxima are different for different particles. Also, the strain everywhere at these instants is zero ($dy/dx = 0$).*

Further, *since at these particular instants, there is no change of pressure and density anywhere, they remain normal all through the medium.*

On the other hand, when cos ωt or cos $2\pi vt/\lambda = \pm 1$ and, therefore, sin $2\pi vt/\lambda = 0$, we have **displacement** $y = maximum$ (*positive or negative*); **particle velocity** $U = dy/dt = 0$; **strain** $dy/dx = maximum$ (positive or negative) and hence also **excess pressure** $p = -Kdy/dx = maximum$ (positive or negative)

This will obviously happen when $2\pi vt/\lambda = m\pi$ or when $(2\pi/\lambda)(\lambda/T)t = m\pi$, or, $t = mT/2$, *i.e.*, when $t = 0$, $T/2$, $3T/2$ etc., again half a period apart from each other.

Thus, *at instants 0, $T/2$, $3T/2$ etc., half a period apart, all particles attain their maximum displacements (positive or negative) simultaneously, though their maxima are all different. Also, the strain on the particles is now maximum compared with that at other instants.*

Further, since at these instants, p is maximum (positive or negative), *the changes of pressure and density are also the maximum.*

It follows at once from the above that (*i*) *all particles pass through their mean positions and attain their maximum displacements (positive or negative) twice in one time-period,* (*ii*) *the particles attain their maximum displacement (positive or negative) an interval $T/4$ later than they pass through their mean positions and* (*iii*) *the pressure changes occur in accordance with the Bernoulli principle, being the maximum where the velocity is zero and vice versa.*

II—When reflection occurs at a free boundary. As before, let the equation of a simple harmonic wave, of *amplitude a* and *wavelength* λ, travelling along the positive direction of the *x-axis* be $y_1 = a\sin\frac{2\pi}{\lambda}(vt - x)$. Then, the equation of the wave reflected at the free boundary will be $y_2 = a\sin\frac{2\pi}{\lambda}(vt + x)$. Since only the direction of travel of the wave is reversed and not the direction of displacement of the particles of the medium. The equation of the resulting stationary or standing wave is, therefore,

$$y = y_1 + y_2 = a\sin\frac{2\pi}{\lambda}(vt - x) + a\sin\frac{2\pi}{\lambda}(vt + x)$$

$$= 2a \sin \frac{2\pi vt}{\lambda} \cos \frac{2\pi x}{\lambda}.$$

Or, $$y = 2a \cos \frac{2\pi x}{\lambda} \sin \frac{2\pi vt}{\lambda} = 2a \cos \frac{2\pi x}{\lambda} \sin \omega t, \quad ...(v)$$

$[\because v/\lambda = n \text{ and } 2\pi n = \omega]$

showing that *the resulting wave is also a simple harmonic wave, of the same time-period and wavelength as each of the two constituent waves but with an amplitude* = $2a \cos 2\pi x/\lambda$.

Clearly, therefore, *particle velocity* $U = \frac{dy}{dt} = \frac{4\pi v}{\lambda} a \cos \frac{2\pi x}{\lambda} \cos \omega t, \quad ...(vi)$

$$strain \; \frac{dy}{dx} = -\frac{4\pi}{\lambda} a \sin \frac{2\pi x}{\lambda} \sin \omega t \quad ...(vii)$$

and $$excess\ pressure\ p = -K\frac{dy}{dx} = K\frac{4\pi}{\lambda} a \sin \frac{2\pi x}{\lambda} \sin \omega t$$

$$= \rho v^2 \frac{4\pi}{\lambda} a \sin \frac{2\pi x}{\lambda} \sin \omega t. \quad ...(viii)$$

$$\left[\because v = \sqrt{K/\rho} \text{ and } \therefore K = \rho v^2\right]$$

Let us now consider the changes (*a*) *with respect to position of a particle* and (*b*) *with respect to time*.

(*a*) **Change with respect to position.**

(*i*) **Displacement.** From equation (*v*) above, for displacement *y*, it is clear that *the displacement at all points varies simple harmonically with time but is zero at points for which* $\cos 2\pi x/\lambda = 0$ or $2\pi x/\lambda = (2m + 1)\,\pi/2$, (where *m* is an integer 0, 1, 2, 3, etc) or, when $x = (2m + 1)\,\lambda/4$, *i.e.*, equal to $\lambda/4$, $3\lambda/4$, $5\lambda/4$ etc., *irrespective of time*.

These points of zero displacement thus occur at distance $\lambda/4$ $3\lambda/4$, $5\lambda/4$ *etc. from the free boundary*, $\lambda/2$ *apart from each other* and *are, as we know, called* **nodal points** *or* **nodes,** *or, more correctly* **displacement nodes.**

On the other hand, the *displacement is the maximum* (*positive or negative*) *or the amplitude* $\pm 2a$ *at points for which* $\cos 2\pi x/\lambda = \pm 1$, *i.e.*, when $2\pi x/\lambda = m\pi$ or $x = m\lambda/2 = 0$, $\lambda/2$, $3\lambda/2$, $5\lambda/2$ etc., *irrespective of time*.

These points of maximum displacement (positive or negative) thus occur at distance 0, $\lambda/2$, $3\lambda/2$, $5\lambda/2$ etc from the free boundary. They are the **antipodal points** or **antinodes,** or more correctly, **displacement antinodes**, *and also lie* $\lambda/2$ *apart but alternating with the nodal points or displacement nodes*.

The displacement at all other points lie between these two extremes, decreasing from the maximum at an antinodal point to zero at the preceding or succeeding nodal point.

(*ii*) **Particles velocity.** Form equation VI for particle velocity *U*, it can be easily seen that *at the nodal points, since* $\cos 2\pi x/\lambda = 0$, *the particle velocity is zero, irrespective of time*. In other words, *the particles of the medium throughout remain at rest at these points*.

On the other hand, *at the antinodal points, since* $\cos 2\pi x/\lambda = \pm 1$, *the particle velocity is the maximum* (*positive or negative*) *and this is again so, irrespective of time*.

(*iii*) **Strain.** *At the nodal points*, $\cos 2\pi x/\lambda = 0$ and, therefore, $\sin 2\pi x/\lambda = \pm 1$. So that *the strain* (*dy*/*dx*), given by equation (*vii*) above, *is the maximum* (positive or negative) *at all times*.

And, *at the antinodal points, since cos* $2\pi x/\lambda = \pm 1$ *and, therefore,* $\sin 2\pi x/\lambda = 0$, *the strain is the minimum or zero at all times*

Pressure variation. As in case I, so also here, putting $\rho v^2\, 4\pi\, a/\lambda = P_m$, the maximum value of pressure, we have (from equation (*viii*)), $p = P_m \sin \frac{2\pi x}{\lambda} \sin \omega t$, so that $P_m \sin \frac{2\pi x}{\lambda}$ is the *amplitude of pressure variation*. Putting it equal to P_x, we, therefore, have

$$p = P_x \sin \omega t,$$

indicating that *pressure too at all points varies simple harmonically with time.*

At displacement nodes or nodal points, where $\cos 2\pi x/\lambda = 0$ *and, therefore,* $\sin 2\pi x/\lambda = \pm 1$, *the pressure and density changes are the maximum at all times*, the pressure (and density) being alternately higher and lower than the normal. These points are thus also referred to as the **pressure antinodes.**

At displacement antinodes or antinodal points, on the other hand, $\cos 2\pi x/\lambda = \pm 1$ and, therefore, $\sin 2\pi x/\lambda = 0$, *so that* $p = 0$, *i.e., there are no pressure and density changes which, therefore, remain normal throughout.* For this reason, these points are referred to as **pressure nodes.**

(*v*) **Phase.** As before (case 1), we can put displacements at two points x_1 and x_2 as $y_1 = 2a \cos \dfrac{2\pi x_1}{\lambda} \sin \omega t = A_1 \sin \omega t$ and $y_2 = 2a \cos \dfrac{2\pi x_2}{\lambda} \sin \omega t = A_2 \sin \omega t$, where $2a \cos (2\pi x_1/\lambda) = A$ and $2a \cos (2\pi x_2/\lambda) = A_2$.

Thus, *although the amplitudes of the two particles are different, their phases, are the same,* showing that *the phase of a particle is independent of its position.* This means, in other words, that all *particles pass through their mean positions or attain their maximum displacements (Positive or negative) simultaneously.*

And, since the displacement of the particles varies cyclically with time, their phases get reversed every half a period; so that the nodal points lying $\lambda/2$ apart, *all particles between one pair of nodal points are in a phase opposite to that of the particles between the preceding or succeeding pair.*

(*b*) **Changes with respect to time.** At instants *t* for which $\sin \omega t = \sin 2\pi vt/\lambda = 0$ and, therefore, $\cos 2\pi vt/\lambda = \pm 1$, we have **displacement** $y = 0$, particle velocity $U = dy/dt$, *the maximum* (positive or negative) though the value of the maximum velocity is different at different points; *strain,* $dy/dx = 0$ and hence also $p = -K\, dy/dx = 0$.

This obviously occurs when $2\pi vt/\lambda = (2\pi/\lambda)(\lambda/T)t = m\pi$. or $t = mT/2 = 0, T/2, T, 3T/2$ etc. Thus, *at instants* $0, T/2, T, 3T/2$ etc., *half a period apart, all particles pass through their mean positions* ($y = 0$), *with their maximum velocities (positive or negative), since* dy/dt *is maximum, but the maximum of velocity are different for different particles.*

Also *strain and hence changes of pressure and density are zero at all points at these instants.*

And, at instants *t* for which $\sin 2\pi vt/\lambda = \pm 1$ and, therefore, $\cos 2\pi vt/\lambda = 0$, we have **displacement** y = maximum (positive or negative); **particle velocity** $U = dy/dt = 0$; **strain** = dy/dx = maximum (positive or negative) and hence also *excess pressure* $p = -K\, dy/dx$ = maximum (*positive* or *negative*).

This clearly occurs when $2\pi vt/\lambda = (2\pi/\lambda)(\lambda/T)t = (2m + 1)\pi/2$ or when $t = (2m + 1)T/4$. *i.e.*, equal to $T/4, 3T/4, 5T/4$ etc., again at intervals of $T/2$.

Thus, *at instants* $T/4, 3T/4, 5T/4$, *an interval* $T/2$ *apart, all particles attain their maximum displacements (different for different particles), with the strain and hence also changes of pressure and density maximum, relative to these at all other instants. Again, therefore, the Bernoulli principle holds good, viz.*, that the pressure is the maximum when the velocity is zero and *vice versa.*

10.30 FLOW OF ENERGY IN A STATIONARY OR STANDING WAVE

Considering the case of stationary waves formed by reflection at a free boundary (*i.e.*, case II), we have *excess pressure* $p = P_x \sin \omega t = P_x \sin 2\pi vt/\lambda$. And, since *particle velocity* $U = dy/dt = \dfrac{4\pi v}{\lambda} a \cos \dfrac{2\pi x}{\lambda} \cos \dfrac{2\pi vt}{\lambda}$, we may put as $U = U_x \cos 2\pi vt/\lambda$, where $U_x = \dfrac{4\pi v}{\lambda} a \cos \dfrac{2\pi x}{\lambda}$.

So that, energy transferred (equal to the work done) per unit area in an interval of time dt is, say, $dI = p.U.dt$.

$\therefore$ energy transferred during the whole time-period T is given by

$$I = \int_0^T p.U\,dt = \int_0^T P_x \sin\frac{2\pi vt}{\lambda}\,U_x \cos\frac{2\pi vt}{\lambda}\,dt.$$

And, therefore, *rate of energy transfer or average energy transferred per* second, say,

$$I_{av} = \frac{P_x U_x}{T}\int_0^T \sin\frac{2\pi vt}{\lambda}\cos\frac{2\pi vt}{\lambda}$$

$$= \frac{P_x U_x}{2T}\int_0^T \sin\frac{4\pi vt}{\lambda}\,dt = 0.$$

The same result may be obtained by considering case I.

Thus, *there is no transference of energy across any section of the medium in the case of a stationary or standing wave.*

This also follows from the fact that an equal amount of energy is transferred by the two constituent waves in *opposite* directions.

This result may also be expressed differently by saying that *no energy is transferred across any section of a linear bounded medium.*

N.B. It will be readily seen that the excess pressure (p) and the particle velocity (U) differ in phase by $\pi/2$. They are, therefore, said to be *in quadrature.* The case is, in fact, similar to that of *wattles current* in an A.C. circuit, where too the voltage and current differ in phase by $\pi/2$ (*i.e.*, are in quadrature) and the wattage (or the power) is zero, *i.e.*, no work is done by the source or no energy is drawn from it. That is why the current in this case is dubbed as '*wattless*' current.

10.31 DISTINCTION BETWEEN PROGRESSIVE AND STATIONARY WAVES

The main differences between progressive and stationary (or standing) waves may, for ready reference, be summarized in parallel columns as shown below.

Progressive waves	Stationary waves
1. The *vibration characteristic** of each particle of the medium is the same and is *handed on from particle to particle,* so that there is an onward propagation of the wave through the medium.	1. The *vibration characteristic* of each particles of the medium is its *own* which it does not pass on to others, so that there is no onward propagation of the wave through the medium, *i.e.*, it remains confined to the limited space in which it is produced.
2. All particles of the medium attain the *same maximum displacement* (positive or negative) but *one after the other.*	2. All particles attain their maximum displacements *simultaneously* but *their maximum are different,* decreasing progressively from an antinode to the adjoining node where it is reduced to zero.
3. All particles pass through their mean positions with the *same maximum velocity but one after the other.*	3. All particles pass through their mean positions *simultaneously but with different maximum velocities.*

* *i.e.*, mode of vibration.

4.	No particles of the medium are permanently at rest (except momentarily at the extremities of their vibrations).	4.	Certain particles of the medium (*viz., the displacement nodes*) *throughout remains at rest.*
5.	All particles of the medium undergo the *same changes of pressure and density but one after the other.*	5.	The *changes of pressure and density are the maximum (positive or negative) at the nodal points and zero at the antinodal points but occur simultaneously* at all points.
6.	There is a *regular transference of energy across every section of the medium.*	6.	*There is no transference of energy across any section of the medium.*

10.32 DIFFERENT MODES OF VIBRATION OF STRINGS, RODS AND AIR COLUMNS

A—Different modes of vibration of a stretched string. Suppose we have a string under tension, fixed a both ends and lying along the axis of x in its *normal*, *undisturbed* position. If it be plucked at any point, two *identical* waves proceed from the points in opposite directions. Each of these two waves then suffers reflection at the fixed end or the rigid boundary, giving rise to stationary or standing waves.

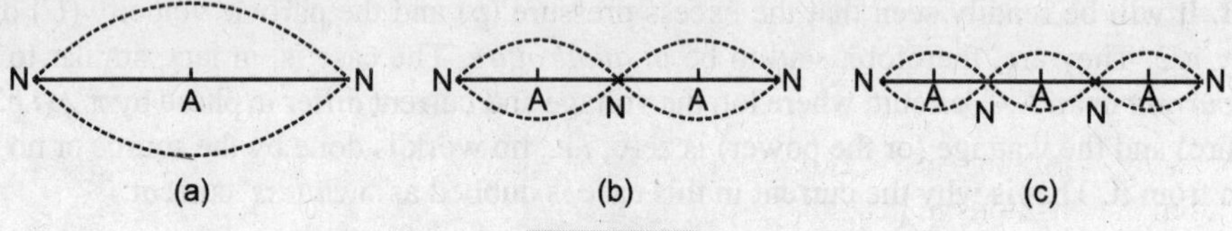

Fig. 10.19

By plucking the string at different suitable points, it can be set into different modes of vibration, *i.e.*, stationary waves of different wavelengths and frequencies may be produced, though the two fixed points, in every case, remain nodal points or displacement nodes.

Thus, if the string be plucked in the middle, it *vibrates as a whole, in one single segment,* as shown in Fig. 10.19 (*a*), *giving its lowest or fundamental note* (*i.e.*, of the lowest frequency).

If pressed in the middle and plucked at the mid-point of either half, it vibrates in two segments, as shown in Fig. 10.19 (*b*), *producing a note of twice the frequency of the fundamental.*

And, if pressed at one-third of its length and plucked at the mid-point of the smaller length, it *vibrates in three segments*, as shown in Fig. 10.19 (*c*), *giving a note of thrice the frequency of the fundamental* and so on.

Let us obtain these results analytically.

Let the equation of the simple harmonic wave travelling along the positive direction of the x-axis be $y_1 = a\sin\frac{2\pi}{\lambda}(vt - x)$. It will naturally get reflected at the fixed end of the string at $x = 0$ and the equation of the reflected wave will, therefore, be $y_2 = -a\sin\frac{2\pi}{\lambda}(vt + x)$. So that, the equation of the resulting stationary wave thus formed will be $y = y_1 + y_2 = a\sin\frac{2\pi}{\lambda}(vt - x) - a\sin\frac{2\pi}{\lambda}(vt + x)$.

Or $$y = -2a\sin\frac{2\pi x}{\lambda}\cos\frac{2\pi vt}{\lambda}.$$

Now, the displacement $y = 0$ at the other fixed point also, *i.e.*, at $x = -l$, where l is the length of the string. So that, we have

$$0 = 2a \sin \frac{2\pi l}{\lambda} \cos \frac{2\pi vt}{\lambda}.$$

Since the displacement at the fixed end is *always* zero, the relation above must be true for all values of t and this is obviously possible only if $\sin 2\pi l/\lambda = 0$, or, $2\pi l/\lambda = p\pi$, *i.e.*, $\lambda = 2l/p$, where p is an integer, 0, 1, 2, 3 etc.

Now, the *frequency* of vibration of the string, or that of the note emitted by it, is given by $n = \frac{v}{\lambda}$. So that, we have

$$n = \frac{v}{\lambda} = \frac{v}{2l/p} = \frac{pv}{2l},$$

where v is, of course, the velocity of the wave.

Since $v = \sqrt{T/\sigma}$, where T is the *tension* in the string and σ, the *line density* or *mass per unit length of the string*, we have

$$n = \frac{p}{2l}\sqrt{\frac{T}{\sigma}}$$

If $p = 1$, we obtain the lowest or the *fundamental tone** of frequency $n_1 = \frac{1}{2l}\sqrt{\frac{T}{\sigma}}$ and $\lambda = 2l$, with the string vibrating as a whole in *one single segment,* as shown in Fig. 10.19 (*a*) having *two displacement nodes at either fixed end and a displacement antinode at its mid-point.*

If $p = 2$, we have $n_2 = \frac{2}{2l}\sqrt{\frac{T}{\sigma}} = \frac{1}{l}\sqrt{\frac{T}{\sigma}}$ = *twice the frequency of the fundamental tone,* and $\lambda = l$, with the string vibrating in *two equal segments*, as shown in Fig. 10.12 (*b*), having nodes and antinodes in the positions indicated.

If $p = 3$, we have $n_3 = \frac{3}{2l}\sqrt{\frac{T}{\sigma}}$ = *thrice the frequency of the fundamental tone*, and $\lambda = 2l/3$, with the string vibrating in *three equal segments* as shown in Fig. 10.12 (*c*) and having nodes and antinodes as indicated in the figure.

In general, therefore, if the string vibrates in p equal segments, we have a note of frequency p times that of the fundamental, *i.e.*, *the frequencies of the notes emitted by the string are proportional to the number of segments of loops into which the string is thrown into vibration, or,*

$$n_1 : n_2 : n_3 \ldots n_p :: 1, 2, 3, \ldots p,$$

Whereas the lowest tone is, as already pointed out, referred to as the fundamental tone or, usually simple *the fundamental*, all the rest (*i.e.*, any integral multiples of the fundamental) are called *overtones*, with the special name *octave* reserved for the first overtone *having twice the frequency of the fundamental.*

Now, if, as is the case here, the fundamental and the overtones have their frequency in the ratio 1 : 2 : 3..., thus forming a *harmonic series*, they are called *harmonics*, the *fundamental* itself being the *first harmonic*, the first overtone, the second harmonic and so on.

N.B. We have, in the above discussion, tacitly assumed that the string vibrates only in 1, 2, 3 etc. segments into which it has been deliberately set vibrating, giving a pure tone of the corresponding frequency. In actual practice, however, it executes two or more of these vibrations *simultaneously* with, of course, the one into which it has actually been set vibrating predominating. The note emitted is thus a mixture of the pure tone sounded and some of its overtones. In fact, it is the presence of these different overtones with the given note sounded on different musical stringed instruments that gives it its characteristic or distinctive quality.

---

* A pure musical sound of one single frequency is called a tone and one, consisting of a number of frequencies, a note.

B. Different modes of longitudinal vibration of a rod. In the case of a rod, set into longitudinal vibration, the following different case arise:

(*i*) The rod is *not clamped anywhere*, so that *the boundary at both ends of the rod is free.* It is referred to as a **free-free rod.**

(*ii*) The rod is *clamped at one end, with the other end free*, so that it has a *fixed or a rigid boundary at the former and a free boundary at the latter end,* It is called a **fixed-free rod.**

(*iii*) The rod is *clamped at its mid-point*, so that *the boundary at either end is free.*

(*vi*) The rod is clamped at both ends, so that there is a *fixed or a rigid boundary at either end.* If is referred to as the **fixed-fixed rod.**

It will be readily seen that in the *first three cases*, the longitudinal wave set up in the rod, or the incident wave is reflected at a free boundary. So that, if the equation of the simple harmonic wave (or the incident wave) set up in the rod, travelling along the positive direction of the *x*-axis along which the rod lies, be $y_1 = a \sin \frac{2\pi}{\lambda}(vt - x)$, that of the reflected wave will be $y_2 = a \sin \frac{2\pi}{\lambda}(vt + x)$.

And the equation of the resulting stationary wave thus formed will be

$$y = y_1 + y_2 = a \sin \frac{2\pi}{\lambda}(vt - x) + a \sin \frac{2\pi}{\lambda}(vt + x).$$

Or, $$y = 2\,a \cos \frac{2\pi x}{\lambda} \sin \frac{2\pi vt}{\lambda} = 2\,a \cos \frac{2\pi x}{\lambda} \sin \omega t \quad \left[\because v/\lambda = n \text{ and } 2\pi n = \omega.\right]$$

Let us now consider each of these cases individually.

Case (*i*) Free-free rod. Here, we shell obviously have *an antinodal point or a displacement antinode at either free end irrespective of time* and, therefore, the strain at these points will always be zero, *i.e.*, $dy/dx = 0$ at $x = 0$ as well as at $x = -l$, whatever the value of ωt.

Since strain $= \frac{dy}{dx} = -\frac{4\pi}{\lambda} a \sin \frac{2\pi x}{\lambda} \sin \omega t$, we have, putting $x = -l$,

$$\frac{4\pi}{\lambda} a \sin \frac{2\pi l}{\lambda} \sin \omega t = 0. \quad \text{Or,} \quad \sin \frac{2\pi l}{\lambda} = 0$$

$\because$ at an antinodal point $\cos 2\pi x/\lambda = \pm 1$ and $\therefore$ $\sin 2\pi\, x/\lambda = 0$. *i.e.*, $2\pi l/\lambda = p\pi$, where p is an integer, 0, 1, 2, 3, etc.

Or, $$\lambda = 2l/p.$$

And, therefore, *frequency of the tone produced, i.e.*,

$$n = v/\lambda = pv/2l = (\rho/2l)\sqrt{Y/\rho}. \qquad [\because v = \sqrt{Y/\rho}.]$$

Hence, if $p = 1$, we have a *tone of frequency* $n_1 = \frac{1}{2l}\sqrt{Y/\rho}$, which is the *lowest* or the *fundamental tone.*

If $p = 2$, we have a *tone of frequency* $n_2 = \frac{2}{2l}\sqrt{Y/\rho} = \frac{1}{l}\sqrt{Y/\rho}$, the *first overtone* (or the *octave of the fundamental tone*).

If $p = 3$, we have a *tone of frequency* $n_3 = \frac{3}{2l}\sqrt{Y/\rho}$, *the second overtone*, having *three times* the *frequency of the fundamental tone.*

Thus, $n_1 : n_2 : n_3 :: 1 : 2 : 3$, *i.e., the tone all form a harmonic series.*

In other words, *all possible harmonics or overtones* (*odd as well as even*) *can be produced in this mode of vibration of the rod.*

Case (*ii*) Fixed-free rod. In this case, we must necessarily have *a nodal point or a displacement node at the fixed end, and an antinodal point or a displacement antinode at the free end, of the rod at all* times *i.e*, $y = 0$ at $x = -l$. Since $y = 2\,a \cos \frac{2\pi x}{\lambda} \sin \omega t$ have, putting $y = 0$ and $x = -l$,

$$0 = 2\,a\cos\frac{2\pi l}{\lambda}\sin\omega t.\ \text{Or, } \cos\frac{2\pi l}{\lambda} = 0.\ \text{Or, } \frac{2\pi l}{\lambda} = (2p+1)\pi/2, \text{ where, } p = 0, 1, 2, 3, \text{ etc.}$$

Or, $$\lambda = \frac{4l}{(2p+1)}.\ \text{So that, } n = \frac{v}{\lambda} = \frac{(2p+1)}{4l}\,v, \text{ i.e.,}$$

$$n = \frac{2p+1}{4l}\sqrt{\frac{Y}{\rho}}. \qquad [\because v = \sqrt{Y/\rho}\,]$$

Thus, the frequency of the lowest or the fundamental tone, corresponding to $p = 0$, is

$$n_1 = \frac{1}{4l}\sqrt{\frac{Y}{\rho}}$$

This, it will be seen, is half the frequency of the fundamental tone in the case of the free-free rod. In other words, *the fundamental tone emitted a rod not clamped anywhere is the octave* (*i.e.*, *has twice the frequency*) *of the fundamental tone emitted by the same rod when clamped at one end.*

The frequency of the second tone emitted by the fixed-free rod, corresponding to $p = 1$ will be

$$n_2 = \frac{3}{4l}\sqrt{Y/\rho}.$$

i.e., three times that of the fundamental.

Similarly, the third tone emitted by the rod, corresponding to $p = 2$, will be

$$n_3 = \frac{5}{4l}\sqrt{Y/\rho},\ \textit{i.e., five times that of the fundamental.}$$

Thus, $$n_1 : n_2 : n_3 :: 1 : 3 : 5.$$

In other words, *we can have only odd harmonics* (*or overtones*) *excited in the rod in this case.*

Case (*iii*) Rod clamped at its mid-point. Here, clearly, *there must always be an antinodal point* (*or displacement antinode*) *at each free end of the rod and a nodal point* (*or displacement node*) at its midpoint where it is clamped.

So that, $y = 0$ at $x = -l/2$ *for all values of t and hence of* ωt.

$\therefore$ substituting these values in the expression for y, we have

$$0 = -2\,a\cos\frac{2\pi}{\lambda}.\frac{l}{2}\sin\omega t = -2\,a\cos\frac{\pi l}{\lambda}\sin\omega t.$$

Or, $\cos\frac{\pi l}{\lambda} = 0$, *i.e.*, $\frac{\pi l}{\lambda} = (2p+1)\,\pi/2$, whence, $\lambda = \frac{2l}{(2p+1)}$ with $p = 0, 1, 2, 3$ etc.

$\therefore$ *frequency of the tone emitted by the rod, i.e.,* $n = \frac{v}{\lambda} = \frac{2p+l}{2l}\,v.$

Or, $$n = \frac{2p+1}{2l}\sqrt{\frac{Y}{\rho}}. \qquad [\because v = \sqrt{Y/\rho}\,]$$

Hence, *frequency of the lowest or the fundamental tone*, corresponding to $p = 0$, will obviously be $n_1 = \frac{1}{2l}\sqrt{\frac{Y}{\rho}}$,

i.e., the same as in the case of the free-free rod, and the *octave of that in the case of the fixed-free rod.*

The frequency of the second tone emitted by the rod, corresponding to $p = 1$, will be

$$n_2 = \frac{3}{2l}\sqrt{\frac{Y}{\rho}},$$

i.e., three times that of the fundamental.

Similarly, *frequency of the third tone* corresponding to $p = 2$, will be $n_3 = \frac{5}{2l}\sqrt{\frac{Y}{\rho}}$ *i.e., five times that of the fundamental.*

Here, again, therefore, $n_1 : n_2 : n_3 :: 1 : 3 : 5$,

i.e., only odd harmonics or overtones can be excited in the rod in this case.

Case (*iv*) Fixed-fixed rod. Here, the longitudinal waves up in the rod, *i.e.*, the incident wave, will be reflected at a rigid boundary, so that the equations of the incident and reflected waves will respectively be

$$y_1 = a \sin \frac{2\pi}{\lambda} (vt - x) \text{ and } y_2 = -a \sin \frac{2\pi}{\lambda}(vt + x)$$

∴ the equation of the resultant stationary wave set up in the rod will be

$$y = y_1 + y_2 = a \sin \frac{2\pi}{\lambda} (vt - x) - a \sin \frac{2\pi}{\lambda} (vt + x).$$

Or,
$$y = -2\, a \sin \frac{2\pi x}{\lambda} \cos \frac{2\pi vt}{\lambda} = -2\, a \sin \frac{2\pi x}{\lambda} \cos \omega t$$

$$[\because v/\lambda = n \text{ and } 2\pi n = \omega]$$

Since there must always be a nodal point or a displacement node at either fixed or clamped end of the rod, we have $y = 0$ at $x = 0$ and at $x = -l$.

Substituting $y = 0$ and $x = -l$ in the expression for y, we therefore have

$$0 = 2\, a \sin \frac{2\pi l}{\lambda} \cos \omega t. \quad \text{Or,} \quad \sin \frac{2\pi l}{\lambda} = 0.$$

Or,
$$2\pi l/\lambda = p\pi, \text{ whence, } \lambda = 2l/p, \text{ where } p = 1, 2, 3, \text{ etc.}$$

Therefore, frequency of the note emitted, *i.e.*, $n = \frac{v}{\lambda} = \frac{p}{2l} v$

$$= \frac{p}{2l}\sqrt{\frac{Y}{\rho}} \qquad [\because v = \sqrt{Y/\rho}\,]$$

So that, *frequency of the lowest or the fundamental tone*, corresponding to $p = 1$, is given by

$$n_1 = \frac{1}{2l}\sqrt{Y/\rho}\,.$$

Similarly, *frequency of the second tone, corresponding to* $p = 2$, is given by

$$n_2 = \frac{2}{2l}\sqrt{Y/\rho} = \frac{1}{l}\sqrt{Y/\rho}$$

and, *frequency of the third tone, corresponding to* $p = 3$ *is given by* $n_3 = \frac{3}{2l}\sqrt{Y/\rho}$, and so on.

Thus, $n_1 : n_2 : n_3 :: 1 : 2 : 3$,

i.e., all possible harmonic (or overtones), odd as well as even, can be excited in the rod in this case.

As will be readily seen, this is thus a case essentially similar to that of the free-free rod.

C—different modes of vibration of air columns. An air column can be set into vibration in what is called an *organ pipe*, which is just a long tube or pipe of wood or metal, rectangular or circular in cross section, fitted with a mouth-piece at one end and either closed or open at the other end. In the former case it is call a *closed pipe* and in the latter, an *open pipe*.

On blowing into the mouth piece, the air column inside the pipe is set into vibration and the longitudinal waves thus produced get reflected at the open or the closed end of the pipe, resulting in the formation of stationary waves.

Since the mouth-piece end of the pipe also serves as an open end, the open and closed pipes, it will be easily seen, correspond to the *free-free* and the fixed-free rod respectively dealt with under **B.** (*i*) and (*ii*) above. So that the equations of the incident and reflected waves here too are respectively

$$y_1 = a\sin\frac{2\pi}{\lambda}(vt - x) \text{ and } y_2 = a\sin\frac{2\pi}{\lambda}(vt + x)$$

And, therefore, the equation of the resultant stationary wave is

$$y = y_1 + y_2 = a\sin\frac{2\pi}{\lambda}(vt - x) + a\sin\frac{2\pi}{\lambda}(vt + x).$$

Or, $$y = 2a\cos\frac{2\pi x}{\lambda}\sin\frac{2\pi vt}{\lambda} = 2a\cos\frac{2\pi x}{\lambda}\sin\omega t.$$

Now, in the case of an open pipe, we have an antinodal point at either end, irrespective of the value of t and hence of ωt. So that, *excess pressure p at either end is zero, i.e., $p = 0$ at $x = 0$ and at $x = -l$ at all times.*

Now, $$p = -K\frac{dy}{dx} = -K\frac{4\pi}{\lambda}a\sin\frac{2\pi x}{\lambda}\sin\omega t.$$

Substituting $p = 0$ and $x = -l$ in the expression for p, therefore, we have $0 = K\frac{4\pi}{\lambda}a\sin\frac{2\pi l}{\lambda}\sin\omega t.$

Or, $\sin\frac{2\pi l}{\lambda} = 0$. Or, $\frac{2\pi l}{\lambda} = m\pi$, where $m = 1, 2, 3$, etc.

Or, $$\lambda = 2\,l/m.$$

And, therefore, frequency of the tone emitted, *i.e.*,

$$n = \frac{v}{\lambda} = \frac{mv}{2l} = \frac{m}{2l}\sqrt{\frac{K}{\rho}}. \qquad \left[\because v = \sqrt{\frac{K}{\rho}}.\right]$$

So that, *frequency of the lowest or the fundamental tone*, corresponding to $m = 1$, is given by

$$n_1 = \frac{1}{2l}\sqrt{\frac{K}{\rho}},$$

and those of the *second* and the *third* tones by

$$n_2 = \frac{2}{2l}\sqrt{\frac{K}{\rho}} = \frac{1}{l}\sqrt{\frac{K}{\rho}} \text{ and } n_3 = \frac{3}{2l}\sqrt{\frac{K}{\rho}} \text{ respectively,}$$

Thus, $n_1 : n_2 : n_3 : 1 : 2 : 3$,

i.e., all possible harmonics or overtones (odd as well as even) can be produced in the case of an open pipe.

In the **case a closed pipe**, *since there must necessarily be a nodal point, at the closed end,* irrespective of the value of t and hence of ωt, we have, as *in the case of a fixed free rod, $y = 0$ at $x = -l$ at all times.*

Substituting these values in the expression for y, therefore, we have

$0 = -2a\cos\frac{2\pi l}{\lambda}\sin\omega t$. Or, $\cos\frac{2\pi l}{\lambda} = 0$. Or, $\frac{2\pi l}{\lambda} = (2m+1)\pi/2$, and, therefore, $\lambda = 4l/(2m+1)$, where $m = 0, 1, 2, 3$ etc.

$\therefore$ *frequency of the tone emitted, i.e.,*

$$n = \frac{v}{\lambda} = \frac{(2m+1)}{4l}v = \frac{2m+1}{4l}\sqrt{\frac{K}{\rho}}.$$

So that, *frequency of the lowest or the fundamental tone*, corresponding to $m = 0$, is given by

$$n_1 = \frac{1}{4l}\sqrt{\frac{K}{\rho}},$$

which is clearly *half* that of the fundamental tone given by an open pipe of the same length. In other words, *the fundamental tone given by an open pipe is the octave of the fundamental tone given by a closed pipe of the same length.*

The *frequencies of the second and third tones* (corresponding to $m = 1$ and $m = 2$) are respectively

$$n_2 = \frac{3}{4l}\sqrt{\frac{K}{\rho}} \text{ and } n_3 = \frac{5}{4l}\sqrt{\frac{K}{\rho}}.$$

Thus, $n_1 : n_2 : n_3 :: 1 : 3 : 5$,

i.e., only odd harmonics or overtones can be produced in the case of a closed pipe.

As in the case of strings, so also here, the note emitted by an air column is usually a mixture of the tone sounded with some of its harmonics or overtones. Obviously, both odd and even harmonics are present if a note is sounded on an open pipe and only odd harmonics when it is sounded on a closed pipe of the same length. This is why the former is always sweeter and richer than the latter.

Note. In our discussion above, we have assumed that reflection of the wave at the open end occurs exactly at the level of the open end itself. In point of fact it occurs just a wee-bit beyond the open end, so that the actual length of the air column involved is slightly greater than the length of the pipe.

Rayleigh has shown that the *effective length* of the air column in the case of a closed pipe is $0.3\ D$ more than the actual length of the pipe, where D is the *internal diameter* of the pipe. And, obviously, in the case of an open pipe, it would be $2 \times 0.3\ D = 0.6\ D$ more than the actual length of the pipe. This is referred to as the end-correction of the pipe.

10.33 TUNING FORK

Chladni regarded the tuning fork as a free bar bent in the from of U elongated. The nodes gradually approach each other, as a bar is bent gradually at the midpoint as shown in fig. 10.20. The midpoint behaves like an antinode. The vibration of antinode, in between the two nodes, is small, compared to that of the free ends. In addition of stem at the mid point causes the nodes to approach closer. It is equivalent to, adding a mass at antinode and to increase the stiffness of the fork between the two nodes causing the reduction of vibration of the midpoint. This small vibration of the stem [Fig. 10.20 (*b*)] fluctuates the sending board or the resonators when the stem is pressed gently into contact with them. The energy of vibration of the fork is rapidly transmitted to them through the stem.

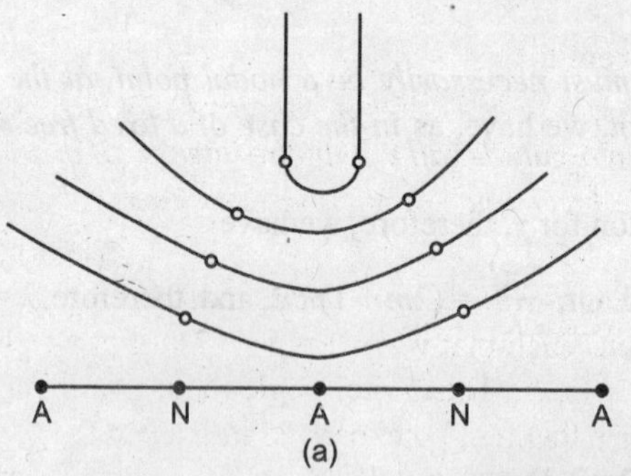

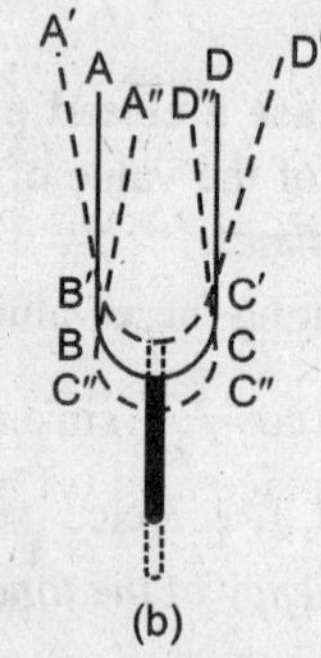

Fig. 10.20

Rayleigh regarded the tuning fork as two clamped free bar mounted parallel to each other on a heavy rigid block of metal. The frequency of a bar clamped at one end and free at the other, may be lowered either by loading the free end or reducing the area of cross-section of the bar near the fixed end. Similarly, the frequency may be increased by reducing the area of cross-section of the bar at the free end or by shortening the length of the bar. The frequency of the bar may be adjusted by using a sliding collar and rigidly fixing at any desired position. *The nearer the sliding collar (weight) the free end, lower is the frequency.* These principles are generally adopted in practice in the construction of a tuning fork and in harmonium reeds.

10.34. FOURIER'S THEOREM

If we examine the wave pattern, *i.e.*, the *time-displacement curve* (or the pressure variation curve) of music from a musical instrument or a song rendered by an artiste, we find that although it is a periodic curve in the sence that it repeats itself periodically, (*i.e.*, after fixed and regular intervals of time) *it is by no means a simple harmonic wave which may be represented by a sine or a cosine curve. Waves of this type, having an irregular profile, are called* **complex waves** and the vibrations which give rise to them, **complex vibrations.**

The French mathematician, **J.B.J. Fourier** (1768–1830) showed, in the year 1822, that such waves may be analysed into a set of simple harmonic waves and that, in fact a periodic motion may, in general, be represented as a combination of sinusoidal or simple harmonic motions, whose frequencies are an integral multiple of that of the periodic motion in question.

The **limitations** under which a periodic functions may be so analysed are that (*i*) *it must be continuous or* may just have a finite number of discontinuities of slope or magnitude within its time-interval of one oscillation but must not be discontinuous as shown at Q in Fig. 10.21. This means, in other words, that it must have only finite values and should never assume an infinite value at any instant. For, an infinite value for a displacement etc, at any given instant, is simply inconceivable; (*ii*) *it must be a single-valued function, i.e.*, it must have only one value at a given instant t, so that the curve representing it may not overhang at any point, as shown at P in the figure, or else it would have two values of y at the same instant t. This is a sheer impossibility in air or in any elastic medium.

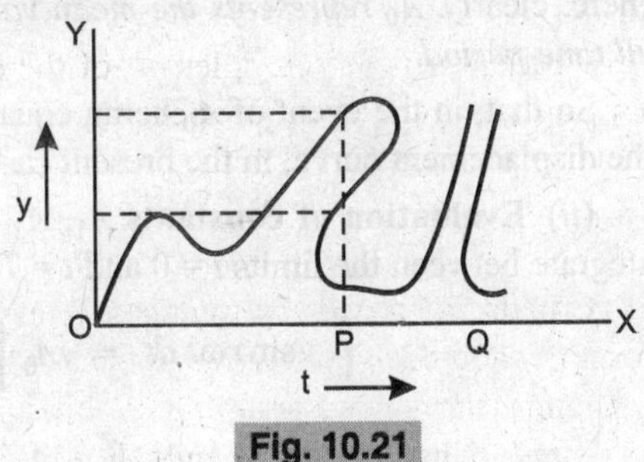

Fig. 10.21

And, naturally enough, the frequencies of the component vibrations should not be incommensurable (like, for instance, 500 and $500\sqrt{3}$). For, then, the resultant vibration is no longer periodic and the theorem, as we know, applies only to periodic vibrations.

All these conditions are satisfied by mechanical waves, in general, and by sound waves, in particular.

We may, therefore, stafe **Fourier's theorem** thus:

Any finite. single-valued periodic function, which is either continuous or which possesses only a finite number of discontinuities of slope or magnitude (*all within the interval of one time-period*), *may be regarded as a combination of simple harmonic vibrations whose frequencies are integral multiples of that of the given function.*

Analytically, then, if we have a *finite, single-valued, continuous function* $y = f(t)$ of t, which is, say, a displacement (or a pressure variation) such that $y = f(t) = f(t + T)$, it is clearly a periodic function of time-period T or of frequency $1/T = \omega/2\pi$. This finite, single-valued, continuous periodic function $f(t)$ may, in accordance with Fourier's theorem be expanded into a summation or a series, called *Fourier series*. Thus,

$$y = f(t) = A_o + A_1 \sin \omega t + A_2 \sin 2\omega t + \ldots\ldots + A_r \sin r\omega t + B_1 \cos \omega t + B_2 \cos 2\omega t + \ldots\ldots + B_r \cos r\omega t,$$

i.e.,
$$y = A_o + \Sigma A_r \sin r\omega t + \Sigma B_r \cos r\omega t. \qquad ...(i)$$

Here, A_o represents the *zero frequency term* (in most cases, equal to zero) and is, in fact, a measure of the mean displacement of the time-axis. The sine and cosine terms represent the component sinusoidal vibrations of frequencies which are integral multiples of frequency $\omega/2\pi$ the periodic function and $A_1, A_2 \ldots A_r$ and $B_1, B_2, \ldots B_r$ are amplitudes of these vibrations, all having definite values for the given periodic function (displacement, in our case) and are referred to as **Fourier coefficients** of the given series.

It is by no means necessary that all the terms of the series should be present in any given case.

Evaluation of Fourier coefficients. The values of the Fourier coefficients may be easily obtained, as we shall presently see-the process of evaluation being termed **Fourier (or harmonic) analysis.**

(*i*) **Evaluation of the constant A_0.** If we integrate both sides of equation (*i*) between the limits $t = 0$ and $t = T$, we have

$$\int_0^T y\,dt = A_0\int_0^T dt + A_1\int_0^T \sin\omega t\,dt + \ldots + A_r\int_0^T \sin r\omega t\,dt$$

$$+ B_1\int_0^T \cos\omega t\,dt + \ldots + B_r\int_0^T \cos r\omega t\,dt = A_0 T,$$

the other integrals all vanishing to *zero* under the limits chosen.

We, therefore, have $$A_0 = \frac{1}{T}\int_0^T y\,dt,$$

where, clearly, A_0 *represents the mean value of the function* (*in our case, displacement*) *during a full time-period.*

So that, in the event of A_0 being equal to *zero*, the axis of the curve representing the function (the displacement curve, in the present case) would lie along the axis of time.

(*ii*) **Evaluation of constants** $A_1, A_2 \ldots A_r$. Multiplying equation (*i*) by $\sin r\omega t$, if we again integrate between the limits $t = 0$ and $t = T$, we have

$$\int_0^T y\sin r\omega t\,dt = A_0\int_0^T \sin r\omega t\,dt + A_1\int_0^T \sin\omega t\sin r\omega t\,dt\ldots$$

$$+A_r\int_0^T \sin^2 r\omega t\,dt + B_1\int_0^T \sin r\omega t\cos\omega t\,dt + \ldots B_r\int_0^T \sin r\omega t\cos r\omega t\,dt$$

Since all other integrals on the right hand side except $A_r\int_0^T \sin^2 r\omega t\,dt$ vanish to *zero* under the chosen limits, we have

$$\int_0^T y\sin r\omega t\,dt = A_r\int_0^T \sin^2 r\omega t\,dt = \frac{A_r}{2}\int_0^T (1-\cos 2r\omega t)\,dt = A_r \times T/2,$$

whence, $$A_r = \frac{2}{T}\int_0^T y\sin r\omega t\,dt = \frac{2}{T}\int_0^T y\sin\frac{2\pi rt}{T}\,dt. \qquad [\because \omega = 2\pi/T]$$

And, therefore, putting $r = 1, 2, 3$, etc., we can easily obtain the values of the coefficients A_1, A_2, A_3 etc.

(*iii*) **Evaluation of constants** $B_1, B_2, \ldots B_r$. Multiplying both sides of equation (*i*) by $\cos r\omega t$ and integrating between the limits $t = 0$ and $t = T$, we have

$$\int_0^T y\cos r\omega t\,dt = A_0\int_0^T \cos r\omega t\,dt + A_1\int_0^T \cos r\omega t\sin\omega t\,dt + \ldots$$

$$\sin r\omega t + A_r\int_0^T \cos r\omega t\,dt + B_1\int_0^T \cos r\omega t\cos\omega t\,dt + \ldots + B_r\int_0^T \cos^2 r\omega t\,dt.$$

Here also, since all the integrals on the right hand side, except $B_r\int_0^T \cos^2 r\omega t\,dt$ vanish to *zero* under the chosen limits, we have

$$\int_0^T y\cos r\omega t\,dt = B_r\int_0^T \cos^2 r\omega t\,dt = \frac{B_r}{2}\int_0^T (1+\cos 2r\omega t)dt = \frac{B_r}{2}\times T,$$

whence, $$B_r = \frac{2}{T}\int_0^T y\cos r\omega t\,dt = \frac{2}{T}\int_0^T y\cos\frac{2\pi rt}{T}\,dt. \qquad [\because \omega = 2\pi/T]$$

Again, putting $r = 1, 2, 3$, etc., we can easily obtain the values of the constants B_1, B_2, B_3 etc.

Incidentally, the very fact that these constants have particular fixed values for a given functions $f(t)$ constitutes a *formal proof of Fourier's theorem.*

N.B. The above process of determining the *Fourier constants* is obviously applicable if the function $f(t)$ can be put into an algebraic form, amenable to integration. In case this is not so, other methods, including a graphical one, are available, for, after all an integration is essentially the same thing as a summation or determination of the area under a curve.

Then, again, a Fourier series may also adopt other forms, *e.g.*, the form of a *series of sine terms or of cosine terms or even an exponential form.*

Thus, if we put $A_r = a_r \sin \phi_r$ and $B_r = a_r \cos \phi_r$, equation (i) takes the following form, consisting of *a constant or zero frequency term* A_0 *and the rest all sine terms*:

$$y = f(t) = A_0 + \sum_{r=1}^{\infty} a_r \sin(r\omega t + \phi_r)$$

$$= A_0 + a_1 \sin(\omega_t + \phi_1) + a_2 \sin(2\omega t + \phi_2) + \ldots a_r \sin(r\omega t + \phi_r).$$

where $a_1, a_2, \ldots a_r$ are the *amplitudes* and $\phi_1, \phi_2, \ldots \phi_r$, the *phase constants of* the constituent harmonic vibrations.

Clearly, $a_r = \sqrt{A_r^2 + B_r^2}$ and $\phi_r = A_r/B_r$. So that, if $A_r = 0$, we have $a_r = B_r$ and $\phi = 0$; and if $B_r = 0$, we have $a_r = A_r$ and $\phi_r = \pi/2$.

In the same manner, the Fourier series may also be expressed wholly as a series of cosine terms. These forms of the Fourier series lend themselves to a much easier physical interpretation than the others.

The *exponential form of Fourier series* may be obtained by putting $2 \sin \omega t = (e^{i\omega t} - e^{-i\omega t})$ and $2 \cos \omega t = (e^{i\omega t} + e^{-i\omega t})$. So that, equation ($i$) becomes

$$y = f(t) = A_0 + \sum_{r=1}^{\infty} A_r(e^{ir\omega t} - e^{-ir\omega t})/2i + \sum_{r=1}^{\infty} B_r(e^{ir\omega t} + e^{-ir\omega t})/2$$

$$= A_0 + \sum_{r=1}^{\infty} \frac{(B_r + iA_r)}{2} e^{-ir\omega t} + \sum_{r=1}^{\infty} \frac{(B_r - iA_r)}{2} e^{-ir\omega t}$$

$$= A_0 + \sum_{r=-1}^{-\infty} \frac{(B_r - iA_r)}{2} e^{ir\omega t} + \sum_{r=1}^{\infty} \frac{(B_r - iA_r)}{2} e^{ir\omega t}.$$

If we put $A_0 = C_o$ and $\dfrac{(B_r - iA_r)}{2} = C_r$, we have

$$y = f(t) = C_0 + \sum_{-\infty}^{\infty} C_r e^{ir\omega t},$$

which is the *exponential form of the Fourier series.*

10.35 SOME ILLUSTRATIVE EXAMPLES OF THE APPLICATION OF FOURIER'S THEOREM

Let us now take up a few examples of Fourier analysis of some typical types of curves.

(i) **The square wave.** Consider a *square wave* of the type shown in Fig. 10.22 (perhaps more appropriately called a *top-hat wave* because of its resemblance with the shape of a top hat).

Here, we have $y = f(t) = a$ from $t = 0$ to $t = T/2$ and $y = f(t) = -a$ from $t = T/2$ to $t = T$.

Now, as we know, the Fourier series gives

$$y = f(t) = A_0 + A_1 \sin \omega t + \ldots + A_r \sin r\omega t + B_1 \cos \omega t + \ldots + B_r \cos r\omega t.$$

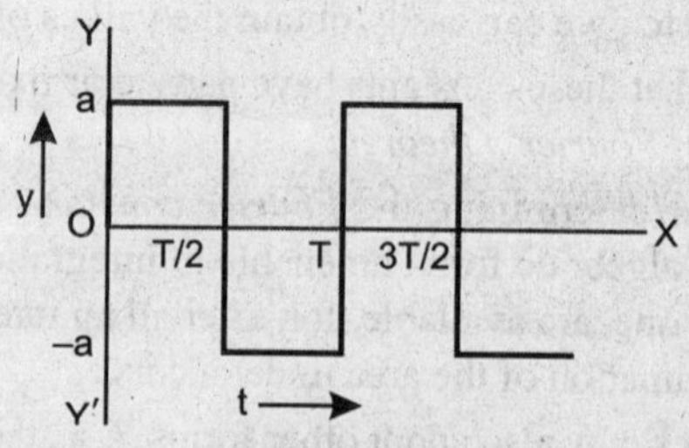

Fig. 10.22

Since $$A_0 = \frac{1}{T}\int_0^T y\,dt, \text{ we have}$$

$$A_0 = \frac{1}{T}\left[\int_0^{T/2} a\,dt - \int_{T/2}^{T} a\,dt\right] = 0,$$

indicating that *the mean value of the displacement over a time-period is zero* or that *the axis of the displacement curve coincides with the time-axis about which the wave is symmetrical.*

And, since $$A_r = \frac{2}{T}\int_0^T y\sin r\omega t\,dt, \text{ we have}$$

$$A_r = \frac{2}{T}\left[\int_0^{T/2} a\sin r\omega t\,dt - \int_{T/2}^{T} a\sin r\omega t\,dt\right]$$

$$= \frac{2a}{T}\left[\left(\frac{-\cos r\omega t}{r\omega}\right)_0^{T/2} + \left(\frac{\cos r\omega t}{r\omega}\right)_{T/2}^{T}\right]$$

$$= \frac{2a}{r\omega t}\left[\left(-\cos\frac{r\omega T}{2} + 1\right) + \left(\cos r\omega T - \cos\frac{r\omega T}{2}\right)\right]$$

Since $\omega = 2\pi/T$ or $\omega T = 2\pi$, we have

$$A_r = \frac{a}{\pi r}(2 - 2\cos\pi r) = \frac{2a}{\pi r}(1 - \cos\pi r)$$

For even values of r, therefore, $Ar = 0$ and for *odd values of r*, $A_r = 4a/\pi r$.

Again, since $$B_r = \frac{2}{T}\int_0^T y\cos r\omega t\,dt, \text{ we have}$$

$$B_r = \frac{2}{T}\left[\int_0^{T} a\cos r\omega t\,dt - \int_{T/2}^{T} a\cos r\omega t\,dt\right]$$

$$= \frac{2a}{T}\left[\left(\frac{\sin r\omega t}{r\omega}\right)_0^{T/2} - \left(\frac{\sin r\omega t}{r\omega}\right)_{T/2}^{T}\right]$$

$$= \frac{2a}{r\omega t}\left[\left(\sin\frac{r\omega T}{2} - 0\right) - \left(\sin r\omega T - \sin\frac{r\omega T}{2}\right)\right]$$

Since $\omega = 2\pi/T$ or $\omega T = 2\pi$, we have

$$B_r = \frac{a}{\pi r}\times 0 = 0.$$

Thus, we have $A_0 = 0, A_1 = 4a/\pi, A_2 = 0, A_3 = 4a/3\pi, A_4 = 0, A_5 = 4a/5\pi$ and so on, and $B_1, B_2, B_3 \ldots B_r$, *all equal to zero i.e., the cosine terms are all absent.* The full Fourier series in this case, therefore becomes $y = \frac{4a}{\pi}\left(\sin\omega t + \frac{1}{3}\sin 3\omega t + \frac{1}{5}\sin 5\omega t + \ldots\right)$.

Or, $$y = \frac{4a}{\pi}\left(\sin\frac{2\pi t}{T} + \frac{1}{3}\sin\frac{6\pi t}{T} + \frac{1}{5}\sin\frac{10\pi t}{T} + \ldots\right),$$

clearly showing that *the combination here is that of the fundamental and its odd harmonics.* In other words, *the ratios of the frequencies of the constituents are proportional to the odd values of r and their amplitudes to their reciprocals, i.e., their frequencies are as* 1 : 3 : 5 *and their amplitudes as* $1 : \frac{1}{3} : \frac{1}{5}$.

A superposition of the displacement curves (or harmonic waves) representing these constituents should thus give the square wave in question.

Thus, in Fig. 10.23, *curves* (1) represents the simple harmonic wave corresponding to $y_1 = \frac{4a}{\pi}\sin\omega t$, the *dotted curve* (2) represents the simple harmonic wave corresponding to $y_3 = \frac{4a}{3\pi}\sin\omega t$, having $\frac{1}{3}$rd the amplitude and *thrice the frequency of the first*, and curve (3) represents the simple harmonic wave, corresponding to $y_5 = \frac{4a}{5\pi}\sin 5\omega t$, with $\frac{1}{5}$th the amplitude and five times the frequency of the first, those corresponding to y_2, y_4, etc. being absent. Their superposition then givens the thick full line curve, which bears only a partial resemblance with the given square wave.

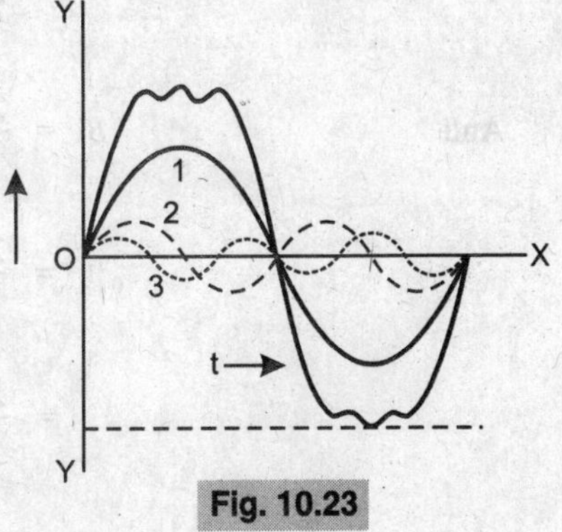

Fig. 10.23

If, however, we add up or superimpose more waves corresponding to y_7, y_9, y_{11} etc, the resultant wave assumes a shape more and more resembling the given square wave. So that, with a still larger number of them, thus superposed, we shall obtain the square wave we have analysed.

(*ii*) **The saw tooth wave.** This wave, (Fig. 10.24) is obviously so called because of its shape and is commonly met with in electronics.

As will be readily seen, here, $y = a$ at $t = 0$, then falls linearly to *zero* at $t = T$. So that, $y = 0$ at $t = T$.

Let the displacement at time t be y. Then, clearly,

$$\frac{y}{a} = \frac{T-t}{T} = \left(1 - \frac{t}{T}\right).$$

So the equation of the wave is

$$y = f(t) = a\left(1 - \frac{t}{T}\right).$$

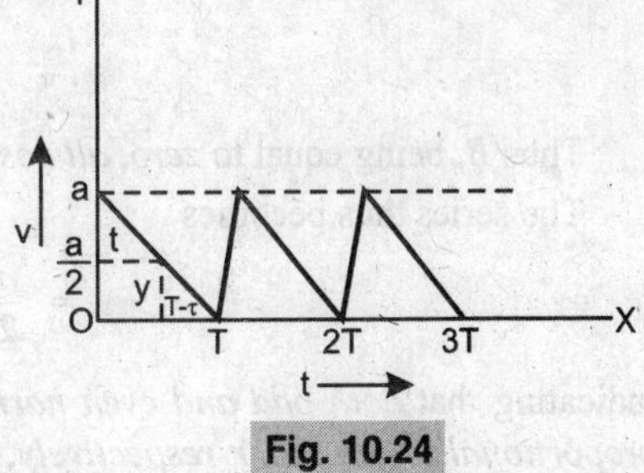

Fig. 10.24

Now, in the *Fourier series* $y = A_0 + A_1 \sin\omega t + \ldots A_r \sin r\omega t + B_1 \cos\omega t + \ldots B_r \cos r\omega t$. Since $A_0 = \frac{1}{T}\int_0^T y\,dt$, we have

$$A_0 = \frac{1}{T}\int_0^T a\left(1 - \frac{t}{T}\right)dt = \frac{a}{T}\left[t - \frac{t^2}{2T}\right]_0^T = \frac{a}{T}\left[T - \frac{T^2}{2T}\right] = \frac{a}{T}\left[\frac{T}{2}\right] = \frac{a}{2},$$

indicating that *the mean value of the displacement over a time-period is a/2 or that the axis of the displacement curve lies at a distance a/2 from the time axis.*

And, clearly, $$A_r = \frac{2}{T}\int_0^T y \sin r\omega t\, dt = \frac{2a}{T}\int_0^T\left(1-\frac{t}{T}\right)\sin r\omega t\, at$$

$$= \frac{2a}{T}\int_0^T \sin r\omega t\, dt - \frac{2a}{T^2}\int_0^T t\sin r\omega t\, dt = \frac{2a}{T}\left[\frac{-\cos r\omega t}{r\omega}\right]_0^T$$

$$-\frac{2a}{T^2}\left[\frac{-t\cos r\omega t}{r\omega}\right]_0^T - \frac{2a}{T^2}\int_0^T \frac{-\cos r\omega t}{r\omega}dt$$

$$= \frac{2a}{Tr\omega}[-\cos r\omega t + \cos 0] - \frac{2a}{Tr\omega}[-\cos r\omega T + 0] - \frac{2a}{T^2}\left[\frac{-\sin r\omega t}{r^2\omega^2} + 0\right]$$

$$= \frac{2a}{Tr\omega}(-\cos r\omega T + 1) - \frac{2a}{Tr\omega}(-\cos r\omega T + 0) = 0$$

$$= \frac{2a}{Tr\omega}[(1-\cos r\omega T) + 1] = \frac{2a}{Tr\omega}(2 - \cos r\omega T).$$

Since $\omega T = 2\pi$, and, therefore, $\cos r\omega T = 1$, we have

$$A_r = \frac{2a}{Tr\omega}(2-1) = \frac{2a}{Tr\omega} = \frac{2a}{T.r.2\pi/T} = a/r\pi.$$

And $$B_r = \frac{2a}{T}\int_0^T y\cos r\omega t\, dt = \frac{2a}{T}\int_0^T\left(1-\frac{t}{T}\right)\cos r\omega t\, dt$$

$$= \frac{2a}{T}\int_0^T \cos r\omega t\, dt - \frac{2a}{T^2}\int_0^T t\cos r\omega t\, dt$$

$$= \frac{2a}{T}\left[\frac{\sin r\omega t}{r\omega}\right]_0^T - \frac{2a}{T^2}\left[\frac{t\sin r\omega t}{r\omega}\right]_0^T - \frac{2a}{T^2}\int_0^T \frac{\sin r\omega t}{r\omega}dt$$

$$= \frac{2a}{Tr\omega}[\sin r\pi - \sin 0] - \frac{2a}{Tr\omega}(\sin r\pi - \sin 0)$$

$$+\frac{2a}{T^2}\left[\frac{\cos r\omega T - \cos 0}{r^2\omega^2}\right] = 0 - 0 + 0 = 0. \quad [\because \omega T = 2\pi]$$

Thus B_r being equal to *zero, all cosine terms of the Fourier series are absent.* The series thus becomes

$$y = \frac{a}{2} + \frac{a}{\pi}\left(\sin\omega t + \frac{1}{2}\sin 2\omega t + \frac{1}{3}\sin 3\omega t + ...\right),$$

indicating that *both odd and even harmonics are present, with their amplitudes and frequencies proportional to* $1/r$ and r *respectively, i.e.,* the frequencies are as 1 : 2 : 3... *and amplitudes as* $1 : \frac{1}{2} : \frac{1}{3} : ....$

Here too, therefore, the superposition of all these constituent harmonic waves should give the given saw-tooth wave. We find, however, that with the superposition of six constituent waves, we obtain a curve of the form shown in Fig. 10.25 (*a*), with only a particle resemblance

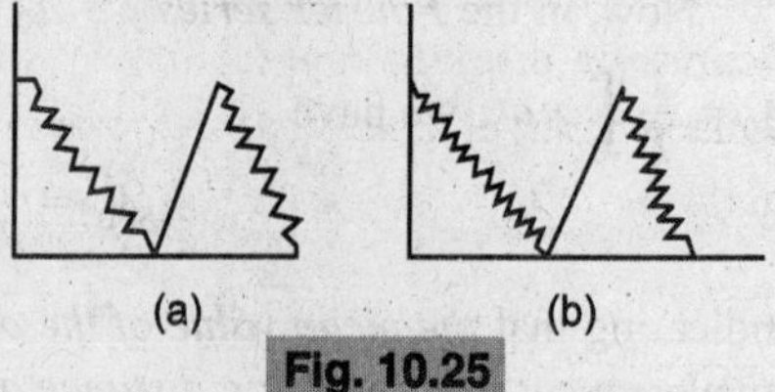

Fig. 10.25

with the given saw-tooth wave. But superposition of 10 or more constituent waves results in its acquiring a closer identity with the given form of the wave, as can be seen from Fig. 10.25 (*b*). If therefore, a still larger number of the constituent waves be superposed, we shall obtain the exact form of the saw-tooth wave analysed.

N.B. Some other types of waves are dealt with under worked examples at the end of the chapter.

10.36 GROUP VELOCITY—ITS RELATIONSHIP WITH WAVE (OR PHASE) VELOCITY

We know that the equation of a plane progressive harmonic wave, travelling in a medium along the positive direction of the *x*-axis is $y = a\sin\frac{2\pi}{\lambda}(vt - x)$, where v is the wave velocity, equal to λ/T.

Let us now put this equation in a slightly different form.

We have from the above, $$y = a\sin\left(\frac{2\pi vt}{\lambda} - \frac{2\pi}{\lambda}x\right)$$

Since $v/\lambda = 1/T = n$, the *frequency* of the wave, and $2\pi/\lambda = k$, the *propagation constant*,* the wave equation takes the form

$$y = a\sin(2\pi nt - kx).$$

Or, since $2\pi n = \omega$, the *angular frequency* of the wave, we have

$$y = a\sin(\omega t - kx),$$

showing that the constant phase $(\omega t - kx)$, of the wave travels along the positive direction of the *x*-axis with velocity dx/dt, *i.e.*, the *phase velocity of the wave* = dx/dt.

Now, since $\omega t - kx$ = constant, we have (on differentiating with respect to t), $\omega - k(dx/dt) = 0$. Or, $\omega = k\,dx/dt$, whence, *phase velocity of the wave* = $dx/dt = \omega/k$.

But $\frac{\omega}{k} = \frac{2\pi n}{2\pi/\lambda} = n\lambda = \lambda/T$ = wave velocity v.

Thus, for a single wave, *in any given medium*,

Wave velocity = Phase velocity = $v = \lambda/T = \omega/k$.

Let us now consider the case of two (or more) wave trains, of slightly different wavelengths, λ and $(\lambda + d\lambda)$, say, [Fig. 10.26 (*a*)], travelling simultaneously along the same path in a given medium, and, for the sake of simplicity, let their amplitudes be equal.

Then, if the medium be *non-dispersive*, *i.e.*, if the velocity of the wave in it does *not* depend upon the wavelength, both the waves travel through it with the same wave (or phase) velocity v.

Since they are both travelling *along the same path* and in the same direction, they get superposed, one over the other (although they have been shown separately in the figure).

This is a case, it will be recalled, exactly similar to that of the formation of *beats* in the case of sound waves. For, at certain points of the medium, where the positive or negative maximum displacements of the two waves come across each other, they get reinforced and we obtain the maxima of displacement of the resulting wave. And, at points where the positive maximum displacements of one wave come across the negative maximum displacements of the other, we obtain the minimum or zero displacement of the resulting wave.

* It is also sometimes referred to as the wave number (see 10.4)

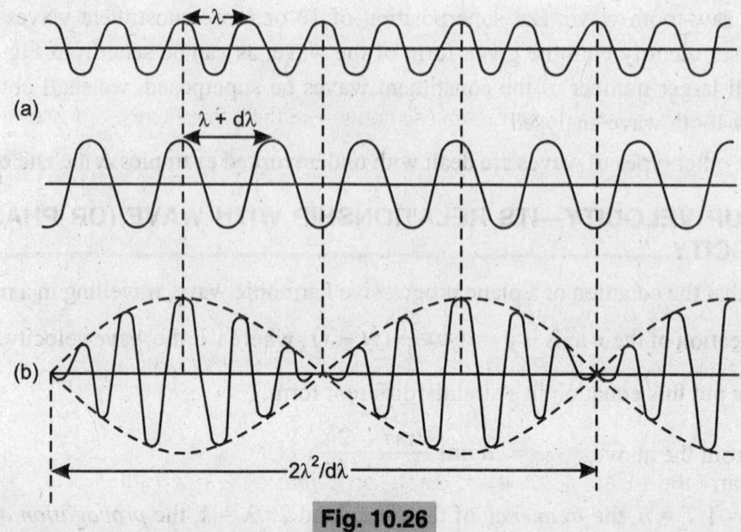

Fig. 10.26

In between these two extremes, the displacements in the resulting wave have intermediate value. The resulting wave or the '*beat wave*' thus consists of groups of waves, shown by the dotted curves in Fig. 10.26 (*b*), each group consisting of a number of waves, with the displacements in the wave at the centre of the group the maximum, with those of the others trailing off gradually to zero on either side, as shown. *The velocity with which the maxima of these groups of waves travel is called the* **group velocity** (*u*) *of the resultant wave.*

In the case we are considering, *i.e.*, in which the two waves are travelling in a *non-dispersive* medium so that their velocities are the same, the resultant wave, consisting of groups of waves, also travels with the same velocity as that of each constituent wave and the shape or profile of the groups, therefore, continues to be maintained throughout. In other words, *the group velocity u is, in this case, equal to the phase velocity v of each wave.* (*We shall presently see this mathematically also.*)

In case, however, the medium be a *dispersive* one, so that the velocities of the two waves of wavelengths λ and (λ + *d*λ) be *v* and (*v* + *dv*) respectively, their wave equations are

$$y_1 = a\sin\frac{2\pi}{\lambda}(vt - x) \text{ and } y_2 = a\sin\frac{2\pi}{(\lambda + d\lambda)}[(v + dv)\,t - x]$$

The equation of the resultant wave (consisting of groups of waves) is thus

$$y = y_1 + y_2 = a\sin\frac{2\pi}{\lambda}(vt - x) + a\sin\frac{2\pi}{(\lambda + d\lambda)}[(v + dv)t - x].$$

Or,
$$y = 2\,a\sin\pi\left\{\left(\frac{v}{\lambda} + \frac{v + dv}{\lambda + d\lambda}\right)t - x\left(\frac{1}{\lambda} + \frac{1}{\lambda + d\lambda}\right)\right\}$$

$$\times\cos\pi\left\{\left(\frac{v}{\lambda} - \frac{v + dv}{\lambda + d\lambda}\right)t - x\left(\frac{1}{\lambda} - \frac{1}{\lambda + d\lambda}\right)\right\} \quad ...(A)$$

Now, $\frac{v}{\lambda} + \frac{v + dv}{\lambda + d\lambda} = \frac{v\lambda + vd\lambda + v\lambda + dv\lambda}{\lambda(\lambda + d\lambda)} = \frac{2v\lambda}{\lambda^2} = \frac{2v}{\lambda}$ very nearly, neglecting the comparatively very small terms;

$$\frac{v}{\lambda} - \frac{v + dv}{\lambda + d\lambda} = \frac{v\lambda + vd\lambda - v\lambda - dv\lambda}{\lambda(\lambda + d\lambda)} = \frac{vd\lambda - \lambda dv}{\lambda^2} \text{ very nearly;}$$

$$\frac{1}{\lambda} + \frac{1}{\lambda + d\lambda} = \frac{\lambda + d\lambda + \lambda}{\lambda(\lambda + d\lambda)} = \frac{2\lambda}{\lambda^2} = \frac{2}{\lambda} \text{ very nearly,}$$

and $$\frac{1}{\lambda} - \frac{1}{\lambda + d\lambda} = \frac{\lambda + d\lambda - \lambda}{\lambda(\lambda + d\lambda)} = \frac{d\lambda}{\lambda^2} \text{ very nearly.}$$

Substituting these values in expression (*A*) above, we therefore have

$$y = 2\,a \sin \pi\left(\frac{2vt}{\lambda} - \frac{2x}{\lambda}\right) \cos x \left\{\left(\frac{vd\lambda - \lambda dv}{\lambda^2}\right) t - \frac{xd\lambda}{\lambda^2}\right\}$$

Or, $$y = 2a \sin \frac{2\pi}{\lambda}(vt - x) \cos \frac{2\pi}{2\lambda^2/d\lambda}\left\{\left(v - \lambda \frac{dv}{d\lambda}\right) t - x\right\}$$

If we put $2\,a \sin \dfrac{2\pi}{\lambda}\,(vt - x) = a'$, $2\,\lambda^2/d\lambda = \lambda'$ and $\left(v - \lambda \dfrac{dv}{d\lambda}\right) = u$,

we have $$y = a' \cos \frac{2\pi}{\lambda'}(ut - x).$$

This is clearly the equation of a wave having an *amplitude* $a = 2\,a \sin \dfrac{2\pi}{\lambda}\,(vt - x)$, *wave length* $\lambda' = 2\,\lambda^2/d\lambda$ and velocity $u = v - \lambda \dfrac{dv}{d\lambda}$.

This means, in other words, that (*i*) *the resultant wave or the beat wave (shown dotted) is divided up into groups, with each group consisting of waves represented by the equation* $y = 2\,a \sin \dfrac{2\pi}{\lambda}\,(vt - x)$ *and its amplitude a′ varying accordingly*, and (*ii*) *the wavelength of the resultant wave is* $2\lambda^2/d\lambda$ and *its velocity i.e., the group velocity* $u = v - \lambda\, dv/d\lambda$.

Thus, group velocity (*u*) = wave velocity (*v*) – $\lambda\, dv/d\lambda$**, which is the required relation between group velocity and wave (or phase)** velocity *in a dispersive medium.*

Since in *a non-dispersive medium,* there is no change in velocity with wavelength, $dv/d\lambda = 0$. Hence, in such a medium, *group velocity = wave* (or phase) velocity and the wave groups continue to travel through the medium with their form or profile intact, as for example, in the case of sound waves in any homogeneous medium or light waves in vacuum.

In a *dispersive medium*, on the other hand, since velocity, in general, increases with wavelength, $dv/d\lambda$ is positive and, therefore, *the group velocity is, in general, less than the wave* (*or phase*) *velocity*. The wave groups in this case, therefore, do not retain their form or profile which keeps on changing as the wave advances.

Alternatively, we may also express group velocity *u* in another form. For, as we have just seen, $u = v - \lambda\, dv/d\lambda$. If, therefore, we denote the wavelengths of the two constituent waves by λ_1 and λ_2 and their velocities by v_1 and v_2 respectively, we have

$$u = v_1 - \lambda_1 \frac{(v_2 - v_1)}{(\lambda_2 - \lambda_1)} = \frac{v_1\lambda_2 - v_1\lambda_1 - v_2\lambda_1 + v_1\lambda_1}{\lambda_2 - \lambda_1} = \frac{v_1\lambda_2 - v_2\lambda_1}{\lambda_2 - \lambda_1}$$

$$= \frac{v_1/\lambda_1 - v_2/\lambda_2}{1/\lambda_1 - 1/\lambda_2}$$

Or, $$u = \frac{(2\pi/\lambda_1)v_1 - (2\pi/\lambda_2)v_2}{2\pi/\lambda_1 - 2\pi/\lambda_2}$$

Since $2\pi/\pi = k$, we have $u = \dfrac{v_1k_1 - v_2k_2}{k_1 - k_2}$.

Again, since $(2\pi/\lambda)v = (2\pi/\lambda)n\lambda = 2\pi n = \omega$, we have $u = \dfrac{\omega_1 - \omega_2}{k_1 - k_2}$, which, in the event of the frequencies and propagation constants being really small, reduces, in the limit, to $u = d\omega/dk = \frac{\Delta\omega}{\Delta k}$

Thus, *whereas the wave (or phase) velocity v, as we have been before, is given by ω/k, the group velocity u is given by its first derivative with respect to k.*

Again, *in a non-dispersive* medium, since wave (or phase) velocity v is the same for all wavelengths, $v = \omega/k$ = constant or $\omega = vk$ and, therefore, *group velocity* $u = d\omega/dk = v$, *i.e., group velocity = wave (or phase) velocity.*

In a dispersive medium, on the other hand, u may be greater or smaller than v.

Further, we may also put $v = d\omega/dk = d(vk)/dk = v + k\, dv/dk$, which again gives $u = v - \lambda\, dv/d\lambda$.

It may as well be pointed out here that whereas it is possible, in some cases, for the phase velocity to be higher than the velocity of light (c), the group velocity can never exceed c. Since it is the group velocity we actually measure by our experiments, the value obtained can never be higher than c.

Thus, taking the case of x-rays (or electromagnetic waves, including light waves, in general, their phase velocity through a carbon block works out to be greater than c but not their group velocity, (see worked example 52). This only shows that although the phase of the waves may travel faster in a medium than the velocity of light c, their velocity of propagation, *i.e.*, the velocity of the wave groups, in the form of which they actually travel through the medium, can never exceed c.

10.37 GROUP VELOCITY IN A CONDUCTING MEDIUM

The wave velocity is given by

$$v = \frac{1}{\sqrt{\varepsilon_r.\mu}} = \frac{1}{\sqrt{\varepsilon_r}} = \varepsilon_r^{-1/2} \quad \text{(for conducting medium } \mu = 1)$$

Differentiating w.r to λ, we get

$$\frac{dv}{d\lambda} = -\frac{1}{2}\varepsilon_r^{-3/2}\frac{d\varepsilon_r}{d\lambda} = -\frac{1}{2\varepsilon_r}.\varepsilon_r^{-1/2}.\frac{d\varepsilon_r}{d\lambda}$$

$$= -v.\frac{1}{2\varepsilon_r}.\frac{d\varepsilon_r}{d\lambda}$$

Now, group velocity, $$v_g = v - \lambda\frac{dv}{d\lambda}$$

$$= v + \lambda v\frac{1}{2\varepsilon_r}.\frac{d\varepsilon_r}{d\lambda}$$

$$= v\left[1 + \frac{\lambda}{2\varepsilon_r}.\frac{d\varepsilon_r}{d\lambda}\right]$$

As the quantity in bracket is greater than 1, $v_g > v$. This is the case of *anomalous dispersion.*

WORKED EXAMPLES

I–Plane progressive harmonic waves

Example 1. If a wave of frequency 500 Hz is travelling with a velocity of 200 ms^{-1}, then find the change in phase at a given point in space between a time interval of 10^{-3} see. Also find the path difference between two points which differ in phase by $\frac{\pi}{2}$ radian. (*PU.*, 2002)

Solution. At a given point in space, the change in phase is 2π during a time interval T, the time period of wave motion.

$\therefore$ For a time interval t, phase change $\phi = \frac{2\pi}{T}t$

Here frequency of the wave $n = 500$ Hz

$\therefore$ Time period $T = \frac{1}{n} = \frac{1}{500}$ sec

Hence phase change in a time interval 10^{-3} sec, $\phi = \frac{2\pi}{T}t$

$$= 2\pi \times 10^{-3} \times 500 = \pi \text{ radian}$$

At a given time, the phase difference two points separated by a distance λ, the wavelength of the wave $= 2\pi$.

$\therefore$ For two points separated by a distance x, phase difference

$$\phi = \frac{2\pi}{\lambda}x$$

Here $\phi = \frac{\pi}{2}$; $\lambda = \frac{v}{n} = \frac{200 \text{ ms}^{-1}}{500 \text{ s}^{-1}} = 0.4$ m

$$\frac{\pi}{2} = \frac{2\pi}{0.4}x \text{ or path difference } x = 0.1 \text{ m}$$

Example 2. A simple harmonic wave travelling along *X*-axis is given by

$$y = 5 \sin 2\pi (0.2\, t - 0.5\, x).$$

Calculate the amplitude, frequency wavelength, wave velocity, particle velocity, velocity amplitude, particle acceleration and acceleration amplitude (*x* is in metres and *t* in seconds).

(*P.U. 2005*)

Solution. The given equation is

$$y = 5 \sin 2\pi (0.2\, t - 0.5\, x) \text{ m}$$

Comparing with the equation

$$y = a \sin \frac{2\pi}{\lambda}(vt - x)$$

$$= a \sin 2\pi\left(\frac{vt}{\lambda} - \frac{x}{\lambda}\right) = a \sin 2\pi\left(nt - \frac{x}{\lambda}\right)$$

We have

Amplitude $a = 5$ m

Frequency $n = 0.2 \text{ s}^{-1}$

Now $\frac{x}{\lambda} = 0.5\, x$

$\therefore$ Wave length $\lambda = \frac{1}{0.5} = 2$ m

Wave velocity $v = n\lambda = 0.2 \times 2 = 0.4 \text{ ms}^{-1}$

Particle velocity $= \frac{dy}{dt} = 5 \cos 2\pi (0.2\, t - 0.5\, x) \times 0.2$

$= \cos 2\pi (0.2\, t - 0.5\, x) \text{ ms}^{-1}$

Particle velocity amplitude $= 1 \text{ ms}^{-1}$

Particle acceleration $= \frac{d^2y}{dt^2} = -\sin 2\pi (0.2\, t - 0.5\, x) \times 0.2$

$$= -0.2 \sin 2\pi (0.2\,t - 0.5\,x) \text{ ms}^{-2}$$

Particle acceleration amplitude $= -0.2 \text{ ms}^{-2}$

Example 3. Find the amplitude, frequency velocity and wavelength of the transfer wave in a string represented by

$$y = 5 \sin 2\pi (t - 0.04\,x) \text{ in S.I. units.} \qquad \textit{(P.U., 2001)}$$

Solution. Compare with Eq. $y = a \sin 2\pi \left(nt - \frac{x}{\lambda} \right)$

Amplitude $a = 5$ m;

Frequency $n = 1 \text{ s}^{-1}$

Wavelength $\lambda = \frac{1}{0.04} = 25$ m

Velocity $v = n\lambda = 25 \text{ ms}^{-1}$

Example 4. Write down the equation of wave travelling in the negative direction along *X*-axis and having an amplitude 0.01 m, a frequency 550 Hz and speed 330 m/s.

(Luck. U., 1995)

Solution. The equation of a wave travelling in the negative *X*-direction is

$$y = a \sin \frac{2\pi}{\lambda} (vt + x)$$

Now $a = 0.01$ m, $v = 330 \text{ m s}^{-1}$, $n = 550$ Hz

$$\therefore \quad \lambda = \frac{v}{n} = \frac{330}{550} = \frac{3}{5} \text{m}$$

Substituting, we get

$$y = 0.01 \sin \left[2\pi \times \frac{5}{3} (330t + x) \right]$$

Or

$$y = 0.01 \sin 2\pi \left(550t + \frac{5}{3} x \right)$$

Examples 5. The displacement equation for a transverse plane wave at any instant is $y(x, t) = 0.03 \sin(3\pi t - 0.03\pi x)$ where *x* and *t* are in metres and seconds. Calculate wavelength, frequency and velocity of the wave. Also calculate phase difference between two particles 0.05 metre apart at same instant. ***(P.U. 2000)***

Solution. The general displacement equation for a transverse plane wave is given by

$$y = a \sin \frac{2\pi}{\lambda} (vt - x) = a \sin \left(2\pi \frac{v}{\lambda} t - \frac{2\pi}{\lambda} x \right)$$

$$= a \sin \left(2\pi\, nt - \frac{2\pi}{\lambda} x \right)$$

Comparing with the given equation

$$y(x, t) = 0.03 \sin (3\pi t - 0.03\pi x)$$

we have $2\pi n = 3\pi$

or $n = \frac{3}{2} = 1.5$ Hertz

$$\frac{2\pi}{\lambda} = 0.03\,\pi$$

or $$\lambda = \frac{2}{0.03} = 66\frac{2}{3}\text{ m}$$

Velocity $$v = n\lambda = \frac{3}{2} \times \frac{200}{3} = 100\text{ ms}^{-1}$$

Phase difference between tw0o particles $x = 0.05$ m apart

$$\phi = \frac{2\pi}{\lambda}x = 0.03\,\pi \times 0.05 = .0015\,\pi$$

Example 6. Equation of a plane progressive wave is given below

$$y = 10 \sin \pi\,[0.01\,x - 2.00\,t]$$

where *y* and *x* are expressed in cm and *t* in seconds. Determine (*i*) amplitude of the wave (*ii*) frequency of the wave (*iii*) phase difference at an instant between two points 40 cm apart.

(*Indore U., 2001*)

Solution. The given equation can be written as

$$y = -10 \sin 2\pi\,[1.00\,t - 0.005\,x]$$

∴ Amplitude $$a = 10\text{ cm}$$

Frequency $$n = 1\text{ s}^{-1}.$$

$$\lambda = \frac{1}{.005} = 200\text{ cm}$$

Hence phase difference $$\phi = \frac{2\pi}{\lambda}x = \frac{2\pi}{200} \times 40 = \frac{2}{5}\pi\text{ rad.}$$

Example 7. A wave of frequency 400 Hz is travelling with a velocity 800 m/s. How far are two points situated whose displacement differ in phase by $\frac{\pi}{4}$? (*P.U. 2002*)

Solution. Frequency of the wave $n = 400$ Hz

Velocity of the wave $$v = 800\text{ ms}^{-1}$$

∴ Wavelength $$\lambda = \frac{v}{n} = \frac{800}{400} = 2\text{ m}$$

Phase difference between two points a distance x apart

$$\phi = \frac{2\pi}{\lambda}x$$

∴ For the displacement to differ in phase by $\frac{\pi}{4}$

$$\phi = \frac{\pi}{4} = \frac{2\pi}{2}x$$

or $$x = \frac{1}{4}\text{ m} = 0.25\text{ m}$$

Example 8. (*a*) Show that $y = x^2 + c^2 t^2$ is a solution of one dimensional wave equation.

(*P.U., 2002*)

(*b*) Prove that 10 sin *kx* cos *ct* cannot be a solution to the one dimensional wave equation (*k* and *c* are constants). (*P.U., 2000 2001,*)

Solution. $$y = x^2 + c^2 t^2$$

∴ $$\frac{dy}{dt} = 2c^2 t \text{ and } \frac{d^2y}{dt^2} = 2c^2$$

Again $$\frac{dy}{dx} = 2x \text{ and } \frac{d^2y}{dx^2} = 2$$

Hence $$\frac{d^2y}{dt^2} = c^2\frac{d^2y}{dx^2}$$

which is the dimensional wave equation for a wave travelling along x-axis with a velocity c.

Hence $y = x^2 + c^2 t^2$ is a solution of one dimensional wave equation.

(*b*) $y = 10 \sin kx \cos ct$

$$\therefore \quad \frac{dy}{dt} = -10\, c \sin kx \sin ct \text{ and } \frac{d^2y}{dt^2} = -10\, c^2 \sin kx \cos ct = -c^2 y$$

Again $$\frac{dy}{dx} = 10\, k \cos kx.\cos ct \text{ and } \frac{d^2y}{dx^2} = -10\, k^2 \sin kx \cos ct = -k^2 y$$

$$\therefore \quad \frac{d^2y}{dt^2} = \frac{c^2}{k^2}\frac{d^2y}{dx^2}$$

This equation does not satisfy one dimensional wave equation.

$\therefore$ $y = 10 \sin kx \cos ct$ cannot be a solution to one dimensional wave equation.

Example 9. A train of simple harmonic waves is travelling in a gas along the positive direction of the *x*-axis, with an amplitude equal to 2 cm, velocity 300 metres/sec and frequency 400 Hz. Calculate the displacement, particle velocity and particle acceleration at a distance of 4 cm from the origin after an interval of 5 seconds.

Solution (*i*) Displacement. As we know, in a simple harmonic wave, the displacement of a particle at a distance x from the origin, after time t, is given by $y = a \sin\frac{2\pi}{\lambda}(vt - x)$, where a is the *amplitude* of the wave, λ, its *wavelength* and v, its *velocity* in the given medium.

Here, $a = 2$ cm, $v = 300$ m/sec. $= 30000$ cm/sec, frequency $n = 400$ Hz and, therefore, *wave length* $\lambda = v/n = 30000/400 = 75$ cm, $x = 4$ cm and $t = 5$ sec. So that,

$$\begin{aligned} y &= 2 \sin \frac{2x}{75}(30000 \times 5 - 4) = 2 \sin\left(\frac{2\pi}{75} \times 149996\right) \\ &= 2 \sin (2\pi \times 1999.9) \\ &= 2 \sin (1999 \times 2\pi + 0.9 \times 2\pi) = 2 \sin (1.8\pi) = 2 \sin (\pi + 0.8\pi) \\ &= -2 \sin (0.8\pi) = -2 \sin (0.8\pi \times 180/\pi)^\circ = -2 \sin 144^\circ \\ &= -2 \sin (180 - 144)^\circ = -2 \sin 36^\circ = -2 \times 0.5878 = -1.1756 \text{ cm.} \end{aligned}$$

Thus, *the displacement of the particle at a distance of* 4 cm *from the origin, after an internal of 5 second is* -1.1756 cm.

(*ii*) **Particle velocity.** We know that *particle velocity U*

$$= \frac{dy}{dt} = \frac{2\pi v}{\lambda} a \cos\frac{2\pi}{\lambda}(vt - x).$$

Now, as we have seen under (*i*) above, $\sin \frac{2\pi}{\lambda}(vt - x) = \sin 36^\circ$, so that,

$\frac{2\pi}{\lambda}(vt - x) = 36^\circ$ and, therefore, $\cos\frac{2\pi}{\lambda}(vt - x) = \cos 36^\circ = 0.8090$,

$\therefore$ *particle velocity* $U = \frac{2\pi v}{\lambda} a \cos 36^\circ = \frac{2\pi \times 30000}{75} \times 2 \times 0.8090 = 4068$ cm/sec

$= 40.86$ m/sec.

(*iii*) **Particle acceleration.** Clearly, *particle acceleration* $= \dfrac{dv}{dt} = \dfrac{d^2y}{dt^2}$

$$= -\frac{4\pi^2 v^2}{\lambda^2} a \sin\frac{2\pi}{\lambda}(vt - x) = -(4\pi^2 v^2/\lambda^2)\, y.$$

Since $y = -1.1756$ cm, we have *particle acceleration* $= -\dfrac{4\pi^2 (30000)^2}{75^2}(-1.1756)$

$$= 7.429 \times 10^6 \text{ cm/sec}^2.$$

Example 10. A wave of frequency 500 cycles/sec has a phase velocity of 360 metres/sec. (*a*) How far apart are two points 60° out of phase? (*b*) What is the phase difference between two displacements at a certain point at times 10^{-3} sec apart?

Solution. (*a*) We have the equation $y = a \sin \dfrac{2\pi}{\lambda}(vt - x)$ representing a simple harmonic wave, where *a* is the *amplitude* and $\dfrac{2x}{\lambda}(vt - x)$, the *phase angle* of a point distance *x* from the origin at time *t*.

$\therefore$ phase angle of a point distant x_1 from the origin at time $t = \dfrac{2\pi}{\lambda}(vt - x_1)$ and phase angle of a point distant x_2 from the origin at time $t = \dfrac{2\pi}{\lambda}(vt - x_2)$

Hence *phase difference between the two points* $= \dfrac{2\pi}{\lambda}(vt - x_1) - \dfrac{2\pi}{\lambda}(vt - x_2)$

$$\frac{2\pi}{\lambda}(x_2 - x_1) = \frac{2\pi v}{\lambda}\frac{(x_2 - x_1)}{v} = 2\pi n\left(\frac{x_2 - x_1}{v}\right),$$

because, as we know, $v = n\lambda$ and, therefore $v/\lambda = r$.

Here, the phase difference between the two points is given to be 60°

$$= \frac{60 \times \pi}{180} = \frac{\pi}{3} \text{ radian.}$$

We, therefore, have $2\pi n \dfrac{(x_2 - x_1)}{v} = \dfrac{\pi}{3}$. Or, $2n \dfrac{(x_2 - x_1)}{v} = \dfrac{1}{3}$

Since $n = 500$ and $v = 360$ m/sec = 36000 cm/sec, we have

$$\frac{2 \times 500\,(x_2 - x_1)}{36000} = \frac{1}{3}. \text{ Or, } (x_2 - x_1) = 36/3 = 12.0 \text{ cm.}$$

Thus, *the two points* 60° *out of phase are* 12.0 cm *apart.*

(*b*) Again, phase angle at a point distant *x* from the origin at time $t_1 = \dfrac{2\pi}{\lambda}(vt_1 - x)$ and phase angle at the same point at time $t_2 = \dfrac{2\pi}{\lambda}(vt_2 - x)$

$\therefore$ phase difference at the point at times $(t_2 - t_1)$ *sec* apart

$$= \frac{2\pi}{\lambda}(vt_2 - x) - \frac{2\pi}{\lambda}(vt_1 - x) = \frac{2\pi v}{\lambda}(t_2 - t_1) = 2\pi n\,(t_2 - t_1)$$

Here, $(t_2 - t_1) = 10^{-3}$ sec and, therefore,

phase difference between displacements at the point at times 10^{-3} sec *apart*

$$= 2\pi \times 500 \times 1/1000 = \pi \text{ radian} = 180°.$$

Example 11. (*a*) Obtain the value of (*i*) frequency, (*ii*) time-period, (*iii*) wave number (in the sense of waves per cm), (*iv*) propagation constant and (*v*) angular frequency for light waves of wavelength 5000 A.U., travelling in free space.

***(b)* The propagation constant of a wave is 120/cm and its velocity 360 m/sec. Obtain the values of *(i)* wave number (*i.e.*, number of waves per cm), *(ii)* wavelength and *(iii)* frequency of the wave.**

Solution. (*a*) The *velocity* of light in free space is $c = \nu\lambda = 3 \times 10^{10}$ cm/sec, where ν is its frequency and λ, its wavelength.

(*i*) Here, since $\lambda = 5000$ A.U. $= 5000 \times 10^{-8}$ cm, we have frequency of the light wave, $\nu = c/\lambda = 3 \times 10^{10}/5000 \times 10^{-8} = 6 \times 10^{14}$ Hz.

(*ii*) Hence, *time-period* $T = 1/\nu = 1/6 \times 10^{14} = 1.7 \times 10^{-15}$ sec.

(*iii*) *Wave number* $\nu = 1/\lambda = 1/5000 \times 10^{-8} = 2 \times 10^{4}$/cm.

(*iv*) *Propagation constant* of the wave (*k*) $= 2\pi/\lambda = 2\pi \times 2 \times 10^{4} = 4\pi \times 10^{4} = 1.257 \times 10^{5}$/cm and

(*v*) *angular frequency* $\omega = 2\pi\nu = 2\pi \times 6 \times 10^{14} = 12\pi \times 10^{14}$ ra/sec $= 3.77 \times 10^{15}$ rad/sec.

(*b*) We know that *propagation constant* $k = 2\pi/\lambda$ and *wave number* $\nu = 1/\lambda$.

(*i*) Here, $2\pi/\lambda = 120$ and, therefore, *wave number* $\nu = 1/\lambda = 120/2\pi = 19.1$ per cm.

(*ii*) $\therefore$ *wavelength* $\lambda = 1/\nu = 1/19.1 = 0.05238$ cm.

(*iii*) Since $v = n\lambda$, we have *frequency* $n = v/\lambda = v \times (1/\lambda) = v$

Here, $v = 360$ m/sec $= 36000$ cm/sec and, therefore,

frequency n of the wave $= 36000 \times 19.1 = 6.876 \times 10^{5}$ c.p.s.

Example 12. Show that *(i)* $y = x^2 + v^2t^2$, *(ii)* $y = (x + vt)^2$, *(iii)* $y = (x - vt)^2$ and *(iv)* $y = 2 \sin x \cos vt$ are each a solution of the one-dimensional wave equation but not *(v)* $y = x^2 - v^2t^2$ and *(vi)* $y = \sin 2x \cos vt$.

Solution. (*i*) Differentiating expression (*i*) with respect to *t*, we have $dy/dt = 2v^2t$ and, therefore, $d^2y/dt^2 = 2v^2$.

And differentiating expression (*i*) with respect to *x*, we have $dy/dx = 2x$ and, therefore, $d^2y/dx^2 = 2$.

Clearly, $2v^2 = (v^2)\,2$, *i.e.*, $d^2y/dt^2 = v^2\,(d^2y/dx^2)$

Expression (i) is therefore a solution of the one-dimensional wave equation,

$$d^2y/dt^2 = v^2\,(d^2y/dx^2).$$

(*ii*) and (*iii*). Differentiating each of the expressions (*ii*) and (*iii*) twice with respect to *t*, we have

$$d^2y/dt^2 = 2v^2$$

And differentiating the two expressions with respect to *x*, we have $d^2y/dx^2 = 2$. Again, therefore

$$2v^2 = (v^2)\,2. \quad \text{Or,} \quad d^2y/dt^2 = v^2\,(d^2y/dx^2).$$

Both expression (*ii*) and (*iii*) are therefore, a solution of the one-dimensional wave equation.

(*iv*) Differentiating expression (*iv*) twice with respect to *t*, we have $d^2y/dx^2 = -v^2y$ and differentiating it twice with respect to *x*, we have $d^2y/dx^2 = -y$.

Now, $$-v^2y = v^2(-y). \quad \text{Or,} \quad d^2y/dt^2 = v^2\,(d^2y/dx^2)$$

So that, *expression (iv) too is a solution of the one-dimensional wave equation.* (*v*) Differentiating expression (*v*) twice with respect to *t*, we have $d^2y/dt^2 = -2v^2$, and differentiating it twice with respect to *x*, we have $d^2y/dx^2 = 2$.

Now $$-2v^2 \neq v^2\,(2) \text{ and, therefore, here, } d^2y/dt^2 \neq v^2(d^2y/dx^2)$$

Expression (*v*) *is not thus a solution of the one-dimensional wave equation,*

(*vi*) Differentiating expression (*vi*) with respect to *t*, we have $d^2y/dt^2 = v^2y$ and differentiating it twice with respect to *x*, we have $d^2y/dt^2 = -2y$.

Again, clearly $-v^2 y \neq v^2(-2y)$ and, therefore, $d^2y/dt^2 \neq v^2(d^2y/dx^2)$.

Expression (*vi*) *too, therefore*, is not a solution of the one-dimensional wave equation.

Example 13. (*a*) A continuous sinusoidal longitudinal wave is sent along a coil spring from a vibrating source attached to it. The frequency of the source is 25 vibrations per second and the distance between successive rarefactions in the spring is 24 cm. Find the wave speed. If the maximum longitudinal displacement of a particle in the spring is 3.0 cm and the wave moves in the –*x* direction, write down the equation of the wave. Let the source be at *x* = 0 and the displacement at *x* = 0 and *t* = 0 be zero.

(*b*) Write down the equation of a harmonic wave travelling along the +*x* direction in terms of *a* = 5 cm, ω = 100 π radian/sec and *v* = 250 cm/sec with *y* = 0 at *x* = 0 and *t* = 0, and obtain the values of λ, *v* and *k*.

Solution. (*a*) We know that in a sinusoidal (or harmonic) longitudinal wave, the wavelength is equal to the distance between two successive condensations or rarefactions. So that, here, $\lambda = 24$ cm and frequency *n*, the same as that of the source of vibrations *i.e.*, 25 Hz.

∴ *velocity* (*or speed*) *of the wave*, $v = n\lambda = 25 \times 24 = 600$ cm/sec.

Now, the *maximum longitudinal displacement of a particle* or *amplitude* of the wave is $a = 3.0$ cm.

Then, since displacement $y = 0$ at $x = 0$ and $t = 0$ and the wave is travelling along the *–ve* direction of the *x*-axis, its equation is $y = a\sin\frac{2\pi}{\lambda}(vt + x)$.

i.e., $$y = 3\sin\frac{2\pi}{24}(600\,t + x) \text{ or, } y = 3\sin\frac{\pi}{12}(600\,t + x).$$

(*b*) For a harmonic wave travelling along the +*x* direction, with $y = 0$ at $x = 0$ and $t = 0$, we have the equation $y = a\sin\frac{2\pi}{\lambda}(vt - x)$.

We may put it as $$y = a\sin\frac{2\pi v}{\lambda}\left(t - \frac{x}{v}\right)$$

Or, since $v/\lambda = n$ and $2\pi n = \omega$, it takes the form $y = a\sin\omega(t - x/v)$

Here, $a = 5$ cm, $\omega = 100\pi$ rad/sec and $v = 250$ cm/sec. So that, the equation becomes

$$y = 5\sin 100\pi(t - x/250).$$

Now, $\omega = 2\pi n = 100\pi$, and, therefore, $n = 100\pi/2\pi = 50$ Hz.

And, since $v = n\lambda = 250$ cm/sec, we have $\lambda = v/n = 250/50 = 5.0$ cm.

Hence, $\nu = 1/\lambda = 1/5 = 0.2$/cm and $k = 2\pi/\lambda = 2\pi \times 0.2 = 0.4\pi = 1.257$/cm.

Example 14. Plane waves of frequency 500 are produced in air with displacement amplitude 1.00 × 10⁻³ cm. Deduce (*i*) the pressure amplitude, (*ii*) the energy density, (*iii*) energy flux in the wave. (Density of air = 1.29 gm/litre, speed of sound in air = 300 m/sec.) ***(Agra, 2002)***

Solution. (*i*) We know that in the case of a plane harmonic wave, $y = a\sin\frac{2\pi}{\lambda}(vt - x)$ and $p = -K\,dy/dx = K\frac{2\pi}{\lambda}a\cos\frac{2\pi}{\lambda}(vt - x)$.

Obviously, *p* will have its maximum value $K\frac{2\pi}{\lambda}a$ when $\cos\frac{2\pi}{\lambda}(vt - x) = 1$.

So that, the *maximum value of p* or *the pressure amplitude* $= K\frac{2\pi}{\lambda}a$.

Or, since $v = \sqrt{K/\rho}$ and, therefore, $K = \rho v^2$, we have *pressure amplitude* $= \rho v^2\frac{2\pi}{\lambda}a$.

Again, because $v = n\lambda$, we have $1/\lambda = n/v$ and, therefore,

$$\text{pressure amplitude} = 2\pi \rho v^2 a\, n/v = 2\pi \rho v a n.$$

Here, $\rho = .00129$ gm/c.c., $v = 34000$ cm/sec, $a = 10^{-3}$ cm and $n = 500$ Hz.

$\therefore$ *Pressure amplitude* $= 2\pi \times .00129 \times 34000 \times 10^{-3} \times 500 = 135.8$ dynes/cm^2.

(*ii*) Energy density $E = 2\pi^2 n^2 a^2 \rho$ (§ 9.10). So that, $E = 2\pi^2 \times (500)^2 \times (10^{-3})^2 \times .00129 = 6.365 \times 10^{-3}$ erg/c.c.

(*iii*) Energy flux or energy current $I = Ev = 6.365 \times 10^{-3} \times 3400 = 2.164 \times 10^2$ erg sec^{-1} cm^{-2}

$= \dfrac{2.164 \times 10^2}{4.2 \times 10^7} = 5.153 \times 10^{-4}$ watt cm^{-2}. [$\because$ 4.2×10^7 erg/sec = 1 watt.]

Example 15. (*a*) Spherical waves are emitted from a 1.0 watt source in an isotropic non-absorbing medium. What is the wave intensity 1.0 metre from the source?

(*b*) A line source emits a cylindrical expanding wave. Assuming the medium absorbs no energy, find how the intensity and amplitude of the wave depend on the distance from the source.

Solution. (*a*) We know that the *intensity (I) of a wave is the quantity of incident energy per area of the wave front per unit time.*

Here, the *energy incident on the wave front per second* = 1 joule.

And, the wave front being spherical, its surface area at distance r from the source $= 4\pi r^2 = 4\pi(1)^2 = 4\pi$ sq.m.

$\therefore$ *Wave intensity at a distance* 1 *metre from the source, i.e.,* $I = 1/4\pi = 0.0796$ *joules per metre*^{2} *per sec* = 0.0796 watt/metre^2.

(*b*) Here, *the wave front being cylindrical, its surface area at a distance r from the line source* $= 2\pi rl$, where l is the *length of the cylindrical wave front or the line source.*

If, therefore, E be the *energy emitted by the source per second*, we have,

intensity of the wave at a distance r from the source, i.e., $I = E/2\pi rl$.

Or, $$I \propto 1/r \text{ or } I \propto r^{-1},$$

i.e., the intensity of the wave is inversely proportional to the distance from the source.

Now, as we know, *the intensity of a wave is directly proportional to the square of its amplitude, i.e.,* $I \propto a^2$. We therefore, have

$$a^2 \propto I \propto r^{-1}. \text{ So that, } a \propto r^{-1/2}$$

i.e., the amplitude of the wave is inversely proportional to the square root of the distance from the source.

Example 16. Two tuning forks produce 4 beats per second when sounded together. One of them is in unison with 1.20 m length of wire and the other with 1.25 m of it. Calculate the frequencies of the forks. ***(Nagpur 2006)***

Solution. It n_1 and n_2 are the frequencies of the forks, then

$$n_1 - n_2 = 4 \qquad \ldots(i)$$

If the string is stretched by a tension T and has mass per unit length m, then

$$n_1 = \frac{1}{2 \times 1.20}\sqrt{\frac{T}{m}} \quad \text{and} \quad n_2 = \frac{1}{2 \times 1.25}\sqrt{\frac{T}{m}}$$

$$\therefore \quad \frac{n_1}{n_2} = \frac{1.25}{1.20} = \frac{25}{24} \quad \text{Or} \quad n_1 = n_2 \times \frac{25}{24}$$

Substituting in Eq. (*i*), we get

$$n_2 \times \frac{25}{24} - n_2 = 4$$

$\therefore$ $$n_2 = 96 \text{ Hz}$$

and $$n_1 = n_2 + 4 = 96 + 4 = 100 \text{ Hz.}$$

Example 17. Calculate the velocity of sound in a gas in which the waves of wavelength 50 cm and 50.5 cm produces 6 beats per second. ***(Nagpur 2007)***

Solution. Let v be the velocity of sound in the gas.

$$\lambda_1 = 50 \text{ cm} = 0.5 \text{ m} \quad \text{and} \quad \lambda_2 = 50.5 \text{ cm} = 0.505 \text{ m}$$

$\therefore$ $$n_1 = \frac{v}{\lambda_1} = \frac{v}{0.500} \qquad n_2 = \frac{v}{0.505}$$

$\therefore$ $$n_1 - n_2 = 6, \qquad \frac{v}{0.500} - \frac{v}{0.505} = 6$$

Or, $$(0.505 - 0.500)\, v = 6 \times 0.500 \times 0.505$$

$\therefore$ $$v = \frac{6 \times 0.500 \times 0.505}{0.005} = 303 \text{ ms}^{-1}$$

Example 18. Calculate the number of beats heard per second if three sources of sound of quencies 400, 401 and 402 Hz, of equal intensity, are sounded together. ***(Delhi 2003)***

Solution. This is a particular example of a general case of three sources of sound simultaneously producing tones of frequencies $(n - 1)$, n and $(n + 1)$ *of equal amplitudes* their intensities being equal and intensity α (amplitude)^2].

Let the displacements due to the three sound waves at a particular point in the medium through which they are passing simultaneously along the same direction be respectively.

$$y_1 = a \sin 2\pi (n - 1)t,\; y_2 = a \sin 2\pi nt \text{ and } y_3 = a \sin 2\pi (n+1)t.$$

Then, in accordance with the principle of superposition, *the resultant displacement at the point is* $y = y_1 + y_2 + y_3 = a \sin 2\pi (n - 1)t + a \sin 2\pi nt + a \sin 2\pi (n + 1)t$.

Or, $$y = [a \sin 2\pi (n - 1)t + a \sin 2\pi (n + 1)t] + a \sin 2\pi nt$$
$$= 2a \sin 2\pi nt \cos 2\pi t + a \sin 2\pi nt = \sin 2\pi nt\, (a + 2 \cos 2\pi t)$$
$$= a\,(1 + 2 \cos 2\pi t) \sin 2\pi nt,$$

indicating that the resultant displacement at the point varies cyclically with time.

Clearly, the *maximum resultant displacement* or the *amplitude of the displacement at the point,* is $a\,(1 + 2 \cos 2\pi t)$.

This amplitude will obviously have the maximum value when $\cos 2\pi t = +1$, *i.e.*, when $2\pi t = 2r\pi$, where, $r = 0, 1, 2, 3$, etc., or, $t = r = 0, 1, 2, 3$ etc.

Thus, the maximum of amplitude, and hence also of intensity, occur at time-intervals of 1 sec each, of the *frequency of maxima* = 1 per sec.

And, *the amplitude, and hence also intensity, will be the minimum or zero when* $2 \cos 2\pi t = -1$, or, $\cos 2\pi t = -1/2$, *i.e.*, when $2\pi t = (2r\pi + 2\pi/3)$ or $t = \left(r + \frac{1}{3}\right)$, where $r = 0, 1, 2, 3$ etc., *i.e.*, when $t = 1/3, 4/3, 7/3$ etc.

Thus, the minima of amplitude, and hence also of intensity, also occur at time-intervals of 1 sec each, or *their frequency too is* 1 per sec, though they alternate with the maxima.

Thus, in all such cases, and hence also in the case given, one maximum and one minimum, *i.e.*, *only one beat, is heard per second.*

II–Transverse vibration of strings

Example 19. A uniform circular hoop of string is rotating clockwise in the absence of gravity. The tangential speed is v_0. Find the speed of the wave travelling on this string.

Solution. Since the circular hoop of the string preserves its shape continues to rotate with a uniform speed v_0, there is *tension* along the string. Indeed, as we know, without any tension in the string, it would be simply impossible for a transverse wave to travel along it. The amplitude of the wave must, however, be very small or else, its presence would alter the tension in the string which would no longer remain constant.

Let us then consider a small circular hump *AB* of the wave, of length δl of a very small amplitude so as to almost coincident with the circumference of the hoop itself and hence of the same radius, *i.e.*, *r*, as shown in Fig. 10.27.

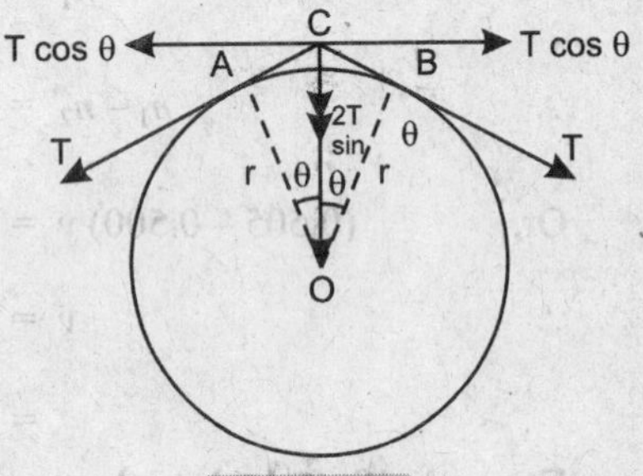

Fig. 10.27

We know that the velocity of this hump (or the wave) along the string or the hoop is given by $\sqrt{T/\sigma}$, where *T* is the *tension* in the string acting tangentially to the hump or the hoop at *A* and *B*, as shown, and σ, the *line density* or *mass per unit length* of the string. Let us obtain the value of $\sqrt{T/\sigma}$.

Resolving the tension *T* at *A* and *B* into its two rectangular components, along the horizontal and the vertical, we find that the horizontal components $T \cos\theta$ are equal and opposite and thus cancel out; so that, the only effective components are the vertical ones along *CO*, each equal to $T \sin\theta$, where *C* is the mid-point of *AB*, *O*, *the centre of the circular hoop* and θ, the angle *AOC* = angle *COB*. The total force acting on the portion *AB* of the string is thus $2T \sin\theta$ towards the centre *O* of the hoop and provides the necessary *centripetal force*, maintaining its rotation with speed v_0 in a circle or radius *r*.

But *centripetal force* acting on portion *AB* of the string is, as we know, given by *mass of portion AB of the string* $\times\, v_0^2/r = \sigma\delta l\, v_0^2/r$, because mass of portion *AB* of the string, of length $\delta l = \sigma\delta l$.

We, therefore, have $2T\sin\theta = \sigma\delta l\, v_0^2/r$.

Since θ is small, we may take $\sin\theta = \tan\theta = \theta$ (*in radian measure*).

So that, $\quad 2T\theta = \sigma\delta l\, v_0^2/r. \quad$ Or, $\quad T\delta l/r = \sigma\delta l\, v_0^2/r. \qquad [\because 2\theta = \delta l/r]$

Or, $\quad T/\sigma = v_0^2. \quad$ Or, $\quad \sqrt{T/\sigma} = v_0,$

i.e., the velocity of the transverse wave along the hoop of string is the same as the velocity of rotation of the hoop, viz., v_0.

Example 20. The equation of a transverse wave travelling along a stretched string is given by $y = 10 \sin\pi\,(2t - 0.01\,x)$, where *y* and *x* are expressed in centimeters and *t* in seconds. (*a*) Find the amplitude, frequency, velocity and wavelength of the wave. (*b*) Find the maximum transverse speed of a particle in the string.

Solution. (*a*) For any type of wave, transverse or longitudinal, we have the equation $y = a \sin \frac{2\pi}{\lambda}(vt - x)$. This can be put in the form $y = a\sin\pi\left(\frac{2vt}{\lambda} - \frac{2x}{\lambda}\right)$.

Or, since $v/\lambda = n$ and $1/\lambda = \bar{v}$, it takes the form $y = a \sin \pi\ (2nt - 2\bar{v}x)$.

Comparing it with the given equation, we find it to be of the form, where $a = 100$ cm, $2nt = 2t$ or $n = 1$, $2\bar{v}x = 0.01\ x$.

So that, $\bar{v} = 1/\lambda = 0.01/2 = 0.005$/cm, whence, $\lambda = 1/0.005 = 200$ cm and, therefore, $v = n\lambda = 1 \times 200 = 200$ cm/sec.

Thus, the *amplitude of the wave* = 10 cm, *frequency* = 1 Hz, velocity = 200 cm/sec and wave length = 200 cm.

(*b*) Clearly, *particle velocity* $U = dy/dt = 10 \times 2\pi \cos(2t - 0.01\ x)$. And, therefore, its *maximum value*, (*i.e.*, when $\cos(2t - 0.01\ x) = 1$), is $10 \times 2\pi = 20\pi = 62.81$ cm/sec.

Since the particles of the string vibrate at right angles to (or transverse to) the length of the string, we have *maximum transverse speed of a particle of the string* = 62.81 cm/sec.

Example 21. One end of a string is continuously moved up and down through a distance of 1/2 cm, five times in on second, so as to send a transverse wave train along the string. If the line density of the string be 0.64 gm per cm and the tension in the string 1600 dynes, (*a*) obtain the value of the amplitude, frequency, velocity and wavelength of the wave; (*b*) taking $y = 0$ at $x = 0$ and $t = 0$, show that the equation of the wave is given by $y = 0.25 \sin(10\ \pi t - 0.2\ \pi x)$ and hence obtain the values of displacement, particle velocity and acceleration of the particle at a distance of 10 cm from the origin, after an interval of 0.4 second.

Solution. (*a*) Since the end of the string is moved a total up and down distance of 1/2 cm, it is clear that it is moved 1/4 or 0.25 cm first up and then down from its mean or equilibrium position. The *amplitude of the wave generated is thus* 0.25 cm. And since the end is moved up and down five times in 1 second, the *frequency of the wave* = 5/sec.

Now, *velocity of the transverse wave along the string, i.e.*, $v = \sqrt{T/\sigma}$.

Since, here, $T = 1600$ *dynes* and $\sigma = 0.64$ gm/cm, we have $v = \sqrt{1600/0.64} = 40/0.8 = 50$ cm/sec.

And, therefore, *wavelength of the wave*, $\lambda = v/n = 50/5 = 10$ cm.

(*b*) We have the *wave equation* $y = a \sin \dfrac{2\pi}{\lambda}(vt - x)$, with $y = 0$ at $x = 0$ and $t = 0$.

Or, $$y = a \sin(2\pi vt/\lambda - 2\pi x/\lambda).$$

Since $v/\lambda = n$ and $2\pi n = \omega$, we have $2\pi vt/\lambda = \omega t$ and since $2\pi/\lambda = k$, we have $2\pi x/\lambda = kx$. The equation of the wave thus, takes the form $y = a \sin(\omega t - kx)$.

Here, $a = 0.25$ cm, $\omega = 2\pi\ n = 2\pi \times 5 = 10\pi$ and $k = 2\pi/\lambda = 2\pi/10 = 0.2\pi$.

The *equation of the wave is thus* $y = 0.25 \sin(10\ \pi t - 0.2\ \pi x)$

For a distance 10 cm from the origin, we have $x = 10$ cm and $t = 0.4$ sec, and, therefore, *displacement there is* $y = 0.25 \sin(10\pi \times 0.4 - 0.2\pi \times 10) = 0.25 \sin 2\pi = 0$.

Thus, *the displacement of the particle at a distance* 10 cm *from the origin* = 0, indicating that *the particle is passing through its mean or equilibrium position.*

Since particle velocity $U = dy/dt$, we have $U = \omega a \cos(\omega t - kx)$,

i.e., $U = 10\pi \times 0.25 \cos(10\pi t - 0.2\pi x) = 2.5\pi \cos(10\pi \times 0.4 - 0.2\pi \times 10) = 2.5\pi \cos 2\pi = 2.5\pi \times 1 = 2.5\pi = 7.852$ cm/sec.

This is obviously the *maximum particle velocity* (*the cosine term being equal to* 1), as is only to be expected, since the particle is passing through its mean or equilibrium position.

And, *particle acceleration*, $dU/dt = d^2y/dt^2 = -\omega^2 a \sin(\omega t - kx) = -\omega^2 y$, the negative sign indicating that it is *oppositely directed to displacement and velocity.*

$\therefore$ *Particle acceleration*, here, $= -(10\pi)^2 \times 0 = 0$.

(Obviously, because the particle is passing through its mean or equilibrium position and has, therefore, its maximum velocity and hence *zero acceleration*).

Example 22. Show that energy flux (or the energy passing through any point in unit time) in the case of a transverse wave along a string is given by the same general expression as deduced in §10.12 for a wave in any medium, with the difference that the volume density (ρ) of the medium is here replaced by the line density (σ) of the string.

Solution. Consider a small or a crest *AB* of a transverse wave travelling along a stretched string, as shown in Fig 10.28. Then, the string is naturally inclined at a small angle θ to the *x*-axis or the equilibrium position of the string.

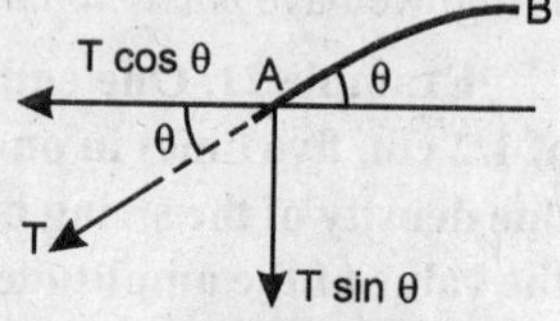

Fig. 10.28

Since the tension *T* of the string acts tangentially to it at *A*, as shown, its downward component is clearly $T\sin\theta$. So that, the force acting at point *A* of the string is $-T\sin\theta$, the negative sign indicating that the pull is *downwards (opposite to the direction of displacement or velocity).*

If, therefore, *U* be the particle velocity at the point *A*, we have *work done or energy supplied by the string to point A*, per unit time $= -T\sin\theta.U$.

$\therefore$ *Energy supplied the string to point A in time* $dt = -T\sin\theta.U.dt$.

Now, θ being small, $\sin\theta = \tan\theta =$ *slope of the curve or the hump at* $A = dy/dx$.

So that, *energy passing through point A in time* $dt = -T.(dy/dx)\,U.dt$.

Again, since $y = a\sin\frac{2\pi}{\lambda}(vt - x)$, we have $U = \frac{dy}{dt} = \frac{2\pi v}{\lambda}a\cos\frac{2\pi}{\lambda}(vt - x)$

and $\frac{dy}{dx} = -\frac{2\pi}{\lambda}a\cos\frac{2\pi}{\lambda}(vt - x)$.

Substituting these values of *U* and *dy*/*dx* in the expression above, we have *energy passing through point A in time* $dt = T\left[\frac{2\pi}{\lambda}a\cos\frac{2\pi}{\lambda}(vt - x)\right]$

$$\left[\frac{2\pi v}{\lambda}a\cos\frac{2\pi}{\lambda}(vt - x)\right]dt = \left(\frac{2\pi a}{\lambda}\right)^2 T v\cos^2\frac{2\pi}{\lambda}(vt - x)dt.$$

$\therefore$ *Energy passing through the point during the whole time-period, from 0 to* τ, (using a symbol τ for *time-period*, since *T* has been used for tension in the string)

$$= \int_0^\tau \left(\frac{2\pi a}{\lambda}\right)^2 T\,v\cos^2\frac{2\pi}{\lambda}(vt - x)\,dt$$

$$= \left(\frac{2\pi a}{\lambda}\right)^2 T\,v\int_0^\tau \frac{1}{2}\left[1 + \frac{\cos 4\pi}{\lambda}(vt - x)\right]dt$$

$$= \frac{4\pi^2 a^2}{\lambda^2}T v\tau/2 = 2\pi^2 a^2 nT\,\tau/\lambda \qquad [\because v/\lambda = n]$$

$\therefore$ *Average energy passing through the point per second* $= \frac{2\pi^2 a^2 nT\tau}{\tau\lambda} = \frac{2\pi^2 a^2 nT}{\lambda}$.

Now, $v = \sqrt{T/\sigma}$, whence, $T = v^2\sigma$.

∴ *Average rate of transfer of energy through the point* or energy flux.

$$= \frac{2\pi^2 a^2 n}{\lambda} v^2 \sigma = \frac{2\pi^2 a^2 nv}{\lambda} v\sigma = 2\pi^2 a^2 n^2 v\sigma. \qquad [\because v/\lambda = n]$$

which is the same expression as obtained for the energy flux of a wave, in general in a given medium, with only the volume density ρ of the medium replaced by the line density σ of the string.

Note. For more examples on vibrations of strings, see section V.

III–Longitudinal wave motion in fluid media and in solid rods

Example 23. A sound wave of frequency 1000 and amplitude 2.5 × 10^{-5} cm is travelling through air at N.T.P. (*a*) Obtain the values of its velocity and wavelength. (*b*) Write down the equation of the wave. (*c*) Obtain the values of particle velocity amplitude and amplitude of pressure variation. (Density of air at N.T.P. = 1.293 gm/litre and γ for air = 1.4.

Solution. (*a*) Since the wave is travelling through air at N.T.P., we have $P = 76$ cm of mercury column = 76 × 13.6 × 981 dynes/cm², ρ = 1.293 gm/litre = 0.001293/gm,' c.c. and γ = 1.4. So that, *velocity of the wave,*

$$v = \sqrt{\gamma P/\rho} = \sqrt{1.4 \times 76 \times 13.6 \times 981 / 0.001293} = 33130 \text{ cm/sec.}$$

And, therefore, *wavelength* $\lambda = v/n = 33130/1000 = 33.13$ cm.

(*b*) The equation of the wave is, as we know, given by $y = a \sin \frac{2\pi}{\lambda}(vt - x)$.

Substituting the values of *a*, λ and *v*, therefore, we have

equation of the wave, $y = 2.5 \times 10^5 \sin \frac{2\pi}{31.13}(33130\, \underline{t} - x)$.

(*c*) Now, particle velocity $U = \frac{dy}{dt} = \frac{2\pi v}{\lambda} a \cos \frac{2\pi}{\lambda}(vt - x)$.

Clearly, therefore, *particle velocity amplitude* $= \frac{2\pi v}{\lambda} a = 2\pi\, na$

$$= 2\pi \times 1000 \times 2.5 \times 10^{-5} = 0.157 \text{ cm/sec.}$$

And, since *pressure variation* $p = -K\frac{dy}{dx} = -K\frac{2\pi}{\lambda} a \cos \frac{2\pi}{\lambda}(vt - x)$,

we have *amplitude of pressure variation* = $K.\ 2\pi/\lambda$ (ignoring the sign) = $v^2 \rho \frac{2\pi}{\lambda} a = 2\pi\, v\rho\, na$

$= 2\pi \times 33130 \times 0.001293 \times 1000 \times 2.5 \times 10^{-5} = 6.726$ dynes/cm². $\qquad [\because v = \sqrt{K/\rho}\,]$.

Example 24. (*a*) prove that at any point in the course of a plane progressive wave the ratio of the excess pressure to the velocity of the air particles at that place is constant, provided the temperature and pressure do not alter. ***(Allahabad, 2005)***

(*b*) In the faintest sound that can be heard at 1000 Hz, the pressure amplitude is 2.0 × 10^{-5} N/m². Find the corresponding displacement amplitude. (Atmospheric pressure = 10^5 N/m², velocity of sound in air = 331 m/sec and ρ for air = 1.22 kg/m³).

Solution. (*a*) We know that particle velocity $U = dy/dt = v(dy/dx)$ and that *excess pressure* $\rho = -K(dy/dx) = -\gamma P\,(dy/dx)$, because K = *elasticity of air (adiabatic)* = γP, where P is the *atmospheric pressure.*

$$\therefore \qquad \frac{P}{U} = \frac{\gamma P(dy/dx)}{v(dy/dx)} = \frac{\gamma P}{v} \qquad \text{[ignoring the sign.]}$$

Since γ is a constant for air and conditions of pressure and temperature of air remaining unaltered, *P* and *v* too are *constant*, we have

$$\frac{P}{U} = \frac{\text{excess pressure}}{\text{particle velocity}} = constant.$$

(*b*) We have for *excess pressure* or *pressure variation*, the relation $p = -K\, dy/dx$.

And, since $y = a \sin \frac{2\pi}{\lambda}(vt - x)$, clearly, $p = -K\frac{2\pi}{\lambda} a \cos\frac{2\pi}{\lambda}(vt - x)$.

Or, *amplitude of pressure variation*, $p_m = K\frac{2\pi}{\lambda} a = v_\rho^2 \frac{2\pi}{\lambda} a$ [$\because v = \sqrt{K/\rho}$] ignoring the sign.

$$\therefore \textit{ displacement amplitude, } a = \frac{\lambda\, p_m}{2\pi v^2 \rho} = \frac{v}{n}\cdot\frac{p_m}{2\pi v^2 \rho} = \frac{p_m}{2\pi v n \rho}$$

$$= \frac{2.0 \times 10^{-5}}{2\pi \times 331 \times 1000 \times 1.22} = 7.883 \times 10^{-12} \text{ metre.}$$

Example 25. (*a*) If the velocity of sound in hydrogen at 0 °C is 1280 m/sec, what will be the velocity of sound (at the same temperature) in a mixture of two parts by volume of hydrogen to one of oxygen? Density of oxygen is 16 times that of hydrogen. ***(Punjab 2001)***

(*b*) The planet Jupiter has an atmosphere of a mixture of ammonia and methane at a temperature –130°C. Calculate the velocity of sound on this planet, assuming γ for the mixture to be 1.3 and the molecular weight of the mixture to be 16.5 (Gas constant R = 8.3 joules per deg. per gm. molecule). ***(Patna, 2001)***

Solution. (*a*) Let ρH be the density of hydrogen and $\rho M'$ that of the mixture of hydrogen and oxygen. Then, if v_H and v_M be the velocities of sound in hydrogen and the mixture respectively, we have

$$v_M = \sqrt{\gamma P/\rho_M} \text{ and } v_H = \sqrt{\gamma P/\rho_H}\text{ . And therefore, } v_M/v_H = \sqrt{\rho_H/\rho_M}\ .$$

Now, the mixture consists of two parts by volume of hydrogen and one part by volume of oxygen. So that, if each part by volume be V, we have

mass of two parts by volume of hydrogen = $2V \times 1$ and *mass of one part by volume of oxygen* = $V \times 16$.

∴ *mass if a volume* $3V$ *of the mixture* = $(2V + 16V) = 18V$ mass units.

So that, *density of the mixture,* $\rho_M = \frac{\text{mass}}{\text{volume}} = \frac{18V}{3V} = 6$ mass units/c.c.

Hence $v_M/v_H = \sqrt{1/6}$ Or, $v_M = v_H\sqrt{1/6} = 1280\ \sqrt{1/6} = 522.43$ m/sec

Or, *the velocity of sound in the given mixture* = 522.43 m/sec.

(*b*) Here, molecular weight of the mixture of ammonia and methane or, *the mass of* 1 gm molecule of the mixture = 16.5. If, therefore, ρ be the *density of the mixture*, the *volume of* 1 gm *molecule of it, i.e.,* $V = 16.5/\rho$.

Now, we have our standard gas equation $PV = RT$,

where, $V = 16.5/\rho$, $R = 8.3$ joules or 8.3×10^7 *ergs per deg. C* per gm *molecule of the mixture* and $T = (-130 + 273) = 143°$ *Abs.*

So that, $P(16.5/\rho) = 8.3 \times 10^7 \times 143$, whence, $P/\rho = 8.3 \times 10^7 \times 143/16.5$.

∴ *velocity of sound in the mixture, i.e., on the planet Jupiter,* is $v = \sqrt{\gamma P/\rho}$

$$= \sqrt{1.3 \times 8.3 \times 10^7 \times 143/16.5} = 30580 \text{ cm/sec} = 305.8 \text{ m/sec.}$$

Example 26 (*a*). Prove that $v = C\sqrt{\gamma/3}$, where *v* is the velocity of sound in a gas, *C*, the root mean square velocity of the molecules and γ the ratio of the two specific heats. (*Punjab 2003*)

(*b*) Show that the velocity of sound in a gas, for which $\gamma = 1.41$ is 0.68 *C*, where *C* is the root mean square velocity of the molecules. (*Agra 2004*)

Solution. (*a*) If *P* be the pressure and ρ, *the density of a gas*, we have

velocity of sound in the gas, $v = \sqrt{\gamma P/\rho}$.

Now, in accordance with the kinetic theory of gases, $P = \frac{1}{3}\rho C^2$ or $P/\rho = C^2/3$,

where *C* is the *root mean square velocity* of the molecules of the gas.

$$\therefore \quad v = \sqrt{\gamma P/\rho} = \sqrt{\gamma C^2/3} = C\sqrt{\gamma/3}.$$

(*b*) If $\gamma = 1.41$ for a gas, we have

velocity of sound in the gas, $v = C\sqrt{1.41/3} = 0.6855\ C \approx 0.68\ C.$

Example 27. (*a*) The speed of sound in a certain metal is *V* cm/sec. One end of a pipe of that metal of length 1 cm is struck a blow. A listener at the other end hears two sound, one from the wave that has travelled along the pipe and the other from the wave that has travelled through air. If *v* is the speed of the sound in air, what time interval *t* elapses between the two sounds? (*b*) suppose *t* = 1.4 sec, Young's modulus for the metal = 7.2×10^{11} dynes/cm², density of the metal = 8 gm/c.c., atmospheric pressure = 10^6 dynes/cm², density of air = 0.0012 gm/c.c. and γ for air = 1.4, find the length *l*.

Solution. (*a*) We have velocity of sound along the pipe, $V = \sqrt{Y/\rho}$, where *Y* is the Young's modulus for the metal and ρ, its *density*.

And, *velocity of sound through air*, $v = \sqrt{\gamma P/\rho'}$, where *P* is the *atmospheric pressure* and ρ', the density of air with $\gamma = Cp/Cv$.

$\therefore$ *time taken by sound travelling along the pipe to cover the length l of the pipe* = l/V

and *time taken by sound travelling through air to cover the same distance l in air* = l/v.

Since *V* is very much greater than *v* ($\because$ the ratio $Y/\rho >> \gamma P/\rho'$), we have *time interval that elapses between the two sounds heard by the listener, i.e.,* $t = l/v - l/V$ $(= l\ 1/v - 1/V) = l(V - v)vV$ sec.

(*b*) It is clear from the above that if *t* = 1.4 sec, we have

$$t = 1.4 = l\left(\frac{V - v}{vV}\right), \text{ whence, } l = \frac{1.4 \times v \times V}{V - v}$$

Now, $$V = \sqrt{\frac{Y}{\rho}} = \sqrt{\frac{7.2 \times 10^{11}}{8}} = 3 \times 10^5 \text{ cm/sec and}$$

$$v = \sqrt{\frac{\gamma P}{\rho'}} = \sqrt{\frac{1.4 \times 10^6}{0.0012}} = 3.415 \times 10^4 \text{ cm/sec}$$

$$\therefore \quad l = \frac{1.4 \times 3.415 \times 10^4 \times 3 \times 10^5}{3 \times 10^5 - 3.415 \times 10^4} = 53940 \text{ cm} = 539.4 \text{ metres.}$$

Thus, *the length l of the pipe* = 539.4 metres.

Example 28. The lowest tone emitted by a cylindrical metal rod has a frequency 1000 Hz and wavelength 300 cm. If the density of the metal be 7.5 gm/c.c., obtain the value of Young's modulus for it.

Solution. We have *velocity of the wave emitted by the rod*, $v = n\lambda = 100 \times 300 = 3 \times 10^5$ cm/sec.

Now, $v = \sqrt{Y/\rho}$, where Y is *Young's modulus* for the material of the rod and ρ, its *density*.

$$\therefore \quad v^2 = Y/\rho \quad \text{or} \quad Y = \rho v^2.$$

Substituting the values of ρ and v, therefore, we have

Young's modulus for the material of the rod $= 7.5 \times (3 \times 10^5)^2 = 7.5 \times 9 \times 10^{10}$

$$= 67.5 \times 10^{10} = 6.75 \times 10^{11} \text{ dynes/cm}^2.$$

(**N.B.** For other example on longitudinal vibrations of rods, sec section V.)

IV–Linear bounded medium (Interference and stationary waves)

Example 29. (*a*) Find the resultant of two plane simple harmonic waves of the same period travelling in the same direction but differing in phase and amplitude. What is the amplitude of the resultant wave if those of the component waves be 3.0 and 4.0 cm respectively and their phase difference $\pi/2$ radian?

(*b*) Explain why the interference fringes are hyperbolic when the prongs of a tuning fork are made to touch the surface of a liquid. ***(Rajasthan 2003)***

Solution. (*a*) Let the two simple harmonic waves, travelling along the same direction have amplitudes a_1 and a_2 and let the second wave lag a phase angle ϕ behind the first. Then, their equations may respectively be represented by

$$y_1 = a_1 \sin \frac{2\pi}{\lambda}(vt - x) \text{ and } y_2 = a_2 \sin\frac{2\pi}{\lambda}[(vt - x) - \phi].$$

The *resultant wave* is thus represented by

$$y = y_1 + y_2 = a_1 \sin \frac{2\pi}{\lambda}(vt - x) + a_2 \sin \frac{2\pi}{\lambda}[(vt - x) - \phi].$$

Or,
$$y = a_1 \sin \frac{2\pi}{\lambda}(vt - x) + a_2 \sin \frac{2\pi}{\lambda}(vt - x) \cos \phi - a_2 \cos \frac{2\pi}{\lambda}(vt - x) \sin$$

$$= \sin\frac{2\pi}{\lambda}(vt - x)(a_1 + a_2 \cos \phi) - \cos\frac{2\pi}{\lambda}(vt - x)(a_2 \sin \phi).$$

Putting $(a_1 + a_2 \cos \phi) = a \cos \theta$ and $a_2 \sin \phi = a \sin \theta$, we have

$$y = a \sin \frac{2\pi}{\lambda}(vt - x) \cos \theta - a \cos \frac{2\pi}{\lambda}(vt - x) \sin \theta$$

Or,
$$y = a \sin\left[\frac{2\pi}{\lambda}(vt - x) - \theta\right],$$

indicating that the resultant wave too is a simple harmonic wave, having the same frequency and wavelength as the two component waves but has an amplitude a and is a phase angle θ behind the first wave, where

$$a = \sqrt{(a\cos\theta)^2 + (a\sin\theta)^2} = \sqrt{a_1^2 + a_2^2\cos^2\phi + 2a_1a_2\cos\phi + a_2^2\sin^2\phi}$$

$$= \sqrt{a_1^2 + a_2^2 + 2a_1a_2\cos\phi}$$

and
$$\tan\theta = \frac{a\sin\theta}{a\cos\theta} = \frac{a_2\sin\phi}{a_1 + a_2\cos\phi}$$

Obviously, for $\phi = 0$, *i.e.*, when the two component waves arrive at a point *in phase*, we have $\cos \phi = +1$ and, therefore, $a = a_1 + a_2$ and for $\phi = \pi$, *i.e.*, when the two waves arrive at a *point out of phase*, we have $\cos \phi = -1$ and, therefore, $a = a_1 - a_2$. At all other points, the amplitude of the resultant wave lies between these two extremes.

If, therefore, $a_1 = 3.0$ cm, $a_2 = 4.0$ cm and $\phi = \pi/2$, we have

amplitude of the resultant wave, $a = \sqrt{3^2 + 4^2 + 2 \times 3 \times 4 \cos \pi/2} = \sqrt{9 + 16 + 0} = \sqrt{25} = 5.0$ cm.

(*b*) In Fig. 10.29, let the two dots, 1 and 2, represent the two points where the prongs of a vibrating tuning fork *just* touch a liquid surface. These points then obviously become the *sources of two identical, transverse, spherical waves, travelling onwards in the form of crests and troughs,* represented respectively by full and broken-line curves in the figure.

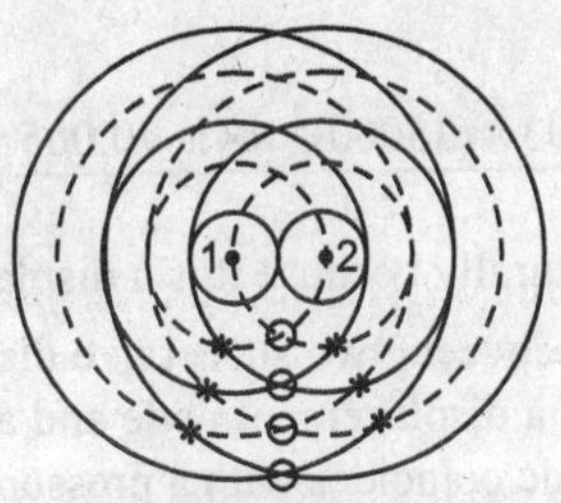

Fig. 10.29

These two sets of waves thus get partially superposed and *interfere* with each other, *constructively at points where the crests or the troughs of the two waves arrive simultaneously and destructively at points where the crest of one wave arrives simultaneously with the trough of the other*. The former are thus points of *maximum*, and the latter, of *minimum*, displacements and are marked in the figure by circles add *crosses* respectively.

Joining by a free hand curve the points marked by circles and so also those marked by crosses, we obtain positions of maxima and minima of displacement in the resultant wave. These curves thus constitutes the *interference fringes* formed by the two wave trains proceeding from the two dots.

Consider any point on one of these curves or interference fringes, such that its distances from dots 1 and 2 respectively are x_1 and x_2. Then, if the point lies on a curve representing a maximum of displacement, we have $(x_1 - x_2) = n\lambda$, *a constant*, and if it happens to be on a curves representing a minimum of displacement, we have $(x_1 - x_2) = (2n + 1)\lambda/2$, *again a constant* (where $n = 0, 1, 2, 3$ *etc*). In either case, therefore, the path difference for the point considered from the two fixed points or dots remains constant.

Now, *the locus of all points for which the path difference from two fixed points remains constant is a hyperbola, with the two fixed points as its two foci.*

This explains why the interference fringes in this case are so many hyperbolic curves, corresponding to $n = 0, 1, 2, 3$ etc, with their two foci at the two dots or points of disturbance.

Example 30. (*a*) A sound wave in air, having an amplitude of 0.005 cm and frequency 700 Hz, and travelling along the positive direction of the *x*-axis with velocity 350 m/sec, suffers reflection at a free boundary. Obtain the values of (*i*) the displacement amplitude and (*ii*) the pressure amplitude in the resulting stationary wave at a point $x = 50$ cm. (Density of air = 1.293 gm/litre).

(*b*) Also obtain the distance between (*i*) two successive displacement nodes and antinodes, (*ii*) two successive pressure nodes and antinodes, (*iii*) a displacement node and an adjacent pressure node.

Solution. (*a*) (*i*) We have the equation of a stationary wave formed by reflection at a free boundary given by $y = 2\,a \cos \dfrac{2\pi x}{\lambda} \sin \dfrac{2\pi vt}{\lambda}$, [10.21, (*ii*)]

whence, clearly, displacement amplitude $= 2\,a \cos 2\pi\, x/\lambda$.

Here, $a = 0.005$ cm, $x = 50$ cm and $\lambda = v/n = 350 \times 100/700 = 50$ cm.

$\therefore$ *displacement amplitude* $= 2 \times 0.005 \cos 2\pi \times 50/50 = 0.01$ cm,

i.e., the *maximum* (the cosine term being equal to 1).

The point is thus a displacement antinode.

(*ii*) We have excess pressure $p = \rho v^2 \dfrac{4\pi a}{\lambda} \sin \dfrac{2\pi x}{\lambda} \sin \dfrac{2\pi vt}{\lambda}$ [10.21, (*ii*)]

So that, *pressure amplitude*

$$= \rho v^2 \frac{4\pi a}{\lambda} \sin \frac{2\pi x}{\lambda} = \frac{0.001293 \times (35000)^2 \times 4\pi \times 0.005}{50} \sin \frac{2\pi \times 50}{50} = 0.$$

i.e., the point is a pressure node (naturally because it is a displacement antinode).

(*b*) We know that the distance between two successive displacement nodes or antinodes is $\lambda/2$ and, therefore, the distance between a displacement node and an adjacent displacement antinode is $\lambda/4$, and also that a displacement node coincides with a pressure antinode and vice versa.

It will thus be easily seen that, in the case above,

distance between two successive displacement nodes = distance between two successive displacement antinodes $= \lambda/2 = 50/2 = 25.0$ cm.

And, therefore, *distance between two successive nodes or antinodes is also equal to* $\lambda/2 = 50/2 = 25.0$ cm, and

distance between a displacement node (or *pressure antinode*) *and an adjacent pressure node* (*or displacement antinode*) $= \lambda/4 = 50/4 = 12.5$ cm.

Example 31. The equation of a stationary wave in a metal rod is given by $y = 0.002 \sin \left(\frac{\pi}{3} x\right) \sin (1000\, t)$. Obtain the values of (*i*) amplitude of particle velocity, (*ii*) maximum tensile stress at a point $x = 2.0$ cm. (Y for the material of the rod $= 8 \times 10^{11}$ dynes/cm^2).

Solution. (*i*) We have, particle velocity $U = dy/dt = 0.002 \times 1000 \sin \left(\frac{\pi}{3} x\right) \cos (1000\, t)$.

So that, *amplitude, of particle velocity*

$$= 0.002 \times 1000 \sin \left(\frac{\pi}{3} x\right) = 2 \sin \left(\frac{\pi}{3} \times 2\right)$$

$$= 2 \sin \frac{2\pi}{3} = 2 \sin 120^\circ = 2\sqrt{3/2} = 1.732 \text{ cm/sec.}$$

(*ii*) Since Young's modulus $Y = \dfrac{\text{tensile stress}}{\text{tensile strain}} = \dfrac{\text{tensile stress}}{dy/dx}$, we have

$$\text{tensile stress} = Y\,(dy/dx)$$

Here, $Y = 8 \times 10^{11}$ dynes/cm^2 and $dy/dx = 0.002 \left(\frac{\pi}{3}\right) \cos\left(\frac{\pi}{3} x\right) \sin (1000\, t)$.

Clearly, *maximum value of strain* $(dy/dx) = 0.002\, (\pi/3) \cos\left(\frac{\pi}{3} x\right)$ [*i.e.*, when $\sin (1000\, t) = 1$].

$\therefore$ *maximum value of stress* $= Y \times 0.002 \times (\pi/3) \cos\left(\frac{\pi}{3} x\right) = Y \times 0.002 \times (\pi/3)$

$\cos 60^\circ = 80 \times 10^{11} \times 0.002 \times (\pi/3) \times 1/2 = 8 \times 10^8 \times \pi/3 = 8.377 \times 10^8$ dynes/cm^2.

V–Different modes of vibration of strings, rods, closed and open pipes

A–Different modes of vibration of strings

Example 32. (*a*) A loaded string, one metre in length and weighing 0.5 gm is hanging from a tuning fork of frequency 200 Hz and is vibrating in 4 loops. Calculate the tension in the string. ***(Delhi, 2003)***

(*b*) In Melde's experiment when the tension is 100 gm wt and the fork vibrates at right angles to the direction of the string. the latter is thrown into four segments. If now the fork is set to vibrate along the string, find what additional load will make, the string vibrate in one segment. ***(Agra, 2004 Vikram, 2006)***

Solution. (*a*) Here, obviously, two cases arise: (*i*) when the prongs of the fork vibrate transversely (*i.e.*, at right angles) to the length of the string, as shown in Fig. 10.30 (*a*), called the *transverse mode* and (*ii*) when the prongs vibrate *along* the length of the string, as shown in Fig. 10.30 (*b*), called the *longitudinal mode*.

In case (*i*) or the *transverse mode*, with the prong in its normal position, the string is horizontal and when the prong moves up or down the string also does so; so that, the frequency of vibration of the *string* in its *fundamental mode of vibration. i.e.,* when it vibrates as a whole, in one single segment, is the same as that of the prong or the tuning fork, say, n, and we, therefore, have

$$n = \frac{1}{2l}\sqrt{\frac{T}{\sigma}}.$$

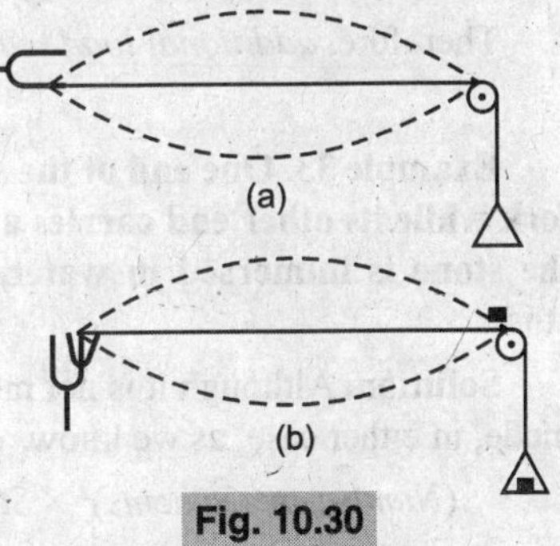

Fig. 10.30

And, if the string vibrates in p segments, the frequency of the note emitted by it is given by $n = \frac{p}{2l}\sqrt{\frac{T_p}{\sigma}}$, where T_p is now the tension in the string.

$\therefore\ T_p = 4l^2 n^2 \sigma/p^2 = 4 \times (100)^2 \times (200)^2 \times 0.5/(4)^2 \times 100 = 5 \times 10^5$ *dynes*. [$\because \sigma = 0.5/100$ gm/cm]

Thus, the *tension required in the string* = 5×10^5 dynes.

In case (*ii*), or the *longitudinal mode*, when the prong of the fork is in its extreme right position, the string takes the lower dotted position show and when the prong has moved to its extreme left position, the string comes to its normal horizontal position, so that, by the time prong has completed half its vibration, the string has completed only one-fourth of its vibration. The frequency of the string is thus *half* that of the fork and we, therefore, have $\frac{n}{2} = \frac{1}{2l}\sqrt{\frac{T}{\sigma}}$.

And, if the string vibrates in p segments, the frequency of the note emitted by it is given by $\frac{n}{2} = \frac{p}{2l}\sqrt{\frac{T'_p}{\sigma}}$, where T'_p is now the tension in the string.

$\therefore\ T'_p = 4\,l^2 n^2 \sigma/4\,p^2 = l^2 n^2 \sigma/p^2 = \frac{1}{4}$th of the tension T_p in case (i) $= \frac{1}{2} \times 5 \times 10^5 = 1.25 \times 10^5$ *dynes*.

Thus, *the tension required in the string, in this case,* = 1.25×10^5 *dynes*.

(*b*) It will be seen from the discussion under (*a*) above that *in the transverse mode, $p^2 \times T_p$ = a constant k*. Or, $p \propto \sqrt{1/T_p}$ and in the *longitudinal mode, $p^2 \times T_p'$ = a constant k'*. Or, $p \propto \sqrt{1/T_p'}$,

i.e., in either case, *the number of segments or loops into which the string is thrown into vibration is inversely proportional to the square root of the stretching force.*

Since, however, T_p is four times T_p', it is clear that the stretching force required to set the string vibrating into a given number of segments in the transverse mode is four times that required to set it vibrating into the same number of segments in the longitudinal mode.

If, therefore, we apply the same tension $T_p = 4T_p'$ in either case, we shall find that whereas in the transverse mode the string vibrates in p segments, in the longitudinal mode, the number of segments is reduced to $p/2$ because the number of segments is inversely proportional to the square root of the stretching force which is now 4 times its previous value. In other words, *for the same tension in the string, the number of segments in the longitudinal mode is half that in the transverse mode.*

Now, in the given problem, a stretching force of 100 gm wt produces 4 loops in the string *in the transverse mode*. In the longitudinal mode, therefore, this stretching force will produce only half the number of loops, *i.e.*, only 2 loops. The problem thus reduces to this that if with a stretching force of 100 gm wt, the string vibrates in 2 loops in the longitudinal mode, what additional force will be needed to make it vibrate in only one loop?

In other words, $p = 2$ when $T_p' = 100$ gm wt. what should be the value of T_p' when $p = 1$?

As we know, $p^2 \times T_p' = constant$. And, therefore, $2^2 \times 100 = (1)^2 \times T_p'$, whence,

$$T_p' = 400 \text{ gm wt.}$$

Therefore, *additional load required to make the string vibrate in* 1 *loop*

$$= 400 - 100 = 300 \text{ gm wt.}$$

Example 33. One end of the string in Melde's experiment is attached to a vibrating tuning fork while its other end carries a piece of stone. The string shows eight vibrating loops. When the stone is immersed in water, 10 loops are formed. Calculate the specific gravity of the stone. ***(Bihar, 2004)***

Solution. Although it is not mentioned here whether it is a case of transverse or of longitudinal mode, in either case, as we know,

$$(\textit{Number of segments})^2 \times \textit{Stretching force} = \textit{Constant.}$$

$\therefore$ if T_1 and T_2 be the tensions in the string when the stone is in air and in water respectively, we have $8^2 \times T_1 = 10^2 \times T_2$, whence, $T_2 = 8^2 \times T_1/10^2 = (16/25)T_1$.

$\therefore$ *Loss of weight of in water* $= T_1 - T_2 = T_1 - (16/25)T_1 = (9/25)T_1$.

And, therefore, *specific gravity of the stone* $= \dfrac{T_1}{(9/25)T_1} = \dfrac{25}{9} = 2.78.$

Example 34. (*a*) A tuning fork of frequency 200 Hz is in unison with a sonometer wire. How many beats per second will be heard if the tension of the wire be increased by one per cent?

(*b*) A stretched sonometer wire gives 2 beats per second with a tuning fork when the length of the wire is 143 cm and also when its lengths is 145 cm. What is the frequency of the tuning fork? ***(Delhi 2005)***

Solution. (*a*) We know that other factors remaining the same, the frequency of the note emitted by a sonometer wire is directly proportional to the square root of the stretching force applied to it or the tension in it.

If, therefore, n_1 and n_2 be the frequencies of the notes emitted by the wire with tension T and $(T + T/100)$ respectively, we have

$$\frac{n_2}{n_1} = \sqrt{\frac{T + T/100}{T}} = \left(1 + \frac{1}{100} + ...\right)^{1/2} = \left(1 + \frac{1}{200}\right) \text{ Or, } \frac{n_2}{n_1} = \frac{201}{200}$$

Since the first note (n_1) of the sonometer wire is in unison with tuning fork, we have $n_1 = 200$ and, therefore, $n_2 = 201$. So that, $(n_2 - n_1) = 201 - 200 = 1$.

Thus, the difference between the frequencies of the second note of the wire and the tuning fork being 1, *only* 1 *beat per second will be heard.*

(*b*) Here, the tension and mass per unit length of the sonometer wire remaining the same, the frequency of the note emitted by it is inversely proportional to the length of the wire. So that, if n_1 and n_2 be the frequencies of the notes when the lengths of the wire are l_1 and l_2 respectively, we have $n_1/n_2 = l_2/l_1$.

Or, $n_1 l_1 = n_2 l_2$. And, therefore, $143\ n_1 = 145\ n_2$, whence,

$$n_2 = 143\ n_1/145.$$

If the frequency of the tuning fork be n, it must be 2 lower than n_1 and 2 higher than n_2 in order to produce 2 beats per second in either case.

We, therefore, have $\quad n_1 - n = 2 \quad$ ...(*i*)

and $\quad n - n_2 = n - \dfrac{143}{145} n_1 = 2 \quad$ ...(*ii*)

Adding relations (*i*) and (*ii*), we have $n_1 - \dfrac{143}{145} n_1 = 4$

Or, $\quad 2n_1 = 4 \times 145$, whence, $n_1 = 4 \times 145/2 = 290$ Hz.

Substituting this value of n_1 in relation (*i*) above, we have $290 - n = 2$.

Or, $\quad n = 288$ Hz.

Thus, the *frequency of the tuning fork* = 288 Hz.

Example 35 (*a*) A sonometer wire of non-magnetic material is stretched across two permanent bridges on metre apart and a permanent horse-shoe magnet *M* placed athwart (*i.e.*, across) it at its mid-point, so that the two poles of the magnet lie on either side of the wire, as shown in Fig. 10.31 (*a*). The tension in the wire is so adjusted that on passing an alternating current under a low voltage (to avoid undue heating of the wire), the wire vibrates up and down with its maximum amplitude. If the line density of the wire be 0.049 gm/cm and the stretching force necessary be 5 kg wt, calculate the frequency of the alternating current. ($g = 980$ cm/sec^2).

(*b*) If the sonometer wire be of a magnetic material, like iron, it can be made to vibrate up and down with maximum amplitude by bringing close to it an electromagnet E.M., energised by the alternating current, [Fig 10.31 (*b*)], and suitable adjusting the length of the wire and the tension in it. Calculate the frequency of the alternating current in this case if the line density of the wire and the tension in it be the same as in case (*a*) but the length of the wire is now 50 cm.

Solution. (*a*) Here, the magnetic field due to the magnet (*M*) being perpendicular to the length of the wire, in the direction *NS* [Fig. 10.31 (*a*)], we have the case of a current-carrying conductor lying in a magnetic field. The conductor or the wire, therefore, gets deflected in accordance with *Fleming's left hand rule**, *i.e.*, upwards during one half cycle of the current and downwards during the other half. It thus executes a forced vibration in one single segment with the frequency of the current.

* This rule states that if the thumb and the first two fingers of the *left hand* be extended so as to be mutually perpendicular to each other, then if the First finger points in the direction of the magnetic field, the second or the Central finger in the direction of the current in the conductor, the thumb points in the direction of Motion of the conductor.

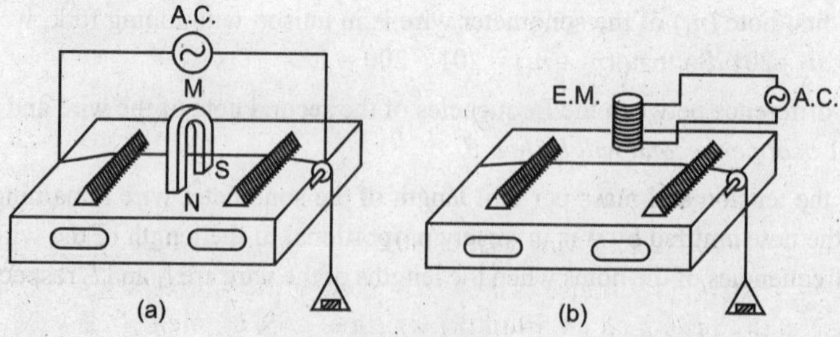

Fig. 10.31

With its length and tensions properly adjusted, the wire vibrates with *maximum amplitude, showing that now its natural frequency n is the same as the frequency f of the alternating current, i.e.*, it now vibrates in resonance with the alternating current.

Clearly, the natural frequency of the wire is $n = \frac{1}{2l}\sqrt{\frac{T}{\sigma}}$

Or, since $T = 5$ kg wt = $5 \times 1000 \times 980$ *dynes* and $\sigma = 0.049$ gm/cm, we have

$$n = \frac{1}{2\times 100}\sqrt{\frac{5\times 1000\times 980}{0.049}} = \frac{10^4}{2\times 100} = 50 \text{ Hz.}$$

Since the wire is in resonance with the alternating current, *the frequency of the alternating current too is* 50 Hz.

(*b*) In this case, as the alternating current is passed around the electromagnet, the pole close to the wire acquires alternately north and south polarities (due to the current flowing in one direction during on half cycle and in the opposite direction during the other half). In either case, however, the wire (being of a magnetic material) is attracted towards it. So that, although the current passing through the electromagnet changes direction only once in one cycle, the wire is attracted upwards *twice* in that one cycle. In other words, the wire is forced to vibrate in one segment with twice the frequency of the alternating current. The length of the wire and its tension have been so adjusted that the wire vibrates with its maximum amplitude.

Again, the *frequency of the wire*, $n = \frac{1}{2l}\sqrt{\frac{T}{\sigma}} = \frac{1}{2\times 50}\sqrt{\frac{5\times 100\times 980}{0.049}}$

$$= \frac{104}{2\times 50} = 100 \text{ Hertz.}$$

Since the frequency of the wire is twice that of the alternating current, we have *frequency of the alternating current* = 100/2 = 50 Hz.

Example 36. A one-metre long sonometer wire is stretched with a force of 4 kg wt. Another wire of the same material and diameter is arranged alongside the first and stretched with a force of 16 kg wt. What should be the length of the second wire so that its second harmonic is the same as the fifth harmonic of the first?

Solution. The two wires being of the same material and diameter, their *line density* σ is the *same*. If, therefore, n_5 be the *fifth harmonic of the first wire*, T_1, the *stretching force* applied to it and l_1, its length, we have $n_5 = \frac{5}{2l}\sqrt{\frac{T_1}{\sigma}}$. And, if n_2 be the *second harmonic of the second wire*, T_2, the *stretching force* applied to it and l_2, its *length*, we have $n_2' = \frac{2}{2l_2}\sqrt{\frac{T_2}{\sigma}} = \frac{1}{l_2}\sqrt{\frac{T_2}{\sigma}}$

Since $n_2' = n_5$, we have $\frac{1}{l_2}\sqrt{\frac{T_2}{\sigma}} = \frac{5}{2l_1}\sqrt{\frac{T_1}{\sigma}}$ Or, $\sqrt{T_2}/l_2 = 5\sqrt{T_1}/2l_1$.

Or, $l_2 \times 5\sqrt{T_1} = 2l_1\sqrt{T_2}$. Or, $l_2 \times 5\sqrt{4} = 2l_1\sqrt{16}$ Or, $10\,l_2 = 8\,l_1$,

whence, $l_2 \times 8\,l_1/10 = 8 \times 100/10 = 80$ cm.

Thus, *the length of the second wire must be* 80 cm.

Example 37. A string 1.3 metre in length is divided into three segments such that their frequencies are in the ratio 2 : 3 : 4. Find the length of each segment. ***(Agra 2004)***

Solution The frequency $n = \frac{1}{2l}\sqrt{\frac{T}{\rho}}$

As T and ρ are constants, the frequency $n \propto \frac{1}{l}$

As the frequency are in the ratio 2 : 3 : 4, the lengths of the segments, l_1, l_2, l_3 are in the ratio $\frac{1}{2}:\frac{1}{3}:\frac{1}{4}$ or 6 : 4 : 3.

Also total length $l = l_1 + l_2 + l_3 = 1.3$ m

$$\therefore \quad l_1 = \frac{1.3}{6+4+3} \times 6 = 0.6 \text{ m}$$

$$l_2 = \frac{1.3}{6+4+3} \times 4 = 0.4 \text{ m}$$

$$l_3 = \frac{1.3}{6+4+3} \times 3 = 0.3 \text{ m}$$

Example 38. A string is stretched by suspending a load of 5 kg. The mass per unit length of the string is 5 gm m^{-1}. The travelling waves are sent through the string by oscillating one of the ends with a frequency of 250 Hz and amplitude 5 mm. Calculate the velocity and the length of the wave. Also write the equation of the travelling wave. Take g = 10 ms^{-2}. ***(P.U., 2002)***

Solution. Load suspended = 5 kg.; $g = 10$ ms^{-2}

$\therefore$ Tension $T = 5 \times 10 = 50$ N

Mass per unit length $\rho = 5$ gm m^{-1} = 5×10^{-3} kg m^{-1}

$\therefore$ Velocity $c = \sqrt{\frac{T}{\rho}} = \sqrt{\frac{50}{5 \times 10^{-3}}} = 100$ ms^{-1}

Frequency $\nu = 250$ Hz

$\therefore$ Wave length $\lambda = \frac{100}{250} = 0.4$ m

Amplitude $a = 5$ mm $= 5 \times 10^{-3}$ m

Wave equation is given by

$$y = a \sin\frac{2\pi}{\lambda}(ct - x) = 5 \times 10^{-3} \sin\frac{2\pi}{0.4}(100\,t - x)$$

$$= 5 \times 10^{-3} \sin 5\pi\,(100\,t - x)$$

Example 39. Two wires of steel of the same length are stretched on a sonometer. The tension of the first and second are 8 kg wt and 2 kg. wt respectively. Find the ratio of the fundamental notes emitted by the two wires when the diameter or cross section of the first wire is half that the second. ***(Cal. 2001)***

Solution. Let d be the density of steel.

Diameter of the second wire = D

$\therefore$ Diameter of the first wire = $\frac{D}{2}$

Mass per unit length of the first wire $\rho_1 = \frac{\pi}{4}\left(\frac{D}{2}\right)^2 d = \frac{\pi}{16}D^2 d$

Mass per unit length of the second wire $\rho_2 = \frac{\pi}{4}D^2 d = \frac{\pi}{4}D^2 d$

$$\therefore \quad \frac{\rho_2}{\rho_1} = 4$$

Tension for first wire $T_1 = 8$ kg wt = 8 g Newton

Tension for the second wire $T_2 = 2$ kg wt = 2 g Newton

Let l be the length of each wire, then

Frequency of the fundamental note of first wire $n_1 = \frac{1}{2l}\sqrt{\frac{T_1}{\rho_1}}$

Frequency of the fundamental note of second wire $n_2 = \frac{1}{2l}\sqrt{\frac{T_2}{\rho_2}}$

$$\therefore \quad \frac{n_1}{n_2} = \sqrt{\frac{T_1}{\rho_1}\cdot\frac{\rho_2}{T_2}} = \sqrt{\frac{8}{2}.4} = 4$$

Example 40. A string *AB* of length 100 cm is kept under uniform tension. A bridge is kept at *C* such that *BC* = 60 cm. When the string is subjected to vibration *BC* part vibrates with frequency 252 Hz. Find the frequency of both parts of the string when the bridge is moved through 10 cm towards *A*. ***(Vid. S. U., 2002)***

Solution. The position of the bridge in the first and second case is shown in Fig 10.32 (*a*) and (*b*) respectively.

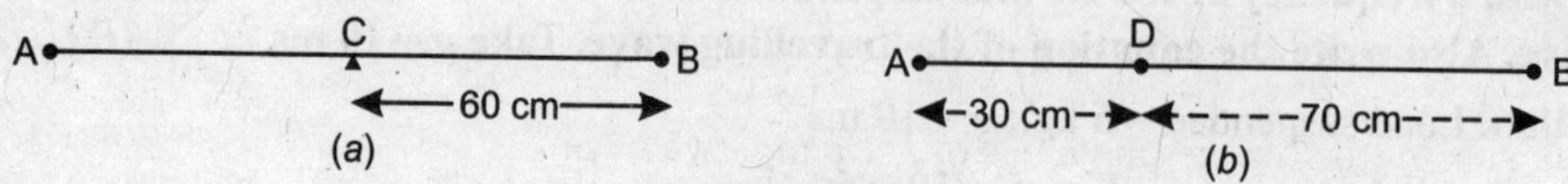

Fig. 10.32

When $BC = 60$ cm, frequency of BC part, $n = \frac{1}{2l}\sqrt{\frac{T}{\rho}}$

Or
$$252 = \frac{1}{120}\sqrt{\frac{T}{\rho}}$$

$$\therefore \quad \sqrt{\frac{T}{\rho}} = 252 \times 120$$

When the bridge is moved 10 cm towards A from C to D

$$BD = 70 \text{ cm and } DA = 30 \text{ cm}$$

$\therefore$ Frequency of part BD, $n_1 = \frac{1}{2\times 70}\sqrt{\frac{T}{\rho}} = \frac{1}{140} \times 252 \times 120 = 216$ Hz

Frequency of part DA, $n_2 = \frac{1}{2\times 30}\sqrt{\frac{T}{\rho}} = \frac{1}{60} \times 252\times 120 = 504$ Hz

Example 41. A stretched string is observed to vibrate with a frequency 30 c.p.s in the fundamental note when the length of the string is 60 cm. The string has a mass of 0.5 gm/cm. Find the velocity of propagation of the transverse wave and compute the tension of the string. ***(Burd. U., 2000)***

Solution. Frequency of the fundamental note $n = 30$ c.p.s.

Length of the string $l = 60$ cm

Mass per unit length $\rho = 0.5$ gm/cm

Let T be the tension of the string, then

$$n = \frac{1}{2l}\sqrt{\frac{T}{\rho}}$$

Or $$30 = \frac{1}{2 \times 60} \times \sqrt{\frac{T}{0.5}}$$

$$T = 30 \times 30 \times 2 \times 2 \times 60 \times 60 \times 0.5 = 6.48 \times 10^6 \text{ dynes/cm}$$

Velocity of propagation $$v = \sqrt{\frac{T}{\rho}} = n \times 2l = 30 \times 2 \times 60 = 3600 \text{ cm/sec.}$$

B–Different modes of vibration of rods

Example 42. Calculate the frequency of the lowest note, or the first harmonic, emitted by a metal rod set in longitudinal vibration when the rod is *(i)* clamped nowhere (free-free rod), *(ii)* clamped in the middle and *(iii)* clamped at both ends (fixed-fixed rod), if the length of the rod be 100 cm, its density 8 gm/c.c. and the value of Young's modulus for its material, 10^{11} dynes/cm^2.

Is it possible to obtain a note of a lower frequency from this rod? If so, how? what is the value of this frequency?

Solution. In all the cases, (*i*), (*ii*) and (*iii*), the frequency of the lowest or the fundamental note, or the first harmonic, is given by $n = \frac{1}{2l}\sqrt{\frac{Y}{\rho}}$.

So that, substituting the given values of l, Y and ρ, we have

frequency of the lowest note, $$n = \frac{1}{2 \times 100}\sqrt{\frac{10^{11}}{8}} = 5591 \text{ Hz.}$$

It is possible to obtain a note of a lower frequency than this (in fact, half of this) if the rod be fixed at one end and be free at the other (fixed-free rod), when the frequency of the lowest note or the first harmonic is given by

$$n' = \frac{1}{4l}\sqrt{\frac{Y}{\rho}} = \frac{1}{4 \times 100}\sqrt{\frac{10^{11}}{8}} = 2796 \text{ Hz.}$$

Example 43. The frequency of the note next higher to the fundamental, as given by a rod of an alloy, 100 cm long and clamped at its mid-point is 1000. If the density of the alloy be 7.5 gm/c.c., calculate the value of Young's modulus for it.

Solution. We know that in the case of a rod, clamped at its mid point, *only odd* harmonics can be excited. So that, the note next to the fundamental has thrice the frequency of the fundamental. If, therefore, n be the frequency of the note, we have

$$n = \frac{3}{2l}\sqrt{\frac{Y}{\rho}}.$$

Substituting the given values, we have $1000 = \frac{3}{2 \times 100}\sqrt{\frac{Y}{7.5}}$.

Or, $\sqrt{\frac{Y}{7.5}} = \frac{1000 \times 2 \times 100}{3}$, whence, $Y = \frac{4 \times 10^{10} \times 7.5}{9} = 3.33 \times 10^{10}$

Thus, *Young's modulus for the alloy of the rod* = 3.33×10^{10} dynes cm^2.

Example 44. A wire, of area of cross section 0.04 sq. cm, is fixed at one end and is stretched by a weight of 20 kg suspended from the other. Obtain the ratio between the frequencies of the notes emitted by it when it is rubbed longitudinally at its mid-point by a resined cloth and when it is plucked at its mid-point. (*Y* for the material of the wire = 4.9×10^{12} dynes/cm^2).

Solution. In the *first case*, when the wire is rubbed at its mid-point, it functions as a rod fixed at both ends and is set in longitudinal vibration, giving out its fundamental note of frequency *n*, say, where

$$n = \frac{1}{2l}\sqrt{\frac{Y}{\rho}}, \qquad \ldots(i)$$

being the (volume) density of the wire.

And, in the *second case*, it function as a string fixed at both ends which, when plucked at its mid-point gives its fundamental note of frequency *n'*, say, where

$$n' = \frac{1}{2l}\sqrt{\frac{T}{\sigma}}, \qquad \ldots(ii)$$

σ being is the *line density* (or *mass per unit length*) of the wire = (area of cross section of the wire × 1) × ρ = 0.04 ρ gm/cm.

So that,
$$n' = \frac{1}{2l}\sqrt{\frac{T}{0.04\rho}}. \qquad \ldots(iii)$$

$\therefore$ *ratio of the two frequencies* = $\frac{n}{n'} = \frac{1}{2l}\sqrt{\frac{Y}{\rho}} \Big/ \frac{1}{2l}\sqrt{\frac{T}{0.04\rho}} = \sqrt{\frac{Y \times 0.04}{T}}$.

Since $Y = 4.9 \times 10^{12}$ dynes/cm^2, $T = 20$ kg *wt* = $20 \times 1000 \times 980 = 1.96 \times 10^7$ dynes, we have

$$\frac{n}{n'} = \sqrt{\frac{4.9 \times 10^{12} \times 0.04}{1.97 \times 10^7}} = 100.$$

Thus, *the ratio between the two notes is* 100 : 1.

C–Different modes of vibration of organ pipes (air columns)

Example 45. A tube 100 cm long is closed at one end. A stretched wire is placed near the open end. the wire is 30 cm long and has a mass of 10 gm. It is held fixed at both ends and vibrates in its fundamental mode. It sets the air column in the tube into vibration at its fundamental frequency by resonance. Find (*a*) the frequency of oscillation of the air column and (*b*) the tension in the wire. (velocity of sound in air = 340 m/sec). Neglect end-correction of the tube.

Solution. (*a*) We know that the fundamental frequency of the air column in a closed pipe is given by $n = \frac{1}{4l}\sqrt{\frac{K}{\rho}} = \frac{v}{4l}$, neglecting the end-correction.

Here, $v = 340 \times 100 = 34000$ cm/sec and $l = 100$ cm. And, therefore,

$$n = 34000/4 \times 100 = 85.$$

Thus, the *frequency of oscillation of the air column* = 85 cps.

(*b*) Since the air column has been set into resonant oscillation by the fundamental frequency of the wire, the latter too is $n = 85$.

Now, with the wire fixed at both ends, its *fundamental frequency* = $\frac{1}{2l}\sqrt{\frac{T}{\sigma}}$.

We, therefore, have $n = 85 = \frac{1}{2l}\sqrt{\frac{T}{\sigma}}$ Or, $\sqrt{\frac{T}{\sigma}} = 85 \times 2l = 85 \times 2 \times 30.$

Or, $$T/\sigma = (85 \times 2 \times 30)^2. \text{ And, therefore, } T = (85 \times 2 \times 30)^2 \times \sigma.$$

Clearly, σ = mass per unit length of the wire = 10/30 = 1/3 gm/cm.

Tension in the wire, $T = (85 \times 2 \times 30)^2 \times 1/3 = 8.672 \times 10^6$ dynes.

Example 46. (*a*) If two pipes, one closed at one end and the other open at both ends, have their first overtones of the same frequency, what is the ratio of their respective lengths?

(*b*) A tuning fork is held above a column of air in a glass tube. The positions of the first and second resonance are 33.0 cm and 100.5 cm respectively. Calculate the end correction.

(Punjab 2006)

Solution. (*a*) Let the lengths of the closed and open pipes be l and l' respectively. Then, the first *overtone of the former has a frequency* = $\frac{3}{4l}\sqrt{\frac{K}{\rho}} = \frac{3v}{4l}$ and the *first overtone of the latter has a frequency* = $\frac{2}{2l'}\sqrt{\frac{K}{\rho}} = \frac{2v}{2l'} = \frac{v}{l'}$ where v is the velocity of sound in air.

Since the frequencies of the two overtones are the same, we have

$$\frac{3v}{4l} = \frac{v}{l'}. \quad \text{Or,} \quad 4l = 3l' \text{ or } l : l' :: 3 : 4$$

Thus, *the ratio of the lengths of the closed and open pipes is* 3 : 4.

(*b*) Here, the glass tube is, obviously, serving as a *closed pipe*. Therefore, if l_1 be the length of the air column at the first *resonance* and x, the *end-correction* of the tube, we have

$$(l_1 + x) = \lambda/4 \quad \ldots(i)$$

And, if l_2 be the length of the air column at the *second resonance*, we have

$$(l_2 + x) = 3\lambda/4 \quad \ldots(ii)$$

$\therefore$ multiplying relation (*i*) by 3, we have $3l_1 + 3x = 3\lambda + 4$.

From relation (*ii*) and (*iii*), therefore, we have $3l_1 + 3x = l_2 + x$.

Or, $$3x - x = l_2 - 3l_1. \text{ Or, } 2x = l_2 - 3l_1. \text{ whence, } x = (l_2 - 3l_1)/2.$$

Here, $$l_1 = 33.0 \text{ cm and } l_2 = 100.5 \text{ cm. So that,}$$

end correction of the tube, $x = (100.5 - 3 \times 33.0)/2 = 1.5/2 = 0.75$ cm.

Example 47. It is found that 4 beats are heard per second when the fundamental note of a closed pipe, 25 cm long, is sounded simultaneously with the second harmonic of an open pipe. What can be possible lengths of the open pipe? The end-correction may be neglected in either case. (Velocity of sound in air = 340 m/sec)

Solution. Here, clearly, the length of the closed pipe being given to be 25 cm, the frequency of its fundamental note is fixed and is equal to

$$n = v/4l = 340 \times 100/4 \times 25 = 340 \text{ Hertz.}$$

In order, therefore, that 4 beats may be heard per second, the frequency of the second harmonic of the open pipe must either be 340 + 4 = 344 Hz or 340 − 4 = 336 Hertz.

If, therefore l' be the length of the open pipe which gives a second harmonic of frequency 344 Hz, we have

$$344 = 2v/2l' = v/l' = 34000/l', \text{ whence, } l' = 34000/344 = 98.83 \text{ cm.}$$

And, if l'' be the length of the open pipe which gives a second harmonic of frequency 336, we have

$$336 = 2v/2l'' = 34000/l'', \text{ whence, } l'' = 34000/336 = 101.2 \text{ cm}$$

Thus, *the two possible lengths of the open pipe are* 98.83 cm and 101.2 cm.

VI–Fourier's theorem

Example 48. Fig 10.33 gives a periodic function. Obtain a Fourier analysis of this up to the fifth harmonic. ***(Nagpur 2002)***

Solution. Here, as we can see, $\xi = f(x) = 0$ from $x = 0$ to $x = a/2$ and $\xi = f(x) = h$ from $x = a/2$ to $x = a$.

Now, the *Fourier series* gives $\xi = A_0 + A_1 \sin \omega x + ... + A_r \sin r\omega x + B_1 \cos \omega x + ... + B_r \cos r\omega x$.

Since $$A_0 = \frac{1}{a}\int_0^a \xi ax, \text{ we have } A_0 = 0 + \frac{1}{a}\int_{a/2}^a h\,dx = \frac{1}{a}[x]_{a/2}^a$$

$$= \frac{1}{a}(ha - ha/2) = h/2,$$

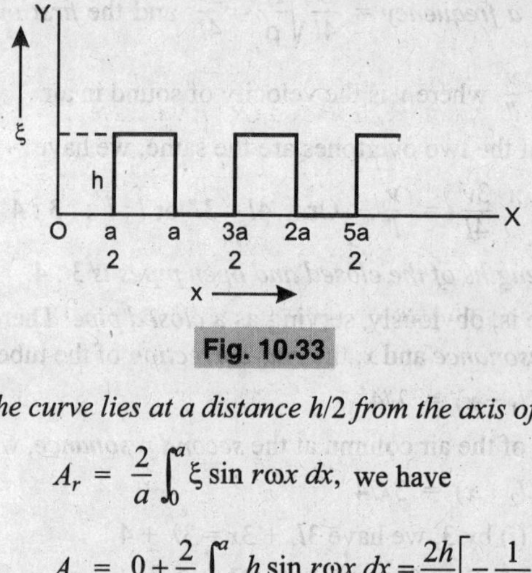

Fig. 10.33

indicating that *the axis of the curve lies at a distance h/2 from the axis of x.*

And, because $$A_r = \frac{2}{a}\int_0^a \xi \sin r\omega x\,dx, \text{ we have}$$

$$A_r = 0 + \frac{2}{a}\int_{a/2}^a h \sin r\omega x\,dx = \frac{2h}{a}\left[-\frac{1}{r\omega}\cos r\omega x\right]_{a/2}^a$$

$$= \frac{2h}{a}\left[-\frac{a}{2\pi r} + \frac{a}{2\pi r}\cos r\pi\right] = \frac{h}{\pi r}(-1 + \cos r\pi) \quad [\because \omega = 2\pi/a.]$$

For *even values of r*, therefore, $A_r = 0$ and *for odd values of r*, $A_r = -2h/\pi r$.

So that, $A_1 = -2h/\pi$, $A_2 = 0$, $A_3 = -2h/3\pi$, $A_4 = 0$ and $A_5 = -2h/5\pi$.

Again, since $$B_r = \frac{2}{a}\int_0^a \xi \cos r\omega x\,dx, \text{ wh have}$$

$$B_r = \frac{2}{a}\int_{a/2}^a h \cos r\omega x\,dx = \frac{2h}{a}\left[\frac{a}{2\pi r}\sin r\omega x\right]_{a/2}^a$$

$$= \frac{2h}{a}\left[\frac{a}{2\pi r}(\sin r\pi - \sin r\pi)\right] = 0.$$

And, therefore, B_1, B_2, B_3 *are all zero, i.e., the cosine terms in the Fourier series are all absent.*

The series, in this case, thus becomes

$$\xi = \frac{h}{2} - \frac{2h}{\pi}\left(\sin\omega x + \frac{1}{3}\sin 3\omega x + \frac{1}{5}\sin 5\omega x + ...\right)$$

Or,
$$\xi = \frac{h}{2} - \frac{2h}{\pi}\left(\sin\frac{2\pi x}{a} + \frac{1}{3}\sin\frac{6\pi x}{a} + \frac{1}{5}\sin\frac{10\pi x}{a} + ...\right)$$

Example 49. Obtain the Fourier series for the complex periodic function represented by Fig. 10.34 when $y = f(t) = at$ $t = 0$ and $t = T$ and $y = f(t) = a$ at $T/2$.

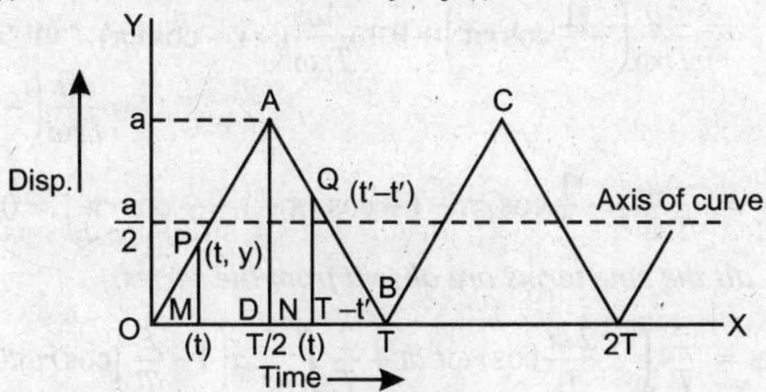

Fig. 10.34

Solution. Let us take a point P on OA, with coordinates t and y and a point Q on AB, with coordinates t', y' and drop perpendiculars PM and QN from P and Q respectively on to the time-axis. Then, from similar right-angled triangles OMP and ODA, we have

$$\frac{PM}{AD} = \frac{OM}{OD}. \text{ Or, } \frac{y}{a} = \frac{t}{T/2}, \text{ whence, } y = \frac{2at}{T} \text{ from 0 to } T/2$$

Similarly, from similar right-angled triangles BNQ and BDA, we have

$$\frac{QN}{AD} = \frac{NB}{DB} \text{ or, } \frac{y'}{a} = \frac{T-t'}{T/2}, \text{whence } y = 2a\left(1 - \frac{t'}{T}\right) \text{ from } T/2 \text{ to } T.$$

Now, the coefficient A_0 of the Fourier series is given by $A_0 = \frac{1}{T}\int_0^T y\,dt$.

We, therefore, have
$$A_0 = \frac{1}{T}\left[\int_0^{T/2}\frac{2at}{T}dt + \int_{T/2}^{T}2a\left(1-\frac{t'}{T}\right)dt'\right]$$

$$= \frac{a}{T}\left[\frac{2t^2}{2T}\right]_0^{T/2} + \frac{2a}{T}\left[t' - \frac{t'^2}{2T}\right]_{T/2}^{T} = \frac{a}{4} + a - \frac{3a}{4} = \frac{a}{2},$$

indicating that the axis of the curve lies at a distance a/2 from the time-axis.

The coefficient A_r of the series is given by

$$A_r = \frac{2}{T}\left[\int_0^{T/2}\frac{2at}{T}\sin r\omega t\,dt + \int_{T/2}^{T}2a\left(1-\frac{t'}{T}\right)\sin r\omega t'\,dt'\right]$$

Or,
$$A_r = \frac{4a}{T^2}\int_0^{T/2} t\sin r\omega t\,dt + \frac{4a}{T}\int_{T/2}^{T}\sin r\omega t' - \frac{4a}{T^2}\int_{T/2}^{T} t'\sin r\omega t'\,dt'.$$

$$= \frac{4a}{T^2}\left[-t\frac{\cos r\omega t}{r\omega}\right]_0^{T/2} + \frac{4a}{T^2}\int_0^{T/2} -\frac{\cos r\omega t}{r\omega}dt$$

$$+ \frac{4a}{T^2}\left[-\frac{\cos r\omega t'}{r\omega}\right]_{T/2}^{T} - \frac{4a}{T^2}\left[-t'\frac{\cos r\omega t'}{r\omega}\right]_{T/2}^{T}$$

$$= \frac{4a}{T^2}\left(-\frac{T}{2}\frac{\cos r\omega T/2}{r\omega}+0\right)+\frac{4a}{T^2}\left[-\frac{\sin r\omega T/2}{r^2\omega^2}\right]$$

$$+\frac{4a}{T}\left[-\frac{\cos r\omega t}{r\omega}+\frac{\cos r\omega T/2}{r\omega}\right]-\frac{4a}{T^2}\left(-\frac{T\cos r\omega t}{r\omega}\right.$$

$$\left.+\frac{(T/2)\cos r\omega T/2}{r\omega}\right)-\frac{4a}{T^2}\left[-\frac{\sin r\omega t}{r^2\omega^2}+\frac{\sin r\omega T/2}{r^2\omega^2}\right]$$

Since $\omega T = 2\pi$ and, therefore, $\omega T/2 = \pi$, we have

$$A_r = \frac{4a}{Tr\omega}\left(-\frac{1}{2}\cos r\pi\right)+0+\frac{4a}{Tr\omega}(-1+\cos r\pi)$$

$$-\frac{4a}{Tr\omega}\left(-1+\frac{1}{2}\cos r\pi\right)+\frac{4a}{T^2}(0)$$

$$= \frac{4a}{Tr\omega}\left(-\frac{1}{2}\cos r\pi-1+\cos r\pi+1-\frac{1}{2}\cos r\pi\right)=0.$$

Thus, A_r *being zero, all the sine terms are absent from the series.*

And, coefficient $B_r = \frac{2}{T}\int_0^{T/2}\frac{2at}{T}\cos r\omega t\,dt+\frac{2}{T}\int_{T/2}^{T}2a\left(1-\frac{t'}{T}\right)\cos r\omega t'\,dt'.$

$$= \frac{4a}{T^2}\int_0^{T/2}t\cos r\omega t\,dt+\frac{4a}{T}\int_{T/2}^{T}\cos r\omega t'\,dt'-\frac{4a}{T^2}\int_{T/2}^{T}t'\cos r\omega t'\,dt'$$

$$-\frac{4a}{T^2}\left[\frac{t'\sin r\omega t'}{r\omega}\right]_{T/2}^{T}+\frac{4a}{T^2}\int_{T/2}^{T}\frac{\sin r\omega t'}{r\omega}dt'.$$

$$=\frac{4a}{T^2}\left[\frac{t\sin r\omega t}{r\omega}\right]_0^{T/2}-\frac{4a^2}{T^2}\int_0^{T/2}\frac{\sin r\omega t}{r\omega}dt+\frac{49}{T}\left[\frac{\sin r\omega t'}{r\omega}\right]_{T/2}^{T}$$

$$=\frac{4a}{T}\left(\frac{1}{2}\frac{\sin r\pi}{r\omega}\right)-\frac{4a}{T^2}\left[\frac{-\cos r\omega T/2+\cos 0}{r^2\omega^2}\right]+\frac{4a}{T}(0)-\frac{4a}{T^2}(0)$$

$$+\frac{4a}{T^2}\left[\frac{-\cos r\omega T+\cos r\omega T/2}{r^2\omega^2}\right]$$

$$= 0-\frac{4a}{T^2r^2\omega^2}(-\cos r\pi+1)+0-0+\frac{4a}{T^2r^2\omega^2}(-1+\cos r\pi)$$

$$= \frac{4a}{T^2r^2\omega^2}(\cos r\pi-1)+\frac{4a}{T^2r^2\omega^2}(\cos r\pi-1)$$

$$= \frac{4a}{T^2r^2\omega^2}[2(\cos r\pi-1)]=\frac{8a}{T^2r^2\omega^2}(\cos r\pi-1)$$

Or, since $\omega = 2\pi/T$, we have $B_r = \frac{2a}{r^2\pi^2}(\cos\pi-1)$.

So that, *for even values of* r, $\cos r\pi = 1$ and, therefore, $B_r = 0$ *and, for odd values of* r, $\cos r\pi = -1$ and, therefore, $B_r = -4a/r^2\pi^2$.

Thus, *the complete Fourier series for the given periodic function is*

$$y = \frac{a}{2}-\frac{4a}{\pi^2}\left(\cos\omega t+\frac{\cos 3\omega t}{3^2}+\frac{\cos 5\omega t}{5^2}+\ldots\right).$$

VII–Group velocity

Example 50. Two sinusoidal waves

$$y_1 = 0.03 \cos (7t - 10x) \text{ m and}$$
$$y_2 = 0.03 \cos (5t - 8x) \text{ m}$$

were superimposed. Calculate the group velocity. ***(P.U., 2000, G.N.D.U., 2003, 2000)***

Solution. Comparing with wave equation $y = a \cos (\omega t - kx)$ we have,

Amplitude $a = 0.03$ m

Angular frequency $\omega_1 = 7;\quad \omega_2 = 5$

Propagation constant $k_1 = 10;\quad k_2 = 8$

$\therefore$ Group velocity $$v_g = \frac{\Delta\omega}{\Delta k} = \frac{\omega_1 - \omega_2}{k_1 - k_2} = \frac{7-5}{10-8} = 1 \text{ ms}^{-1}.$$

Example 51. Calculate the group velocity when the two waves

$$y_1 = 10 \sin (2\pi t - 5x)$$
$$y_2 = 15 \sin (5\pi t - 5x)$$

superimpose, y_1 and y_2 are in metres. ***(P.U; 2003)***

Solution. Comparing with the wave equation $y = a \sin (\omega t - kx)$ we have,

Angular frequency $\omega_1 = 2\pi,\quad \omega_2 = 5\pi$

Propagation number (constant) $k_1 = +5;\quad k_2 = -5$

$\therefore$ Group velocity $$v_g = \frac{\Delta\omega}{\Delta k} = \frac{\omega_1 - \omega_2}{k_1 - k_2} = \frac{2\pi - 5\pi}{+5-(-5)}$$
$$= -\frac{3}{10}\pi = -0.3\pi \text{ ms}^{-1}$$

Example 52. The velocity of water waves, under the combined action of gravity and surface tension is given by the relation $v = \sqrt{\lambda g/2\pi + 2\pi T/\lambda\rho}$, where T stands for surface tension, and ρ for the density of water. Obtain an expression for the group velocity of the wave and show that the group velocity of surface waves or ripples (due in main to surface tension) is thrice the group velocity of gravity waves (due in main to gravity).

Solution. We know that the *wave velocity* of the water waves is given by $v = \omega/k$, where $k = 2\pi/\lambda$. We, therefore, have

$$v = \frac{\omega}{k} = \sqrt{\frac{1}{k}\left(g + \frac{k^2 T}{\rho}\right)}, \text{ whence, } \omega = \sqrt{kg + k^3 T/\rho}.$$

$\therefore$ *Group velocity of the wave,* $$u = \frac{d\omega}{dk} = \frac{1}{2}\frac{g + 3k^2 T/\rho}{\sqrt{kg + k^3 T/\rho}} = \frac{1}{2}\frac{g + 3k^2 T/\rho}{\omega}.$$

Or, dividing the numerator and denominator by k, we have

$$u = \frac{g/2k + 3k\,T/2\rho}{\omega/k} = \frac{g/2k + 3k\,T/\rho}{v}$$

And $\therefore$ $$\frac{u}{v} = \frac{g/2k + 3k\,T/2\rho}{v^2} = \frac{g/2k + 3k\,T/2\rho}{g/k + k\,T/\rho}$$

Or, *group velocity,* $$u = \frac{g/2k + 3kT/2\rho}{g/k + kT/\rho}\, v. \qquad \ldots(i)$$

Now, if we consider the case of *rupples* in which the surface tension along plays the dominant part, we obtain the group velocity of ripples by neglecting the terms involving g in expression (i) above. Thus,

$$\textit{group velocity of ripples, } u_{(\text{ripples})} = \frac{3k\,T/2\rho}{k\,T/\rho}\,\nu = \frac{3}{2}\nu,$$

i.e., the group velocity of ripples is 3/2 times the waves velocity.

If, on the other hand, we are interested in the waves in deep water or the *gravity waves*, in which gravity plays the major part, we obtain their group velocity by neglecting the terms involving surface tension in expression (i) above. Thus

$$\textit{group velocity of gravity waves, } u_{(\text{gravity wave})} = \frac{g/2k}{g/k}\,\nu = \frac{1}{2}\nu,$$

i.e., the group velocity of gravity waves (if the water be deep enough) is half the wave velocity.

It will thus be easily seen that *the group velocity of ripples* $\left(\frac{3}{2}\nu\right)$ *is thrice the group velocity of gravity waves* $\left(\frac{1}{2}\nu\right)$.

Example 53. Show that the group velocity of de Broglie waves associated with a moving particle is the same as the velocity of the particle on both non-relativistic and relativistic considerations but their phase velocity is half the particle velocity in the former, and much higher than the velocity of light (c) in the latter, case.

Solution. *Ignoring first any relativistic considerations*, let m be the *mass* of a moving particle and v, its *velocity*, so that its *momentum* $p = mv$.

Then, the *de Broglie wavelength of the wave associated with the particle, say*, λ, is given by $\lambda = h/p$, where h is the *Planck's constant.*

The *frequency of the wave* $\nu = \omega/2\pi$ and the *energy associated with it* $= h\nu$.

We thus have – energy $E = h\nu = h\omega/2\pi$. Also, $E = \frac{1}{2}mv^2 = p^2/2m = h^2/2m\lambda^2$, (because $p = h/\lambda$).

Or, putting $2\pi/\lambda = k$ and, therefore, $\lambda = 2\pi/k$, we have $E = h^2 k^2/8\pi^2 m$.

Equating the two values of E, we have

$$h\omega/2\pi = h^2 k^2/8\pi^2 m, \text{ whence, } \omega = hk^2/4\pi m.$$

Hence, *group velocity of de Broglie waves*, $u = \dfrac{d\omega}{dk} = \dfrac{2hk}{4\pi m} = \dfrac{hk}{2\pi m} = \dfrac{h}{\lambda m}$. $[\because k = 2\pi/\lambda]$

Since $p = mv = h/\lambda$, we have particle velocity $v = h/\lambda m$.

Thus, *group velocity of de Broglie waves associated with the particle = velocity of the particle itself.*

Now, *under relativistic considerations*, the mass m of the particle is its *relativistic mass* $= m_0/\sqrt{1 - v^2/c^2}$, where m_0 is its *rest mass* and c, the *velocity of light in free space.*

We, therefore, have $E = h\nu = h\omega/2\pi$, whence, $\omega = 2\pi E/h$.

Since $E = mc^2$, we have $\omega = 2\pi\, mc^2/h = 2\pi\, m_0\, c^2/h\,\sqrt{1 - v^2/c^2}$ ...(i)

And, clearly, $k = 2\pi/\lambda = 2\pi/\dfrac{h}{p} = 2\pi\, p/h = 2\pi\, mv/h = 2\pi\, m_0 v/h\,\sqrt{1 - v^2/c^2}$ ...(ii)

From relation (i) we have $\dfrac{d\omega}{dv} = \dfrac{2\pi m_0 v}{h(1 - v^2/c^2)^{3/2}}$, ...($iii$)

and from relation (*ii*) we have $\dfrac{dk}{dv} = \dfrac{2\pi m_0}{h(1-v^2/c^2)^{3/2}}$ ...(*iv*)

From relations (*iii*) and (*iv*), therefore, we have

group velocity of de Broglie waves, $u = \dfrac{d\omega}{dk} = \dfrac{d\omega/dv}{dk/dv} = \dfrac{2\pi m_0 v / h(1-v^2/c^2)^{3/2}}{2\pi m_0 / h(1-v^2/c^2)^{3/2}} = v.$

Thus, *the group velocity of de Broglie waves here too is equal to the velocity of the particle itself.*

Let us now calculate the *phase velocity in the two cases*:

Under non-relativistic considerations, we have

$$\lambda = 2\pi/k = h/mv, \text{ whence, } k = \frac{2\pi}{h} mv.$$

And, $E = \dfrac{1}{2}mv^2 = hv = \dfrac{h\omega}{2\pi}$, whence, $\omega = \dfrac{2\pi}{h}hv = \dfrac{2\pi}{h} \times \dfrac{1}{2}mv^2 = \dfrac{\pi mv^2}{h}$.

$\therefore$ *phase velocity of de Broglie waves* $= \dfrac{\omega}{k} = \dfrac{\pi mv^2}{h} \times \dfrac{h}{2\pi mv} = \dfrac{1}{2}mv^2/mv = \dfrac{1}{2}v,$

i.e., the phase velocity here is equal to half the particle velocity.

Under relativistic considerations, we have ω given by expression (*i*) and *k* by expression (*ii*) above. And, therefore,

phase velocity of de Broglie waves $= \dfrac{\omega}{k} = \dfrac{2\pi m_0 c^2/h\sqrt{1-v^2/c^2}}{2\pi m_0 v/h\sqrt{1-v^2/c^2}} = \dfrac{c^2}{v}$

Since $v << c^2$, *the phase velocity, in the case, in very much greater than c, the velocity of light in free space.*

EXERCISE

I–Plane Progressive Harmonic Waves

1. (*a*) What is wave motion? What are longitudinal and transverse waves? Give the condition regarding the direction to oscillation and direction of propagation of longitudinal and transverse waves. ***(P.U. 2000, 2001, G.N.G.D. 2001)***

   (*b*) State the characteristics of progressive wave. Derive on expression for the progressive wave of wavelength λ and amplitude a moving with a velocity *V* in the positive *X*-direction. ***(Mithila U. 2000, Luck.U. 2002, Burd. U. 2002)***

2. (*a*) Show that the slope of the displacement curve for a given wave gives the volumetric strain in the medium in which it travels.

   (*b*) Derive a relation between *v* (velocity), *dy*/*dt* (Particle velocity) and *dy*/*dx* (volumetric strain) ***(Mithila U. 2001; Kan.U. 2003; Vid. S.U. 2001)***

3. What is meant by a plane progressive harmonic wave? Distinguish between transverse and a longitudinal wave and obtain an expression for a plane progressive wave, in general.

4. Show that the particle velocity at a point affected by a plane progressive wave is equal to wave velocity × slope of the displacement curve at that point.

5. Show that particle velocity *dy*/*dt* in the case of a plane progressive wave is given by $dy/dt = -v\, dy/dx$. Hence derive the differential equation of a wave motion.

6. Show that the most general differential equation of a one-dimensional wave is $d^2\xi/dt^2 = v^2 d^2\xi/dx^2$. Discuss the solutions for this in the case of a medium with rigid boundaries separated by length *L*.

7. What do you understand by *energy density* and *energy current* (or *intensity*) of a plane progressive wave? Obtain the usual expressions for them.

8. Obtain the expression for the energy of a plane progressive wave and show that, at any given instant, it is, on an average, half kinetic and half potential in form.

9. What is ment by the *principle of superposition* of waves? Explain in brief how is gives rise to the phenomena of '*beats*' and '*stationary waves*'. Is any loss of energy involved in either of these cases?

10. Show that the wave equation $y = a \sin \frac{2\pi}{\lambda}(vt - x)$ for a wave travelling along the $+x$ direction may be written in any one of the following forms:

(*i*) $y = a \sin(\omega t + kx)$ (*ii*) $y = a \sin 2\pi(vt - x/\lambda)$

(*iii*) $y = a \sin \omega(t - x/v)$ (*iv*) $y = a \sin 2\pi(t/T - x/\lambda)$ and

(*v*) $y = a \sin 2\pi(nt - x/\lambda)$.

11. A longitudinal harmonic wave train is travelling along a spring in the positive direction of the x-axis. If the frequency of the wave be 50 Hertz and the distance between a condensation and an adjacent rarefaction in the spring, 10 cm, obtain the velocity of the wave.

Assuming the amplitude of the wave to be 2.0 cm, write down the wave equation, taking $y = 0$ at $x = 0$ and $t = 0$. [**Ans.** 1000 cm/sec; $2 \sin 0.1\pi(1000t - x)$]

12. A plane progressive harmonic wave, travelling along the $+x$ direction has an amplitude of 5.0 cm and frequency, 100 Hz. If its velocity be 6000 cm/sec, obtain the values of (*i*) the wave number (in the sense of waves per unit length), (*ii*) displacement, (*iii*) particular velocity and (*iv*) particle acceleration at $x = 150$ cm and $t = 2$ sec. [**Ans.** (*i*) 0.0166/cm, (*ii*) 0, (*iii*) 3142 cm/sec, (*iv*) 0]

13. A plane progressive wave travelling along the $+x$ direction has the following characteristers; $a = 0.2$ cm, $v = 360$ cm/sec and $\lambda = 60$ cm.

(*a*) Write down the equation for it (*i*) when displacement is zero at $x = 0$ and $t = 0$ and (*ii*) when displacement is maximum at $x = 0$ and $t = 0$.

(*b*) Obtain the displacement in either case at $x = 120$ cm and $t = 2$ sec.

[**Ans.** (*a*) (*i*) $y = 0.2 \sin 2\pi(6t - x/60)$, (*ii*) $y = 0.2 \cos 2\pi(6t - x/60)$
(*b*) (*i*) $y = 0$, (*ii*) $y = 0.2$ cm.]

14. A plane progressive wave train of frequency 400 Hz has a phase velocity of 480 m/sec. (*a*) How far apart are two points 30° out of phase? (*b*) What is the phase difference between two displacements at a given point at times 10^{-3} sec apart? [**Ans.** (*a*) 0.1 *m*, (*b*) 144°.]

15. Which of the following are solutions of the one-dimensional wave equation? (*i*) $y = x^2 - v^2t^2$, (*ii*) $y = 7x - 10t$, (*iii*) $y = 2 \sin x \cos vt$ and (*iv*) $y = \sin 2x \cos vt$ [**Ans.** (*ii*) and (*iii*)]

16. (*a*) Obtain the phase difference between two progressive waves represented by the following equations: (*i*) $y_1 = a \cos(\omega t - kx)$ and $y_2 = a \sin(\omega t - kx)$, (*ii*) $y_1 = f(Wt - kx)$ and $y_2 = F(Wt - kx - \phi)$.

(*b*) Find the *frequency*, *angular frequency*, *wave number* and the *propagation constant* for light waves of wavelength 6×10^{-5} cm.

[**Ans.** (*a*) (*i*) $\pi/2$ [$\because$ *phase difference* $= \cos(\omega t - kx) - \sin(\omega t - kx)$
$= (\cos \omega t - kx) - \cos(\omega t - kx - \pi/2) = \pi/2$
(*ii*) *The two being different types of fundamental of* $(t - x/v)$, *their phase difference cannot be determined.*
(*b*) 5×10^{14} Hz; 3.142×10^{15} rad/sec; $1 - 7 \times 10^4$ cm^{-1}; 1.05×10^5]

17. A plane progressive harmonic wave is travelling with a velocity of 340 m/sec in a fluid medium of density 0.0015 gm/c.c. If the amplitude of the wave be 10^{-4} cm and its frequency 300 Hz, obtain the values of (*i*) *energy density* and (*ii*) *energy current* for it.

[**Ans.** (*i*) 2.665×10^{-5} erg/c.c., (*ii*) 0.9059 erg/cm^2-sec.]

18. Determine (*i*) the velocity of sound in a gas in which two waves of lengths 50 cm and 50.5 cm produce 6 beats per second and (*ii*) the velocity of sound in water in which waves of lengths 500 cm and 512 cm produce 6 beats per second. [**Ans.** (*i*) 303 m/sec; (*ii*) 1280 m/sec.]

[**Hint.** Number of beats per second = $n_1 - n_2$, where $n_1 = v/\lambda_1$ and $n_2 = v/\lambda_2$, v being the velocity of sound in air in case (*i*) and in water in case (*ii*) So that,

$$\textit{number of beats} \text{ per sec } = (n_1 - n_2) = v/\lambda_1 - v/\lambda_2 = v(1/\lambda_1 - 1/\lambda_2).$$

whence, $(n_1 - a_2)$, λ_1 and λ_2 being known, v can be evaluated.]

19. Sound waves from a vibrating body reach a point by two paths. When the paths differ by 12 cm or by 36 cm, there is silence at the point. Calculate the frequency of the vibrating body if the velocity of sound in air is 330 m/sec. [**Ans.** 1375 Hz.]

[**Hint.** It is clearly a case of *destructive interference*. For, when the path difference is 12 cm, the two waves arrive at the point in opposite phases and thus annul each other, producing silence. This path difference must be equal to an odd number of half wavelengths, *i.e.*, equal to $(2n + 1)\ \lambda/2$ or equal to $\lambda/2$, $3\lambda/2$ $5\lambda/2$ etc., the successive values of path difference differing from each other by λ. So that, again, when the path difference is 36 cm and there is silence at the point, it is clear that the difference between these two successive values of path difference must be equal to λ, the wavelength of each wave, *i.e.*, $\lambda = (36 - 12) = 24$ cm. If, therefore, n be the frequency of the vibrating body, or of the waves produced by it, we have $v = n\lambda$, whence $n = v/\lambda = 33000/24 = 1375$.]

20. A source S and a detector D of high frequency waves are a distance d apart on the ground (Fig. 10.35). The direct wave from S is found to be in phase at D with the wave from S that is reflected from a horizontal layer at an altitude H. The incident and reflected rays make the same angle with the reflecting layer. When the layer rises a distance h, no signal is detected at D. Neglect aborption in the atmosphere and find the relation between d, h, H and the wave-length λ of the waves.

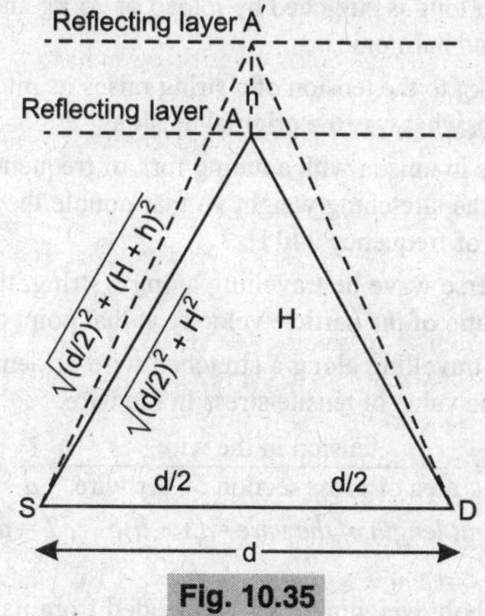

Fig. 10.35

[**Ans.** $\lambda = 2[\sqrt{d^2 + 4(H+h)^2} - \sqrt{d^2 + 4H^2}]$]

[**Hint.** Obviously, first the waves arrive at D, directly along SD and by reflection along SAD. The path difference between the two = $(SA + AD) - SD$. Since they arrive *in phase*, this path difference = $n\lambda$., *i.e.*, $2\sqrt{(d/2)^2 + H^2} - d = n\lambda$.

Next, the waves arrive at D, directly along SD and by reflection along $SA'D$. The path difference now is $(SA' + A'D) - SD$. Since they arrive *in opposite phases* and thus annual each other, this path difference = $(2n + 1)\ \lambda/2$, *i.e.*, $2\sqrt{(d/2)^2 + (H+h)^2} - d = (2n+1)\ \lambda/2$. Therefore, $(2n + 1)\ \lambda/2 - n\lambda$ $= \lambda/2 = (2\sqrt{(d/2)^2 + (H+h)^2} - d) - (2\sqrt{(d/2)^2 + H^2} - d)$, whence λ may be evaluated.]

II–Vibration of strings

21. Discuss the transverse vibrations of strings and derive an expression for the velocity of propagation of a transverse wave along a string. Suggest a method for determining this velocity experimentally.

22. (*a*) Derive an expression for the velocity of transverse waves in a stretched uniform string.

(*b*) Calculate the velocity of a transverse wave along a string of length 2 metres and mass 0.06 kg under a tension of 500 newton. **[Ans.** 130 m/sec.]

23. A transverse harmonic wave is travelling along a string. Show that the energy per unit length of the string is given by $2\pi^2 a^2 n^2 \sigma$, where a is the amplitude and n, the frequency of the wave and σ, the mass per unit length of the string. Also show that the power or the average rate of transfer of energy is given by $2\pi^2\, a^2\, n^2\, \sigma\, v$/sec, where v is the wave velocity.

[Hint. See worked example 22]

24. Outline a method for the determination of the frequency of an alternating current with the help of a sonometer when the sonometer wire is (*i*) of a *magnetic* material, (*b*) of a *non-magnetic material.*

[Hint. See worked example 35]

25. (*a*) Show that the time taken for a disturbance to pass along a string of length l cm and of mass m gm per cm is constant when the tension is ml^2 gm wt and calculate this time.

[Hint. Wave velocity $v = \sqrt{T/m} = \sqrt{ml^2 g/m} = l\sqrt{g}$ cm/sec, because $T = ml^2$ gm wt $= ml^2 g$ dynes.

Therefore, *time taken to cover the length of the string*, say

$$t = l/l\sqrt{g} = 1/\sqrt{g} = 1/\sqrt{981}]$$

(*b*) Calculate the speed of a transverse wave in a wire of 1.0 mm^2 cross section under the tension produced by 0.1 kilogram weight. (Specific gravity of material of the wire = 9.81 and g = 981 cm/sec^2.) **[Ans.** (*a*) 0.3192 sec; (*b*) 10^3 cm/sec.]

26. (*a*) A piece of wire 50 cm long is stretched by a load of 25 kg and has a mass of 1.44 gm. Find the frequency of the second harmonic.

(*b*) If an addition of 11.5 kg to the tension of a string raises its pitch (or frequency) by a fifth (*i.e.*, to 3/2 of its initial value), what was the original tension? **[Ans.** (*a*) 583.2 (*b*) 9.1 kg wt]

27. A sonometer wire vibrates in unison with a tuning fork of frequency 320 when the stretching weight is 4 kg. What should be the stretching weight so that double the length of the wire may vibrate in unison with a tuning fork of frequency 240 Hz?

28. (*a*) Show that if a transverse wave be travelling along a string, the slope of the string at any given point is equal to the ratio of the particle velocity at that point to the wave velocity.

(*b*) A transverse wave is travelling along a stretched wire of density 7.5 gm/c.c. with a velocity of 105 cm/sec. Obtain the value of tensile stress in the wire. **[Ans.** 7.5×10^{10} dynes/cm^2.]

[Hint. *Tensile stress* $= \dfrac{\text{tension in the wire}}{\text{area of cross section of the wire}} = \dfrac{T}{a}$. Since $v = \sqrt{T/\sigma}$, clearly, $T = \sigma v^2$, where σ = *mass per unit length of the wire* $= (1 \times a)\rho$. $\therefore\ T = a\rho v^2$. Hence *tensite stress* $= a\rho v^2/a = \rho v^2$.]

29. (*a*) A long thin wire has bob, weighing 2 kg, suspended from its lower free end and functions as a pendulum. When the wire is plucked at its mid-point, it emits a note of frequency 252 Hz. What should be the weight of the bob in order that the wire, when plucked in the middle, gives an *octave* of first note (*i.e.* a note of twice its frequency)?

(*b*) A string of mass 2 gm/metre carries progressive waves of amplitude 1.5 cm, frequency, 60 sec^{-1} and speed, 200 m/sec. Calculate (*i*) the energy per unit length per metre length of the wave, (*ii*) the rate of energy propagation in the wave.

[Ans. (*a*) 8 kg wt; (*b*), (*i*) 3.2×10^{-2} joule, (*ii*) 6.4 Joules/sec.]

Note. More problems on vibrations of strings will be found under section *V*.

30. Problem that the wave equation for a transverse wave in a string is given by

$$\frac{\delta^2 y}{\delta x^2} = \frac{1}{v^2}\frac{\delta^2 y}{\delta t^2}$$

where $v = \sqrt{\dfrac{T}{\rho}}$, T being the tension and ρ the linear density of the string. What are its possible solutions?

(Pbi. U., 2003, 2002, P.U. 2002, 2001, 2000; Kerala U., 2001, Cal. U. 2003; H.P.U., 2002; G.N.D.U. 2001)

31. (*a*) Show that for a transverse in a string $T/\rho = v\frac{1}{2}$ where T is the tension with which the string is stretched, ρ the mass per unit length of the string and v the velocity of the wave produced in it. Hence find the frequency of the fundamental note and the first octave of the vibrating string fixed at both ends. ***(Indore U., 2001; Pbi.U., 2000; G.N.D.U., 2000)***

(*b*) The wave velocity in a string is a functions of elasticity and inertia of the medium. Comment ***(P.U., 2002)***

32. When a rod is clamped at the end horizontally and free end is pressed down and released, show that for the smallest frequency of vibration, the wavelength is four times the length of the rod.

33. Obtain an expression for the energy of a transversely vibrating string. Hence derive the expression for the rate of flow of energy along the stretched string. ***(P.U. 2003; Gauhati U., 2000)***

34. Explain why we hear a 'flick' at the end of a string. ***(P.U. 2001; Pbi U., 2001)***

35. (*a*) What happens if incident waves fall at a common boundary of two strings having different impedances but joined in such a way that tension is the same throughout?

(*b*) Define reflection coefficient and transmission coefficient of amplitude. What is the amplitude of transverse waves reflected at the dense medium (*i.e.*, $Z_2 \cong \infty$)? ***(P.U., 2004)***

36. Show that all energy arriving at the boundary in the incident wave leaves the boundary in the reflected and transmitted wave. Define reflection and transmission coefficients of energy. Show that the sum of the reflection and transmission coefficients of energy is always unity.

(P.U., 2004, 2004, 2001, 2000 Pbi. U., 2001; G.N.D.U. 2000)

37. Derive the relation for the characteristic impendence of a string. Explain the factors on which it depends. ***(G.N.D.U. 2004; P.U., 2001, 2000)***

38. What does the term 'the matching of impedance' imply? show that for perfect matching the impedance of the coupling element is the geometric mean of the impedances of the media to be matched when the impedances of the two media are not equal. ***(P.U., 2003)***

39. State the conditions for perfect impedance matching between two media. What are the uses of impedance matching? Give application for anti-reflection films. ***(P.U., 2001; G.N.D.U., 2004)***

40. Two electric transmission cables are joined at a point. What special care should be taken for proper transmission of power? ***(G.N.D.U., 2000)***

III–Longitudinal wave motion in fluid media and in solid rods

41. Obtain Netwton's expression for the velocity of sound in a gaseous medium and explain La' place's correction of the same.

42. Show that the excess pressure p and particle velocity ξ in plane longitudinal waves in a medium of volume elasticity E are related by $p = E\,\xi/v$, where v is the speed of the waves.

[**Hint.** We have $p = -E.\frac{d\xi}{dx}$ and $\xi = -v\frac{d\xi}{dx}$. So that, $\frac{d\xi}{dx} = -\xi/v$]

43. Show that in the case of a sound wave in a gas, the pressure amplitude (p_m) is $2\pi\, v^2\rho/\lambda$ times the displacement amplitude (a). Hence, or otherwise, show that the intensity of a sound wave in terms of displacement amplitude is given by $I = 2\pi^2 a^2 n^2 \rho v$ and in terms of pressure amplitude it is given by $I = Pm^2/2\rho v$, where the symbols have their usual meanings.

[**Hint.** $p = -K\, dy/dx$ and since $y = a\sin\frac{2\pi}{\lambda}(vt - x), dy/dx = -\frac{2\pi}{\lambda}a\cos\frac{2\pi}{\lambda}(vt - x)$.

So that, $p = K.\frac{2\pi}{\lambda}a\cos\frac{2\pi}{\lambda}(vt - x) = v^2\rho\frac{2\pi}{\lambda}a\cos\frac{2\pi}{\lambda}(vt - x)$, because $v = \sqrt{K/\rho}$ and ∴ $K = v^2\rho$.

Thus, *pressure amplitude*, $pm = \frac{2\pi}{\lambda}v^2\rho a$]

44. Particle displacement in a plane longitudinal wave in a medium of density ρ is given by $\xi = A\cos 2\pi n\,(t - x/v)$. Deduce expressions for (*i*) pressure amplitude, and (*ii*) energy flux.

45. One sound wave is travelling in water and another in air. (*a*) If their intensities be equal, obtain the ratio between their pressure amplitudes and (*b*) If their pressure amplitudes be equal, obtain the ratio between their intensities.

[Ans. (*a*) $\sqrt{\rho_\omega v_\omega} : \sqrt{\rho_{a_{wa}}}$ (*b*) $\rho_a v_a$: $\rho_w v_w$ where ρ_w and ρ_a are the densities of water and air and v_w and v_a, the velocities of sound in water and air respectively.**]**

46. (*a*) Discuss the effect of temperature and pressure on the velocity of sound in air.

(*b*) The velocity of sound in air at normal temperature and pressure is 330 m/sec. Find the velocity at a temperature of 27°C and a pressure of 74 cm of mercury. **[Ans.** 345.9 m/sec]

47. The planet Jupiter has an atmosphere of a mixture of ammonia and methan at a temperature of – 130°C. Calculate the velocity of sound on this planet, assuming γ for the mixture to be 1.3 and the molecular weight of the mixture to be 16.5. (Gas constant $R = 8.3$ joules per deg. per gm mol.

[Ans. 305.8 m/sec.]

48. Show that in the case of a plane acoustic wave (*i.e.*, sound wave), (*i*) the displacement, (*ii*) the particle velocity, (*iii*) the strain and (*iv*) the excess pressure each satisfy the differential wave equation $d^2\phi/dt^2 = v^2 d^2 \phi/dx^2$.

[Hint. (*i*) This has already been shown in § 9.8.

(*ii*) Putting the wave equation in the form $y = a \sin k(vt - x)$, where $k = 2\pi/\lambda$, we have *particle velocity* $U = dy/dt = kv\, a \cos k(vt - x) = \phi$, say.

Then, $d^2\phi/dt^2 = -k^3v^3\, a \cos k(vt - x)$ and $d^2\phi/dx^2 = -k^3\, v\, a \cos k(vt - x)$.

Or,
$$d^2\phi/dt^2 = v^2 d^2\, \phi/dx^2.$$

(*iii*) Putting $dy/dx = -k\, a \cos (vt - x) = \phi$, we have

$d^2\phi/dt^2 = k^3v^2\, a \cos k(vt - x)$ and $d^2\phi/dx^2 = k^3\, a \cos (vt - x)$. Again, therefore,
$$d^2\phi/dt^2 = v^2\, d^2\phi/dx^2.$$

(*iv*) Since $p = -K\, dy/dx$, proceeding as in (*iii*) above, we again have
$$d^2\phi/dt^2 = v^2\, d^2\phi/dx^2.]$$

49. Show that in plane harmonic sound wave, the excess pressure (p) is ahead of the displacement in phase by $\pi/2$.

[Hint. Displacement $y = a \sin \frac{2\pi}{\lambda}(vt - x)$ *and, therefore, excess pressure*]

$$P = -K\frac{dy}{dx} = -\rho v^2 \frac{dy}{dx} = \rho v^2 \frac{2\pi}{\lambda} a \cos \frac{2\pi}{\lambda}(vt - x) = p_m \cos \frac{2\pi}{\lambda}(vt - x)$$

$= p_m \sin \frac{2\pi}{\lambda}\, [(vt - x) + \pi/2]$, where $K = \rho v^2$ ($\because v = \sqrt{K/\rho}$) and $\rho v^2 \frac{2\pi}{\lambda} a = p_m$, the amplitude of pressure variation.]

50. Obtain an expression for the velocity of a longitudinal wave in a solid rod. If the frequency of the waves produced be 1000/sec, the density of the material of the rod, 9 gm/c.c., the value of Young's modulus for it, 9×10^{12} dynes/cm^2, calculate the wavelength of the waves. **[Ans.** 1000 cm.]

[Hint. $v = n\lambda = \sqrt{Y/\rho}$ and $\therefore \lambda = \frac{1}{n}\sqrt{Y/\rho}$]

51. In a plane progressive wave in a fluid, the angular frequency is ω sec^{-1} and the displacement amplitude is A cm. Deduce the values of (*i*) pressure amplitude, (*ii*) energy density in terms of ω, A and ρ.

[Ans. (*i*) $\omega^2 A\rho/k$; (*ii*) $\omega^2 A^2 \rho/2$.]

52. (*a*) The velocity of a longitudinal wave in a wire of area of cross section 0.004 sq. cm is twice the velocity of a transverse wave along it. Determine the ratio between the Young's modulus for the material of the wire and the tension to which the wire is subjected.

(*b*) The velocities of the longitudinal and transverse waves along a wire are the same. Show that the stress in the wire is equal to the value of Y for its material. **[Ans.** (*a*) $Y : T :: 1000 : 1$]

[Hint. (*a*) $v = \sqrt{T/m} = \sqrt{T/a \times 1 \times \rho} = \sqrt{T/0.004\rho}$ and $2v = \sqrt{Y/\rho}$.

(*b*) $v = \sqrt{T/a \times 1 \times \rho} = \sqrt{T/a \times \rho} = \sqrt{Y/\rho}$. So that, stress, $T/a = Y$]

Note. More problem on longitudinal waves in gases and solids are given under section *V*.

IV–Linear bounded medium—(Stationary waves)

53. Explain analytically the formation of waves in a linear bounded medium. Why are they referred to as stationary or standing waves?

How do they differ from ordinary progressive waves?

54. Discuss the changes (*i*) with respect to position, and (*ii*) with respect to time in the case of standing waves in air.

55. Discuss the solution of the differential wave equation $d^2y/dx^2 = (1/c^2)\, d^2y/dt^2$ for a bounded system with boundary conditions $y = 0$ at $x = 0$ and $x = L$.

N.B. Here *c* represents the wave velocity. **[Ans.** $y = a \sin\left(\frac{r\pi x}{L}\right) \cos\left(\frac{r\pi vt}{L}\right)$.]

56. Show that there is no transference of energy across any section in the case of a wave in a linear bounded medium.

57. A sound wave in air is represented by the equation 5 sin 0.3142 (500*t* + *x*), where *t* is in see and *x* in cm. Write the equation of the wave which, on superposition with it, would produce a standing wave.

[Ans. (*i*) –5 sin 0.3142 (500 *t* + *x*) or (*ii*) 5 sin 0.3142 (500*t* + *x*)]

58. A progressive wave train in air, of amplitude 0.005 cm, frequency, 1000 cps and wavelength, 80 cm, and travelling along the positive direction of *x*, is reflected normally at a rigid boundary. Obtain the values of (*i*) displacement amplitude, (*ii*) particle velocity amplitude, and (*iii*) amplitude of pressure variation at *x* = 50 cm. **[Ans.** (*i*) 0.01 cm (*ii*) 62.84 cm/sec, (*iii*) 0]

[Hint. See §10.29 Case I]

V–Different modes of vibration of strings, rods and air columns

59. Show that in the case of a sonometer (*i.e.*, in the medium with both boundaries rigid), the frequencies of the notes emitted form a harmonic series.

60. One end of a string, 100 cm long and of mass 5 gm, is attached to a prong of an electrically driven tuning fork, with weights suspended from the other so that it is quite horizontal and under tension. The fork vibrates in a direction perpendicular to the length of the string which is thrown into vibration in 4 loops emitting a note of frequency 60 Hz. Calculate the tension in the string.

What would happen in the fork be turned so as to vibrate parallel to the length of the string?

[Ans. 4.5×10^5 dynes; *frequency of the note emitted* = 30 Hz.]

[Hint. See worked example]

61. A sonometer wire is stretched by means of a piece of metal hanging from its other end. With the effective length of the wire (*i.e.*, the distance between the two bridges) equal to 100 cm, it emits its fundamental note, in unison with that of a given tuning fork. When the suspended piece of metal is immersed in water, the length of the wire has to be shortened by 7 cm in order that the fundamental note emitted by the wire may again be in unison with that of the fork. Obtain the value of the density of the metal piece.

[Hint. If *m* be the mass of the metal piece, tension *T* in the wire, *in the first case* (*i.e.*, when the metal piece is in air) = *m* gm wt = mg dynes.

When immersed in water, the weight of the metal piece, and therefore the tension in the wire = $(m - m/\rho) = m(1 - 1/\rho)$ gm wt = $m(1 - 1/\rho)\, g$ dynes, where ρ is the density of the metal piece.

If *n* be the frequency of the tuning fork and hence that of the fundamental note emitted by the wire in either case, we have

$$n = \frac{1}{2l_1}\sqrt{mg/\sigma} = \frac{1}{2l_2}\sqrt{\frac{m(1-1/\rho)g}{\sigma}}$$

where l_1 and l_2 are the lengths of the wire in the two cases and, obviously, therefore, equal to 100 cm and 100 – 7 = 93 cm respectively.]

62. Show that when a given rod is clamped (*i*) at one end or (*ii*) in the middle, only odd harmonics can be excited but the frequencies of the various notes in case (*i*) are half those of the corresponding notes in case (*ii*).

63. Show that whether a rod be free at both ends or clamped at both ends, both odd and even harmonics can be excited and that the frequencies of the corresponding notes are the same in either case.

64. A metal rod, 200 cm long, is clamped at one end and emits a fundamental note of frequency 800 Hz when set into longitudinal vibration. If the value of Young's modulus for the material of the rod be 8×10^{11} dynes/cm^2, obtain the values of its density.

What would be the frequency of the fundamental note emitted by the rod if it were clamped (*i*) in the middle. (*ii*) at both ends or (*iii*) nowhere? [**Ans.** 7.8 gm/cc; 1600 Hz in all three cases.]

65. (*a*) Show that the fundamental note given by an open pipe is the octave of the fundamental note given by the pipe if it were closed at one end.

(*b*) Also show that the frequencies of the second harmonics of a closed and open pipe of the same length are in the ratio 3 : 4.

66. What is meant by the *end correction* of a pipe? How may it be obtained for (*i*) a closed, and (*ii*) an open pipe?

67. (*a*) Tuning forks are usually mounted or their resonance boxes which are just rectangular boxes with one side open, so that the air column inside the box has the same fundamental frequency as that of the fork and is thus set into resonance with it. If the frequency of the fork be 320 Hz and the velocity of sound in air, 342 m/sec, what should be the length of the box? (Ignore end correction).

(*b*) A tuning fork of frequency 256 Hz is held above a column of air in a closed tube. The positions of the first and the second resonance are 33.0 cm and 100.5 cm respectively. Calculate the velocity of sound in air. [**Ans.** (*a*) 0.267 m; (*b*) 345.6 m/sec.]

VI–Fourier's theorem

68. State *Fourier's theorem* and mention the conditions under which it holds good. Also evaluate the various Fourier coefficients.

69. Obtain the Fourier series for a complex periodic function given by $y = a$ from $t = 0$ to $T/2$ and $y = 0$ from $T/2$ to T.

[**Ans.** $y = \frac{a}{2} + \frac{2a}{\pi}\left(\sin\omega t + \frac{1}{3}\sin 3\omega t + \frac{1}{5}\sin 5\omega t + ...\right)$]

70. State the conditions under which Fourier's theorem may be applicable. Apply it to deduce the harmonic components of a saw-tooth curve of frequency $\frac{n}{2\pi}$ and form given by $y = -\frac{a}{2} + a\frac{n}{2\pi}t$ for $t = 0$ to $2\pi/n$.

[**Ans.** $y = -\frac{a}{\pi}\left(\sin nt + \frac{1}{2}\sin 2nt + \frac{1}{3}\sin 3nt\right)$]

71. A quantity y has a value a from $x = 0$ to $x = \pi$ and $-a$ from $x = \pi$ to $x = 2\pi$. Express y as a Fourier expansion in x. [**Ans.** $y = \frac{4a}{\pi}$ [sin x + (sin 3x)/3 + (sin 5x)/5 + ...]]

72. In a displacement curve $y = 4\,at/T$ from $t = 0$ to $t = T/4$, $y = 2a - 4\,at/T$ from $T/4$ to $3T/4$ and $y = 4\,at/T - 4a$ from $3T/4$ to T. Find the amplitude of the fundamental and the first two harmonics.

[**Ans.** $8a/\pi^2$, $8a/9\pi^2$, $8a/25\pi^2$.]

73. A function is displaced by half the range and the new function thus obtained is added to the first. Show that the result gives twice the sum of the independent term and the even harmonics. And, if the new function obtained is subtracted from the first, the result is twice the sum of the odd harmonics.

VII–Group velocity

74. Distinguish between *phase velocity* and *group velocity* of a train of waves and establish relationship between the two. Show that in a non-dispersive medium they are the same.

75. Deduce the relation $v = \omega/k$, where v is the phase (or wave) velocity and ω and k have their usual meanings, and show that its first derivative with respect to k gives the group velocity.

76. Show that when $dv/d\lambda = v/\lambda$, the group velocity, is zero and when $v = A + B\lambda$ (where A and B are constants), the group velocity is equal to A.

77. For what wavelength will the group velocity of surface waves in a liquid, of surface tension T and density ρ, be a minimum? [**Ans.** $\lambda = 16\sqrt{T/g\rho}$.]

11 Chapter

DYNAMICS OF RIGID BODIES

Brief Contents

11.1 RIGID BODY — TRANSLATIONAL AND ROTATIONAL MOTION

A rigid body is defined as a solid body in which the particles are compactly arranged so that the inter-particle distance is small and fixed and is not disturbed by any external forces applied. Such a body thus preserves its shape or configuration intact and does not bend, stretch or vibrate when in motion.

There is no such thing as an ideally rigid body but bodies, in which the small forces required to move them produce little or no bending, stretching etc., may be taken to be rigid.

A rigid body may either move *bodily, i.e., as a whole*, in any direction, or it may turn around or rotate in two or three dimensions. In the former case, it is said to execute a *translatory motion* and in the latter, a *rotational motion*. A body may also execute both translational and rotational motions simultaneously. We can imagine the translational motion of a rigid body to be that of one single point, namely, its centre of mass, with the whole mass of the body is supposed to be concentrated there.

The rotational motion, on the other hand, can be quite a complicated affair but we shall restrict ourselves here to the *simplest case* of rotation, *viz.*, *the rotation of a rigid body about a line or axis fixed in the reference frame in which we are making our observation*, this line or axis being referred to as the *axis of rotation* of the body. A given point in the body thus obviously moves in a plane perpendicular to this axis of rotation and the rotation is referred to as *plane rotation* or *rotation in two dimensions*.

Let us consider a rigid body free to rotate about the axis *OZ* through *O*, with the axis fixed in an *inertial reference frame,* (Fig. 11.1).

All the particles of the body describe circles about the axis of rotation (*OZ*) in a plane perpendicular to it and have their centres lying on it, with their radii equal to their respective perpendicular distances from it (except, of course, those that lie on the axis itself) and the radius of each obviously sweeps through the same angle $\delta\theta$, say, in the same time δt.

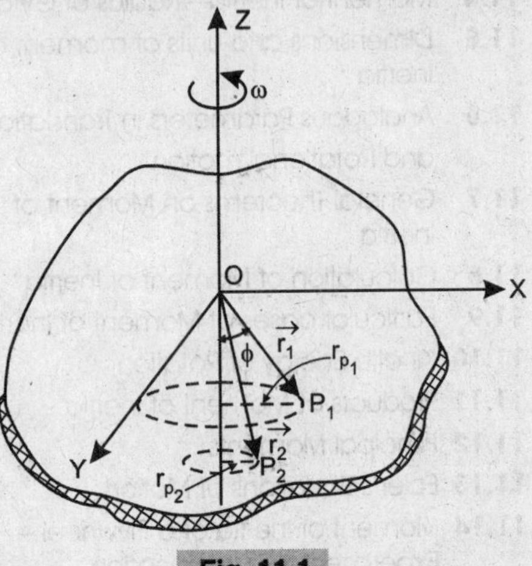

Fig. 11.1

Thus, for example, particles P_1 and P_2, with position vector $\vec{r_1}$ and $\vec{r_2}$ with respect to origin *O* and distant r_{p_1} and r_{p_2} from the axis, describe circles of radii $P_1A = r_{p_1}$ and $PB = r_{p_2}$ with their centres at *A* and *B* respectively, where P_1A and P_2B are perpendiculars dropped from P_1 and P_2 on to the axis, and both sweep through the same angle $\delta\theta$ in time δt.

The angular velocity of both P_1 and P_2, and in fact of all the particles, and hence of the body, as a whole, is thus the same, *viz.*, $\omega = \delta\theta/\delta t$, which, in the limit $\delta t \to 0$ gives $\omega = d\theta/dt$.

Since infinitesimally small angular displacements are vectors, we have $\omega = d\theta/dt$ (a vector quantity $d\theta$ divided by a scalar quantity dt) also a vector, the direction of which (in accordance with the right hand rule*) is along the axis of rotation (or the *Z*-axis), upward, if the rotation of the body be anticlockwise about the axis. This is indicated in the figure by the thick arrow, the length of which is proportional to the magnitude of ω.

* That is, if we coil the fingers of our right hand around the axis in the direction of rotation of the body, the extended thumb gives the direction of the angular velocity vector.

It may be noted that nothing actually moves in the direction of the angular velocity vector; *it merely represents conventionally the angular velocity of the rotational motion* that is taking place in the plane perpendicular to it (*i.e.*, in the $x - y$ plane, in the case shown).

The *angular acceleration* of the body is given by $\alpha = d\omega/dt$ which, again, is a vector, since, as before, a *vector* ($d\omega$) is divided by a scalar (dt).

The *linear speed* of a particle P is, as we know, given by $v = \omega r$ P (*i.e., its angular velocity × radius of the circle in which it rotates*), where v and ω are respectively the *magnitudes* of the linear speed and the angular velocity.

Now, in Fig. 11.2, if $\vec{r}$ be the position vector of a particle P of a rigid body with respect to the origin O, it obviously rotates about the axis in a circle of radius $r_p = r \sin POA = r \sin \theta$, where θ is the angle that the position vector $\vec{r}$ makes with the axis. So that, $v = \omega r \sin\theta$.

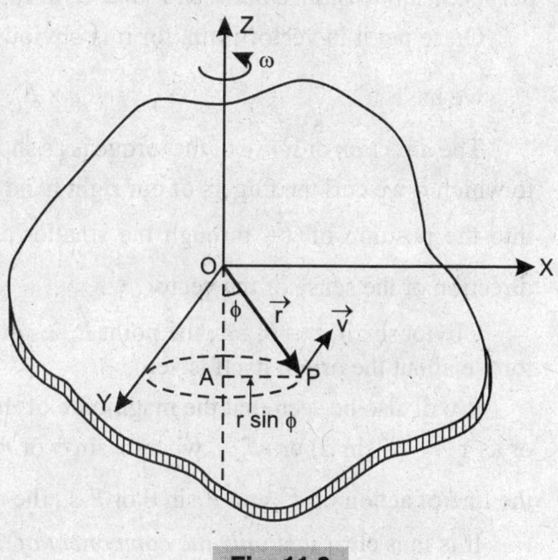

Fig. 11.2

And therefore,

linear velocity vector $\vec{v} = \vec{\omega} \times \vec{r}$, its direction being *tangential to the circular path at P and perpendicular to the position vector* $\vec{r}$, as shown.

As mentioned already, we are concerned here with only this plane rotational motion of a rigid body and the study of its relationship with the properties of the body or the causes of its rotation, and we call it the study of the *rotational dynamics* of the rigid body.

As will be readily seen, however, and as will be further observed as we proceed along, the analogous translational and rotational parameters, like linear and angular displacements (r and θ), linear and angular velocities ($\vec{v}$ and $\vec{\omega}$), linear and angular acceleration ($\vec{a}$ and $\vec{\alpha} = d\omega/dt$ etc., differ dimensionally in most cases only by a length factor r; for example, $v = r\omega$, $a = r\, d\omega/dt$ and so on.

11.2 TORQUE

The one important difference between translational and rotational motion that is clearly apparent is that for linear acceleration, in the case of the former, we need to know only the magnitude of the force applied; for angular acceleration in the case of the latter, we must know also the actual point of application of the force and the way it is directed, or, in other words, the *moment of the force* which, in the terminology used in the context of rotational motion, we refer to as the *torque* (from the Latin word *torquere* meaning *to twist*).

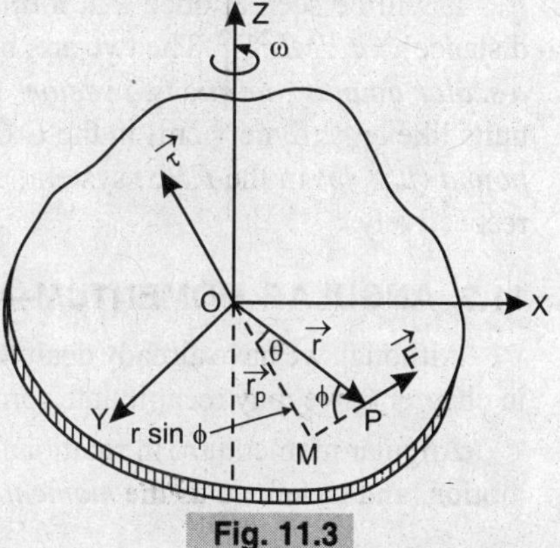

Fig. 11.3

Thus, in Fig. 11.3, if $\vec{F}$ be the *force* acting on a particle P of a rigid body, the *moment of the force* about the origin O in an inertial reference frame, or the *torque* τ acting on the particle, with respect to O, is $\vec{F} \times \vec{r}_p$, where

$\vec{r}_p$ is the perpendicular distance between the line of action of the force and the origin O (or the axis passing through O).

If $\vec{r}$ be the position vector of P with respect to O, we have $r_P = r \sin \phi$, where ϕ is the angle between $\vec{F}$ and $\vec{r}$.

So that, *magnitude of the torque acting on the particle* = $Fr \sin \phi$, where $r \sin \phi = r_P$, the *perpendicular distance between F and O*, is called the *moment arm*.

Or, to put it in vector form, for it is obviously a *vector quantity*,

we have $$\vec{\tau} = \vec{r} \times \vec{F}.$$

The *direction* or *sense* of the torque is as shown, given by the *right-handed screw rule*, according to which if we curl the fingers of our right hand in the direction in which $\vec{r}$ must be swung to move into the position of $\vec{F}$, through the smaller angle between them, the extended thumb gives the direction or the sense of the vector $\vec{\tau}$.

Obviously, if $\vec{r}$ *=0, i.e.*, the point P lies at the origin O, the torque is zero. In other words, the torque about the origin itself is zero.

It will also be seen that the magnitude of the torque may be put either as $\tau = F(r \sin \phi)$ or $Fr \perp$ or as $\tau = r(F \sin \phi)$ or $rF \perp$, where $r \sin \phi$ or $r \perp$ represents the component of $\vec{r}$ perpendicular to the line of action of $\vec{F}$ and $F \sin \theta$ or $F \perp$, the component of $\vec{F}$ perpendicular to $\vec{r}$.

It is thus clear that *only the component of* $\vec{F}$ *perpendicular to* $\vec{r}$ *is responsible for the torque.* For, if $\theta = 0$ or π, this perpendicular component of $\vec{F}$, and hence also the torque, vanishes; for, then, $F \sin \theta = 0$ and the line of action of $\vec{F}$ thus passes through the origin O.

It may as well be noted that reversing either $\vec{F}$ or $\vec{r}$ reverses only the direction of the torque, its magnitude remaining unaffected (because a reversal of the direction of one vector in a vector product means a reversal of direction of the product itself). If, however, both $\vec{r}$ and $\vec{F}$ be reversed simultaneously, both magnitude and direction of $\vec{\tau}$ remain unaffected (because a reversal of the direction of both the vectors in a vector product leaves the direction of the product unaffected).

And, obviously, *for a rigid body*, consisting of a large number of particles, the torque

$$\vec{\tau} = \Sigma \vec{r} \times \vec{F}$$

It will be seen at once that *torque has the same dimensions as work* (both being force times distance), *viz.*, ML^2T^{-2}. The two are, however, entirely different physical quantities; *whereas work is a scalar quantity, torque is a vector*. To distinguish between the two, therefore, we express work in units like *ergs* (dyne × cm) in the *C.G.S.* system, *joules* ($N \times m$) in the *MKS* or *SI* system and *foot-pound* (*ft* × *lb*) in the *F.P.S.* system, and torque in *dyne-cm*, *N-metre* and *lb-ft* in the three systems respectively.

11.3 ANGULAR MOMENTUM—ANGULAR IMPULSE

Although we have already dealt with angular momentum in connection with angular momentum in chapter 6, we may recapitulate some salient points here.

Angular momentum, in rotational motion, is the analogue of linear momentum, in translational motion, and is defined as the *moment of linear momentum*.

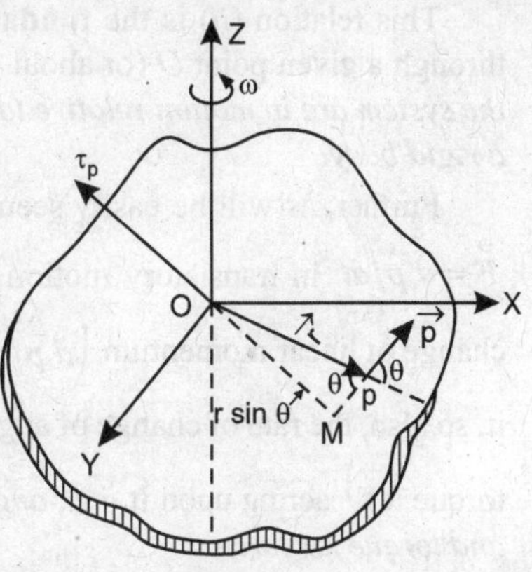

Fig. 11.4

Now, linear momentum for a particle of mass *m*, moving with velocity $\vec{v}$ is given by $\vec{p} = m\vec{v}$ and for system of particles or a rigid body, by $\vec{P} = M \times \vec{v}\ c.m.$, where *M* is the mass of the whole system or body and $\vec{v}\ c.m.$, the velocity of its *centre of mass*.

Thus, considering a particle of a rigid body, free to turn about the fixed axis *OZ* through *O* (Fig. 11.4), if its linear momentum $\vec{p}$ be directed as shown, such that the momentum vector makes an angle θ with its position vector $\vec{r}$ (with respect to the origin *O*) in an inertial frame of reference, its angular momentum is given by

$$J_p = \vec{r} \times \vec{p} = \vec{r} \times m\vec{v} = m \times (\vec{r}\,\omega) \qquad ...[\because\ \vec{v} = \vec{r}\,\omega]$$

It is obviously a vector and its magnitude is given by $J_p = pr \sin\theta$, with its sense or direction given by the usual right handed screw rule for the vector product of two vectors as in the case of torque in § 11.2 above. So that, in the case shown, it is perpendicular to the plane of $\vec{r}$ and $\vec{p}$, directed as indicated.

This direction of the angular momentum vector $\vec{J}_p$, it will be noted, is not, in general, the same as that of the angular velocity vector $\vec{\omega}$, for the simple reason that $\vec{J}_p$ is *not* the product of a scalar with ω.

Again, as in the case of torque, so also here, we may write the magnitude of $\vec{J}_p$ as $J_p = p\,(r \sin\theta)$ or $pr\perp$, or, as $J_p = r\,(p \sin\theta)$ or $rp\perp$, where $r \sin\theta = r\perp$, called the *moment arm*, is the component of $\vec{r}$ at right angles to the line of action of *p* and $p \sin\theta = p\perp$, the component of *p* at right angles to $\vec{r}$.

It follows, therefore, that *only the component of $\vec{p}$ perpendicular to $\vec{r}$ is responsible for the angular momentum*. For, if angle θ between $\vec{r}$ and $\vec{p}$ be *zero* or π the line of action of $\vec{p}$ passes through the origin *O*, and $p \sin\theta$ being zero, the angular momentum $\vec{J}_p$ is also zero.

Obviously enough, *the angular momentum of the whole rigid body* $(\vec{J})$ *about the point O will be the vector sum of the angular momenta of all the particles constituting it about the same point (O), i.e.,*

$$\vec{J} = \Sigma m\,\vec{r} \times \vec{v} = \Sigma m\,\vec{r} \times (\vec{\omega} \times \vec{r}) \qquad ...(i)$$

its direction, as pointed out earlier, being not, in general, the same as that of $\vec{\omega}$.

As shown under § 6.9, *the rate of change of angular momentum, i.e.,*

$$\frac{d\vec{J}}{dt} = \Sigma\vec{r} \times \frac{d}{dt}(m\vec{v}) = \Sigma\vec{r} \times \vec{F} = \vec{\tau}, \qquad ...(ii)$$

where $\Sigma\vec{r} \times \vec{F}$ is the sum of the torques, or the total torque, *due to all the external forces acting on the system or the rigid body*. The reason why we explicity use the word *external* as explained already under § 6.13, is that internal forces all form *collinear pairs of opposite forces* (of *action* and *reaction* in accordance with Newton's third law of motion), having equal and opposite moments about the given point, so that their sum is zero and they produce no effect.

This relation (*ii*) is the **fundamental equation of motion** of a rigid body about a fixed axis through a given point *O* (or about *O*) and *applies irrespective of whether the particles constituting the system are in motion relative to each other or in fixed spatial relationship with each other, as in a rigid body*.

Further, as will be easily seen, this relation is the rotational analogue of the familiar relation $\vec{F} = d\vec{p}/dt$ in translatory motion (*i.e.*, Newton's second law of motion). For, just as the rate of change of linear momentum $\left(d\vec{p}/dt\right)$ of a particle (or a body) is equal to the force $\left(\vec{F}\right)$ acting upon it, so also, the rate of change of angular momentum $\left(d\vec{J}/dt\right)$ of a particle (or a body) is equal to the torque $\left(\vec{\tau}\right)$ acting upon it, *i.e.*, *angular momentum has here been substituted for linear momentum and torque for force.*

Now, since the direction of the angular momentum vector $\vec{\tau}$ is not, in general, the same as that of the angular velocity vector $\vec{\omega}$, the torque vector $\vec{\tau}$ will not, in general, lie along the vector $\vec{\omega}$, *i.e.*, along the axis of rotation. Only a component of it will thus lie along the axis, with its other component perpendicular to it. The former component alone, however, produces rotation of the body about the axis, the latter merely tending to turn the axis away from its fixed position.

Let us, therefore, proceed to obtain the value of this *axial component* of $\vec{J}$ and hence also that of the *axial component of torque* $\vec{\tau}$.

Simplifying the triple vector product in expression I for $\vec{J}$ above, with the help of the vector identity $\vec{A}\times\left(\vec{B}\times\vec{C}\right) = \vec{B}\left(\vec{A}\cdot\vec{C}\right) - \vec{C}\left(\vec{A}\cdot\vec{B}\right)$, where $\vec{A}$ may be replaced by $\vec{r}, \vec{B}$ by $\vec{\omega}$ and $\vec{C}$ by $\vec{r}$, we have

$$\vec{J} = \Sigma m[\vec{r}\times(\vec{\omega}\times\vec{r})] = \Sigma m[\vec{\omega}(\vec{r}\cdot\vec{r}) - \vec{r}(\vec{r}\cdot\vec{\omega})]$$

Or,
$$\vec{J} = \Sigma m[r^2\vec{\omega} - (\vec{r}\cdot\vec{\omega})\vec{r}]$$

Since the angle between $\vec{r}$ and $\vec{\omega}$ is ϕ (Fig 11.4), the magnitude of the component of $\vec{r}$ along the direction of $\vec{\omega}$, *i.e.*, along the axis, is $r \cos\phi$, as shown separately in Fig 11.5 (*a*) for the sake of clarity. And, therefore, *magnitude of the component of* $\vec{J}$ *along the axis, i.e., its axial component*, is given by $J_A = \Sigma m\,[r^2\omega - (r\,\omega\cos\phi)\,r\cos\phi)]$ $= \Sigma mr^2\,\omega\,(1 - \cos^2\phi) = \Sigma mr^2\,\omega\,\sin^2\phi$. Or, since $r\sin\phi = r_p$ $= PA$ and ω is the same for all particles of the body, we have $J_A = \omega\Sigma mr_p^2$.

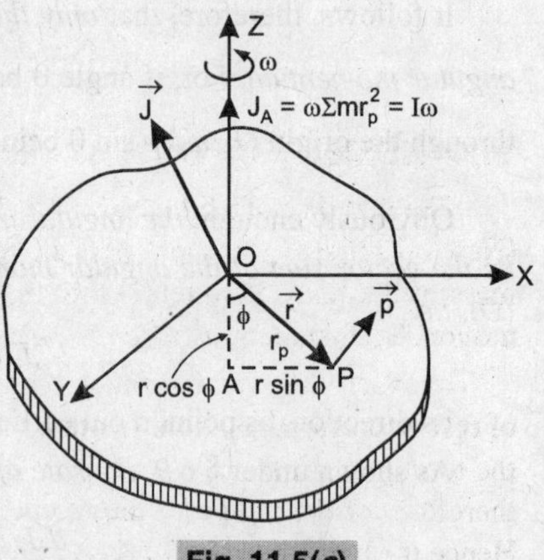

Fig. 11.5(*a*)

This summation Σmr_p^2 is called *rotational inertial or the moment of inertia* of the body about the axis of rotation and is represented by the symbol *I* (see § 11.4). So that, axial *component of angular momentum*, $J_A = I\omega$. Since *torque* $\vec{\tau} = d\vec{J}/dt$, we have *axial component of the torque, i.e.*, $\tau_A = dJ_A/dt = \dfrac{d}{dt}I\omega$.

Or, since I is constant for the body for a given axis of rotation, we have $\tau_A = Id\omega/dt$.

If, however, the axis of rotation passes through the centre of mass of the body, and coincides with its axis of symmetry, the components of the angular momenta of the various particles, and hence also those of the torque perpendicular to the axis, form equal and collinear pairs and thus cancel out. The entire angular momentum vector $\vec{J}$ *and hence also the entire torque vector* $\vec{\tau}$, *then lies along the angular velocity vector.* There is thus no component of the torque tending to turn the axis away from its fixed position and *the whole of it is, therefore, effective in producing rotation of the body.*

In such a case, in which the axis of rotation passes through the centre of mass and coincides with the axis of symmetry of the body, we drop the subscript (A) from $\vec{J}$ and $\vec{\tau}$ and simply write

$$\vec{J} = I\vec{\omega} \text{ and } \vec{\tau} = Id\vec{\omega}/dt.$$

With the axis of rotation passing through the centre of mass of the body, these relations for $\vec{J}$ and $\vec{\tau}$ still hold good even if the axis of rotation be not fixed in an inertial frame but be a moving one, *provided that it always moves parallel to itself, i.e.*, its position at one instant is parallel to that at another.

To summarise, then, the relation $\vec{\tau} = I\,d\vec{\omega}/dt$ is applicable (i) when the axis of rotation passes through the centre of mass of the body and is itself its axis of symmetry (even though it may be moving parallel to itself) or (ii) when the axis of rotation is a fixed one.

Angular impulse. We have the relation $I\,d\vec{\omega}/dt = \vec{\tau}$, whence, we have $Id\vec{\omega} = \vec{\tau}\,dt$, where $\vec{\tau}$ is the torque acting on the body.

Integrating with respect to t, we have

$$\textit{angular momentum} = I\vec{\omega} = \int_0^t \vec{\tau}\,dt,$$

the expression being true *howsoever* $\vec{\tau}$ *may vary with time.*

If, however, $\vec{\tau}$ be constant, we have $I\vec{\omega} = \int_0^t \vec{\tau}\,dt = \vec{\tau}\,t.$

If t be small and $\vec{\tau}$ quite large, the expression $\int_0^t \vec{\tau}\,dt$ is called the *angular impulse* given to the body and, as we have just seen, with $\vec{\tau}$ constant, it is equal to $\vec{\tau}\,t$.

Also if I remains constant during the time t, we may express it as

$$\int_0^t \vec{\tau}\,dt = \int I\frac{d\vec{\omega}}{dt}dt = \int_{\omega_1}^{\omega_2} Id\vec{\omega} = I(\vec{\omega}_2 - \vec{\omega}_1)$$

11.4 MOMENT OF INERTIA—RADIUS OF GYRATION

The inability of a body to change by itself its state of rest or uniform motion along a straight line (Newton's first law of motion) is an inherent property of matter and is called *inertia*. The greater the mass of the body, the greater the resistance offered by it to any change in its state of rest or linear motion. So that, *mass is taken to be a measure of inertia for linear or translatory motion.*

In exactly the same manner, a body free to rotate about an axis opposes any change in its state of rest or uniform rotation. In other words, it possesses inertia for rotational motion, *i.e.*, it opposes the torque or the moment of the couple applied to it to change its state of rotation. It must also be, therefore, of the nature of the moment of a couple, for only a couple can oppose another couple. Hence the name *moment of inertia* given to it.

It will thus be seen at once that the moment of inertia (usually written as *M.I.* for brevity) about a given axis plays the same part in rotational motion about that axis as the mass of a body does in translational motion. In other words, *moment of inertia, in rotational motion, is the analogue of mass in linear or translational motion.*

Now, in § 11.3 above, we have put $\Sigma mr_p^2 = \text{I}$, where I is the moment of inertia of the rigid body about the axis of rotation.

This means, obviously, that if r_1, r_2, r_3 etc. be the perpendicular distances from the axis, of particles of respective masses m_1, m_2, m_3, etc., we have

$$I = \Sigma m\, r^2 = m_1 r_1^2 - m_2 r_2^2 + m_3 r_3^2 + \ldots$$

We may, therefore, define *the moment of inertia of a rigid body about a given axis of rotation as the sum of the products of the masses of the various particles of the body and the squares of their respective distances from the axis*. We usually put it as

$$I = \Sigma m r^2 = MK^2,$$

where M is the *total mass of the body* (*i.e.*, equal to $m_1 + m_2 + m_3$ etc.) and K_2 the *effective distance of its particles from the axis,* called its *radius of gyration about the axis of rotation.*

In the case of a body which does not consist of separate, discrete particles but has a continuous and homogeneous distribution of matter in it, the summation becomes an integration, the integral being taken over the entire body. So that, $I = \int r^2 dm = MK^2$, where dm is the mass of an infinitesimally small element of the body at distance r from the axis.

Also, since for a body free to rotate about a fixed axis of rotation, we have $\tau = I\, d\omega/dt$, it follows that if $d\omega/dt = 1$, $I = \tau$, *i.e., the moment of inertia of a body about a fixed axis of rotation may also be defined as the torque that must be applied to the body to produce unit angular acceleration in it about that axis.*

Again, as we shall shortly see (§ 11.10), the kinetic energy of rotation of a body rotating about a fixed axis $= \frac{1}{2} I\omega^2$. So that, if ω be *unity*, the kinetic energy of rotation of the body $= \frac{1}{2}\, I$, and, therefore, $I = 2$ (*kinetic energy of rotation*).

This gives us another method of defining moment of inertia, *viz.*, that *the moment of inertia of a body about a fixed axis of rotation is twice the kinetic energy of rotation of the body, rotating about that axis with unit angular velocity.*

Radius of gyration. It follows from the above discussion and Fig. 11.5 (*b*) that K, the *radius of gyration* of a body about its axis of rotation, which we have called the *effective distance* of its particles from the axis, is actually *that distance from the axis at which if its entire mass (M) be supposed to be concentrated, its moment of inertia about the given axis would be the same as with its actual distribution of mass.*

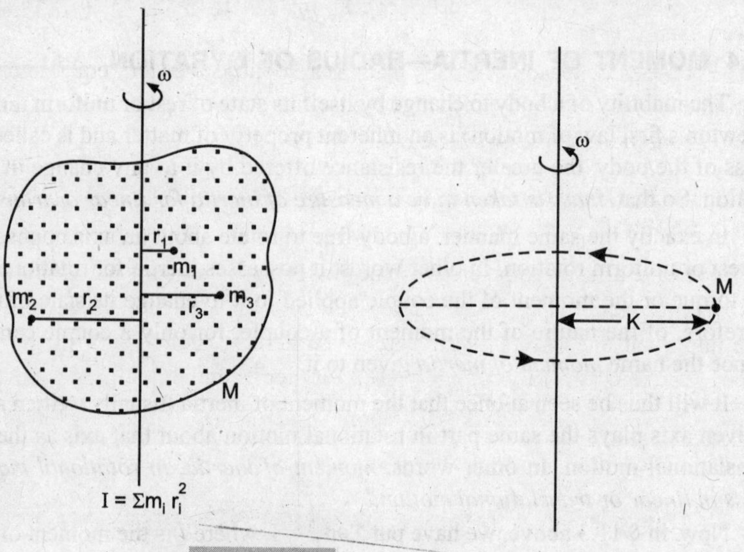

Fig. 11.5 (*b*)

Clearly, therefore, a change in the position or inclination of the axis of rotation of a body will bring about a change in the relative distances of its particles and hence in their *effective distance* or the *radius of gyration* of the body about the axis. And so will a change in the distribution of mass about the axis *e.g.*, the transference of a portion of matter (or mass) of the body from one part to another, despite the fact that the total mass of the body remains unaltered.

Thus, whereas the mass of a body remains the same irrespective of the location or inclination of its axis of rotation, its radius of gyration about the axis depends upon (*i*) *the position and inclination of the axis* and (*ii*) the *distribution of mass of the body about the axis*.

This may be illustrated by a simple example: As we shall presently see, the *M.I.* of a circular hoop or ring about an axis passing through its centre and perpendicular to its plane (MR^2) is twice the *M.I.* of a circular disc of *exactly the same mass and radius and about an identical axis*, *i.e.*, an axis passing through its centre and perpendicular to its plane, ($MR^2/2$). The masses in the two cases being the same, obviously, K^2 for the hoop or ring is twice as large as K^2 for the disc, due, no doubt, to the average, and hence the effective, distance of the particles from the axis of rotation being greater in the case of the hoop or ring than in that of the disc.

11.5 DIMENSIONS AND UNITS OF MOMENT OF INERTIA

Since the moment of inertia of a body about a given axis of rotation is MK^2, where M is the *mass* of the body and K, its *radius of gyration* about the axis, *its dimensions* are 1 *in mass*, 2 *in length* and *zero in time*. Its dimensional formula is thus ML^2T^0 or ML^2.

Obviously, therefore, it is expressed in gm-cm² in the C.G.S. system, kg-m² in the MKS (*or* SI) *system* and *lb-ft²* in the F.P.S. *system*.

Further, it may be noted that since the moment of inertia of a body about a given axis remains unaffected by reversing its direction of rotation about that axis, it is a **scalar quantity**, once its axis of rotation is fixed.

It follows, therefore, that the total *M.I.* of a number of bodies about a given axis is equal to the sum of the moments of inertia of the individual bodies about that axis, *i.e.*, $I = I_1 + I_2 + I_3 + \ldots$, where I is the total *M. I.* of the bodies and I_1, I_2, I_3 etc. their individual moments of inertia about the given axis.

For the same reason, if a body has a *M.I.* about a given axis equal to I, and a portion of it, having a moment of inertia I' about the same axis be removed from it, the *M.I.* of the remaining part of the body about the given axis will be $I-I'$.

11.6 ANALOGOUS PARAMETERS IN TRANSLATIONAL AND ROTATIONAL MOTION

We have already come across some analogous parameters in translational and rotational motion, like *linear and angular velocity, linear and angular acceleration*. There are, of course, many others, the important ones among which are given here in tabular form for purposes of ready reference, along with the symbols commonly used for them and their various relationships.

	Translational motion	Rotational motion
1.	*Mass* (or *translational inertia*) *m* or *M*	*Moment of inertia* $I = MK^2$ (or *rotational inertia*)
2.	*Distance covered* (or *linear displacement*) $\vec{s}$	*Angle described* $\vec{\theta}$ (*radians*) (or *angular displacement*)

3.	*Linear velocity* $\vec{v} = d\vec{s}/dt$	*Angular velocity* $\vec{\omega} = d\vec{\theta}/dt$ *(radian/sec)*
4.	Linear acceleration $\vec{a} = d\vec{v}/dt = d^2s/dt^2$	*Angular acceleration* $\vec{\alpha} = d\vec{\omega}/dt = d^2\theta/dt^2$
5.	*Linear momentum* $\vec{p} = m\vec{v}$	*Angular momentum* $\vec{J} = I\vec{\omega}$
6.	*Force (or rate of change of linear momentum)* $\vec{F} = d\vec{p}/dt = ma$	*Torque* or moment of couple (or rate of change of angular momentum) $\vec{\tau}$ or $\vec{C} = d\vec{J}/dt = I\,d\vec{\omega}/dt$
7.	*Work done by force,* $W = \int F d\vec{s} = Fs$	Work done by torque or couple, $W = \int \vec{\tau}\, d\vec{\theta}$ or $\int C d\theta$ or $\tau\theta$ or $C\theta$.
8.	*Power* $P = Fv$	*Power* $P = \tau\omega$ or $C\omega$
9.	*Translational kinetic energy* $= \frac{1}{2}mv^2$	*Rotational kinetic energy* $= \frac{1}{2}I\omega^2$
10.	*Equations of translational motion*: (*i*) $v = u + at$ (*ii*) $s = ut + \frac{1}{2}at^2$ (*iii*) $v^2 - u^2 = 2as$	*Equations of rotational motion*: (*i*) $\omega_2 = \omega_1 + \alpha t = \omega_1 + (d\omega/dt)\,t$ (*ii*) $\theta = \omega_1 t + \frac{1}{2}\alpha t^2 = \omega_1 t + \frac{1}{2}(d\omega/dt)t^2$ (*iii*) $\omega_2^2 - \omega_1^2 = 2\alpha\theta = 2\,(d\omega/dt)\,\theta$

Further, corresponding to Newton's three laws of translational motion, we have the following **three laws of rotational motion:**

1. *Unless an external torque is applied to it, the state of rest or uniform rotational motion of a body about its fixed axis of rotation remains unaltered.*

2. *The rate of change of angular momentum (or the rate of change of rotation) of a body about a fixed axis of rotation is directly proportional to the torque applied and takes place in the direction of the torque.*

3. *When a torque is applied by one body on another, an equal and opposite torque is applied by the latter on the former about the same axis of rotation.*

11.7 GENERAL THEOREMS ON MOMENT OF INERTIA

There are two important theorems on moment of inertia which, in some cases, enable the moment of inertia of a body to be determined about an axis, if its moment of inertia about some other axis be known. Let us now proceed to discuss these.

I—The theorem (or principle) of perpendicular axes.

(*a*) **For a plane laminar body.** The theorem states that *the moment of inertia of a plane lamina about an axis perpendicular to the plane of the lamina is equal to the sum of the moments of inertia of the lamina about two axes perpendicular to each other, in its own plane, and intersecting each other at the point where the perpendicular axis passes through it.*

Thus, if I_x and I_y be the moments of inertia of a plane lamina (Fig. 11.6), about the perpendicular axis *OX* and *OY* respectively, which lie *in the plane of the lamina* and intersect each other at *O*, its moment of inertia (*I*) about an axis passing through *O* and *perpendicular to its plane* is given by $I = I_x + I_y$.

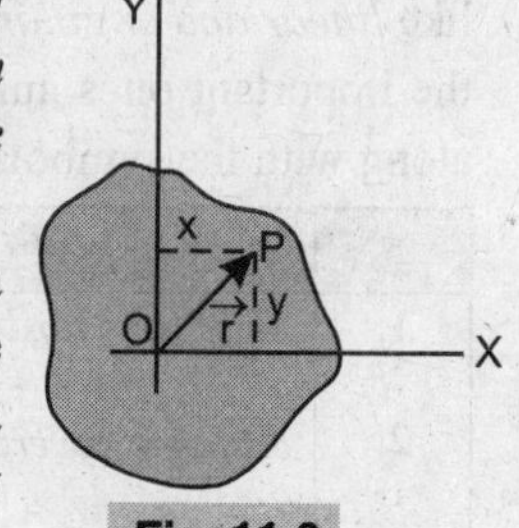

Fig. 11.6

For, considering a particle of mass m at P, distant r from O and x and y from the axes OY and OX respectively, we have

$I = \Sigma mr^2$, $I_x = \Sigma my^2$ and $I_y = \Sigma mx^2$.

So that, $I_x + I_y = \Sigma my^2 + \Sigma mx^2 = \Sigma m\,(y^2 + x^2) = \Sigma mr^2$, $[\because y^2 + x^2 = r^2]$.

i.e., $I_x + I_y = I$.

(*b*) **For a three-dimensional body.** In this case, the theorem demands that *the sum of the moments of inertia of a three-dimensional body about its three mutually perpendicular axes is equal to twice the summation Σmr^2 about the origin.* This may be seen from the following.

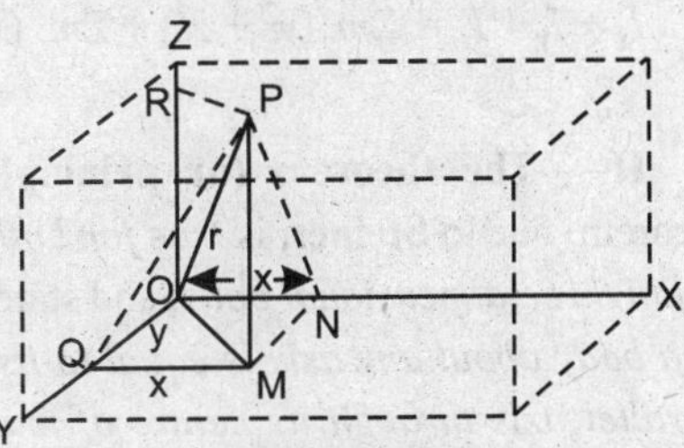

Fig. 11.7

Suppose we have a three dimensional or a cubical body, shown dotted in Fig 11.7, with OX, OY and OZ as its three mutually perpendicular axes, representing its *length, breadth* and *height* respectively.

Consider a small element of *mass m* of the body at a point P somewhere inside it. Drop a perpendicular PM from P on the $x-y$ plane to meet it in M. Join OM and OP and from M draw MQ parallel to the x-axis and MN parallel to the y-axis. Also, from P draw PR parallel to OM. Then, clearly, the coordinates of the point P are $x = ON = QM$, $y = OQ = NM$ and $z = MP = OR$.

Since plane $x - y$ is perpendicular to the z-axis, any straight line drawn on this plane is also perpendicular to it. So that, both OM and PR are perpendicular to the z-axis (PR being parallel to OM).

Clearly, therefore, $\angle OMP$ is a *right angle* $[\because OM \,//\, PR$ and $PM \,//\, OR]$. We, therefore, have

$OM^2 + MP^2 = OP^2$. Or, $OM^2 + z^2 = r^2$ ... (*i*) $[\because OP = r]$

But $OM^2 = QM^2 + OQ^2 = x^2 + y^2$.

[$\because$ OQM is a right angle, being the angle between the axes of x and y].

$\therefore$ Substituting the value of OM^2 in relation (*i*) above, we have

$$x^2 + y^2 + z^2 = r^2. \quad \ldots (ii)$$

Join PN and PQ. Then, PN and PQ are the respective normals to the axes of x and y. For $\angle PMN$ being a *right angle* (the angle between the axes of y and z), we have $PN^2 = MN^2 + PM^2 = y^2 + z^2$ and, therefore, $x^2 + PN^2 = x^2 + y^2 + z^2 = r^2$. Or, $ON^2 + PN^2 = r^2$ ($\because x = ON$). Angle PNO is thus a right angle and, therefore, PN perpendicular to the x-axis.

Similarly, in the right-angled ΔPMQ, we have

$PQ^2 = MQ^2 + PM^2 = x^2 + z^2$.

Again, because $x^2 + y^2 + z^2 = r^2$, we have $PQ^2 + y^2 = r^2$.

Or, $PQ^2 + OQ^2 = OP^2$. $[\because y = OQ$ and $r = OP]$

Angle PQO too is thus a right angle and, therefore, PQ perpendicular to the y-axis.

Now, moment of inertia of the element at P about the z-axis $= m \times PR^2 = m \times OM^2$, because $PR = OM$ is the perpendicular distance of the mass from the axis.

$\therefore$ *Moment of inertia of the whole body about the z-axis, i.e.,*

$$I_z = \Sigma m.\,OM^2 = \Sigma m\,(x^2 + y^2).$$

Similarly, *moment of inertia of the body about the y-axis, i.e.,*

$$I_y = \Sigma m.PQ^2 = \Sigma m(x^2 + y^2),$$

because PQ is the perpendicular distance of mass m from this axis.

And, *moment of inertia of the body about the x-axis, i.e.,*

$$I_x = \Sigma m.\ PN^2 = \Sigma m\ (y^2 + z^2),$$

because PN is the perpendicular distance of mass m from the x-axis.

$\therefore$ Adding up the moments of inertia of the body about the three axes, we have

$$I_x + I_y + I_z = \Sigma m.\ (y^2 + z^2) + \Sigma m.\ (x^2 + z^2) + \Sigma m.\ (x^2 + y^2) = 2\ \Sigma m.\ (x^2 + y^2 + z^2)$$
$$= 2\ \Sigma mr^2.$$

II— The theorem (or principle) of parallel axes. This theorem, due to **Steiner,** is *true for both a plane laminar body and a thin three-dimensional body*, and states that *the moment of inertia of a body about any axis is equal to its moment of inertia about a parallel axis through its centre of mass, plus the product of the mass of the body and the square of the distance between the two axes.*

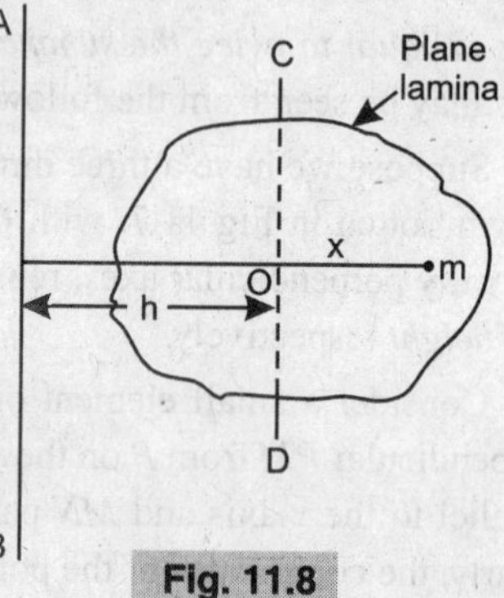

Fig. 11.8

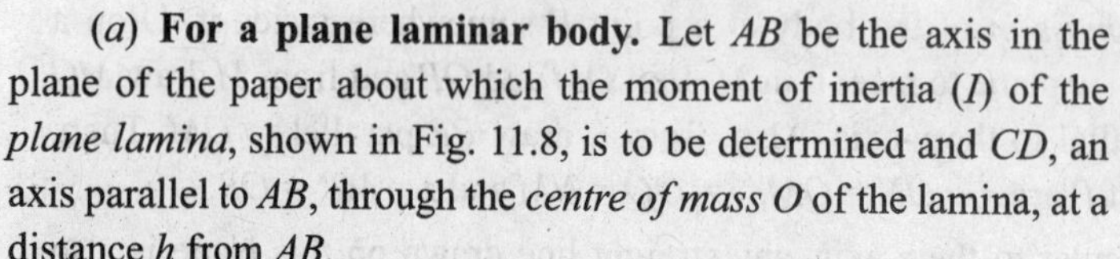
(*a*) **For a plane laminar body.** Let AB be the axis in the plane of the paper about which the moment of inertia (I) of the *plane lamina*, shown in Fig. 11.8, is to be determined and CD, an axis parallel to AB, through the *centre of mass O* of the lamina, at a distance h from AB.

Considering a small element of mass m of the lamina at the point P, distant x from CD, we have *moment of inertia of the element about the axis AB* $= m\ (x + h)^2$.

And, therefore, *moment of inertia of the whole lamina about the axis AB, i.e.,* $I = \Sigma m\ (x + h)^2$.

Or, $I = \Sigma mx^2 + \Sigma mh^2 + 2\Sigma mxh$.

Obviously, $\Sigma mx^2 = I_{c.m.}$, the moment of inertia of the lamina about the axis CD, through its centre of mass. So that,

$$I = I_{c.m.} + \Sigma mh^2 + 2\Sigma mxh.$$

Now, $\Sigma mh^2 = h^2\Sigma m$ (h being constant) $= Mh^2$, where M is the mass of the whole lamina, and Σmx = the sum of the moments of all the particles of the lamina about the axis CD, passing through its centre of mass and, therefore, equal to *zero*; for, as we know, a body always balances about its c.m., showing that the algebraic sum of the moments of all its particles about the *c.m.* is *zero*.

We, therefore, have $I = I_{c.m.} + Mh^2$,

i.e., the *moment of inertia of the lamina about the axis AB = its moment of inertia about a parallel axis CD through its centre of mass + mass of the lamina* × (*distance between the two axes*)^2.

(*b*) **For a three-dimensional body.** Let AB be the axis about which the moment of inertia of a cubical or a three-dimensional body, shown dotted in Fig. 11.9, is to be determined.

Draw a parallel axis CD through the centre of mass O of the body at a distance h from it.

Imagine an element of the body, of mass m, at a point P outside the plane of the axes AB and CD and let PK and PL be perpendiculars drawn from P to AB and CD respectively and PT, the

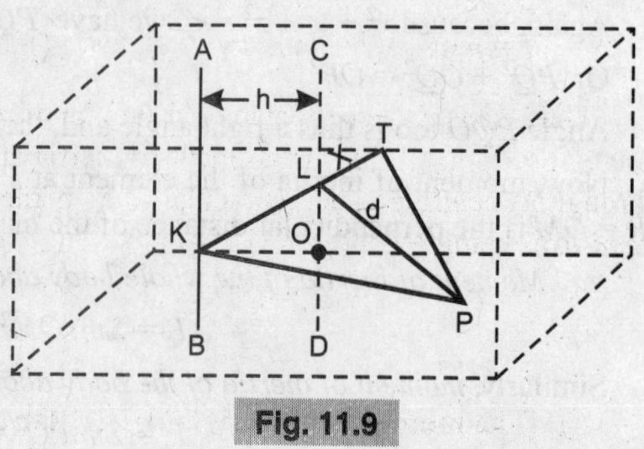

Fig. 11.9

perpendicular dropped from P on to KL produced.

Put $PL = d$, $LK = h$, $LT = x$ and $\angle PLK = \theta$.

Then, if I be the moment of inertia of the body about the axis AB and $I_{c.m.}$, its moment of inertia about the axis CD (through its centre of mass O), we have

$$I = \Sigma m.\ PK^2 \text{ and } I_{c.m.} = \Sigma mPL^2 = \Sigma md^2.$$

Now, from the geometry of the figure, we have $PK^2 = PL^2 + LK^2 - 2PL.\ LK \cos PLK = d^2 + h^2 - 2d.\ h \cos\theta$.

And, in the right-angled triangle PTL, we have $\cos PLT = LT/PL$, where $\angle PLT = 180° - \angle PLK = 180° - \theta$. So that, $\cos(180 - \theta) = x/d$.

Or, $-\cos\theta = x/d$, whence, $d\cos\theta = -x$.

Substituting this value of $d\cos\theta$ in the expression for PK^2 above,

we have $PK^2 = d^2 + h^2 + 2hx$. And, therefore, $I = \Sigma mPK^2 = \Sigma m\,(d^2 + h^2 + 2hx)$

$$= \Sigma md^2 + \Sigma mh^2 + 2h\Sigma mx.$$

Or, $$I = I_{c.m.} + Mh^2 + 2h\,\Sigma mx$$

[$\because$ $\Sigma m = M$, mass of the body and h is constant.

Clearly $\Sigma mx = 0$, being the total moment about an axis passing through the centre of mass of the body. We, therefore, have

$$I = I_{c.m.} + Mh^2,$$

the same result as for a plane laminar body.

11.8 CALCULATION OF MOMENT OF INERTIA

In the case of a *continuous, homogeneous* body of a definite geometrical shape, its moment of inertia is calculated by (*i*) *first obtaining an expression for the moment of inertia of an infinitesimal element* (*of the same shape*) *of mass dm about the given axis, i.e., dm.h*^{2}, where h is the distance of the infinitesimal element from the axis, and then (*ii*) *integrating this expression over appropriate limits so as to cover the entire body*, making full use of the theorems of perpendicular and parallel axes, where necessary, as we shall shortly see under § 11.9.

The moments of inertia of certain bodies of a regular geometrical shape *about any one of their three perpendicular axes of symmetry, passing through their centres of mass* may, however, be directly obtained by the application of what is known as **Routh's rule**.

According to this rule:

(*i*) The moment of inertia of a rectangular lamina or a parallelopiped about any one of these axes (passing through its centre of mass) is given by

$$I = \textit{mass of the lamina} \times \frac{1}{2}\ (\textit{sum of the squares of the other two semi-axes}).$$

Thus, considering a rectangular lamina of *mass M, length l* and *breadth b*, (Fig. 11.10), its moment of inertia about an axis passing through its centre and perpendicular to its plane is given by the two *semi-axes* being $l/2$ and $b/2$.

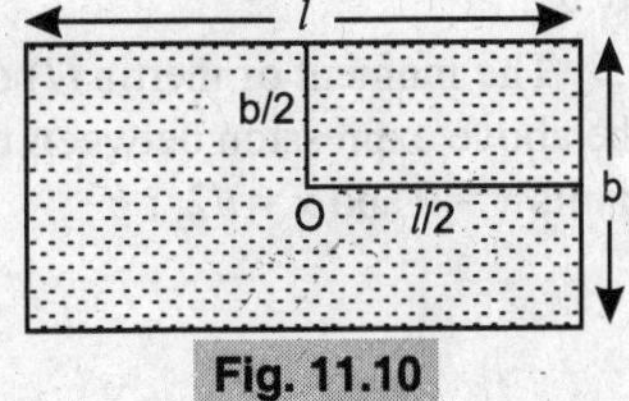

Fig. 11.10

$$I = M\left[\frac{(l/2)^2 + (b/2)^2}{3}\right] = M\left(\frac{l^2 + b^2}{12}\right),$$

(*ii*) **The moment of inertia of a circular or elliptical lamina** about any one of the three axes of symmetry (and passing through its centre mass) is given by

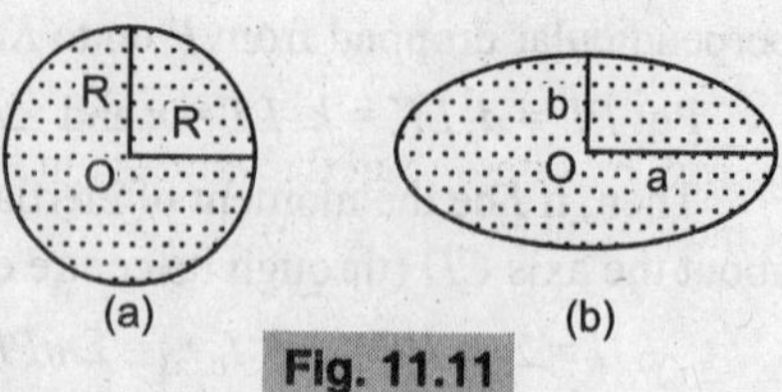

Fig. 11.11

I = mass of the lamina × $\frac{1}{4}$ *(sum of the squares of the other two semi-axes)*

Thus, in the case of a **circular lamina** of *mass M* and *radius R* [Fig. 11.11 (*a*)] its moment of inertia about an axis passing through its centre and perpendicular to its plane is given by the two *semi axes* being *R* and *R*.

$$I = M\left(\frac{R^2 + R^2}{4}\right) = M\frac{R^2}{2},$$

And in the case of an **elliptical lamina** of *mass M* and *major* and *minor axes* 2*a* and 2*b* respectively, [Fig. 11.11 (*b*)], its moment of inertia about an axis passing through its centre and perpendicular to its plane is given by the two semi-axes being *a* and *b*.

$$I = M\left(\frac{a^2 + b^2}{4}\right),$$

(*iii*) **The moment of inertia of a sphere or spheroid** about any axis of symmetry (passing through its centre of mass) is given by

I = mass of the sphere or spheroid × $\frac{1}{5}$ *(sum of the squares of the other two semi-axes)*

Thus, the moment of inertia of a solid sphere, of mass *M* and radius *R*, about any axis of symmetry, *i.e.*, about any diameter, is given by the two semi-axes being *R* and *R*.

$$I = M\left(\frac{R^2 + R^2}{5}\right) = \frac{2}{5}MR^2,$$

11.9 PARTICULAR CASES OF MOMENT OF INERTIA

Let us now see how to obtain expressions for moments of inertia in some typical and important cases, with regular geometrical shapes.

1. Moment of inertia of a uniform rod

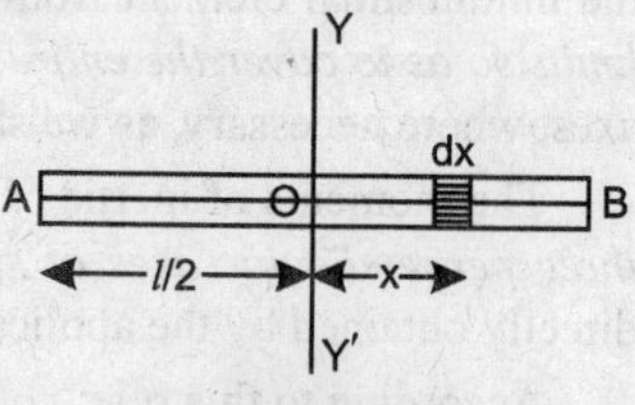

Fig. 11.12

(*i*) **about an axis through its centre and perpendicular to its length**. Let *AB* be a *thin uniform* rod, of *length l* and mass *M*, free to rotate about an axis *YOY'* passing through its centre *O* and perpendicular to its length, as shown in Fig. 11.12. Since the rod is uniform, its *mass per unit length* is clearly *M/l*.

Considering a small element of the rod, of length *dx* at a distance *x* from the axis through *O*, we have *mass of the element* = (*M/l*).*dx* and, therefore, its *M.I.* about the axis (*YOY'*) through *O* = (*M/l*) *dx*. x^2.

The moment of inertia (*I*) of the whole rod about the axis *YOY'* is thus given by the integral of the above expression between the limits *x* = – *l*/2 and *x* = + *l*/2 or by twice its integral between the limits *x* = 0 and *x* = *l*/2, *i.e.*,

$$I = 2\int_0^{l/2}\frac{M}{l}x^2dx = \frac{2M}{l}\left[\frac{x^2}{3}\right]_0^{l/2} = \frac{2M}{l}\cdot\frac{l^3}{24} = \frac{Ml^2}{12}.$$

(*ii*) **about an axis through one end of the rod and perpendicular to its length.**

Proceeding as in case (*i*) above, we obtain the moment of inertia of the rod about the axis, now passing through one end *A* of the rod, by integrating the expression for the *M.I.* of the element *dx* of the rod, between the limits $x = 0$ at *A* and $x = l$ at *B*, *i.e.*,

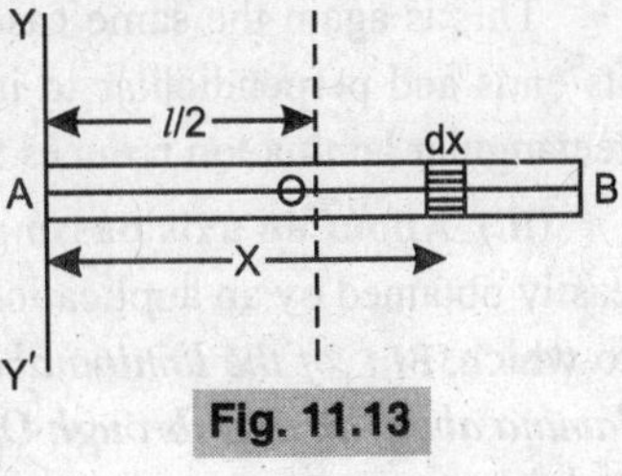

Fig. 11.13

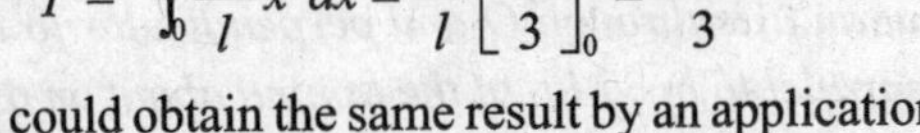

$$I = \int_0^l \frac{M}{l} x^2 dx = \frac{M}{l}\left[\frac{x^3}{3}\right]_0^l = \frac{Ml^2}{3}$$

Alternatively, we could obtain the same result by an application of the *principle of parallel axes*, according to which

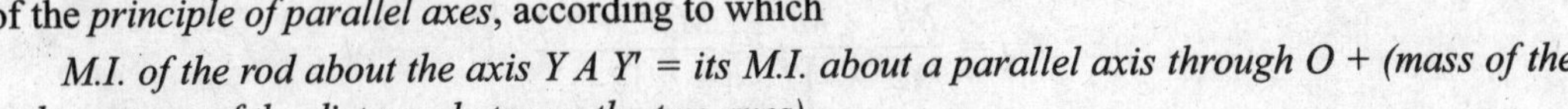

M.I. of the rod about the axis Y A Y′ = its M.I. about a parallel axis through O + (mass of the rod × square of the distance between the two axes).

So that, $$I = \frac{Ml^2}{12} + M\left(\frac{l}{2}\right)^2 = \frac{Ml^2}{12} + \frac{Ml^2}{4} = \frac{Ml^2}{3}.$$

2. Moment of inertia of a rectangular lamina (or bar)

(*i*) **about an axis through its centre and parallel to one side.** Let *ABCD* be a rectangular lamina, of *length l*, *breadth b* and *mass M* and let *YOY′* be the axis through its centre *O* and parallel to the side *AD* or *BC* about which its moment of inertia is to be determined.

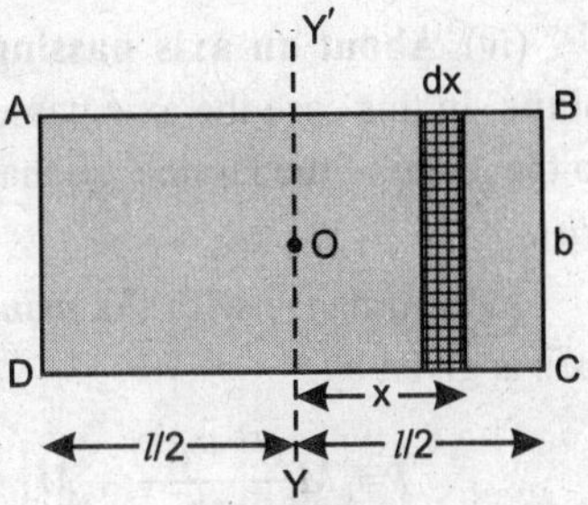

Consider an element, or a small rectangular strip of the lamina, parallel to, and at a distance *x* from the axis. The area of the strip or element = $dx \times b$. And, since the *mass per unit area of the lamina* = $M/(l \times b)$, we have

Fig. 11.14

$$\textit{mass of the strip or element} = \frac{M}{l \times b} \times dx \times b = \frac{M}{l} dx.$$

And, therefore, *M.I. of the element about the axis YOY′*

$$= \frac{M}{l} dx.\, x^2.$$

The moment of inertia (I) of the whole rectangular lamina is thus given by twice the integral of the above expression between the limits $x = 0$ and $x = l/2$.

i.e., $$I = 2\int_0^{l/2} \frac{M}{l} x^2 dx = \frac{2M}{l} \int_0^{l/2} x^2 dx = \frac{2M}{l}\left[\frac{x^3}{3}\right]_0^{l/2}$$

$$= \frac{2M}{l} \cdot \frac{l^3}{24} = \frac{Ml^2}{12}$$

As will be readily seen, if *b* be small, the rectangular lamina becomes a *rod* of length *l* whose *M.I.* about the axis *YOY′* passing through its centre and perpendicular to its length would be $Ml^2/12$, as obtained under case 1, (*i*) above.

(*ii*) **About one side.** In this case, since the axis coincides with *AD* or *BC*, we integrate the expression for the *M.I.* of the element of length *dx* and distance *x* from the axis, *i.e.*, $(M/l)\, dx.x^2$, between the limits $x = 0$ at *AD* and $x = l$ at *BC*. So that *M.I.* of the lamina about side *AD* or *BC* is given by

$$I = \int_0^l \frac{M}{l} x^2 dx = \frac{M}{l}\left[\frac{x^3}{3}\right]_0^l = \frac{Ml^2}{3}$$

Alternatively, by the *principle of parallel axes*, $I = \frac{Ml^2}{12} + M\left(\frac{l}{2}\right)^2 = \frac{Ml^2}{3}.$

This is again the same case as that of the *M.I.* of a rod about an axis passing through one of its ends and perpendicular to its length [*case I (ii)*]; for, as pointed out above, if b be small, the rectangular lamina too reduces to a thin rod of length l.

(*iii*) **About an axis passing through its centre and perpendicular to its plane**. This may be easily obtained by an application of the principle of perpendicular axes to case (*i*) above, according to which, *M.I. of the lamina about an axis through O and perpendicular to its plane = M.I. of the lamina about an axis through O parallel to b + M.I. of the lamina about an axis through O parallel to l, i.e.,*

$$I = \frac{Ml^2}{12} + \frac{Mb^2}{12} = \frac{M(l^2+b^2)}{12}$$

This relation is true for both *thin* (*i.e., laminar*) as well as *thick* plates or bars, because no stipulation has been made in deducing it as to the thickness of the lamina. And, in fact, *a thick rectangular plate or bar may be regarded as a combination of thin or laminar plates or bars, piled up one over the other.*

(*iv*) **About an axis passing through the mid-point of one side and perpendicular to its plane**. In this case the axis passes through the mid-point of side AD or BC, say, and perpendicular to the plane of the lamina, so that it is parallel to the axis through O (the *c.m.* of the lamina) in case (*iii*).

In accordance with the *principle of parallel axes*, therefore, the *M.I.* of the lamina about this axis is given by

$$I = M\frac{(l^2+b^2)}{12} + M\left(\frac{l}{2}\right)^2 = M\left(\frac{l^2+b^2}{12} + \frac{l^2}{4}\right) = M\left(\frac{l^2}{3} + \frac{b^2}{12}\right)$$

And, if the axis passes through the mid-point of AB or DC, we, similarly, have

$$I = M\left(\frac{l^2+b^2}{12}\right) + M\left(\frac{b}{2}\right)^2 = M\left(\frac{l^2+b^2}{12} + \frac{b^2}{4}\right) = M\left(\frac{l^2}{12} + \frac{b^2}{3}\right)$$

(*v*) **About an axis passing through one of its corners and perpendicular to its plane**. Let the axis pass through the corner D of the lamina. Since it is perpendicular to the plane of the lamina, it is parallel to the axis through its centre of *mass O* in case (*iii*). Again, therefore, by the *principle of parallel axes*, we have moment of inertia of the rectangular lamina about this axis through D given by

$$I = M\frac{(l^2+b^2)}{12} + Mh^2,$$ where h is the distance between the two axes.

Clearly, $h^2 = (l/2)^2 + (b/2)^2 = (l^2 + b^2)/4.$

So that, $$I = M\left(\frac{l^2+b^2}{12}\right) + M\left(\frac{l^2+b^2}{4}\right) = M\left(\frac{l^2+b^2+3l^2+3b^2}{12}\right)$$

$$= M\left(\frac{l^2+b^2}{3}\right)$$

3. Moment of inertia of a hoop or a thin circular ring.

(*i*) **About an axis through its centre and perpendicular to its plane.** Let thr radius of the hoop or the thin circular ring be R and its mass M, (Fig. 11.15).

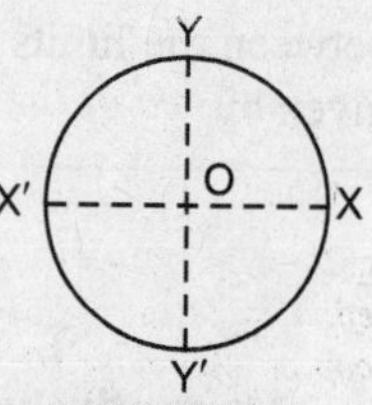

Fig. 11.15

Consider a particle of mass m of the hoop or the ring. Clearly, its *M.I* about an axis passing through the centre O of the hoop or the ring and perpendicular to its plane $= mR^2$.

$\therefore$ *M.I. of the entire hoop or ring about this axis passing through its centre and perpendicular to its plane,* $\mathbf{I} = \Sigma mR^2 = \mathbf{MR^2}$* [$\Sigma m = M$, the mass of the hoop or ring.]

(*ii*) **About its diameter.** Obviously, due to symmetry, the *M.I.* of the hoop or the ring will be the same about one diameter as about another. Thus, if I be its *M.I.* about the diameter XOX' (Fig. 11.15), it will also be I about the diameter YOY' perpendicular to XOX'.

By the principle of perpendicular axes, therefore, the *M.I.* of the hoop or the ring about the axis through its centre O and *perpendicular to its plane* is equal to the sum of its moments of inertia about the perpendicular axes XOX' and YOY' in its own plane and intersecting at O, *i.e.*,

$I + I = MR^2$. Or, $2I = MR^2$, whence, $I = MR^2/2$.

4. Moment of inertia of a circular lamina or disc:

(*i*) **About an axis through its centre and perpendicular to its plane.**

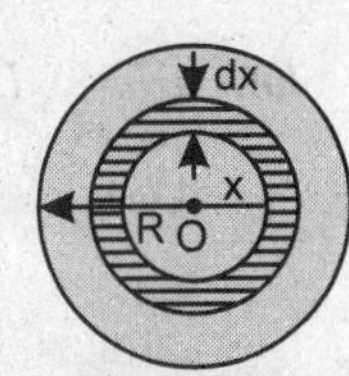

Fig. 11.16

Let M be the mass of the disc and R, its *radius*, so that its *mass per unit area* is equal to $M/\pi R^2$. Considering a ring of the disc, of width dx. and distant x from the axis passing through O and perpendicular to the plane of the disc (Fig. 11.16), we have

Area of the ring = Circumference × Width $= 2\pi x dx$, and hence

its mass $= (M/\pi R^2) \times 2\pi x dx = 2\ Mxax/R^2$.

And, therefore, its *M.I.* about the perpendicular axis through O

$$= \frac{2Mxdx}{R^2}x^2 = \frac{2Mx^3dx}{R^2}.$$

Since the whole disc may be supposed to be made up of such like concentric rings of radii ranging from O to R, the *M.I. of the whole disc* about the axis through O and perpendicular to its plane, *i.e.*, I, is obtained by integrating the above expression for the *M.I.* of the ring, between the limits $x = 0$ and $x = R$. Thus

$$I = \int_0^R \frac{2M}{R^2}x^3dx = \frac{2M}{R^2}\left[\frac{x^4}{4}\right]_0^R = \frac{2M}{R^2}\frac{R^4}{4} = MR^2/2.$$

(*ii*) **About a diameter.** Here, again, due to symmetry, the *M.I.* of the disc about one diameter is the same as about another. So that, if I be the *M.I.* of the disc about each of the perpendicular diameters XOX' and YOY', (Fig. 11.17), we have, by the *principle of perpendicular axes,*

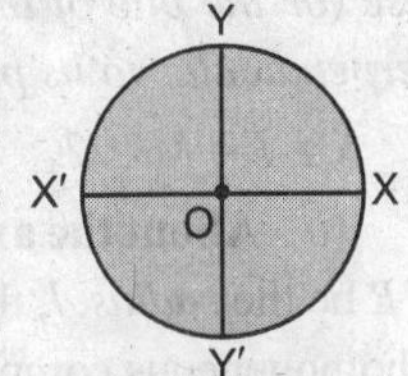

Fig. 11.17

$I + I$ = *M. I. of the disc about an axis through O and perpendicular to its plane,*

i.e., $2I = MR^2/2$, whence, $I = MR^2/4$.

5. Moment of inertia of an annular ring or disc

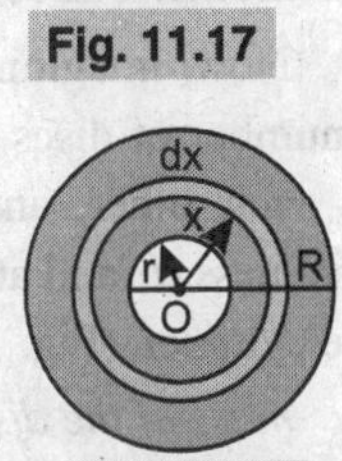

(*i*) **About an axis through its centre and perpendicular to its plane.** An annular disc is just an ordinary disc, with a smaller coaxial disc removed from it, leaving a concentric circular hole in it, as shown in Fig. 11.18.

Fig. 11.18

If R and r be the outer and inner radii of the disc and M, its mass, we have *mass per unit area of the disc = mass/area* $= M/\pi\ (R^2 - r^2)$.

* Since as we know, $I = MK^2$, we have here $MK^2 = MR^2$, whence, $K = R$, *i.e.*, the radius of the hoop or the ring is equal to its radius of gyration about the axis through its centre and perpendicular to its plane. This gives us *another definition of the radius of gyration of a body about a given axis, viz.*, that *it is numerically equal to the radius of a hoop or a circular ring, infinitely thin, of the same mass as the body and having the same moment of inertia about the axis passing through its centre and perpendicular to its plane as the body has about the given axis.*

Now, the disc may be imagined to be made up of a number of circular rings, with their radii ranging from r to R. So that, considering one such ring of radius x and width dx, we have

face area of the ring $= 2\pi x\, dx$ and $\therefore$ *its mass* $= 2\pi x\, dx\ [M/\pi (R^2 - r^2)] = [2\, Mx/(R^2 - r^2)]\, dx$.

And hence *its M.I. about the axis through O and perpendicular to its plane*

$$= \frac{2Mx}{(R^2 - r^2)} dx \cdot x^2 = \frac{2Mx^3}{(R^2 - r^2)} dx\,.$$

The *M.I.* of the whole annular disc *i.e.*, I, is, therefore, given by the integral of the above expression between the limits $x = r$ and $x = R$.

Or, $$I = \int_r^R \frac{2Mx^3}{(R^2 - r^2)} dx = \frac{2M}{(R^2 - r^2)} \int_r^R x^3 dx = \frac{2M}{(R^2 - r^2)} \left[\frac{x^4}{4}\right]_r^R$$

$$= \frac{2M}{(R^2 - r^2)} \left[\frac{(R^4 - r^4)}{4}\right] = \frac{M(R^2 + r^2)}{2}\,.$$

(*ii*) **About a diameter.** Due to symmetry, the *M.I.* of the annular disc about one diameter is the same as about another, say I. Then, clearly, in accordance with the *principle of perpendicular axes*, the sum of its moments of inertia about two perpendicular diameters must be equal to its *M.I.* about the axis passing through its centre (where the two diameters intersect) and perpendicular to its plane, *i.e.*, $I + I = M(R^2 + r^2)/2$. Or, $2I = M(R^2 + r^2)/2$, whence, $I = M(R^2 + r^2)/4$.

6. Moment of inertia of a solid cylinder:

(*i*) **About its own axis of cylindrical symmetry.** A solid cylinder is just a thick circular disc or a number of thin circular discs (all of the same radius) piled up one over the other, so that its axis of cylindrical symmetry is the same as the axis passing through the centre of the thick disc (or the pile of thin discs) and perpendicular to its plane.

$\therefore$ *M.I. of the solid cylinder about its axis of cylindrical symmetry, i.e.,* $I =$ *M.I. of the thick disc (or the pile of thin discs) of the same mass and radius about the axis through its centre and perpendicular to its plane.*

Or, $I = MR^2/2$. [*case* 4(*i*)

(*ii*) **About the axis through its centre and perpendicular to its axis of cylindrical symmetry.** If R be the *radius*, l, the *length* and M, the *mass* of the solid cylinder, supposed to be uniform and of a homogeneous composition, we have its *mass per unit length* $= M/l$.

Now, imagining the cylinder to be made up of a number of discs each of radius R, placed adjacent to each other, and considering one such disc of thickness dx and at a distance x from the centre O of the cylinder, (Fig. 11.19), we have

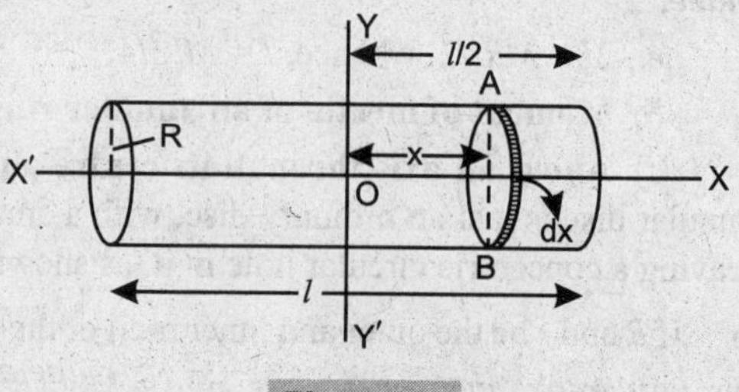

Y
l/2
A
R
X′
x
X
O
dx
B
l
Y′

Fig. 11.19

mass of the disc $= (M/l)\, dx$, and *radius* $= R$.

And $\therefore$ *M.I. of the disc about its diameter*

$$AB = \frac{M}{l} dx \cdot \frac{R^2}{4}\,.$$

and *its M.I. about the parallel axis YOY′, passing through the centre O of the cylinder and perpendicular to its axis of cylindrical symmetry* (*or its length*), *in accordance with the principle of parallel axes*,

$$= \frac{M}{l}dx\frac{R^2}{4} + \frac{M}{l}dx \cdot x^2$$

Hence, *M.I. of the whole cylinder about this axis, i.e., I = twice the integral of the above expression between the limits x = 0 and x = l/2, i.e.,*

$$I = 2\int_0^{l/2}\left(\frac{M}{l}\cdot\frac{R^2}{4}dx + \frac{M}{l}x^2dx\right) = \frac{2M}{l}\int_0^{l/2}\left(\frac{R^2}{4}dx + x^2dx\right)$$

$$= \frac{2M}{l}\left[\frac{R^2x}{4} + \frac{x^3}{3}\right]_0^{l/2}$$

Or,
$$I = \frac{2M}{l}\left[\frac{R^2}{4}\cdot\frac{l}{2} + \frac{l^3}{8\times 3}\right] = \frac{2M}{l}\left(\frac{R^2l}{8} + \frac{l^3}{24}\right) = M\left(\frac{R^2}{4} + \frac{l^2}{12}\right).$$

7. Moment of inertia of a solid cone:

(*i*) **About its vertical axis.** Let *M* be the *mass* of the solid cone, *h* its *vertical height* and *R*, the *radius of its base* (Fig. 11.20).

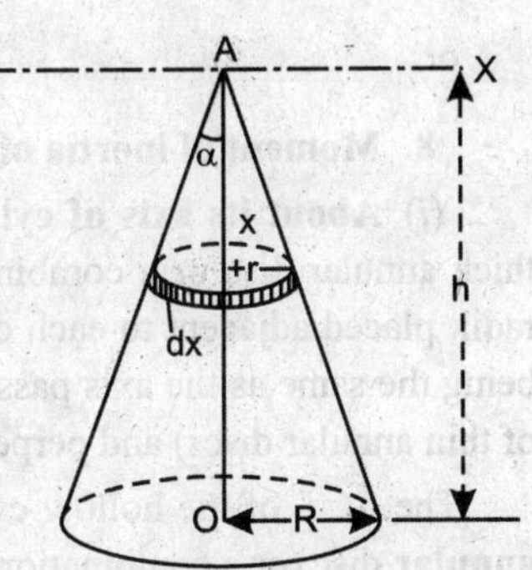

Fig. 11.20

Clearly, *volume of the cone* = $\frac{1}{3}\pi R^2 h$ and if ρ be the density of its material its *mass* $M = \frac{1}{3}\pi R^2 h\rho$, whence, $\rho = 3M/\pi R^2 h$.

Now, the cone may be imagined to consist of a number of discs of progressively decreasing radii, from *R* to *0*, piled up one over the other.

Considering one such disc of thickness *dx* and at a distance *x* from the vertex (*A*) of the cone, we have

radius of the disc, $r = x\tan\alpha$, where α is the semi-vertical angle of the cone, and therefore, its volume = $\pi r^2\,dx = \pi x^2\tan^2\alpha dx$ and, its *mass* = $\pi x^2\tan^2\alpha\rho dx$.

Hence, *M.I. of the disc about the vertical axis AO of the cone* (*i.e.*, an axis passing through its centre and perpendicular to its plane) = *mass* × (*radius*)^2/2 = $\pi x^2\tan^2\alpha\rho\,dx.\,r^2/2 = \pi x^2\tan^2\alpha\rho\,dx.x^2\tan^2\alpha/2$

$$= (\pi\rho\tan^4\alpha/2)\,x^4\,dx.$$

And ∵ *M.I. of the entire cone about its vertical* axis *AO* is given by

$$I = \int_0^h \frac{\pi\rho\tan^4\alpha}{2}x^4dx = \frac{\pi\rho\tan^4\alpha}{2}\int_0^h x^4dx = \frac{\pi\rho\tan^4\alpha}{2}\left[\frac{x^5}{5}\right]_0^h$$

$$= \frac{\pi\rho\tan^4\alpha}{2}\cdot\frac{h^5}{5} = \frac{\pi\rho R^4}{2h^4}\cdot\frac{h^5}{5},$$

substituting *R/h* for tan α.

Or, substituting the value of ρ obtained above, we have

$$I = \frac{\pi 3M}{\pi R^2 h}\cdot\frac{R^4}{2h^4}\cdot\frac{h^5}{5} = \frac{3MR^2}{10}.$$

(*ii*) **About an axis passing through the vertex and parallel to its base.** Again, considering the disc at a distance *x* from the vertex of the cone, we have *its M.I. about its diameter* = *mass* × (*radius*)^2/4

$= \pi x^2\tan^2\alpha\rho\,dx.\,r^2/4 = \pi x^2\tan^2\alpha\rho\,dx.\,x^2\tan^2\alpha/4 = (\pi\rho\tan^4_\alpha/4)\,x^4\,dx.$

∴ Its *M. I. about the parallel axis XX′, distant x from it*

$$= (\pi\rho\tan^4\alpha/4)\,x^4\,dx + \pi x^2\tan^2\alpha\rho x^2 dx$$

$$= (\pi\rho \tan^4\alpha /4)\, x^4\, dx + \pi\rho \tan^2 \alpha x^4 dx$$

Hence *M.I. of the entire cone* about the axis *XX′*, *parallel to its base* is given by

$$I = \int_0^h \frac{\pi\rho \tan^4 \alpha}{4} x^4 dx + \pi\rho \tan^2\alpha\, x^4 dx$$

$$= \frac{\pi\rho \tan^4 \alpha}{4} \int_0^h x^4 dx + \pi\rho \tan^2 \alpha \int_0^h x^4 dx$$

$$= \frac{\pi\rho}{4} \cdot \frac{R^4}{h^4}\left[\frac{x^5}{5}\right]_0^h + \pi\rho \cdot \frac{R^2}{h^2}\left[\frac{x^5}{5}\right]_0^h = \frac{\pi\rho R^4}{4h^4} \cdot \frac{h^5}{5} + \frac{\pi\rho R^2}{h^2} \cdot \frac{h^5}{5}$$

[$\because \tan\alpha = R/h$.]

Or, substituting the value of ρ, we have

M.I. of the cone about the axis XX′, i.e.,

$$I = \frac{\pi \cdot 3M}{4\pi R^2 h} \cdot \frac{R^4}{h^4} \cdot \frac{h^5}{5} + \frac{\pi \cdot 3M}{\pi R^2 h} \cdot \frac{R^2}{h^2} \cdot \frac{h^5}{5}$$

or. $$I = \frac{3MR^2}{20} + \frac{3Mh^2}{5}.$$

8. Moment of inertia of a hollow cylinder

(*i*) **About its axis of cylindrical symmetry.** A hollow cylinder may be considered to be a thick annular disc or a combination of thin annular discs, each of the same external and internal radii, placed adjacent to each other, the axis of the cylinder (*i.e.*, its axis of cylindrical symmetry) being the same as the axis passing through the centre of the thick annular disc (or the combination of thin annular discs) and perpendicular to its plane.

The *M. I.* of the hollow cylinder about its own axis is, therefore, the same as that of a **thick annular** disc (or a combination of thin annular discs) of the same mass *M* and external and internal radii *R* and *r* respectively about the axis passing through its centre and perpendicular to its plane, *i.e.*,

$$I = M(R^2 + r^2)/2$$

Alternatively, we may obtain the same result directly as follows:

Let *R* and *r* be the external and internal radii respectively of a hollow cylinder of length *l* and mass *M*, (Fig. 11.21). Then, *face-area* of the cylinder = $\pi(R^2 - r^2)$ and its *volume* = $\pi(R^2 - r^2)$ and, therefore, its *mass per unit volume* = $M/\pi(R^2 - r^2)l$.

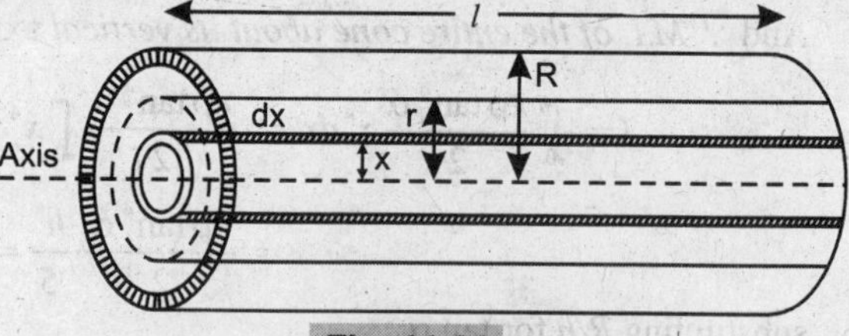

Fig. 11.21

Imagining the cylinder to be made up of a large number of thin, coaxial cylinders, with their radii varying from *r* to *R*, and considering one such cylinder of radius *x* and thickness *dx*, we have its *face area* = $2\pi x dx$ and its *volume* = $2\pi x dx l$ and hence its *mass* = $2\pi x dx.l \times M/\pi(R^2 - r^2)l = 2Mxdx/R^2 - r^2)$.

And, therefore, its *M. I. about the axis of the cylinder*

$$= \frac{2Mxdx}{(R^2 - r^2)} \cdot x^2 = \frac{2M}{(R^2 - r^2)} x^3 dx$$

Hence *M. I. of the entire cylinder about its axis, i.e., I,* is given by

$$I = \int_r^R \frac{2M}{(R^2 - r^2)} x^3 dx = \frac{2M}{(R^2 - r^2)} \int_r^R x^3 dx = \frac{2M}{(R^2 - r^2)} \left[\frac{x^4}{4}\right]_r^R$$

$$= \frac{2M}{(R^2 - r^2)} \left(\frac{R^4 - r^4}{4}\right) = M\left(\frac{R^2 + r^2}{2}\right)$$

(ii) **About an axis passing through its centre and perpendicular to its own axis.** Again, if R and r be the *external and internal radii* respectively of the hollow cylinder, l, its *length* and M, its *mass*, we have *mass per unit volume of the cylinder* $= M/\pi(R^2 - r^2)l$.

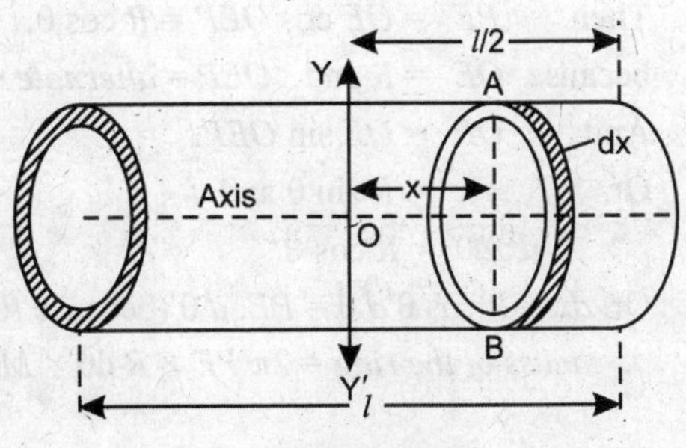

Fig. 11.22

Imagining the hollow cylinder to be made up of a large number of *annular discs*, of external and internal radii R and r respectively, placed adjacent to each other, and considering one such disc at a distance x from the axis YOY' passing through the centre O of the cylinder and perpendicular to its own axis as shown in Fig. 11.22. We have

surface area of the disc $= \pi(R^2 - r^2)$, its *volume* $= (R^2 - r^2)\,dx$ and, therefore, its *mass* $= \pi(R^2 - r^2)\,dx \times M/\pi(R^2 - r^2)l = Mdx/l$.

So that, *M. I. of the disc about its diameter (AB)* $= \dfrac{Mdx}{l} \cdot \dfrac{(R^3 + r^2)}{4}$ [Case 6 *(ii)*]

And, therefore, *its M. I. about the parallel axis YOY'* distant x from it, in accordance with the *principle of parallel axes,*

$$= \frac{M}{l} dx \cdot \left(\frac{R^2 + r^2}{4}\right) + \frac{M}{l} dx \cdot x^2.$$

Hence, *M. I. of entire hollow cylinder about the axis YOY'* is equal to twice the integral of the above expression between the limits $x = 0$ and $x = l/2$, *i.e.*,

$$I = 2\int_0^{l/2} \left[\frac{M(R^2 + r^2)}{4l} dx + \frac{M}{l} x^2 dx\right]$$

$$= \frac{2M}{l} \int_0^{l/2} \left[\frac{R^2 + r^2}{4} dx + x^2 dx\right]$$

$$= \frac{2M}{l} \left[\frac{(R^2 + r^2)x}{4} + \frac{x^3}{3}\right]_0^{l/2}$$

Or,

$$I = \frac{2M}{l} \left[\frac{(R^2 + r^2)l}{4 \times 2} + \frac{l^3}{8 \times 3}\right] = M\left[\frac{(R^2 + r^2)}{4} + \frac{l^2}{12}\right]$$

9. Moment of inertia of a spherical shell

(ii) **About its diameter.** Let $ABCD$ be the section through the centre O, of a spherical shell of radius R and mass M, (Fig. 11.23) whose moment of inertia is to be determined about a diameter AB, say, its value being obviously the same about any other diameter.

Clearly, *surface area of the shell* $= 4\pi r^2$ and, therefore, *mass per unit area of the shell* $M/4\pi R^2$.

Now, consider a thin slice of the shell, lying between two planes EF and GH, perpendicular to the diameter AB at distances x and $x + dx$ respectively from its centre O. This slice is, obviously, a *ring* of radius PE and width EG (and not PQ which is equal to dx, the distance between the two planes).

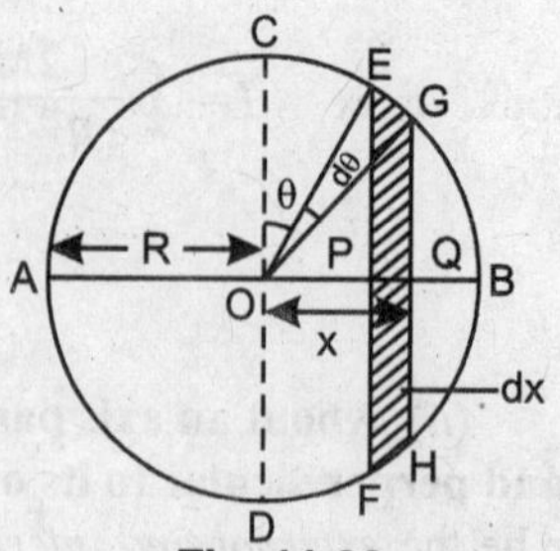

Clearly, *area of the ring = circumference × width* $= 2\pi PE \times EG$ and hence its *mass* $= 2\pi PE \times EG \times M/4\pi R^2$.

Join OE and OG and let angle COE be equal to θ and angle $EOG = d\theta$.

Fig. 11.23

Then, $PE = OE \cos OEP = R\cos\theta$,

because $OE = R$ and $\angle OEP =$ *alternate* $\angle COE = \theta$.

And, $OP = OE \sin OEP$.

Or, $x = R\sin\theta$ and $\therefore$

$dx/d\theta = R\cos\theta$. $[\because OP = x \text{ and } OE = R]$.

Or, $dx = R\cos\theta\, d\theta = PE.\,d\theta$ (because $R\cos\theta = PE$) and $EG = OE\, d\theta = R d\theta$.

$\therefore$ *mass of the ring* $= 2\pi\, PE \times R\, d\theta \times M/4\pi R^2 = Mdx/2R$.

$[\because PE.d\theta = dx]$

Hence, *M. I. of the ring about diameter AB of the shell (i.e., an axis passing through the centre of the ring and perpendicular to its plane = mass × (radius)² = (Mdx/2R)* $(R^2 - x^2)$,

[because $PE^2 = OE^2 - OP^2 = R^2 - x^2$]

And, therefore, *M. I.* of the whole spherical shell about the diameter (AB) is equal to twice the integral of this expression between the limits $x = 0$ and $x = R$, *i.e.*,

$$I = 2\int_0^R \frac{M}{2R}(R^2 - x^2)dx = \frac{M}{R}\int_0^R (R^2 - x^2)dx = \frac{M}{R}\left[R^2x - \frac{x^3}{3}\right]_0^R$$

$$= \frac{M}{R}\left[R^3 - \frac{R^3}{3}\right] = \frac{M}{R}\cdot\frac{2}{3}R^3$$

or, $$I = \frac{2}{3}MR^2.$$

10. Moment of Inertia of a solid sphere

(i) **About a diameter.** Figure 11.24 represents a section, through the centre, of a solid sphere of radius R and mass M, whose moment of inertia is to be determined about a diameter AB, say, its value being the same about *any* other diameter.

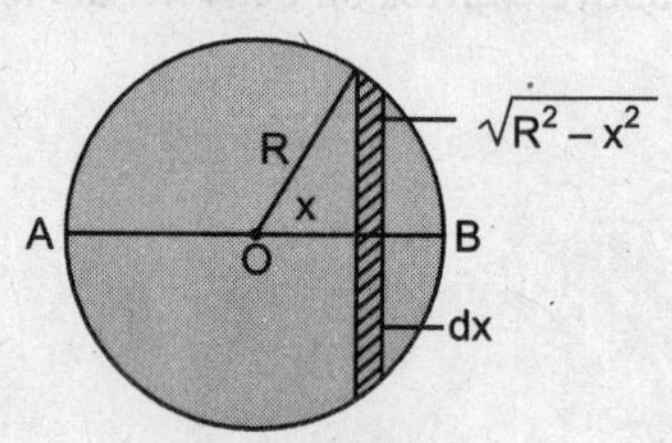

Fig. 11.24

Since the volume of sphere $= 4\pi R^3/3$, its *mass per unit volume* (or *density*) $= M\Big/\frac{4}{3}\pi R^3 = 3M/4\pi R^3$.

Considering a thin *circular* slice of the sphere at a distance x from its centre O and of thickness dx, we have *surface area of the slice* (which is obviously a disc of radius $\sqrt{R^2 - x^2} = \pi(R^2 - x^2)$ and *its Volume = Area × Thickness* $= \pi(R^2 - x^2)\, dx$ and hence its *mass = volume × density* $= \pi(R^2 - x^2)\, dx \times 3\, M/4\pi R^3/ = 3M\, (R^2 - x^2)\, dx/4R^3$.

And $\therefore$ *M.I. of this slice or disc about AB (i.e., an axis passing through its centre and perpendicular to its plane) = its mass × (radius)²/2*

$$= \frac{3M(R^2 - x^2)}{4R^3}dx\cdot\frac{R^2 - x^2}{2} = \frac{3M(R^2 - x^2)^2}{8R^3}dx.$$

Hence *M. I.* of the whole sphere about its diameter (*AB*) is equal to twice the integral of the above expression between the limits $x = 0$ and $x = R$, *i.e.*,

$$I = 2\int_0^R \frac{3M(R^2 - x^2)^2}{8R^3}dx = \frac{2 \times 3M}{8R^3}\int_0^R (R^2 - x^2)^2 dx$$

$$= \frac{3}{4}\frac{M}{R^3}\int_0^R (R^4 - 2R^2x^2 + x^4)dx$$

Or,
$$I = \frac{3M}{4R^3}\left[R^4x - 2R^2\frac{x^3}{3} + \frac{x^5}{5}\right]_0^R = \frac{3M}{4R^3}\left(R^5 - \frac{2}{3}R^5 + \frac{1}{5}R^5\right)$$

$$= \frac{3M}{4R^3} \times \frac{8R^5}{15} = \frac{2}{5}MR^2.$$

(*ii*) **About a tangent.** A tangent drawn to the sphere at any point will clearly be parallel to one or the other diameter of it (*i.e.*, an axis passing through its centre or centre or mass) and at a distance equal to the radius of the sphere, *R*, from it. We therefore have, by the principle of parallel axes, *moment of inertia of the sphere about a tangent, i.e.* ,

$$I = \frac{2}{5}MR^2 + MR^2 = \frac{7}{5}MR^2.$$

11. Moment of inertia of a hollow sphere or a thick shell

(*i*) **About its diameter.** A hollow sphere (or a thick shell) is just a solid sphere from the inside of which a small concentric solid sphere has been removed.

Since the *M.I.* about a given axis is a scalar quantity, we have *moment of inertia of hollow sphere about a diameter = moment of inertia of the solid sphere minus moment of inertia of the smaller solid sphere removed from it, both about the same diameter.*

Let *R* and *r* be the external and internal radii of the hollow sphere, *i.e.*, the radius of the bigger solid sphere and the smaller solid sphere (removed from it) respectively. Then, if ρ be the density of the material of the given hollow sphere, we have

mass of the bigger sphere $= \frac{4}{3}\pi R^3\rho$ and

mass of the smaller sphere $= \frac{4}{3}\pi r^3\rho$

so that *mass of the hollow sphere,* $M = \frac{4}{3}\pi(R^3 - r^3)\rho$, and therefore,

$$\rho = \frac{3M}{4\pi(R^3 - r^3)}$$

And, clearly, moments of inertia of the bigger and the smaller spheres about a given diameter are respectively $\frac{2}{5}\left(\frac{4}{3}\pi R^3\rho\right)R^2$ and $\frac{2}{5}\left(\frac{4}{3}\pi r^3\rho\right)r^2$.

And, therefore, *M. I. of the hollow sphere about the same diameter* is given by

$$I = \frac{2}{5}\left(\frac{4}{3}\pi R^3\rho\right)R^2 - \frac{2}{5}\left(\frac{4}{3}\pi r^3\rho\right)r^2 = \frac{2}{5}\cdot\frac{4}{3}\pi\rho(R^5 - r^5).$$

Or, substituting the value of ρ obtained above, we have

$$I = \frac{2}{5}\cdot\frac{4}{3}\pi\frac{3M}{4\pi(R^3 - r^3)}(R^5 - r^5) = \frac{2}{5}M\left(\frac{R^5 - r^5}{R^3 - r^3}\right).$$

(*ii*) **About a tangent.** A tangent to the sphere at any point being parallel to one diameter or the other (*i.e.*, the axis passing through the centre of mass) of the sphere and at a distance equal to its external radius R from it, we have, by the principle of parallel axes,

M. I. of hollow sphere about a tangent, i.e., $\mathbf{I} = \dfrac{2}{5}M\left(\dfrac{R^5 - r^5}{R^3 - r^3}\right) + MR^2.$

11.10 KINETIC ENERGY OF ROTATION

Here, we must distinguish between (*i*) *pure rotation, in which the centre of mass of the rotating body has zero linear velocity, e.g.,* the rotation of a body about an axis through its centre of mass, and (*ii*) *rotation in which the centre of mass of the rotating body has also a linear velocity, e.g.,* the rolling of a body along a plane or an inclined surface. Let us consider the two cases separately.

(*i*) **Kinetic energy of a body rotating about an axis through its centre of mass** (*i.e., in the case of pure rotation*). Consider a body of mass M, rotating with angular velocity ω about an axis AB, passing through its *centre of mass, O* (Fig. 11.25), so that *the centre of mass has zero linear velocity.* It is thus a case of *pure rotation.*

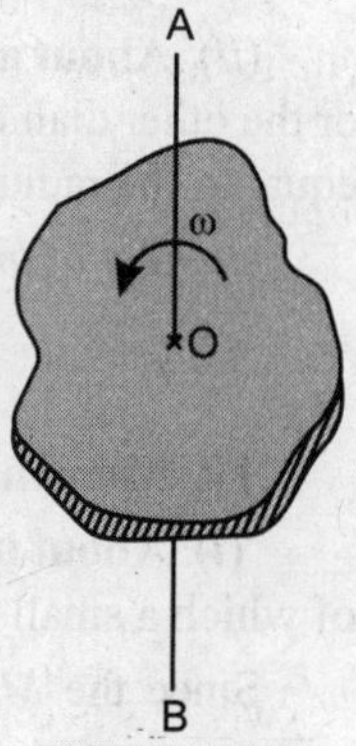

Fig. 11.25

Obviously, the body possesses kinetic energy in virtue of its motion of rotation which is, therefore, aptly called its *kinetic energy of rotation.* Let us obtain an expression for it.

The body is clearly made up of a large number of particles of masses m_1, m_2, m_3...etc. at respective distances r_1, r_2, r_3...etc. from the axis AB through O. Since their angular velocity is the same (ω), their linear velocities are respectively $r_1\omega = v_1, r_2\omega = v_2, r_3\omega = v_3$...etc. and hence their respective kinetic energies equal to $\frac{1}{2}m_1v_1^2 = \frac{1}{2}m_1r_1^2\omega^2$, $\frac{1}{2}m_2v_2^2 = \frac{1}{2}m_2r_2^2\omega^2$, $\frac{1}{2}m_3v_3^2 = \frac{1}{2}m_3v_3^2\omega^2$ ... etc.

$\therefore$ *total K.E. of all the particles, i.e., the K.E. of the body* itself

$$= \frac{1}{2}m_1r_1^2\omega^2 + \frac{1}{2}m_2r_2^2\omega^2 + \frac{1}{2}m_3r_3^2\omega^2 + ...$$

$$= \frac{1}{2}\omega^2(m_1r_1^2 + m_2r_2^2 + m_3r_3^2 + ...)$$

$$= \frac{1}{2}\omega^2\Sigma mr^2 = \frac{1}{2}\omega^2 MK^2,$$

where $\Sigma mr^2 = MK^2$, with M, as the mass of the body and K, its *radius of gyration* about the axis of rotation AB.

Since $MK^2 = I$, the *moment of inertia* of the body about the axis AB, we have

Kinetic energy of rotation of the body about the axis (AB) through its centre of mass $= \frac{1}{2}I\omega^2$. It is naturally expressed in *ergs* in the *C.G.S. system,* in *joules* in the *M.K.S.* (*or the SI system* and in *foot-poundals* or *foot-pounds* in the *F.P.S. system*)

(*ii*) **Kinetic energy of a rotating body whose centre of mass has also a linear velocity.**

(*a*) **Case of a body rolling along a plane surface.** Let us consider a body, like a circular disc, a cylinder, a sphere etc. (*i.e.*, a body with a circular symmetry), of *mass M, radius R and* with its *centre of mass* at *O*, (Fig. 11.26), rolling, *without*

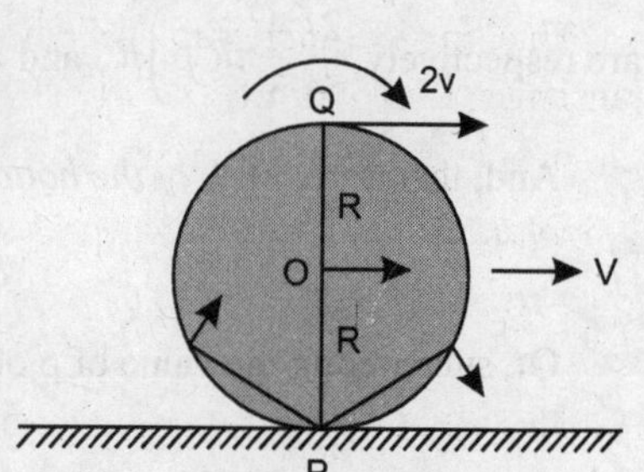

Fig. 11.26

slipping, along a plane or a level surface, such that it rotates clockwise and moves along the + x direction, as indicated.

At any given instant, the point P, where the body touches the surface, is at rest, so that an axis through P, perpendicular to the plane of the paper is its *instantaneous axis of rotation* and the linear velocities of its various particles are perpendicular to the lines joining them with the point of contact P, their magnitudes being proportional to the lengths of these lines, as shown by the directions and lengths of the arrows at the various points. Thus, if the linear velocity of the centre of mass O (where $PO = R$) be v, that of the particle at Q (where $PQ = 2R$) is $2v$.

This means clearly that the particles have all the *same* angular velocity *with respect to the point* P or that *the body is rotating about the fixed axis through P with an angular velocity ω, say, given by v/R,* where v is the linear velocity of the centre of mass.

The motion of the body is thus equivalent to one of pure rotation about the axis through P, with an angular velocity ω. The whole of the kinetic energy of the body is, therefore, the same as its kinetic energy of rotation about this axis and hence equal to $I_P\omega^2$, where I_P is the *M. I.* of the body about the axis through R.

Clearly, if $I_{c.m.}$ be the moment of inertia of the body about a parallel axis through its centre of mass, we have, by the principle of parallel axes, $I_P = I_{c.m} + MR^2$.

So that, *K.E. of the rolling body* $= \frac{1}{2}(I_{c.m.} + MR^2)\omega^2$

$$= \frac{1}{2}I_{c.m.}\omega^2 + \frac{1}{2}MR^2\omega^2 = \frac{1}{2}I_{c.m.}\omega^2 + \frac{1}{2}Mv^2, \quad \ldots (i)$$

where v is the linear speed of its centre of mass with respect to P,

Now, $I_{c.m} = \boldsymbol{MK^2}$, where K is the *radius of gyration* of the body about the axis through its centre of mass, and $\omega = v/R$. So that,

$$K.E.\ of\ the\ rolling\ body = \frac{1}{2}MK^2\frac{v^2}{R^2} + \frac{1}{2}Mv^2 = \frac{1}{2}Mv^2\left(\frac{K^2}{R^2}+1\right) \quad \ldots (ii)$$

It will be readily seen that in expression I above for *K.E.* of a rotating body, the first term gives its *K.E. of pure rotation* about the centre of mass, *i.e.*, its *K.E.* when it is simply rotating with angular velocity ω about the axis through its centre of mass, without executing any translational motion (*i.e.*, with the linear velocity of its centre of mass zero). And, the second term gives its *K. E. of pure translation, i.e.*, its *K.E.* when it is simply moving with linear velocity v (or the linear speed of the centre of mass) without performing any rotational motion (*i.e.*, with its angular velocity zero). Thus,

K. E. of a rolling body rotating with angular velocity ω *and moving with linear velocity* v $(= R\omega)$ = *its K. E. of pure rotation (with the same angular velocity* ω *) about its centre of mass + its K. E. of pure translation, with its centre of mass moving with linear velocity v.*

This, in fact, applies to all bodies, rolling or otherwise, which are simultaneously executing a translational motion and a rotational motion about an axis perpendicular to their planes of motion.

It follows at once from the above that

rotation of the body about the fixed axis through P, with angular velocity ω

= *its pure rotation about the c. m. (O) with the same angular velocity* ω + *the pure translational motion of its c.m. with linear velocity v* $(= R\omega)$.

This may be very interestingly seen from Fig. 11.27 where Fig. (*a*) represents the rotation of the body about the fixed axis through the point of contact P, when as we have seen, the linear velocity of the particle at P is *zero*, that of O, the centre of mass, $+ v$ along the $+ x$ direction and that of the particle at Q, $+ 2v$ in the $+ x$ direction.

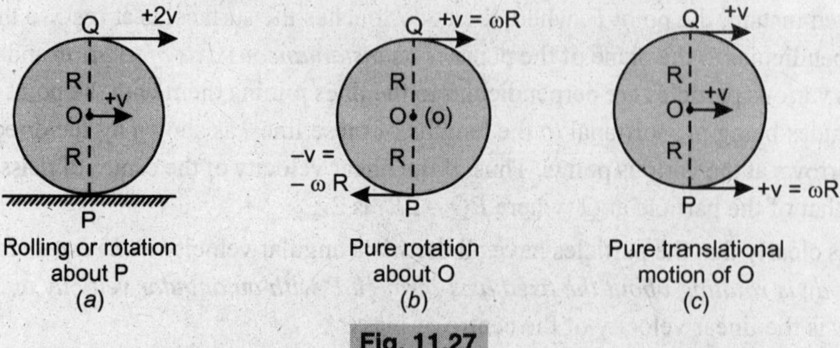

Fig. 11.27

Figure 11.27 (*b*) represents the pure rotation of the body about the axis through its centre of mass O, when, obviously, the centre of mass (O) is at rest, *i.e.*, its linear velocity is *zero*, that of the particle at P, $- v = -\omega R$ along the $- x$ direction and that of the particle at Q, $+ v = \omega R$ along the $+ x$ direction.

Figure 11.27 (*c*) represents the pure translational motion of the body, with the linear velocity of the centre of mass O equal to $+ v$ so that the linear velocities of all other particles at P, Q etc are also the same, *viz.*, $+ v$.

Now, if really the rotation of the body about the fixed axis through P is equivalent to its pure rotation about O *plus* the translational motion of its centre of mass (O), the respective velocities of the particles at P, O and Q in Fig. 11.27 (*b*) and (c) must add up to give the same values as in Fig. 11.27 (*a*), as indeed they do, thereby fully confirming the conclusious arrived at above.

(*b*) **Case of a body rolling down an inclined plane — Its acceleration along the plane.** Let a body of circular symmetry (*e.g.*, a *disc, sphere, cylinder etc.*,) of *mass M*, roll freely down a plane, inclined to the horizontal at an angle θ, (Fig. 11.28) and rough enough to prevent *slipping* and hence any work done by friction.

If v be the linear velocity acquired by the body on covering a distance S *along the plane*, obviously, its vertical distance of descent $= S \sin \theta$.

$\therefore$ *potential energy lost by the body* $= Mg.\ S \sin \theta$.

This must obviously be equal to the kinetic energy gained by the body, *i.e.*, equal to its *K. E.* of rotation *plus* its *K. E.* of translation.

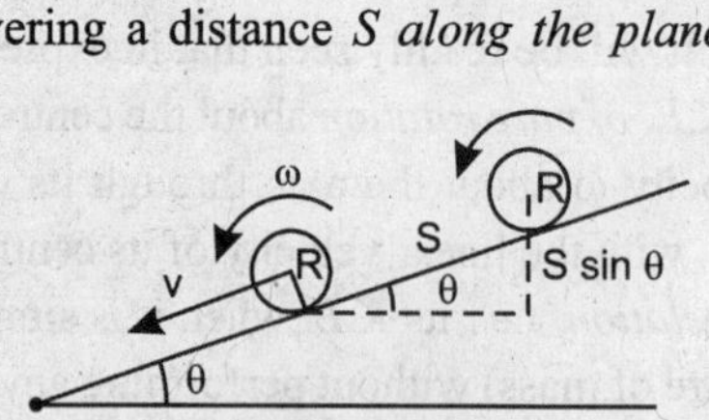

Fig. 11.28

Now, *K. E. of rotation of the body* $= \frac{1}{2} I\omega^2$, where ω is its *angular velocity* about a perpendicular axis through its centre of mass, and its *K. E. of translation* $= \frac{1}{2} Mv^2$, because its centre of mass has a linear velocity v.

$$\therefore \quad \textit{Total K. E. gained by the body} = \frac{1}{2} I\omega^2 + \frac{1}{2} Mv^2 = \frac{1}{2} MK^2 \frac{v^2}{R^2} + \frac{1}{2} Mv^2$$

because $I = MK^2$, where K is the radius of gyration of the body about the axis through its centre of mass, and $\omega = v/R$.

$$\text{Or, } \textit{total K.E. gaimed by the body} = \frac{1}{2} Mv^2 (K^2/R^2 + 1)$$

[See equation (*ii*), *case* (*a*) above]

$\therefore$ Equating this gain of $K. E.$ against the loss of $P. E.$, we have

$\frac{1}{2}Mv^2(K^2/R^2+1) = Mg\,S\sin\theta$. Or, $v^2(K^2+R^2)/R^2 = 2\,g\sin\theta.\,S$,

whence, $$v^2 = 2\frac{R^2}{K^2+R^2}g\sin\theta.S.$$

Comparing this with the kinematic relation $v^2 = 2\,aS$ for a body starting from rest, we have *acceleration of the body along the plane,*

i.e., $$a = \frac{R^2}{K^2+R^2}g\sin\theta,$$

i.e., the acceleration is proportional to $R^2/(K^2+R^2)$ for a given angle of inclination (θ) of the plane.

Clearly, therefore, (*i*) *the greater the value of K, as compared with R, the smaller the acceleration of the body rolling down along the plane* and hence the greater the time taken by it in reaching the bottom of the plane, and (*ii*) *the acceleration, and hence the time of descent, is quite independent of the mass of the body*.

Special cases (*i*) **Cylinder.** The moment of inertia of a cylinder about its axis of symmetry about which it rolls $= \frac{1}{2}Mr^2$

$$\therefore \qquad I = \frac{1}{2}Mr^2 = Mk^2 \text{ or } k^2 = \frac{r^2}{2} \text{ and } \frac{k^2}{r^2} = \frac{1}{2}$$

Hence $$a = \frac{g\sin\theta}{1+\frac{k^2}{r^2}} = \frac{g\sin\theta}{1+\frac{1}{2}} = \frac{2}{3}g\sin\theta$$

(*ii*) **Solid sphere.** The moment of inertia of a solid sphere about a diameter about which it rolls $= \frac{2}{5}Mr^2$

$$\therefore \qquad I = \frac{2}{5}Mr^2 = Mk^2 \text{ or } k^2 = \frac{2}{5}r^2 \text{ and } \frac{k^2}{r^2} = \frac{2}{5}$$

Hence $$a = \frac{g\sin\theta}{1+\frac{k^2}{r^2}} = \frac{g\sin\theta}{1+\frac{2}{5}} = \frac{5}{7}g\sin\theta$$

(*iii*) **Hollow sphere.** The moment of inertia of a hollow sphere about a diameter about which it rolls $= \frac{2}{3}Mr^2$

$$\therefore \qquad I = \frac{2}{3}Mr^2 = Mk^2 \text{ or } k^2 = \frac{2}{3}r^2 \text{ and } \frac{k^2}{r^2} = \frac{2}{3}$$

Hence $$a = \frac{g\sin\theta}{1+\frac{k^2}{r^2}} = \frac{g\sin\theta}{1+\frac{2}{3}} = \frac{3}{5}g\sin\theta$$

As an example for $g = 9.8\text{ ms}^{-2}$ and $\theta = 30°$; $\sin\theta = \frac{1}{2}$, we have

For cylinder $a = \frac{2}{3}\times\frac{1}{2}\times 9.8 = 3.27\text{ ms}^{-2}$

For solid sphere $a = \frac{5}{7}\times\frac{1}{2}\times 9.8 = 3.5\text{ ms}^{-2}$

For hollow sphere $a = \frac{3}{5}\times\frac{1}{2}\times 9.8 = 2.94\text{ ms}^{-2}$

11.11 PRODUCTS OF MOMENT OF INERTIA

When a rigid body moves with one point stationary, the total angular momentum about that point is

$$\vec{J} = \sum_i \vec{v}_i \times \vec{p}_i = \sum_i \vec{v}_i \times m_i \vec{v}_i = \sum_i m_i \vec{v}_i \times \vec{v}_i \qquad ...(i)$$

where $\vec{r}_i$ and $\vec{v}_i$ are the radius vector and velocity vector respectively of the ith particle relative to the given point. Since $\vec{r}_i$ is a fixed vector to the body, the velocity $\vec{v}_i$ with respect to the space set of axes solely form the rotational motion of the body about the fixed point.

We know, $$\vec{v}_i = \vec{\omega} \times \vec{r} \qquad ...(ii)$$

Substituting equation (*ii*) in equation (*i*), we have

$$\vec{J} = \sum_i m_i[(\vec{r}_i \times (\vec{\omega} \times \vec{r}_i)] \qquad ...(iii)$$

Expanding the triple cross product using

$$[\vec{A} \times (\vec{B} \times \vec{C}) = \vec{B}(\vec{A} \cdot \vec{C}) - \vec{C}(\vec{A} \cdot \vec{B})]$$

We write equation (*iii*) as

$$\vec{J} = \sum_i m_i[\vec{\omega}(\vec{r}_i \cdot \vec{r}_i) - \vec{r}_i(\vec{r}_i \cdot \vec{\omega})]$$

$$= \sum_i m_i[\vec{\omega} r_i^2 - \vec{r}_i \cdot (\vec{r}_i \cdot \vec{\omega})]$$

$$= \sum_i m_i r_i^2 \vec{\omega} - m_i \vec{r}_i(\vec{r}_i \cdot \vec{\omega}) \qquad ...(iv)$$

Expanding angular momentum J, in cartesian co-ordinates, Eq. (*iv*) can be written as

$$J_x = \omega_x \sum_i m_i r_i^2 - \omega_x \sum_i m_i x_i^2 - \omega_y \sum_i m_i x_i y_i - \omega_z \sum_i m_i x_i z_i$$

$$= \omega_x \sum_i m_i (r_i^2 - x_i^2) - \omega_y \sum_i m_i x_i y_i - \omega_z \sum_i m_i x_i z_i \qquad ...(v)$$

With similar equations for other components J_y and J_z of $\vec{J}$.

Eq. (*v*), may be written as

$$J_x = I_{xx}\, \omega_x + I_{xy}\, \omega_y + I_{xz}\, \omega_z \qquad ...(vi)$$

where $$I_{xx} = \sum_i m_i (r_i^2 - x_i^2) = \sum_i m_i (y_i^2 + z_i^2)$$

$$I_{xy} = -\sum_i m_i x_i y_i$$

$$I_{xz} = -\sum_i m_i x_i z_i$$

By analogy, we can write for J_y and J_z from eq. (*vi*) as

$$J_y = I_{yx}\, \omega_x + I_{yy}\, \omega_y + I_{yz}\, \omega_z$$

$$J_z = I_{zx}\, \omega_x + I_{zy}\, \omega_y + I_{zz}\, \omega_z.$$

In general, $$J = \sum_k I_{jk} \omega_k \qquad ...(vii)$$

where j and k takes values x, y, z.

Such nine coefficients I_{xx}, I_{xy}, ... are the nine elements of the transformation (3 × 3) matrix, *i.e.*, nine quantities I_{jk} form a *symmetric tensor*

$$\Pi = \begin{pmatrix} I_{xx} & I_{xy} & I_{xz} \\ I_{yx} & I_{yy} & I_{yz} \\ I_{zx} & I_{zy} & I_{zz} \end{pmatrix} \quad \text{...(viii)}$$

In vector notation, we have

$$\vec{J} = \Pi \cdot \vec{\omega} \quad \text{...(ix)}$$

The diagonal elements are known as "*Moments of inertia coefficients*", while the off-diagonal elements are named as "*Products of M. I.*"

11.12 PRINCIPAL MOMENTS

The methods of matrix algebra enables us to show that for any point in a rigid body one can find a set of cartesian axes for which the inertia tensor will be diagonal and the axes are called "*Principal axes*" and the corresponding diagonal elements I_1, I_2, I_3 are known as "*Principal moments of inertia*". In practice, the principal *M. I.*, being the eigen values of *I*, are found as roots of the following determinant

$$\begin{vmatrix} I_{xx} - I & I_{xy} & I_{xz} \\ I_{yx} & I_{yy} - I & I_{yz} \\ I_{zx} & I_{zy} & I_{zz} - I \end{vmatrix} = 0 \quad \text{...(x)}$$

The above equation is cubic in *I* whose three roots are the desired principal moments.

11.13 EULER'S EQUATIONS OF MOTION

For a rotational motion about a fixed point or about the centre of mass, the direct Newtonian approach leads to a set of equations known as *Euler's equations of motion.* Let us consider the equation of motion for rotational motion for a fixed coordinate system with origin at centre of mass is

$$\text{Torque,} \qquad \vec{\tau}_j = \frac{d\vec{J}_j}{dt} \text{ where } J_j = \sum_k I_{jk}\omega_k \quad \text{...(xi)}$$

The moment and product of inertia I_{jk} are with respect to a fixed coordinate frame. By choosing *body-fixed* coordinate system simplifies analysis of motion. Hence, moments and products of inertia both are time-independent.

$$\text{Now using relation,} \qquad \frac{d\vec{r}}{dt} = \frac{\delta\vec{r}}{\delta t} + \vec{\omega} \times \vec{r}$$

Eq. (*xi*), may be written as

$$\tau_j = \frac{\delta J_j}{\delta t} + (\vec{\omega} \times \vec{J})_j \quad \text{...(xii)}$$

If we select the axes of rotation in the body where all the products of inertia vanish

i.e., $\qquad i_{ij} = 0$ for $I \neq j$

Axes for which $I_{ij} = 0$, $i \neq j$ are called the *principal axes of the body,*

$$J_1 = I_{11}\,\omega_1 = I_1\omega_1$$

$$J_2 = I_{22}\,\omega_2 = I_2\omega_2$$

$$J_3 = I_{33}\,\omega_3 = I_3\omega_3$$

where I_1, I_2, I_3 are the principal M.I.

From Eq. (*xii*) in cartesian co-ordinates, the Euler's equations of motion of a rigid body as

$$\tau_1 = I_1 \dot{\omega}_1 - \omega_2\omega_3 (I_2 - I_3)$$
$$\tau_2 = I_2 \dot{\omega}_2 - \omega_3\omega_1 (I_3 - I_1) \qquad ...(xiii)$$
$$\tau_3 = I_3 \dot{\omega}_3 - \omega_1\omega_2 (I_1 - I_2)$$

Eq. (*xii*) and (*iii*) are called Euler's equations of motion for a rigid body with one point fixed.

11.14 MOMENT OF INERTIA OF A FLYWHEEL – EXPERIMENTAL DETERMINATION

A flywheel* is just a *large, heavy wheel, with a long cylindrical axle passing through* its centre (Fig. 11.29), and with its *c.g.* lying on its axis of rotation, so that, when properly mounted on ball bearings (to minimise friction), *it may continue to be at rest in any desired position.*

In order that its *M. I.* about its axis of rotation may be large, *practically the whole of its mass is concentrated on its rim.* In fact, the larger its *M. I.,* the better its performance in making the running of a machine, coupled to the engine, smoother and steadier. It therefore, finds extensive use in the case of stationary engines, where, as we know, power is delivered to the shaft (to which the machine is connected *not continuously* but only once in a cycle of four strokes. Without the flywheel, therefore, (also connected to the shaft), the machine would be driven in jerks. The flywheel, so to speak, absorbs the power delivered to the shaft and makes it available to the machine during the intervening three strokes. For, on account of its large *M. I.,* the flywheel gets hardly accelerated by the power transmitted to it intermittently (after every three strokes) and it, therefore, continues to rotate with the same speed throughout, thus making for a smooth running of the machine.

For our purpose here, however, we may regard a flywheel to be just a thick disc (or a short cylinder) from which a smaller concentric disc (or cylinder) has been removed. In other words, we may take it to be an annular ring, whose moment of inertia is to be determined about an axis passing through its centre and perpendicular to its plane, or a hollow cylinder whose *M. I.* is to be determined about its axis of symmetry. So that, if *R* and *r* be the *external and internal radii* respectively of the annular ring (or the hollow cylinder) and *M* its *mass*, its *M. I.* about *this* axis = $\boldsymbol{M(R^2 + r^2)/2}$

[§11.9 cases 6 and 9.

The axle, again, is a disc (or a solid cylinder) of radius *r* and its *M. I.* about the axis passing through its centre and perpendicular to its plane (or about the axis of symmetry of the solid cylinder) = $mr^2/2$, where *m* is the *mass of axle*. [§ 11.9 cases 5 and 7]

So that, *M. I. of the flywheel* as a whole, (*i.e.*, of the wheel and the axle) *about the axis of rotation, i.e.,*

$$I = M.\,I.\ of\ the\ wheel + M.\,I.\ of\ the\ axle = M\frac{(R^2 + r^2)}{2} + m\frac{r^2}{2}.$$

Experimental determination. The axle of the flywheel, whose moment of inertia is to be determined, is arranged to lie in a horizontal position, as shown in Fig. 11.29 at a convenient height from the floor.

A small loop at the end of a piece of find cord is slipped on to a tiny peg *P* on the axle and almost the whole length of it wound *evenly* round the latter, with a suitable mass *M* suspended from its other free end, as shown.

---

*The flywheel is dispensed with in a mobile type of engine, like a locomotive or a motor car engine, because the motion of the locomotive or the car itself conserves motion. The former has a considerable mass of its own, ensuring a smooth motion and in the case of the latter this smoothness of motion is partly achieved by using a multicylinder engine, with the cylinders so arranged that they deliver power to the shaft one after the other in quick succession so as to make it almost continuous. Incidentally, this also increases the power of the engine.

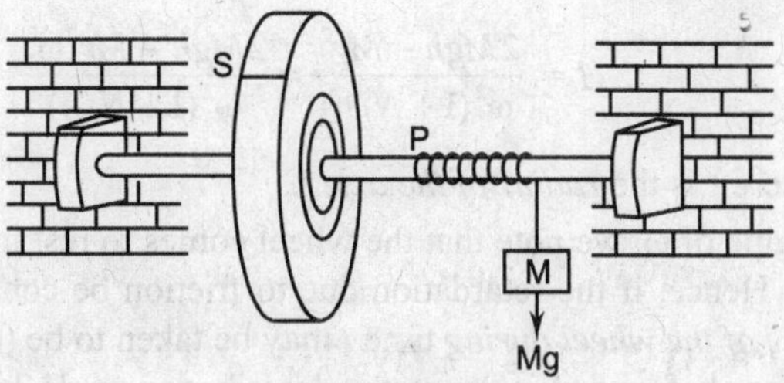

Fig. 11.29

This mass is initially kept properly supported at a known height h from the floor, the length of the cord being so adjusted that when the mass is allowed to fall, resulting in the rotation of the wheel, *the cord just gets completely unwound as the mass touches the floor and the loop slips off the peg.* The number of rotations made by the wheel during this interval of time is counted (with the help of a *reference mark S* made on the wheel) and is obviously equal to the number of turns of the cord round the axle, say, N.

The wheel having acquired kinetic energy due to the falling mass continues to rotate until brought to rest by the frictional forces at the bearings. The time t taken by it to come to rest after the mass gets detached from the axle is noted with the help of a stop watch, as also the number of rotations made by it during this time, say, n.

The calculations are then made as follows:

The potential energy lost by the mass in falling through a vertical height h is clearly Mgh. This energy is gained in the form of kinetic energy of rotation by the flywheel and in the form of kinetic energy of translation by the mass. So that, if I be the *M. I.* of the flywheel about the axis of rotation and ω, its *angular velocity* at the time the cord slips off the peg, the *K. E. of rotation acquired by the flywheel* $= \frac{1}{2}I\omega^2$. And, if v be the linear velocity of the mass on falling through vertical height h, the *K. E. of translation acquired by the mass* $= \frac{1}{2}Mv^2$.

We, therefore, have

$$Mgh = \frac{1}{2}I\omega^2 + \frac{1}{2}Mv^2 + \textit{Work done against friction.}$$

Now, if the frictional force be taken to be uniform and the work done against it per rotation of the wheel to be w, clearly, work done against friction during N rotations made by the wheel before the mass gets detached from the axle $= Nw$. So that, we have

$$Mgh = \frac{1}{2}I\omega^2 + \frac{1}{2}Mv^2 + Nw.$$

Again, since, after the mass gets detached from the axle, the wheel makes *n rotations* before coming to rest, the work done against friction during n rotations $= nw$. This must obviously be equal to the *K. E.* of rotation of the wheel and, therefore,

$$nw = \frac{1}{2}I\omega^2, \text{ whence, } w = \frac{1}{2}I\omega^2/n.$$

Substituting this value of w in the energy equation above, we have

$$Mgh = \frac{1}{2}I\omega^2 + \frac{1}{2}Mv^2 + \frac{1}{2}NI\omega^2/n = \frac{1}{2}Mv^2 + \frac{1}{2}I\omega^2(1 + N/n)$$

Or, $$2Mgh = Mv^2 + I\omega^2\,(1 + N/n). \text{ Or, } 2\,Mgh - Mv^2 = I\omega^2\,(1 + N/n),$$

whence,
$$I = \frac{2Mgh - Mv^2}{\omega^2(1+N/n)} = \frac{2Mgh - Mr^2\omega^2}{\omega^2(1+N/n)} = \frac{M(2gh/\omega^2 - r^2)}{(1+N/n)},$$

because $v = r\omega$, where r is the *radius of the axle**.

To determine the value of ω, we note that the wheel comes to rest in time t after the mass gets detached from the axle. Hence, if the retardation due to friction be considered to be uniform, the *average angular velocity of the wheel during* time t may be taken to be $(\omega + 0)/2 = \omega/2$. And, since the wheel makes n rotations before coming to rest, it describes an angle $2\pi n$ in time t, and its average angular velocity is, therefore, also equal to $2\pi n/t$. So that,

$$\omega/2 = 2\pi n/t, \text{ Or, } \omega = 4\pi n/t.$$

Substituting this value of ω in the expression for I above, we have

$$I = \frac{M[(2ght^2/16\pi^2 n^2) - r^2]}{1 + N/n} = \frac{M[ght^2/8\pi^2 n^2) - r^2]}{(n+N)/n}$$

Or,
$$I = M\left(\frac{n}{n+N}\right)\left(\frac{ght^2}{8\pi^2 n^2} - r^2\right) = \frac{M}{n+N}\left(\frac{ght^2}{8\pi^2 n} - nr^2\right)$$

whence, the value of I, the *moment of inertia of the flywheel about its axis of rotation*, may be easily obtained.

11.15 PRECESSION

We know that when a body rotates about a *fixed* axis, under the action of a torque, the axial component of the torque alone is effective in producing rotation (§ 11.3), its component perpendicular to the axis being neutralised by an equal and opposite torque due to the constraining forces applied to the axis to maintain its original position, *i.e.*, to keep it fixed.

In the absence of any such costraining forces, obviously, the axis of rotation, and hence also the plane of rotation, of the body will turn from its initial position under the action of the *component of the torque perpendicular to the axis*, which we may denote by the symbol τ_1.

Since this torque τ_1 (*i.e.*, the axis of this torque) is perpendicular to the axis of rotation of the body, the magnitude of the angular velocity, and hence also that of the angular momentum, of the body remains unaltered, with only its direction changed in exactly the same manner that in a linear motion, a constant force (viz., the centripetal force), acting on a body in a direction perpendicular to that of its velocity, simply changes its direction and not its magnitude. So that, if the torque, τ_1 be a constant one, the rotation-axis and the plane of rotation of the rotating body continue to change their direction at a constant rate, with the axis of the torque always perpendicular to the axis of rotation of the body.

This change in the direction of the rotation-axis, or in the direction of the plane of rotation, of the rotating body under the action of a constant torque perpendicular to the axis of rotation is called precession.

The torque τ_1 which brings this about is, therefore, called the **precessional torque** and the rate of rotation of the axis of rotation or the plane of rotation of the body is called the **rate of precession**, usually denoted by the symbol ϕ.

Let us obtain the value of this *precessional torque* (τ_1) and the *rate of precession* (ϕ).

We shall consider here only the case of a symmetrical body rotating about one of its axes of symmetry, for in such a case alone, does the position of the axis of rotation remain the same, or very nearly the same, with respect to the rotating body itself.

* If the cord be appreciably thick, the effective value of r is taken to be the radius of the axle plus half the thickness of the cord.

Thus, let us consider the case of a uniform circular disc D rotating with a constant angular velocity ω, in the anticlockwise direction, about its geometric axis OY (*i.e.,* about the axis passing through its centre (or centre of mass) and perpendicular to its plane), in its own plane and hence perpendicular to OY, (Fig. 11.30).

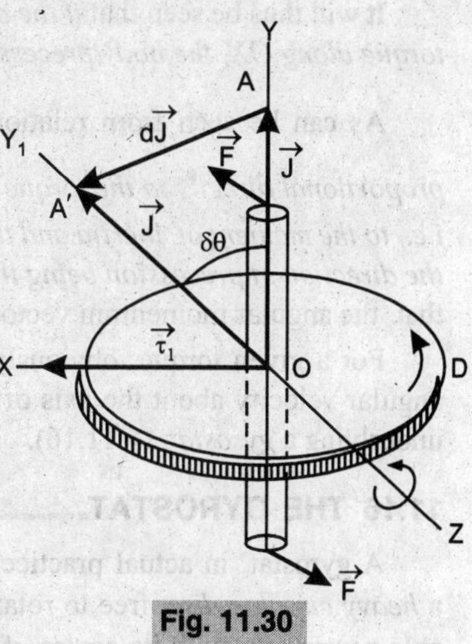

Fig. 11.30

Clearly, if I be the *M.I.* of the disc about its axis of rotation (OY), its angular momentum J will be equal to $I\omega$.

Let it be represented by the vector $\overrightarrow{OA}$, perpendicular to its plane of rotation or along the axis of rotation OY.

Under the action of the component of the torque $\left(\vec{F}, \vec{F}\right)$ perpendicular to it, (*i.e.,* with the axis of the torque perpendicular to it and hence in the plane of the disc, along OX), let the axis of rotation OY, and hence also the plane of rotation of the disc, turn or *precess* through a small angle $\delta\theta$, in a small interval of time δt, about the axis OZ through O and perpendicular to both OX and OY, *i.e.,* perpendicular to the plane of the paper.

The angular momentum of the disc will now be represented by the vector $\overrightarrow{OA'}$, perpendicular to its new plane of rotation, or along its new axis of rotation OY_1. It will be seen that the torque vector being perpendicular to the angular momentum vector, the angular momentum of the disc remains unaltered in magnitude, with only its direction changing through angle $AOA = \delta\theta$ and, therefore, $\overrightarrow{OA'} = \overrightarrow{OA} = \vec{J}$.

Since even a change in its direction constitutes a change in momentum, we have, in accordance with the principle of addition of vectors, the change in angular momentum $d\vec{J}$ represented by the vector AA' which forms the third side of the triangle of vectors OAA'.

This means that the torque $\vec{\tau}_1 = d\vec{J}/\delta t$, also directed along $\overrightarrow{AA'}$ or OX, is again perpendicular to the axis of rotation in its new position (OY_1) and the axis, therefore, goes on precessing at a constant rate (ϕ) about the axis OZ through O, *in the direction of the torque.*

To obtain the value of ϕ, we note that $\vec{\tau}_1 = d\vec{J}/\delta t = Id\vec{\omega}/\delta t.$

So that, *change in angular momentum* $d\vec{J} = \vec{\tau}_1 \delta t$.

Since from the figure, $\delta\theta = AA'/OA = dJ/J$, we have $\delta\theta = \tau_1 \delta t/J$,

whence, the *rate of precession* $\phi = \delta\theta/\delta t = \tau_1/J = \tau_1/I\omega$. ...(*i*)

$[\because \vec{J} = I\omega]$.

And, therefore, *precessional torque* $\vec{\tau}_1 = \vec{\phi} \times (I\vec{\omega}) = \vec{\phi} \times \vec{J}$,

its magnitude being equal to $\phi \times J \times$ *sine of the angle between them* (which is clearly 90° here). ...(*ii*)

Thus, *the precessional torque vector* $\vec{\tau}_1$ *is the cross product of the precessional rate vector* $\vec{\phi}$ *and the angular momentum vector* $\vec{J}$. So that, if we know the directions of vectors $\vec{\phi}$ and $\vec{J}$, the direction of the torque vector may be easily obtained from the *right hand rule for a vector product.*

It will thus be seen that *if the axis of rotation of a body lies along OY and the axis of the applied torque along OX, the body precesses about the third mutually perpendicular axis OZ.*

As can be seen from relation (*i*) above, *the rate of precession* ($\vec{\phi}$) *of the rotation-axis is proportional directly to the torque* $\left(\vec{\tau}_1\right)$ *applied and inversely to the angular momentum* $\left(\vec{J} = I\vec{\omega}\right)$, *i.e., to the moment of inertia and the angular velocity of the rotating body about the axis of rotation, the direction of precession being the direction of the change of angular momentum or the torque.* So that, the angular momentum vector, so to speak, changes the torque vector.

For a given torque, obviously, the larger the moment of inertia of a body and the higher its angular velocity about the axis of rotation, the smaller the rate of precession. This is the principle underlying a *gyrostat*, (§ 11.16).

11.16 THE GYROSTAT

A gyrostat, in actual practice, usually takes the form of a *heavy circular disc,* free to rotate at a high speed about an axle passing through its centre of mass and perpendicular to its plane, *i.e.*, about its axis of symmetry, and is so mounted that the disc, along with the axle can turn freely about any one of the three mutually perpendicular axes.

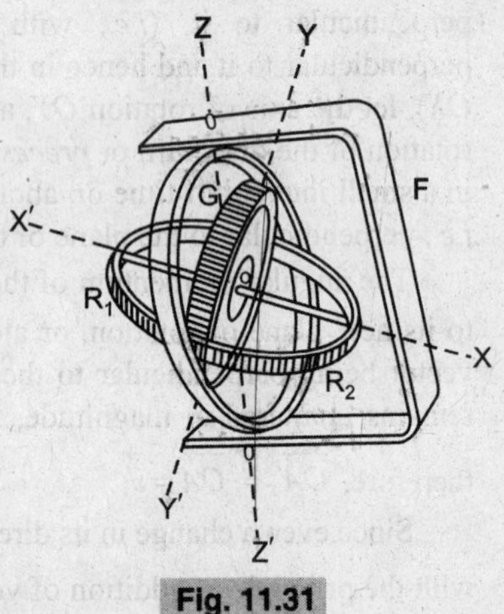

Fig. 11.31

Thus, in Fig. 11.31, the disc or the gyrostat G is free to rotate about the axle, coincident with the axis of x and is carried by a circular ring R_1 which is itself free to turn about the axis of y inside another ring R_2, which is free to rotate about the axis of z, within a rigid framework F. The three axes being obviously perpendicular to each other, intersect in the same point O and therefore, for any given position of F, the disc or the gyrostat G can turn freely about any one of them.

Now, from the discussion under §11.15 above, it is clear that *with the disc rotating fast,* (*i*) *any rotation of the framework leaves the position and direction of the axis of rotation of the disc unaffected with respect to it and* (*ii*) *any torque applied to the axis of rotation of the disc results in its precession.*

Since the rate of precession is inversely proportional to the angular momentum $I\omega$ of the disc, the greater its *M.I.* and the higher its angular velocity about the axis of rotation, the smaller the precession of the latter. Obviously, therefore, a massive disc rotating at a high speed makes for a greater stability of its axis of rotation. Hence the use of gyrostats for studying of motions and ensuring stability of direction. For examples of such use, see §11.17.

11.17 GYROSTATIC APPLICATIONS

The following are a few example of the use of a gyroscope for steadying of motions and ensuring directional stability, the underlying principle in each case being that the gyroscope is made to precess in such a manner that the reaction couple due to the rotating disc or wheel offsets *exactly* the effect of the disturbing couple.

* The direction of the torque may also be obtained from what is called Lanchaster's rule, viz., that if we view the spinning disc from a point in its plane, with the line of sight perpendicular to the axis of precession and the disc slightly moves in the direction of precession, a point on its circumference would be seen to describe an ellipse, the sense (*i.e.*, direction) of which would be the direction of the precessional torque with the line of slight as its axis.

(*i*) **The Gyrostatic or the Gyro-Compass.** Used in aeroplanes and ships and, particularly in submarines, it is a disc or a flywheel of a large moment of inertia (*i.e.*, a gyrostat), G, with its axle PQ mounted in a horizontal ring R_1 free to rotate about its axis AB inside a vertical ring R_2 which can turn freely about the axis CD within a framework F, carried on horizontal *gimbals*, of which only one pair G_1G_1 is shown here, (Fig. 11.32). This ensures that the disc or the flywheel has three degrees of freedom, irrespective of the position of the framework F.

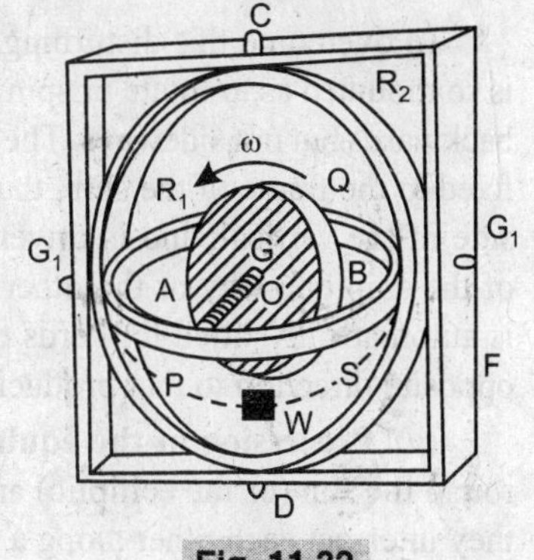

Fig. 11.32

Rotated at a high speed by means of an electric motor, with its axis in the magnetic meridian (*i.e.*, in the vertical plane passing through the geographic north and south of the earth), the conservation of momentum of the disc or the wheel and its directional stability ensure that its axis POQ always lies in the direction of the meridian, *i.e.*, along the geographic north and south.

In view of the complete freedom of movement of the disc, irrespective of the position of the supporting frame (F), any movement of the latter produces no deflecting couple or torque on it and *this particular (North-South) direction of the axis thus continues to be maintained in space all the time, despite any changes in the direction of the ship or the submarine or any tossings or pitchings of it.*

This compass, appropriately called the *gyro-compass*, is therefore more dependable than the ordinary compass, the more so because *it remains quite unaffected by any type of magnetic disturbances.*

(*ii*) **Rifling of barrels of guns and rifles.** This is another familiar example of the directional stability of a rapidly spinning body. For, if the shot or the bullet be given a rapid spin about an axis along its direction of motion, it is less responsive to small deflective forces through air and its uniformity of flight is thus greatly improved.

This is achieved by what is called '*rifling*' the barrel of the gun or the rifle, *i.e.*, by cutting spiral grooves inside it, so that before emerging out, the shot or the bullet first moves along these, thereby acquiring the necessary spin to ensure its almost linear motion on emergence.

(*iii*) **Riding of bicycles and rolling of hoops or discs.** Both these are cases of what is called *statical instability*, for neither of the two, when at rest, can possibly remain in equilibrium in the position in which it does when in motion.

Here, again, the gyroscopic action does the trick by appropriately deflecting their axes of rotation, thereby changing their planes of rotation to counteract the disturbing effect due to gravity.

Thus, if a person riding a bicycle, without holding the handle, wishes to turn to one side, all he has to do is to tilt a little to that side, thus producing a couple about the horizontal direction of motion of the front wheel (here functioning as a rotating gyrostat) which then turns the axle of the wheel about the vertical, and hence its plane of rotation, in the desired direction.

The same is true for a hoop or a disc, projected with its plane vertical to roll over a horizontal surface.

(*iv*) **Stabilising of ships.** Although a ship is intrinsically stable, it is subject to disturbing oscillations in a rough or heavy sea, both about its transverse and longitudinal axes. The former type of oscillation is called pitching and the latter type, rolling. The amplitude in the case of rolling being much greater than that in the case of pitching, it is the more troublesome of the two. Efforts are, therefore, directed towards minimising rolling rather than pitching.

Now, rolling is caused by the torque generated as a result of the difference in the buoyancy on the two sides of the centre line of the ship when it happens to lie on a wave slope. This torque has its maximum value when the ship lies on either side of a wave at the point of maximum slope and, the minimum or zero value when it lies on either the crest or the trough of a wave.

To overcome this disturbing torque, a large gyroscope, here called a gyro-stabiliser, is used. It is so mounted as to rotate or spin about a vertical shaft or axle which can be tilted only forwards and backwards but not sideways. The shaft is, in fact, enclosed in a casing which is supported in bearings fixed to the frame of the ship, thus allowing for its precessional motion through about 60° on either side of the vertical, and is driven by an electric motor. The arrangement is such that during a roll of the ship one way or the other (*i.e.*, clockwise or anticlockwise), the shaft of the gyro-stabiliser is automatically titled forwards or backwards, such that its precession gives rise to a torque in the opposite direction to that producing the roll.

(*v*) **Precession of the equinoxes.** The equatorial plane of the earth and the plane of its orbit round the sun (or the ecliptic) are, as we know, inclined to each other at an angle of 23.5°, so that they intersect each other along a line, called the *line of equinoxes*. The earth, therefore, crosses this line *twice* in one full round about the sun, near about the 21st of March and the 22nd of September every year,—its position in the orbit at these two points being referred to as the *vernal* and the *Autumnal equinox* respectively. .

Now, the earth, as is well known, is not an exact sphere but slightly bulges out at the equator (its equatorial radius being about 13 miles greater than its polar radius) and thus has the form of a *flattened ellipsoid of revolution*. Further, the sun and the moon do not usually lie in its equatorial plane but rather in the plane of its orbit or the ecliptic. In consequence, the gravitational attraction due to the sun and the moon on the equatorial bulge of the earth gives rise to a torque, bringing about the precession of its axis. And since the earth acts like a gigantic top, its precessing axis describes a circular cone relative to the fined stars, *e.g.*, the pole star. This precession of the earth's axis brings about a corresponding change in the direction of the line of equinoxes and the phenomenon is called *precession of the equinoxes*.

The torque on the earth due to the attractive force of the sun and the moon is, however, so small that it takes 25800 years for the earth's axis to describe the complete cone, at which rate of rotation the star *Vega* will be the pole star in about 1200 years hence.

(*vi*) **Other applications.** Among other applications of gyrostatic action may be mentioned the modern aircraft appliances like the *automatic pilot*, the *steering* of *torpedoes*, the *artificial horizon*, the *bomb sights* and the *turn and bank indicators* etc.

The function of all these instruments is to record the effects of a change of orientation between a relatively fixed plane (provided by a fast rotating gyrostat), serving as the *datum plane*, and some other movable plane in the machine. This they do with greater precision and reliability than is possible by human judgement alone, however trained and practised.

11.18 MOMENT OF INERTIA OF A DIATOMIC MOLECULE

In a diatomic molecule, in its stable equilibrium position, the two atoms are a certain distance r_0 apart, where r_0 is called its *internuclear distance* or *bond length*. For our present purpose, however, we may imagine it to consist of two tiny spheres at either end of a thin weightless rod, as shown in Fig. 11.33.

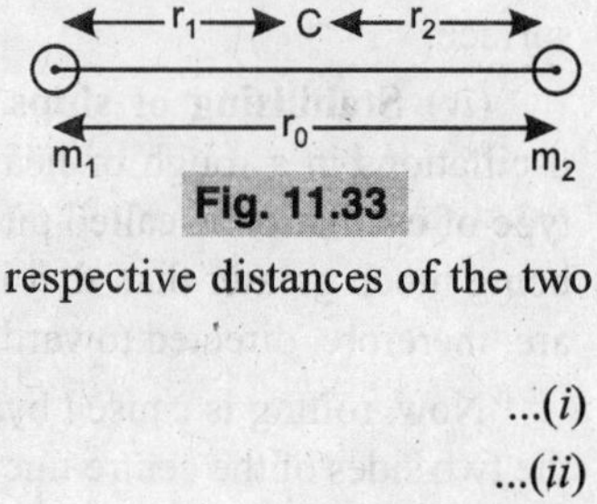

Fig. 11.33

Let C be the centre of mass of the molecule and r_1 and r_2, the respective distances of the two atoms from it.

Then, clearly $$r_1 + r_2 = r_0 \quad ...(i)$$

and $$m_1 r_1 = m_2 r_2, \quad ...(ii)$$

where, m_1 and m_2 are the masses of the two atoms respectively.

From relations (*i*) and (*ii*), therefore, we have

$$r_1 = \frac{m_2}{m_1 + m_2} r_0 \quad \text{and} \quad r_2 = \frac{m_1}{m_1 + m_2} r_0$$

Now, the moment of inertia of the molecule (*i.e.*, of the two atoms) about an axis passing through the centre of mass C and perpendicular to r is clearly

$$I = m_1 r_1^2 + m_2 r_2^2 .$$

Or, substituting the values of r_1 and r_2, we have

$$I = m_1 \left(\frac{m_2}{m_1 + m_2} \right)^2 r_0^2 + m_2 \left(\frac{m_1}{m_1 + m_2} \right)^2 r_0^2 .$$

Or,
$$I = \left[\frac{m_1 m_2^2 + m_2 m_1^2}{(m_1 + m_2)^2} \right] r_0^2 = \left[\frac{m_1 m_2 (m_1 + m_2)}{(m_1 + m_2)^2} \right] r_0^2 = \frac{m_1 m_2}{m_1 + m_2} r_0^2 .$$

But, as we know, $m_1 m_2/(m_1 + m_2) = \mu$, the *reduced mass* of the molecule. So that,

$$I = \mu r_0^2 .$$

Or, *M.I. of diatomic molecule* = (*reduced mass of the molecule*) × (*internuclear distance or bond length*)^2.

11.19 ROTATIONAL ENERGY STATES OF A DIATOMIC MOLECULE

As we have just seen in §11.18 above, the *M.I.* of a diatomic molecule about an axis through its centre of mass and perpendicular to the distance r_0 (the bond length) between the two atoms is μr_0^2, where μ is its reduced mass. If, therefore, ω be the angular velocity of the molecule about its axis of rotation, its *angular momentum* $j = I\omega$, and the *angular momentum vector* $\vec{j}$ lies in the plane perpendicular to the plane of rotation or *along the axis of rotation.*

Thus,
$$j^2 = I^2 \omega^2 . \quad \text{Or,} \quad \omega^2 = j^2 / I^2 .$$

Now, as we know, the kinetic energy of rotation of a rigid body about an axis, about which its *M.I.* is I, is given by $E = \frac{1}{2} I\omega^2$, where ω is its angular velocity about the axis.

So that, substituting the value of ω^2 as obtained above, we have

$$E = \frac{1}{2} I \frac{j^2}{I^2} = \frac{j^2}{2I} = \frac{j^2}{2\mu r_0^2} .$$

This is the relation for the kinetic energy of rotation of a diatomic molecule on the basis of classical mechanics, where j and, therefore, E may have any possible values and not only certain specified ones.

As we have seen under §11.14, however, the angular momentum in the case of small particles is *quantised* and, as deduced on the basis of wave mechanics, may have only discrete values $\sqrt{j(j+1)}$ in terms of $\hbar$ or $h/2\pi$ units, where j is the *total angular momentum quantum number,* equal to 0, 1, 2, 3 etc., *i.e.*, the *magnitude of the angular momentum of the molecule* = $\sqrt{j(j+1)} \frac{h}{2\pi}$.

Substituting this in place of j, therefore, in the expression for rotational kinetic energy of the diatomic molecule, we have

$$E = \frac{j(j+1)h^2}{8\pi^2 I},$$

an expression which is also borne out by actual experiment.

This means, then, *that the rotational kinetic energy of a diatomic molecule is also quantised and may have only discrete values corresponding to j* = 0, 1, 2, 3 etc., *and no other intermediate values.*

Putting $h^2/8\pi^2 I = A$, we have $E = Aj(j+1)$. So that,
for $j = 0$, $E = 0$; for $j = 1$, $E = 2A$; for $j = 2$, $E = 6A$ and so on.

These are called the *rotational energy states,* (*or rotational energy levels*) *of the diatomic molecule,* indicating that it can have no rotational energy between 0 and $2A$, between $2A$ and $6A$ and so on.

For convenience, these are usually shown in what is called an *energy level diagram,* as indicated in Fig. 11.34, which consists of a set of parallel lines, one above the other, representing the various energy levels, the lowest or the base line representing the *ground state* of the molecule, with $j = 0$ and hence also $E = 0$. The upper lines correspond to $j = 1, j = 2$ etc. and therefore, $E = 2A$, $6A$ etc., the distances of the lines (or energy levels) from the base line (or the ground state) being proportional to the values of energy represented by them.

At or near the absolute zero, the molecule is in the ground state, with $E = 0$ corresponding to $j = 0$. As the temperature rises, the energy state or the energy level of the molecule also rises as shown, so that E attains the values $2A$, $6A$, $12A$, $20A$, $30A$ etc., corresponding to $j = 1, 2, 3, 4$ and 5 etc. respectively, *i.e., there is a transition of the molecule from a lower to a higher energy state* as it absorbs more and more energy.

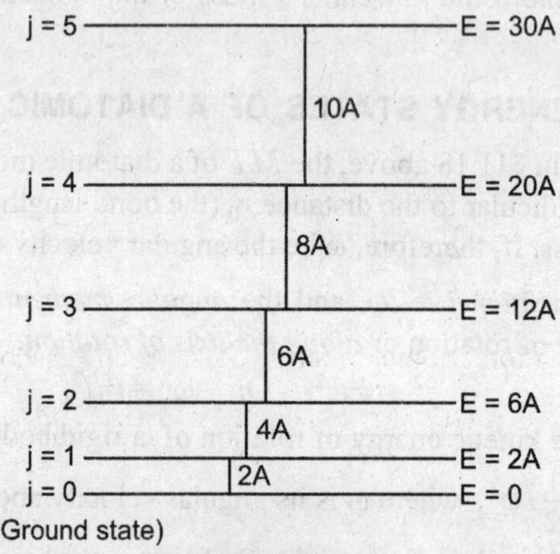

Fig. 11.34

On the other hand, if the transition occurs from a higher to a lower energy state, the molecule gives out its surplus energy which appears in the form of an electromagnetic radiation. These transitions are indicated by vertical lines in the figure along with the surplus energy emitted as electromagnetic radiation in each successive transition.

In either case, however, only those transitions are possible for which the value of j changes by $\Delta J = \pm 1$, *i.e.,* from j to $(j+1)$ or from j to $(j-1)$.

The change in energy corresponding to a change $\Delta j = \pm 1$ in the value of j can be easily obtained from the difference in energy at energy levels corresponding to j and $(j-1)$.

Thus, the change in energy,

$$\Delta E = E_{(j)} - E_{(j-1)} = j(j+1)\,A - (j-1)jA = 2Aj.$$

Or,
$$\Delta E = 2\frac{h^2}{8\pi^2 I}\,j = \frac{h^2}{4\pi^2 I}\,j \qquad ...(i)$$

So that, $h\nu = \dfrac{h^2}{4\pi^2 I}\,j$ and , therefore, $\nu = \dfrac{h}{4\pi^2 I}\,j = \dfrac{2Aj}{h}$ ...(ii)

This shows that the frequencies (ν) of the transition radiations emitted differ by the same amount $2A/h$ for successive pairs of energy levels.

Thus, the frequency of radiation due to transition between energy levels corresponding to $j = 1$ and $j = 0$ is $2A/h$; that of the radiation due to transition between energy levels corresponding to $j = 2$ and $j = 0$ is $4A/h$ and so on, the common difference between the frequencies emitted between successive pairs of energy levels being $2A/h$ all along. This means, clearly, that the spectral lines emitted due to transition between successive pairs of energy levels must all be equally spaced. The frequencies of these spectral lines being quite small (and hence their wavelengths large) because of the small amount of the energy involved in the transition, they are found in the infra-red or the micro-radio wave region of the electromagnetic spectrum.

It will be readily seen that this common difference ($2A/h$) in the frequencies of the successive spectral lines enables us to obtain the value of the *M.I.* of a diatomic molecule about its own axis of rotation. For, $\quad 2A/h = h/4\pi^2 I, \quad$ whence, $\quad I = h^2/8\pi^2 A.$

And, since $I = \mu r_0^2$, where μ is the reduced mass of the molecule and r_0, the internuclear distance or bond length, we can also obtain the value of r_0.

Now, defining *wave number* ν as the *number of wavelengths per cm*,

we have $$\nu = 1/\lambda = v/c \text{ per cm},$$

where c is the velocity of light or electromagnetic radiation, in general.

If, therefore, E be the energy of radiation, we have

$$E = h\nu \quad \text{or,} \quad \nu = E/h,$$

Or, $\bar{\nu} = 1/\lambda = E/hc = E$, where $E/hc = \in$ is referred to as *energy in wave numbers*.

We can thus put our equation I above in terms of $\in$, when it becomes

$$\nu = \frac{E_{(j)}}{hc} - \frac{E_{(j-1)}}{hc} = E_{(j)} - E_{(j-1)} = \frac{2A}{hc} j = \frac{hj}{4\pi^2 Ic} = \frac{hj}{4\pi^2 \mu r_0^2 c} \qquad ...(iii)$$

This shows at once that the common spacing between the spectral lines emitted is $h/4\pi^2 Ic = h/4\pi^2 \mu r_0^2 c$. So that, knowing the spacing between the spectral lines we can again obtain the *M.I.* of the diatomic molecule and its intranuclear distance or bond length.

Further, knowing the energy in wave numbers ($\in$) for two successive energy levels, say, corresponding to j and $(j - 1)$, we can straightaway obtain the wave number ν and hence the wavelength (λ) of the spectral line emitted during transition between the two energy levels. For $\nu = E_{(j)} - E_{(j-1)}$, as shown above.

WORKED EXAMPLES

I–Angular momentum—Torque

Example 1. Prove that $J^2 = 2EI$, where J, E, and I are the angular momentum, kinetic energy of rotation and moment of inertia respectively.

Solution. The angular momentum of a rotating body $J = I\omega$ where I is the moment of inertia of the body about the axis of rotation and ω the angular velocity.

Kinetic energy of rotation $\quad E = \frac{1}{2} I\omega^2$

$$\therefore \quad J^2 = I^2\omega^2 = 2 \times \frac{1}{2} I\omega^2 \times I = 2EI$$

Example 2. The inter-molecular distance between two atoms of hydrogen molecule is 0.77Å and mass of the proton is 1.67×10^{-27} kg. Calculate the moment of inertia of the molecule.

Solution. The hydrogen molecule consists of two atoms of hydrogen which are point masses each $m = 1.67 \times 10^{-27}$ kg separated by a distance 0.77 Å $= 0.77 \times 10^{-10}$ m. The molecule has a moment of inertia only about an axis perpendicular to the line joining the two atoms.

Hence the moment of inertia of the hydrogen molecule about an axis passing through the mid-point of the line joining the two atoms and perpendicular to it

$$I = 2m\left(\frac{l}{2}\right)^2 = \frac{ml^2}{2} = \frac{1.67 \times 10^{-27}(0.77 \times 10^{-10})^2}{2}$$

$$= 0.495 \times 10^{-47} \text{ kg m}^2$$

Example 3. A particle of mass *m* is released from rest at the point *A* a distance $x = b$ from the origin *O* so as to fall vertically parallel to the *y*-axis, as shown in Fig. 11.35. (*a*) Calculate the angular momentum of the particle and the torque acting on it at any given instant *t* after its release from the point *A*. (*b*) Verify from your result the relation $\vec{\tau} = d\vec{J}/dt$.

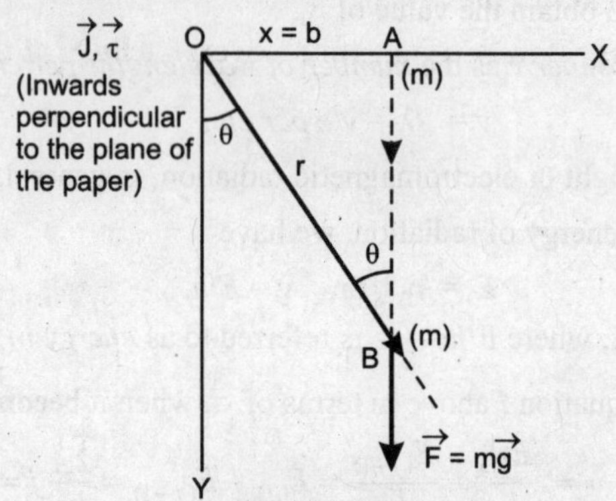

Fig. 11.35

Solution. (*a*) Let *B* be the position of the particle at a given instant *t* after its release from rest at the point *A*, so that its position vector with respect to the origin *O* is *r*, as shown.

Now, *angular momentum about the origin O is* $\vec{J} = \vec{r} \times \vec{p}$, where $\vec{p}$ is the *linear momentum*. And the magnitude of $\vec{J}$ is $J = r\,p \sin\theta = p\,r \sin\theta = pb$, because $r \sin\theta = b$.

Since the particle is falling under the action of gravity, its velocity at instant *t* is, say, $v = 0 + gt = gt$.

$\therefore\ \vec{p} = m\vec{v} = mgt$ and $J = mgbt$, the angular momentum vector $\vec{J}$ being, in accordance with the right hand rule, directed *inwords* at *O*, *perpendicular to the plane of the paper*.

And, clearly, the torque acting on the particle is $\vec{\tau} = \vec{r} \times \vec{F}$, where $\vec{F}$ is the force *mg* acting on it vertically downwards, as indicated.

$\therefore$ *magnitude of the torque*, $\tau = r\,F \sin\theta = F(r \sin\theta) = Fb = mgb$.

Again, in accordance with the right hand rule, the torque vector τ must also be directed inwards at *O*, perpendicular to the plane of the paper, *i.e.*, *in the same direction as* $\vec{J}$.

Let us now see whether we obtain the same value for the magnitude of the torque by the application of the relation $\vec{\tau} = d\vec{J}/dt$.

Since the change in angular momentum $d\vec{J}$ and the torque $\vec{\tau}$ both have the same direction, *i.e.*, are parallel vectors, we can write this relation in the scalar form

$$\vec{\tau} = \frac{d\vec{J}}{dt}$$

(*b*) Now, $J = mgbt$ and we, therefore, have $\vec{\tau} = \frac{d\vec{J}}{dt} = \frac{d(mgbt)}{dt} = mgb$, the same result as obtained above.

The relation $\vec{\tau} = d\vec{J}/dt$ thus stands verified.

Example 4. Two masses of 4 gm and 6 gm respectively are attached to the two ends of a light rod, 10 cm long, of negligible mass and the rod rotates anticlockwise at the rate of 2 revolutions per second about an axis passing through its centre of mass and perpendicular to its length. Obtain the values of (*a*) the angular momentum of each mass about the centre of mass, (*b*) the total angular momenutm of the system about the centre of mass, (*c*) the angular momentum of the system about the axis of rotation.

How will things change if the axis of rotation were inclined at the angle of 30° to the length of the rod and why?

Solution. (*a*) Let m_1 and m_2 be the two masses of 4 gm and 6 gm respectively at the ends of the rod *AB* of negligible mass and of length 10 cm, (Fig. 11.36). Then, if x be the distance of the centre of mass (*C*) of the system from mass $m_1 = 4$ gm at *A*, we have

$$4x = 6(10 - x). \quad \text{Or,} \quad 10x = 60. \quad \text{Or,} \quad x = 6 \text{ cm}.$$

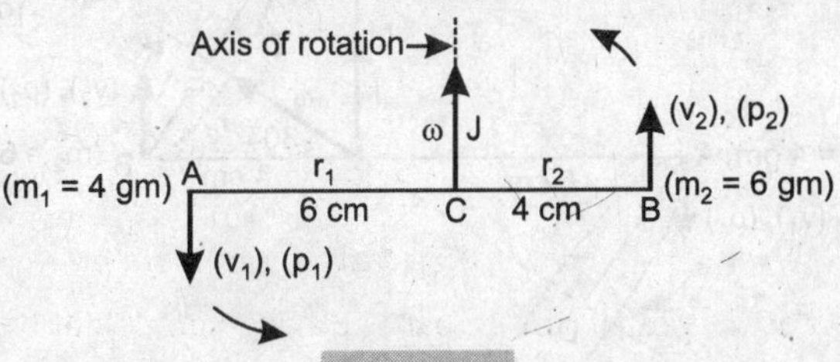

Fig. 11.36

Thus, the centre of mass of the system (*C*) lies at 6 cm from *A* and 4 cm from *B*, with the axis of rotation passing through it, perpendicular to the length of the rod, as shown.

Since the rod is rotating *anticlockwise* about this axis through *C* with an angular velocity of $2 \times 2\pi \approx 12.5$ radians/sec, the angular velocity vector ω has a magnitude 12.5 rad/sec and lies along the axis of rotation, as indicated in the figure.

Now, since mass $m_1 = 4$ gm at *A* rotates about *C* in a circle of radius $CA = 6$ cm, its *linear velocity* $v_1 = CA \times$ (*angular velocity*) $= 6(12.5) = 75.0$ cm/sec, the *linear velocity vector* v_1, and hence also the *linear momentum vector* p_1 ($= m_1v_1$), being perpendicular to *CA*, in the direction shown.

Similarly, *linear velocity of mass* $m_2 = 6$ gm at *B* about *C* in a circle of radius $CB = CB \times$ (*angular velocity*) $= 4(12.5) = 50.0$ cm/sec, with the *linear velocity vector* v_2, and hence also the *linear momentum vector* $p_2 (= m_2v_2)$ perpendicular to *CB*, in the direction indicated.

The *angular momentum of mass* m_1 *about C* is thus $r_1 \times p_1 = r_1 \times (m_1v_1)$ and its *magnitude* $= 6 \times 4 \times 75 = 1800$ gm cm^2/sec.

Similarly, *angular momentum of mass* m_2 *about* $C = r_2 \times p_2 = r_2 \times (m_2v_2)$ and its *magnitude* $= 4 \times 6 \times 50 = 1200$ gm cm^2/sec.

(*b*) The linear momentum vectors $p_1 = m_1v_1$ and $p_2 = m_2v_2$ of the two masses respectively are oppositely directed but since their position vectors r_1 and r_2 are also oppositely directed with respect to the centre of mass *C*, their angular momenta about *C* are both directed upwards perpendicular to the length of the rod. Hence the *total angular momentum vector about the centre of mass is J, directed upwards at C, perpendicular to the rod AB,* or *along the axis of rotation, with its direction thus coinciding with that of the angular velocity vector* $\vec{\omega}$ *i.e.,* $\vec{J}$ and $\vec{\omega}$ are parallel vectors, and the magnitude of $\vec{J}$ is 1800 + 1200 = 3000 gm cm²/sec.

(*c*) Since the total angular momentum vector **J** lies along the axis of rotation, the angular momentum of the system about the axis of rotation (*i.e.,* the component of the total angular momentum along the axis of rotation) is the same as the total angular momentum about the centre of mass *C*, *i.e.*, equal to 3000 gm cm²/sec.

Alternatively, we could obtain the angular momentum of the system about the axis of rotation directly from the relation $\vec{J} = I\vec{\omega}$, where *I* is the *moment of inertia* of the system about the axis of rotation, equal to $m_1r_1^2 + m_2r_2^2 = 4(6)^2 + 6(4)^2 = 144 + 96 = 240$ gm cm² and ω, the angular velocity of the system about the axis of rotation, equal to 12.5 radian/sec. So that, *angular momentum of the system about the axis of rotation* = 240 × 12.5 = 3000 cm gm²/sec.

Let us now take the case when the axis of rotation of the rod is inclined at an angle of 30° to its length, (Fig. 11.37).

In this case also, the *angular velocity vector* ω naturally lies along the axis of rotation and its magnitude is the same as before, viz., 12.5 radian/sec.

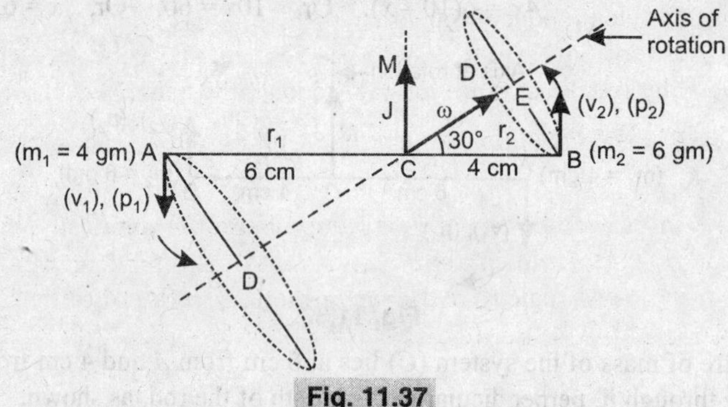

Fig. 11.37

Since mass m_1 = 4 gm here rotates about the axis in a circle of radius *AD* = *CA* sin 30° = 6 × 1/2 = 3 cm, its *linear velocity* $v_1 = AD \times \omega = 3 \times 12.5 = 37.5$ cm/sec and the *linear velocity vector* v_1, and hence also the *linear momentum vector* $p_1(= m_1v_1)$ is perpendicular to *CA*, as shown.

Similarly, since mas m_2 = 6 gm rotates about the axis in a circle of radius *BE* = *CB* sin 30° = 4 × 1/2 = 2 cm, its *linear velocity* $v_2 = BE \times \omega = 2 \times 12.5 = 25.0$ cm/sec and the *linear velocity vector* v_2, and hence also the *linear momentum vector* p_2, is perpendicular to *CB* but directed oppositely to v_1 and p_1.

∴ *angular momentum of* m_1 *about* $C = \vec{r_1} \times \vec{p_1} = \vec{r_1} \times (m_1\vec{v_1})$ and its *magnitude* = 6 × 4 × 37.5 = 900 gm cm²/sec.

And, *anular momentum of* m_2 *about* $C = \vec{r_2} \times \vec{p_2} = \vec{r_2} \times (m_2\vec{v_2})$ and its *magnitude* = 4 × 6 × 25 = 600 gm cm²/sec.

Now, although the linear momenta of the two masses about *C* are oppositely directed, their position vectors too with respect to *C* being oppositely directed, their angular momenta about *C* are both directed upwards, perpendicular to the rod at *C*.

∴ *total angular momentum of the system about C (the centre of mass), i.e.,* $\vec{J}$ *is directed upwards along CM at C, perpendicular to the rod,* as shown, and *its magnitude* = 900 + 600 = 1500 gm cm^2/sec.*

Clearly, therefore, *the total angular momentum vector* $\vec{J}$ *here is not in the same direction with the angular velocity vector* $\vec{\omega}$ *but is inclined to it at an angle of* (90 – 30) = 60°.

∴ *magnitude of the angular momentum of the system about the axis of rotation* (*i.e.,* the component of the total angular momentum (about *C*) along the axis of rotation) = 1500 cos 60° = 1500 × 1/2 = 750 gm-cm^2/sec.

Alternatively, we could directly obtain the value of the angular momentum about the axis of rotation from the relation $J = I\omega$ which gives its magnitude to be

$$[4 \times (AD)^2 + 6 \times (BE)^2] \times 12.5 = [4 \times (3)^2 + 6 \times (2)^2] \times 12.5 = (36 + 24) \times 12.5 = 60 \times 12.5$$
$$= 750 \text{ gm-cm}^2/\text{sec.}$$

This case thus differs from the previous one in that the total angular momentum vector $\vec{J}$ and the angular velocity vector $\vec{\omega}$ are here not parallel vectors as there but are inclined to each other at an angle of 60°. This is so because when the axis of rotation of a body is not also its axis of symmetry, not the whole of the applied torque vector but only a component of it lies along the axis and it is this component which produces rotation about the axis. The component at right angles to the axis merely tends to turn the axis from its fixed position and is neutralised by an equal and opposite torque applied by the bearings to the shaft to keep the axis fixed. This component of the torque, in the case shown, is perpendicular to the plane of $\vec{J}$ and $\vec{\omega}$, *i.e.*, the plane of the paper, acting outwards at *C*.

Example 5. (*a*) A force *F* equal to 10 kg wt is applied to the spoke of a wheel at a distance of 50 cm from the axis of rotation. If the spoke and the applied force make an angle of 45° and 75° respectively with the *x*-axis, calculate the torque acting on the wheel.

(*b*) An engine rotating at the rate of 1500 rev/min develops 50 H.P. What is the torque supplied by it?

Solution. (*a*) Let *OA* be the spoke of a wheel *W*, (Fig. 11.38), inclined at an angle of 45° to the *x*-axis and let *P* be the point distant 50 cm from *O* where the force is applied in the direction shown, the force vector $\vec{F}$ making an angle of 75° with the *x*-axis.

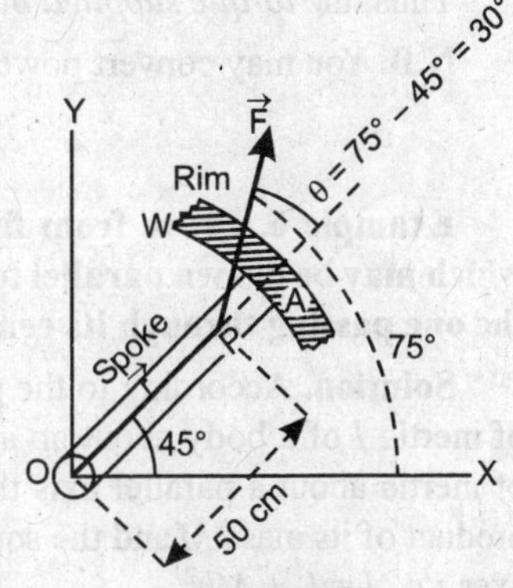

Fig. 11.38

Clearly, then, the angle between the *position vector* $\vec{r}$ of point *P* and the force vector $\vec{F}$ is θ = (75° – 45°) = 30°. If, therefore, τ be the *torque* acting on the wheel, we have $\tau = \vec{r} \times \vec{F}$ and its *magnitude* is thus given by $\tau = r\,F \sin\theta$ = 50(10 × 1000 × 980) (sin 30°) = 50(98 × 10^5) (1/2) = 2.45 × 10^8 dyne cm and its *direction*

---

*We could also obtain the total angular momentum of the system about *C* by resolving its angular velocity ω into two rectangular components, along and perpendicular to the rod, equal to ω cos 30° and ω sin 30° respectively. Since the *M.I.* of the two masses about the length of the rod is *zero*, the former component of ω contributes no angular momentum. So that, the total angular momentum of the system about *C* is due to the component ω sin 30° = 12.5 × 1/2 = 6/25 rod/sec. Since *M.I.* of the two masses about the axis perpendicular to the rod and passing through *C. i.e.,* about the axis *CM*, is 4 × 6^2 + 6 × 4^2 = 144 + 96 = 240 gm-cm^2, we have *total angular momentum of the system about C* = 240 × 6.25 = 1500 gm-cm^2/sec.

is perpendicular to the plane of $\vec{r}$ and $\vec{F}$, *i.e.*, perpendicular to the plane of the paper outwards or along the axis through *O*.

N.B. It may be noted that since $\tau = rF \sin\theta$, we could obtain its value by either the relation $\tau = rF\perp$, where $F\perp$ is the component of *F* perpendicular to **r** or the relation $\tau = Fr\perp$, where $r\perp$ is the component of $\vec{r}$ perpendicular to $\vec{F}$, (Fig. 11.39).

In the former case, $\tau = 50(F \sin\theta) = 50(98 \times 10^5)(1/2) = 2.45 \times 10^8$ dyne cm and in the latter case, $\tau = (98 \times 10^5)(r \sin\theta) = (98 \times 10^5)(50)(1/2) = 2.45 \times 10^8$ dyne cm.

(*b*) Clearly, *work done by the engine per second* = *50 × 550 ft lb and the angle through which it rotates in one second* = $(1500/60)(2\pi) = 25 \times 2\pi = 50\pi$ radian.

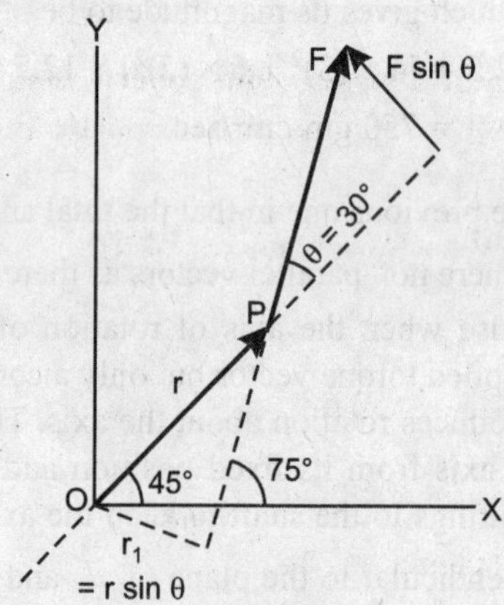

Fig. 11.39

Now, *work done* = *torque* × *angle, i.e.*, $w = \tau\theta$. So that,

$50 \times 500 = \tau \times 50\pi$, where τ is the torque supplied by the engine.

Or, $\tau = 50 \times 550/50\pi = 550/\pi = 175$ *ft lb.*

Thus, the *torque supplied by the engine* = 175 *ft. lb.*

N.B. You may convert power using 1 H.P. = 0.7457 kilo watts.

II–Moment of inertia

Example 6. Prove from first principles that out of an infinite number of straight lines which may be drawn parallel to a given direction the moment of inertia of a body is least about the one passing through its centre of gravity.

Solution. According to the principle of parallel axes, the moment of inertia *I* of a body about an axis is equal to the sum of its moment of inertia about a parallel axis through its centre of gravity I_g and the product of its mass *M* and the square of the distance *h* between the two axes *i.e.*, $I = I_g + Mh^2$

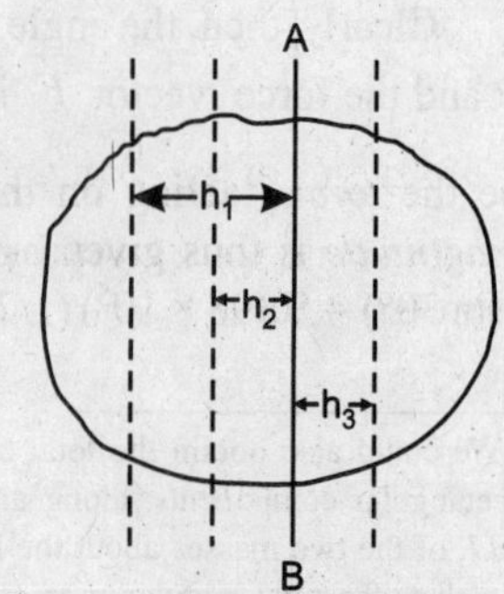

Fig. 11.40

Hence for a number of axes which are all parallel to each other at distances h_1, h_2, h_3 etc. from the axis *AB* passing through the centre of gravity the moment of inertia is respectively given by

$$(I_g + Mh_1^2), (I_g + Mh_2^2)$$

and so on. The value of h^2 is always positive whether *h* is towards the left or right of *AB*. Hence Mh^2 is a positive quantity.

The least value of I is obtained when $h = 0$ *i.e.*, when the axis passes through the centre of gravity.

Example 7. Assuming earth to be a sphere of uniform density 5520 kg. m^{-3} and radius 6400 km, calculate the M.I. about its axis of rotation.

Solution. Density of earth $\rho = 5520$ kgm^{-3}

Radius of earth $R = 6400$ km $= 6400 \times 10^3$ m

$\therefore$ Mass of earth $M = \frac{4}{3}\pi R^3 \rho = \frac{4}{3}\pi [6400 \times 10^3]^3 \times 5520 = 6.06 \times 10^{24}$ kg

Moment of inertia of the earth about its axis $= \frac{2}{5}MR^2$

$$= \frac{2}{5} \times 6.06 \times 10^{24} \times [6400 \times 10^3]^2 = 9.93 \times 10^{37} \text{ kg m}^2$$

Example 8. Moment of inertia of a bigger solid sphere about its diameter is *I*. 64 smaller, equal spheres are made out of bigger sphere. What will be the moment of inertia of such smaller sphere about its diameter?

Solution. Moment of inertia of the bigger sphere $I = \frac{2}{5}MR^2$

where M is its mass and R its radius. Let ρ be the density of the material of the sphere, then

$$M = \frac{4}{3}\pi R^3 \rho$$

Let m be the mass of the smaller sphere, then $m = \frac{M}{64}$

If r is the radius of the smaller sphere, then

$$m = \frac{4}{3}\pi r^3 \rho = \frac{1}{64} \times \frac{4}{3}\pi R^3 \rho$$

or $\quad r^3 = \frac{R^3}{64}$ or $r = \frac{R}{4}$

$\therefore$ Moment of inertia of the smaller sphere $= I_s = \frac{2}{5}mr^2$

$$= \frac{2}{5}\frac{M}{64}\frac{R^2}{16} = \frac{1}{1024} \times \frac{2}{5}MR^2 \text{ or } I_s = \frac{I}{1024}$$

Example 9. Calculate the radius of gyration of a solid sphere rotating about its diameter if its radius is 5.0 cm. ***(M.D.U. 2003)***

Solution. M.I of solid sphere $= \frac{2}{5}Mr^2 = Mk^2$

$$\therefore \quad k^2 = \frac{2}{5}r^2 = \frac{2}{5} \times 5^2 = \frac{2}{5} \times 25 = 10 \text{ cm}^2$$

or radius of gyration $k = \sqrt{10}$ cm

Example 10. A hollow steel sphere has its inner and outer radii 5 cm and 12 cm respectively. Calculate its moment of inertia about a diameter. Density of steel is 7.8 × 10^3 kg m^{-3}.

Solution. Outer radius $R = 12$ cm $= 0.12$ m, Inner radius $r = 5$ cm $= 0.05$ m

Mass of hollow sphere $\quad M = \frac{4}{3}\pi(R^3 - r^3)\rho$

M.I. of hollow sphere $\quad I = \frac{2}{5}M\left(\frac{R^5 - r^5}{R^3 - r^3}\right) = \frac{2}{5} \times \frac{4}{3}\pi(R^3 - r^3).\rho\left(\frac{R^5 - r^5}{R^3 - r^3}\right)$

$$= \frac{8}{15} \times 3.142 \times 7.8 \times 10^3 (R^5 - r^5)$$

$$= 13.07 \times 10^3 (0.12^5 - 0.05^5) = 0.3211 \text{ kg m}^2$$

Example 11. The flat surface of a hemisphere of radius *r* is cemented to one flat surface of a cylinder of radius *r* and length *L*. If the total mass is *M*, show that the M.I. of combination about the axis of the cylinder will be

$$Mr^2 \frac{(L/2 + 4r/15)}{(L + 2r/3)}$$

Solution. Suppose m is the mass of cylinder and m' that of the hemisphere and ρ the density of the material, then

M.I. of cylinder about its axis $= \frac{mr^2}{2} = \pi r^2 L\rho \times \frac{r^2}{2} = \frac{\pi r^4 L\rho}{2}$

M.I. of hemisphere about the axis of cylinder $= \frac{2}{5} m' r^2 = \frac{2}{5} \times \frac{2}{3} \pi r^3 \rho r^2 = \frac{4}{15} \pi r^5 \rho$

M.I. of the combination about the axis of the cylinder,

$$I = \pi r^4 \rho (L/2 + 4r/15)$$

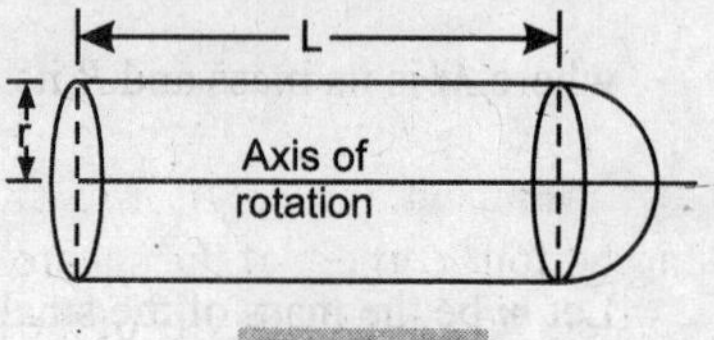

Now $$M = m + m' = \pi r^2 L\rho + \frac{2}{3} \pi r^3 \rho$$

$$= \pi r^2 \rho (L + 2/3\, r)$$

Hence $$I = Mr^2 \frac{(L/2 + 4r/15)}{(L + 2/3r)}$$

Fig. 11.41

Example 12. A flat thin uniform disc *D* of radius *a* and centre *O* has a hole of radius *b* in it at a distance *c* from *O* (Fig. 11.42). If its mass be 90 gm and *a*, *b* and *c* equal to 7 cm, 2 cm and 4 cm respectively, calculate its moment of inertia (*i*) about an axis through *O* and perpendicular to its plane, (*ii*) about an axis through the centre of the hole and perpendicular to its plane and (*iii*) about an axis passing through *O* and the centre of the hole.

Solution. *Area of the disc with the hole in it = area of the complete disc – area of the hole* $= \pi a^2 - \pi b^2 = \pi(a^2 - b^2) = \pi(49 - 4) = 45\pi$ sq cm.

Since its mass is 90 gm, *mass per unit area of the disc* $= 90/45\pi = 2/\pi$ gm/cm^2.

$\therefore$ *Mass of the complete disc*

$= \frac{2}{\pi} \times$ *area of complete disc* $= \frac{2}{\pi} \times \pi \times 49 = 98$ gm and

mass of the small disc of radius $b = 2$ cm (which is removed to produce the hole in the disc) $= (2/\pi) \times$ area of the disc $= (2/\pi)$ $(\pi \times 4) = 8$ gm.

Now, M.I. *of the complete disc about the axis through its centre O and perpendicular to its plane* =(*mass of the disc*) $\times$ (*radius*)$^2/2 = 98 \times 49/2 = 49 \times 49 = 2401$ gm cm^2.

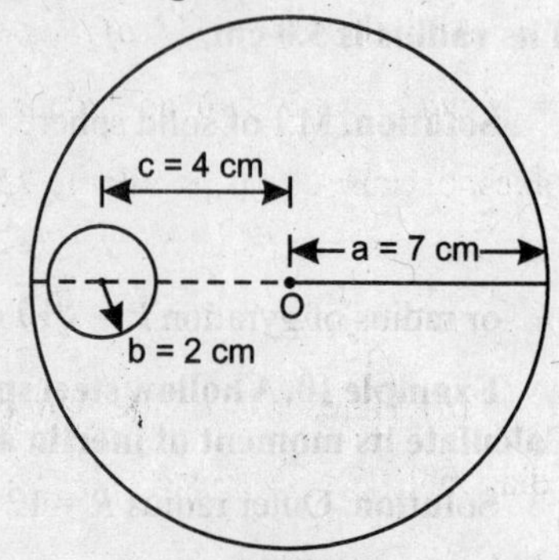

Fig. 11.42

And, *M.I. of the small disc of radius* $b = 2$ cm about the axis through O and *perpendicular to its plane* is, in accordance with the principle of parallel axes, equal to *M.I. of the small disc about the axis through its centre and perpendicular to its plane + mass of the small disc* $\times c^2 = 8(2)^2 + 8 \times (4)^2 = 32 + 128 = 160$ gm cm^2.

$\therefore$ *(i) M.I. of the disc (D), with the hole,, about the axis through O and perpendicular to its plane = M.I. of the complete disc about this axis—M.I. of the small disc about this axis = 2401 – 160* = 2241 gm cm^2.

(ii) M.I. of the disc (D), with the hole, about the axis through the centre C of the hole and perpendicular to its plane = M.I. of the complete disc about the perpendicular axis through C—M.I. of the small disc about the perpendicular axis through C = (M.I. of the complete disc about the perpendicular axis through O + its mass × c^2) – M.I. of the smaller disc about the perpendicular axis through C = $2401 + 98(4)^2 - 8(2)^2 = 2401 + 98 \times 16 - 32 = 3969 - 32 = 3937$ gm-cm^2.

(iii) M.I. of the disc (D), with the hole, about the axis passing through O and the centre C of the hole, i.e., about the common diameter of the complete disc and the hole = M.I. of the complete disc about its diameter–M.I. of the small disc about its diameter $= 98 \times \frac{a^2}{4} - 8 \times \frac{b^2}{4} = \frac{98 \times 49}{4} - \frac{8 \times 4}{4}$
$= 600 - 8 = 592$ gm-cm^2.

Example 13. (*a*) Four solid spheres, *A*, *B*, *C* and *D*, each of mass *m* and radius *a*, are placed with their centres on the four corners of a square of side *b*, (Fig. 11.43). Calculate the moment of inertia of the system about one side of the square.

(*b*) Also calculate the moment of inertia of the system about a diagonal of the square.

(Punjab 2002, Purvanchal 2006)

Solution. (*a*) Let *A*, *B*, *C* and *D* be the four solid spheres, each of mass *m* and radius *a* placed at the four corners of the square *PQST*, as shown, and let it be required to calculate the *M.I.* of the system about the side *PQ* of the square.

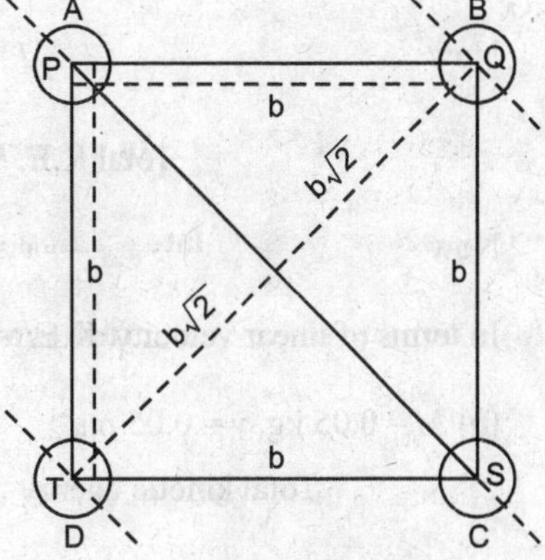

Fig. 11.43

Clearly, *PQ* lies along the diameter of each of the spheres *A* and *B*; so that, *M.I.* of each about $PQ = \frac{2}{5}ma^2$ and, therefore,

M.I. of the pair of spheres A and B about PQ
$= 2 \times \frac{2}{5}ma^2 = \frac{4}{5}ma^2$.

Similarly, *M.I. of the pair of spheres C and D about the side TS of the square,* (which lies along their diameters) $= 2 \times \frac{2}{5}ma^2 = \frac{4}{5}ma^2$.

And, therefore, *M.I. of the pair C and D about side PQ*
$= \frac{4}{5}ma^2 + 2mb^2$, in accordance with the principle of parallel axes, because *PQ* is parallel to *TS* and distant *b* from it.

So that, *M.I. of the whole system about the side PQ (or, in fact, any side) of the square*
$= \frac{4}{5}ma^2 + \frac{4}{5}ma^2 + 2\,mb^2 = \frac{8}{5}ma^2 + 2mb^2 = \frac{2}{5}m(4a^2 + 5b^2)$.

(*b*) Here, *M.I.* of the pair of spheres *A* and *C* about their common diameter, *i.e.*, along the diagonal $PS = 2 \times \frac{2}{5}ma^2 = \frac{4}{5}ma^2$; *M.I. of sphere B about its diameter* $= \frac{2}{5}ma^2$ and therefore, *its M.I. about the diagonal PS,* parallel to its diameter and distant $b\sqrt{2}$ from it $= \frac{2}{5}ma^2 + m(b\sqrt{2})^2 =$
$\frac{2}{5}ma^2 + mb^2/2$.

Similarly, *M.I. of sphere D* about the diagonal *PS*, parallel to its diameter and distant $b\sqrt{2}$ from it $= \frac{2}{5}ma^2 + mb^2/2$.

∴ *M.I. of the whole system about the diagonal PS* (*as also along the diagonal QT*)

$$= \frac{4}{5}ma^2 + 2\left(\frac{2}{5}ma^2 + mb^2/2\right) = \frac{8}{5}ma^2 + mb^2 = \frac{2}{5}m\left(4a^2 + \frac{5}{2}b^2\right).$$

III–Kinetic energy of rotation—Rolling bodies

Example 14. (*a*) A circular disc of mass *M* and radius *r* is set rolling on a table. If ω is the angular velocity show that its total energy *E* is given by $\frac{3}{4}Mr^2\omega^2$.

(*b*) A flat circular disc of mass 0.05 kg and diameter 0.02 m rolls on its edge on a smooth horizontal surface with a velocity 0.05 ms^{-1}. Calculate its total energy.

Solution. (*a*) When a circular disc rolls on a table a point on its circumference rotates about an axis passing through its centre and perpendicular to its plane. In addition, the point moves forward. In other words it possess an angular velocity and a linear velocity. Therefore, it possesses two kinds of energies:

(*i*) Energy due to linear motion, and (*ii*) Energy due to rotation about an axis through its centre.

If v is the linear velocity, the energy due to linear motion = $\frac{1}{2}Mv^2$.

If ω is the angular velocity, then the kinetic energy due to rotational motion = $\frac{1}{2}I\omega^2$ where I is the moment of inertia of the disc about an axis perpendicular to its plane and passing through its C.G.

Now $\quad I = \frac{1}{2}Mr^2 \quad \therefore$ K.E. due to rotation = $\frac{1}{2}\times\frac{1}{2}Mr^2\omega^2 = \frac{1}{4}Mr^2\omega^2$

∴ $\quad$ Total K.E. = $\frac{1}{2}Mv^2 + \frac{1}{4}Mr^2\omega^2$

Now $\quad v = r\omega \quad \therefore$ K.E. = $\frac{1}{2}Mr^2\omega^2 + \frac{1}{4}Mr^2\omega^2 = \frac{3}{4}Mr^2\omega^2$

In terms of linear velocity, K.E. = $\frac{3}{4}Mv^2$

(*b*) $M = 0.05$ kg, $v = 0.05$ ms^{-1}

∴ $\quad$ Total kinetic energy = $\frac{3}{4}Mv^2 = \frac{3}{4}\times 0.05\times(0.05)^2$

$= 93.75 \times 10^{-6}$ kg m^2 s^{-2} or Joule

Example 15. An annular disc of mass 0.2 kg and radii 0.2 m and 0.25 m rolls such that the centre has a velocity of 0.5 ms^{-1}. Calculate its kinetic energy.

Solution. Here $M = 0.2$ kg, $v = 0.5$ ms^{-1}

∴ K.E. due to linear motion = $\frac{1}{2}mv^2 = \frac{1}{2}\times 0.2\times(0.5)^2 = 0.025$ J

M.I. of annular disc about the axis of rotation $I = \frac{1}{2}M(R_2^2 + R_1^2)$

Now $R_2 = 0.25$ m and $R_1 = 0.20$ m

∴ $\quad I = \frac{1}{2}\times 0.2\,(0.25^2 + 0.2^2) = 1.025\times 10^{-2}$ kg m^2

Angular velocity $\omega = \frac{v}{R_2} = \frac{0.5}{0.25} = 2$ rad s^{-1}

$\therefore$ K.E. of rotation $= \frac{1}{2}I\omega^2 = \frac{1}{2} \times 1.025 \times 10^{-2} \times 4 = 2.05 \times 10^{-2}$ J

Total K.E. = 0.025 + 0.0205 = 0.0455 J

Example 16. A solid sphere of mass 0.1 kg and radius 2.5 cm rolls without slipping with a uniform velocity of 0.1 ms^{-1} along a straight line on a horizontal table. Calculate its total energy.

Solution. As the sphere rolls without slipping it has both energy of translation and rotation.

Here $M = 0.1$ kg, $r = 2.5$ cm $= 0.025$ m, $v = 0.1$ ms^{-1}

$$\therefore \qquad \omega = \frac{v}{r} = \frac{0.1}{0.025} = 4 \text{ rad s}^{-1}$$

K.E. of translation $= \frac{1}{2}Mv^2 = \frac{1}{2} \times 0.1 \times 0.1 \times 0.1 = 0.0005$ J

K.E. of rotation $= \frac{1}{2}I\omega^2 = \frac{1}{2} \times \frac{2}{5}Mr^2\omega^2 = \frac{1}{5} \times 0.1 \times (.025)^2 \times 16 = 0.0002$ J

Total energy = 0.0005 + 0.0002 = 0.0007 J = 7×10^{-4} J.

Example 17. (*a*) A solid sphere of mass 100 gm and radius 2.5 cm rolls without sliding with a uniform velocity of 10 cm/sec along a straight line on a smooth horizontal table. Calculate its total energy in ergs. ***(Delhi 2004)***

(*b*) A hoop of radius 100 cm and mass 19 kg is rolling along a horizontal surface, so that its centre of mass has a velocity of 20 cm/sec. How much work will have to be done to stop it?

Solution. (*a*) The sphere possesses only kinetic energy, so that its total energy is equal to its *K.E.*

Now, *K.E. of a rolling body,* as we know, is given by $\frac{1}{2}Mv^2(1 + K^2/R^2)$.

For a *solid sphere,* $K^2 = \frac{2}{5}R^2$. And, therefore,

K.E. or the total energy of the rolling sphere, $E = \frac{1}{2}Mv^2\left(1 + \frac{2}{5}R^2/R^2\right)$

$$= \frac{1}{2}Mv^2\left(1 + \frac{2}{5}\right) = \frac{7}{10}Mv^2.$$

Or, substituting the values of M and v, we have $E = \frac{7}{10} \times 100 \times 10^2 = 7 \times 10^3$ ergs.

(*b*) Obviously, *work required to be done to stop the rolling hoop* = *its K.E.* $= \frac{1}{2}Mv^2(1 + K^2/R^2) = \frac{1}{2}Mv^2(1 + R^2/R^2) = Mv^2 = 10^4\,(20)^2 = 4 \times 10^6$ *ergs.*

Example 18. A small solid sphere rolls without slipping along a loop the loop track, shown in Fig. 11.44 from a height OR from the bottom of the track, where *R* is the radius of the circular part of the track. Calculate the horizontal and the vertical forces acting on the sphere when it rises up to the point *P*. in a level with the centre *O* of the circular part.

Solution. The kinetic energy acquired by the sphere when it arrives at P in the circular part of the loop will be the same as that at Q in a level with P and the centre O of the circular part, *i.e.*, at a distance $(8R - R) = 7R$ from the top of the track. If, therefore, v be the velocity of the sphere at Q or P, its *K.E. of rotation* $= \frac{1}{2}Mv^2(1 + K^2/r^2)$, where M is its *mass*, r, its *radius* and K, its *radius of gyration about its diameter* (about which it is rotating as it is rolling down).

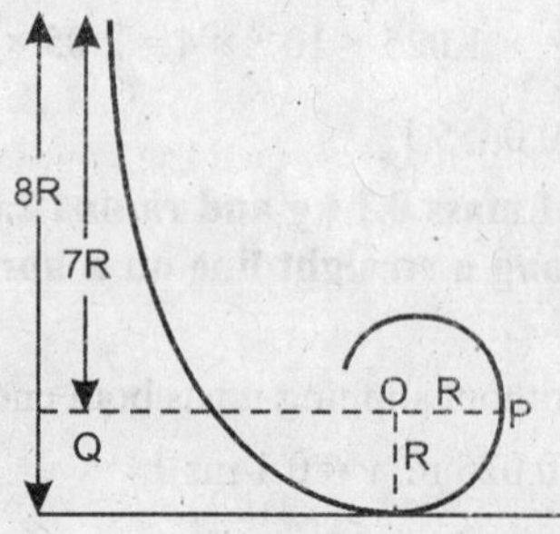

Fig. 11.44

Since $K^2 = \frac{2}{5}r^2$ in the case of a sphere, we have

K.E. acquired by the sphere on falling through a height 7R

$$= \frac{1}{2}Mv^2\left(1+\frac{2}{5}r^2/r^2\right) = \frac{1}{2}Mv^2\left(\frac{7}{5}\right) = \frac{7}{10}Mv^2.$$

And *P.E. lost by the sphere on falling through this height 7R* = 7 *MgR*.

Since gain in *K.E.* of the sphere = loss in its *P.E.*, we have

$$\frac{7}{10}Mv^2 = 7\,MgR, \text{ whence, } v^2 = 10\,gR.$$

Obviously, this velocity v of the sphere at the point P is tangential to the circular part of the track at P. *The horizontal force acting on it, therefore, towards O is the centripetal force* $Mv^2/R = M(10\,gR)/R = 10\,Mg$. And, the *vertical force acting on it is clearly its weight Mg.*

Example 19. A symmetrical body is rotating about its axis of symmetry, its moment of inertia about the axis of rotation being 1 kg m² and its rate of rotation 2 rev/sec.

(*a*) What is its angular momentum? (*b*) What additional work will have to be done to double its rate of rotation?

Solution. (*a*) Since the body is rotating about its axis of symmetry, *the angular momentum vector coincides with its axis of rotation* and we have its *angular momentum* $J = I\omega$.

And since its *K.E.* of rotation, $E = \frac{1}{2}I\omega^2$, we have $I\omega^2 = 2E$, and therefore,

$$I^2\omega^2 = 2EI, \quad \text{whence,} \quad J = I\omega = \sqrt{2EI}$$

Here, $I = 1$ kg m² and $\omega = 2$ rev/sec $= 2 \times 2\pi$ or 4π radian/sec,

So that, $$E = \frac{1}{2}(1)(4\pi)^2 = 8\pi^2 \text{ joules and, therefore}$$

$$J = \sqrt{2EI} = \sqrt{2\times 8\pi^2 \times 1} = \sqrt{16\pi^2} = 4\pi = 12.57 \text{ kg m}^2\text{/sec.}$$

(*b*) When doubled, the rate of rotation of the body will be 4 rev/sec = 8π radian/sec.

$\therefore$ *its K.E. of rotation* will be $\frac{1}{2}I(8\pi)^2 = \frac{1}{2}(1)(64\pi^2) = 32\pi^2$ joules.

Hence, *additional work required to be done = its final K.E. of rotation*—its *initial K.E. of rotation* $= 32\pi^2 - 8\pi^2 = 24\pi^2 = 236.8$ *joules*.

Example 20. A flat thin uniform disc of radius *a* has a hole of radius *b* in it at a distance *c* from the centre of the disc {*c* < (*a* – *b*)}. If the disc were free to rotate about a smooth circular rod of radius *b* passing through the hole, calculate the moment of inertia about the axis of rotation.

Solution. Let M be the mass of the disc of radius a and having a hole of radius b at a distance c from the centre of the disc.

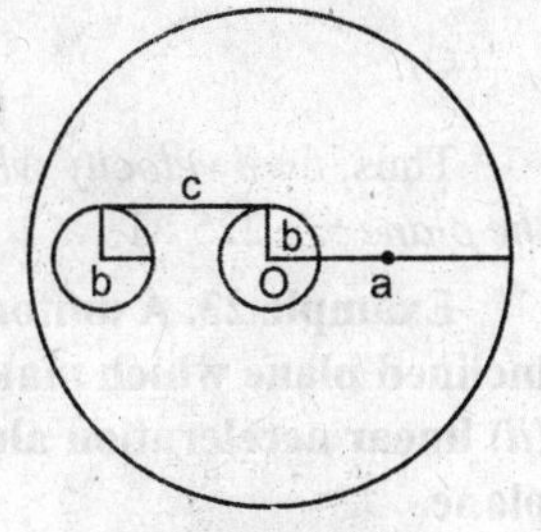

Fig. 11.45

If the hole were supposed to be at the centre, then the moment of inertia of the disc about an axis through O and perpendicular to the plane of the disc

$$I_0 = \frac{M(a^2+b^2)}{2}$$

Applying the principle of parallel axes, moment of inertia about an axis, passing through the centre of a circle of radius b at a distance c from the centre of the disc

$$I = I_0 + Mc^2$$

$$= \frac{M(a^2+b^2)}{2} + Mc^2$$

IV–Motion along an inclined plane

Example 21. A body of radius *R* and mass *m* is rolling horizontally without slipping with speed *v*. It rolls up a hill to a maximum height $h = 3v^2/4g$. Neglecting friction, find the moment of inertia of the body. What can be the shape of the body?

Solution. Kinetic energy due to linear motion $= \frac{1}{2}mv^2$

Kinetic energy due to rotation $= \frac{1}{2}I\omega^2 = \frac{1}{2}I\frac{v^2}{R^2}$

$\therefore$ Total kinetic energy $= \frac{1}{2}mv^2 + \frac{1}{2}Iv^2/R^2$

As the body rolls up the hill to a height h, the whole of the K.E. is converted into potential energy given by $mgh = mg\frac{3v^2}{4g} = \frac{3}{4}mv^2$

$$\therefore \quad \frac{1}{2}mv^2 + \frac{1}{2}Iv^2/R^2 = \frac{3}{4}mv^2 \quad \text{or} \quad \frac{1}{2}Iv^2/R^2 = \frac{1}{4}mv^2 \quad \text{or} \quad I = \frac{1}{2}mR^2$$

The shape of the body is, therefore, a circular disc of radius R.

Example 22. A solid cylinder (*a*) rolls, (*b*) slides from rest down an inclined plane. Neglect friction and compare the velocities in both cases when the cylinder reaches the bottom of the incline.

Solution. We know that the acceleration of a body *rolling* down an inclined plane cf angle of inclination θ is given by $a = [R_2/(K^2 + R^2)]g \sin\theta$. [11.10 (*ii*) (*b*)]

For a solid cylinder, $K^2 = R^2/2$ and therefore, $a = \left[R^2 \Big/ \left(\frac{R^2}{2} + R^2\right)\right] g \sin\theta = \frac{2}{3} g \sin\theta$.

Hence, if v_1 be the *velocity acquired by the cylinder on reaching the bottom of the incline of length l*, we have

$$v_1^2 - 0 = 2\,al. \quad \text{Or,} \quad v_1^2 = 2.\frac{2}{3}g\sin\theta.\,l = \frac{4}{3}g\sin\theta.\,l \qquad [\because u = 0]$$

And, when the cylinder *slides* down the plane, its acceleration $a = g \sin\theta$.

$\therefore$ if v_2 be the velocity acquired by the cylinder on reaching the bottom of the incline, we have

$$v_2^2 - 0 = 2\,al. \quad \text{Or,} \quad v_2^2 = 2g\sin\theta.\,l \qquad [\because u = 0]$$

$\therefore v_2^2 : v_1^2 :: 2g \sin\theta\, l : \frac{4}{3} g \sin\theta.l.$ Or, $v_2^2 : v_1^2 :: 2 : \frac{4}{3}$.

Or, $$v_2/v_1 = \sqrt{2\times\frac{3}{4}} = \sqrt{\frac{3}{2}} = 1.225.$$

Thus, *final velocity when the cylinder slides down the plane* : *final velocity when it rolls down the plane* :: 1.225 : 1.

Example 23. A uniform sphere of mass 2 kg and radius 10 cm is released from rest on an inclined plane which makes 30° angle with the horizontal. Deduce (*i*) its angular acceleration, (*ii*) linear acceleration along the plane and (*iii*) kinetic energy as it travels 2 metres along the plane.

Solution. As we know, [11.10 (*ii*) (*b*)], the acceleration of a body rolling down an inclined plane is given by $a = [R^2/(K^2 + R^2)]g \sin\theta$.

Here, $R = 10$ cm $= 0.1$ m and $K^2 = \frac{2}{5}R^2 = \frac{2}{5}(0.1)^2$, $g = 9.8$ m/sec^2 and $\sin\theta = \sin 30° = 1/2$.

$\therefore$ *linear acceleration of the sphere along the plane* $= \dfrac{(0.1)^2}{\frac{2}{5}(0.1)^2 + (0.1)^2} \times 9.8 \times 1/2$

$$= \frac{4.9}{1+2/5} = \frac{4.9\times 5}{7} = 3.5 \text{ m/sec}^2.$$

If v be the *linear velocity* of the sphere along the plane at any given instant, we have $v = R\omega$, where ω is its *angular velocity*.

$\therefore \dfrac{dv}{dt} = R\dfrac{d\omega}{dt} = R\alpha = a$, where $d\omega/dt$ is the *angular acceleration* α.

So that, *angular acceleration of the sphere*, $\alpha = a/R = 3.5/0.1 = 35$ radian/sec^2.

And, *K.E. acquired by the sphere on covering a distance $S = 2$ metres along the plane = P.E. lost by it in falling through a vertical distance* $h = S \sin\theta$, (Fig. 11.46). $= \text{Mg } S \sin\theta = 2(9.8)(2)(1/2) = 1.96$ *joules*.

Example 24. Two spheres are identical in mass and volume, but one is hollow and the other solid. How will you identify them experimentally? ***(Delhi; Gujarat; Punjab)***

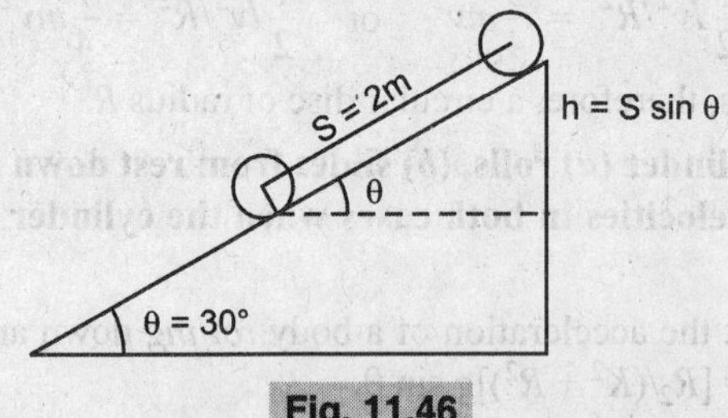

Fig. 11.46

Solution. As we know, the acceleration of a body rolling down an inclined plane is given by $a = [R^2/(K^2 + R^2)]g \sin\theta$. So that, *the greater the value of the radius of gyration (K) of the body about the axis of rotation, the smaller its acceleration and hence the longer the time taken by it to roll down the plane.*

Now, *in the case of a solid sphere*, $K^2 = \frac{2}{5}R^2$, where R is its *radius*.

In the case of a hollow sphere, $K^2 = \frac{2}{5}\left(\frac{R^5 - r^5}{R^3 - r^3}\right)$, where R and r are its *external and internal radii* respectively.

Clearly, $\frac{2}{5}\left(\frac{R^5 - r^5}{R^3 - r^3}\right) = \frac{2}{5} \cdot \frac{R^5(1 - r^5/R^5)}{R^3(1 - r^3/R^3)} = \frac{2}{5}R^2\left(\frac{1 - r^5/R^5}{1 - r^3/R^3}\right)$

Since $(r^5/R^5) < (r^3/R^3)$, we have $(1 - r^5/R^5) > (1 - r^3/R^3)$

And, therefore, $\frac{1 - r^5/R^5}{1 - r^3/R^3} > 1$,

i.e., for a hollow sphere, $K^2 = \frac{2}{5}R^2 \times$ *(a quantity greater than* 1), or K^2 for a hollow sphere is greater than $\frac{2}{5}R^2$, which is the value of K^2 for a solid sphere.

It follows, therefore, that *the acceleration of the hollow sphere down the plane will be less than that of the solid sphere. The latter will thus roll down the plane faster than the former and the two may thus be easily distinguished from each other despite their outward identical appearance.*

V–Flywheel

Example 25. A flywheel of mass 6.4 kg is made in the form of a circular disc of radius 18 cm; it is driven by a belt whose tensions at the points where it run on and off the rim of the wheel are 2 kg and 5 kg weight respectively. If the wheel is rotating at a certain instant at 60 revolutions per minute, find how long will it be before the speed has reached 210 revolutions per minute. While the flywheel is rotating at this latter speed, the belt is slipped off and a brake applied. Find the constant breaking couple required to stop the wheel in 7 revolutions.

Solution. Here, obviously, the *resultant tension in the belt* = 5 – 2 = 3 kg wt = 3 × 1000 × 981 *dynes*.

∴ *Moment of the couple due to this tension* = 3 × 1000 × 981 × 18 *dyne* cm.

But, if $I = MR^2/2$ be the moment of inertia of the flywheel (of the form of a circular disc) about its axis of rotation and α, its *angular acceleration,* the couple acting on the wheel is also $I\alpha$. We, therefore, have

$$I\alpha = 3 \times 1000 \times 981 \times 18.$$

Or, $$(MR^2/2)\alpha = 3 \times 1000 \times 981 \times 18.$$

Or, $(65.4 \times 1000 \times 18^2/2)\alpha = 3 \times 1000 \times 981 \times 18$, whence, $\alpha = \frac{3 \times 1000 \times 981 \times 18}{65400 \times 18 \times 9} = 5\,radian/sec^2$.

Now, we have the relation $\omega_2 = \omega_1 + \alpha t$, where $\omega_2 = 210$ *rev/min* $= 210 \times 2\pi/60 = 7\pi$ *radians/sec*, $\omega_1 = 60$ *rev/min* $= 60 \times 2\pi/60 = 2\pi$ *radians/sec* and $\alpha = 5$ *radians/sec*^{2}.

So that, $$7\pi = 2\pi + 5t.$$

Or, $$5\pi = 5t. \text{ Or, } \quad t = \pi = 3.142 \text{ sec.}$$

The flywheel will thus acquire the speed of 210 *rev/min* in 3.142 *sec.*

Let the angular retardation produced in the wheel by the braking couple be α'. And, Clearly, angle turned through by the wheel before coming to rest, say, $\theta = 7 \times 2\pi = 14\pi$ *radians*. So that applying the relation $\omega_2^2 - \omega_1^2 = 2\alpha\theta$, where $\omega_2 = 0$ and $\omega_1 = 7\pi$ radian/sec, we have

$0 - (7\pi)^2 = 2\alpha'(14\pi)$, because, here, $\alpha = \alpha'$. Or, $\alpha' = -49\pi^2/28\pi = -7\pi/4$ radian/sec^2.

∴ *Braking couple required to be applied* $= 1\alpha' = (65.4 \times 1000 \times 18^2/2)(7\pi/4)$

gm-wt-cm $= (65.4 \times 1000 \times 18 \times 9)(7\pi/4)/1000 = 59.37$ kg wt-cm.

Example 26. A flywheel of mas 10 kg and radius 20 cm is mounted on an axle of mass 8 kg and radius 5 cm. A rope is wound round the axle and carries a weight of 10 kg. The flywheel and the axle are set into rotation by releasing the weight. Calculate (*i*) the angular velocity

and the kinetic energy of the wheel and the axle, and (*ii*) the velocity and kinetic energy of the weight, when the weight has descended 20 cm from its original position.

Solution. *P.E.* lost by the weight in descending through a distance of 20 cm must be equal to the *K.E.* gained by the flywheel and axle and the weight itself, *i.e.*, $Mg \times 20 = \frac{1}{2}I\omega^2 + \frac{1}{2}Mv^2$, where M is the *mass of the weight, I, the moment of inertia of the flywheel and the axle,* ω, *its angular velocity* and *v*, the *linear velocity of the mass* $M = r\omega$ (*r* being the radius of the axle).

Now, $$I = \textit{mass of the flywheel}\left(\frac{R^2 + r^2}{2}\right) + \frac{1}{2}\textit{ mass of the axle } (r^2),$$

where *R* is the *radius of the flywheel* and *r that of the axle.*

Or, $$I = 80 \times 1000\ (20^2 + 5^2)/2 + \frac{1}{2}.8 \times 1000 \times 5^2 = 17 \times 10^6 + 10^5$$

$$= 171 \times 10^5 \text{ gm-cm}^2.$$

∴ substituting the values of the various quantities in the energy equation above, we have

$$10 \times 1000 \times 981 \times 20 = \frac{1}{2}171 \times 10^5, \omega^2 + \frac{1}{2} \times 10 \times 1000\ (5\omega)^2.$$

Or, $$1962 \times 10^5 = 855 \times 10^4 \times \omega^2 = 125 \times 10^3 \times \omega^2 = 8675 \times 10^3 \times \omega^2,$$

whence, $$\omega^2 = 1962 \times 10^5/8675 \times 10^3 = 1962 \times 10^2/8675,$$

Or, $$\omega = \sqrt{1962 \times 10^2/8675} = 4.755 \text{ rad/sec.}$$

Thus, *angular velocity of the flywheel and axle* = 4.755 radians/sec and, therefore, *linear velocity of the weight,* $v = r\omega = 5\omega = 5 \times 4.755 = 23.785$ cm/sec.

Clearly, *K.E. of the flywheel and the axle* $= \frac{1}{2}I\omega^2 = 855 \times 10^4 \times (4.755)^2 = 19.34 \times 10^7$ ergs and *K.E. of the weight* $= \frac{1}{2}Mv^2 = \frac{1}{2} \times 10 \times 1000(5 \times 4.755)^2 = 28.27 \times 10^5$ ergs.

Example 27. A flywheel of mass 500 kg, radius 1 metre makes 500 revolutions per minute. Assuming the mass to be concentrated along the rim, calculate the energy of the flywheel.

(*Nagpur U. 2007*)

Solution. Mass of the flywheel $M = 500$ kg

As the mass is concentrated along the rim, distance of the mass from the axis or radius of gyration

$$k = 1 \text{ m}$$

Angular velocity $$\omega = 500 \text{ rev/min.} = \frac{500 \times 2\pi}{60} \text{ rad/sec}$$

Moment of inertia $$I = Mk^2 = 500 \times 1 = 500 \text{ kg-m}^2$$

∴ $$\text{K.E. of flywheel} = \frac{1}{2}Iw^2 = \frac{1}{2}Mk^2\omega^2 = \frac{1}{2} \times 500 \times \left(\frac{500 \times 2\pi}{60}\right)^2$$

$$= 6.871 \times 10^5 \text{ J.}$$

VI–Precession

Example 28. A bicycle wheel of mass 2 kg and radius 50 cm is rolling along on a road at 20 km/hr. What torque will have to be applied to the handle to turn it through half a radian in 0.1 sec? (Take the mass of the wheel to be concentrated at the rim).

Solution. We know that the torque producing precession is given by

$$\tau_1 = J\,\delta\theta/\delta t = J\phi,$$

where J is the *angular momentum* of the body about its axis of rotation and ϕ, the *rate of precession* of the axis.

Now, $J = I\omega = mr^2\,\omega$, where $I = mr^2$ is the *moment of inertia* of the wheel about its axis of rotation (its mass being concentrated at the rim) and ω, its *angular velocity*.

Here, $I = 2000 \times 2500 = 5 \times 10^6$ gm-cm² and $\omega\ v/r = \frac{20 \times 1000 \times 100}{3600 \times 50} = \frac{100}{9}$ radian/sec, and $\phi = \delta\theta/\delta t = 0.5/0.1 = 5$ radian/sec.

∴ *torque required to be applied to the handle, i.e.,*

$$\tau_1 = J\phi = I\omega\phi = 5 \times 10^6 \times \frac{100}{9} \times 5 = \frac{25 \times 10^8}{9} = 2.78 \times 10^8 \text{ gm-cm}^2/\text{sec}.$$

VII–Quantisation of angular momenutm—Rotational energy states of a diatomic molecule

Example 29. The internuclear distance between the two hydrogen atoms in a hydrogen molecule is 0.71 A and mass of a proton is 1.6 × 10^{-24} gm. Calculate the moment of inertia and energy of the first and third rotational energy levels in ergs, in electron volts and in cm^{-1}. Given h = 6.6 × 10^{-27} erg-sec.

Solution. Here, *reduced mass of the hydrogen molecule,* $\mu = \frac{mHmH}{mH + mH} = \frac{mH}{2}$ where mH is the mass of a hydrogen atom.

Or, since $m_H \approx mp$, the *mass of a proton*, we have $\mu = mp/2 = 1.6 \times 10^{-24}/2 = 0.8 \times 10^{-24}$ gm.

∴ *Moment of inertia of the hydrogen molecule about the axis passing through its centre of mass and perpendicular to the line joining the two nuclei (or the two protons)*, say $I = \mu\, r_0^2$ (§11.15) = $0.8 \times 10^{-24} \times (0.71 \times 10^{-8})^2 = 4.03 \times 10^{-41}$ gm-cm².

Now, as we know, (§11.20), *energy corresponding to the jth energy level is given* by $E = Aj(j+1)$, where $A = h^2/8\pi^2 I$. So that,

energy of the hydrogen molecule corresponding to the first rotational energy level, i.e., for $j = 1$, is given by $E_1 = 2A = \frac{2h^2}{8\pi^2 I} = 2\frac{(6.6 \times 10^{-27})^2}{8\pi^2 \times 4.03 \times 10^{-41}} = 2.72 \times 10^{-14}$ ergs.

Since 1.6×10^{-12} ergs = 1 *electron volt*, we have

$$E_1 = \frac{2.72 \times 10^{-14}}{1.6 \times 10^{-12}} = 1.7 \times 10^{-2} \text{ eV}.$$

And, in cm^{-1}, *i.e.*, in *wave numbers*, E_1 is given by

$$\nu_1 = E_1/hc = \frac{2.72 \times 10^{-14}}{6.6 \times 10^{-27} \times 3 \times 10^{10}} = 137.4 \text{ cm}^{-1}.$$

Similarly, *energy of the hydrogen molecule corresponding to the third rotational energy level, i.e.,* for $j = 3$, is given by

$$E_3 = 12A = \frac{12h^2}{8\pi^2 I} = 12\frac{(6.6 \times 10^{-27})^2}{8\pi^2 \times 4.03 \times 10^{-41}} = 16.3 \times 13^{-14} \text{ ergs}.$$

Or, *in electron volts,* $$E_3 = \frac{16.3 \times 10^{-14}}{1.6 \times 10^{-12}} = 10.2 \times 10^{-2} \text{ eV},$$

and *in wave numbers,* $$\bar{\nu}_3 = \frac{E_3}{hc} = \frac{16.3 \times 10^{-14}}{6.6 \times 10^{-27} \times 3 \times 10^{10}} = 823 \text{ cm}^{-1}.$$

Example 30. The spacing between successive spectral lines in the rotational spectrum of Hcl is found to be 20.8 cm^{-1}. Calculate the internuclear distance or the bond length for the Hcl molecule. (Atomic weight of Cl = 35.5 *amu* and 1 *amu* = 1.6 × 10^{-24} gm; *h* = 6.6 × 10^{-27} erg-sec).

Solution. We know that the spacing between the successive spectral lines in the rotational spectrum of a diatomic molecule $= \dfrac{h}{4\pi^2 Ic} = \dfrac{h}{4\pi^2 \mu r_0^2 c}$, [§11.19 (*iii*)]

where μ is the *reduced mass of the molecule and* r_0, its *internuclear distance* or *bond length.*

We, therefore, have $\dfrac{h}{4\pi^2 \mu r_0^2 c} = 20.8^{-1}$ cm. Or, $r_0^2 = \dfrac{h}{4\pi^2 \mu (20.8) c}$,

whence, $$r_0 = \sqrt{\frac{h}{4\pi^2 \mu (20.8) c}}$$

Here, $\dfrac{1}{\mu} = \left(\dfrac{1}{1} + \dfrac{1}{35.5}\right) = \dfrac{36.5}{35.5}$. Or, $\mu = \dfrac{35.5}{36.5}\, amu = \dfrac{35.5}{36.5} \times 1.6 \times 10^{-24} = 1.56 \times 10^{-24}$ gm.

And, therefore, $$r_0 = \sqrt{\frac{6.6 \times 10^{-27}}{4\pi^2 \times 1.56 \times 10^{-24} \times 20.8 \times 3 \times 10^{10}}}$$

$$= \sqrt{\frac{6.6 \times 10^{-13}}{4\pi^2 \times 1.56 \times 20.8 \times 3}} = 1.31 \times 10^{-8} \text{ cm.}$$

Or, since 10^{-8} cm = 1 *Angstrom unit,* we have *internuclear distance or the bond length for the hydrogen molecule* = 1.31 *A.*

EXERCISE

I–Torque—Angular momentum

1. Deduce the fundamental equation of a motion of rigid body about a fixed axis and show how it is the rotational analogue of the equation $\vec{F} = d\vec{p}/dt$ in the case of translational motion.
2. Show that the dimensions of *torque* are the same as those of *work* or *energy* and those of *angular momentum* the same as those of *energy* × *time*.
3. Show that the torque on a rigid body about a given axis is equal to the product of moment of inertia of the body and its angular acceleration about that axis and that its angular momentum about the given axis is equal to the product of its moment of inertia and its angular velocity about that axis.
4. Describe the vector representing the angular velocity of the earth (*i*) about its own axis, (*ii*) about the sun.
5. Show that the angular momentum about any point of a single particle moving with constant velocity remains the same throughout its motion.
6. A heavy disc rotating about the axis through its centre and perpendicular to its plane is slowed down due to friction at the bearings, such that its initial rate of rotation of 100 rotations per second is reduced to 90 rotations per second at the end of the first minute. If the frictional resistance be assumed to be constant, what will be its rate of rotation at the end of the second minute?

[**Ans.** 80 *rotations per second.*]

II–Moment of Inertia

7. What is the physical significance of Moment of inertia?

(Nagpur U., 2007, 2003; M.D.U., 2002; Gharwal U., 2000; Indore U., 2001; Gauhati U., 2007, 2000)

8. Moment of inertia plays the same role in rotation as mass does in translation. Justify.

9. Determine the moment of inertia of a circular disc. (*a*) about a diameter (*b*) about a tangent.

10. Find the moment of inertia of a thin uniform rod about an axis passing through one end and perpendicular to its length. ***(Kerala 2001)***

11. What must be the relation between l and R if the moment of inertia of the cylinder about its axis is to be the same as the moment of inertia about the equatorial axis? **[Ans.** $l = \sqrt{3}R$]

12. What do you mean by product of inertia, principal moment of inertia and principal axes of inertia? ***(Nagpur U. 2007, 2008)***

13. Derive Euler's equation of motion of a rigid body. ***(Nagpur U. 2007, 2008; D.A.U. Agra 2008, 2007, 2005, 2004)***

14. How can a solid-sphere be distinguish from a hollow sphere, the two being identical in all respects?

15. Explain Moment of Inertia and Radius of Gyration. Give the dimensions and units of moment of inertia. Is it a vector or scalar quantity?

(Kerala U., 2001; M.D.U. 2003, 2001; Gauhati U. 2007; Nagpur U., 2009, 2007, 2003; Purvanchal U. 2005)

16. Prove that $J^2 = 2EI$ weher J, E and I are the angular momentum, kinetic energy of rotation and moment of inertia respectively. ***(M.D.U. 2000)***

17. State and prove the theorem of perpendicular axis for moment of inertia.

(Meerut U., 2001; Gauhati U., 2007; Nagpur U. 2009, 2008; D.A.U. Agra, 2008, 2007, 2004; Purvanchal U. 2005)

18. State and prove theorem of parallel axes for moment of inertia.

(M.D.U., 2003; Meerut U., 2002, 2001; Gharwal U., 2000; Cal. U., 2003, Nagpur U. 2007, Purvanchal U. 2006, 2005, 2004; Agra U. 2006)

19. Determine the M.I. of circular disc about an axis through its centre perpendicular to its plane. ***(Gauhati U. 2007; Madurai U., 2003)***

20. Calculate the moment of inertia of a solid cylinder about

(*i*) axis of cylindrical symmetry. ***(Gauhati U. 2000; Gharwal U. 2000)***

(*ii*) about the axis passing through its centre and perpendicular to its own axis of symmetry. ***(M.D.U., 2002, Purvanchal U. 2004)***

21. Calculate the moment of inertia of a thin rod of mass M and length l about an axis passing through its centre and perpendicular to its length. If this rod rotates about the above axis with a constant angular speed ω, determine its angular momentum and kinetic energy.

22. Obtain an expression for the moment of inertia of an annular ring about an axis (*a*) passing through the centre and perpendicular to its plane. (*b*) about its diameter.

23. Obtain an expression for the moment of inertia of a hollow cylinder about its own axis of symmetry.

24. Derive an expression for the moment of inertia of a hollow cylinder about an axis through the centre and perpendicular to its own axis. ***(K.U. 2000)***

25. Derive the formula for the moment of inertia of a uniform solid sphere (*i*) about its diameter and (*ii*) about its tangent. ***(M.D.U. 2001; K.U. 2000; Purvanchal U. 2006; Meerut 2004)***

26. (*a*) Calculate the moment of inertia of a thin spherical shell (hollow sphere) about a diameter.

(*b*) Hence derive the moment of inertia of (*i*) a solid sphere about a diameter and a tangent and (*ii*) a thick shell about an axis through the centre.

(Meerut U. 2003; K.U. 2001; Kerala U. 2001; M.D.U. 2003, 2001; Gauhati U. 2000)

27. Obtain an expression for the moment of inertia of a solid cone (*i*) about its vertical axis and (*ii*) about an axis through its vertex and parallel to its base.

28. Calculate the moment of inertia of a rectangular lamina about an axis perpendicular to its plane and passing through its centre of gravity.

29. Find an expression for the moment of inertia of a rectangular solid bar of length l about an axis perpendicular to its length and passing through its centre of gravity. ***(K.U., 2002, 2000)***

30. Deduce an expression for the moment of inertia of a rectangular bar about an axis perpendicular to the length of the bar and passing through one of its sides. Hence find the moment of inertia of a square bar about the same axis. ***(M.D.U. 2000; Kerala U. 2001)***

31. Define Moment of inertia and Radius of gyration. Explain their physical significance. State the laws of (*i*) parallel and (*ii*) perpendicular axes and prove any one of them. ***(Bombay)***

32. Define moment of inertia of a body about an axis. Establish the parallel axes theorem. Evaluate the moment of inertia of a uniform circular disc about a diameter. ***(Delhi (Hons.))***

33. Define moment of inertia of a body and discuss its physical significance. Derive an expression for the moment of inertia of a sphere about an axis tangent to its surface. ***(Delhi (Hons.))***

34. (*a*) Find the moment of inertia of a solid cylinder about a line parallel to its axis and touching its surface. ***(Vikram)***

(*b*) Derive an expression for the moment of inertia of an annular ring (*i*) about an axis passing through its centre and perpendicular to its plane (*Calcutta, Bombay*), (*ii*) about its diameter, (*Punjab, Bombay*).

35. From the results obtained in Question 34(*b*) above, deduce the moments of inertia of (*i*) a plane circular disc about a perpendicular axis through its centre, (*ii*) a ring or a hoop about its diameter.

36. A thin and uniform metal rod of mass M and length $2l$ is bent sharply at its mid-point so that its two halves are inclined to each other at an angle θ. Show that its moment of inertia about an axis through its mid-point and perpendicular to its plane is $Ml^2/3$ irrespective of the value of θ.

37. Calculate the moment of inertia of a thin spherical shell and hence or otherwise, that of a solid and a hollow sphere, about an axis through its centre.

38. The cross section of five bodies of different geometrical shapes but the same mass (M) are shown in Fig. 11.47, each cross section having the same height and maximum width ($2a$).

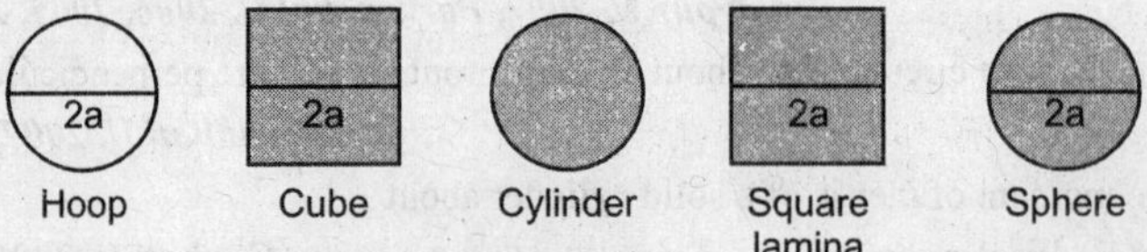

Fig. 11.47

Obtain the values of their moments of inertia about perpendicular axes passing through their respective centres of cross section, pointing out clearly the highest and the lowest values.

[**Ans.** (*i*) Ma^2 (*highest*), (*ii*) $\frac{2}{3}Ma^2$, (*iii*) $\frac{1}{2}Ma^2$, (*iv*) $\frac{2}{3}Ma^2$, (*v*) $\frac{2}{5}Ma^2$ (*lowest*)]

39. (*a*) About which axis will (*i*) a plane square lamina, (*ii*) a cube have the least moment of inertia?

(*b*) Will the moment of inertia of two circular discs of the same mass and radius but of materials of different densities be different about the axes through their centres of mass and perpendicular to their cross sections?

40. A uniform thin bar of mass 3 kg and length 0.9 metre is bent to make an equilateral triangle. Calculate the moment of inertia about an axis passing through the centre of mass and perpendicular to the plane of the triangle. ***(Agra)*** [**Ans.** 0.045 kg-m^2.]

41. A thin uniform disc of radius 25 cm and mass 1 kg has a hole of radius 5 cm in it. If the centre of the hole be at a distance of 10 cm from the centre of the disc, calculate the moment of inertia about an axis perpendicular to the plane and passing through the centre of the hole. ***(Gorakhpur)***

[**Ans.** 4.25×10^5 gm-cm^2.]

42. Five masses, each of 2 kg, are placed on a horizontal circular disc (of negligible mass) which can be rotated about a vertical axis passing through its centre. If the masses be equidistant from the axis and at a distance of 10 cm from it, what is the moment of inertia of the whole system?

[**Ans.** 10^6 gm-cm^2.]

43. Calculate the moment of inertia of a sphere about its diameter and also about a tangent. ***(Delhi)***

44. Obtain an expression for the moment of inertia of a uniform right circular cone of mass M about its axis, the radius of the base being r and deduce from it the moment of inertia of the cone about an axis through its vertex and parallel to its base.

45. State and illustrate *Routh's rule* for the moments of inertia of bodies of geometrical shapes about any one of their axes of symmetry.

46. On what factors does radius of gyration depend. ***(Nagpur U. 2008)***

47. Centres of four solid spheres of diameter $2a$ and mass m make a square of side b. Calculate the moment of inertia of the system about one side of the square. $\left[\textbf{Ans.} \frac{2}{5} m(4a^2 + 5b^2)\right]$

48. State the expression for the moment of inertia of a uniform cylinder of length l and radius R about an axis through its centre and normal to its length. If the above moment of inertia is to be a minimum, determine the ratio $\frac{l}{R}$, when the mass of the cylinder is kept constant and show that the ratio is $\sqrt{3} : \sqrt{2}$.

49. The flat surface of a hemisphere of radius r is cemented to one flat surface of a cylinder of radius r and length L. If the total mass is M, show that the M.I. of combination about the axis of the cylinder will be

$$Mr^2 \frac{(L/2 + 4r/15)}{(L + 2r/3)}$$

50. A uniform thin bar of mass 3 kg and length 0.9 m is bent to make an equilateral triangle. Calculate the moment of inertia about an axis passing through the centre of mass and perpendicular to the plane of the triangle. [**Ans.** 0.6225 kg m^2]

51. Two thin discs each of mass 0.1 kg and radius 0.05 m are placed at either end of a rod 0.2 m long and 0.01 m in diameter. What is the moment of inertia of the system about an axis passing through the centre of the rod and perpendicular its length? Density of the material of the rod is 7.8×10^3 kg m^{-3}. [**Ans.** 2.5342×10^{-3} kg m^2.]

52. Determine the moment of inertia of the earth, assuming it to be a uniform sphere of radius 6400 km and mass 6×10^{24} kg. [**Ans.** 98.3×10^{35} kg m^2.]

III–Kinetic energy of rotation—Rolling bodies

53. A hoop of radius 0.5 m and mass 16 kg is rolling along a horizontal floor, such that its centre of mass has a velocity of 0.25 m/sec. What work will have to be done to stop it? [**Ans.** 1 joule.]

54. A thin hollow cylinder, open at both ends and of mass M, (a) slides with a velocity v *without rotating*, (b) rolls *without slipping*, with the same speed. Compare the kinetic energies it possesses in the two cases. [**Ans.** 1 : 2.]

55. A solid spherical ball rolls on a table. Find the ratio of its translational and rotational kinetic energies and the total energy of the spherical ball. What fraction of the total energy is rotational? ***(Kerala U. 2001; Gauhati U. 2000)***

56. Derive an expression for the acceleration of a body rolling down a smooth inclined plane without slipping. What are the values of acceleration for a cylinder, solid sphere and hollow sphere of the same radius? ***(K.U., 2002, 2001; M.D.U. 2003, 2001, Gharwal U., 2001; Bang. U., 2000)***

57. A sphere, a solid cylinder, a spherical shell and a ring of the same mass and radius are allowed to roll down from rest simultaneously on an inclined plane from the same height without slipping. Prove that the sphere reaches down first, then the cylinder, thereafter the shell and the last the ring.

58. (*i*) Define products of moment of inertia, principal axes and principal moment of inertia.
(*ii*) Derive Euler's equation of motion of a rigid body.
(*iii*) Using law of parallel axes, calculate the moment of inertia of a disc of mass 0.2 kg and radius 0.5 m about an axis passing through its edge and perpendicular to the plane of the disc. ***(Nagpur U. 2008)*** [**Ans.** 0.075 kg m^2]

59. (*a*) A solid spherical ball rolls on a horizontal table. What fraction of its total kinetic energy is rotational?

(*b*) A circular disc of mass m and radius r is set rolling on a table. If ω is its angular velocity, show that its total energy E is given by $E = \frac{3}{4} mr^2\omega$. ***(Punjab)*** **[Ans.** (*a*) 2/7th.]

60. A symmetrical diatomic molecule of a gas, of mass 5.30×10^{-28} kg and moment of inertia about the axis through the centre of its bond length and perpendicular to it, 1.94×10^{-46} kg-m^2, is moving with a speed of 500 m/sec. If its kinetic energy of rotation be two thirds of its kinetic energy of translation, calculate its mean angular velocity.. **[Ans.** 6.747×10^{12} radians/sec.]

61. A body of mass M and radius R, rolling on a horizontal surface, without slipping, with a velocity v, rises up an incline to a maximum height $h = 7\ Mv^2/10$. What is the body? **[Ans.** A solid sphere.]

62. What is inertia? Obtain an expression for the kinetic energy of a rotating body.

(Kerala U. 2001, M.D.U. 2003)

63. A string is wrapped round a cylinder of mass M and radius R. The string is pulled vertically upward to prevent the centre of mass of the cylinder falling as the string round it gets unwound. (*i*) What is the tension in the string? (*ii*) What is the work done on the cylinder when it has attained an angular velocity ω? (*iii*) What is the length of the string unwound during this time?

[Ans. (*i*) Mg, (*ii*) $MR^2\omega^2/4$, (*iii*) $R^2\omega^2/4g$,]

64. A wheel of radius 6 cm is mounted so as to rotate about a horizontal axis through its centre. A string of negligible mass, wrapped round its circumference, carries a mass of 200 gm attached to its free end. When let fall, the mass descends through 100 cm in the first 5 seconds. Calculate the angular acceleration of the wheel and its moment of inertia. **[Ans.** $\frac{4}{3}$ radian/sec^2; 8.75×10^5 gm-cm^2.]

65. A small sphere of radius r and mass m rolls without slipping on the inner surface of a large hemisphere of radius R, whose axis of symmetry is vertical (Fig. 11.48), where $R >> r$. If the sphere starts from rest at the top of the hemispherical surface, calculate (*i*) the kinetic energy of the sphere at the bottom of the surface, (*ii*) the rotational and translational fraction of this energy and (*iii*) the normal force exerted by the sphere on the bottom of the hemispherical surface.

[Ans. (*i*) $mg(R - r)$, (*ii*) 2/7, 5/7, (*iii*) (17/7) mg.]

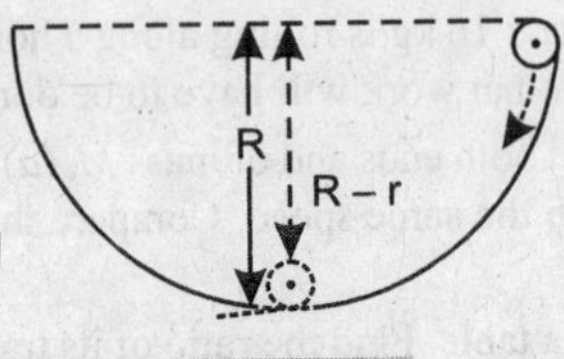

Fig. 11.48

66. A flywheel in the form of a solid circular disc of mass 500 kg and radius 1 meter is rotating, making 120 rev/min. Compute the kinetic energy and the angular speed if the wheel is brought to rest in 2 seconds; friction is to be neglected. ***(Punjab)*** **[Ans.** 1.974×10^{12} ergs; 3.142×10^{11} radian/sec.]

67. The moment of inertia of a reel of thread about its axis is MK^2. If the loose end of the thread is held in the hand and the reel is allowed to unroll itself while falling under the action of gravity, show that it falls down with an acceleration $ga^2/(a^2 + K^2)$, where a is the radius of the reel. ***(Nagpur)***

68. A metre stick is first held vertically with its lower end resting on a horizontal surface and is then allowed to fall. Assuming that its lower end does not slip, calculate the velocity of the upper end as it hits the horizontal surface. **[Ans.** 5.4 m/sec.]

69. Starting from rest at the top of a zigzag path, with its right hand end horizontal, as shown in Fig. 11.49, small solid sphere rolls without slipping until it finally rolls off the horizontal end. If the top of the path be 195 cm and its horizontal end 20 cm above the ground level, how far from the latter will the sphere hit the ground? **[Ans.** 100 cm.]

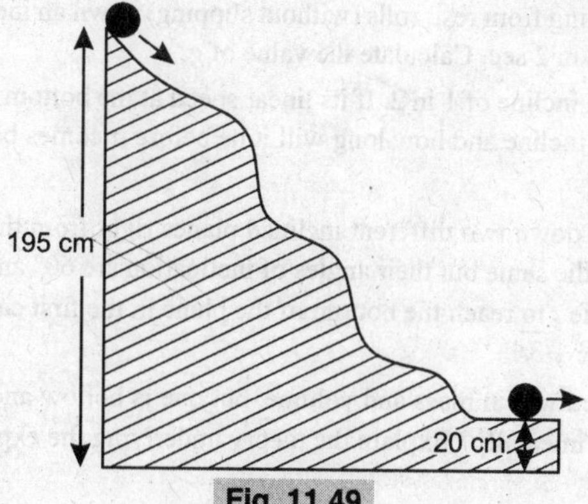

Fig. 11.49

70. A sharp impulse is given to a stationary billiard ball of mass m by means of a cue held horizontally at a height h above the centre line, as shown in Fig. 11.50. As a result, the ball starts moving away from the cue with velocity v but soon acquires a final velocity $(9/7)v$. Show that $h = (4/5)r$, where r is the radius of the ball.

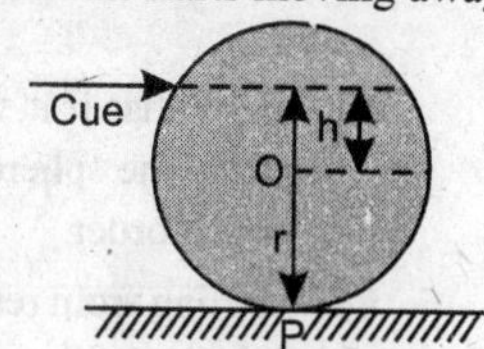

Fig. 11.50

[Hint. Angular momentum imparted to the ball about the point $P = mv(r + h)$. This must be equal to $I\omega$, where I is the *M.I.* of the ball about the axis through P and parallel to the one through O, *i.e.*,

$= \frac{2}{5}mr^2 + mr^2 = \frac{7}{5}mr^2$ and, ω, the angular velocity of the ball.

So that, $\frac{7}{5}\ mr^2\ \omega = mv(r + h)$,

whence, $\omega = 5v(r + h)/7r^2$. And, therefore,

$$\frac{9}{7}v\ =\ \omega \times r = \frac{5v(r+h)}{7r^2} \times r, \text{ which gives } h = \frac{4}{5}r$$

71. The free end of a string wrapped round the axle of a flywheel of moment of inertia 27.61×10^5 gm-cm^2 carries a weight of 5 kg which is allowed to fall. What is the number of revolutions made by the wheel when the weight has fallen through 1 meter. The kinetic energy of the weight may be neglected. **[Ans.** 3]

72. A pair of rails is supported in a horizontal position and the axle of a wheel rests on the rails. A thread is wrapped round the axle and a weight hung on the end of the thread. As the weight falls, the wheel moves along the rails. How would you determine the moment of inertia of the wheel with this arrangement?

73. A solid sphere and a hollow sphere of the same mass and same radius are allowed to roll down an inclined plane from the same position. Which one will come down with greater acceleration? Justify your answer. **[Ans.** Solid sphere, because acceleration is proportional to $R^2/(k^2+R^2)$ for a given angle of inclination θ]

74. A solid sphere and a hollow sphere have the same mass and the same radius. Will they have the same moment of inertia about their principal axis? Explain. ***(Purvanchal 2005)***

[Ans. Hollow sphere has larger M.I.]

75. A solid cylinder (*a*) rolls, (*b*) slides from rest down an inclined plane. Neglect friction and compare the velocities in both cases when the cylinder reaches the bottom of the inclined plane.

$$\left[\textbf{Ans. } \frac{v_1}{v_2} = \sqrt{\frac{2}{3}} = 0.8166\right]$$

IV–Motion along an inclined plane

76. Obtain an expression for the acceleration of a body rolling down an inclined plane.

77. Show that for a sphere to be able to roll along an inclined plane of inclination θ, the coefficient of static friction must not be less than $\frac{2}{7}\tan\theta$.

78. A circular disc, starting from rest, rolls (without slipping) down an inclined plane of 1 in 8 and covers a distance of 5.32 ft in 2 sec. Calculate the value of *g*. [**Ans.** 31.92 ft/sec^2.]

79. A sphere rolls up an incline of 1 in 2. If its linear speed at the bottom of the incline be 22 km/hr, how far will it go up the incline and how long will it be before it comes back to the bottom?

[**Ans.** 5.33 m; 3.50 sec.]

80. A solid sphere rolls down two different inclined planes right from their tops. The heights of the two inclined planes are the same but their angles of inclination are 60° and 30° respectively. Show that if the sphere takes time *t* to reach the bottom of the plane in the first case, the time taken by it to do so in the second case is $\sqrt{3t}$.

81. Two spheres are identical in mass and volume, but one is hollow and the other, solid. How will you identify them experimentally? Explain the theory underlying the experiment.

(Delhi; Gujarat; Punjab)

82. A solid cylinder (*a*) rolls, (*b*) slides from rest down an inclined plane. Neglect friction and compare the velocities in both cases when the cylinder reaches the bottom of the incline. ***(Punjab)***

[**Ans.** 1 : 1.225]

83. Show that if a sphere, a disc, a cylinder, a spherical shell and a hoop roll down the same inclined plane, the sphere, the disc, the cylinder, the spherical shell, the hoop reach the bottom of the incline in that order.

84. Starting from rest, a solid sphere, a circular disc and a spherical shell roll down an inclined plane. The velocity of the disc as it reaches the bottom of the plane is 20 cm/sec. Calculate the velocities of the sphere and the spherical shell when they too reach the bottom of the plane.

[**Ans.** 20.7 cm/sec; 18.97 cm/sec.]

85. Two identical heavy circular discs are attached to the two ends of a short rod of a very much smaller radius and the assembly is placed on an inclined plane with the rod touching the plane and the two discs overhanging on either side of the plane, such that the rod rolls down the plane without slipping. Near the bottom of the plane as the discs touch the horizontal surface of the table, the assembly starts moving with a very much higher linear velocity. Explain why?

V–Flywheel

86. A flywheel in the form of a solid disc of 5000 kg and 1 m radius is rotating making 120 r.p.m. Compute (*i*) K.E. and (*ii*) angular impulse if the wheel is brought to rest in 2 seconds.

[**Ans.** 1.974×10^5 J, 1.571×10^4 N ms^{-1}]

87. Define moment of inertia. Describe how you would determine experimentally the moment of inertia of a flywheel about its usual axis of rotation. Discuss briefly the part played by a flywheel in a machine. ***(Delhi)***

88. A thin string is slipped on to a small peg on the axle of a flywheel and wound round it, with a mass of 2 kg suspended from its lower free end which is initially held in position at a height of 100 cm from the floor. The mass is then allowed to fall. When it just touches the floor and the string slips off the peg, the flywheel comes to rest after making 20 revolutions in 8 sec. If the radius of the axle be 1.0 cm, obtain the value of the moment of inertia of the wheel about its axle and the kinetic energy of the 2 kg mass as it just touches the floor. [**Ans.** 2.20×10^5 gm-cm^2; 9.87×10^5 ergs.]

IV–Precession—Gyrostat

89. What is meant by the term '*precession*'? Show that if the axis of the torque applied to a body be perpendicular to its axis of rotation, the body precesses about an axis perpendicular to either of the first two axes.

90. What is a gyrostat? Explain its working and mention some of its important applications.

91. Explain the theory underlying a gyrastatic pendulum and obtain an expression for its time-period.

IV–Quantisation of angular momentum Rotational energy states of a diatomic molecule

92. What is meant by the quantisation of the angular momenta of electrons around the nucleus? How does it lead to the conclusion that the radii of the permissible orbits around the nucleus are proportional to n^2, where $n = 1, 2, 3$ etc?

93. What is meant by the spin angular momentum of a fundamental particle? Why is it referred to as intrinsic angular momentum of the particle?

94. What are *fermions* and *bosons*? What is the characteristic property of fermions which has led to *Pauli's exclusion principle* and hence to the arrangement of electrons in an atom?

95. Two point-masses m_1 and m_2 separated by a massless link of length r rotate about an axis passing through the centre of mass of the system and perpendicular to the link. If the angular momentum is $\sqrt{j(j+1)}\ h/2\pi$, find the rotational energy. ***(Rajasthan)***

[**Ans.** $E = h^2 j(j+1)/8\pi^2 I$, where $I = \mu r^2$ and $\mu = \dfrac{m_1 m_2}{m_1 + m_2}$]

96. Deduce an expression for the wavelength of light absorbed by a molecule of moment of inertia I in rotational transition $j = 0$ to $j = 1$, assuming that the angular momentum J is quantised according to the relation $J^2 = (h/2\pi)^2\, j(j+1)$. ***(Agra)***
[**Hint.** See ϕ 11.20]

97. Obtain the values of the three longest wavelengths in the rotational spectrum of HF, given that the bond length of the HF molecule is 0.92×10^{-8} cm and the atomic weight of F is 19.

[**Ans.** 0.024 cm; 0.012 cm; 0.008 cm.]

98. The internuclear distance between the tow protons in a hydrogen molecule is 0.74 A. Calculate its moment of inertia and the first two rotational energy levels. (Given that angular momentum J is quantised by the rule $J^2 = j(j+1)h^2/4\pi^2$, with $j = 0, 1, 2, 3$ etc.

[**Ans.** 9.6×10^{-4} gm-cm^2; 0.153 eV and 0.046 eV.]

99. It is found that the wave numbers of the successive spectral lines in the rotational spectrum of CO differ by 3.82 cm^{-1}. Obtain the value of energy for the third rotational energy level. What is the maximum wavelength of the radiation emitted? What is the bond length of the molecule and its moment of inertia about the right bisector of the bond length?

[**Ans.** 4.5×10^{-15} ergs; $\lambda_{max} = 0.26$ cm; 1.13×10^{-8} cm or 1.13 A; 1.46×10^{-39} gm cm^2.]

[**Hint.** The longest wavelength is emitted or absorbed during transition between states $j = 1$ and $j = 0$.]

100. A solid cylinder of diameter 8 cm and mass 0.25 kg rolls down an inclined plane rising 3 in 20 without slipping. Find the acceleration and total energy of the cylinder after 5 sec.

[**Ans.** 0.98 ms^{-2}; 4.5 J]

12 Chapter

GRAVITATION: FIELDS AND POTENTIAL

INVERSE SQUARE LAW FORCES—FUNDAMENTAL LENGTHS

Brief Contents

INTRODUCTION

Gravitation or gravity is a natural phenomenon by which physical bodies attract with a force proportional to their masses. In everyday life, gravitation is most familiar as the agent that gives weight to objects with mass and causes them to fall to the ground when dropped. Gravitation causes dispersed matter to coalesce, and coalesced matter to remain intact, thus accounting for the existence of the Earth, the Sun, and most of the macroscopic objects in the universe, Gravitation is responsible for keeping the earth and the other planets in their orbits around the Sun; for keeping the Moon in its orbit around the Earth; for the formation of tides; for natural convection, by which fluid flow occurs under the influence of a *density gradient* and gravity; for heating the interiors of forming stars and planets to very high temperatures; and for various other phenomena observed on Earth.

Gravitation is one of the four fundamental interactions of nature, along with the strong force, electromagnetic and the weak force. Modern physics describes gravitation using the *general theory of relativity*, in which gravitation is a consequence of the curvature of *space-time* which governs the motion of inertial objects. The simpler *Newton's law of universal gravitation* provides an accurate approximation for most calculations.

History of gravitational theory

Modern work on gravitational theory began with the work of Galileo Galilei in the late 16th and early 17th centuries. In his famous experiment dropping balls from the *Tower of Pisa*, and later with careful measurements of balls rolling down inclines, Galileo showed that gravitation accelerates all objects at the same rate. This was the major departure from Aristotle's belief that heavier objects accelerate faster. Galileo correctly postulated air resistance as the reason that lighter objects may fall more slowly in an atmosphere. Galileo's work set the stage for the formulation of Newton's theory of gravitation.

In 1687, English mathematician Sir Isaac Newton published *Principia* which hypothesizes the *inverse-square law* of universal gravitation. Newton's this theory enjoyed its greatest success when it was used to predict the existence of *Neptune* based on motions of Uranus that could not be accounted for by the actions of the other planets. With calculations based on this law, John Adams and Urbain Le Verrier predicted the general position of the planet and led to the discovery of Neptune.

A discrepancy in Mercury's orbit pointed out flaws in Newton's theory. But the issue was resolved in 1915 by Albert Einstein's new theory of '*general relativity*' which accounted for the small discrepancy in Mercury's orbit.

Earth's gravity. Every planetary body (including the Earth) is *surrounded by its own gravitational field*, which exerts an attractive force on all objects. Assuming a spherically symmetrical planet (a reasonable approximation), the strength of this field at any given point is proportional to the planetary body's mass and inversely proportional to the distance from the centre of the body.

The strength of the gravitational field is numerically equal to the acceleration of objects under its influence, and its value at the Earth's surface, denoted by g, is approximately expressed as the standard average and is $g = 9.81 \text{ m/s}^2 = 32.2 \text{ ft/s}^2$. This means that, ignoring air resistance, an object falling freely near the Earth's surface increases its velocity by 9.81 m/s (32.2 ft/sec or 22 mph) for each second of its descent. Thus, an object starting from rest will attain a velocity of 9.81 m/s (or 32.2 ft/s) after 1 sec, 19.6 m/s (64.4 ft/s) after 2 seconds, and so on. Also, ignoring air resistance, any and all objects, when dropped from the same height, will hit the ground at the same time.

The discovery and application of Newton's law of gravitation accounts for the detailed information we have about the planets in our solar system, the mass of the Sun, the distance to stars, *quasars* and even the theory of *dark matter*. Although we have not travelled to all the planets, nor to the Sun, we know their masses. In space an object maintains its orbit because of the force of gravity acting upon it. Planets orbit stars, stars orbit *galactic centres*, *galaxies* orbit a centre of mass in *clusters*, and clusters orbit *super clusters*.

12.1 BASIC FORCES OF NATURE

There are only four known ways for the interaction of matter leading to four fundamental types of forces, *viz*; (*i*) *gravitational interaction*, leading to gravitational forces, (*ii*) *electromagnetic interaction*, leading to electromagnetic forces, (*iii*) *strong interaction*, and (*iv*) *weak interaction* leading to what are referred to as nuclear forces. The latter two forces being operative at only very small distances, of the order of the size of the nucleus (*i.e.* 10^{-13} cm) are thus short-range forces compared to the former two long-range ones.

Of these, *the gravitational interaction is the weakest* and yet it is the gravitational force which is responsible for (*a*) holding the earth together and retaining on it the atmosphere, as we know it, with its life-giving constituent oxygen; (*b*) binding the earth and the other planets to that perennial source of energy, the sun, into a well-knit solar system, and (*c*) similarly binding the stars together into what are called galaxies, etc.

The *electromagnetic interaction* is equally important in that the electromagnetic force binds the electrons in an atom to the nucleus, the atoms into molecules and the molecules into crystals. It further accounts for such properties of matter as elasticity, viscosity, surface tension, refractive index, conductivity, specific heat and latent heat etc. The reason why it is so called is that it operates not only between electric charges but also between a moving charge and a magnetic field (since a moving charge too, as we know, develops a magnetic field about itself). In Chemistry and Biology, this alone is the dominating force.

Among the short-range nuclear forces, the *strong interaction* provides the strong force which binds together the *nucleons*, *i.e.*, *protons*, carrying positive charges and *neutrons* (carrying no charge) into a stable nucleus despite the force of repulsion between the similar charges carried by the protons. This force is, in fact, the strongest of all the four fundamental forces and its importance is obvious from the fact that all material bodies in the universe are actually made up of atoms and these atoms are, in a majority of cases, stable in consequence of this force.

Finally, the *weak interaction* gives rise to comparatively *feebler forces* which operate between lighter fundamental particles (like *electrons leptons, muons* and *neutrinos*) or between a light fundamental particle and a heavier particle. They cannot, however, form any such stable systems as the solar system formed by gravitational forces.

In this chapter, we shall, for the most part, concern ourselves only with gravitational forces.

12.2 NEWTON'S LAW OF GRAVITATION

This law was first announced by *Newton* in the year 1687 in his monumental work *Principia*, hailed as *the greatest production of the human mind.*

The law states that *every particle of matter in the universe attracts every other particle with a force which is directly proportional to the product of their masses and inversely proportional to the square of the distance between them.*

Thus, if the masses of two particles, distant r from each other, be m and m', the force of gravitational attraction between them, say, $F \propto mm'/r^2$.

Or, $$F = \frac{mm'}{r^2} G,$$

where G is a *universal constant*, called the *universal gravitational constant*, or usually simply the *Gravitational constant*.

Clearly, if $m = m' = 1$ gm and $r = 1$ cm, we have $F = G$,

i.e., the *Gravitational constant is the force of gravitational attraction between two unit masses unit distance apart.*

Its dimensions are $M^{-1} L^3 T^{-2}$ and its accurate value (determined by *Heyl* in 1930) is taken to be 6.669×10^{-8} dynes-cm^2/gm^2.

The reason why the law is said to be a universal law is that it operates from enormous inter-planetary distances down to the small terrestrial ones. The minimum distance up to which it holds good is probably not yet known with absolute certainty but it appears to break down at molecular distances, of the order of 10^{-7} cm.

There is a whole lot of evidence in favour of the law and there are also some small deviations from it, which we shall discuss a little later in the chapter

12.3 EXPERIMENTAL DETERMINATION OF THE GRAVITATIONAL CONSTANT (G)

1. Cavendish's method. *Cavendish* was the first to have made use of a *torsion balance* to devise a laboratory method for determining the value of G in the year 1798.

Apparatus. The apparatus used by Cavendish, shown in Fig. 12.1, consisted of a *cross bar PQ* about 6 ft (or 180 cm) long, suspended from the ceiling of a chamber, so as to be free to rotate about a vertical axis by means of a wheel and string arrangement, manipulated from outside the chamber. Two *metal rods* attached to the two ends of the cross bar carried two *equal lead spheres C* and *D* at their lower free ends, 20 to 25 cm in diameter and weighing about 160 kg each.

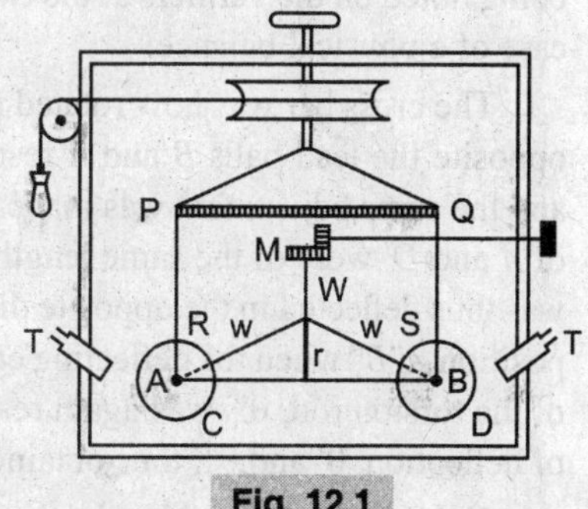

Fig. 12.1

Directly below the mid-point of the cross bar, was a *torsion head M*, also manipulated from outside from which was suspended a lighter, deal rod *RS* (of the same length as *PQ*) by means of a fine *torsion wire W* of sliver-plated copper. To increase the strength of the rod without increasing its moment of inertia, two *wires w, w* were fastened to its two ends *R* and *S* and to a small vertical rod *r* fixed at its mid-point and attached to the suspension wire. Two smaller lead balls *A* and *B*, about 5 cm in diameter and weighing about 740 gm each, were suspended from the two ends of the deal rod *RS*, such that their centres, along with those of the lead spheres *C* and *D* lay in the same horizontal plane, roughly in a horizontal circle of about 3 ft (or 90 cm) radius. A small vernier carried by each end of the torsion rod (*RS*) moved over a fine ivory scale fixed to vertical stands, with each division equal to 0.05″.

As a safeguard against any changes of temperature and consequent setting up of air draughts (or convection currents) which might mask the rather feeble gravitational effect, the chamber was kept completely closed and the observations taken with the help to telescopes *T, T* fixed into the walls of the chamber, as shown. Further, to shield the apparatus from the effect of any outside electric charges, it was enclosed in a gilded glass case, supported on four levelling screws.

Working. The cross bar *PQ* was first rotated until the line joining the centres of the lead spheres *C* and *D*, carried by it, way at right angles to the torsion rod *RS* carrying the smaller lead balls *A* and *B* at its two ends, as shown in Fig. 12.2 (*a*), it being so arranged that *in this position there was no* *twist in the suspension wire W*, and the readings on the verniers at either end of the torsion rod taken.

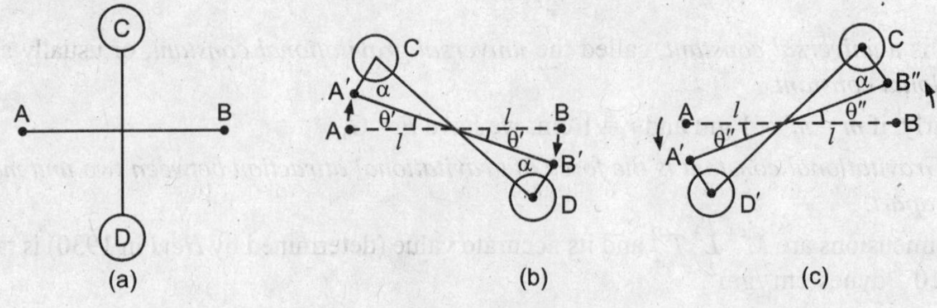

Fig. 12.2

The cross bar *PQ* was then rotated until the lead spheres *C* and *D* lay on opposite sides of the lead balls *A* and *B* respectively as shown in Fig. 12.2 (*b*), such that lines joining the centres of *A* and *C* and of *B* and *D were equal in length and perpendicular to the torsion rod*. Obviously, then, the gravitational force of attraction on ball *A* due to sphere *C* was equal and opposite to that on ball *B* due to sphere *D*. This pair of equal and opposite forces constituted a couple tending to rotate the torsion rod clockwise. This was resisted by the restoring torsional couple set up in the suspension wire *W*, tending to bring the torsion rod back into its original position. Equilibrium was naturally attained when the two couples balanced each other, when the torsion rod had been deflected, say through an angle 0 into the position *A′B′*, from its initial position *AB* (shown dotted), this angle being noted on the verniers at the two ends of the torsion rod by the method of oscillations, as in the case of a physical balance.

The cross bar was now rotated the other way about, such that the lead spheres *C* and *D* now lay opposite the lead balls *B* and *A* respectively, in the positions *C′* and *D′*, as shown in Fig. 12.2 (*c*), and the same adjustment was made as before, *viz.*, that the lines joining the centres of *B* and *C′* and of *A* and *D′* were of the same length as before and perpendicular to the torsion rod. The torsion rod was thus deflected in the opposite direction to that in the first case, *i.e.*, anticlockwise, occupying the position *A″B″* when the deflecting couple just balanced the restoring torsional couple. The deflection of the torsion rod, θ'', was again read on the verniers at its two ends. The mean of these two values of deflection, θ' and θ'', thus obtained, was taken as the true deflection θ of the torsion rod.

Calculations. Let *M* and *m* be the masses of each lead sphere and lead ball respectively and *d* the distance between their centres in the deflected position of the torsion rod [Fig. 12.2 (*b*) or (*c*)]. Then, clearly, forces of attraction exerted by the spheres on the lead balls near to them = MmG/d^2 each, but oppositely directed, thus constituting a *deflecting couple* $(MmG/d^2).2l$, where $2l$ is the *length of the torsion rod*. And, if *C* be torsional couple per unit twist in the suspension wire (*W*), the restoring torsional couple set up in the wire = $C\theta$, where θ is the twist in the wire (or the deflection of the torsion rod). Since in the equilibrium position of the torsion rod, the two couples balance each other, we have

$$\frac{Mm}{d^2}G.2l = C\theta, \quad \text{whence, } G = \frac{Cd^2}{Mm.2l}\theta.$$

To determine the value of *C*, the torsion rod (*RS*), together with the lead balls *A* and *B* suspended from its two ends, was set into torsional vibration about the suspension wire (*W*) and its time-period *t* noted, (found to be 28 minutes in Cavendish's own experiment). Then, if *I* be the moment of inertia of the torsion rod (along with the lead balls) about the wire *W* as axis, we have $t = 2\pi\sqrt{I/C}$, whence, $C = 2\pi^2 I/t$.

Substituting this value of *C* in the expression above, we have

$$G = \frac{2\pi^2 Id^2}{Mmlt^2}\theta.$$

And, if δ be the *displacement* of each end of the torsion rod, clearly, $\theta = \delta/l$. so that,

$$G = \frac{2\pi^2 Id^2}{Mml^2t^2}\delta.$$

Or, if we ignore the mass of the torsion rod compared with that of the balls *A* and *B*, we have $I = 2m\,(2l/2)^2 = 2ml^2$. And, therefore,

$$G = \frac{4\pi^2 ld^2}{Mt^2}\theta = \frac{4\pi^2 d^2}{Mt^2}\delta.$$

Corrections applied. Corrections were applied *for the force of attraction between* (*i*) *a lead sphere distant small ball*, (*ii*) *the two lead spheres and the torsion rod* and (*iii*) *the rods carrying the lead spheres and the smaller lead/balls.*

Sources of error: The following are the chief sources of error in the experiment:

(*i*) The force of attraction between each pair of lead sphere and lead ball being small, the torsion rod had to be a long one to increase the deflecting couple. This necessitated a large chamber in which convection currents could hardly be avoided.

(*ii*) The suspension wire (*W*) required a large torque per unit angular twist and hence for a given deflecting couple; the deflection of the torsion rod was rather small.

(*iii*) The suspension wire was not perfectly elastic, so that the torque (or the couple) required was not strictly proportional to the deflection of the torsion rod.

(*iv*) The lead spheres tended to decrease the deflection of the torsion rod due to their force of attraction on the distant small balls, whereas the rods carrying the lead spheres tended to increase its deflection due to their force of attraction on the small balls.

(*v*) The method of measuring the angle of deflection was far from sensitive.

Result. The value of G obtained by *Cavendish*, as the mean of twenty-nine observations, was 6.754×10^{-8} dyne-cm^2/gm^2 in the C.G.S. units or 6.754×10^{-11} newton-metre^2/kg^2 in the M.K.S (SI) units.

2. Boys' method. Sir Charles Vernon Boys devised, in the year 1895, a far more accurate method for the determination of the value of *G*. He removed all the sources of error of Cavendish's method, greatly reduced the size of the apparatus and yet increased its sensitiveness (by reducing the dimensions of different parts of it in different proportions).

Apparatus. The apparatus used by Boys, shown diagrammatically in Fig. 12.3, consists of *two coaxial glass tubes*, with the bore of the inner one abut 4 cm. This inner tube is fixed and the outer one can be rotated about their common axis, with the whole assembly mounted on a suitable platform provided with levelling screws. A large chamber is thus done away with.

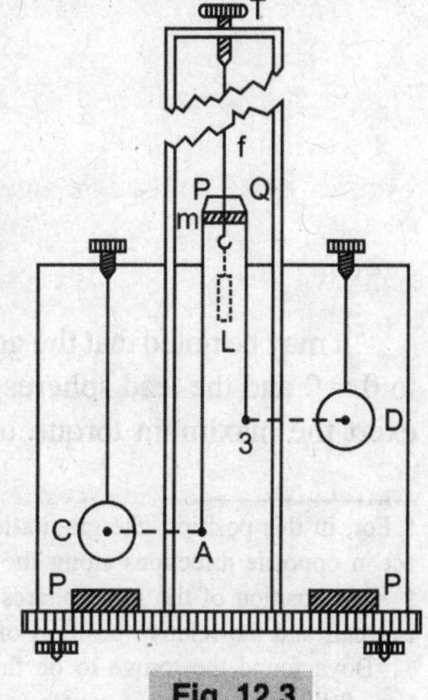

Fig. 12.3

The moving system here consists of two *gold balls*, *A* and *B*, about 0.5 cm in diameter and weighing 2.65 gm each, suspended by fine gold wires from the two ends of a small beam *PQ* which is itself suspended by a fine *quartz fibre f* from a torsion head *T*, inside the inner tube. This serves to protect the system from any outside disturbances. Also, if suspended *centrally* inside the tube, the system remains unaffected by the effects due to attraction by the tube itself.

Immediately below the beam PQ is a *plane mirror strip m*, 2.5 cm long and rigidly attached to the beam, with grooves in its two vertical edges inside which slide the wires carrying the gold balls. This ensures that (*i*) *the two wires are kept a constant horizontal distance apart* and (*ii*) *the effective points of suspension of the gold balls on the two edges of the mirror strip,* which thus replaces the long torsion rod of Cavendish's apparatus.

Two large lead spheres C and D, about 11.0 cm in diameter and weighing 74 kg each, are suspended in the outer tube as indicated, such that the centre of C is in a level with that of ball A and that of D in a level with that of ball B (to ensure greater precision in the measurement of the distance between each pair), *the distance between each pair being the same.* And, to minimise of effect of a large sphere on the distant small ball (*i.e.*, of C on B and of D on A), one of the pairs, say, BD, is arranged to lie some 15 cm above the level of the other (AC), the centres of both, the sphere and the ball, lying in the same vertical plane, with no twist in the suspension fibre.

The deflection of the torsion rod (*i.e.*, the mirror strip) m is measured accurately by a scale and telescope arrangement and a half-millimetre scale is placed at a distance of about seven metres from it for the purpose.

Finally, as a safeguard against damage to the tube by an accidental fall of the lead spheres (C and D), rubber pads P and P are placed directly below them, as shown.

Working. The outer tube is rotated unit *the lead spheres C and D lie on opposite sides of the two gold balls A and B respectively* (*but not in a line with the mirror strip**), so as to exert the maximum torque on the suspended system and its deflection is, therefore, the largest†. This deflection is noted on the half-millimetre scale.

The outer tube is next rotated until the lead spheres now lie *on the other sides* of the gold balls *in a similar position to the previous one*, again exerting the maximum torque on the suspended system and hence producing the maximum deflection of the mirror strip. The mean of the two deflections is then taken. Let it be θ.

Calculations. Let A, B and C, D (Fig. 12.4) be the positions of the gold balls and the lead spheres respectively when they are in equilibrium in the position of maximum deflection θ, with their centres in the same vertical plane again, as to start with.

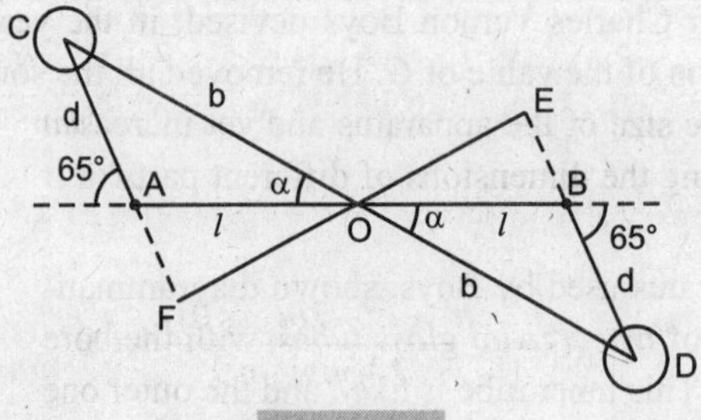

Fig. 12.4

It may be noted that the gold balls A and B are here shown in their initial positions, corresponding to $\theta = 0$ and the lead spheres C and D in their final positions into which they have been rotated to exert the maximum torque on the suspended system and to produce the maximum deflection θ.

* For, in this position, the gravitational force of attraction due to the large spheres on the small balls near to them will act in opposite directions along the same line and will thus neutralize each other.

† This position of the lead spheres in chosen because, with the torque on the system a maximum, its rate of variation is small and the relative position of the spheres and the balls need not be known with any great precision.

Boys found the torque to be the maximum when the lines joining the centres of each pair of a sphere and a ball (*i.e.*, the lines joining the centres of the pairs AC and BD) were inclined to the line AB (Fig 12.4) at an angle of 65°

In this position, therefore, the deflecting gravitational couple exerted by the lead spheres on the suspended system is just balanced by the restoring torsional couple set up in the suspension fibre.

Now, let O be the mid-point of the mirror strip and l, its half-length (*i.e.*, $OA = OB = l$) and let $OC = OD = b$, $AC = BD = d$, $\angle AOC = \angle BOD = \alpha$ and $OE = OF$, where EF is the perpendicular through O on to DB and CA produced.

Obviously, in ΔOBD, we have

$$BD = \sqrt{OD^2 + OB^2 - 2OD.OB\cos\alpha}, \textit{ i.e.},$$

$$d = (b^2 + l^2 - 2bl\cos\alpha)^{1/2}.$$

Again, in the same triangle, $\dfrac{\sin\alpha}{\sin BDO} = \dfrac{OD}{OB} = \dfrac{d}{l}$.

Or, $$\sin BDO = \frac{l\sin\alpha}{d}.$$

And, in the right-angled triangle OED, we have $OE = OD\sin EDO = b\sin BDO$ or, substituting the value of $\sin BDO$, we have

$$OE = bl\sin\alpha/d \text{ and } \therefore\ EF = 2OE = 2bl\sin\alpha/d$$

Now, if M be the mass of each lead sphere and m, that of each gold ball, we have *force of attraction between each pair of lead sphere and gold ball* $= MmG/d^2$. The two forces being *equal opposite and parallel*, constitute *a couple or torque* $= (MmG/d^2)$. EF, where EF is the perpendicular distance between the two forces.

Substituting the value of EF obtained above, we therefore have

$$\textit{deflecting couple or torque} = \frac{Mm}{d^2}G.\frac{2bl\sin\alpha}{d} = \frac{2Mmbl\sin\alpha}{d^3}G.$$

Again, substituting the value of d, we have

$$\textit{deflection couple or torque} = \frac{2Mmbl\sin\alpha}{(b^2 + l^2 - 2bl\cos\alpha)^{3/2}}G.$$

And, if C be the torsional couple per unit twist of the suspension fibre*, the *restoring torsional couple or torque* $= C\theta$.

Since the two couples just balance each other in the position of equilibrium of the system, we have

$$\frac{2Mmbl\sin\alpha}{(b^2 + l^2 - 2bl\cos\alpha)^{3/2}}G = C\theta, \text{ whence, } G = \frac{(b^2 + l^2 - 2bl\cos\alpha)^{3/2}}{2Mmbl\sin\alpha}C\theta.$$

Since a quartz fibre is nearly perfectly elastic, the value of α may be taken to be the same as that of θ, and we therefore have

$$G = \frac{(b^2 + l^2 - 2bl\cos\theta)^{3/2}}{2Mmbl\sin\theta}C\theta,$$

whence, the value of G may be easily obtained. Its value, as obtained by Boys, was 6.6576×10^{-8} dyne-cm^2/gm^2 in CGS units and 6.6576×10^{-11} newton-metre^2/kg^2 in M.K.S. (or SI) units.

Advantages over Cavendish's method. The following are the obvious advantages of the method over Cavendish's method.

* The value of C may be obtained in the same manner as in Cavendish's experiment, *i.e.*, by setting the strip (together with the gold balls suspended from it) into torsional vibration in the absence of the lead spheres and noting its time-period.

Boys, however, determined it by removing from the mirror strip both the gold balls and their suspension wires and suspending from it a small cylinder L (shown dotted in the figure), this cylinder having the same mass as the gold balls and their suspension wires and a known *M.I.* about its own axis.

(*i*) The size of the chamber was greatly reduced, thus almost completely eliminating convection currents and enabling its temperature to be controlled.

(*ii*) The two pairs of lead spheres and gold balls being arranged at different levels, the gravitational force of a lead sphere on the distant gold ball is almost negligible.

(*iii*) The deflection of the mirror strip is measured more accurately by the scale and telescope method.

(*iv*) A quartz fibre is used as the suspension wire which, besides being fine and strong, (*a*) is almost perfectly elastic and (*b*) requires a small torque per unit twist. The angular deflection of the mirror strip is thus quite appreciably large as well as proportional to the applied torque.

3. Heyl's method. The method adopted by *P.R. Heyl*, in the year 1930, for the determination of the value of *G* is taken to be the most accurate to date. It is a modification of *Braun's Torsion balance experiment* which itself was a revised version of Boys' method, dealt with under (2) above,

Apparatus. Heyl arranged his apparatus in a constant *temperature enclosure* (in fact, the constant temperature room of the American Bureau of Standards, 12 metres below ground level) with the pressure inside it reduced to 2 mm of mercury column to minimise convection currents.

The attracting *large masses* used by him were massive *cylinders of steel* (with 0.9% of carbon), each weighing about 66.3 kg and suspended from a system free to rotate about a vertical axis midway between the two.

The reason why he took his large masses in the form of cylinders rather than that of the spheres (which obviously make the calculation easier) was that it was difficult to machine a sphere of such a huge mass. As someone well remarked, *the burden was thus 'shifted to the broad shoulders of the malhematician'*.

The *smaller masses*, each weighing 2.44 gm, were *balls of gold, platinum* and *optical glass* in three different sets of experiments respectively, and were suspended from the two ends of a *light aluminum torsion rod R*, 28.6 cm long (Fig. 12.5), supported by a *tungsten thread T.W.* (1 metre long and 0.25 mm in diameter) and two inclined copper wires (*w*, *w*), so that almost the whole moment of inertia of the assembly remains in the balls themselves. *Heyl* preferred a tungsten thread to a quartz fibre as suspension wire because the latter is sometimes found to break quite unexpectedly and for no apparent reason.

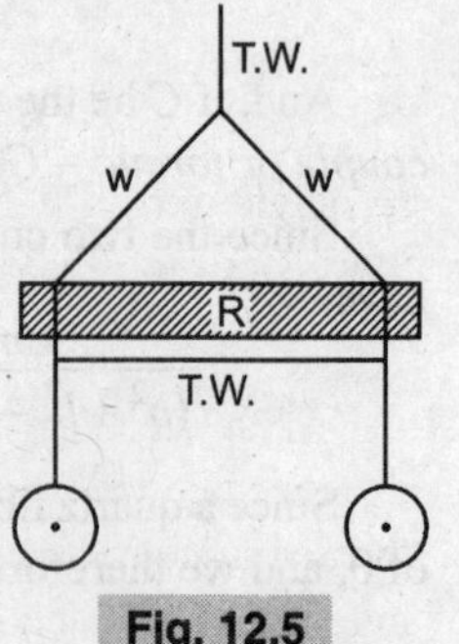

Fig. 12.5

It may be mentioned that the gold balls, first used by Heyl, were discarded by him when he found that in the near complete vacuum in the chamber, they absorbed mercury from the mercury gauges used to measure the pressure there. He next tried platinum balls, coated with lacquer, and finally preferred balls of optical glass in which any internal cavities could be easily detected visually.

Working. The suspension system (*i.e.*, the torsion rod together with the two small masses) was made to oscillate in the gravitational field of the two large masses which were first arranged with their centres in the same horizontal line with those of the smaller masses as shown in Fig. 12.6 (*a*) and then with the line joining their centres along the right bisector of the torsion rod, as shown in Fig. 12.6 (*b*), the two positions being referred to as the *near and* the *distant* positions respectively. The gravitational attraction obviously accelerates the oscillations in the first case and retards them in the second.

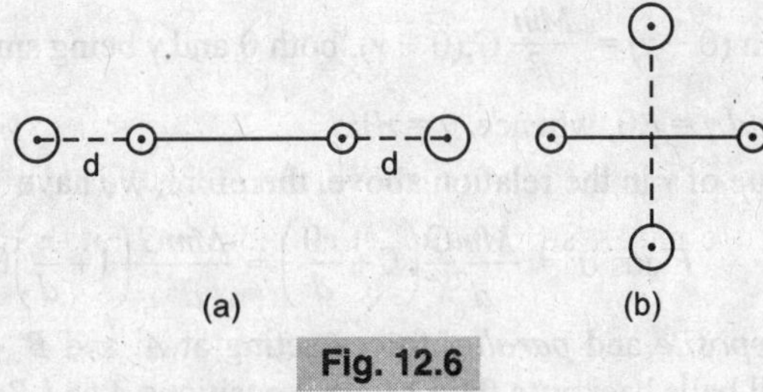

Fig. 12.6

Or, as a variation of this, the time-period of the suspended system was first noted with no other masses in the neighbourhood and then with the large masses in the *near position,* shown in Fig. 12.6 (*a*).

The system was set oscillating by bringing bottles of mercury near to the small masses for a while and then removing them. It was found that for an angular displacement of 4°, the system continued oscillating for about 20 hours. The usual scale and telescope method was used to observe the oscillations, the passage of the lines of the image of a scale across a vertical cross wire of the telescope being recorded automatically by a pen on a chronograph, with another pen marking down on it the second signals from a standard clock.

Calculation. From the time-periods of the suspended system in the near and distant positions, the value of G was obtained as indicated in brief outline below.

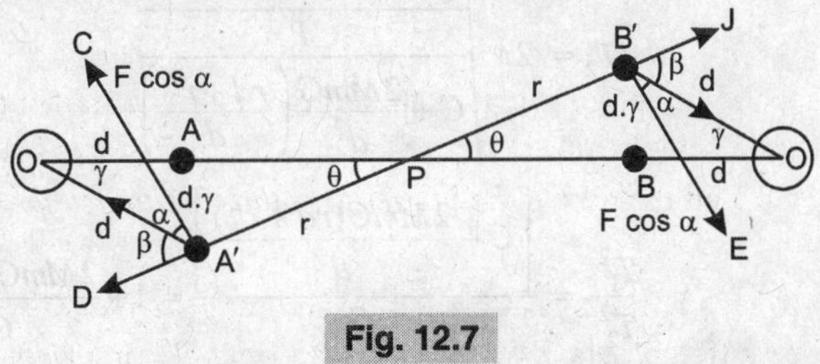

Fig. 12.7

Let T_1 be the time-period of the suspended system when the large masses are not yet brought in its neighbourhood. Then, if C be the couple or torque per unit twist of the suspension wire and I, the moment of intertia of the system about it, we have

$$T_1 = 2\pi\sqrt{I/C}.$$

With the large masses brought into the *near position*, as shown in Fig. 12.7, such that the distance between each pair of large and small masses is the same, say, d, the gravitational pull due to each large mass on the small mass near to it will clearly be $F = MmG/d^2$, where M and m are the magnitudes of each large mass and small mass respectively. The value of F remains unaffected due to each small mass being deflected through a small angle θ from its initial position A or B into the position A' or B'.

This force F will naturally be directed in either case from the centre of the small mass towards the centre of the neighbouring large mass, *i.e.*, along $A'O$ and $B'O'$ respectively. Resolving F into two rectangular components, along $A'B'$ (the line joining the centres of the two small masses in their displaced positions) and perpendicular to it, we have *component perpendicular to A′B′ (in either case)* $= F\cos\alpha = (MmG/a^2)\cos\alpha$, represented by $A'C$ and $B'E$ in the two cases respectively. where, $\angle OA'C = \angle O'B'E = \alpha$.

Since $\angle OA'D = \angle O'B'J = (90 - \alpha) = \beta$, we have

$F\cos\alpha = (MmG/d^2)\sin\beta$.

Now, since $\angle A'OP = \angle B'O'P = \gamma$, we have $\beta = (\theta + \gamma)$, And, therefore.

$$F\cos\alpha = \frac{Mm}{d^2}G.\sin(\theta+\gamma) = \frac{Mm}{d^2}G.(\theta+\gamma), \text{ both } \theta \text{ and } \gamma \text{ being small.}$$

Clearly, $A'A = B'B = d.\gamma = r.\theta$, whence, $\gamma = r\theta/d$.

Substituting this value of γ in the relation above, therefore, we have

$$F\cos\alpha = \frac{MmG}{d^2}\left(\theta+\frac{r\theta}{d}\right) = \frac{MmG}{d^2}\left(1+\frac{r}{d}\right)\theta.$$

These two *equal, opposite* and *parallel* forces acting at A' and B' obviously form a couple, tending to bring the small balls back into their original positions A and B respectively and, clearly,

$$\textit{moment of the couple} = \frac{MmG}{d^2}\left(1+\frac{r}{d}\right)\theta.2r \qquad [\because A'B' = 2r].$$

And, if C be the torsional couple per unit twist of the suspension wire, the restoring couple also, tending to bring the small balls back into their original positions after being deflected through angle θ, is equal to $C\theta$. So that,

total couple acting on the suspended system

$$= C\theta + \frac{MmG}{d^2}\left(1+\frac{r}{d}\right)\theta.2r = \left[C+\frac{2MmG}{d^2}\left(\frac{rd+r^2}{d}\right)\right]\theta.$$

If, therefore, T_2 be the time-period of the suspended system *now*, we have

$$T_2 = 2\pi\sqrt{\frac{I}{C+\frac{2MmG}{d^2}\left(\frac{rd+r^2}{d}\right)}}$$

And thus,
$$\frac{T_1^2}{T_2^2} = \frac{\left[C+\frac{2MmG(rd+r^2)}{d^3}\right]}{C} = 1+\frac{2MmG(rd+r^2)}{Cd^2}.$$

Or,
$$\frac{2MmG(rd+r^2)}{Cd^2} = \frac{T_1^2}{T_2^2}-1 = \frac{T_1^2-T_2^2}{T_2^2},$$

whence,
$$G = \frac{T_1^2-T_2^2}{T_2^2}\cdot\frac{Cd^2}{2Mm(rd+r^2)}.$$

The mean results (for the different masses, mentioned earlier) gave the value of G to be 6.670×10^{-8} dyne-cm^2/gm^2 in *C.G.S.* units and 6.670×10^{-11} newton-metre^2/kg^2 in *M.K.S.* (or *SI*) units.

Birge later estimated the probable error in the result to be 0.005. So that, the *true value of G* (obtained to date) = $(6.67 \pm 0.005) \times 10^{-8}$ dyne-cm^2/gm^2 or $(6.67 \pm 0.005) \times 10^{-11}$ newton-metre^2/kg^2.

12.4 DENSITY OF THE EARTH

The weight of a body on the surface of the earth (or the gravitational force of attraction on it due to the earth) is, as we know, given by *mg*, where *m* is the mass of the body and *g*, the acceleration due to gravity at the place. If *M* be the *mass of the earth* and *R*, *its radius,* this gravitational force of attraction, in accordance with Netwton's law of gravitation, is equal to MmG/R^2, We, therefore, have $-mg = -MmG/R^2$. *Or,* $g = MG/R^2$, or, $M = gR^2/G$.

Taking the earth to be a homogeneous sphere and hence of volume $V = 4\pi R^3/3$ and its density to be Δ, we have $M = V\Delta = 4\pi R^3\Delta/3 = gR^2/G$, whence,

density of the earth, $\Delta = 3g/4\pi RG$ and may be easily evaluated.

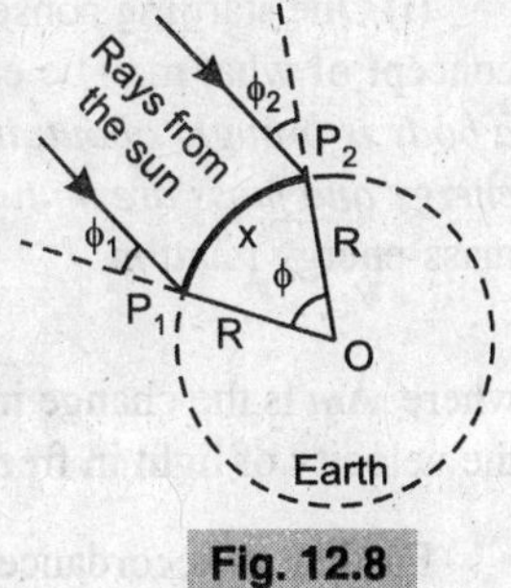

Fig. 12.8

N.B. The radius of the earth (R) may be easily estimated by choosing two points P_1 and P_2 on the earth's surface, a known distance x apart and in the same latitude (Fig. 12.8) and measuring the altitudes of the sun at both the points *simultaneously* at about 12.0 noon. If these be ϕ_1 and ϕ_2 at P_1 and P_2 respectively, the angle subtended by them at the centre of the earth is clerly $\phi_1 \approx \phi_2 = \phi$, say. So that, $\tan \phi = x/R$. Or, since $\phi = (\phi_1 \sim \phi_2)$ is small, we have $\phi = x/R$, whence, $R = x/\phi = x/(\phi_1 \sim \phi_2)$.

Taking the value of G to be 6.6576×10^{-8} dynes-cm²/gm², (as found by *Boys*), *the density of the earth,* Δ, works out to be 5.5270 gm/c.c. and with Heyl's value of G(*i.e.*, 6.670×10^{-8} dyne-cm²/gm²) it comes to (5.515 ± 0.004) gm/*c.c.*

The most probable value of Δ is, however, taken to be 5.5247 gm/*c.c.* and since the density of the outer layers of the earth is found to be only 2.7 gm/c.c., obviously, the density of the inner layers must be very much greater than 5.5247 gm/c.c.

Interestingly enough, Newton had intuitively guessed the probable density of the earth to lie between 5 and 6 gm/c.c.

12.5 MASS OF THE EARTH AND THE SUN

Knowing the density of the earth, it is but an easy step to obtain its mass, equal to *volume* × *density*.

The earth, however, is not actually a sphere but a spheroid of revolution about its polar axis; so that, if its equatorial and polar radii be R_1 and R_2 respectively, we have

$$\textit{its volume} = \frac{4}{3}\pi R_1^2 R_2 \text{ and hence } \textit{its mass} = \frac{4}{3}\pi R_1^2 R_2 \Delta.$$

Now, taking the orbit of rotation of the earth around the sun to be circular (though, in actual fact, it is elliptical), of radius r, it is clear that the centripetal force acting on the earth towards the centre of its orbit (*i.e.*, the centre of the sun) is $M_C r\,\omega^2$,* where M_C is the mass of the earth and ω, its angular velocity = $(2\pi / 365 \times 24 \times 60 \times 60)$ radians/sec.

This centripetal force is obviously supplied by the *force of gravitational attraction exerted by the sun on the earth* = $M_{CMg}G/r^2$, where M_S is the mass of the sun. We, therefore, have

$$M_e M_S\, G/r^2 = M_e r\omega^2, \text{ whence,}$$

$$\textit{mass of the sun, } M_S = r^3\omega^2/G \text{ and can be easily evaluated.}$$

This, incidentally, enables us to obtain an expression for the time-period of the earth's revolution, (T, say) around the sun in terms of the mass of the sun and the radius of the earth's orbit. For $\omega^2 = M_S G/r^3$ and, therefore, $\omega = \sqrt{M_S G/r^3}$.

Hence, $$T = 2\pi/\omega = 2\pi\sqrt{r^3/M_S G}.$$

12.6 LAW OF GRAVITATION AND THE THEORY OF RELATIVITY

As mentioned already, it was only when *Einstein* came forward with his *theory of relativity* that the infallibility of Newton's law of gravitation began to be seriously questioned and it came to be realised that it was only an approximation, although an extremely close one, to the true or a more fundamental law of gravitation.

A detailed discussion of this new law is beyond our present scope but we shall consider here how Newton's law lays itself open to criticism in view of some of the salient points of Einstein's theory of relativity.

---

* Or, we could take it to be $M_C v^2/r$, where v is the speed of the earth in its orbit round the sun. (See worked example).

(*i*) One startling consequence of Einstein's theory, as we have already seen in Chapter 3, is the concept of what may be called the *inertia of energy, viz.*, that *whenever a change in the energy of a body is brought about, it is accompanied by a corresponding change in its mass.* In other words, *energy and mass are mutually convertible,* the relation between the two being given by the famous mass-energy relation

$$\Delta mc^2 = \Delta E,$$

where Δm is the change in the mass of the body corresponding to a change ΔE in its energy and c, the velocity of light in free space (equal to 3×10^{10} cm/sec).

Further, in accordance with this theory $m = m_0/\sqrt{1-u^2/c^2}$, where m is the mass of a body when moving with velocity u, called its *moving mass* and m_0 its mass when at rest, called its *rest mass.*

Thus, the mass of a body is different when in motion from that when at rest, *i.e.*, it changes with the velocity of the body, and *Newton* has not specified which one of them is to be used in his formula for gravitational attraction. This is, indeed, a noticeable omission.

Another consequence of the theory, as we have seen in Chapter 3, is that the numerical value of the distance between two points varies according to the system of space-time coordinates chosen. Thus, the distance between them varies with the situation of the observer making the measurement.

The effect of these two discrepancies is, of course, only very slight but it is there all the same. Einstein has taken both these factors into account in the formulation of his law of gravitation which satisfactorily explains the deviations from the Newtonian law.

Thus, the correct law of gravitation is the one due to *Einstein*, which is true for both strong and weak gravitational fields. However, although Newton's law is true only for weak gravitational fields, it is a most satisfactorily close approximation to the correct law for most of our ordinary purposes (engineering and others), any slight discrepancies becoming noticeable only at extremely small distances.

12.7 GRAVITATIONAL FIELD–INTENSITY OF THE FIELD

The area round about a body within which its force of gravitational attraction is perceptible (no other body being near about it) is called its *gravitational field.*

The *intensity* (or *strength*), E, of the gravitational field of a particle of mass m at a point distant r from it is the *force experienced by a unit mass placed at that point in the field* (it being assumed that the presence of the unit mass does not in any way affect the gravitational field of mass m).

Thus, $E = -\dfrac{m}{r^2} G\vec{r}$, where $\vec{r}$ is the unit vector along the direction of $\vec{r}$.

Or, $$E = -mG/r^2.$$

It is thus clear that the intensity of the field is directed towards the particle, *i.e.*, opposite to the vector $\vec{r}$.

The intensity of the field at a point is quite often referred to simply as the *field at the point*, and may also be defined as the *space rate of change of gravitational potential* (or the *potential gradient*) at the point, *i.e.*, $E = dV/dr$, where dV is the small change of gravitational potential for a small distance dr. (See §12.8)

12.8 GRAVITATIONAL POTENTIAL AND GRAVITATIONAL POTENTIAL ENERGY

The gravitational potential V at a point distant **r** from a body of mass m is equal to *the amount of work done in moving a unit mass from infinity* (*where the gravitational force and potential are zero*) *to that point.* Thus,

$$V = -\int_{\infty}^{r} \mathbf{E}d\mathbf{r} = -\int_{\infty}^{r} \frac{m}{r^2} G = -\frac{m}{r} G.$$

Clearly, *this is also the potential energy of unit mass at the point distant* **r** *form the body of mass m*. So that *the gravitational potential at a point is equal to the potential energy of unit mass at that point.*

It follows, therefore, that the potential energy of a mass m' at the point in question will be $U = m'V = -mm'G/r$.

It will be noted that the *gravitational potential (V) and the potential energy (U) are always negative in sign, their highest value being zero at infinity*. This is clearly a consequence of the fact that in the case of gravitation we come across only forces of attraction and never those of repulsion.

12.9 VELOCITY OF ESCAPE FROM THE EARTH

Ordinarily, as we know, when a body, say, a rifle bullet, is projected upwards, it comes down to the earth due to the gravitational pull of the earth on it. If, however, it can be given a velocity which can take it beyond the gravitational field of the earth, it will never come back and escape into space. This velocity of the body is, therefore, called the *velocity of escape*. Let us try to obtain its value.

If m be the mass of the body, M, that of the earth and R, its radius, clearly, the gravitational force acting on the body at a distance x from the centre of the earth is mMG/x^2.

Therefore, work done by the body against the gravitational field of the earth in moving upwards through distance $dx = (mMG/x^2)dx$.

Therefore, total work done by the body in escaping away from the surface of the earth, *i.e.*, in moving away to an infinite distance from it $= \int_R^\infty \frac{mMG}{x^2}dx = \frac{mM}{R}G = m \times$ *the gravitational potential on the surface of the earth.*

If v_e be the initial or the *escape velocity* that thus takes the body away from its surface, into space, the *initial kinetic energy of the body* $= \frac{1}{2}mv_e^2$. This must obviously be equal to the work done by the body in escaping away from the earth. We therefore, have

$$\frac{1}{2}mv_e^2 = mMG/R. \text{ Or, } v_e^2 = MG/R. \text{ Or, } v_e = \sqrt{2MG/R} \quad \ldots(i)$$

Or, since $MG/R^2 = g$, we also have

$$v_e = \sqrt{(2MG/R^2)R} = \sqrt{2gR}. \quad \ldots(ii)$$

Thus, *velocity of escape from the surface of the earth,*

$$v_e = \sqrt{2MG/R} = \sqrt{2gR}.$$

Substituting the values of M, G and R in relation (*i*) or of g and R in relation (*ii*), we have velocity of escape,

$v_e = 1.19 \times 10^5$ cm/sec ≈ 11.2 km/sec or, approximately 25000 miles/hr.

The smallest value of the velocity of escape (v_e) is for the planet *Mercury*, being only 4.2 km/sec and the highest, *viz.*, 61 km/sec, for the planet *Jupiter*, not to speak of the *sun* for which it is as high as 618 km/sec but from which *only atoms*, and no other bodies or rockets, can escape.

Velocity to become a satellite of the earth. Let us now calculate the velocity with which the body should be projected from the surface of the earth so as to revolve *close* around it, *i.e.*, to become its *satellite*. Let it be v_o. Then, clearly, the centrifugal force on the body, tending to take it away from the surface of the earth will be $\frac{mv_0^2}{R}$, where R, the radius; around the earth, is practically the same as the radius of the earth, (it being close to the earth). This must obviously be just balanced by the gravitational pull mMG/R^2 on it due to the earth. So that, we have

$$mv_0^2/R = mMG/R^2. \text{ Or, } v_0^2 = MG/R. \text{ Or, } v_o = \sqrt{MG/R}.$$

Or, since $MG/R^2 = g$, we also have $v_o = \sqrt{(MG/R^2)R} = \sqrt{gR}$.

Thus, *velocity of projection of a body to becomes a satellite of the earth,*

$$v_o = \sqrt{MG/R} = \sqrt{gR}.$$

Clearly, therefore, $v_o/v_o = \sqrt{gR/2gR} = 1/\sqrt{2}$.

Or, $v_o = v_o/\sqrt{2} = 0.7073\ v_o$.

The following table shows at a glance how the path of a satellite of the earth depends upon its velocity of projection v in relation to v_o and v_e.

Velocity of satellite	Nature of path
(*i*) $v = v_o$	*Circular path around the earth*
(*ii*) $v < v_o$	*Elliptical path–Return to earth*
(*iii*) $v > v_o$ *but* $< v_o$	*Elliptical path around the earth*
(*iv*) $v = v_o$	*Parabolic path – Escape from the earth*
(*v*) $v > v_o$	*Hyperbolic path – Escape from the earth*

When the orbit of the satellite is elliptical, the *closest point* to the earth is referred to as the **perigee** and the farthest point as the **apogee**, the speed of the satellite being the highest, *i.e.*, $\sqrt{(GM/a)\left(\frac{1+e}{1-e}\right)}$ at the former, and lowest, *i.e.*, $\sqrt{(GM/a)\left(\frac{1-e}{1+e}\right)}$, at the latter point, where a and e are respectively the *semi-major axis* and the *eccentricity* of the ellipse.

12.10 VELOCITY OF ESCAPE FROM THE SOLAR SYSTEM

If a body of mass m be situated on the earth in the gravitational field of the sun, its potential energy, say, $U = \frac{M_s m}{R_s} G$, where M_s is the mass of the sun $= 1.33 \times 10^{33}$ gm and R_s, the distance between the sun and the earth $= 1.49 \times 10^{13}$ cm.

In order that the body may escape from the solar system, it should be projected with a velocity v (*i.e.*, its *escape velocity* should be v) such that its kinetic energy $\frac{1}{2}mv^2 = U = M_s mG/R_s$, whence,

its *escape velocity* $v = \sqrt{\frac{2M_s}{R_s} G} = \sqrt{\frac{2 \times 1.33 \times 10^{33}}{1.49 \times 10^{13}} \times 6.67 \times 10^{-8}} = 4.2 \times 10^6$ cm/sec or 42 km/sec.

If, however, we take into account the rotation of the earth around the sun, *i.e.* the fact that the earth has a relative velocity of 3×10^6 cm or 30 km/sec with respect to the sun, the escape velocity $v = 42–30 = 12$ km/sec.

12.11 AN INTERESTING CONSEQUENCE OF ESCAPE VELOCITY

An obvious, interesting and important consequence of escape velocity is that it enables us to form an idea as to the probable nature of the atmosphere on other planets as also, of course, on our own. For, clearly, the nearer the average velocity of the molecules of a gas to the velocity of escape, the greater the chances of their escaping away from the upper regions of the atmosphere which may thus get completely denuded of them in course of time.

Thus, for example, on the moon, landing on which has now been effected, the escape velocity is only 2.4×10^5 cm/sec or 2.4 km/sec as against 11.2 km/sec on the earth. No wonder, then, that all the constituents of the atmosphere (as we know it here on earth), *like oxygen, nitrogen, carbon dioxide* and *water vapour*, the *root mean square velocities* of which (at 0°C) lie between 0.4×10^5 and 0.8×10^5 cm/sec – not to speak of *hydrogen* and *helium*, whose *r.m.s.* velocities are very much greater, about 2×10^5 cm/sec – should all be absent from its surface and that the latter two lighter gases (*hydrogen* and *helium*) should be so rare even in our own atmosphere on the earth. Again, the presence of these two latter gases in relative abundance in the atmosphere of the sun should not surprise us in view of the much stronger gravitational field of the sun and consequently a much higher escape velocity of 618 km/sec there.

12.12 EQUIPOTENTIAL SURFACE

A surface, *at all the points of which the gravitational potential is the same*, is called an *equipotential surface.*

Thus, as we shall presently see, the gravitational potential at all points on the surface of a spherical shell is the same, *viz.*, $-MG/R$, where M is the mass of the shell and R, its radius'. The surface of the shell is thus an *equipotential surface.*

A consequence of this is that the difference of potential between any two points on such a surface being *zero, no work is done against the gravitational force in moving a unit, or any other, mass along it.* This means, in other words, that there is *no component of the gravitational field along an equipotential force* or that *the field is at every point perpendicular to it.*

Thus, consider two points P and Q, a small distance δr apart, on an equipotential surface AB (Fig. 12.9), and let the intensity of the gravitational field at P be E, directed along PR at an angle θ with PQ. Then clearly, component of the field along $PQ = E \cos\theta$ and, therefore, work done in moving a unit mass from P to $Q = E\cos\theta.\,\delta r$.

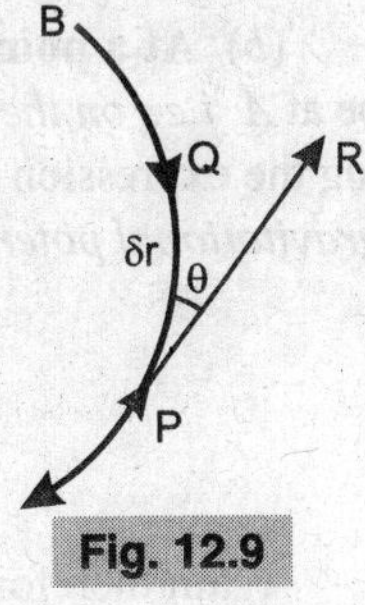

Fig. 12.9

Since P and Q lie on an equipotential surface, the work done, *i.e.*, $E \cos\theta.\,\delta r = 0$ and since neither E nor δr is zero, we have $\cos\theta = 0$ or $\theta = 90°$, *i.e.*, the field is directed along the perpendicular to the surface at P. And, obviously, what is true of the point P, is also true of all other points on the surface AB. Thus, *the direction of the field at every points on an equipotential surface is perpendicular to the surface at that point.*

We shall now proceed to calculate gravitational fields and potentials in particular cases.

12.13 GRAVITATIONAL POTENTIAL AND FIELD DUE TO A SPHERICAL SHELL

1. Gravitational potential

(*a*) **At a point outside the shell.** Let P be a point, distant r from the centre O of a spherical shell of *radius R* (Fig. 12.10) and *surface density* (*i.e.*, mass per unit area of surface) σ.

Join OP and cut out a slice $CEFD$ in the form of a ring by two planes CD and EF close to each other and perpendicular to the radius OA of the shell, and let angle EOP be θ and the small angle $COE = d\theta$.

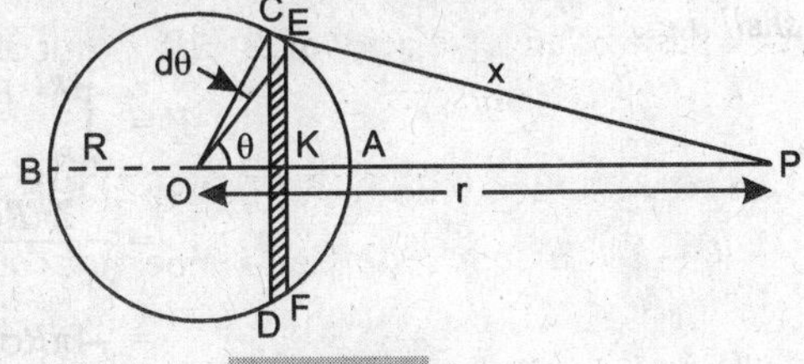

Fig. 12.10

Clearly, radius of the ring, $EK = OE \sin\theta = R\sin\theta$, so that its *circumference* $= 2\pi R\sin\theta$ and its *width* $= CE = R\,d\theta$.

Therefore, *surface area of the ring = circumference × width* $= 2\pi R \sin\theta.\, R\,d\theta$ and hence its *mass* $= 2\pi R\sin\theta.R\,d\theta\,\sigma = 2\pi R^2 \sin\theta\,d\theta\,\sigma$.

If $EP = x$, every point of the slice or the ring is at a distance x from P and, therefore, *Potential at P due to the ring*, say,

$$dV = -\frac{mass\ of\ slice}{x}G = -\frac{2\pi R^2 \sin\theta d\theta\sigma}{x}G. \quad ...(i) \quad [\S\ 12.8]$$

Now, in Δ OEP, $EP^2 = OE^2 + OP^2 - 2OE.OP\cos\theta$ Or, $x^2 = R^2 + r^2 - 2Rr\cos\theta$, which, on differentiation, gives $2xdx = 0 + 0 + 2Rr\sin\theta\, d\theta$, whence, $x = Rr\sin\theta d\theta/dx$.

[R and r being constants]

$$dV = \frac{2\pi R^2 \sin\theta d\theta\sigma}{Rr\sin\theta d\theta} G dx = -\frac{2\pi R\sigma G}{r} dx.$$

The integral of this between the limits $x = AP = (r - R)$ and $x = BP = (r + R)$ then clearly gives the potential V at P due to the whole shell. Thus,

$$V = \int_{(r-R)}^{(r+R)} -\frac{2\pi R\sigma G}{r} dx = -\frac{2\pi R\sigma G}{r}\int_{(r-R)}^{(r+R)} dx$$

$$= -\frac{2\pi R\sigma G}{r}[x]_{(r-R)}^{(r+R)} = -\frac{2\pi R\sigma G}{r} 2R = -\frac{4\pi R^2\sigma G}{r}.$$

Clearly, $4\pi R^2$ is the *surface area* of the shell and, therefore $4\pi R^2\sigma$, its mass M. We, therefore, have *gravitational potential at P due to the whole shell*, $V = -\frac{M}{r}G$, *i.e.*, the same as due to a mass M at O.

In other words, *the mass of the shell behaves as though it were concentrated at its centre.*

(*b*) **At a point on the surface of the shell.** In Fig. 12.10 above, if we imagine the point P to be at A, *i.e., on the surface of the shell itself,* we obtain the gravitational potential there by integrating the expression for dV (obtained above) between the limits $x = PA = 0$ and $x = PB = 2R$. So that, *gravitational potential at a point on the surface of the shell, i.e.,*

$$V = \int_o^{2R} -\frac{2\pi R\sigma G}{r} dx = -\frac{2\pi R\sigma G}{r}[x]_o^{2R}$$

$$= -\frac{4\pi R^2\sigma G}{r} = -\frac{M}{r}G = -\frac{M}{R}G. \qquad [\because \text{ here } r = R]$$

Again therefore, the mass of the shell behaves as though it were concentrated at its centre.

(*c*) **At a point inside the shell.** Let the point P now lie anywhere inside the spherical shell (Fig. 12.11), such that $OP = r$. Then, proceeding as in case (*a*) above, we have *potential at P due to the ring CEFD*, *i.e.*,

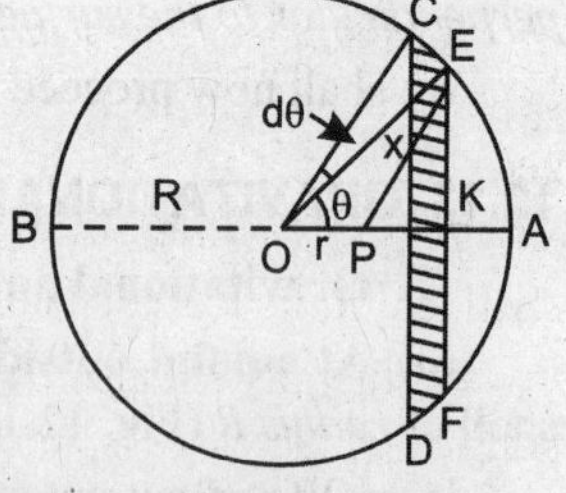

Fig. 12.11

$$dV = -2\pi\frac{R\sigma G}{r}dx.$$

Differentiating this expression between the limits $x = PA = (R - r)$ *and* $x = PB = (R + r)$, we therefore have *potential* at *P due to the whole shell. i.e.,*

$$V = \int_{(R-r)}^{(R+r)} -\frac{2\pi RsG}{r}dx$$

$$= -\frac{2\pi R\sigma G}{r}[x]_{(R-r)}^{(R+r)} = -\frac{2\pi R\sigma G}{r}\cdot 2r$$

$$= -4\pi R\sigma G.$$

Or, multiplying and dividing by R, we have

$$V = -\frac{4\pi R^2\sigma G}{R} = -\frac{M}{R}G, \qquad [\because\ 4\pi R^2\sigma = M]$$

the same as at a point on the surface of the shell.

Since the point P has been taken *anywhere* inside the shell, it follows that the *gravitational potential at all points inside a spherical shell is the same and is numerically equal to the value of the gravitational potential on the surface of the shell itself, which is also its maximum (negative) value.*

2. Gravitational field

(*a*) **At a point outside the shell.** Since the potential at a point *outside the shell*, distant *r* from its centre (Fig. 12.10), *i.e.*, when $r > R$, is given by $V = -MG/r$, we have *intensity of the gravitational field at the point*, $E = dV/dr = -\frac{d}{dr}\left(-\frac{M}{r}G\right) = -\frac{M}{r^2}G$r.

Or, $$E = -\frac{M}{R^2}G,$$

i.e., the same as though the whole mass of the shell were concentrated at its centre.

Force on a point mass *m*. If instead of a unit mass at *P* (Fig. 12.10), we have a point-mass *m* there, its potential energy will be given by $U = mV = -mMG/r$ and the force acting on it by $F = -dU/dr = -(mM/r^2)G$, the same as due to a mass *M* at *O*.

Thus, *for all points lying outside it (i.e., for all values of $r > R$), a spherical shell behaves as though its whole mass where concentrated at its centre.*

(*b*) **At a point on the outer surface of the shell.** As we know, the gravitational potential at a point on the outer surface of the shell is given by $V = -MG/R$.

Therefore, *intensity of the gravitational field at the point, i.e.,*

$$E = -\frac{d}{dr}\left(-\frac{MG}{R}\right) = -\frac{M}{R^2}G,$$

again, as though the mass of the shell were concentrated at its centre?

(*c*) **At a point inside the shell.** We have seen under 12.13(*c*) above that the gravitational potential at all points inside a spherical shell is the same.

Now, the gravitational field at a point is given by the space rate of change of potential (*i.e.*, the potential gradient) there. Therefore, *field at the point is given* by $E = -dV/dr$.

Since *V* is constant for all points inside the shell, $dV/dr = 0$, *i.e.*, the field in the interior of the shell is zero at all points. In other words, *there is no gravitational field inside a spherical shell.*

Force acting on a mass m at a point inside the shell. Since the gravitational field inside a spherical shell is *zero*, the force acting on a unit mass or any mass *m* at any point inside the shell is zero. This may also be seen from the following:

Considering a *mass m* at *P*, we have its *P.E.* $= U = mV = -mMG/R$, where *M* is the mass of the shell and *R*, its radius. And, therefore, force acting on mass *m*, *i.e.*, $F = -dU/dR = 0$.

Further, it will also be readily seen that whereas the gravitational field at a point on the inner surface of the shell is *zero*, that at a point on its outer surface is $-MG/R^2$, *i.e.*, there is a sudden change in the value of the field from $-MG/R^2$ on its outer surface to *zero* on its inner surface. *There is thus a definite, sharp discontinuity in the gravitational intensity at the surface of a spherical shell* [*See* Fig. 12.12 (*a*)].

12.14 COMPARISON OF GRAVITATIONAL POTENTIAL AND FIELD DUE TO A SPHERICAL SHELL WITH ELECTROSTATIC POTENTIAL AND FIELD TO A CHARGED SPHERICAL SHELL

We have seen under § 5.7 that the *electrostatic potential* due to a charge *Q* at a distance *r* from it is given by $V = Q/kr$, where *k* is the *dielectric constant* of the intervening medium. And, therefore, intensity of the electrostatic field there is given by

$$E = dV/dr = \frac{Q}{kr^2}\cdot r. \quad \text{Or, } E = \frac{Q}{kr^2}.$$

For *air*, $k = 1$ and, therefore, *in air*, $V = Q/r$ and $E = Q/r^2$.

Considering the case of a spherical shall carrying a charge Q, and proceeding exactly as in deducing an expression for gravitational potential due to a spherical shell, (§ 12.13,1) and taking σ as the *surface density of the charge* on the shell, (equal to $Q/4\pi R^2$), the *electrostatic potential at a point distant r from the centre of the shell*, where $r>R$ (*i.e.*, the point lies outside the shell) is given by $V = Q/kr$ and the *intensity of the electrostatic field* at the point, given by

$$E = \frac{Q}{kr^2}r \quad \text{or, } E = \frac{Q}{kr^2},$$

Thus, M and G in the case of gravitational potential and field are here replaced by Q and $1/k$ respectively and the negative sign by a positive one.

In case the intervening medium between the spherical shell and the point in question be *air*, $k = 1$ and, therefore, $V = Q/r$ and $E = Q/r^2$.

And, at a point *inside the shell, i.e.*, when $r = R$, the potential due to the shell is given by $V = Q/R$, *the same as on the surface of the shell* and the intensity of the electrostatic field there is, therefore, $E = dV/dr = 0$, because all points inside the shell are at the same potential.

If now we plot gravitational potential (V) due to a spherical shell of mass M and radius R, against distance (r) from its centre, we obtain a curve of the form shown in Fig. 12.12 (a), indicating that the gravitational potential *inside the shell* (*i.e.*, for $r < R$) has the maximum negative value, $-MG/R$ but *outside the shell* (*i.e.*, for $r > R$), the $-ve$ value goes on decreasing, or the gravitational potential goes on increasing with distance r from the centre, tending to its *highest value, zero*, as $r \to \infty$.

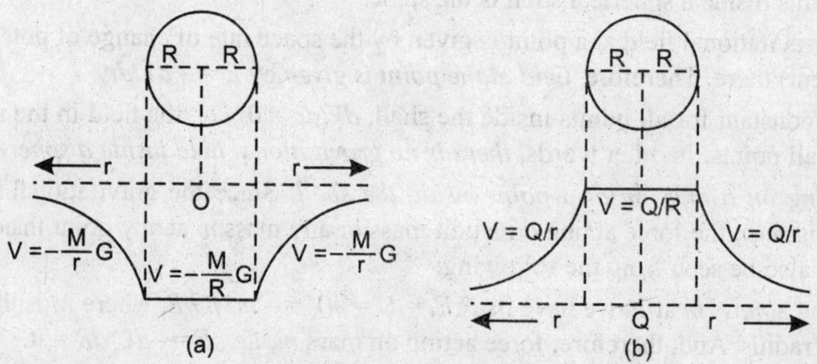

Fig. 12.12

On the other hand, if we plot electrostatic potential (V) due to a spherical shell, of radius R and carrying a charge Q, against distance (r) from the centre of the shell, we obtain a curve of the form shown in Fig. 12.12 (b), which is the *reciprocal* of that in Fig. 12.12 (a), indicating that *inside the shell* (*i.e.*, for $r < R$) the potential has its maximum value, Q/R, but *outside the shell*, (*i.e.*, for $r > R$) it goes on progressively decreasing, tending to *lowest value*, zero, as $r \to \infty$.

Similarly, if we plot intensities of gravitational field and electrostatic field against distance r from the centre of the shell, we obtain curves such as those shown in Figs. 12.13 (a) and (b) respectively.

Curve (a) shows that the intensity of the *gravitational field inside the shell* (*i.e.* for $r < R$) is *zero* at all points; *just outside the shell*, it falls to its highest negative value, $-MG/R^3$ and then becomes $-MG/r^2$, *i.e.*, its negative value goes on decreasing , or the intensity goes on increasing with distance r (where $r > R$), tending to its *highest value* 0 as $r \to \infty$.

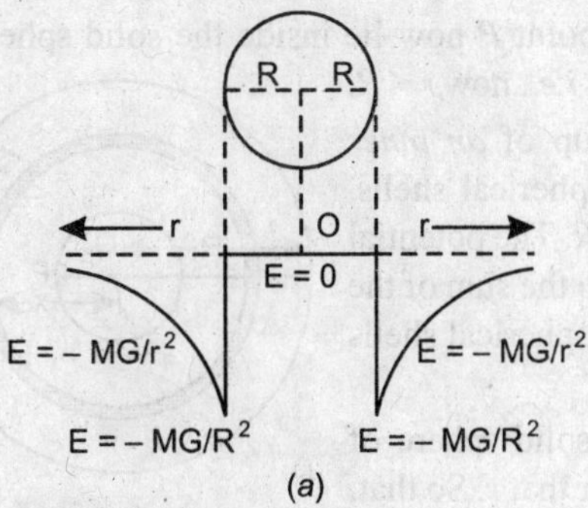

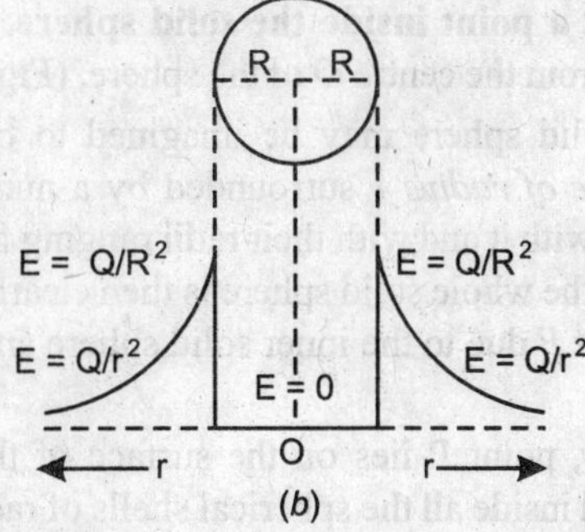

Fig. 12.13

Curve (*b*), on the other hand, shows that the intensity of the *electrostatic field inside the shell* (*i.e.* for $r < R$) is *zero* at all points but at the surface of the shell itself it suddenly rises to its highest value Q/R^2 and thereafter becomes Q/r^2, *i.e.*, goes on falling with distance r (where $r > R$), tending to its lowest value, 0, as $r \to \infty$.

Again, if we plot gravitational potential energy (U) of a mass m at a point P against its distance r from the centre of the shell, we obtain a curve identical in form with the one in Fig. 12.12 (*a*). And, if we plot *P.E.* of a charge Q' at a point P against its distance r from the centre of the shell, we obtain a curve identical in form with that in Fig. 12.12 (*b*).

And, similarly, the graph between gravitational force on a mass m and its distance r from the centre of the shell is of the same form as that in Fig. 12.13 (*a*) and that between electrostatic force on a change Q' and its distance r form the centre of the shell, of the same form as that in Fig. 12.13 (*b*)

12.15 GRAVITATIONAL POTENTIAL AND FIELD DUE TO A SOLID SPHERE

1. Gravitational potential

(*a*) **At a point outside the solid sphere.** Let P be a point distant r from the centre O of a solid sphere, of mass M and radius R, outside the sphere, *i.e*, with $r > R$, (Fig. 12.14), where the gravitational potential due to the sphere is to be determined.

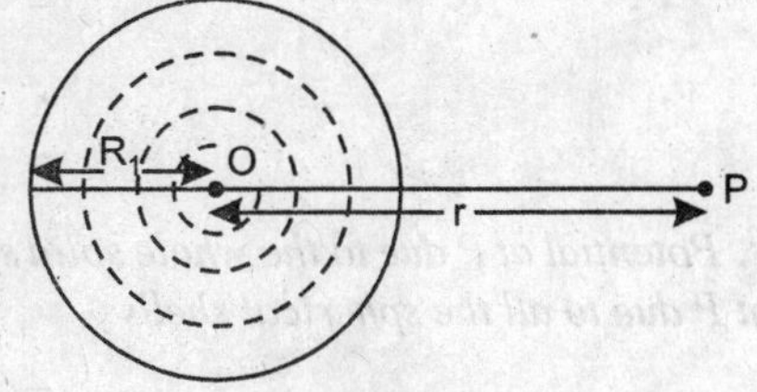

Fig. 12.14

Imagine the sphere to consist of a number of spherical shells (shown dotted), one inside the other, concentric with the sphere, and of masses m_1, m_2, m_3. etc. Then, as we have seen under §12.13, 1 (*a*), above, *gravitational potential* at P due to each spherical shell = – (*mass of spherical shell*) × G/R. So that potentials at P due to different shells are $-m_1\, G/R$, $-\, m_3\, G/R/m_3\, G/R$ etc. And, therefore, *potential at P due to all the shells constituting the sphere, i.e., due to the whole solid sphere* is given by $V = (m_1 + m_2 + m_3 + \ldots)G/R$, *because potential is a scalar quantity.*

Clearly, $(m_1 + m_2 + m_3 + \ldots) = M$. the mass of the solid sphere. So that,

gravitational potential at P due to the solid sphere, i.e., $V = -\dfrac{M}{r}G.$

Again, therefore, *the sphere behaves as though its whole mass is concentrated at its centre.*

(*b*) **At a point on the surface of the solid sphere.** Clearly, if the point P lies on the surface of the solid sphere, we have $r = R$, the radius of the sphere.

So that, *gravitational potential at a point on the surface of a solid sphere* = $-\dfrac{M}{R}G.$

(*c*) **At a point inside the solid sphere.** Let the point P now lie inside the solid sphere at a distance r from the centre O of the sphere, (Fig. (12.15), *i.e.*, now $r < R$.

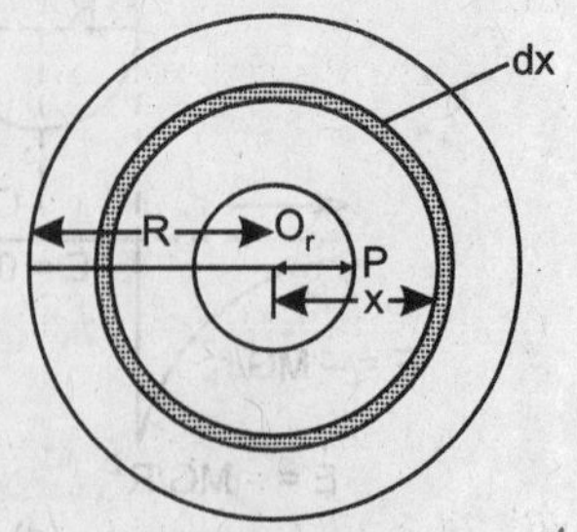

Fig. 12.15

The solid sphere may be imagined to be made up of *an inner solid sphere of radius r* surrounded by a number of spherical shells, concentric with it and with their radii ranging from r to R. The potential at P due to the whole solid sphere is then clearly equal to the sum of the potentials at P due to the inner solid sphere and all the spherical shells outside it.

Clearly, point P lies on the surface of the inner solid sphere of radius r and inside all the spherical shells of radii greater that r. So that, *potential at P due to the inner solid sphere of radius r.*

$$= -\frac{\text{mass of the sphere}}{r}G = -\frac{4}{3}\pi r^3\rho G/r = -\frac{4}{3}\pi r^2\rho G,$$

because mass of the inner solid sphere $= \frac{4}{3}\pi r^2\rho$, where ρ is the *volume density* of the sphere.

To determine the potential at P due to all the outer shells, let us consider one such shell of radius x and thickness dx, *i.e.*, of *volume = area × thickness* $= 4\pi x^2 dx$ and hence of *mass* $= 4\pi x^2 dx\rho$. Since potential at a point inside a shell is the same as that at a point on its surface [§ 12.13, 1 (*c*)], we have

$$\textit{potential at P due to this shell} = -\frac{4\pi x^2 dx\rho}{x}G = -4\pi x dx\rho G.$$

$\therefore$ *Potential at P due to all the shells*

$$= \int_r^R -4\pi\rho G x dx$$

$$= -4\pi\rho G\int_r^R x dx = -4\pi\rho G\left[\frac{x^2}{2}\right]_r^R$$

$$= -4\pi\rho G\left(\frac{R^2 - r^2}{2}\right)^* = -\frac{4}{3}\pi\rho G.\frac{3(R^2 - r^2)}{2}$$

$$= -\frac{4}{3}\pi\rho G\frac{(3R^2 - 3r^2)}{2}$$

$\therefore$ *Potential at P due to the whole solid sphere = potential at P due to inner solid sphere + potential at P due to all the spherical shells*

$$= -\frac{4}{3}\pi r^2\rho G - \frac{4}{3}\pi\rho G\left(\frac{3R^2 - 3r^2}{2}\right)$$

$$= -\frac{4}{3}\pi\rho G\left(r^2 + \frac{3R^2}{2} - \frac{3r^2}{2}\right) = -\frac{4}{3}\pi\rho G\left(\frac{3R^2 - r^2}{2}\right)$$

$$= -\frac{4}{3}\pi R^2\rho G\left(\frac{3R^2 - r^2}{2R^3}\right). \quad \text{[Multiplying and dividing by } R^3\text{]}$$

Clearly, $\frac{4}{3}\pi R^3\rho$ is the mass of the whole solid sphere *i.e.*, M.

$\therefore$ *Gravitational potential at P due to the solid sphere, i.e.,*

$$V = -\frac{M(3R^2 - r^2)}{2R^3}G.$$

---

* This expression is equal to $-2\pi\rho G(R^2 - r^2)$; so that potential at P due to all the shells is $-2\pi\rho G(R^2 - r^2)$ and, therefore, *potential at P due to the whole solid sphere* is also equal to $-\frac{4}{3}\pi r^2\rho G - 2\pi\rho G(R^2 - r^2) = -2\pi\rho G\left(\frac{2}{3}r^2 + R^2 - r^2\right) = -2\pi\rho G\left(R^2 + \frac{2r^2 - 3r^2}{3}\right) = -2\pi\rho G\left(R^2 - \frac{r^2}{3}\right)$

It follows at once, therefore, that if the point *P lies at the centre of the sphere*, we have $r = 0$. So that,

gravitational potential at the centre of the solid sphere

$$= -M\left(\frac{3R^2}{2R^2}\right)G = -\frac{3}{2}\cdot\frac{M}{R}G.$$

But $-\frac{M}{R}G$, as we know, is the gravitational potential on the *surface* of the sphere.

We thus have *gravitational potential at the centre of solid sphere* = $\frac{3}{2}$ *time the gravitational potential on its surface.*

Or, *gravitational potential at the centre of the solid sphere*: *gravitational potential on the surface of the sphere* : : 3 : 2.

This means, in other words, that *the gravitational potential due to a solid sphere has its maximum (negative) value at its centre.*

2. Gravitational field

(*a*) **At a point outside the solid sphere.** We know that the gravitational potential at a point *P* outside a solid sphere distant *r* from its centre (*i.e.*, with $r > R$) is given by $V = -MG/r$, (§12.15. 1 (*a*).

And, since intensity of the gravitational field at a point is equal to the potential gradient there, we have

Gravitational field due to a solid sphere at a point P distant r from its centre ($r > R$), *i.e.*, $E = -dV/dr = -\frac{d}{dr}\left[-\frac{MG}{r}\right] = -\frac{MG}{r^2}$, *the same as though the whole mass* (*M*) *of the sphere were concentrated at its centre.*

Alternatively, we may imagine the sphere to consist of a number of concentric spherical shells one inside the other, with their radii ranging from θ to *R*. Then, considering one such spherical shell of radius *x* and thickness *dx* and hence of mass $4\pi x^2 dx\rho$, we have

gravitational field at point P distant r from the centre of the shell = $4\pi x^2 dx\rho G/r^2$

And, therefore, *gravitational field at P due to the whole solid sphere*

$$= -\frac{4\pi\rho G}{r^2}\int_0^R x^2 dx$$

$$= -\frac{4}{3}\pi R^2 \rho G/r^2.$$

Clearly, $\frac{4}{3}\pi R^3\rho = M$, the mass of the sphere. So that,

gravitational field at P due to the solid sphere, i.e., $E = -MG/r^2$.

Force on a point-mass *m*. If we replace the unit mass at *P* by a point-mass *m*, we have *P.E.* of the mass, $U = mV = -mMG/R$.

And, *therefore, force acting on the point-mass m,i.e.*,

$$F = -dU/dr = mMG/r^2.$$

(*b*) **At a point on the surface of the solid sphere.** For a point on the surface of the solid sphere, obviously, $r = R$, the radius of the sphere. We, therefore, have

gravitational field at a point on the surface of the solid sphere,

i.e., $$E = -MG/R^2.$$

(*c*) **At a point inside the solid sphere.** As we know, the gravitational potential at a point inside a solid sphere distant *r* from its centre (*i.e.*, with $r < R$) is given by the potential gradient there, we have

gravitational field due to a solid sphere at a point P inside it, distant r from its centre, i.e.,

$$E = -\frac{dV}{dt} = -\frac{d}{dr}\left[-MG\frac{(3R^2 - r^2)}{2R^3}\right]$$

$$= -MG\frac{2r}{2R^3} = -\frac{MG}{R^3}r^*, \text{ showing that } E \propto r.$$

Thus, *the intensity of the gravitational field at a point inside a solid sphere is directly proportional to the distance of the point from the centre of the sphere.*

Obviously, therefore, *at the centre of the sphere*, since $r = 0$, *the intensity of the gravitational field is zero*, whereas the gravitational potential there, as we have seen under 12.15, 1 (*c*) above, has its maximum (negative) value.

It will also be readily seen that in the expressions for the intensities of the gravitational field (E) outside and inside a solid sphere, deduced above under (*a*) and (*c*), if we put $r = R$, the radius of the sphere, we have $E = MG/R^2$ as the field on the surface of the sphere in either case, *i.e.*, whether the point P lies on the outer or the inner side of the surface of the sphere.

This shows clearly that *there is a continuity in the intensity of the gravitational field at the surface of a solid sphere* [See § 12.16, Fig. 12.17 (*a*)], unlike the case of a spherical shell, where there is a sharp discontinuity in the intensity of the gravitational field at the surface of the shell [§ 12.14, Fig. 12.13 (*a*)].

Force on a point-mass *m*. As usual, the potential energy of a point-mass m at a point P inside the solid sphere at a distance r from its centre is given by $U = mV = -mMG\left(\frac{3R^2 - r^2}{2R^3}\right)$ and, therefore,

force acting on the mass, i.e., $F = -\frac{dU}{dr} = -\frac{mMG}{R^3}r,$

i.e., the force acting on a mass m placed at a point inside a solid sphere is also directly proportional to its distance from the centre of the sphere and is, therefore, zero at the centre of the sphere.

12.16 COMPARISON OF GRAVITATIONAL POTENTIAL AND FIELD DUE TO A SOLID SPHERE WITH ELECTROSTATIC POTENTIAL AND FIELD DUE TO A CHARGED SOLID SPHERE

Here *two cases* arise, *viz.*, (*i*) the sphere may be *of a conducting material*, a metallic sphere, for instance, (*ii*) the sphere may be a homogeneous one of a *non-conducting material*.

Since in the case of a conducting sphere, the charge on it is not uniformly distributed over the whole of its volume but resides only on its surface, it *effectively* functions as a charged spherical shell which we have considered already under § 12.14.

We shell, therefore, consider here only the case of a homogeneous *non-conducting sphere*, in which the charge is uniformly distributed over its entire volume.
non-conducting sphere, in which the charge is uniformly distributed over its entire volume.

Proceeding in the same manner as for gravitational potential and field due to a solid sphere and taking charge Q on the sphere in place of its mass M, with ρ now representing the volume density of its charge (*i.e.*, $\rho = Q\Big/\frac{4}{3}\pi R^3$), instead of the volume density of its mass $\left(M\Big/\frac{4}{3}\pi R^3\right)$, we obtain expressions similar to those for gravitational potential and field, *viz.*, ***for points outside the charged***

*Taking the value of V at a distance r from the centre of the sphere to be $-2\pi\rho G(R^2 - r^2/3)$ (see footnote of 12.15, 1(*c*), we have *intensity of the gravitational field there, i.e.,* $E = -dV/dr$.

Or, $E = -\frac{d}{dr}[-2\pi\rho G(R^2 - r^2/3)] = -2\pi\rho G.2r/3 = -\frac{4}{3}\pi\rho Gr.$

Again, therefore, $E \propto r$.

sphere, (*i.e.*, for $r > R$), ***electrostatic potential,*** $V = Q/kr$ and ***intensity of the electrostatic field,*** $E = \dfrac{Q}{kr^2}\mathbf{r}$ Or, $E = \dfrac{Q}{kr^2}$. And, ***on the surface of the sphere,*** $V = Q/kR$ end $E = Q/kR^2$.

Thus, M in the case of gravitational potential field is here replaced by Q and G by $1/k$, with, of course, the negative sign replaced by a positive one.

If the charged sphere and the point in question be *in air*, $k = 1$, and we have $V = Q/r$ and $E = Q/r^2$, And, **on the surface of the sphere**, $V = Q/R$ and $E = Q/R^2$. *i.e., the sphere behaves as though the whole of the charge on it is concentrated at its centre.*

And, *for points inside the sphere,* $V = \dfrac{Q}{k}\left(\dfrac{3R^2 - r^2}{2R^3}\right)$

and $$E = \frac{Qr}{kR^3}\mathbf{r} \quad \text{Or, } E = \frac{Q}{kR^3}r.$$

At the centre of the sphere, (*i.e.*, for $r = 0$), clearly, $V = \dfrac{3}{2}\dfrac{Q}{kR}$ and $E = 0$.

If, therefore, we plot gravitational and electrostatic potentials against distances from the centre of a uniform solid sphere and a uniformly charged solid sphere respectively, we obtain curves such as those shown in Figs. 12.16 (*a*) and (*b*).

Curves (*a*) shows that the gravitational potential (negative) due to a uniform solid sphere is the *highest*, $-\dfrac{3}{2}\dfrac{M}{R}G$ *at its centre*, $-MG\left(\dfrac{3R^2 - r^2}{2R^3}\right)$ for points between the centre and the surface of the sphere, $-\dfrac{M}{R}G$ at the surface of the sphere and $-\dfrac{M}{r}G$, thereafter, tending to zero as $r \to \infty$.

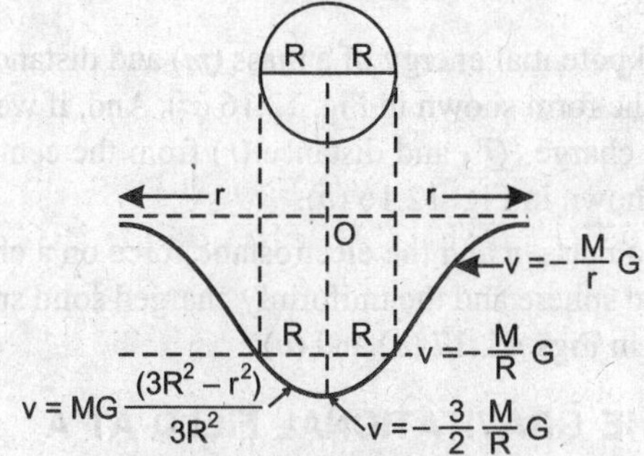

(a) Gravitational potential due to a uniform solid sphere.

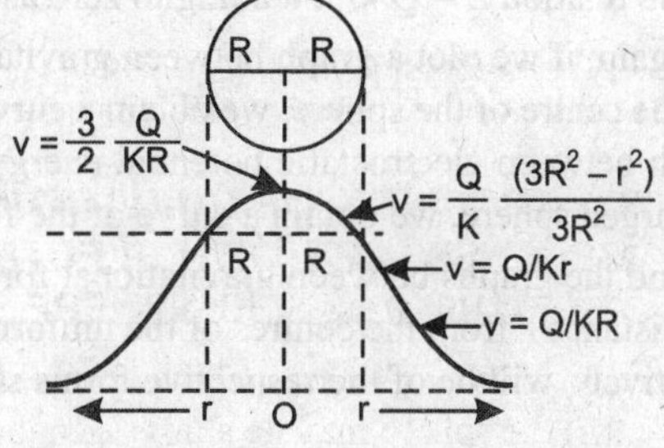

(b) Electrostatic potential due to a uniformly charged solid sphere.

Fig. 12.16

Curve (*b*), as will be readily seen, is the exact reciprocal for curve (*a*), because although the electrostatic potential due to the charged sphere varies with distance from its centre precisely in the manner of the gravitational potential in case (*a*), its sign is reversed and is now positive. So that, here, electrostatic potential is $\dfrac{3}{2}\dfrac{Q}{kR}$ at the centre of the charged sphere, $\dfrac{Q}{k}\left(\dfrac{3R^2 - r^3}{2R^3}\right)$ for points between the centre and the surface of the sphere, Q/kR at the surface of the sphere, and Q/kr thereafter, tending to zero as $r \to \infty$.

Similarly, if we plot intensities of the gravitational and electrostatic fields due to a uniform solid sphere and a uniformly charged solid sphere respectively against distances from their centres, we obtain curves of the form shown in Fig. 12.17(*a*) and (*b*).

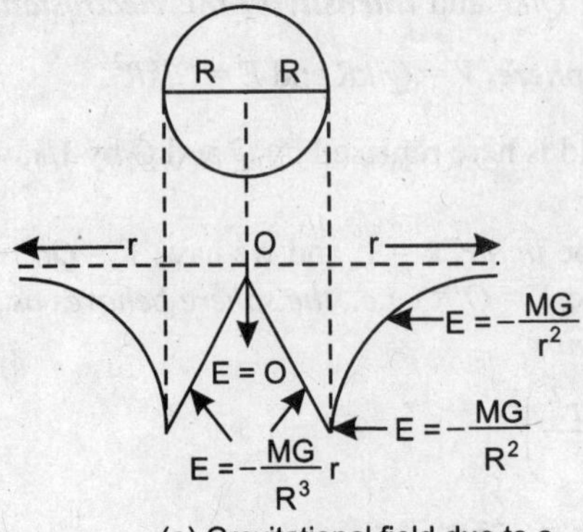

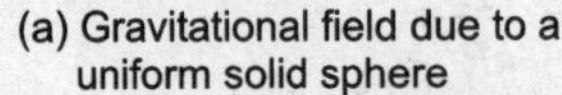
(a) Gravitational field due to a uniform solid sphere

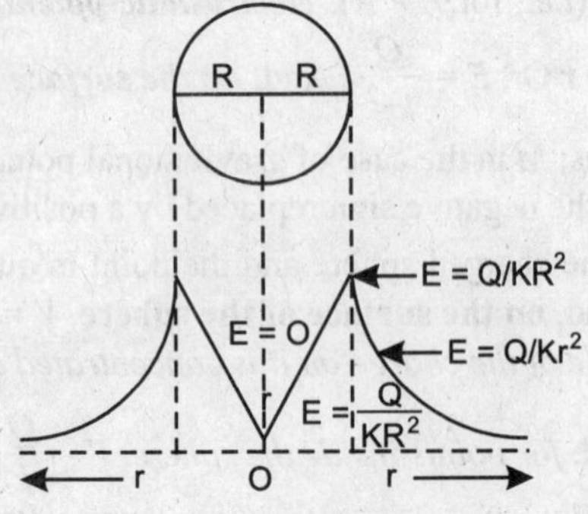

(b) Electrostatic field due to a uniformly charged solid sphere.

Fig. 12.17

Clearly, Fig. 12.17(*a*) shows that the gravitational field E is *zero* at the centre of the uniform solid sphere and its (negative) value increases linearly with distance r from the centre in accordance with the relation $E = -(MG/R^3)r$, so that at the surface of the sphere it attains its maximum (negative) value $-MG/R^2$ ($\therefore$ here, $r = R$). Thereafter, its (negative) value goes on decreasing with distance r in accordance with the relation $E = -MG/r^2$, tending to *zero* as $r \to \infty$.

Similarly, Fig (*b*) shows that the electrostatic field due to a uniformly charged solid sphere is zero at its centre and its value goes on increasing linearly with distance r from the centre in accordance with the relation $E = (Q/kR^3)r$, so that at the surface of the sphere it attains its maximum value $E = Q/kR^2$ ($\therefore$ here, $r = R$). Thereafter, its value goes on decreasing with distance r in accordance with the relation $E = Q/kr^2$, tending to zero as $r \to \infty$.

Again, if we plot a graph between gravitational potential energy of a mass (m) and distance (r) from the centre of the sphere, we obtain a curve of the form shown in Fig. 12.16 (*a*). And, if we plot a graph between electrostatic potential energy of a charge (Q') and distance (r) from the centre of the charged sphere, we obtain a curve of the form shown in Fig. 12.16 (*b*).

And the graphs between gravitational force of a mass m and the electrostatic force on a charge Q' at distance r from the centres of the uniform solid sphere and the uniformly charged solid sphere respectively, will be of the respective forms shown in Figs. 12.17 (*a*) and (*b*).

12.17 INTENSITY AND POTENTIAL OF THE GRAVITATIONAL FIELD AT A POINT DUE TO A CIRCULAR DISC

Let AB, (Fig. 12.18), represent a circular disc of radius R with its plane perpendicular to the plane of the paper and let P be a point on its axis, distant r from its centre O where the intensity and potential due to its gravitational field are to be determined.

Imagining the disc to consist of an infinite number of concentric rings with O as their common centre and considering one such ring CD of *radius* x and *width* dx, we have

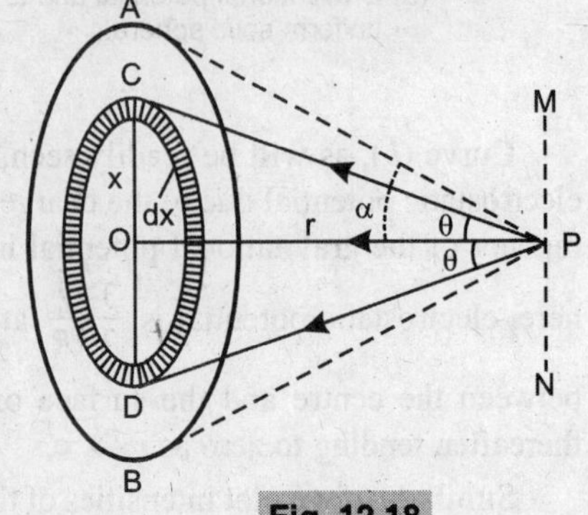

Fig. 12.18

$OC = x = r \tan\theta$, where $\angle OPC = \theta$.

Differentiating it with respect to θ, we have $d/d\theta = r \sec^2\theta$ Or, $dx = r\sec^2\theta\, d\theta$ and $CP = r\sec\theta$.

Now, *Area of the ring* = *Circumference* × *Width* = $2\pi x dx$.

$\therefore$ *Mass of the ring* = $2\pi x dx\sigma$, where σ is the *surface density* (*i.e., mass per unit area*) of the disc.

Considering a small element of mass δm of the ring at C, we have *gravitational intensity at P due to the elements* = $\delta mG/CP^2$ *along the direction PC.*

Resolving it into its rectangular components along and perpendicular to PO, we have *component along PO* = $\frac{\delta m}{CP^2}G\cos\theta$ and component at right angles to it, *vertically upwards* = $-\frac{dm}{CP^2}G\sin\theta$, along PM.

Similarly, for an equal element at D, diametrically opposite to C, we may resolve the gravitational intensity at P due to it (*i.e.*, $-\delta m\, G/DP^2$) into similar components, *viz.*,

$$\text{component } -\frac{\delta m}{DP^2}G\cos\theta = -\frac{\delta m}{CP^2}G\cos\theta \textit{ along PO}$$

$$\text{and component } -\frac{\delta m}{DP^2}G\sin\theta = -\frac{\delta m}{CP^2}G\sin\theta, \text{ perpendicular to it.}$$

vertically downwards, along PN. $[\because DP = CP]$

The two vertical components (along PM and PN) being equal and opposite along the same line of action, cancel out and the components along PO alone being *effective* are added up. The same will obviously be the case with all other elements into which the ring may be supposed to be broken up. So that, the gravitational intensity at P due to the whole ring is equal to the sum of the components along PO due to the different elements, *i.e.*,

$$= -\frac{\sum\delta m}{CP^2}G\cos\theta = -\frac{\textit{mass of the ring}}{CP^2}G\cos\theta$$

$$= -\frac{2\pi x dx\sigma}{CP^2}G\cos\theta.$$

Or, substituting the value of x, dx and CP obtained above, we have *gravitational intensity at P due to the ring*

$$= \frac{2\pi\sigma.\, r\tan\theta.\, r\sec^2\theta d\theta}{r^2\sec^2\theta}G\cos\theta$$

$$= -2\pi\sigma\, G\sin\theta\, d\theta, \text{ along } PO.$$

Clearly, therefore, the intensity at P due to all the rings into which the disc is supposed to be divided up, *i.e., due to the whole disc*, can be easily obtained by integrating the above expression between the limits $x = 0$ and $x = R$ or $\theta = 0$ and $\theta = \alpha$, where α is the angle that each extremity of the diameter AB of the disc makes with PO.

Thus, *gravitational intensity* at *P due to the whole disc, i.e.*,

$$E = -2\pi\sigma G\int_0^\alpha \sin\theta d\theta.$$

Or,
$$E = -2\pi\sigma G[-\cos\theta]_0^\alpha = -2\pi\sigma G[-\cos\alpha - (-\cos 0)]$$

$$= -2\pi\sigma G(1-\cos\alpha) \qquad \ldots(i)$$

Or, since $\cos\alpha = OP/AP = r/\sqrt{r^2+R^2}$, we also have

$$E = -2\pi\sigma G\left(1 - \frac{r}{\sqrt{r^2+R^2}}\right) \qquad \ldots(ii)$$

Again, because $2\pi(1-\cos\alpha)$ is the solid angle ω subtended by the disc at the point P, we have, from relation (*i*) above.

$$E = -\alpha G\omega. \qquad \ldots(iii)$$

Now, *potential at the point P due to the ring of radius x*

= intensity at the *point P due to the ring* $\times r$

$= -2\pi\sigma G \sin\theta d\theta \times r$.

[∴ *Intensity of the field at P = Potential gradient there*].

Hence, *gravitational potential at P due to the whole disc, i.e.,*

$$V = -2\pi\sigma Gr \int_0^{\alpha} \sin\theta d\theta = -2\pi\sigma Gr(1-\cos\alpha) \qquad ...(iv)$$

Or, since $\cos\alpha = r/\sqrt{r^2+R^2}$, we have

$$V = -2\pi\sigma Gr\left(1 - \frac{r}{\sqrt{r^2+R^2}}\right) \qquad ...(v)$$

Or, again, since $2\pi(1-\cos\alpha) = \omega$, we have $V = -\sigma G\omega r$. ...(*vi*)

12.18 INTENSITY AND POTENTIAL OF THE GRAVITATIONAL FIELD AT A POINT DUE TO AN INFINITE PLANE

In the case of the disc above (§ 12.17) if the radius *R* becomes infinite, the disc becomes an *infinite plane*, when, obviously, $\alpha = \pi/2$ and, therefore, $\cos\alpha = 0$, and $\omega = 2\pi$.

Thus, if we put $R = \infty$ in expression (*ii*), $\cos\alpha = 0$ in expression (*i*) or $\omega = 2\pi$ in expression (*iii*), we have

gravitational intensity at P due to an infinite plane $= -2\pi\sigma G$,

which is, clearly, quite independent of the distance *r* from it.

Similarly, putting these values of *R*, cos α and ω in relations (*v*), (*iv*) and (*vi*) respectively, we have

gravitational potential at a point P distant r from an infinite plane $= -2\pi\sigma Gr$.

12.19 FLUX OF GRAVITATIONAL INTENSITY—GAUSS'S THEOREM

Let *P* be a point in the gravitational field of mass *m* at *O*, (Fig. 12.19) distant *r* from it. Then, clearly, *gravitational intensity or field at P due to mass m, i.e.,* $E = -mG/r^2$, directed along *OP*. Let it be represented by *PQ*.

Draw any closed and finite surface through *P*, enclosing mass *m* and consider a surface element *ab* of it, of area *ds*, with *PN* as the *outward drawn normal* to it at point *P*.

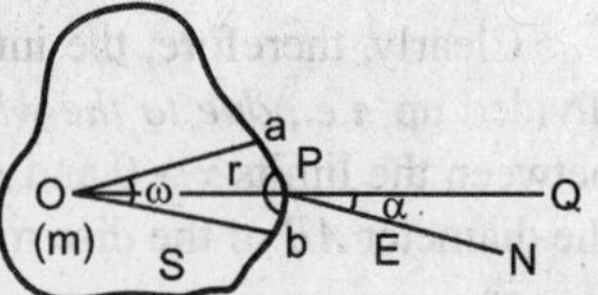

Fig. 12.19

If ∠*QPN*, that the intensity *E* makes with the normal *PN* and *P*, be α, we have

component of gravitational intensity E along the normal PN

$= E_n = E\cos\alpha$,

The product $E_n ds$, of the normal component E_n of intensity *E* and the small area *ds* of the surface element *ab*, is called the *flux of gravitational intensity or field* across the area *ds*, And therefore,

flux of gravitational intensity over the whole closed surface $S = \int E_n.ds = \int E\cos\alpha.ds$, where the integration extends over the entire closed surface.

Gauss's theorem. This theorem states that *the total flux of gravitational intensity over a closed surface (having a unique outward drawn normal to it at every point) in a gravitational field is* $-4\pi G$ *time the total mass enclosed by the surface, i.e.,* $\int E_n\, ds = -4\pi G\Sigma m$, *where* Σm *is the total mass enclosed by the surface.* This may be easily proved as follows:

We have just seen above (Fig. 12.19) that the flux of gravitational intensity over the surface element *ab* of area *ds* is $E_n\, ds = E\cos\alpha\, ds = -(mG/r^2)\cos\alpha\, ds$.

Now $ds \cos\alpha/r^2 = d\omega$, the solid angle subtended by area ds at O. SO that, *flux of gravitational intensity over area ds* $= -mG.d\omega$.

And, therefore, *flux of gravitational intensity over the whole of the closed surface* $= \int mG.d\omega. = G\,\omega\Sigma m = -4\pi\, G\, \Sigma m$,
where ω is the solid angle subtended by the whole of the closed surface at the point $O = 4\pi$ and Σm is the total mass enclosed by the surface.

Thus, if there be a number of masses m_1, m_2, m_3 etc. enclosed by the surface $\Sigma m = m_1 + m_2 + m_3 + \ldots$ and the *total flux of gravitational intensity over the closed surface* $= -4\pi G(m_1 + m_2 + m_3 + \ldots)$

And, *if there be no mass enclosed by the surface*, $\Sigma m = 0$ and, therefore, *total flux of gravitational intensity over the closed surface* $= 0$.

Some simple applications of Gauss's theorem

(*i*) Gravitational intensity due to a solid sphere

(*a*) *At a point outside the sphere.* Consider a solid sphere of mass M and radius R, the gravitational intensity E due to which is to be determined at a point P, distant r from its centre O, (Fig. 12.20)

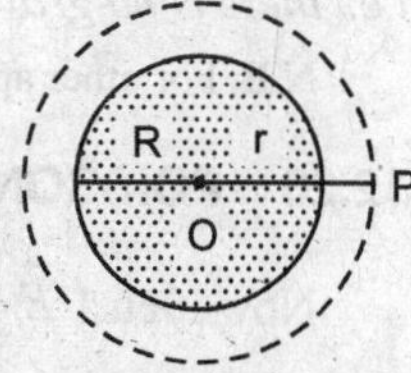

Fig. 12.20

Imagine a sphere to be drawn with centre O, and radius r as shown dotted in the figure, so as to completely enclose within it the given sphere, with point P lying on its surface.

By sheer symmetry, the gravitational intensity will be the *same* at every point on the surface of *this* sphere in a direction normal to the surface at that point. We, therefore, have $E_n = E$.

Since the surface area of the sphere is $4\pi r^2$, we have *total flux of gravitational intensity across its surface* $= 4\pi r^2 E$.

This should, in accordance with Gauss's theorem, be equal to $-4\pi GM$. So that, we have $4\pi r^2 E = -4\pi GM$, whence, $E = -MG/r^2$, the same result as obtained earlier [§12.15, 2 (*a*)].

(*b*) *At a point on the surface of the sphere.* In this case, obviously $r = R$, so that, proceeding as above, we have $E = -MG/R^2$. [see § 12.15, 2(*b*)]

(*c*) *At a point inside the sphere.* Let the point P now lie inside the sphere at a distance r from the centre O of the sphere, (Fig. 12.21).

Again, draw a sphere with centre O and radius r, as shown dotted in the figure, with point P lying on its surface.

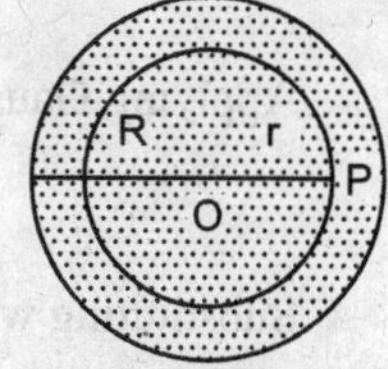

Fig. 12.21

As before, due to symmetry, the gravitational intensity (E) will be the *same* at every point on *this* sphere, in a direction normal to its surface at that point, *i.e.*, $E_n = E$.

Therefore total flux of gravitational intensity across the surface of this sphere $= 4\pi r^2 E$.

By *Gauss's theorem*, this should be equal to $-4\pi G$ times the mass enclosed by the sphere. Thus,

$4\pi r^2 E = -4\pi G\left(\frac{4}{3}\pi r^3 \rho\right)$ where ρ is the density (*i.e.*, volume density) of the material of the sphere.

Or, $$E = -\frac{4}{3}\pi G r\rho = -\frac{MG}{R^3}r, \qquad \left[\because \frac{4}{3}\pi R^3\rho = M. \text{Or, } \frac{M}{R^3} = \frac{4}{3}\pi\rho.\right]$$

i.e., the intensity varies directly as the distance (r) from the centre of the sphere. [see 12.15.2 (*c*)].

At the centre of the sphere, since $r = 0$, $E = 0$, the same result as obtained before..

(*ii*) Gravitational intensity due to a spherical shell

(*a*) *At a point outside the shell.* Proceeding exactly as in the case (*i*) (*a*), we have here too, $E = -MG/r^2$, where M is the mass of the spherical shell. [§ 12.13, 2 (*a*)] (*b*) *At a point on the surface of the shell.* Here, clearly, $r = R$, the radius of the spherical shell. So that, proceeding as in case (*a*) above, we have

$$E = -MG/R^2. \qquad [\S\ 12.13, 2\ (b)]$$

(*c*) *At a point inside the shell.* Here, we describe a sphere with O as centre and r as radius, such that the point P (inside the shell) lies on its surface, (Fig. 12.22).

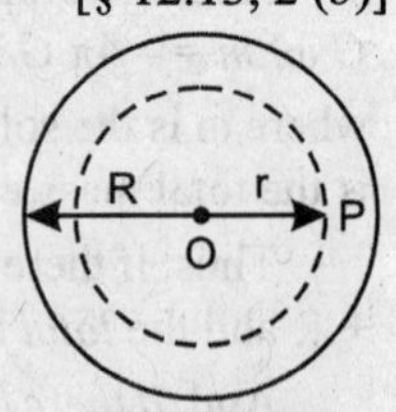

Fig. 12.22

Then by symmetry $E_n = E$. And. Therefore,

$$4\pi r^2 . E = 4\pi G\ (\textit{mass enclosed by the sphere}).$$

Since the mass enclosed by the sphere is clearly *zero*, we have

$$4\pi r^2 E = -4\pi G \times \theta. \text{ Or, } E = 0,$$

i.e., there is no gravitational field or intensity inside a spherical shell. [§ 12.14, 2 (*c*)]

N.B. For other applications of Gauss's theorem, see worked example,

12.20 POISSON'S EQUATION

Now if curl $\vec{E} = \vec{\nabla} \times \vec{E} = 0$. We can define the potential as

$$\vec{E} = -\text{grad } V = -\vec{\nabla} V \qquad \ldots(iii)$$

Now $$\phi = \int_S \hat{n} \cdot \vec{E}\, dA$$

But $$\phi = -4\pi GM.$$

∴ For a continuous mass distribution,

$$\phi = -\int_m 4\pi G dm = --\int_m 4\pi G \rho d\tau \qquad \ldots(iv)$$

where $dm = \rho d\tau$ and ρ is mass density.

$$\therefore \qquad -\int_S \hat{n} \cdot \vec{E}\, dA = -\int_\tau 4\pi G \rho d\tau \qquad \ldots(v)$$

Applying Gauss's divergence theorem to the *L.H.S.*, we get

$$\int_S \hat{n} \cdot \vec{E}\, dA = -\int_\tau \vec{\nabla} \cdot \vec{E}\, d\tau \qquad \ldots(vi)$$

Substituting we have

$$\int_\tau \vec{\nabla} \cdot \vec{E}\, d\tau = -\int_\tau 4\pi \rho d\tau \qquad \ldots(vii)$$

Or $$-\int_\tau (\vec{\nabla} \cdot \vec{E} + 4\pi G \rho) d\tau = 0$$

Since this is for any volume, we get

$$\vec{\nabla} \cdot \vec{E} = -4\pi G \rho.$$

By definition of potential, we have $\vec{E} = -\vec{\nabla} V$ where V is the potential

$$\therefore \qquad \vec{\nabla} \cdot \vec{E} = \vec{\nabla} \cdot (-\vec{\nabla} V) = -4\pi G \rho$$

or $$\nabla^2 V = 4\pi G \rho$$

In Cartesian form

$$\frac{\partial^2 V}{dx^2} + \frac{\partial^2 V}{dy^2} + \frac{\partial^2 V}{dz^2} = 4\pi G \rho$$

This is called the **Poisson's equation.**

12.21 INERTIAL AND GRAVITATIONAL MASS

(*i*) **Inertial mass.** We are aware of the property of inertia possessed by a material body, *i.e.*, its property of resisting any change in its position of rest or uniform motion along a straight line. Thus, we know that some effort or force has to be applied to put into motion a block, of whatever material, lying at rest on a smooth, frictionless horizontal surface, or to stop or even to slow it down or decrease its acceleration if it be in motion, and also that the bulkier the block, *i.e.*, the greater its mass, the greater the effort required for the purpose. Obviously, gravity does not come into the picture in this case (the motion being perpendicular to the direction in which the gravity acts). In fact, the effort or the force required to set the block in motion or to stop it would still be the same if the experiment were performed in gravity-free space.

This inertness or reluctance of the block, or a material body, in general, to change its state of rest or uniform motion along a straight line is thus an *inherent property of the body in virtue of its mass which, since it represents the inertia of the body*, is called its *inertial mass*. It can obviously be measured in terms of the ratio between the force (F) applied and the acceleration (a) produced in the body. For, in accordance with Newton's second law of motion, we have

$$F = ma \text{ and, therefore, } m = F/a.$$

Here, m represents the *inertial mass* of the body and may, therefore, more appropriately, be denoted by the symbol m_i.

If we apply the same force F to two bodies of inertial masses m_i and m_i', and if the accelerations produced in them be a and a' respectively, we have

$$F = m_i a = m'_i a', \text{ whence, } m_i/m'_i = a'/a.$$

Thus, *the inertial masses of two bodies are inversely proportional to the accelerations produced in them by a given force*. This holds good irrespective of the magnitude of the force applied.

We can, therefore, measure the inertial mass (m_i) of a body by comparing the acceleration produced in it with that produced in *standard mass* (M), such as the *standard kilogramme* (preserved at Sevres) by the application of the same force F to both. If the acceleration produced in the two masses be a and A respectively, we have

$$F = m_i a = MA, \text{ whence, } m_i/M = A/a. \text{ Or, } m_i = (A/a)M.$$

So that, m_i can be easily evaluated.

(*ii*) **Gravitational mass.** We can also measure the mass of a body in terms of the gravitational force of attraction exerted on it by another body, such as the earth. For, as we know, we have to exert an upward force to prevent a body from falling under the gravitational force of the earth and again, the bulkier the body, the greater the force required to hold it. Here clearly, the property of inertia plays no part but only the action of gravity. *This mass of a body, measured in terms of the gravitational force of attraction on it due to another body, usually the earth, is called its gravitational mass. Thus* if F and F' be the forces of attraction exerted by a given body A, of mass M, on two bodies B and C, of masses m and m' respectively, at the same distance R from it, we have

$$F = mMG/R^2 \quad \text{and} \quad F' = m'MG/R^2, \text{ whence, } F/F' = m/m'.$$

Here, m and m' are the *gravitational masses* of the two bodies and may be denoted by m_s and m'_s respectively to distinguish them from their inertial masses m_i and m'_i. So that, $F/F' = m_g/m'_g$.

Thus, we see that *the gravitational masses of the two bodies B and C, are directly proportional to the forces of attraction exerted on them by the body A*.

If the body A happens to be the *earth*, clearly $F = w$ and $F' = w'$, where w and w' are the weights of bodies B and C respectively at the given place. We, therefore, have

$$w = \frac{m_g M}{R^2}G \text{ and } w' = \frac{m'_g M}{R^2}G, \text{ whence, } \frac{w}{w'} = \frac{m_g}{m'_g}.$$

Or, *the ratio between the gravitational masses of two bodies is equal to the ratio between their weights at a given place.*

If follows, therefore, that the mass of a body, as measured by a spring balance or by balancing it in one pan against a standard mass in the other, of a physical balance, is its *gravitational mass*.

Equality of inertial and gravitational masses. The question naturally arises whether the inertial mass of a body is any different from, or the same as, its gravitational mass. As a first step to enquire into the problem, let us try to see whether the inertial masses of two bodies too are proportional to their weights at a given place. For this, we first determine the inertial masses m_i and m'_i of the two bodies in the manner discussed under (*i*) above. Then, since in free space (or vacuum) all bodies fall with are same acceleration (*g*) at a given place, under the action of gravity, we have forces acting on the two bodies due to attraction by the earth, *i.e.*, their weights w and w', equal to m_ig and m'_ig respectively. And, if mg and m'_g be the gravitational masses of the two bodies, their weights w and w′ are also equal to m_gMG/R^2 and $m'gMG/R^2$ respectively, as we have just seen above.

So that, $m_ig = m_gMG/R^2$ and $m_ig = m_gMG/R^2$, whence, $m_i/m'_i = m_g/m'_g$, showing that the *ratio of the inertial masses of two bodies is the same as that of their gravitational masses.*

The inertial and gravitational masses of a body are thus clearly proportional to each other. Newton, Eotvos and others have conclusively shown that inertial and gravitational masses agree with each other to within 1 part in 10^{10}. We can thus safely assert that the two are equal.

12.22 PRINCIPLE OF EQUIVALENCE

It has already been mentioned in the article above how the mass of a body, when *subjected to a gravitational attraction but no acceleration,* (*i.e., its gravitational mass*) comes out to be the same as when it is *subjected to an acceleration but no gravitational attraction* (*i.e., its inertial mass*). *This gave* **Einstein** *the idea that a gravitational field can be imitated by a field of acceleration* and this, ultimately, led to the formulation of his *general theory of relativity*, wherein he showed *that non-accelerating or inertial frame of reference in which there is a gravitational field is physically equivalent to a reference frame accelerating uniformly with reference to the inertial frame but in which there is no gravitational field.* This means, in other words, that experiments carried out in the two frames, under the *same* conditions, will yield identical results. This is called the *principle of equivalence.*

Thus, if we have two reference frames *S* and *S′*, the former an *inertial* or *non-accelerating* frame on the surface of the earth, so as to have a uniform gravitational field in it, and the latter, a frame of reference moving away from the earth with an acceleration – *g* with respect to *S* into far space where there is no gravitational field in it, all physical phenomena occurring in the two frames of reference will be identical. For instance, just as an object dropped in the inertial frame *S* will fall freely with an acceleration *g* with respect to it, so also will an object dropped in frame *S′* fall freely with an acceleration *g* with respect to it; or, just as a person sitting in frame *S* will experience an upward force equal to his weight *mg* by way of reaction of the floor, so will a person sitting in frame *S′* experience an identical reaction equal to his weight. So that, if the frame *S* be a closed ship, a person inside it would not be able to say from any observations he makes inside it whether he is in a uniformly accelerating frame without a gravitational field or in a non-accelerating frame with a uniform gravitational field.

Einstein thus showed that just as, in accordance with his special theory of relativity, we can only talk of *relative*, and *not absolute*, velocity of a frame of reference, so also in accordance with the *principle of equivalence*, we can only talk of *relative* and *not absolute* acceleration of frame of reference.

The principle of equivalence thus demands the equality of inertial and gravitational mass. *Indeed, this equality of inertial and gravitational mass is itself sometimes referred to as the principle of equivalence.*

It thus follows from this principle that in a reference frame accelerating towards the inertial frame of the earth, with an acceleration g (*e.g.* a *falling lift*), all particles, originally subject to its gravitational field, will become free because of the gravitational effect getting cancelled by the effect due to acceleration. This explains the *weightlessness* of a person inside an earth satellite.

It is very interesting to note here that a person standing in a lift whose rope has unfortunately broken during his downward journey, can save his life by jumping out just before the lift strikes the ground? Answer is 'No'. The person is falling freely with the same acceleration that of acceleration due to gravity g. Hence he feels weightlessness. The acceleration of the floor of lift on which he is standing and that of the person being same, he can't push the floor as there is 'no' reaction' to his 'action' on the floor. Hence, he can't jump out and unfortunately strikes on the ground along with the lift.

12.23 CENTRAL FORCES – INVERSE SQUARE LAW FORCES

As we have seen already in Chapter 5, *a central force between two particles is one which is directed along the line joining the two particles and whose magnitude is a function of the distance r between them.*

Thus, if r be the distance between the two particles, the *central force* operating between them is given by $\vec{F} = F_{(r)}\hat{r} = F_{(r)}\vec{r}/r$, where $F_{(r)}$ is a *function of distance r* and $\hat{r}$ or $\vec{r}/r$, the unit vector along $\vec{r}$.

This central force is *–ve* or + *ve*, *i.e.*, of attraction or repulsion, according as $P_{(r)} < 0$ or > 0.

Now, if one of the particles be fixed in its position, the central force on the other is $\vec{F} = F_{(r)}\vec{r}/r$.

If, therefore, $\vec{J}$ be the *angular momentum* of the second particle about the fixed particle or the origin, we have

$$\textit{torque acting on it, } \vec{\tau} = d\vec{J}/dt = \vec{r}\times\vec{F} = \vec{r}\times F_{(r)}\vec{r}/r = 0.$$

Since the *torque* $\vec{\tau} = 0$, it is clear that $\vec{J}$ = *Constant*.

In other words, *if a particle be moving under the influence of a central force, its angular momentum* ($\vec{J}$) *remains conserved*, (meaning, obviously, that there is no change in its magnitude and direction).

Further, *the constancy of* $\vec{J}$ *also implies that motion of the particle remains confined to a plane.* For if $\vec{p}$ be the linear momentum of the moving particle, we have $\vec{J} = \vec{r}\times\vec{p}$. So that, $\vec{r}.\vec{J} = \vec{r}\cdot(\vec{r}\times\vec{p})$.

Or, since in a triple vector product, we may interchange the *dots* and *crosses*, we have

$$\vec{r}\cdot\vec{J} = (\vec{r}\times\vec{r})\cdot\vec{p} = 0. \qquad [\because \text{the cross product } \vec{r}\times\vec{r} = 0.]$$

This shows clearly that *vectors* $\vec{r}$ *and* $\vec{J}$ *are perpendicular to each other or that the motion of the particle is confined to a plane.*

The general form of central force is represented by what may be called the **inverse n^{th} power law**, *viz.*, $\mathbf{F} = \frac{C}{r^n}\hat{r}$, where C is a *constant*.

The force is *–ve* or *attractive* or *+ve* or repulsive according as $C < 0$ or > 0.

Since a central force is a conservative force (*see* chapter 5), we have

$$F_{(r)} = -grad\ U = -\frac{dU}{dr} = \frac{C}{r^n}, \text{ where } U \text{ is the } P.E. \text{ of the particle.}$$

So that, $\quad dU = -\frac{C}{r^n}dr$, whence, no integration, we have

$$U_{(r)} = \frac{C}{(n-1)r^{(n-1)}} + C_1, \text{ where } C_1 \text{ is a constant of integration.}$$

Since at $r = \infty$, $P.E. = 0$, we have $C_1 = 0$. And, therefore,

$$U_{(r)} = \frac{C}{(n-1)r^{(n-1)}}.$$

Now, if $n = -1$ and C negative, we have $F_{(r)} = -Cr$ and $U_{(r)} = \frac{C}{2}r^2$, which, as we know, is the case of a *simple harmonic oscillator*, the force being always directed towards the fixed point or the origin.

And, if $n = 2$, we have $F_{(r)} = C/r^2$ and $U = C/r$, where C may be positive or negative if the force be an electrostatic one, depending upon the same or opposite signs of the two point-charges, and *always* negative if the force be a gravitational one.

Clearly, in this case, the force between the two particles (or point-charges) is *inversely proportional to the square of the distance between them.* This force is, therefore, known as the *central inverse square law force*, or more commonly, simply as the **Inverse square law force** and the law pertaining to it, the **Inverse square law**, *viz.*, that *the force between two particles (or two point-charges) is inversely proportional to the square of the distance between them.*

This is the one law that occurs most frequently in the entire field of Physics. One notable example of it is the force of gravitational attraction between two masses m_1 and m_2, ***viz.***, $\vec{F} = -\frac{m_1 m_2}{r^2} G\hat{r}$, which is the familiar **Newton's law of gravitation,** and where the constant $C = m_1 m_2 G$, *the force being always one of attraction.*

Another equally familiar example is *Coulomb's law of electrostatic attraction or repulsion* (in *C.G, S. Gaussian units) between two point-charges* q_1 and q_2 (in air or vacuum), ***viz.***, $\vec{F} = -\frac{m_1 m_2}{r^2}\hat{r}$, where the constant C is obviously equal to q_1, q_2, its sign being $+ve$ or $-ve$ according as the force is one of repulsion or attraction, *i.e.*, according as the two charges are of the same or opposite signs.

The inverse square law of force may also be expressed as the **inverse first power law of potential energy.** For, the inverse square law force (F) being a *central*, and *hence a conservative, force*, we have $F_{(t)} = -dU/dr = C/r^2$, whence, $dU = -(C/r^2)dr$, which, on integration, gives $U = \frac{C}{r} + C_1$ where C_1 is a constant of integration.

Since we assume *P.E.* to be *zero* for an infinite distance between the two particles, the constant $C_1 = 0$ and we, therefore, have

$U_{(r)} = C/r$, *i.e., the potential energy* of system of two particles at a separation of r is C/r.

Thus, if $C = -m_1 m_2 G$, we have *gravitational potential energy of a system of two particles of masses* m_1 and m_2 *given by* $U = -m_1 m_2 G/r$. And, if $C = q_1 q_2$, we have *electrostatic potential energy of a system of two charges* q_1 *and* q_2 given by $U = q_1 q_2 / r$ *in C.G.S. Gaussian units.*

12.24 INVERSE SQUARE LAW FORCES AND STABLE EQUILIBRIUM

If we have a group of point-charges, or masses, subject to inverse law forces, they cannot all remain at rest.

This follows at once from a consideration of the equipotential lines or surfaces due to the charges or masses constituting the group. For, as we know, in the case of a point-change, the equipotential lines are all concentric circles of increasing radii and decreasing values of potential about the point-charge as centre. And so also for a charged sphere, where the charge behaves as though it were concentrated at its centre, the equipotential surface are all concentric spheres of increasing values of potential about the charged sphere. Now, for a test charge to be in stable equilibrium at any point in an electrostatic field, the potential at *all* other neighbouring points must be higher or lower than at the point in question according as the test charge is positive or negative. And this is obviously impossible in the field either of the point-charge or of the charged sphere.

Similarly, if we have two equal positive (or negative) charges or charged spheres, in fixed positions, the equipotential lines due to them will be somewhat like those shown in Fig. 12.23. So that, if a test charge be placed at any point in the electrostatic field of the two charges, the potential there will again be neither lower nor higher than that at all other neighbouring points and the test charge will not therefore remain in static equilibrium at that or at any other point in the electrostatic field of the two charges. And what is true of two charges is equally true for any number of them.

A charged particle, positive or negative, may of course remain in equilibrium in an electrostatic field in the sense that the electrostatic force on it is *zero*, as for example, at a point somewhere between two similar charges (positive or negative) where the intensity of the field due to them is

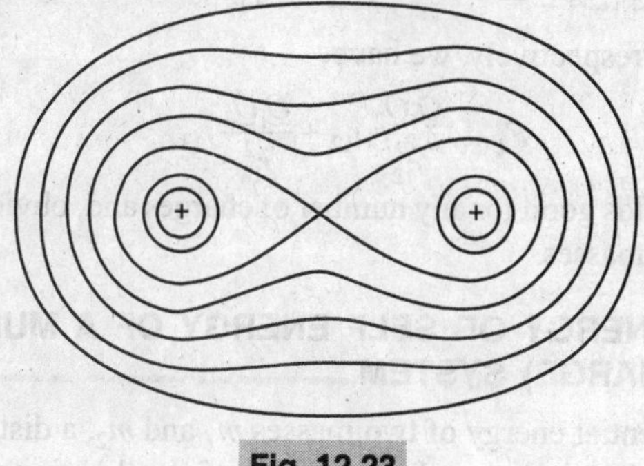

Fig. 12.23

zero. But then, it will not be in *stable* equilibrium, for its slightest displacement from the equilibrium position will alter the very configuration of the field and it will never be able to come back to its previous position.

The same would be the case with a small mass-particle if we place it in the gravitational field of either a single large mass or that of two or more large masses.

We can, therefore, safely state that *no static equilibrium is possible in an inverse square law force field*. This means that in any system of bodies in which inverse square law forces are operative, no state in which the kinetic energy of the system becomes zero can possibly be stable. This is true whether the system of bodies be the electrons in an atom, the atoms in a star or the stars in a galaxy. It follows, therefore, that *the entire known universe must consist of moving bodies, in which we may have a steady state in the sense that no great changes may occur but never a static state in which all bodies are motionless*.

12.25 THE SUPERPOSITION PRINCIPLE

This principle states that the resultant force on a charge or a mass placed at a point, due to a group or a combination of charges of masses is the vector sum of the forces exerted on it by the individual charges or masses comprising the group or the combination.

The principle of superposition thus asserts, in effect, the physical independence of the interaction of each pair of charges of *r* masses that the individual charges or masses form with the given charge or mass at the point. It means, in other words, that each such pair of charges or masses interacts in the same manner as it would in the absence of the other charges or masses and that the total effect is thus *additive*, *i.e.*, the vector sum of all the individual effects. In fact, this is the reason why an electrostatic or gravitational force can be expressed as the negative gradient of a potential energy function of the interacting charges or masses moving in electrostatic or gravitational fields.

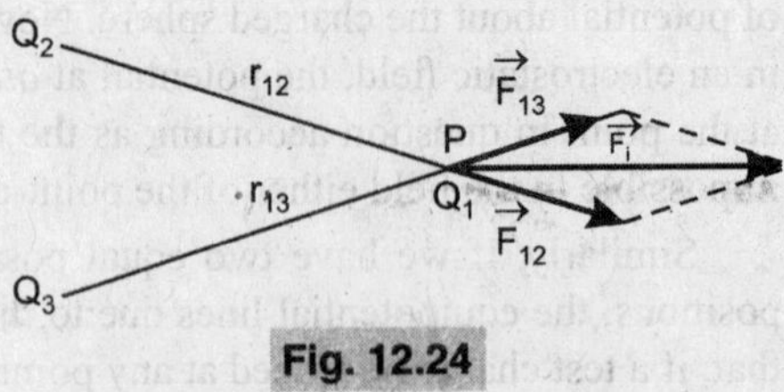

Fig. 12.24

The principle holds good, however, only in classical physics. It breaks down in the case of very small distances or very strong forces and, as such, is not applicable to quantum phenomena.

To illustrate the principle (in classical physics), let us consider a combination of three charges Q_1, Q_2 and Q_3, with Q_1 placed at a point P in air distant r_{12} and r_{13} respectively from Q_2 and Q_3 (Fig. 12.24).

Then if $\vec{F}_{12}$ and $\vec{F}_{13}$ be the forces exerted by Q_2 and Q_3 on the charge Q_1 at P, we have resultant force $\vec{F}_1$ at P equal to the vector sum of $\vec{F}_{12}$ and $\vec{F}_{13}$, *i.e.*,

$$\vec{F}_1 = \vec{F}_{12} + \vec{F}_{13}.$$

Or, since $\vec{F}_{12} = (Q_1Q_2/r_{12}^2)\,\hat{r}_{12}$ and $\vec{F}_{13} = (Q_1Q_3/r_{13}^2)\,\hat{r}_{13}$, where $\hat{r}_{12}$ and are $\hat{r}_{13}$ are the unit vectors directed along $\vec{r}_{12}$ and $\vec{r}_{13}$, respectively, we have

$$F_1 = \frac{Q_1Q_2}{r_{12}^2}\hat{r}_{12} + \frac{Q_1Q_3}{r_{13}^2}\hat{r}_{13}$$

The same naturally holds good for any number of charges and, obviously, similar considerations apply to a combination of masses.

12.26 POTENTIAL ENERGY OR SELF ENERGY OF A MULTI-PARTICLE (OR MULTI-CHARGE) SYSTEM

The gravitational potential energy of two masses m_1 and m_2, a distance r_{12} apart, is defined, as we know, as the amount of work done in bringing them from their initial infinite separation to their present distance apart.

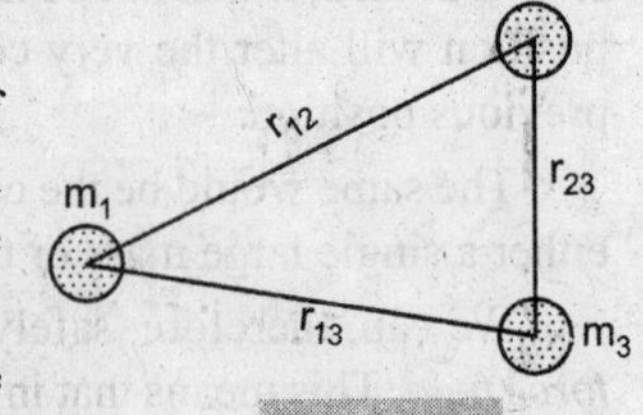

Fig. 12.25

Similarly, the gravitational potential energy of a system of three masses, placed as shown in Fig. 12.25, is equal to the amount of work done in assembling them from their initial infinite separation into their present configuration. This may, therefore, equally well be called the *self energy* of this configuration of the system.

To calculate the gravitational *P.E.* (or the self energy) of the system, all we need to do is to calculate the work done in arranging them in this particular manner.

Clearly, the *potential energy* U_{12} of masses m_1 and m_2 or the *work done* W_{12} *in bringing them from infinity to their present distance* r_{12} *apart* is given by the relation U_{12} (or W_{12}) $= \int_\infty^{12} F_{12}\cdot ds_{12}$

$$= \int_\infty^{r_{12}} -\frac{m_1m_2G}{r_{12}^2}d_{\mathbf{r}}\cdot ds_{12} = \int_\infty^{r_{12}} -\frac{m_1m_2G}{r_{12}^2}.dr_{12} = -\frac{m_1m_2}{r_{12}}G.$$

Similarly, *work done in bringing mass* m_3 *from infinity to distance* r_{13} *from* m_1 *and* r_{23} *from* m_2 *is given by* U_{13} *(or* W_{13}*)* + U_{13} *(or* W_{23}*)*.

$$= \int_\infty^{13} F_{13}dr_{13} + \int_\infty^{23} F_{23}dr_{23}$$

$$= \int_\infty^{13} -\frac{m_1m_3G}{r_{13}^2}dr_{13} + \int_\infty^{23} -\frac{m_2m_3G}{r_{23}^2}dr_{23}$$

$$= -\frac{m_1m_2}{r_{13}}G - \frac{m_2m_3}{r_{23}}G.$$

Hence, *potential energy or gravitational self energy U_s of the system* is equal to the total work done in bringing the three masses into their present configuration, *i.e.*,

$$U_s = U_{12} + U_{13} + U_{23} = W_{12} + W_{13} + W_{23}.$$

Or,
$$U_s = -\left(\frac{m_1 m_2}{r_{12}} + \frac{m_1 m_3}{r_{13}} + \frac{m_2 m_3}{r_{23}}\right) G.$$

If we had three charges Q_1 Q_2 and Q_3 (in air) in place of the three masses m_1, m_2 and m_3, the *potential energy* or the electrostatic self energy of the system would similarly be given by $U_s = U_{12} + U_{13} + U_{23}$.

$$= \int_{\infty}^{r_{12}} \frac{Q_1 Q_2}{r_{12}^2} dr_{12} + \int_{\infty}^{r_{13}} \frac{Q_1 Q_3}{r_{13}^2} dr_{13} + \int_{\infty}^{r_{23}} \frac{Q_2 Q_3}{r_{23}^2} dr_{23}$$

$$= \frac{Q_1 Q_2}{r_{12}} + \frac{Q_1 Q_3}{r_{13}} + \frac{Q_2 Q_3}{r_{23}}.$$

Here, of course, we leave out of account any energy that may have been spent in initially creating these charges. We are actually not concerned with that but only with the ready-made charges, so to speak, as given to us.

In case we have n masses or particles in the system, the total potential energy or the gravitational self energy of the n-particle system will given by

$$U_s = -G \sum \frac{m_i m_j}{r_{ij}} \quad \text{all pairs } i \neq i$$

where the summation extends over all pairs of masses i and j excluding the particular case $i=j$, which is not a pair at all but a case of self-interaction which contributes nothing to the potential energy of the system.

Or, to indicate more explicitly that that *each pair of masses i, j is to be counted only once* (*e.g.*, either 3, 2 or 2, 3), we may put the above expression in the form

$U_s = -G \sum_{i>j}^{n} \sum_{j=1}^{n} \frac{m_i m_j}{r_{ij}}$. And, similarly, the expression for the system of charges in the form,

$$U_s = -\sum_{i>j}^{n} \sum_{j=1}^{n} \frac{Q_i Q_j}{r_{ij}},$$

where the first summation refers to all values of i greater than j, *ensuring that the same pair is not counted twice.*

Alternatively, we may count *all possible pairs*, which obviously means counting each pair twice, first as I, j and then as j, i (*e.g.*, 2.3 and 3.2), omitting, however, the case $i = j$ for the reason explained. Thus, *the number counted is twice the actual number of pairs*. To correct for it we put ½ before the expression for U_s obtained. So that, now it takes the form $U_s = -\frac{1}{2} G \sum_{i=1}^{n} \sum_{\substack{j=1 \\ \neq i}}^{n} \frac{m_i m_j}{r_{ij}}$.

Similarly, for a system of n charges, we have *potential energy* or *electrostatic self energy* given by

$$U_s = -\frac{1}{2} \sum_{i=1}^{n} \sum_{\substack{j=1 \\ \neq i}}^{n} \frac{Q_i Q_j}{r_{ij}}.$$

A positive sign would indicate that the charges are all similar, *i.e.*, either all positive or all negative.

It must be emphasised very clearly here that the forces involved being conservative, it does not matter which of the masses or charges we move first or last and by what path we bring them into their assigned positions in the system, *The potential energy or the self energy of the system or the work done in assembling it will always be the same so long as its configuration remains the same.*

It follows, therefore, that the potential energy (U_s), given by the expressions above, is the potential energy of the system, as a whole, and cannot be assigned proportionately of otherwise to the individual masses or charges comprising the system. It is, in fact, a sort of *binding energy* which keeps the masses or the charges bound into a system of this particular configuration.

So that, just as we associate the elastic potential energy of a spring with its compressed or stretched configuration and consider it to be stored up in the spring itself, so also we must associate the potential energy or the self energy of a system of masses or charges with the configuration of the system and consider it to be stored up in their gravitational or electrostatic field respectively. Any change in the configuration of the system (of the spring, the masses or the charges) will thus inevitably result in a change in its potential energy.

Further, the negative sign of the expression for the *P.E.* or self energy (U_s) of the system indicates that energy is liberated when the masses are brought into their respective assigned positions in the system. And the positive sign of the expression for U_s in the case of a system of similar charges indicates that energy has to be supplied to the charges to be brought into their respective assigned positions in the system.

12.27 GRAVITATIONAL SELF ENERGY OF A BODY

Just as the gravitational self energy of a multi-particle system is its potential energy or the work done in assembling the particles into a system of a given configuration, the gravitational self energy of any material body may be defined as its potential energy or the amount of work done in assembling the body from its infinitesimal particles initially supposed to lie infinite distance apart from each other. *It is thus the energy of the total mass content of the body.*

If there be n such infinitesimal particles which, assembled together, comprise the body, we have, as explained under § 12.25 above,

Gravitational self energy of the body,

$$U_s = -\frac{1}{2}G\sum_{i=1}^{n}\sum_{\substack{j=1\\ \neq i}}^{n}\frac{m_i m_j}{r_{ij}},$$

the negative sign again indicating that as the particles assemble together to form the body, this much energy is released which may get converted into kinetic energy of the particles and ultimately into heat energy and get dissipated in the form of radiation.

12.28 GRAVITATIONAL SELF ENERGY OF A UNIFORM SOLID SPHERE

The gravitational self energy (Us) of a uniform solid sphere is obviously equal to the amount of work done in assembling together its infinitesimal particles initially lying infinite distance apart, so that it may be obtained from the expression for U_s above (§ 12.26). This will, however, be somewhat tedious to first convert the two summations into integrals and then perform multiple integrations.

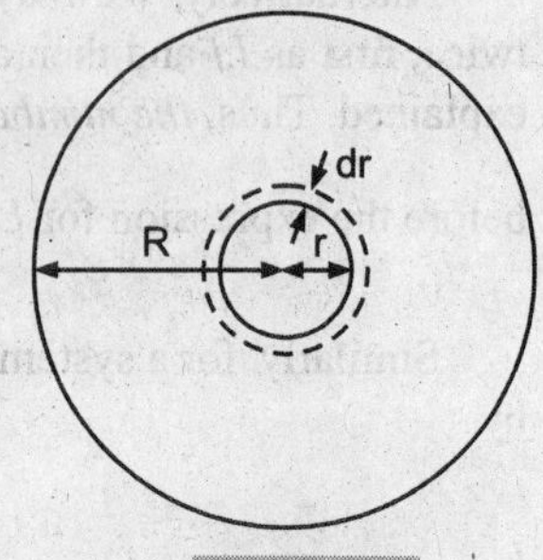

Fig. 12.26

We shall, therefore, adopt a simpler method and imagine the sphere to be formed by continuous deposition of mass particles (brought, of course, from ∞) in the form of successive spherical shells around an inner spherical core of radius r until it becomes a full-fledged solid sphere of radius R, (Fig. 12.26).

If ρ be the density of the material of the sphere, and hence of the spherical core, we have

mass of the inner spherical core = its volume × density $= \frac{4}{3}\pi r^3\rho$.

And, if *the thickness of the spherical shell deposited on it be dr*, we have

Mass of this shell = Its surface area × Its thickness × Density

$$= 4\pi r^2 dr\rho.$$

∴ *Change in P.E. or self energy of the core due to this additional mass deposited on it*, say dU_s = *potential of the core (i.e., its P.E. per unit mass) × additional mass*.

$$= -\frac{\textit{mass of the core}}{\textit{radius of the core}} G \times 4\pi r^2 dr\rho$$

$$= \frac{-\left(\frac{4}{3}\pi r^3\rho\right)(4pr^2 dr\rho)G}{r} = -\frac{16}{8}\pi^2\rho^2 Gr^4 dr.$$

This, then, is the *increase in the self energy of the core* as its radius increases, from r to $(r + dr)$.

The integral of this expression for dU_s, between the limits $r = 0$ and $r = R$, then give the self energy of the whole sphere on being built from the very start, *i.e.*,

$$U_s = -\int_0^R \frac{16}{3}\pi^2\rho^2 Gr^4 dr = -\frac{16}{3}\pi^2\rho^2 G\left[\frac{r^5}{5}\right]_0^R$$

$$= -\frac{16\pi^2\rho^2 R^5 G}{15} = -\frac{3}{5}\left(\frac{16}{9}\frac{\pi^2 R^5\rho^2}{R}\right)G = -\frac{3}{5}\frac{\left(\frac{4}{3}\pi R^3\rho\right)^2}{R}G.$$

Since $\frac{4}{3}\pi R^3\rho = M$, *the mass of the solid sphere*, we have,

gravitational self energy of the solid sphere,

$$U_s = -\frac{3}{5}\frac{M^2}{R}G.$$

As mentioned earlier, under § 12.26, the *–ve* sign of the expression for U_s indicates that this much energy is actually evolved or released during the process of assembling the solid sphere.

12.29 GRAVITATIONAL SELF ENERGY OF GALAXY

There are number of galaxies in the universe and each galaxy contains large number of stars, planets and other matter. Our own galaxy is estimated to contain 1.6×10^{11} stars including solar system. All the objects in the galaxy are bounded by the gravitational force. Similarly gravitational force also exists between various galaxies.

Let the Galaxy be made number of N number of stars, each of mass M_1, M_2, M_3, …….. M_N. During its formation, let star of mass M_2 be brought from infinity to distance R_{12} near star M_1 then *P.E.* of star of mass M_1 will be

$$u_1 = -\frac{GM_1M_2}{R_{12}}$$

When star of mass M_3 is brought at distance R_{13}, it will contribute to *P.E.* of M_1 as

$$u_2 = -\frac{GM_1M_3}{R_{13}} \quad \text{and so on.}$$

Thus total *P.E.* of star of mass M_1 will be

$$U_1 = u_1 + u_2 + \ldots\ldots\ldots + u_s$$

$$= -\frac{GM_1M_2}{R_{12}} - \frac{GM_1M_3}{R_{13}} - \frac{GM_1M_4}{R_{14}} \ldots\ldots - \frac{GM_1M_N}{R_{1N}}$$

$$= -GM_1\left(\frac{M_2}{R_{12}} + \frac{M_3}{R_{13}} + \ldots + \frac{M_N}{R_{1N}}\right)$$

$$= -GM_1 \sum_{K=2}^{N} \left(\frac{M_K}{R_{1K}} \right) \qquad ...(i)$$

This summation excludes the term $k = 1$

Similarly, the *P.E.* of M_2 will be

$$U_2 = -GM_2 \sum_{K=1}^{N} \left(\frac{M_K}{R_{2K}} \right), \text{ excluding term } k = 2 \qquad ...(ii)$$

....

....

$$U_N = -GM_N \sum_{K=1}^{N} \left(\frac{M_K}{R_{NK}} \right), \text{ excluding term } k = N \qquad ...(iii)$$

In summing $U_1, U_2, \ldots\ldots U_N$, it is found each term appears twice, Hence, the sum should be divided by 2, to find total *P.E.* of the galaxy.

$$U = \frac{1}{2}[U_1 + U_2 + U_3 + \ldots + U_N]$$

$$= \left(-\frac{G}{2}\right)\left[M_1 \sum_{\substack{k=2 \\ K \neq 1}}^{N} \frac{M_K}{R_{1K}} + M_2 \sum_{\substack{k=1 \\ K \neq 2}}^{N} \frac{M_K}{R_{2K}} + \ldots \right]$$

$$= \left(-\frac{G}{2}\right)\left[\sum_{j=1}^{N} M_j \sum \frac{M_K}{R_{1K}} \right]_{j \neq K}$$

$$= \left(-\frac{G}{2}\right)\left[\sum_{j=1}^{N} \sum_{K=1}^{N} \frac{M_j M_K}{R_{jK}} \right]_{j \neq K} \qquad ...(iv)$$

As the distance between two stars is same

$$R_{jk} = R$$

$$U = \left(-\frac{G}{2R}\right) \sum_{j=1}^{N} M_j \sum_{k=1}^{N} M_k, \text{ where } j \neq k$$

$$= \left(-\frac{G}{2R}\right)\left[M_1 \sum_{\substack{K=2 \\ K \neq 1}}^{N} M_K + M_2 \sum_{\substack{K=1 \\ K \neq 2}}^{N} M_K + M_3 \sum_{\substack{K=1 \\ K \neq 3}}^{N} M_K + \ldots \right]$$

$$= \left(-\frac{G}{2R}\right)[M_1(M_2 + M_3 + \ldots + M_N) + M_2(M_1 + M_3 + \ldots + M_N) + \ldots + M_N(M_1 + M_2 + \ldots + M_{N-1})]$$

In each bracket there are $(N - 1)$ terms and these are N terms. Also $M_1 = M_2 = M_3 = \ldots\ldots = M$,

Hence,

$$U = -\left(\frac{G}{2R}\right) M^2 (N - t) N$$

Since N is very large, $(N - 1)$ is taken nearly equal to N.

Thus, the gravitational energy of the Galaxy is

$$U = -\frac{GM^2 N^2}{2R} \qquad ...(v)$$

12.30 ELECTROSTATIC SELF ENERGY OF A CHARGED BODY

Like the gravitational self energy of a material body, the electrostatic self energy of a charged body too is defined as its electrostatic potential energy or the work done in bringing infinitesimal charges, initially lying infinite distance apart, on to it until the charge on it builds up to its given value Q. Again, therefore, if n be the number of such infinitesimal charges, we have, as explained under §12.26 above, *electrostatic self energy of the charged body in air, i.e.,*

$$U_s = \frac{1}{2}\sum_{i=1}^{N}\sum_{j=1}^{N}\frac{Q_i Q_j}{r_{ij}},$$

the +ve sign of the expression indicating that here this much energy has to be supplied in thus assembling the charge (Q) on the body.

12.31 ELECTROSTATIC SELF ENERGY OF A CHARGED SPHERE

Here, obviously, the sphere may be of (*i*) a *conducting material* (say a metal) or (*ii*) a *non-conducting material*. We shall consider both the cases separately.

***(i)* When the sphere is of a conducting material.** In this case, as we know, the charge on the sphere resides only on its outer surface and is not, therefore, distributed uniformly through its volume. It thus functions as a charged spherical shell.

To obtain an expression for its self energy (or *P.E.*), consider infinitesimal charges, dQ each, to be brought to it from their initial positions infinite distance apart. Then, work done in increasing the charge on the sphere from Q to $(Q + dQ)$ is clearly equal to the potential of the sphere × dQ = $(Q/C) \times dQ$, where C is the capacitance of the conducting sphere.

Therefore work done in raising the charge on the sphere from 0 to Q, i.e., self energy of the sphere,

$$U_s = \int_0^Q \frac{Q}{C}dQ = \frac{Q^2}{2C}.$$

Since for a spherical conductor, $C = R$, we have

$$\textit{self energy of the conducting sphere} = \frac{1}{2}\frac{Q^2}{R}.$$

***(ii)* When the sphere is of a non-conducting material.** Here, the charge on the sphere is distributed uniformly throughout its volume. So that, proceeding exactly as in the case of gravitational self energy of a uniform solid sphere (§ 12.28), where the mass of the sphere is distributed uniformly throughout its volume, and taking ρ as the volume density of the charge on the sphere (so that $Q = \frac{4}{3}\pi R^3 \rho$), we have *electrostatic self energy of the non-conducting sphere* $= \frac{3}{5}\frac{Q^2}{R}$.

12.32 CLASSICAL RADIUS OF THE ELECTRON

We have just seen under § 12.31 above how the self energy of a charged sphere works out to be $\frac{1}{2}(Q^2/R)$ if it be a *conducting one* and $\frac{3}{5}(Q^2/R)$ if it be a *non-conducting one.*

In the absence of any accurate knowledge about the structure of an electron, we cannot possibly decide on any one of these two expressions as representing the self energy of the electron. We, there-fore, tentatively take it to be $\approx Q^2/R$, a factor common to both the expressions.

Since the *charge on an electron is e* and *its classical radius*, r_0, we have $Q = e$ and $R = r_0$. So that, *self energy of the electron*, $U_s = e^2/r_0$.

Now, in accordance with *Einstein's mass-energy relation*, the energy E, associated with a mass m is given by $E = mc^2$, where c is the velocity of light in free space, equal to 3×10^{10} cm/sec.

We, therefore, have $e^2/r_0 = mc^2$, whence, $r_0 = e^2/mc^2$.

Since e (the charge on an electron) = 4.8×10^{10} *esu* and m (mass of an electron) = 9.1×10^{-28} gm, we have *classical radius of the electron,*

$$r_0 = \frac{(4.8\times10^{-10})^2}{9.1\times10^{-28}\times(3\times10^{10})^2} \approx 2.80 \times 10^{-13} \text{ cm.}$$

This length r_0 is regarded to be a *fundamental length*, (see § 12.33).

12.33 FUNDAMENTAL LENGTHS AND NUMBERS

In physics we come across quite a few constants, dimensional as well as non-dimensional, various combinations of which give what are regarded as *fundamental lengths and numbers*.

Among familiar examples of *dimensional constants* are G, the *gravitational constant*, having dimensions $M^{-1} L^3T^{-2}$, c, the *velocity of light*, having dimensions LT^{-1} or M^0LT^{-1} and h, *Planck's, constant*, having dimensions of *energy* × *time* or ML^2T^{-1} etc.

And, although the electronic charge e has no dimensions in *mass*, *length* and *time*, because, as we have seen in § 12.32 above, e^2/r_0 is taken to be the self energy of an electron and has thus the dimensions of energy. Obviously, therefore, e^2 has dimensions of *energy* × *length*.

Among the *non-dimensional constants* may be mentioned π and *Reynold's number k*. These non-dimensional constants as well as expressions like $T\sqrt{g/l}$ in the case of a simple pendulum (which too have no dimensions and are pure numbers) are usually referred to as *numerics*.

Now let us see how various combinations of these enable us to obtain other fundamental lengths and numbers.

The **fine structure constant** α. The name *fine structure* for this constant is derived from its having been used first in connection with seemingly single spectral lines observed to consist of (or split into) thinner lines, thus revealing their *fine structure*. Its value can be obtained from e, $\hbar$ and c, $\hbar = h/2\pi$ (and read as *h bar*). Thus,

$$\alpha = \frac{e^2}{\hbar c} = \frac{e^2}{(h/2\pi)c} = \frac{2\pi e^2}{hc} = \frac{1}{137.04}.$$

So that, dimensions of α are those of $\dfrac{energy \times length}{(energy \times time)(length/time)}$, *i.e.*, it has no dimensions in M, L and T.

It is thus a *non-dimensional constant* (*or numeric*) and its great importance lies in the fact that quite a number of important fundamental lengths can be obtained by dividing the classical radius of an electron, r_0(*see* § 12.32), by various powers of α

Thus, for example, one such fundamental length we often meet with in Quantum physics is the **Crompton wavelength of an electron**, $\bar{\lambda}_c$ (read as λ *bar* and equal to $\lambda/2\pi$). It is obtained by dividing r_c by the first power of α. Thus,

$$\textit{Crompton wavelength of an electron, } \bar{\lambda}_c = r_0/\alpha = \frac{e^2}{mc^2}\Big/\frac{2\pi e^2}{hc},$$

[$\therefore r_0 = e^2/mc^2$, where m is the mass of the electron]

Or,
$$\bar{\lambda}_c = \left(\frac{e^2}{mc^2}\right)\left(\frac{hc}{2\pi e^2}\right) = \frac{h}{2\pi mc} = 3.86 \times 10^{-11} \text{ cm.}$$

Another important fundamental length thus obtained is the *Bohr's radius of the ground state of hydrogen* which is, in effect, the *radius of the hydrogen atom*, a_0. It is given by r_0/α^2. So that,

$$a_0 = \frac{r_0}{\alpha^2} = \frac{e^2/mc^2}{(2\pi e^2/hc)^2} = \frac{e^2}{mc^2} \times \frac{h^2c^2}{4\pi^2e^4} = \frac{h^2}{4\pi^2me^2}$$

$$= 0.529 \times 10^{-8} \text{ cm.}$$

Yet another important length we may mention here is what is called the **gravitational length of a body**, (R_o), such that the gravitational self energy of the body (of mass M) is given by M^2G/R_0.

To obtain the value of R_0 for the given body, we equate its self energy M^2G/R_0 against Mc^2. So that, $M^2G/R_0 = Mc^2$, whence $R_0 = MG/c^2$.*

By way of an example, let us calculate the *gravitational length of the sun*. Taking the mass of the sun to be $\approx 2 \times 10^{33}$ gm, we have

$$R_o = \frac{2\times10^{23}\times6.7\times10^{-8}}{(3\times10^{10})^2} \approx 10^5 \text{ cm},$$

which, it may be noted, is very much smaller than the radius of the sun = 7×10^{10} cm.

Similarly, let us calculate the *gravitational length of our known universe*, whose mass can be obtained from the total number of nucleons (*i.e., protons and neutrons*) in it, which is estimated to be 10^{80}. Since each nucleon weighs nearly 10^{24} gm, total mass of the universe (M) comes to $10^{80} \times 10^{-24} = 10^{56}$ gm.

$$\therefore \qquad R_0 = \frac{10^{56}\times6.7\times10^{-8}}{(3\times10^{10})^2} \approx 10^{28} \text{ cm}$$

which is near about the same as its estimated radius.

It is interesting to observe that in accordance with the general theory of relativity, *no photons can escape from the surface of a body whose radius* (R) *is smaller than, or equal to, the gravitational length* (R_o) *for it* and it is, therefore, non-luminous and hence invisible.

Thus, the reason why the sun is intensely visible is that its radius $R \approx 7 \times 10^{10}$ cm being very much larger than its gravitational length $R_0 \approx 10^5$ cm, there is an enormously large number of photons escaping from it, which make it so dazzlingly luminous.

12.34 TWO-BODY PROBLEM REDUCED TO ONE-BODY PROBLEM

A two-body problem, involving central forces, can always be reduced to the form of a one-body problem, thereby greatly simplifying calculations. This will be seen from the following.

A central force between two point-particles, or two uniform spherical bodies, as we know, is one whose magnitude depends only upon their separation, *i.e.*, is a function of the distance between the two particles (or the centres of the two spherical bodies) and which is directed along the line joining them, the force being reckoned *negative* or *positive*, according as it is one of *attraction or repulsion.*

Further, a central force may, in general, be *any function* of the distance between the two particles (or spherical bodies) and not necessarily the familiar inverse square law force, and may, of course, be gravitational or electrostatic.

We shall now proceed to consider the motion of a system of two particles, subjected to such a force, – an obviously two-body problem, –and see how it may be reduced to a one-body problem.

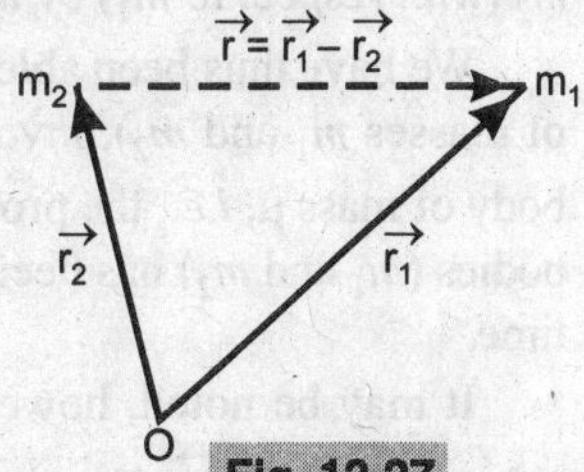

Suppose we have two particles of masses m_1 and m_2, whose instantaneous position vectors in an inertial frame are $\vec{r_1}$ and $\vec{r_2}$, with respect to the origin O, (Fig. 12.27)

Then, clearly, *vector distance* of particle m_1 from particle m_2 is $\vec{r} = \vec{r_1} - \vec{r_2}$.

Fig. 12.27

So that, *central force exerted by the second particle on the first, i.e.,* F_{12} is given by the relation

$$\vec{F_{12}} = m_1(d^2\vec{r_1}/dt^2) \qquad \text{... (i)}$$

* Sometimes, Crompton wavelength of an electron is taken to be $2\pi\lambda_c$.

And, *central force exerted by the first particle on the second, i.e.,*F_{21} is given by the relation

$$\vec{F}_{12} = m_2(d^2\vec{r}_2/dt^2), \qquad \text{...(ii)}$$

Both the forces acting along the line joining m_1 and m_2.

Since, there is no external force acting on the system, we have, in accordance with Newton's third law of motion, $\vec{F}_{12} = -\vec{F}_{21} = \vec{F} = F\hat{r}$ ($\hat{r}$ being the unit vector along $\vec{r}$). The magnitude F of the forces $\vec{F}$ may be any function of distance r between m_1 and m_2.

We may, therefore, express relations (*i*) and (*ii*) in the forms

$$\frac{d^2\vec{r}_1}{dt^2} = \frac{\vec{F}}{m_1} = \frac{F\hat{r}}{m_1} \qquad \text{...(iii)}$$

and

$$\frac{d^2\vec{r}_2}{dt^2} = -\frac{\vec{F}}{m_2} = -\frac{F\hat{r}}{m_2}. \qquad \text{...(iv)}$$

Subtracting relation (*iv*) from relation (*iii*), we have

$$\frac{d^2\vec{r}_1}{dt^2} - \frac{d^2\vec{r}_2}{dt^2} = \frac{\vec{F}}{m_1} + \frac{\vec{F}}{m_2}.$$

Or,

$$\frac{d^2}{dt^2}\left(\vec{r}_1 - \vec{r}_2\right) = \left(\frac{1}{m_1} + \frac{1}{m_2}\right)\vec{F} = \left(\frac{1}{m_1} + \frac{1}{m_2}\right)F\hat{r}. \qquad \text{...(v)}$$

Or, putting $\left(\frac{1}{m_1} + \frac{1}{m_2}\right) = \frac{1}{\mu}$, where, $\mu = \frac{m_1 m_2}{m_1 + m_2}$, called the reduced mass of m_1 and m_2 and $\vec{r}_1 - \vec{r}_2 = \vec{r}$, we have

$$\frac{d^2\vec{r}}{dt^2} = \frac{\vec{F}}{\mu} = \frac{F\hat{r}}{\mu} \qquad \text{...(vi)}$$

which may also be put as $\vec{F} = F\hat{r} = \mu\dfrac{d^2\vec{r}}{dt^2}$. ...(*vii*)

This equation (v*ii*), it will readily be seen, is the equation of motion of a particle of mass μ at a vector distance $\vec{r}$ from one of the particles relative to the other (in our case m_2, because $\vec{r}$ is the vector distance from m_2 to m_1), *i.e.*, as though the latter (m_2) were fixed at the origin O of the inertial frame and exerting a force of attraction $\vec{F} = F\hat{r}$ on the former (m_1). In other words, *considering m_2 as a fixed centre which exerts a force $\vec{F} = F\hat{r}$ on m_1 at vector distance $\vec{r}$ form it, we can obtain the relative motion of m_1 (with respect to m_2) by using μ in place of m_1 as the mass.*

Similarly, *considering m_1 as a fixed centre which exerts a force $\vec{F} = -F\hat{r}$ on m_2 at vector distance $\vec{r}$ from it (because the distance from m_1 to m_2 is... $\vec{r}$), we can obtain the relative motion of m_2 (with respect to m_1) by using μ in place of m_2 as the mass.*

We have thus been able to reduce a two-body problem (of the motion of two particles or bodies of masses m_1 and m_2), involving a central force, to a one-body problem of the motion of a single body of mass μ, *i.e.*, the problem of calculating two position vector $\vec{r}_1$ and $\vec{r}_2$ of the two particles or bodies (m_1 and m_2) has been reduced to the calculation of a single vector distance r as a function of time.

It may be noted, however, that if we solve relation (*vi*) above for $\vec{r}$, we can also obtain the values of $\vec{r}_1$ and $\vec{r}_2$. For, at any given instant, $\vec{r}_1 - \vec{r}_2 = \vec{r}$ and $m_1\vec{r}_1 + m_2\vec{r}_2 = (m_1 + m_2)\vec{R}_{c.m.}$, where $\vec{R}_{c.m.}$, is the position vector of the centre of mass of the system. So that, solving these two equations, we have

$$\vec{r}_1 = \vec{R}_{c.m.} + \frac{m_2\vec{r}}{m_1 + m_2} = \vec{R}_{c.m.} + \frac{\mu}{m_1}\vec{r} \text{ and } \vec{r}_2 = \vec{R}_{c.m.} - \frac{m_1\vec{r}}{m_1 + m_2}$$

$$= \vec{R}_{c.m.} - \frac{\mu}{m_2}\vec{r} \text{ in the inertial frame,}$$

and $$\vec{r_1} = \frac{\mu}{m_1}\vec{r} \text{ and } \vec{r_2} = -\frac{\mu}{m_2}\vec{r} \text{ in the centre-of-mass frame}$$

$[\because \vec{R}_{e.m.}$ is in then *zero*].

Further, as we know, in the absence of any external force acting on the system and, therefore, its total linear momentum remaining conserved, the velocity of the centre of mass remains constant in the inertial frame and, in the centre-of-mass frame, *zero*. The two particles or bodies, therefore, move around the centre of mass in such a way that the vector distance $\vec{r}$ between them changes in the same manner as the vector distance of a single particle or body of mass μ would do when moving around a fixed centre. The actual paths of two particles or bodies will, of course, depend on the law of force operating (*i.e.*, inverse square law or any other) and on initial positions and velocities.

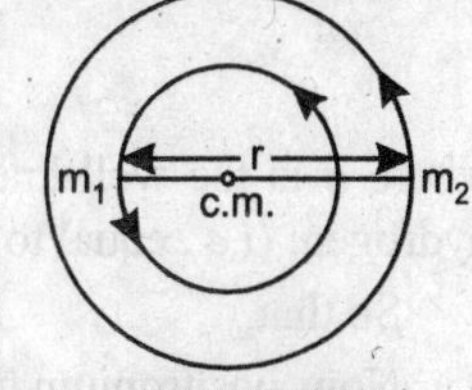

Fig. 12.28

In the case of rotational motion around the centre of mass, the two particles or bodies will move with identical angular velocities, such that the distance r between them remains intact throughout, as shown in Fig. 12.28.

12.35 REDUCED MASS

We have mentioned under 12.34 that $(m_1m_2)/(m_1 + m_2)$ is referred to as the *reduced mass* μ of the two particles or bodies of masses m_1 and m_2. This is obviously so because the introduction of $1/\mu$ in place of $(1/m_1 + m_2)$ in relation (v) there reduces a two-body problem into a simpler one-body problem. And perhaps also because the reduced mass of two particles is always less than the mass of either particle, *i.e.*, $\mu < m_1$ or m_2. This may be easily seen from the fact that if $m_1 = m_2 = m$, their reduced mass $\mu = m \times m/(m + m) = m/2$, *i.e., equal to half the mass of either particle.*

And, *if one of the masses, say, m_1, be very much smaller than the other*, (m_2), we have

$$\mu = \frac{m_1m_2}{m_1 + m_2} = m_1\left[\frac{1}{(m_1/m_2)+1}\right]$$

$$= m_1\left(1+\frac{m_1}{m_2}\right)^{-1} = m_1\left(1-\frac{m_1}{m_2}\right).$$

Or, since $m_1/m_2 \approx 0$ (m_1 being $<< m_2$), we have $\mu \approx m_1$, showing that *the value of the reduced mass tends to be nearest to the value of the smaller mass.*

This may perhaps best be seen if we calculate the **reduced mass of a hydrogen atom** which consists, as we know, of a single proton in the nucleus with a single electron going round it, where a proton is 1836 times heavier than an electron. If, therefore m_e be the *mass of the electron* and m_2, *that of the proton*, we have

reduced mass of the hydrogen atom, $\mu_H \approx m_e\left(1-\dfrac{m_e}{m_p}\right) \approx m_e\left(1-\dfrac{1}{1836}\right) \approx m_e$,

i.e., nearly the same as that of the electron !

On the other hand, the **reduced mass of the positronium atom,** a short-lived combination of a positron (having *the same mass as an electron* but a positive charge) and an electron is given by

$$\mu_p = \frac{m_em_e}{m_e + m_e} = \frac{1}{2}m_e$$

i.e., equal to *half the mass of an electron* and, therefore, *nearly half the reduced mass of a hydrogen atom.*

Thus, in calculating the time-period of an electron or its energy state etc. as it moves in its orbit around the nucleus, we must, *in the case of hydrogen*, imagine a mass μ_H revolving round the fixed proton and, *in the case of positronium,* a mass μ_v revolving round the fixed positron, rather than a mass m_e.

Since, however, $\mu_H \approx m_e$, the error involved in the case of hydrogen in taking the revolving mass to be m_e (the actual mass of the electron) instead of μ_H will only be a marginal one. But, since u_p is only half the actual mass of the electron, *i.e.*, m_e, the error involved in the case of positronium, in taking the revolving mass to be m_e instead of μ_p will obviously be quite considerable.

Incidentally, the fact of the reduced mass of positronium being half that of hydrogen is amply borne out by examining their respective spectra. For, the frequency (ν) of a spectral line in a hydrogen spectrum is, *in accordance with Bohr's theory,* given by the relation

$$\nu = \frac{2\pi^2 e^2 \mu}{h^3}\left(\frac{1}{n^2} - \frac{1}{m^2}\right),$$

where h is the well known *Planck's constant* (= 6.625×10^{-27} erg-sec), μ, the reduced mass of hydrogen, (*i.e.*, equal to μ_H) and n and m, simple integers, such that $m > n$.

So that, $\nu \propto \mu H \propto m_e$, [because $\mu = \mu_H \approx m_e$]

Now, positronium too, being hydrogen-like in structure, gives a pattern of spectral lines similar to that of hydrogen, with the frequencies of its spectral lines also given by the above relation, where μ is now equal to μ_p, the reduced mass of positronium. We, therefore, have

$$\nu \propto \mu_P \propto m_e/2, \quad \text{[because, as we know, } \mu_P \approx m_e/2]$$

indicating clearly that *the frequencies of the spectral lines of positronium are half those of hydrogen.*

And, since wavelength is inversely proportional to frequency ($\because c = \nu\lambda$ and, therefore, $\lambda = c/\nu$), it follows that *the wavelengths of the spectral lines by positronium are twice those of the spectral lines given by hydrogen.*

This being an experimental fact, in stands fully confirmed that $\mu_p = \frac{1}{2}\mu H$, *i.e.*, the reduced mass of positronium is half the reduced mass of hydrogen.

12.36 CASE OF GRAVITATIONAL FORCE (IN A TWO-BODY PROBLEM)

We have seen under § 12.34 above how a two-body problem, in general, where the two bodies, distant $\vec{r}$ from each other, interact through a central force, may be reduced to a one-body problem by means of the relation $F = \mu(d^2r/dt^2)$. Let us consider it now in the particular case of *gravitational* force as the central force.

As we know the gravitational force of attraction two particles or bodies of masses m_1 and m_2 is given by

$\vec{F} = -G\frac{m_1m_2}{r^2}\hat{r}$ where $\hat{r}$ is the unit vector along $\vec{r}$, the distance of particle m_1 from particle m_2.

We thus have

$$\vec{F} = F\hat{r} = \mu(d^2\vec{r}/dt^2) = -G\frac{m_1m_2}{r^2}\hat{r}.$$

Here also, the motion of particle m_1 with respect to particle m_2 would be the same as that of a particle of reduced mass μ [of m_1 and m_2, *i.e.*, $m_1m_2/(m_1 + m_2)$] under the force of attraction of a fixed mass or a fixed centre m_2 at a vector distance **r** from it, and may thus be obtained *by replacing* m_1 by μ.

We cannot, however, replace m_1 by μ in the expression for force above, *i.e.*, we cannot take the central force between the two particles to be $-G\frac{\mu m_2}{r^2}\hat{r}$ for the simple reason that the force between the two particles is not merely a function of the distance $\vec{r}$ between them but also involves the masses of both the particles. The actual masses (m_1 and m_2) of the two particles have, therefore, to be used in the expression for force. So that,

$$\mu \frac{d^2 \vec{r}}{dt^2} = -G\frac{m_1 m_2}{r^2}\hat{r}. \text{ Or, } \frac{d^2 \vec{r}}{dt^2} = \frac{1}{\mu}\frac{Gm_1 m_2}{r^2}\hat{r}.$$

Or, substituting the value of μ, we have

$$\frac{d^2 \vec{r}}{dt^2} = -\left(\frac{m_1 + m_2}{m_1 m_2}\right)\frac{Gm_1 m_2}{r^2}\hat{r} = -G\frac{m_1 + m_2}{r^2}\hat{r}.$$

$$= -F\hat{r}, \text{ say, where, } F' = G\frac{m_1 + m_2}{r^2}.$$

This is clearly the equation of motion of a particle of unit mass, or negligible mass, compared with $(m_1 + m_2)$, at a vector distance $\vec{r}$ (equal to the distance between the two particles) from a fixed mass $(m_1 + m_2)$ exerting a force of attraction on it.

This is the reason why when calculating the angular velocity of a satellite, of mass m, going round the earth, of mass M, we must take the total mass $(M + m)$ as the value of the attracting mass and not merely the mass of the earth M. Of course, if the mass of the satellite (m) be negligible compared with that of the earth, we may take M as the attracting mass without causing any appreciable error in the result. In cases, however, where the mass of the satellite is not negligible, as for example the earth and the other planets going round the sun, or the moon going round the earth, this will cause considerable error and is not, therefore, permissible.

12.37 EQUIVALENT ONE-BODY PROBLEM

We have just seen in the article above how, in the case of two bodies of masses m_1 and m_2, interacting through gravitational force as the central force along the line joining them, we may determine the motion of m_1 relative to m_2 by taking m_2 to lie at the fixed origin of an inertial frame and replacing m_1 by their reduced mass μ, *i.e.*, we can take

$$\mu \frac{d^2 \vec{r}}{dt^2} = -G\frac{m_1 m_2}{r^2}\hat{r},$$

where $\hat{r}$ is the unit vector along $\vec{r}$, thus reducing the two-body problem effectively to a one-body problem.

Now, as we know, *for a particle moving about a fixed centre of force, the angular momentum remains conserved.* So that, *the angular momentum in our effective or equivalent one-body problem, viz.,*

$$\vec{J} = \vec{r} \times \mu \frac{d\vec{r}}{dt} \qquad ...(i)$$

must also remain conserved in both magnitude and direction.

Or course, the value of the angular momentum is its usual value for the system of the two bodies whose position vectors with respect to their centre of mass $(\vec{R}_{c.m.})$ are $\vec{r}_1$ and $\vec{r}_2$, *i.e.*,

$$\vec{J} = \vec{r}_1 \times m_1 d\vec{r}_1/dt + \vec{r}_2 \times m_2 d\vec{r}_2/dt. \qquad ...(ii)$$

Since the reduced mass $\mu = m_1 m_2/(m_1 + m_2)$, we may write relation (i) in the form

$$\vec{J} = \frac{m_1 m_2}{m_1 + m_2}\left(\vec{r}_1 - \vec{r}_2\right)\left(\frac{d\vec{r}_1}{dt} - \frac{d\vec{r}_2}{dt}\right)$$

In a centre-of-mass frame, the centre of mass being at rest, $d\vec{R}_{c.m.}/dt = 0$ and, as we have seen before,

$$\frac{d\vec{r}_1}{dt} = -\frac{m_2}{m_1}\frac{d\vec{r}_2}{dt} \text{ and } \frac{d\vec{r}_2}{dt} = -\frac{m_1}{m_2}\frac{d\vec{r}_1}{dt}.$$

So that, in that case, $$\vec{J} = \frac{m_1 m_2}{m_1+m_2}(\vec{r_1}-\vec{r_2})\left(\frac{m_1}{m_2}\frac{d\vec{r_1}}{dt}-\frac{m_2}{m_1}\frac{d\vec{r_2}}{dt}\right).$$

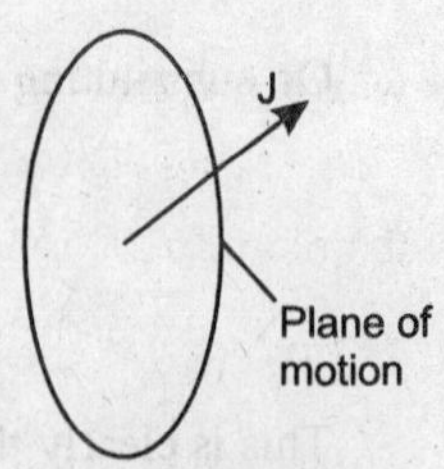

Fig. 12.29

Now, angular momentum is said to be conserved when both its magnitude and direction remain constant. Thus, in order that $\vec{J}$ in expression (*i*) above may remain constant (or conserved), $\vec{r} \times d\vec{r}/dt$ must necessarily remain constant in direction. In other words, the motions must be in a plane, indicated in Fig. 12.29.

It is found to be easier and more useful to describe the motion of a particle in a plane in terms of the *polar coordinates* $\vec{r}$ and *q*, where $\hat{r}$ is the unit vector from the fixed origin directed towards the particle (*p*) and $\hat{\theta}$, the unit vector in the plane, perpendicular to $\hat{r}$, as shown in Fig. 12.30.

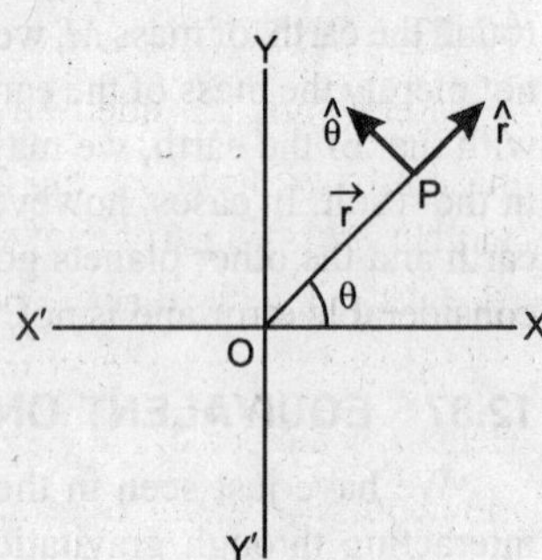

Fig. 12.30

The velocity of the particle *P* will thus have a component along $\vec{r}$ as also a component along $\hat{\theta}$. So that,

$$\frac{d\vec{r}}{dt} = \frac{d\vec{r}}{dt}\hat{r} + r\omega\hat{\theta}.$$

We may, therefore, write expression (*i*) for $\vec{J}$ above as

$$\vec{J} = \vec{r} \times \mu\left[\frac{d\vec{r}}{dt}\hat{r} + r\omega\hat{\theta}\right]$$

Or, since $\hat{r}\times\hat{r} = 0$ and $\hat{r}\times\hat{\theta} = \hat{z}$, the unit vector normal to the plane of motion of the particle, we have

$$\vec{J} = \mu r^2\,\omega\hat{z}. \text{ Or, } J = \mu r^2\omega.$$

We shall make use of this equivalent one-body problem later in deducing Kepler's laws. (See *Alternative method*, § 12.40).

12.38 VIBRATION OF A DIATOMIC MOLECULE

Suppose we have a non-rotating molecule, consisting of two atoms, a distance r_0 apart, in their stable equilibrium position, this distance being really the distance between their nuclei, or *their inter-nuclear distance*, since the mass of an atom is almost wholly concentrated in its nucleus. And, since the atoms are linked together by what are called valency bonds, this distance is also referred to as *bond length* of the molecule.

Now, if a force $\vec{F}$ be applied along the line joining the two atoms, so as to increase the distance between the two atoms a little to, say, **r** the potential energy acquired by the molecule will be $U = \frac{1}{2}(r-r_0)^2$, where $(r-r_0)/r << 1$ and *C*, a constant

So that, the force to which the two atoms of the molecule are subjected is given by $F = -dU/d(r-r_0) = -C\,(r-r_0)$.

But we know that the force between the two atoms is gravitational and, therefore, a *central force*, and that in the event of free vibration, although the atoms are in motion, their centre of mass remains constant. Reducing the two-body problem to one-body problem, therefore, we have $\vec{F} = \mu(d^2\vec{r}/dt^2)$, where μ is the *reduced mass* of the two atoms (or the molecule) and $\vec{r}$, the vector distance between them.

Substituting this value of $\vec{F}$ in the expression above, we thus have

$$\mu \frac{d^2 \vec{r}}{dt^2} = -C(\vec{r} - \vec{r_0})\hat{r},$$

where $\hat{r}$ is the unit vector along the direction of $\vec{r}$.

Since the molecule is a non-rotating one, the direction of $\vec{r}$ remains the same throughout and, therefore, $d^2 \vec{r}/dt^2 = (d^2r/dt^2)\,\hat{r}$.

Hence, $$\mu \frac{d^2 r}{dt^2}\hat{r} = -C(r - r_0)\hat{r}. \quad \text{Or, } \mu \frac{d^2 r}{dt^2} = -C(r - r_0)$$

which is clearly the equation of motion of a simple harmonic oscillator, with C as the *force constant.*

The diatomic molecule thus vibrates as a simple harmonic oscillator of *angular frequency* $\omega_o = \sqrt{C/\mu}$.

12.39 ORBITS

Let us first consider the general case of the orbit of a particle of mass m moving under the action of a *central force* $\vec{F}$ exerted by another *massive* particle of mass M fixed in position at the point O (Fig. 12.31), with $\vec{r}$ as the position vector of m with respect to O.

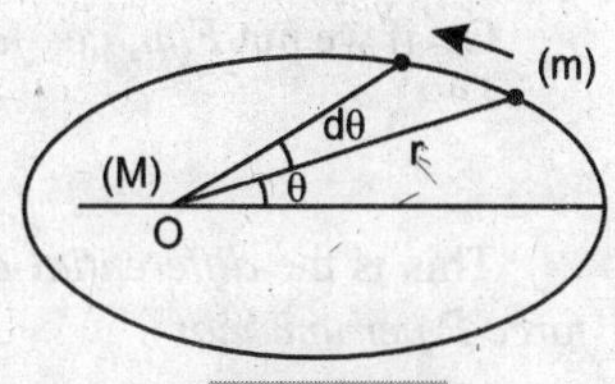

Fig. 12.31

Since the force is directed towards O, it has no moment about O. Hence, by the law of conservation of angular momentum, its angular momentum $\vec{J}$ about O remains conserved in both magnitude and direction, *i.e., it must move in a plane.*

Thus, $J = mvr = m\omega r^2 = m\,(d\theta/dt)r^2 = constant.$

This, it will be noted, is the same result as obtained under § 12.37 (on equivalent one-body problem).

If we denote *angular momentum per unit mass, i.e., J/m*, by h, we have

$$h = r^2(d\theta/dt) = constant. \qquad \text{...(I)}$$

where r and θ are the *polar coordinates* of the particle.

Now, if the position vector (or the radius vector) turns through an infinitesimal angle $d\theta$ in time dt, it sweeps out an area $ds = \frac{1}{2}r^2 d\theta$ and, therefore, its *areal velocity* $ds/dt = \frac{1}{2}r^2 d\theta/dt$ ...(II)

Since $r^2(d\theta/dt) = h$, it follows that the *areal velocity of the particle* $= h/2$.

We thus arrive at the *important result* that, *in motion under a central force, the areal velocity is constant.*

Let us now try to determine the *orbit of the particle.*

We see from relation (I) above that $d\theta/dt$ (or ω) $= h/r^2$. If, therefore, we put $1/r = u$, we have

$$d\theta/dt = hu^2.$$

So that, $$\frac{dr}{dt} = \frac{d}{dt}\left(\frac{1}{u}\right) = -\frac{1}{u^2}\frac{du}{dt} = -\frac{1}{u^2}\frac{du}{d\theta}\frac{d\theta}{dt} = -\frac{1}{u^2}\frac{du}{d\theta}hu^2$$

Or $$\frac{dr}{dt} = -h\frac{du}{d\theta}. \qquad \text{...(III)}$$

And, therefore, $$\frac{d^2 r}{dt^2} = -h\frac{d^2 u}{d\theta^2}\frac{d\theta}{dt} = -h^2 u^2 \frac{d^2 u}{d\theta^2} \qquad \text{...(IV)}$$

Now, *force acting on the particle,* $F = -\mu\left[\frac{d^2 r}{dt^2} - r\left(\frac{d\theta}{dt}\right)^2\right]$, the $-ve$ sign indicating an attractive force.

where μ is the *reduced mass* of the system of particles M and m and $\frac{d^2r}{dt^2} - r\left(\frac{d\theta}{dt}\right)^2$, the acceleration along the radius vector, or the *radial acceleration*.

Since particle M is much more massive than m. we have $\mu \approx m$.

So that,
$$F = -m\left[\frac{d^2r}{dt^2} - r\left(\frac{d\theta}{dt}\right)^2\right] = -m\left(-h^2u^2\frac{d^2u}{d\theta^2} - rh^2u^4\right)$$

Or,
$$F = m\left(h^2u^2\frac{d^2u}{d\theta^2} + \frac{1}{u}h^2u^4\right) = m\left(h^2u^2\frac{d^2u}{d\theta^2} + h^2u^3\right)$$
$$= mh^2u^2\left(\frac{d^2u}{d\theta^2} + u\right),$$

whence,
$$\frac{d^2u}{d\theta^2} + u = \frac{F}{mh^2u^2}.$$

Or, if we put F/m, *i.e., force per unit mass* $= P$, we have
$$\frac{d^2u}{d\theta^2} + u = \frac{P}{h^2u^2}. \quad \text{...(V)}$$

This is the *differential equation of the orbit of a particle moving under an attractive central force P per unit mass.*

If we solve this equation, obtaining u as a function of θ, we have the equation of the orbit in polar coordinates.

We shall now express relation (V) above in terms of energy. For, if we consider P to be a function of r alone, the work done in passing from one position to another will be quite independent of the path taken and the system will thus be *conservative*, with the principle of energy easily applicable. So that, if T, U and E be the *kinetic*, *potential and total energies* respectively, per unit mass, we have
$$T + U = E. \quad \text{Or} \quad T = E - U. \quad \text{...(VI)}$$

Now,
$$T = \frac{1}{2}\left[\left(\frac{dr}{dt}\right)^2 + r^2\left(\frac{d\theta}{dt}\right)^2\right] = \frac{1}{2}h^2\left[\left(\frac{du}{d\theta}\right)^2 + u^2\right]$$

And since $\mathbf{P} = -grad\ U$, the magnitude of its inward component P is given by $P = dU/dr$. and therefore, $U = \int_{r_0}^{r} P\,dr$, where r_0 is some constant.

Equation (VI) thus becomes $\frac{1}{2}h^2\left[\left(\frac{du}{d\theta}\right)^2 + u^2\right] = E - U.$

Or,
$$\left(\frac{du}{d\theta}\right)^2 + u^2 = \frac{2(E-U)}{h^2}. \quad \text{...(VII)}$$

This equation is really the same as equation (V) above, as may be easily seen on differentiation, if only we remember that U, being a function of r, is also a function of u.

Particular case of inverse square law forces. If the force acting on the moving particle towards the fixed particle or the origin O be an inverse square law force, we have *force per unit mass towards the centre of force, i.e.,* $P = K/r^2$, where K is a constant.

Our differential equation (V) for the orbit now becomes $(d^2u/d\theta^2) + u = K/h^2$, the general solution of which is
$$u = K/h^2 + A\cos(\theta - \theta_o) \quad \text{..(VIII)}$$
where A and θ_o are constants of integration.

This, in polar coordinates, is the equation of the most general orbit described under a central inverse square law force.

Now, the *potential energy per unit mass*, $U = \int P dr = \int (K/r^2)\, dr = -K/r = -Ku$, the constant of integration having been so chosen that $U = 0$ at ∞.

From relations (VII) and (VIII), therefore, we have

$$A^2 + \frac{K^2}{h^4} + 2A\frac{K}{h^2}\cos(\theta - \theta_0) = \frac{2}{h^2}\left[E + \frac{K^2}{h^2} + K\,A\cos(\theta - \theta_0)\right]$$

Or, $$A^2 + \frac{K^2}{h^4} + \frac{2AK\cos(\theta - \theta_0)}{h^2} = \frac{2E}{h^2} + \frac{2K^2}{h^4} + \frac{2KA\cos(\theta - \theta_0)}{h^2}.$$

Or, $$A^2 = \frac{K^2}{h^4} + \frac{2E}{h^2},$$

thus obtaining the value of constant A in terms of the total energy and angular momentum per unit mass.

If we rotate the base line $\theta = 0$ to make $\theta_o = 0$ and $A > 0$, relation (VIII) above will assume the form

$$u = \frac{K}{h^2}\left(1 + \sqrt{1 + \frac{2Eh^2}{K^2}}\cos\theta\right) \quad \text{...(IX)}$$

From the focus-directrix property of a conic, we know that its equation in polar coordinates may be written as

$$u = \frac{1}{l}(1 + \in\cos\theta). \quad \text{Or, } \frac{l}{r} = (1 + \in \cos\theta), \quad \text{...(X)} \quad [\because u = 1/r]$$

where l is the *semi latus rectum* (*i.e.*, half the focal chord parallel to the directrix) and $\in$, the *eccentricity*, with θ measured from the perpendicular dropped on the directrix from the focus.

The conic may be of any one of the following types:

(*i*) *ellipse*, if $\in < 1$, (*ii*) *parabola*, if $\in = 1$, (*iii*) *hyperbola*, if $\in > 1$, (in this case, relation (*X*) gives only the branch adjacent to the focus) and (iv) *circle*, if $\in = 0$, This is shown in Fig. 12.32.

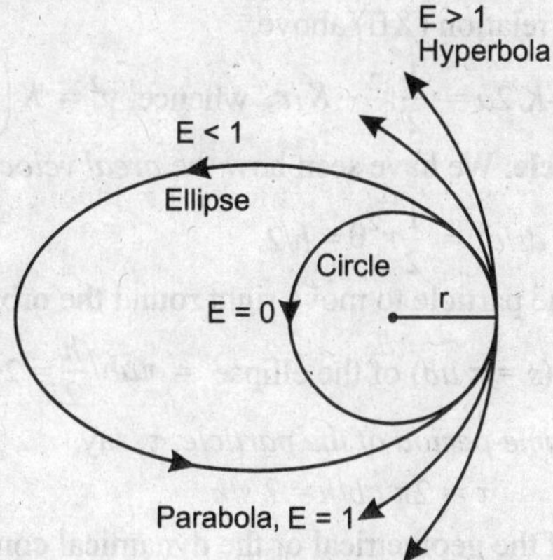

Fig. 12.32

It may be noted that relations (IX) and (X) become identical if we choose

$$l = h^2/K \quad \text{and} \quad \in = \sqrt{1 + \frac{2Eh^2}{K^2}}. \quad \text{...(XI)}$$

Thus, we arrive at the result that *the orbit described by a particle, attracted by a central inverse square law force towards a fixed point or origin, is a conic having the fixed point or centre of force as focus,* (its semi latus rectum and eccentricity being given by relation (XI) in terms of E and h).

The orbit may take the following forms:

(*i*) If $E < 0$ or $-ve$, it is an *ellipse*, (*ii*) if $E = 0$, if is a parabola and (*iii*) if $E > 0$, it is a hyperbola.

Actually, *most of the orbits of the planets are ellipses*. A body describing a parabolic or a hyperbolic orbit would pass out of the solar system, never to return. We shall, therefore, consider here only the constants of the elliptical orbit.

Constants of the elliptical orbit.* It can be seen at once from relation (X) above that *the shape and size of the orbit are given by the constants l and $\in$ but not its orientation in space*. These two constants are related to the constants E and h in the manner shown by expression (XI).

So that, we have five constants in all appearing in our various relations deduced above, *viz.*, K, l, $\in$, E and h. Of these, K (the intensity of the force-centre) has obviously a fixed or constant value and is to be known once for all, but the other four constants take on different values for different orbits. Of these four also, only two are really independent, as can be seen from relation (XI). We may, however, use any two of them, as an independent pair to suit our convenience in any given case.

In fact, it is much better to use a and e as our *fundamental constants* instead of l and e, where a is the *semi major axis* of the ellipse.

$$l = \frac{b^2}{a} = a(1-e^2),$$

where b is the *semi minor axis of the ellipse*.

The constants a and e are usually referred to as *geometrical constants* and constants E and h, as *dynamical constants*, their inter-relationship being as follows:

$$a = K/2E; \quad e = \sqrt{1+(2Eh^2/K^2)}; \quad E = -K/2a$$

and $$h = \sqrt{Ka(1-e^2)}. \qquad \text{...(XII)}$$

Speed of the particle. We have *energy per unit mass* given by

$$E = \frac{1}{2}v^2 - K/r.$$

Or, substituting for E from relation (XII) above,

$$-K/2a = \frac{1}{2}v^2 - K/r, \text{ whence, } v^2 = K\left(\frac{2}{r}-\frac{1}{a}\right) \qquad \text{...(XIII)}$$

Periodic time of the particle. We have seen how the *areal velocity*.

$$ds/dt = \frac{1}{2}r^2\theta = h/2.$$

Therefore, time taken by the particle to move right round the orbit,

or to sweep the entire area ($s = \pi\, ab$) of the ellipse $= \pi ab/\dfrac{h}{2} = 2\pi ab/h = 2s/h.$

And this is obviously, the *time-period of the particle*, τ, say.

So that, $$\tau = 2\pi\, ab/h = 2\, s/h.$$

Or, to express it in terms of the geometrical or the dynamical constants, we note that

$b = a\sqrt{1-e^2}$ and from relation (XII) above,

$$h^2 = Ka(1-e^2). \text{ So that, } (1-e^2) = h^2/Ka.$$

$$\therefore \quad \tau^2 = \frac{4\pi^2a^2b^2}{h^2} = \frac{4\pi^2a^2[a^2(1-e^2)]}{h^2} = \frac{4\pi^2a^4}{h^2}\left(\frac{h^2}{Ka}\right) = \frac{4\pi^2a^3}{K},$$

* The kinetic energy, as we know, can never be negative but is *zero* at infinite separation. On the other hand, potential energy is always negative and is also *zero* at infinite separation. The meaning of total negative energy, therefore, is that the body or the particle remains bound to the attracting centre at O and cannot escape from it, or, in other words, that the system is *closed one*.

whence, $$\tau = 2\pi\sqrt{a^3/K}.$$

Or, *in terms of energy,* $$\tau = \frac{2\pi K}{\sqrt{(-2E)^3}}, \qquad \text{...(XIV)}$$

remembering that $E < 0$ for an elliptical orbit.

Thus, the expression for time-period of the particle contains either one geometrical constant (a) or one dynamical constant (E).

It will easily be seen from the two expressions for τ that *for orbits, having the same semi major axis, the periodic time is the same and so also for orbits with the same total energy.*

Circular orbits and their stability. For a circular orbit, clearly, r and, therefore, u is constant. Hence, the possible radii of circular orbits are determined by the relation $u = P(u)/h^2u^2$ [see relation (V) above].

Thus, *with force per unit mass, P, directed towards the centre of force, we can obtain a circular orbit of any radius by projecting the particle at right angles to the radius vector (or position vector) with a velocity such that*

$$h^2 = P(u) / u^3. \qquad \text{...(XV)}$$

The question, however, arises whether these circular orbits will all be stable, *i.e.*, whether, due to any slight temporary disturbance, which will almost always be there, the orbit would continue to lie close to the original circular orbit or will deviate far from it.

Let us put $u = u_0$ and $h = h_0$ for a circular orbit, so that relation (XV) becomes

$$h_0^2 = P(u_0)/u_0^3.$$

To study the effect of a disturbance, let us put $u = u_0 + \xi$, where ξ and its derivatives are supposed to be small and so is $(h - h_o)$.

Substituting these values in relation (V) above, we have

$$\frac{d^2\xi}{d\theta^2} + u_0 + \xi = \frac{P(u_0 + \xi)}{h^2(u_0 + \xi)^2} \qquad \text{...(XVI)}$$

which, on expansion in powers of ξ, gives

$$\frac{P(u_0 + \xi)}{h^2(u_0 + \xi)^2} = \frac{1}{h^2u_0^2}\left(1 + \frac{\xi}{u_0}\right)^{-2}(P_0 + \xi P_0' + \ldots)$$

$$= \frac{P_0}{h^2u_0^2}\left[1 + \xi\left(\frac{P_0'}{P_0} - \frac{2}{u_0}\right) + \ldots\right]$$

where $P' = dP/du$ and the subscript *0* indicates evaluation for $u = u_0$.

Then, neglecting higher than the first order of small quantities, relation (XVI) takes the form

$$d^2\xi/d\theta^2 + A\xi = B, \qquad \text{...(XVII)}$$

$$\text{where constant } A = 1 - \frac{P_0}{h_0^2u_0^2}\left(\frac{P_0'}{P_0} - \frac{2}{u_0}\right) = 3 - \frac{u_0P_0'}{P_0}, \qquad \text{...(XVIII)}$$

and we need not bother about the value of constant B in which we are not at present interested.

Now, expression (XVII) has three solutions (for ξ) corresponding to $A > 0$, $A < 0$ and $A = 0$. Of these, the only solution which remains permanently small corresponds to $A > 0$, the other two increasing indefinitely with θ.

Clearly, therefore, a circular orbit (of radius $1/u_0$) will be stable *only* if

$$A > 0. \text{ Or, } \left(3 - \frac{u_0P_0'}{P_0}\right) > 0. \quad \text{Or, } \frac{u_0P_0'}{P_0} < 3.$$

Now, suppose the force obeys the *inverse n^{th} power law, i.e.,*

$$P = K/r^n = Ku^n. \qquad \text{...(XIX)}$$

Then, clearly, $uP'/P = n$. So that, circular orbits under the force directed towards the centre of force, *i.e.*, under the attractive force given by relation (XIX) above will be stable *only if* $n < 3$.

It follows, therefore, that *circular orbits will be stable for a force varying inversely as the distance or the square of the distance (i.e., inverse square law force) and will be unstable for the inverse cube (or a higher power) law.*

12.40 KEPLER'S LAWS

Kepler, on the basis of the data on the motion of planet Mars collected by his chief, Tycho Brahe, at the Royal Observatory at Prague, succeeded after 22 years of ceaseless work in evolving the famous three laws, known after him –the first two in the year 1609 and the third, ten years later, in 1619. These laws have an historical importance in that they provided the original experimental evidence on the validity of Newton's laws of mechanics as also his theory of gravitational attraction. The three laws may be stated thus:

First Law. *The path of a planet is an elliptical orbit around the sun, with the sun at one of its foci.* This is aptly known as the **law of elliptical orbits** and obviously gives the shape of the orbit of a planet around the sun.

Second Law. *The radius, drawn from the sun to a planet, sweeps out equal areas in equal time, i.e., its areal velocity (or the area swept out by it per unit time)is constant.* This is referred to as the **law of areas** and gives the relationship between the orbital speed of the planet and its distance from the sun.

Third Law. *The square of a planet's year, i.e., its time-period (or its time of one complete round of the sun) is proportional to the cube of the semi-major axis of its orbit.* This is known as the **harmonic law** and gives the relationship between the size of the orbit of a planet and its time of revolution.

Let us discuss these laws on the basis of the theory of orbits we have dealt with in § 12.39.

We know that in the case of an inverse square law attractive force, the *force per unit mass of the planet towards the centre of the force, (in this case, the sun) is given by $P = K/r^2$, where r is now the distance of the planet from the sun and K,* a constant equal to MG, M being the *mass of the sun and* G, the *gravitational constant.* ($\because F = MmG/r^2$ and $\therefore P = K/r^2 = F/m = MG/r^2$, whence, $K = MG$. See Fig. 12.31, where the sun may be imagined at O.

Our differential equation (V) for the orbit thus becomes

$$\frac{d^2u}{d\theta^2} + u = \frac{MG}{h^2},$$

the general solution for which is $u = MG/h^2 + A\cos(\theta - \theta_0)$, where A and θ_0 are constants of integration.

Now θ_0 can be made equal to 0 by rotating the base line $\theta = 0$, with $A > 0$. Hence, the above solution becomes $u = MG/h^2 + A\cos\theta$.

Or, $\quad 1/r = MG/h^2 + A\cos\theta$.

This may be put as, $\quad \dfrac{h^2/Mg}{r} = 1 + \dfrac{h^2A}{MG}\cos\theta$

This equation is of the same form as equation (X), of a conic in polar coordinates, *viz.*, $u = \frac{1}{l}(1 + \in\cos\theta)$. Or, $\frac{l}{r} = 1 + \in\cos\theta$, with l, the *semi latus rectum, equal to* h^2/MG and $\in$, *the eccentricity*, equal to h^2A/MG.

So that, *with e ,i.e., h^2A/MG less than* 1, *the orbit of the planet around the sun is an ellipse*. This, than, establishes *Kepler's first law*.

Or, if we obtain the *value of $\in$ in terms of the total energy of the system*, we arrive at the result. For as we have seen in § 12.39,

$$l = h^2/K \text{ and } \in = \sqrt{(1+2Eh^2)K^2}$$

So that, here, $l = h^2/MG$ and $\in = \sqrt{(1+2 \in h^2)/M^2G^2}$,

where *E represents the total energy per unit mass.*

In case E_m be taken to be the total energy of the planet (or the system), we have $E = E_m/m$ in the expression above. Also, remembering that $h = J/m$ and $K = MG$, we have

$$l = h^2/K = J^2/m^2MG \text{ and } \in = \sqrt{(1+2E_mh^2)/mM^2G^2}$$

$$= \sqrt{(1+2E_mJ^2)/m^3M^2G^2}, \text{ whence, } E_m = -\frac{m^3M^2G^2}{2J^2}(1-\in^2).$$

So that, if $\in < 1$, the total energy E_m is negative *i.e., the planet is bound in an orbit of the form of a closed ellipse.*

For a circular orbit, since $\in = 0$, we have $E_m = -\dfrac{m^3M^2G^2}{2J^2}$.

Alternatively, we could proceed *on the basis of the equivalent one-body problem as follows*: If μ be the reduced mass of the system of the planet and the sun, we have

$$\mu\frac{d^2r}{dt^2} = -\frac{MmG}{r^2} + \frac{\mu v^2}{r} = \frac{\mu\omega^2r^2}{r} - \frac{MmG}{r^2}.$$

Or, $$\mu\frac{d^2r}{dt^2} = \mu\omega^2r - \frac{MmG}{r^2}. \qquad \ldots(i)$$

But, as we know, $$J = \mu r^2\omega \qquad \text{[see § 12.37]} \ldots.(ii)$$

So that, $$\omega^2 = J^2/\mu^2r^4. \qquad \ldots(iii)$$

$\therefore$ $$\mu\frac{d^2r}{dt^2} = \frac{\mu J^2r}{\mu^2r^4} - \frac{MmG}{r^2} = \frac{J^2}{\mu r^3} - \frac{MmG}{r^2}. \qquad \ldots(iv)$$

Solving relation (*iv*) for *r* as a function of $r(\theta)$ of the angle θ, we have

$$\frac{dr}{dt} = \frac{dr}{d\theta}\cdot\frac{d\theta}{dt} = \frac{dr}{d\theta}\omega = \frac{dr}{d\theta}\cdot\frac{J}{\mu r^2}. \qquad \ldots(v)$$

Differentiating again, we have

$$\frac{d^2r}{dt^2} = \frac{d^2r}{d\theta^2}\left(\frac{J}{\mu r^2}\right)^2 + \frac{dr}{d\theta}\cdot\frac{J}{\mu}\frac{d}{dt}\left(\frac{1}{r^2}\right).$$

Or, $$\frac{d^2r}{dt^2} = \frac{d^2r}{d\theta^2}\left(\frac{J}{\mu r^2}\right)^2 - \frac{2}{r^3}\cdot\frac{J}{\mu}\cdot\left(\frac{dr}{d\theta}\right)^2\cdot\frac{J}{\mu r^2}. \qquad \ldots(vi)$$

[Using $J = \mu r^2\omega$ and relation (*v*)]

Now, let us put the function $u(\theta) = \dfrac{1}{r}(\theta)$. Then, on differentiating, we have

$$\frac{du}{d\theta} = -\frac{1}{r^2}\frac{dr}{d\theta}; \text{ and } \frac{d^2u}{d\theta^2} = -\frac{1}{r^2}\frac{d^2r}{d\theta^2} + \frac{2}{r^3}\left(\frac{dr}{d\theta}\right)^2 \qquad \ldots(vii)$$

Comparing relations (*vi*) and (*vii*) we see that

$$\frac{d^2r}{dt^2} = -\frac{1}{r^2}\left(\frac{J}{\mu}\right)^2\frac{d^2u}{d\theta^2}. \qquad ...(viii)$$

We may, therefore, write relation (*iv*) as

$$-\mu\left[\frac{1}{r^2}\left(\frac{J}{\mu}\right)^2\frac{d^2u}{d\theta^2}\right] = \frac{1}{r^3}\frac{J^2}{\mu} - \frac{1}{r^2}MmG.$$

Remembering that $1/r = u$, we have

$$-u^2\frac{J^2}{\mu}\frac{d^2u}{d\theta^2} = u^3\frac{J^2}{\mu} - u^2 MmG. \quad \text{Or,} \quad -\frac{d^2u}{d\theta^2} = u - \frac{\mu MmG}{J^2}.$$

Or,

$$\frac{d^2u}{d\theta^2} + u = \frac{\mu MmG}{J^2}, \qquad ...(ix)$$

the solutions of which $u = \dfrac{\mu MmG}{J^2} + A\cos\theta.$ Or, $\dfrac{1}{r} = \dfrac{\mu MmG}{J^2} + A\cos\theta.$

Or,

$$\frac{J^2/\mu MmG}{r} = 1 + \frac{J^2 A}{\mu MmG}\cos\theta,$$

which is an equation similar to that of a general conic section.

$$\frac{l}{r} = 1 + \in \cos\theta, \text{ where, } l = \frac{J^2}{\mu MmG} \text{ and } \in = \frac{J^2 A}{\mu MmG}.$$

Thus *for* $\in < 1$, *i.e.*, $(J^2A/\mu MmG) < 1$, *the planet will describe an elliptical orbit round the sun.*

Again, let us obtain the value of $\in$ in terms of the total energy E_m of the system.

We have $E_m = \dfrac{1}{2}mv^2 - \dfrac{mM}{r}G$, where m is the *mass of the planet*.

Now, at *minimum* and *maximum* distances from the sun, *i.e.*, at positions respectively called *perihelion* and *aphelion*, the velocity vector is perpendicular to the position vector **r** and $\theta = 0$ and π respectively. So that, at these points, $v = r\,d\theta/dt = h/r = J/\mu r$. Hence

$$E_m = \frac{J^2}{2\mu}\left(\frac{1}{r_{min}}\right)^2 - \frac{mMG}{r_{min}} = \frac{J^2}{2\mu}\left(\frac{1}{r_{max}}\right)^2 - \frac{mMG}{r_{max}}. \qquad ...(i)$$

Therefore, from the relation, $l/r = 1 + \in \cos\theta$, we have

$$\frac{l}{r_{min}} = 1 + \in \text{ and } \frac{l}{r_{max}} = 1 - \in \qquad ...(ii)$$

which gives $\in = \dfrac{r_{max} - r_{min}}{r_{max} + r_{min}}$, a convenient relation to remember.

Substituting relation (*ii*) in (*i*) and solving out, we obtain, as before,

$$\in = \sqrt{\frac{1 + 2E_m J^2}{\mu M^2 m^2 G^2}} \text{ and } E_m = \frac{-\mu M^2 m^2 G^2}{2J^2}(1 - \in^2).$$

So that, again, for $\in < 1$, the total energy E_m is constant and negative and the planet describes a closed ellipse around the sun.

For $\in = 0$, the orbit would be a circle and the total energy of the system would be $E_m = -\mu M^2 m^2 G^2/2J^2$.

N.B. It will be seen that if m be $<< M$, $\mu \approx m$ and the expressions for $\in$ and E_m respectively become $\sqrt{(1 + 2E_m J^2)/m^3 M^2 G^2}$ and $-(m^3M^2G^2/2J^2)(1 - \in^2)$, as obtained above.

Now, in § 12.39 at the very outset we have shown how, in the case of a body moving under a central force, its areal velocity is constant. Therefore, since a planet moves around the sun under the central gravitational force directed towards the sun, its areal velocity must remain constant. This, then, takes care of *Kepler's second law.* In fact, we have proceeded on this very assumption in deducing Kepler's first law above.

Finally, as shown in § 12.39. (under constants of the elliptical orbit), the time-period of a body describing an ellipse around a fixed body, and therefore, here, of a planet describing an elliptical orbit around the sun, given by

$$\tau = \frac{\textit{area of ellipse}}{\textit{areal velocity}} = \frac{\pi ab}{h/2}.$$

Or,
$$\tau^2 = \frac{4\pi^2 a^2 b^2}{h^2}.$$

Again, $l = h^2K = h^2/MG$. Also $l = b^2/a$. So that, $b^2/a = h^2/MG$.

Or,
$$b^2 = h^2a/MG.$$

∴ substituting this value of b^2 in the expression for τ^2 above, we have

$$\tau^2 = \frac{4\pi^2 a^2}{h^2}\left[\frac{h^2 a}{MG}\right] = \frac{4\pi^2 a^3}{MG}.$$

Or,
$$\tau^2 \propto a^3 \qquad ...(iii)$$

since $4\pi^2/MG$ is clearly a constant for all planets.

And, this is *Keper's third law*, a consequence of which is that *all planets, with the same major axis of their elliptical orbits have the same periodic time.*

This relation (*iii*) actually enables us to *weigh* the sun, as it were, if we know the time-period and the major axis of the orbit of any planet around it.

In worked example at the end of the chapter, it has been done from the time-period of the earth around the sun, its orbit being assumed circular. Relation (*iii*), however, tells us that we can do so even for an elliptical orbit if we use the *semi-major axis* of the orbit in place of the *radius* of the circular orbit.

12.41 DEDUCTION OF NEWTON'S LAW OF GRAVITATION FROM KEPLER'S LAWS

In the discussion above (§ 12.40), we have deduced *Kepler's laws* from Newton's laws of motion and gravitation. Let us now take up the reverse problem of deducing Newton's law of gravitation from Kepler's laws, for that is how, historically, the law of gravitation was deduced by *Newton.*

Kepler's *second law* tells us that $h = J/m$, the *angular momentum per unit mass* = $r^2\,(d\theta/dt)$ = *constant*. Hence the force on the planet must be directed towards the sun.

And from the *first law*, as we have seen, the equation of the orbit of the planet around the sun may be written as

$$u = \frac{1}{l}(1 + \in\cos\theta).$$

So that, in accordance with relation (*V*) (§12.40), *force per unit mass of the planet* is given by $P = h^2u^2(d^2u/d\theta^2 + u) = h^2u^2/l.$

Now, *force per unit mass means acceleration*. Therefore, *radial acceleration* of every planet towards the sun is, say,

$$a_r = -h^2u^2/l = -\frac{h^2/l}{r^2} = -\frac{K}{r^2}, \text{ where } K = h^2/l, \text{ a constant}$$

Thus, *the acceleration, and hence the force acting on a planet, is inversely proportional to the square of its distance from the sun*, the negative sign merely indicating that it is directed inwards, towards the sun, or that it is a force of attraction.

And, the time-period of a planet, in accordance with Kepler's *third law*, is given by

$$\tau = \pi ab\frac{h}{2}.$$

Or, $$\tau^2 = 4\pi^2a^2b^2/h^2,$$

where a and b are the semi-major and minor axes of the elliptical orbit respectively.

Since $b^2/a = l$, the *semi-latus rectum* of the elliptical orbit, we have

$$b^2 = al.$$

And, therefore, $$\tau^2 = (4\pi^2 l/h^2)a^3$$
$$= (4\pi^2/K)a^3,$$

indicating that $\tau \propto a^3$ *for every planet*, or that $4\pi^2/K$, and hence K, is constant for every planet and thus quite *independent of its nature*.

Hence, if m and M be the masses of a planet and the sun respectively, the force of attraction by the sun on the planet is, say, $F = -Km/r^2$ and its reaction, *i.e.*, the force of attraction by the planet on the sun, say, $F' = -kM/r^2$, where K and k are *constants*.

Since by Newton's third law of motion, $F = F'$, we have

$$Km/r^2 = kM/r^2.$$

Or, $Km = kM.$ Or, $K/M = k/m$, constant, say G.

So that, $K = MG.$

Substituting this value of K in the expression for F we, therefore, have

$$F = -\frac{Mm}{r^2}G,$$

showing that the force of attraction between the planet and the sun is *directly proportional to the product of their masses and inversely proportional to the square of the distance between them*, which is Newton's *law of gravitation*.

WORKED EXAMPLES

I–Law of gravitation

Example 1. The radius of the Moon's orbit r is 240,000 miles and period of revolution is 27 days; the diameter of the Earth is 8000 miles and the value of gravity on its surface is 32 ft/sec². Verify the statement that the gravitational force varies inversely as the square of the distance.

Solution. Clearly *velocity of the Moon*, $v = \frac{Distance\ covered}{Time\ taken} = \frac{2\pi\times 240000\times 1760\times 3}{27\times 24\times 60\times 60}$ m/s

$\therefore$ *Centripetal acceleration of the Moon towards the centre of the earth, i.e.,*

$$g_M = \frac{v^2}{r} = \left(\frac{2\pi\times 24\times 176\times 3\times 10^5}{27\times 24\times 36\times 10^2}\right)^2\times\left(\frac{1}{24\times 176\times 3\times 10^5}\right)$$

$$= \frac{4\pi^2\times 176\times 3\times 10}{(27\times 36)^2\times 24} = 0.009189 \text{ ft/sec}^2.$$

Let the gravitational force be inversely proportional to the nth power of distance. Then, if the acceleration due to gravity on the surface of the Earth be g_E (equal to 32 ft/sec²), we have

$$g_M/g_E = (R/r)^n, \text{ where } R \text{ is the radius of the earth,}$$

Or, $\frac{0.009189}{32} = \left(\frac{4000 \times 1760 \times 3}{240000 \times 1760 \times 3}\right)^n = \left(\frac{1}{60}\right)^n$.

Or, taking logarithms, we have $\bar{4}.4582 = n\,(\bar{2}.2218)$ Or, $n = \bar{4}.4582/\bar{2}.2218 \approx 2$.

Thus, g and *hence the gravitational force varies inversely as the square of the distance.*

Example 2. Find the mass of sun from the following data: Radius of earth orbit $r = 1.5 \times 10^8$ km, $G = 6.67 \times 10^{-11}$ Nm^2 kg^{-2}. ***(Gharwal U. 2000)***

Solution. The earth revolves round the sun in more or less circular orbit of radius r. The gravitational force of attraction between the sun of mass M and earth of mass m is balanced by the centripetal force $mr\omega^2$, where ω is the angular velocity of earth

$$\therefore \qquad \omega = \frac{2\pi}{365 \times 24 \times 3600} = 1.99 \times 10^{-7} \text{ rad s}^{-1}$$

$$r = 1.5 \times 10^8 \text{ km} = 1.5 \times 10^{11}\ m$$

Now
$$\frac{GMm}{r^2} = mr\omega^2$$

$$\therefore \qquad M = \frac{r^3\omega^2}{G} = \frac{(1.5 \times 10^{11})^3 \times (1.99 \times 10^{-7})^2}{6.67 \times 10^{-11}} = 2.004 \times 10^{30} \text{ kg}$$

Example 3. The earth is moving round the sun under gravitational force and its orbit has semi-major axis 1.495×10^8 km. When the earth passes closest to the sun at its perihelion its distance is 1.47×10^8 km and its orbital velocity is 0.303 kms^{-1}. Find the velocity of the earth at the aphelion and its angular velocities at the two points.

Solution. As the motion of the earth round the sun is under gravitational force which is a central force, the angular momentum of the earth at the two positions, the perihelion and the apehilion, is conserved.

Or Angular momentum at apehilion = angular momentum at perihelion

Or
$$mv_{ap}\, r_{ap} = mv_{peri}\, r_{peri}$$

Now
$$r_{peri} = 1.47 \times 10^8 \text{ km}$$

Semi major axis $a = 1.495 \times 10^8$ km $\quad \therefore$ Major axis $= 2a = 2.990 \times 10^8$ km ...(*i*)

Now
$$r_{ap} + r_{peri} = 2a$$

$$\therefore \qquad r_{ap} = 2a - r_{peri} = 2.990 \times 10^8 - 1.47 \times 10^8 = 1.520 \times 10^8 \text{ km}$$

Substituting in (*i*), we have $v_{ap} \times 1.52 \times 10^8 = 0.303 \times 1.47 \times 10^8$

$\therefore$ Velocity of the earth at apehilion $v_{ap} = \frac{0.303 \times 1.47 \times 10^8}{1.52 \times 10^8} = 0.293$ kms^{-1}

The angular velocity at the perihelion $\omega_{peri} = \frac{v_{\text{peri}}}{r_{\text{peri}}} = \frac{0.303}{1.47 \times 10^8} = 0.206 \times 10^{-8}$ rad s^{-1}

The angular velocity at the apehilion $\omega_{ap} = \frac{v_{\text{ap}}}{r_{\text{ap}}} = \frac{0.293}{1.520 \times 10^8} = 0.193 \times 10^{-8}$ rad s^{-1}

Example 4. The motion of a particle under the influence of a central force is described by $r = a \sin\theta$. Find an expression for the force.

Solution. The motion of the particle is given by

$$r = a \sin\theta$$

$$\therefore \qquad u = \frac{1}{r} = \frac{1}{a\sin\theta} = \frac{\text{cosec}\,\theta}{a}$$

Hence
$$\frac{du}{d\theta} = -\frac{\text{cosec}\theta \cot\theta}{a}$$

and
$$\frac{d^2u}{d\theta^2} = -\frac{1}{a}(-\text{cosec}\,\theta\,\text{cosec}^2\theta - \text{cosec}\theta\cot\theta\cot\theta)$$
$$= \frac{1}{a}\cos\theta\,(\text{cosec}^2\,\theta + \cot^2\theta)$$

The differential equation of motion of the orbit of a particle moving under a central force is given by

$$\frac{d^2u}{d\theta^2} = -u - \frac{m}{j^2u^2}F\left(\frac{1}{u}\right)$$

$$\therefore \quad \frac{m}{J^2u^2}F\left(\frac{1}{u}\right) = -u - \frac{d^2u}{d\theta^2}$$
$$= -\frac{1}{a}[\text{cosec}\,\theta + \text{cosec}\,\theta\,(\text{cosec}^2\,\theta + \cot^2\theta)]$$
$$= -\frac{1}{a}\text{cosec}\,\theta\,(1 + \text{cosec}^2\,\theta + \cot^2\theta)]$$
$$= -\frac{2}{a}\text{cosec}^2\theta = -2a^2u^3$$

$$\therefore \quad F\left(\frac{1}{u}\right) = -\frac{(2J^2u^5a^2)}{m} = \frac{-2J^2a^2u^5}{m} \therefore F(r) = \frac{-2J^2a^2}{m}\left(\frac{1}{r^5}\right)$$

This is the required force law.

Example 5. Calculate the period of revolution of Neptune round the sun given that the diameter of the orbit is 30 times the diameter of the earth's orbit round the sun, both orbits being assumed to be circular.

Solution. Let a_1 and a_2 be the mean radii of the orbit of the earth and Neptune respectively.

$$\therefore \quad \frac{a_2}{a_1} = 30$$

Period of revolution of earth T_1 = one year.

Let T_2 be the period of revolution of Neptune. Then according to Kepler's third law

$$\frac{T_2^2}{T_1^2} = \left(\frac{a_2}{a_1}\right)^3 \therefore T_2^2 = T_1^2\left(\frac{a_2}{a_1}\right)^3 = 30 \times 30 \times 30$$

or
$$T_2 = 30\sqrt{30} \text{ years} = 164.3 \text{ years}$$

Example 6. A sphere of mass 19 kg. is attracted by another sphere of mass 150 kg. when their centres are separated by a distance 0.28 m with a force equal to the weight of 0.25 mg. Calculate the gravitational constant. If the distance is halved, what would be the new force in Newton? Assume $g = 9.8$ ms^{-2}.

Solution. Here $\quad m_1 = 19$ kg; $m_2 = 150$ kg; $r = 0.28$ m

Force $\quad F = 0.25$ mg. $wt = 0.25 \times 10^{-6} \times 9.8$ N

Now
$$F = \frac{Gm_1m_2}{r^2} \text{ or } G = \frac{Fr^2}{m_1m_2}$$
$$= \frac{0.25\times10^{-6}\times9.8\times(0.28)^2}{19\times150} = 6.74 \times 10^{-11} \text{ Nm}^2\text{ kg}^{-2}.$$

When the distance is halved, the force F' between the two masses becomes 4 times as the force is inversely proportional to the square of the distance between the centres of the two masses.

$$F' = 4F = 4 \times 0.25 \times 10^{-6} \times 9.8 = 9.8 \times 10^{-6} \text{ Newton.}$$

Example 7. If the mass of sun is 2 × 10^{-30} kg, distance of earth from the sun is 1.5 × 10^{11} m and period of revolution of the former around the latter is 365.3 days, find the value of *G*.

Solution. The force of attraction F between the sun of mass M and earth of mass m separated by a distance r is given by $F = \frac{GMm}{r^2}$

This force is balanced by the centripetal force $m\omega^2$ where w is the angular velocity of earth

$$\therefore \quad \frac{GMm}{r^2} = mr\omega^2 \text{ or } G = \frac{r^3\omega^2}{M}$$

Now $M = 2 \times 10^{30}$ kg, $r = 1.5 \times 10^{11}$ m, $G = ?$

$$\omega = \frac{2\pi}{365.3 \times 24 \times 3600} = 11.991 \times 10^{-7} \text{ rad s}^{-1}$$

$$\therefore \quad G = \frac{(1.5 \times 10^{11})^3 \times (1.991 \times 10^{-7})^2}{2 \times 10^{30}} = 6.668 \times 10^{-11} \text{ Nm}^2\text{-kg}^2$$

Example 8. A satellite revolves in a circular orbit at a height of 200 km from the surface of earth. If the period of revolution of satellite is 90 mts, $G = 6.66 \times 10^{-11}$ Nm^2 kg^{-2} and mean radius of earth is 6 × 10^6 m, calculate the average density of earth,

Solution. Distance of satellite from the centre of earth

$$R_1 = 6 \times 10^6 + 0.2 \times 10^6 = 6.2 \times 10^6 \, m$$

If M is the mass of earth and m that of satellite, then $\frac{GMm}{R_1^2} = mR_1\omega^2$

Or $$M = \frac{R_1^3\omega^2}{G} = \frac{4}{3}\pi R^3\rho$$

Or $$\rho = \frac{3R_1^3\omega^2}{4\pi R^3 G}$$

$$= \frac{3 \times (6.2 \times 10^6)^3}{4\pi \times (6 \times 10^6)^3 \times 6.66 \times 10^{-11}} \times \left(\frac{2\pi}{90 \times 60}\right)^2$$

$$= 5.355 \times 10^3 \text{ kg m}^{-3}$$

II–Gravitational potential and field intensity–Potential energy – Gauss's theorem

Example 9. Show that the intensity and potential at any point on the surface of the earth are *g* and *gR* respectively, assuming the earth to be a uniform sphere. ***(Poona)***

Solution. Let the earth be a uniform sphere of radius R and mass M. Then, clearly,

intensity of the gravitational field at any point on its surface, $E = -\frac{M}{R^2}G.$

Now, weight of a body of mass m on the surface of r the earth of the gravitational force on it due to attraction by the earth $= mg - mMG/R^2$, where g is the acceleration due to gravity at the place.

$\therefore$ *Force on unit mass on the surface of the earth,* or *intensity of the gravitational field on the surface of the earth, i.e,.* $E = -\frac{M}{R^2}G = g.$

This is the reason why g is also quite often referred to as *intensity of gravity.*

And, since *potential at any point on the surface of the earth, i.e.,* $V = -\frac{M}{R}G,$

we have $$V = -\left(\frac{M}{R^2}G\right)R = gR.$$

Example 10. Two bodies of mass M_1 and M_2 are placed distance d apart. Show that at the position where the gravitational field due to them is zero, the potential is given by

$$V = -\frac{G}{d}(M_1 + M_2 + \sqrt{M_1 M_2}) \qquad \textit{(Rajasthan, 2001)}$$

Solution. Let the gravitational field E be *zero* at a point distant x from mass M_1, and, therefore, distant $(d-x)$ *from mass* M_2. Then, clearly,

$$-\frac{M_1}{x^2}G = -\frac{M_2}{(d-x)^2}G. \text{ Or, } \frac{x}{d-x} = \sqrt{\frac{M_1}{M_2}}.$$

Or, $$\frac{x}{d} = \frac{\sqrt{M_1}}{\sqrt{M_1}+\sqrt{M_2}}.$$

whence, $x = \dfrac{d\sqrt{M_1}}{\sqrt{M_1}+\sqrt{M_2}}$ and, therefore, $(d-x) = d - \dfrac{d\sqrt{M_1}}{\sqrt{M_1}+\sqrt{M_2}}$

Or, $$d - x = \frac{d\sqrt{M_2}}{\sqrt{M_1}+\sqrt{M_2}}.$$

Hence, *potential at the point due to the two masses* $= -\left(\dfrac{M_1}{x}G + \dfrac{M_2}{(d-x)}G\right)$

$$= -G\left[\frac{M_1(\sqrt{M_1}+\sqrt{M_2})}{d\sqrt{M_1}} + \frac{M_2(\sqrt{M_1}+\sqrt{M_2})}{d\sqrt{M_2}}\right]$$

$$= -\frac{\sqrt{M_1}+\sqrt{M_2}}{d}G(\sqrt{M_1}+\sqrt{M_2}).$$

Or, *potential at the point* $= -\dfrac{G}{d}(\sqrt{M_1}+\sqrt{M_2})^2 = -\dfrac{G}{d}(M_1 + M_2 + 2\sqrt{M_1 M_2}).$

Example 11. A smooth straight tunnel is bored through the earth and a small particle is allowed to move in it from a position of rest. Find the periodic time of one vibration. Given that $G = 6.67 \times 10^{-8}$ c.g.s. units and the mean density of earth = 5.6 gm per c.c. ***(Delhi, 2000)***

Solution. Let a tunnel AB be bored through the earth (Fig. 12.33) and let a particle of mass m be placed in it at P, such that its distance from the centre O of the earth is r and that from the mid-point C of the tunnel, x. And, let the angle OPC be θ.

As we know, the only force of attraction on the particle will be due to a sphere of radius $OP = r$. (shown dotted in the figure), on the surface of which the particle lies, there being no effect on it due to the outer shells around this sphere. So that,

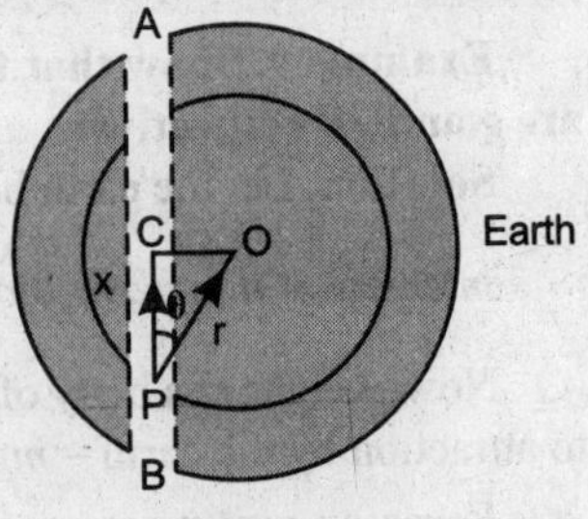

Fig. 12.33

gravitational force acting on the particle, i.e.,

$$F = -\frac{m(\textit{mass of sphere of radius } r)}{r^2}G,$$

the $-ve$ sign indicating that it is directed towards O, the centre of the sphere.

Or, $$F = -\frac{m\left(\frac{4}{3}\pi r^3 \rho\right)}{r^2}G = -\frac{4}{3}\pi r \rho m G.$$

And, clearly, *component of this force acting on the particle along* $PC = F\cos\theta = -\frac{4}{3}\pi r\rho mG\cos\theta$

$$= -\frac{4}{3}\pi r\rho mG \times \frac{x}{r} = -\frac{4}{3}\pi r\rho mGx,$$ directed towards C, the mid-point of the tunnel.

$\therefore$ *acceleration of the particle towards* $C = \dfrac{force}{mass} = \dfrac{-\frac{4}{3}\pi\rho mGx}{m} = \frac{4}{3}\pi\rho Gx$

$= -\mu x$, say, where $4/3\ \pi\rho G = \mu =$ constant.

Thus, the acceleration of the particle is proportional to its displacement (x) from C and is directed towards it. It, therefore, executes a *simple harmonic motion* about (C) and its time-period is given by

$$T = 2\pi\sqrt{\frac{1}{\mu}} = 2\pi\sqrt{\frac{3}{4\pi\rho G}} = \sqrt{\frac{3\pi}{\rho G}} = \sqrt{\frac{3\pi}{5.6\times 6.67\times 10^{-8}}} = 5023 \text{ sec}$$

$$= 83.72 \text{ min} \approx 84 \text{ min}$$

Example 12. One uniform shell of mass m_2 lies inside, and concentric with, a larges uniform shell of mass m_1. Obtain the gravitational field due to the system (*i*) at a point outside the two shells, (*ii*) at a point in the space between the two shells and (*iii*) at a point inside the smaller shell.

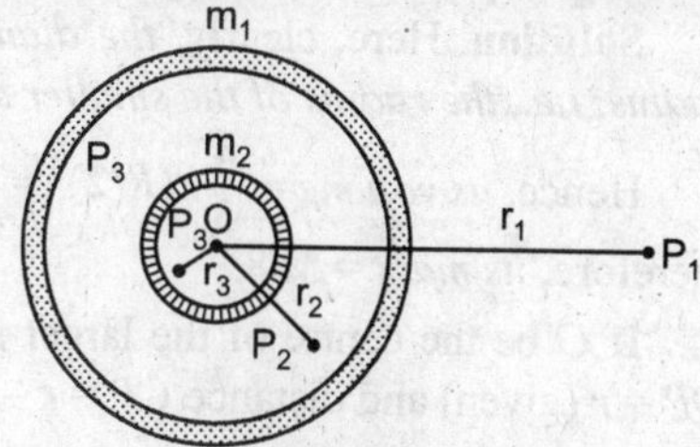

Fig. 12.34

Solution. Let Fig. 12.34 represent the two shells with their common centre O, and let points P_1, P_2, and P_3 lie outside the two shells, in between the two shells and inside the inner shell at distances r_1, r_2 respectively from O.

(*i*) Since point P_1 lies outside both the shells, at distance r_1 from their common centre O, we have

intensity of the gravitational field at P due to the system

= intensity due to one shell + intensity due to the other

i.e.,
$$E = -\frac{m_1}{r_1^2}G - \frac{m_2}{r_1^2}G = -\left(\frac{m_1+m_2}{r_1^2}\right)G.$$

(*ii*)Point P_2 lies inside the outer, but outside, the inner shell. The field at P_2 due to the former is, therefore, *zero* and due to the latter $-(m_2/r_2^{\,2})G$.

Therefore, *intensity at P_2 due to the system, as a whole, i.e.,*

$$E = 0 - \left(\frac{m_2}{r_2^2}\right)G = -\frac{m_2}{r_2^2}G.$$

(*iii*) Point P_3 lies inside both the shells, so that the field there due to either shell is *zero*. Hence the *intensity of the gravitational field at P_3 due to the system as a whole* = 0

Example 13. Two satellites *A* and *B* of the same mass are orbiting the earth at altitudes *R* and 3*R* respectively, where *R* is the radius of the earth. Taking their orbits to be circular, obtain the ratios of their kinetic and potential energies.

Solution. Distance of satellite A from the centre of the earth $= R + R =$ 2R and *that of satellite* $B = R + 3R = 4R$.

If, therefore, m be the *mass of each satellite* and M, the *mass of the earth, we have*

P E. of satellite A $= mMG/2R$ and *P.E. of satellite B* $= mMG/4R$

$\therefore$ *P E. of satellite A* : *P.E. of satellite B* :: $mMG/2R$: $mMG/4R$ or as 2:1.

If v_1 and v_2 the velocities of the two satellites respectively, we have

K.E. of satellite A $= \frac{1}{2}mv_1^2$, and *K.E. of satellite B* $= \frac{1}{2}mv_2^2$

Or, since $v_1 = \sqrt{MG/2R}$, and $v_2 = \sqrt{MG/4R}$, [See § 12.9]

we have

$$K.E.\ of\ satellite\ A = \frac{1}{2}\frac{mMG}{2R} = \frac{mMG}{4R}$$

and

$$K.E.\ of\ satellite\ B = \frac{1}{2}\frac{mMG}{4R} = \frac{mMG}{8R}.$$

$\therefore$ $K.E.\ satellite\ A: of\ satellite\ B :: \frac{mMG}{4R} : \frac{mMG}{8R}$, *i.e.*, as 2 : 1.

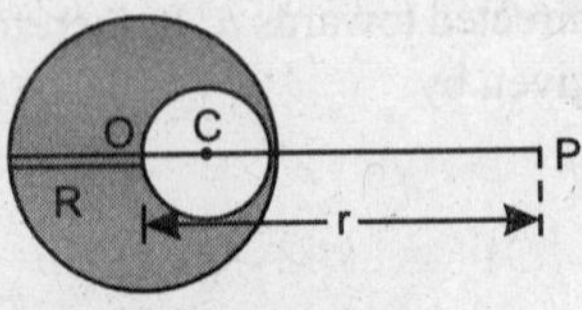

Fig. 12.35

Example 14. From a large metallic sphere of radius *R* and mass *M*, a smaller sphere is scooped out such that the spherical hollow thus formed just touches the surface of the larger sphere on one side and its centre on the other, as shown in Fig. 12.35. Obtain an expression for the gravitational field due to the hollowed sphere at a point *P* lying on a line passing through the centres of the larger sphere and the spherical hollow at a distance *r* from the centre of the former.

Solution. Here, clearly, *the diameter of the spherical hollow formed* = *R and, therefore, its radius, i.e., the radius of the smaller sphere removed* = *R*/2.

Hence, *its volume* = $\frac{4}{3}\pi(R/2)^3 = \frac{4}{3}\pi R^3/8 = \frac{1}{8}$ of the volume of the larger sphere $\left(\frac{4}{3}\pi R^3\right)$ and, therefore, *its mass* = *M*/8.

If *O* be the centre of the larger sphere and *C*, that of the spherical hollow, we have distance $OP = r$ (given) and distance $CP = r - R/2 = (2r - R)/2$.

Clearly, *intensity of the gravitational field at P due the hollowed sphere* = *intensity at P due to the complete larger sphere of radius R* – *intensity of the gravitational field at P due to the smaller sphere of radius R*/2, *i.e.*,

$$E = -\frac{MG}{r^2} - \left(-\frac{MG}{8}\cdot\frac{1}{CP^2}\right) = -MG\left(\frac{1}{r^2} - \frac{1}{8}\cdot\frac{4}{(2r-R)^2}\right)$$

$$= -MG\left(\frac{1}{r^2} - \frac{1}{2(2r-R)^2}\right).$$

Example 15. A satellite of mass M_s is orbiting the earth in a circular orbit of radius *R*. It starts losing energy slowly at a constant rate *C* due to friction. If M_e and R_e denote the mass and radius of the earth respectively, show that the satellite falls on the earth in time

$$t = \frac{GM_eM_S}{2C}\left(\frac{1}{R_e} - \frac{1}{R}\right).$$

[*Delhi* (*Hons.*), *2001*]

Solution. Let the velocity of the satellite in its orbits of radius *R* be v_1. Then, clearly,

$$\frac{M_S v_1^2}{R} = \frac{M_S M_e}{R^2}G, \text{ whence, } v_1^2 = M_eG/R.$$

(Because centripetal force on the satellite = force of attraction due to the earth).

Similarly, if v_2 be the velocity of the satellite when its orbit touches the earth, *i.e.*, when the radius of its orbit is R_e, we have

$$\frac{M_s v_2^2}{R_e} = \frac{M_s M_e}{R_e^2}, \text{ whence, } v_2^2 = M_eG/R_e.$$

$\therefore$ *K.E. of the satellite in orbit of radius* $R = \frac{1}{2}M_s v_1^2 = \frac{1}{2}M_s M_e G/R =$

and *K.E. of the satellite in orbit for radius* R_e (*when it touches the earth*)

$$= \frac{1}{2}M_S v_2^2 = \frac{1}{2}M_S M_e G/R_e.$$

Now, *P.E. of the satellite when at distance R form the centre of the earth*

$$= -M_s M_e G/R$$

and its P.E. when at a distance R_e from the centre of the earth (i.e., when it touches the earth) $= -M_sM_eG/R_e$.

$\therefore$ *total energy of the satellite when in orbit of radius R = its P.E + its K.E.*

$$-\frac{M_SM_eG}{R}+\frac{1}{2}\frac{M_SM_eG}{R} = \frac{1}{2}-\frac{M_SM_eG}{R}.$$

and *total energy of the satellite when on the surface of the earth*

$$= -\frac{M_sM_eG}{R_e}+\frac{1}{2}\frac{M_SM_eG}{R_e} = -\frac{1}{2}\frac{M_SM_e}{R_e}G.$$

Hence, *loss of energy in falling to the earth* $= -\frac{1}{2}\frac{M_SM_eG}{R}-\left(-\frac{1}{2}\frac{M_SM_eG}{R_e}\right)$

$$= \frac{1}{2}M_SM_eG\left(\frac{1}{R_e}-\frac{1}{R}\right)$$

If the satellite takes time t to fall to the earth, clearly, *energy lost by it* $= Ct$.

$$\therefore \quad Ct = \frac{1}{2}M_SM_eG\left(\frac{1}{R_e}-\frac{1}{R}\right), \text{ whence, } t = \frac{M_SM_eG}{2C}\left(\frac{1}{R_e}-\frac{1}{R}\right).$$

Example 16. Assuming that the interior of the earth can be treated as homogenous spherical mass in hydrostatic equilibrium, express the pressure within the earth as a function of distance r from the centre. Taking radius of the earth, $R = 6.3 \times 10^8$ cm and its uniform density, $\rho = 5.5$ gm/cm^3, calculate the pressure at the centre of the earth.

Solution. In Fig. 12.36 let R be the *radius of the earth* and r, the distance of a point P from its centre O where the pressure is to be determined.

Consider a shell of radius x and thickness dx, where $r < x < R$. Clearly, *volume of the shell* $= 4\pi x^2\, dx$ *and hence its mass* $= 4\pi x^2\, dx\rho$.

And, *mass of the solid sphere of radius x enclosed by the shell* $= \frac{4}{3}\pi x^3 r$.

Obviously, *gravitational pull exerted by the sphere on the shell inwards*

$$= \frac{\text{mass of the sphere} \times \text{mass of the shell}}{x^2}G$$

$$= \frac{4\pi x^3\rho \times 4\pi x^2 dx\rho}{3\times x^2}G = \frac{16}{3}\pi^2\rho^2 Gx^3 dx.$$

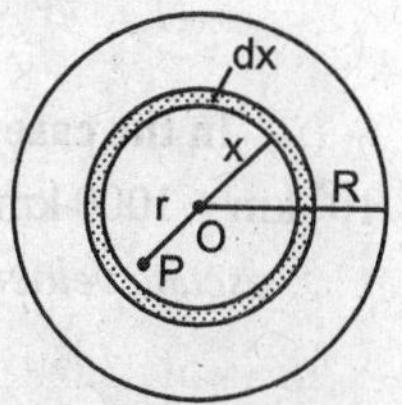

Fig. 12.36

Since the whole spherical mass (of the earth) is in hydrostatic equilibrium, the shell does not move inwards due to this force. This clearly means that equal and opposite force $\left(\frac{16}{3}\pi^2\rho^2 Gx^3 dx\right)$ must be acting radically outwards on its surface.

Since the area of the inner surface of the shell $= 4\pi x^2$, we have *outward pressure on the shell at distance x from the centre, say,*

$$dp = \frac{16}{3}\pi^2\rho^2 Gx^3 dx/4\pi x^2,$$

i.e.,
$$dp = \frac{4}{3}\pi\rho^2 Gx dx.$$

Now, the solid sphere of radius x also attracts all other shells outside the shell of radius x, *i.e.,* all other shells of radii greater than x and less than R.

These shells too do not move inwards under its force of attraction, showing that there must be an equal and opposite force acting on their inner sides, pushing them outwards.

Hence, to determine the *total pressure P at the point P*, distant r form O, we must integrate the expression for *dp* between the limits $x = r$ and $x = R$. Thus,

$$\textit{total pressure at P, i.e.,}\ \rho = \frac{4}{3}np^2G\int_r^R x\,dx = \frac{4}{3}\pi\rho^2G\left[\frac{x^2}{2}\right]_r^R$$

$$= \frac{2\pi}{3}\rho^2G(R^2 - r^2)$$

Since at O, $r = 0$, we have *pressure at the centre of the earth*

$$= \frac{2\pi}{3}\rho^2GR^2 = \frac{2\pi}{3}(5.5)^2\,(6.67\times10^{-8})(6.3\times10^8)^2$$

$$= 1.7\times10^{12}\ \text{dyne/cm}^2.$$

Example 17. Obtain the values of the escape velocity for an atmospheric particle 1000 km above the surface of (*i*) the earth, (*ii*) the moon, (*iii*) the sum. Given, mass of the earth = 5.98 × 10^{24} kg, radius of the earth = 6.37 × 10^6 metre: mass of the moon = 7 .34 × 10^{22} kg, radius of the moon = 1.74 × 10^6 metre: mass of the sun = 1.99 × 10^{30} kg, radius of the sun = 6.96 × 10^8 metre; and gravitational constant $G = 6.67\times10^{-11}$ *N–m²/kg²*.

Solution. We know that *escape velocity* $v_e = \sqrt{2MG/R}$. [§ 12.9]

Now, (*i*) **in the case of the earth,** $M = 5.98\times10^{24}$ kg and R = *radius of the earth* + 1000 km = 6.37 × 10^3 km + 1000 km = 7.37 × 10^3 km = 7.37 × 10^6 ≠ 73.7 × 10^5 *metre.*

∴ *escape velocity of the atmospheric particle, i.e.,*

$$v_e = \sqrt{2\times5.98\times10^{24}\times6.67\times10^{-11}/73.7\times10^5}$$

$$= \sqrt{2\times5.98\times6.67/73.7\times10^8} = 1.04\times10^4\ \text{m/sec}$$

(*ii*) **In the case of the moon,** $M = 7.34\times10^{22}$ kg and R = *radius of the moon* + 1000 km = 1.74 × 10^8 km + 1000 km = 27.4 × 10^5 metre.

∴ *escape velocity of the atmospheric particle, i.e.,*

$$v_e = \sqrt{2\times7.34\times10^{22}\times6.67\times10^{-11}/27.4\times10^5}$$

$$= \sqrt{2\times7.34\times6.67/27.4\times10^6} = 1.89\times10^3\ m/\text{sec}.$$

(*iii*) **In the case of the sun,** $M = 1.99\times10^{30}$ kg and R = *radius of the sum* + 1000 km = 6.96 × 10^5 km + 1000 km = 69.7 × 10^7 metre.

∴ *escape velocity of the atmospheric particle,*

i.e.,
$$v_e = \sqrt{2\times1.99\times10^{30}\times6.67\times10^{11}/69.7\times10^7}$$

$$= \sqrt{2\times1.99\times6.67/69.7\times10^{12}}$$

$$= 6.172\times10^5\ m/\text{sec}.$$

Example 18. The radius of earth is 6.637 × 10^6 m, its mean density 5.57 × 10^3 kg^{-3} and gravitational constant 6.66 × 10–^{11} N m² kg^{-2}. Calculate the earth's surface potential.

Solution. Considering the earth to be a homogenous sphere, the magnitude of gravitational

$$\text{potential on its surface} = \frac{GM}{r} = \frac{G\frac{4}{3}\pi r^3\rho}{r} = \frac{4G\pi r^2\rho}{3}$$

$$= \frac{4\times6.66\times10^{-11}\times\pi\times(6.637\times10^6)^2\times5.57\times10^3}{3}$$

$$= 6.845\times10^7\ \text{J/kg}$$

Example 19. The earth's mass is 80 times that of the moon and their diameters are 12800 km and 3200 km respectively. What is the value of g on the moon? g on earth is 9.8 ms^{-2}.

Solution. The acceleration due to gravity on the surface of a sphere is given by $g = \frac{GM}{R^2}$ where M is the mass and R the radius of the sphere. Taking the earth and moon to be spheres, acceleration due to gravity on the surface of the earth

$$g = G\frac{80m}{(64\times10^5)^2}\text{ ms}^{-2}$$

where m is the mass of the moon and 64×10^5 m the radius of the earth.

Acceleration due to gravity on the surface of the moon

$$g' = \frac{Gm}{(16\times10^5)^2} \text{ where } 16\times10^5 \text{ m is the radius of the moon.}$$

$$\therefore \quad \frac{g'}{g} = \frac{(64\times10^5)^2}{80\times(16\times10^5)^2} = \frac{1}{5} \qquad \therefore\ g' = 9.8\times\frac{1}{5} = 1.96 \text{ ms}^{-2}$$

III– Inverse square law forces–self energy

Example 20. Three electrical charges A, B, C, of values + 40, – 70 , 12 esu respectively are placed such that distances AB, BC, CA are 10, 30, 30 cm respectively. Calculate the work required to separate the three charges to infinity. ***(Agra, 2003)***

Solution. Let the three charges A, B, C be placed as shown in Fig. 12.37

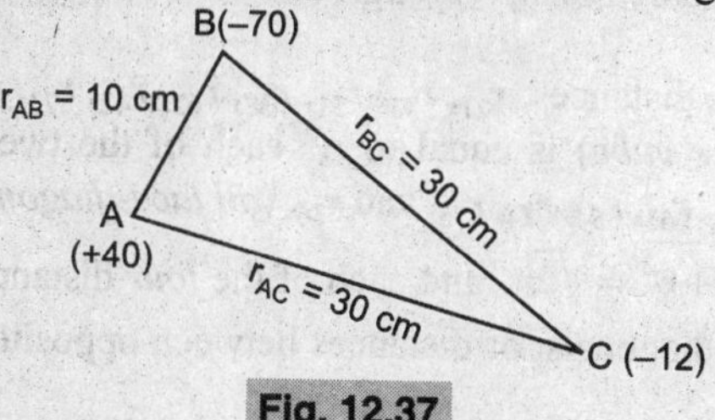

Fig. 12.37

The work required to separate them to infinity will obviously be equal to the potential energy of the system, with its sign reversed.

Now, *potential energy of the system,*

$$U = U_{AB} + U_{BC} + U_{CA} = \frac{AB}{r_{AB}} + \frac{BC}{r_{BC}} + \frac{AC}{r_{AC}}.$$

Or,

$$U = \frac{(+40)(-70)}{10} + \frac{(-70)(-12)}{30} + \frac{(+40)(-12)}{30}$$

$$= 280 + 28 - 16 = -268 \textit{ ergs}$$

Therefore, *work required to separate the three charges to infinity* = 268 *ergs*.

Example 21. Determine the potential energy of a galaxy consisting of n stars, where $n = 16 \times 10^{11}$, each equal to the mass of the sun and with an average distance $r = 10^{21}$ metres between each pair of stars. Ignore the self energy of each star. (Take mass of the sun = 2×10^{30} kg and $G = 7 \times 10^{-11}$ N – M/kg^2).

Solution. As we have seen in § 12.26, *gravitational potential energy or self energy of n stars* is given by

$$U_s = -\frac{1}{2}G\sum_{i=1}^{n}\sum_{\substack{j=1\\ \neq 1}}^{n}\frac{m_i m_j}{r_{ij}}.$$

Here, $m_i = m_j = m$ and there are n equal terms in $\sum_{i=1}^{n}$ and $(n-1)$ terms in $\sum_{\substack{j=1\\ \neq 1}}^{n}$ So that,

$$= \sum_{i=1}^{n} = n \text{ and } \sum_{\substack{j=1\\ \neq 1}}^{n} = (n-1).$$

$$\therefore \quad U_s = -\frac{1}{2} Gn(n-1)\frac{m^2}{r}.$$

Substituting the given values, therefore, we have *gravitational potential energy of the galaxy*

$$= -\frac{1}{2}\frac{7\times10^{-11}\times1.6\times10^{11}\times(1.6\times10^{11}-1)\times(2\times10^{30})^2}{10^{21}} \approx -4\times10^{51} \text{ joules}$$

Example 22. Calculate the gravitational potential energy of a system of 8 masses of 10 kg each placed at the corners of a cube of each edge equal to 0.25 metre. ($G = 6.67 \times 10^{11}$ N-m/kg^2).

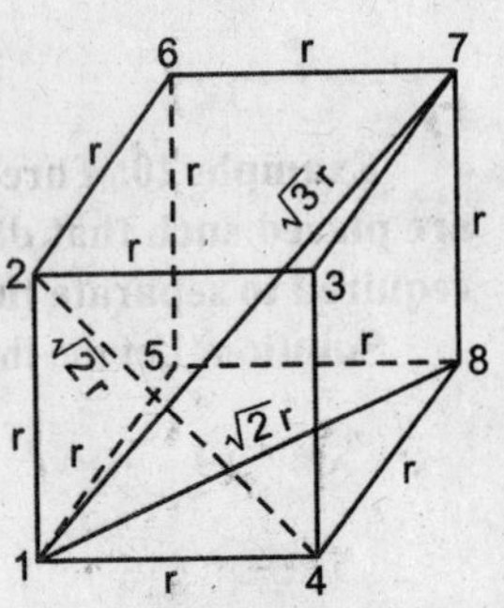

Fig. 12.38

Solution. Figure 12.38 shows a cube of each edge, 0.25 metre in length, with a mass of 10 kg placed at each corner, The gravitational potential energy or self energy of the system is thus obviously given by

$$U_s = -G\sum_{i>j}^{8}\sum_{j=1}^{8}\frac{m_i m}{r_{ij}}, \text{ where } m_i = m_j = 10 \text{ kg}.$$

Now, each of the *twelve* distances, r_{21}, r_{41}, r_{51}, r_{38}, r_{62}, r_{42}, r_{73}, r_{84}, r_{76}, and r_{87} (*all edges of the cube*) is equal to r, each of the twelve distances, r_{31}, r_{61}, r_{42}, r_{52}, r_{72}, r_{63}, r_{54}, r_{74}, r_{75}, and r_{36}, (*all face-diagonals of the cube*) is equal to $\sqrt{r^2+r^2} = \sqrt{2}r$, and each of the *four* distances, r_{71}, r_{52}, r_{53} and r_{64} (all long diagonals, or distances between opposite corners, of the cube) is equal to $\sqrt{2r^2+r^2} = \sqrt{3r^2} = \sqrt{3}r$.

$$\therefore \quad U_s = -Gm^2\ 12/r + 12/\sqrt{2}r + 4/\sqrt{3}r)$$

$$= -\frac{4Gm^2}{r}(3+3/\sqrt{2}+1/\sqrt{3})$$

$$= -\frac{4Gm^2}{r}(5.7).$$

Substituting the given values of G, m and r, therefore, we have *gravitational potential energy of the system,*

$$U_s = -\frac{4\times6.67\times10^{-11}\times(10)^2}{0.25} = -1.067 \times 10^{-7} \textit{ joule}.$$

Example 23. Calculate the self energy of the sun, taking its mass to be equal to 2×10^{30} kg and its radius to be very nearly 7×10^8 metre. ($G = 7 \times 10^{-11}$ N-m/kg^2).

If its radius contracts by 1 km per year, without affecting its mass, calculate the rate at which it radiates out energy. ***(Nagpur 2008)***

Solution. We know that the self energy of a solid sphere is given by $U_s = -\frac{3}{5}\frac{M^2}{R}G$.

$$\therefore \quad \textit{self energy of the sun} = -\frac{3}{5}\frac{(2\times10^{30})^2}{7\times10^8}\times7\times10^{11} = -\frac{12}{5}\times10^{41}$$

$$= -2.4 \times 10^{11} \textit{ joules}.$$

The *–ve* sign is because the gravitational force is attractive.

Now, *rate of change of energy of the sun, i.e.,* $\frac{dU_s}{dt} = \frac{dU_s}{dR}\cdot\frac{dR}{dt} = \frac{3}{5}\frac{M^2G}{R^2}\cdot\frac{dR}{dt}$.

Here, $\frac{dR}{dt} = \frac{1000}{365\times24\times60\times60}$ metre/sec ($\because$ 1 km = 1000 metres)

$\therefore$ *rate of energy radiated out by the sun*

$$= \frac{3}{5}\frac{M^2G}{R^2}\frac{dR}{dt} = \frac{2.4\times10^{41}}{7\times10^{8}}\times\frac{1000}{365\times24\times3600}$$

$$= 1.087 \times 10^{28} \text{ joules/sec.}$$

Example 24. Charges of + 100 esu are placed at the corners of a square of 10 cm side and a charge of $-50\sqrt{2}$ esu at the point of interaction of its diagonals. Calculate

(*i*) the resultant force on each charge, (*ii*) the potential energy of the system, (*iii*) work done in separating the charge to infinity.

If the charge were initially infinite distance apart, what would be the work done in assembling them into their present configuration?

Solution. Let *ABCD* be the square of side 10 cm, at the four corners of which charges of 100 esu each are placed and let a charge of $-50\sqrt{2}$ *esu* be placed at the point of intersection *O* of its diagonals, (Fig. 12.39)

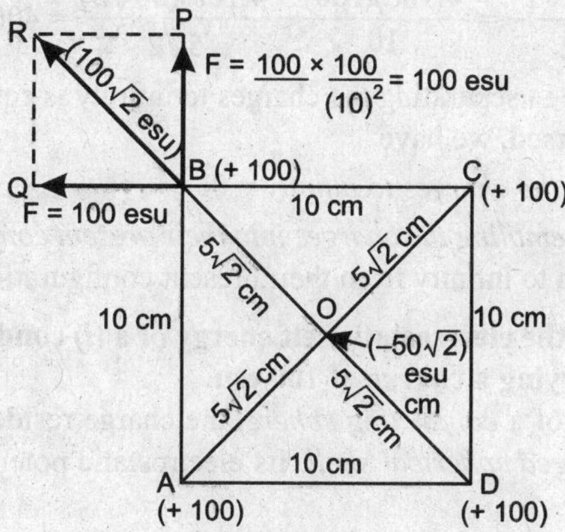

Fig. 12.39

Then, clearly, diagonal $AC = BD = \sqrt{10^2+10^2} = 10\sqrt{2}$ cm

And, therefore, $AO = OC = OB = OD = 10\sqrt{2}/2 = 5\sqrt{2}$ cm.

(*i*) Hence, *force on the charge at O due to the charge at A*

$$= (100)\ (-50\sqrt{2})(5\sqrt{2})^2 = -5000\sqrt{2}/50$$

$$= -100\sqrt{2} \text{ dynes along } OA.$$

And, *force on the charge at O due to the charge at C*

$$= (100)\ (-50\sqrt{2})/(5\sqrt{2})^2 = -5000\sqrt{2}/50$$

$$= -100\sqrt{2} \text{ dynes } along\ OC,$$

The two, being *equal and opposite*, cancel out.

Similarly, forces on the charge at O due to the charges at B and D are $-100\sqrt{2}$ dynes and $-100\sqrt{2}$ *dynes* along OB and OD respectively and they too, being equal and opposite, cancel out.

So, *the resultant force on the charge at* $O = 0$.

Now, force on the charge at B due to the charge at $A = 100 \times 100/(10)^2 = 100$ dynes *along AB*.

Let it be represented in magnitude and direction by BP.

Similarly, force on the charge at B due to the charge at $C = 100 \times 10/(10)^2 = 100$ dynes along CB. Let it be represented by BQ.

Then, the *resultant force on the charge at B due to the charges at A and C is represented by BR* $= \sqrt{100^2 + 100^2} = 100\sqrt{2}$ dynes, *along OB*.

And, force on the charge at B due to the charge at $O = 100(-50\sqrt{2})/(5\sqrt{2})^2 = 100\sqrt{2}$ dynes along BO.

These too, again being equal and opposite, the resultant force on the charge at B is *zero*.

Similarly, it can be shown that the resultant force on the charges at A, C and D is also *zero*.

In other words, *the resultant force on each charge of the system is zero.*

(*ii*) The *potential energy of the system of charges* is clearly

$$= \frac{(100)(100)}{10} + \frac{(100)(100)}{10} + \frac{(100)(100)}{10} + \frac{(100)(100)}{10} - \frac{(100)(50\sqrt{2})}{5\sqrt{2}} - \frac{(100)(5\sqrt{2})}{5\sqrt{2}}$$

$$- \frac{(100)(50\sqrt{2})}{5\sqrt{2}} - \frac{(100)(5\sqrt{2})}{5\sqrt{2}} = \frac{4(100)(100)}{10} - \frac{4(100)(50\sqrt{2})}{5\sqrt{2}} = 4000 - 4000 = 0.$$

(*iii*) Since the work done in separating the charges to infinity is equal to the potential energy of the system, with its sign reversed, we have

work done in separating the charges to infinity = 0.

Finally, *work done in assembling the charges into their present configuration*, being equal to the work done in separating them to infinity from their present configuration, is also equal to *zero*.

Example 25. Calculate the electrostatic self energy of a (*i*) conducting, (*ii*) non-conducting sphere of radius 10 cm carrying a charge of 100 esu.

Solution (i) In the case of a *conducting sphere*, the charge resides only on its surface and it, therefore, *behaves as a charged spherical shell*. Its electrostatic potential energy or self energy is thus given by $U_s = -Q^2/2R$. [*See* § 12.31 case (*i*)]

Substituting the given values of Q and R, therefore, we have

electrostatic self energy of the conducting sphere

$$= (100)^2/2\,(10) = 10000/20 = 500 \text{ ergs},$$

(*ii*) In the case of a *non-conducting sphere*, the charge is spread over its entire volume and its *electrostatic self energy* is given by $U_s = \frac{3}{5}(Q^2/R)$. [*See* § 12.31 case (*ii*)]

So that, *electrostatic self energy of the non-conducting sphere*

$$= \frac{3}{5} \times (100)^2/10 = \frac{3}{5}(10000/10) = 600 \text{ ergs}.$$

Example. 26. A meteor of mass 500 kg falls to the surface of the earth. How does the potential energy of the meteor-earth system change? If the meteor be supposed to start from rest, with what velocity does it strike the earth? (Radius of the earth = 6.37 × 10⁶ metre; g = 9.80 m/sec²)

Solution . Potential energy (or self energy) of the meteor-earth system will decrease by MmG/R when the meteor falls to the surface of the earth, where M is the *mass of the earth, m, the mass of the* *meteor and R,* the *radius of the earth*, or the distance of the meteor (now lying on the surface of the earth) from the centre of the earth.

Now, as we know, $MG/R^2 = g$ and, therefore, $MG/R = (MG/R^2)\,R = gR$.

$\therefore$ loss in *P.E. of meteor-earth system* $= mg\,R = 500\times 9.8\times 6.37\times 10^6 = 3.121\times 10^{10} J.$

Obviously, *loss in P.E. of the system = gain in K.E. of the meteor.*

Since the meteor is supposed to start from rest, the gain in its *K.E.* $= \frac{1}{2}mv^2$, where *v is the velocity with which it strikes the earth.* We, therefore, have

$$= \frac{1}{2}mv^2 = mgR. \quad \text{Or, } v^2 = 2gR. \text{ Or, } v = \sqrt{2gR}$$

= *velocity of escape from the surface of the earth*

$$= \sqrt{2\times 9.8\times 6.37\times 10^6} = 11.17\times 10^3\ m/\text{sec} \approx 11.20 \text{ km/sec.}$$

The meteor thus strikes the earth with a velocity 11.20 km/sec.

Example 27. Estimate the temperature of the interior of the sun, taking its mass to be nearly equal to 2 × 10^{33} gm, its radius to be nearly equal to 7 × 10^{10} cm., $G = 7\times 10^{-8}$ C.G.S. units and the average mass of an atom in the sun to be equal to 3 × 10^{-24} gm.

Solution. We know that the potential energy (or self energy) of the sun, *i.e.*,

$U_s = -\frac{3}{5}\frac{M^2}{R}G$, where *M* is its *mass* and *R* its *radius.*

In accordance with the *virial theorem*, we have

average K.E. of the atoms in the sun $= -\frac{1}{2}$ *(average P.E. of the sun)*

Now, *K.E. of the atom* $= \frac{3}{2}kT$, where *k* is the familia *Boltzmann constant* $= 1.38\times 10^{-16}$ erg/^0K and *T*, the average temperature of the sun, measured in degrees Kelvin (or *K*).

If, therefore, there be *N* atoms in all in the sun, their *average K.E.* $= \frac{3}{2}NkT$.

We, thus, have $$\frac{3}{2}NkT = -\frac{1}{2}\left(-\frac{3}{5}\frac{M^2}{R}G\right) = \frac{3M^2G}{10R},$$

whence, $$T = \frac{3M^2G}{10R}\times\frac{2}{3Nk} = \frac{M^2G}{5RNk} = \frac{MMG}{5RNk}.$$

Clearly, *M/N* is the *average mass of an atom in the sun* $= 3\times 10^{-24}$ gm.

So that, $$T = \frac{MG}{5Rk}(3\times 10^{24}) = \frac{2\times 10^{33}\times 7\times 10^{-8}\times(3\times 10^{-24})}{5\times 7\times 10^{10}\times 1.38\times 10^{-16}} = \frac{6\times 10^7}{6.9}\approx(10^7)°\text{K}$$

Thus, *the average temperature of the interior of the sun* $= (10^7)°K$.

EXERCISE

I–Law of Gravitation

1. State the law of gravitational attraction and hence define the gravitational constant *G*. Describe a method of measuring *G*. ***(Delhi, 2002)***
2. Describe an accurate method for the determination of *G*.
   A sphere of mass 40 kg is attracted by a second sphere of mass 15 kg, when their centres are 20 cm apart, with a force equal to 1/10 of a milligram weight. Calculate the constant of gravitation.
   (Bombay, Punjab) [**Ans.** 6.53 × 10^{-8} C.G.S units.]
3. (*a*) Describe an accurate method of determining the gravitational constant in the laboratory.

(*b*) A smooth tunnel is bored through the earth and a small particle is allowed to move in it from a position of rest. Find the periodic time of one vibration. Given that $G = 6.67 \times 10^{-8}$ cgs units and the mean density of the earth = 5.6 gm per c.c. **[*Delhi (Hons)*]**

If mail were to be delivered through the tunnel, how long would it be between depositing it at one end and its delivery at the other end? **[Ans.** 84 min; 42 min.]

4. Calculate the mass of the earth from the following data: Radius of the earth = × 10^8 cm; acceleration due to gravity = 980 cm/ sec^2 and gravitational constant = 6.6×10^{-8} cm^3 gm^{-1} sec^{-2}. (*Punjab 2004*)

[Ans. 53.47×10^{26} gm.]

5. Calculate the mass of the sun, given that the distance between the sun and the earth is 1.49×10^{13} cm and $G = 6.66 \times 10^{-8}$ C.G.S. units. Take the year to consist of 365 days.

(Agra; Aligarh; Bombay; Punjab) **[Ans.** 19.72×10^{34} gm.]

6. Obtain an expression for the limiting velocity required by an artificial satellite for orbiting around the earth. If the radius of the earth be 6.4×10^8 cm and $g = 980$ cm/sec^2, calculate the value of this velocity. **[Ans.** *Limiting velocity* $v_0 = \sqrt{gR} = 7.92 \times 10^5$ cm/sec.]

7. It is said that the first artificial satellite was revolving round the earth at a distance of 560 miles from it. Estimate its velocity and period of revolution, taking the radius of the earth to be 4000 miles and the value of g to be 32 ft/sec^2. ***(Punjab)*** **[Ans.** 24340 ft/sec; 6207 sec.]

[Hint. Let distance of the satellite from the centre of the earth be $R' = R + 560 = 4000 + 560 = 4560$ miles.

Then, $mv_0^2/R' = mMG/R'^2$ whence, $v_0^2 = MG/R'$. But $MG = gR^2$.

$$v_0^2 = gR^2/R' \text{ or } v_0 = R\sqrt{g/R'}$$

Hence, time-period of revolution or $T = 2\pi R'/v_0$]

8. Show that the time-period of oscillation of a particle dropped in a tunnel right through the earth is the same whether or not the tunnel passes through the centre of the earth. What is the value of this time-period? **[Ans.** 83.72 *min.*]

9. Imagine a particle at a point P inside a spherical shell of uniform thickness and denslty and construct a narrow double cone with apex at P so as to intercept areas A_1 and A_2 on the shell on either side of P. Show that the resultant gravitational force exerted on the particle at P by the intercepted mass elements of the shell is zero and hence show that the gravitational field due to the entire shell is zero at any point inside it.

II–Gravitational potential and field intensity–Potential energy—Velocity of escape—Gauss's theorem

10. Explain the terms 'gravitational potential' and ' gravitational field'. Obtain expressions for the gravitational potential and gravitational field at a point (*i*) inside. (*ii*) outside a hollow spherical shell.

(Vikram, Bombay; Banaras)

11. Derive expressions for gravitational field and potential at a point inside and outside a thin uniform spherical shell. ***(Agra, 2006)***

12. Define and explain gravitational potential. Calculate the gravitational potential due to a sphere at a point (*i*) outside the sphere (*ii*) inside the sphere. ***(Delhi, Bombay)***

Show that the potential at the centre of the sphere is one and a half times that on its surface.

13. (*a*) How may the density of the earth be determined?

(*b*) The radius of the earth is 6.37×10^8 cm, its mean density, 5.5 gm/c.c. and the gravitational constant, 6.66×10^{-8} *C.G.S.* units. Calculate the earth's surface potential. ***(Agra, Bombay)***

[Ans. 6.227×10^{11} erg/gm.]

14. Obtain an expression for the gravitational attraction at a point (*i*) outside and (*ii*) inside a solid sphere and show that in the latter case, it is proportional to the distance from the centre of the sphere.

(Bombay, Patna)

15. Show that in the case of a hollow sphere (or a thick shell) of density ρ and inner and outer radii, R_1 and R_2 respectively, the gravitational potential at a point inside the hollow sphere is $V = -2\pi\rho G (R_2^2 - R_1^2)$ and the field at the point, *zero*.

Also show that the field at a point in the material of the hollow sphere (or thick shell) at a distance r from its centre is given by $E = -\left(\frac{r^3 - R_1^3}{R_2^3 - R_1^3}\right)\frac{M}{r^2}G.$

16. Show that if a body be projected vertically upward from the surface of the earth so as to reach a height nR above the surface, (*i*) the increase in its potential energy is $[(n+1)]MgR$ and (*ii*) the velocity with which it must be projected is $\sqrt{[2n/(n+1)gR}$, where R is the radius of the earth and M, its mass.

[**Hint.** At the surface of the earth, *i.e.*, at a distance R from its centre, the *P.E.* of the body $= -MmG/R = -mgR^2/R = mgR$ ($\because MG = gR^2$). And, at a distance $(nR + R)$ or $(n+1)R$ from the centre of the earth, its *P.E.* $= -MmG/(n+1)R = -mgR^2/(n+1)R = -mgR/(n+1)$.

$\therefore$ increase in *P.E.* of the body $= -mgR/(n+1) - (-mgR) = [n/(n+1)]mgR$.

If v be its velocity of projection, its *K.E.* $= \frac{1}{2}mv^2 = \left(\frac{n}{n+1}\right)mgR$, whence,

$$v = \sqrt{\left(\frac{2n}{n+1}\right)gR}.\ ]$$

17. Deduce an expression for the gravitational potential due to a sphere at an external point. Hence calculate the amount of work required to send a body of mass m form the earth's surface to a height (*i*) $R/2$, (*ii*) $10\ R$ and (*iii*) $1000\ R$, where R is the radius of the earth. Express the result in m, R and g.

(Rajasthan) [**Ans.** (*i*) $\frac{1}{3}mgR$, (*ii*) $\frac{10}{11}mgR$, (*iii*) $\frac{1000}{1001}mgR$.]

18. If the density (ρ) of the earth increases with depth below the surface, show that the value of g may also icrease. How should the density vary with depth in order that the value of g may remain unaffected?

Ans. ρ *should be proportional to* $1/r$ *or* ρr *should remain constant, where r is the distance from the centre of the earth.*

[**Hint.** On the surface of the earth, *i.e.*, at distance R from the centre of the earth, $g = MG/R^2 = \frac{4}{3}\pi R^3\rho G/R^2 = \frac{4}{3}\pi GR\rho$. And, at a distance r from the centre of the earth, $g' = \frac{4}{3}\pi R^3\rho' G/r^2 = \frac{4}{3}\pi GR\rho'$, where ρ' is now the density. $\therefore g'/g = (r/R)(\rho'/\rho)$. In order that $g' = g$, we must have $(r/R)\ \rho'/\rho = 1$, or, $\rho/\rho' = r/R$.]

19. In question 17 above, what should be the velocities given to the body to attain the heights $R/2$, $10R$ and $1000\ R$ respectively? [**Ans.** (*i*) $\sqrt{\frac{2}{3}gR}$, (*ii*) $\sqrt{\frac{20}{11}gR}$, (*iii*) $\sqrt{\frac{2000}{1001}gR}$.] [*see* Hint under Q. 16]

20. (*a*) Explain the terms.

(*i*) Gravitational Field

(*ii*) Gravitational intensity

(*iii*) Gravitational potential ***(Nagpur U. 2008, 2007, 2006)***

(*b*) What will be gravitational potential and intensity of a thin spherical shell of mass 10 kg and radius. 0.1 *m* at a point 0.2 *m* outside of its surface? ($G = 6.67 \times 10^{-11}$ Nm^2/kg^2)

(Nagpur, 2008, 2004) [**Ans.** -1.66×10^{-8} N/kg]

21. (*a*) Obtain an expression for the gravitational potential and attraction due to a thin uniform spherical shell at a point (*i*) outside, (*ii*) at the surface and (*iii*) inside the shell.

(Nagpur U. 2008; Meerut U. 2005, 2001; Gharwal U. 2000; Agra U. 2005, 2003)

(*b*) Graphically represent the variation of potential with distance due to a thin spherical shell.

(Kerala U. 2001)

22. Find the intensity of gravitational field due to a thin spherical shell at a point (*i*) external to the shell, (*ii*) at the surface of the shell and (*iii*) inside the shell.

(Nagpur U. 2008. 2001; Grarwal U., 2000; Guwahati. U. 2000)

23. (*a*) Define gravitational potential.

(*b*) Derive an expression for the gravitational potential at a point (*i*) outside, (*ii*) on the surface and (*iii*) inside a solid sphere.

(Kerala U. 2001; Guwahati U. 2000; Indore U. 2001; Meerut U. 2003, 2000, M.S.U. Tiruneveli, 2007; Purvanchal U. 2004; D.A.V. Agra, 2008; 2006)

(*c*) Hence find gravitational field (attraction) at these points and show that it is proportional to the distance from the centre of the sphere for a point inside it.

(Indore U. 2001; Meerut U. 2000, Kerala. U. 2001)

24. The gravitational potential at a point at a distance *r* from the centre of a solid sphere is given by $V = -\frac{GM(3a^2 - r^2)}{2a^3}$ where *M* is the mass and *a* the radius of the sphere. Find the field intensity at this point. ***(Meerut U., 2003)***

25. Find the gravitational potential and attraction due to a spherical shell bounded by spheres of radii *a* and *b* at a point (*i*) inside the shell, (*ii*) outside the shell and (*iii*) between the two surfaces.

(Arga U. 2007; Cal U., 2003)

26. Explain the terms gravitational field and gravitational potential. Find the relation between them

(Nagpur U., 2007, 2003, 2001; Meerut U. 2003, 2002, 2000, Agra, 2005; M.S.U. Tiruneveli, 2007)

27. Two particles having masses *M* and *m* respectively are initially at rest an infinite distance apart and attract each other according to the law of gravitation. Show that their velocity of approach $v = \sqrt{\frac{2G(M+m)}{a}}$ where *a* is their separation.

28. Derive the expressions for gravitational potential energy and force inside a sphere of uniform density. Calculate the time taken by an earth satellite moving in a circular orbit, close to its surface, in completing one round. Take the radius of the earth = 6×10^8 cm. ***[Delhi (Hons)]***

[**Ans.** 1 *hr* 21 *min* 56 sec.]

29. Show that the *escape velocity* from the surface of the earth is $\sqrt{2}$ times the velocity of projection of an artificial satellite orbiting close around the earth.

30. Two satellites of equal mass *m* are moving in the same circular orbit of radius *r* and around the earth, in opposite directions, so as to eventually collide with each other. (*i*) Obtain an expression in terms of *M*, *m*, *r* and *G* (where *M* is the mass of the earth) for the total mechanical energy of the two satellite-earth system before collision. (*ii*) Taking the collision to be perfectly elastic, obtain the total mechanical energy of the system immediately after collision. (*iii*) Describe the subsequent motion of the wreckage of the two satellites.

[**Ans.** MmG/r, (*ii*) $-2\ MmG/r$, (*iii*) *the wreckage falls down to the earth.*]

31. The minimum and maximum distance of a comet from the sun are 7×10^{10} and 1.4×10^{12} *m* respectively. If the speed of the comet at the nearest point is 6×10^4 m/s, calculate the speed at the farthest point. ***(Gharwal. U., 2000)***[**Ans.** $V = 3 \times 10^3$ m/s]

[**Hint:** $7 \times 10^{10} \times 6 \times 10^4 = 1.4 \times 10^{12}$ V]

32. A sphere of mass 19 kg is attracted by another sphere of mass 150 kg when their centres are separated by a distance 0.28 m with a force equal to the weight of 0.25 mg. Calculate the gravitational constant. If the distance is halved what would be the new force in Newton? Assume $g = 9.8$ ms^{-2}.

33. Suppose the earth is revolving round the sun in a circular orbit of radius one astronomical unit (1.5×10^8 km). Find the mass of the sun. $G = 6.67 \times 10^{-11}$ Nm^2 kg^{-2}.

(Gharwal U. 2000) [**Ans.** 2.004×10^{30} kg]

34. If the mass of the sun is 1.5×10^{11} *m* and period of revolution of the earth around the sun is 365.3 days, find the value of *G*. [**Ans.** 6.688×10^{11} Nm^2/kg^2]

35. Show that gravitational potential at the centre of a solid sphere is 3/2 times that on its surface.

36. A satellite revolves round a planet in an elliptical orbit. Its maximum and minimum distances from the planet are 1.5×10^7 *m* and 0.5×10^7 m respectively. If the speed of the satellite at the farther point is 5×10^3 ms^{-1}, calculate the speed at the nearest point. [**Ans.** 15×10^{-3} ms^{-1}]

37. A spherical mass of 20 kg situated at the surface of the earth is attracted by another mass of 150 kg with a force equal to the weight of 0.25 mg when the centres of masses are 30 cm apart. Calculate the mass and mean density of the earth assuming the radius of the earth to be 6×10^5 cm.

[**Hint:** $0.25 \times 10^3 g = \frac{Gm_1m_2}{r^2}$ and $M = \frac{g}{G}R^2$. Calculate $\frac{g}{G}$ from the first relation and substitute in the second.]

[**Ans.** M = 4.8×10^{27} gm and mean density = 5.31 gm/cc]

38. The moon describes a circular orbit of radius 3.8×10^5 kilometres about the earth in 27 days and the earth describes a circular orbit of radius 1.5×10^8 kms round the sun in 365 days. Determine the mass of the sun in terms of the earth.

[**Hint:** $\frac{GM}{d^2} = d\left(\frac{2\pi}{T_1}\right)^2$ or $T_1^2 = \frac{4\pi^2}{GM}d^3$. Similarly $T_2^2 = \frac{4\pi^2}{GE}\cdot x^3$. Hence $\frac{M}{E} = \frac{d^3}{x^3}\cdot\frac{T_2^2}{T_1^2}$

[**Ans.** 3.3666×10^5 *E*]

39. Show by cogent argument why the following two time-periods are the same, *viz.*, 84 minutes: (*i*) period of oscillation of a particle in a tunnel bored through the earth and (*ii*) period of revolution of an artificial satellite close to the earth's surface.

40. The mean distance of Mars from the sun is 1.524 times that of the *Earth* from the sun. How many years would be required for *Mars* to make one revolution around the sun? [**Ans.** 1.88 years]

41. Estimate (*i*) the value of *g*, (*ii*) the escape velocity, on Mars. Given, mass of *Mars* ≈ 0.11 of the mass of the earth and its radius, 42/79 that of the earth, (Radius of the earth = 6.37×10^8 cm.)

[**Ans.** (*i*) 381.5 cm/sec^2; (*ii*) 5×10^5 cm/sec.]

III–Inverse square law forces–self energy

42. (*a*) What are central and non-central forces? Give three characteristics of each. Give two examples of central and non-central forces.

(Pbi. U. 2001; P.U. 2000; G.N.D.U. 2000; H.P.U. 2003, Luck. U. 2001; Purvanchal U. 2006, 2005; Kerala U. 2001; Gharwal U. 2000; Osm. U.2004; Nagpur U. 2009)

(*b*) (*i*) Why gravitational and Coulomb forces are called inverse square law forces? ***(H.P.U. 2000)***

(*ii*) Why nuclear force is called non-central force? ***(H.P.U., 2001)***

43. When a particle moves under a central force, prove that the angular momentum of a particle is conserved. ***(Calicut U. 2003; Meerut U. 2005, 2003; Purvanchal U. 2005; D.A.U. Agra 2008)***

44. Derive the polar equation of the orbit of a particle of mass *m* moving under the action of a force field $F = \frac{c}{r^2}$ about a fixed centre. ***(P.U. 2001)***

45. What is central force? Show that motion of a particle under central force is always confined to a single plane, if the motion of the particle is not parallel to the force direction. ***(Nagpur U. 2007, Kolkata U. 2002)***

46. Why gravitational and Coulomb's forces are called central forces?

47. Why nuclear forces are called non-central forces?

48. Show that a conservative force can be expressed as $\vec{F} = -$ *grad U*, where *U* is potential energy. ***(Meerut U. 2000; Purvanchal U.,2005)***

49. Show that work done in a conservative field around a closed path is zero. ***(Nag. U. 2007)***

50. The equation of the orbit of a particle of mass *m* moving under the action of a central force field about a fixed centre is $r = 1/2\theta$. Find the force law. ***(P.U. 2000)***

51. State Newton's law of gravitation. What is meant by gravitational constant? What are its dimensions? ***(Nag. U. 2007, 2006)***

52. (*a*) Explain the term Gravitational self-energy of a Galaxy.

(*b*) Obtain an expression for Gravitational self-energy of a Galaxy in terms of number of stars in Galaxy, mass of each star and average distance between each pair of stars. ***(Nagpur Uni. 2009)***

53. Explain the concept of self energy of a body. Deduce an expression for gravitational self energy of any uniform solid sphere. ***(Nagpur, 2006, 2003; Agra U. 2007, 2004)***

54. What do you understand by the term '*gravitational self energy*' of a body or a system of particles? Show that the gravitational self energy of a system of n particles, each of mass m, at an average distance r from each other is given by $U_s = \frac{1}{2} Gn(n-1)m^2/r$.

55. Calculate the gravitational self energy of (*i*) the sun, (*ii*) the earth-sun system, given that the mass of the sun = 2×10^{-30} kg and its radius = 7×10^8 metres, mass of the earth = 6×10^{24} kg and mean earth-sun distance = 1.50×10^8 km. Take $G = 7 \times 10^{-11}\ N-m^2/kg^2$.

[Ans. (*i*) -2.4×10^{41} Joules, (*ii*) -5.6×10^{33} joules, **]**

[Hint. Self energy of the sun = $\frac{3}{5}\frac{M_s^2}{R_s}G$. Self energy of the earth-sun system = $-\frac{M_sM_e}{r_{es}}G$, where M_s and M_e are the masses of the sun and the earth respectively; R_s, the radius of the sun and r_{es}, the distance between the sun and the earth.]

56. The gravitational self energy of a uniform sphere of mass M and radius R is given by $-\frac{3}{5}G\frac{M^2}{R}$. Explain what is meant by this. What happens if the sphere contracts in radius by a small amount a?

***(Agra, 1971)* [Ans.** *It results in release of energy* = $\frac{3}{5}G\frac{M^2}{R}a$. **]**

57. Deduce an expression for the electrostatic self energy of a charge q spread uniformly over the surface of a sphere of radius r. ***[Agra (supp), 1967]***

58. 10^5 Stars are distributed spherically in a globular cluster, with each star having the same mass as the sun. If the diameter of the cluster be 40 *parsec*, where 1 *parsec* = 3×10^{18} cm, calculate (*i*) the number of stars per cube parsec, (*ii*) the gravitational self energy of the cluster (neglecting the self energy of individual stars). (Mass of the sun = 2×10^{33} gm, $G = 6.67 \times 10^{-8}$ *c.g.s* units).

[Ans. (*i*) *number of stars per cubis parsec* = 3; (*ii*) nearly 10^{49} *ergs*.**]**

[Hint. (*i*) Number of stars per cubic parsec = $\frac{\textit{total number of stars}}{\textit{volume of cluster}} = \frac{10^5}{\frac{4}{3}\pi(20)^3}$

(*ii*) Self energy of the cluster, $U_s = \frac{3}{5}\frac{M^2}{R}G = \frac{3}{5}\frac{(10^5 \times 2\times 10^{33})^2}{20\times 3\times 10^{18}} \times 6.67\times 10^{-8}$]

59. Calculate the rate of contraction of the sun's radius if the energy released due to its contraction (with no apprectable change in its mass) is radiated and received on the surface of the earth at the rate of 2 calories *per sq* cm *per minute*. Distance between the sun and the earth = 1.5×10^{13} cm. (Mass of the sun = 2×10^{33} gm; radius of the sun = 7×10^{10} cm). **[Ans.** 2.3 km/year.**]**

[Hint. See worked example 14]

60. Show that the gravitational energy of a galaxy is given by $U_s = -\frac{GN^2M^2}{2R}$ where N = Number of stars; M = Mass of each star. R = Average distance between each pair of stars. ***(Nagpur. 2003)***

61. (*a*) Show that the radius vector joining the sun to a planet sweeps out equal areas in equal interval of time. ***(Purvachal U. 2005)***

(*b*) Show that the square of the time period of revolution of a planet is proportional to the cube of semi-major axis of the orbit. ***(Bhopal U. 2004; Osm. U. 2004; P.U. 2001, 2000, Gharwal U. 2000; G.N.D.U. 2002, 2001, 2000; Pbi. U. 2003, 2000 Indore U. 2001; Kerala U. 2001; Meerut U. 2002)***

62. Find the force field associated with the potential energy $V = Ae^{\alpha(x+y+z)}$ where A and α are constant. ***(H.PU. 2003)***

63. Prove that all ellipses with the same major axes have the same energy.

64. A particle moves under a central force. Show that (*i*) its orbit lies in a plane and (*ii*) the radius vector from the centre of the force to the particle sweeps area at a constant rate.

(Meerut U. 2002; P.U. 2001; G.N.D.U 2003)

65. State the relation showing total energy for a particle moving under a central force. Hence derive a relation between (*i*) r and t (*ii*) θ and t and (*iii*) θ and r.

66. (*a*) Discuss the nàturae of orbital motion under a central force field when the force obeys inverse square law and is (*i*) repulsive (*ii*) zero and (*iii*) attractive.

(*b*) What is potential energy curve? Making use of potential energy curve explain the naturae of motion when total energy is (*i*) positive (*ii*) zero (*iii*) negative but greater than minimum value and (*iv*) minimum. ***(Utkal U. 2003; P.U. 2004, 2003, 2000; G.N.D.U. 2000)***

67. Establish the differential equation of motion under a central force and deduce its solution for attractive inverse square force field. ***(H.P.U. 2003, 2001)***

68. (*a*) A particle of mass m traces a circle of radius r under attractive inverse square force $-\frac{c}{r^2}$. Show that the energy of the particle at any point on the circle is $-\frac{c}{2r}$.

(*b*) Show that the differential equation of motion of a particle of mass m under the influence of a central isotropic force can be written as

$$\frac{d^2u}{d\theta^2}+u = -\frac{m}{J^2u^2}F\left(\frac{1}{u}\right)$$

where $u=\frac{1}{r}$, (r, θ) are the plane polar co-ordinates of the particles and J the angular momentum.

69. (*a*) Prove that the shape of the orbit traced by a particle moving under attractive inverse square force depends on the angular momentum and total energy of the particle. What are turning points? What is the number of turning points in an elliptic orbit? ***(P.U. 2001, G.N.D.U. 2000; Pbi. U. 2003)***

(*b*) What will be the shape of the orbit of a particle moving under repulsive inverse square force? Explain.

70. (*a*) State the expression for acceleration of a particle moving in a plane in polar coordinates and derive (*i*) the radial equation of motion (*ii*) equation of motion of θ-coordinates.

71. If $\vec{r}$ is the radius vector joining a particle of mass m with centre of force and $\vec{A}$ the area swept by the radius vector, show that $\vec{A}=\frac{1}{2}\vec{r}\times d\vec{r}$ and $\frac{d\vec{A}}{dt}=\frac{J}{2m}$ where J is the angular momentum of the particle about the centre of force. ***(P.U. 2004)***

72. A particle moving under a central force describes spiral orbit given by $r = a\ \exp.(b\theta)$ where a and b are some constants. Obtain the force law. ***(Pbi. U. 2000, G.N.D.U. 2002)***

73. A particle follows a spiral orbit given by $r = c\theta^2$ under an unknown force law. Prove that such an orbit is possible in a central field. Also find the form of the force law.

74. A planet moving round the sun is suddenly stopped. Find the time taken by the planet to fall into the sun in terms of the period of revolution of the planet around the sun.

75. What parameters determine the shape and size of an elliptic orbit of a planet? Explain.

IV–Fundamental lengths and numbers

76. What is meant by *fundamental lengths and numbers*? Illustrate their importance in Physics by a couple of examples.

77. Construct any three fundamental quantities from the following basic parameters:

(*i*) velocity of light (*c*), (*ii*) Planck's constant (*h*), (*iii*) mass of electrons (*m*), (*iv*) charge of electron (*e*), (*v*) Gravitational constant (*G*).

Express the dimensions of the above and the constructed quantities in terms of mass (*M*), length (*L*) and time (*T*). ***[Delhi (Hons); 1972]***

Ans. The *dimensions of the given quantities are* (*i*) M^0LT^{-1}, (*ii*) ML^2T^{-1}, (*iii*) ML^0T^0, (*iv*) $M^{1/2}L^{3/2}T^{-1}$ and (*v*) $M^{-1}L^3T^{-2}$.

The *three constructed quantities* are

(*i*) *Fine structure constant* $\alpha = \dfrac{e^2}{(h/2\pi)c} = \dfrac{2\pi e^2}{hc} = \dfrac{1}{137.04}$

Its *dimensions* are $\dfrac{ML^3T^{-2}}{(ML^2T^{-1})(LT^{-1})} = M^0L^0T^0$, *i.e., no dimension in M,L,T.*

(*ii*) *Radius of the hydrogen atom,* $\alpha_0 = r_0/\alpha^2 = \dfrac{e^2/mc^2}{(2\pi e^2/hc)^2} = \dfrac{h^2}{4\pi^2 me^2} = 0.529 \times 10^{-8}$ cm.

Its *dimensions* are $\dfrac{M^2L^4T^{-2}}{(M)(ML^3T^{-2})} = M^0L^0T^0.$

(*iii*) *Planck's length,* $l = \left(\dfrac{Gh}{c^3}\right)^{\frac{1}{2}} \approx 10^{-33}$ cm.

Its *dimensions* are $\left[\dfrac{(M^{-1}L^3T^{-2})(ML^2T^{-1})}{L^3T^{-3}}\right]^{1/2} = M^0L^0T^0.$

V–Kepler's laws

78. Enunciate *Kepler's laws* and show how they may be deduced from Newton's law of gravitation. ***(Meerut 2005)***

79. (*a*) With the help of Kepler's first two laws of planetary motion and Newton's laws of motion, show that the force acting on a planet is directed towards the sun and is inversely proportional to the square of its distance from the sun.

(*b*) With the help of Kepler's third law, show that the forces on the planets are proportional to their masses.

(*c*) Finally, with the help of Newton's third law, show that the force on a planet is proportional to the product of the masses of the sun and the planet.

80. State Kepler's laws of planetary motion and Newton's laws of gravitation. ***(Nagpur Uni. 2009, 2007)***

81. Deduce Newton's law of gravitation from Kepler's laws.

82. (*a*) State and prove Kepler's laws of planetary motion. ***(Guwahati U. 2007, Nagpur U. 2005)***
(D.A.U. Agra 2008, 2003; Nag. U. 2007, 2008; Calicut U., 2003)

(*b*) Show that the areal velocity of a planet round the sun is constant.

13 Chapter

ELASTICITY (Strength of Materials)

Brief Contents

13.1 INTRODUCTION

In the previous chapters of mechanics, we had started with the concept of a small massive particle and then the rigid body which we defined as one, the distance between any two particles remains unaltered whatever the external forces applied to it, and in whatever in manner they may vary. In other words, the body remains un-deformated in its shape, size, and volume.

However in practice, we never find such a body. Every material body gets deformated, to a smaller or larger extent, depending upon the way in which the forces act. Moreover, it has a tendency to recover its original shape and size on the removal of external applied forces; within some limit, called an elastic limit. This property of a body is known as elasticity.

Elasticity is the property by the virtue of which the material bodies recover (or regain) their original shape and size on the removal of the external deforming forces.

When an external force acts on a body, there is a change in its length, volume or shape. The body is then said to be strained. On the removal of the deforming force, the strained body tries to regain its original state or condition. Such a body in known as elastic body. Some of the examples are steel, ivory, quartz, rubber *etc.* If the deformation of a body under a given deforming force, at a given temperature, remains unchanged (*i.e.*, neither increases nor decreases) by the prolonged application of that force and which completely regains its original state on the removal of that force, it is said to be **perfectly elastic**.

On the other hand, if the body remains deformed and shows no tendency to recover its original condition on the removal of the deforming force, it is said to be **perfectly plastic.**

In practice, however, there exist no such perfectly elastic or perfectly plastic bodies. The nearest approach to the former is a quartz fibre and to the later, ordinary putty. All other bodies lie between these two extremes, there being only differences of degree as to their elasticity or plasticity when compared to one another.

We shall confine ourselves here to bodies which are homogeneous and isotropic, *i.e.*, which have a uniform composition and whose properties are the same at all points and in all directions. Almost all fluids (*i.e.*, liquids and gases) belong to this category but not all solids, some of which, (like wood and crystals, show different properties in different directions and are thus non-isotropic or anisotropic, including also some metals which are crystalline in structure. As a class, in general, however, metals, particularly if they be in the form of wires or rods, behave as isotropic bodies in respect of at least their elastic properties, if not also others.

13.2 LOAD, STRESS AND STRAIN

1. Load. Any combination of external forces acting on a body (*e.g.*, its own weight, along with the forces connected with it, like centrifugal force, force of friction *etc.*) whose net effect is to deform the body, *i.e.*, to change its form or dimensions, is referred to as a *load*.

2. Stress. A body in equilibrium under the influence of its internal forces is, as we know, in its natural state. But when external or deforming forces are applied to it, there is a relative displacement of its particles and this gives rise to internal forces of reaction tending to oppose and balance the deforming forces, until the elastic limit is reached and the body gets permanently deformed. The body is then said to be *stressed or under stress*.

If this opposing or recovering force be uniform, *i.e.*, proportional to area, it is clearly a distributed force like fluid pressure and is measured in the same manner, as *force per unit area*, and termed *stress*. Being obviously equal in magnitude, though opposite in direction, to the applied or deforming force per unit area, if is generally measured in terms of the latter. Thus if F be the deforming force applied uniformly over an area A , we have *stress* $= F/A$.

In case the stress is not uniformly distributed over a surface, let a force δF act normally on an elemental area δ A of the surface, when *stress at a point on the surface* = $\delta F/ \delta A$ which in the limit $\delta A \to 0$ is equal to dF/dA.

If the deforming force be inclined to the surface, it components perpendicular to and along the surface are respectively called normal and tangential (or shearing) stress. The stress is, however, always normal in the case of a change of length or volume and tangential in the case of a change of shape of a body.

Further, the stress may be tensile (extensional or expansive) or compressive according as it results in an increase or decrease in length or volume. And, since like pressure, it is force per unit area, its dimensions are the same us those of pressure, *viz.*, $ML^{-1} T^{-2}$ and it is measured in the same units, *viz.*, *dynes/cm*^{2}, *poundal/ft*^{2} and *newton/metre*^{2} in the C G.S., F.P.S, and M.K.S (or *SI*) systems of units respectively.

3. Strain. As we have seen, a body under stress, *i.e.*, under a system of forces or couples of equilibrium undergoes a change in form, *i.e.*, in length, volume or shape. This change in the dimensions of body measured per unit dimension, *i.e.*, per unit length, per unit volume or the angular deformation produced in it, is called *strain* and is referred to as *linear*, *volume* and *shearing strain* (or *shear*) in the three cases respectively.

Being thus just a ratio between two similar quantities, it is a mere number and hence a dimensionless quantity, having no units.

13.3 HOOKE'S LAW

This is the fundamental law of elasticity and was first enuniciated in the year 1679 by Robert Hooke in the concise form '*Ut tensio sic vis, i.e.*, '*As the tension, so the strain*'. It may, however, be formally stated thus:

'Provided the strain is small, the stress is proportional to the strain.'

It follows, therefore, that if the strain be small, *the ratio between stress and strain is a constant*, called **modulus of elasticity** (a name given to it by Thomas Young) or **coefficient of elasticity** (*E*). Thus *E* = *stress/strain* or *stress per unit strain.*

Since stress has the same dimensions and units as those of pressure and strain is a mere number having no dimensions, *the dimensions and units of the modulus or coefficient of elasticity are the same as those of stress or pressure.*

13.4 ELASTIC LIMIT

In the case of a solid, if the stress be gradually increased, the strain too increases with it in accordance with *Hooke's law* until a point is reached at which the linear relationship between the two just ceases and beyond which the strain increases much more reapidly than is warranted by the law. *This value of the stress for the which Hooke's law just ceases to be obeyed is called the elastic limit of the material of the body for the type of stress in question.*

The body thus recovers its original state on removal of the stress within this limit but fails to do so when this limit is exceeded, acquiring a permanent residual strain or a *permanent set*, as it is usually referred to.

The elastic limit is also sometimes defined in terms of the load or the forece which produces the maximum reversible or recoverable deformation in the body.

13.5 BEHAVIOUR OF A WIRE OR A BAR UNDER INCREASING STRESS

If we subject a wire (or a bar) to gradually increasing stress and plot a graph between the stress applied and the corresponding strain produced, we obtain a curve of the form shown in Fig. 13.1, called the **stress-strain diagram**, from which the following points emerge :

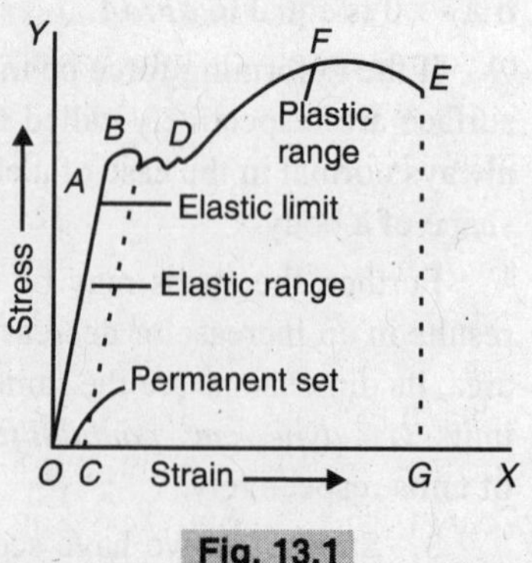

Fig. 13.1

(*i*) There is linear relationship between stress and strain, *i.e.*, Hooke' law is fully obeyed (or the wire is perfectly elastic) up to the point *A*, as shown by the straight and sloping part *OA* of the curve. So that, on the stress being removed at any point up to *A*, the wire recovers its original condition of zero strain represented by the point *O*.

Obviously, therefore, the tensile stress corresponding to *A* thus gives the elastic limit of the material of the wire, sometimes referred to as the *elastic strength* of the wire.

It will also be seen that *the strain, within the elastic limit, is very small*. The increase in the length of the wire, which is purely elastic, (*i.e.*, due to tension in it), hardly ever exceeds 1/1000*th* of its original length.

(*ii*) Beyond the elastic limit (*A*), Hooke's law ceases to be obeyed, the strain increasing more rapidly with stress than warranted by the law, as shown by the bent part *AB* of the curve. The increase in lenth of the wire is now partly elastic and partly plastic (*i.e.*, due to shearing stress): so that if the stress be removed at *B*, the wire does not recover its original condition of zero strain along *BAO* but takes the path *BC* to come to the position *C*, with a *residual strain* or a *permanent set OC* in it.

(*iii*) Beyond the point *B*, there starts a large but irregular increase in strain up *D* with little or no increase in stress, the stress being just a little smaller at *D* than at *B*. This point *B*, where the large, erratic increase in strain just starts is called the **yield point** (or the commercial elastic limit) of the material of the wire, and the *stress corresponding to it is naturally* referred to as the **yielding stress**.

Points *B* and *D* are also sometimes called the *upper* and the *lower yield* points respectively.

(*iv*) Beyond the point *D*, the yielding comes to a stop and any further extension in the wire (which is now purely plastic) can be produced only by increasing the stress, there being a corresponding decrease in the area of cross-section of the wire, so that its volume remains unaffected. This continues up to the point *F*, beyond which the extension goes on even without any addition to the load applied, the wire being in a state of virtual *flow*. Its cross-section decreases faster at some section of it and a local constriction, called a *neck* or a *waist* is developed there. This results in an automatic decrease in stress and gives the portion *FE* of the curve, where *E* represents the **breaking point** of the wire since it *breaks* or *snaps* (or, technically speaking, is *destroyed*) there.

Obviously, the maximum stress to which the wire can be subjected (*i.e., the maximum load or force applied divided by the original cross section of the wire*) is the one represented by the point F. It is fittingly called the **breaking stress** and measures the **tensile or ultimate strength** of the wire.

In actual practice, however, no part of machinery is, as a safeguard, subjected to a stress as high as this. The maximum stress to which it is subjected is very much less and always within the elastic limit. It is, therefore, called the **working stress**, *working strength or tenacity, and the ratio between the breaking stress and the working stress is appropriately called the* **factor of safety** (or, amusingly enough, the *factor of ignorance*), its value being kept 10 in the United Kingdom and only five in the USA.

N.B. If we plot a load extension diagram for the given wire (or ba.), it is found to be of the same general shape as the stress-strain diagram (Fig. 13.1), leading to the same deductions as above.

13.6 ELASTIC BEHAVIOUR OR SOLIDS IN GENERAL

(*i*) **Elastic after-effect.** Only a few solids, like quartz, phosphor-bronze, silver and gold, recover their original condition almost immediately after the deforming force is removed, provided, of cource the elastic limit has not been exceeded*. Solids, in general, however, take appreciable time to do so or, so to speak, only *creep* back to it, glass being particulary notorious in this respect. This delay in recovery on removal of the deforming force is known as *elastic after-effect.*

(*ii*) **Elastic hysteresis.** This is purely a consequence of the elastic after effect, due to which, as we have seen under (*i*) above, the strain persists even when the stress is removed and thus lags behind the stress. As a result, if a material be subjected to a full cycle of increasing and decreasing load, the strain is found to be greater for the same value of the stress when it is being unloaded than when it is being loaded, as shown exaggerated in Fig. 13.2.

The lagging behind of strain is called elastic hysteresis (hysteresis literally meaning lagging behind), the phenomenon being similar to the familiar magnetic hysteresis will all its implications.

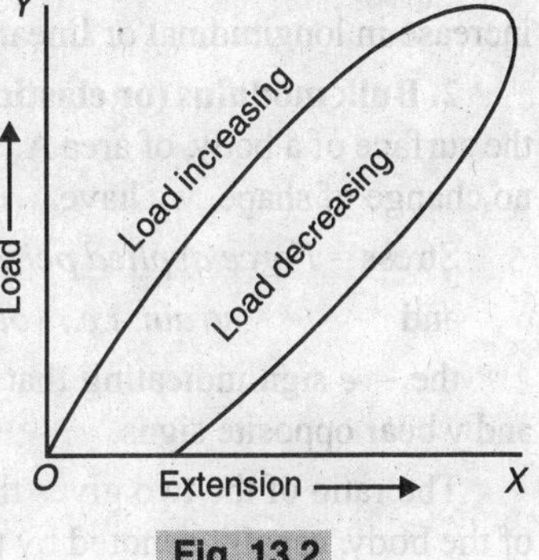

Fig. 13.2

Obviously, materials which show little or no elastic after-effect also show no elastic hysteresis.

(*iii*) **Elastic fatigue.** *Kelvin*, while investigating the rate of decay of torsional vibrations of wires, found that the vibrations decayed much sooner if a wire is kept vibrating for a long enough time than when it is quite fresh, as though on vibrating continuously it gets tired or fatigued and finds it difficult to continue vibrating. Kelvin aplty called the phenomenon *elastic fatigue*.

Apart from the above peculiar traits, it is found that operations, like *hammering* and *rolling*, which break up the crystal grains of a material into smaller units, make for a strengthening of its elastic properties, whereas operations like *annealing*, which tend to orient the crystal grains into one particular direction (thus forming a larger crystal, as it were) result in a weakening of its elastic properties or a strengthening of its plastic properties.

Again, the *addition of impurities* (as are sometimes added to metals to bind their crystals better together) like carbon to iron or potassium to gold, affect the elastic properties of the metal according as they are themselves more elastic or plastic than the metal in question. In the two cases mentioned here, the effect is a strengthening of the elastic properties of both iron and gold.

Finally, a *change in temperature* also affects the elastic properties of a material, – a rise in temperature resulting in general, in a weakening of the elastic properties and a fall in temperature in strengthening them. Thus, carbon which is highly elastic at the ordinary temperature, becomes plastic when heated by a current through it and lead, which is hardly elastic at the ordinary temperature, becomes highly so when cooled in liquid air.

13.7 DIFFERENT TYPES OF ELASTICITY

Corresponding to the different types of strain, we have the following different types of elasticity.

1. **Young's modulus (or elasticity of length).** If a deforming force be applied to a body *only along a. particular direction, i.e.*, if the body be subjected to a simple tension or a simple compression (no external force being applied to prevent the accompanying small lateral contraction or expansion), the force applied per unit area of cross-section is called *longitudinal or linear stress* and the change per unit length is called *longitudinal* or *linear strain.* The ratio between the two,

* This exaplains the use of quartz fibres in the torsion balance experiments of *Cavendish* and *Boys* for the determination of the value of G as also in *electrometers* and in fact, as suspension fibres, in general.

within the elastic limit, gives the *coefficient of linear elasticity* or *Young's modulus* of the material in question, usually denoted by the letter Y, or, in engineering practice, by the letter E.

Thus, if F be the force applied normally to a cross sectional area A, such that an increase in length l is produced in an original length L, we have

linear stress = F/A and linear strain = l/L.

So that, Young's modulus Y (or E) = $\dfrac{F/A}{l/L} = \dfrac{F/L}{Al}$

In case the increase in length be not proportional to the force applied, we have

$$Y \text{ (or } E) = \frac{dF/A}{dL/L} = \frac{L}{A}\frac{dF}{dL}$$

where dF/A is the infinitesimal increase in longitudinal or linear stress and dL/L, the corresponding increase in longitudinal or linear strain.

2. Bulk modulus (or elasticity of volume). If a force F be applied normally and uniformly over the surface of a body, of area A, such that there is a change of volume v in its original volume V, but no change of shape, we have

Stress = *Force applied per unit area,* or *Pressure* $P = F/A$

and *strain, i.e., volume strain* $= -v/V$,

the *–ve* sign indicating that if pressure increases, the volume decreases and vice versa, *i.e.*, P and v bear opposite signs.

The ratio of the two gives the coefficient of cubical elasticity or Bulk modulus for the material of the body, usually denoted by the letter K. Thus,

$$K = -\frac{F/A}{v/V} = -\frac{F}{A}\cdot\frac{V}{v} = -\frac{PV}{v}.$$

In case the change in volume be not proportional to the stress (or pressure) applied, we have $K = -dPV\ dV$, where dP is the infinitesimal increase in pressure and dV, the change in volume corresponding to it.

K is also sometimes referred to as incompressibility of the material of the body and, therefore, $1/K$ is called its **compressibility**.

Obviously, since *liquids and gases* can permanently sustain only a hydrostatic pressure, *the only elasticity they possess is* ***Bulk modulus*** (K).

3. Modulus of rigidity (Torsion modulus or Elasticity of shape). Here, there is a movement of the contiguous layers of the body one over the other under a tangential force, very much like that of the individual members of a pack of playing cards pressed on the table and pushed to one side; so that although there is a change in the shape of the body there is no change in its volume.

Thus, if a tangential force F be applied to the upper face *ABfe* of a cube, of each edge L, whose lower face *Ddgc* is fixed on a horizontal surface, as shown in Fig.13.3, an equal and opposite force comes into play on the lower face, thus forming a couple, tending to rotate the cube. The rotation of the cube is prevented, however, by another equal and opposite couple due to the weight of the cube (along with any vertical force applied) and the reaction of the surface on which the cube rests. The result is that the layers of the cube

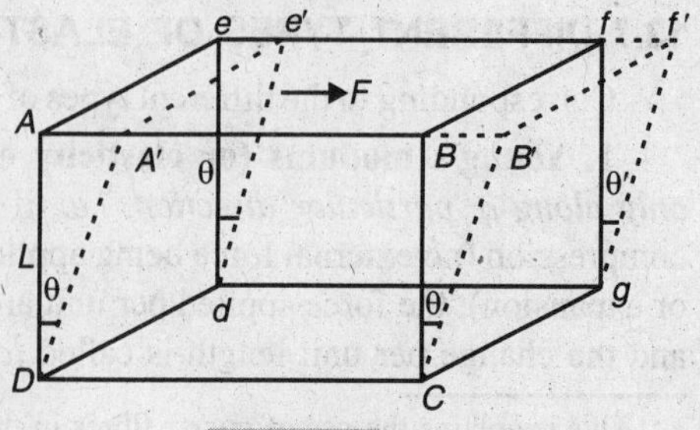

Fig. 13.3

parallel to the upper and lower faces move one over the other, with point A shifting to A', B to B', e to e' and f to f', through an angle θ, where $AA' = BB' = ee' = ff' = l$.

This angle θ through which a line originally perpendicular to the fixed face *is turned thus gives* the shear strain or the angle of shear of the face $ABCD$.

Clearly, $\theta = l/L$, where l is the relative displacement of the upper face of the cube with respect to the lower fixed face, distant L from it. If, therefore, $L = 1$, we have $\theta = l =$ *relative displacement of the upper surface* (or plane) $ABfe$.

We may, therefore, also define *shear strain as the relative displacement between any two planes in the body unit distance apart.*

And, of course, tangential stress = F/A where $A = L^2$, the area of face $ABfe$.

The ratio between tangential stress and shear strain (or angle of shear) then gives the coefficient or modulus of rigidity or the coefficient of transverse elasticity, as it is also sometimes called. It is denoted by the letter n. We thus have

$$n = \frac{F/A}{\theta} = \frac{F/L^2}{l/L} = \frac{F/A}{l/L}$$

As will be readily seen, this is a relation similar to that for Young's modulus. Only, F/A here is the tangential, and *not linear, stress* and l, the displacement *at right angles to*, and *not along*, L.

Obviously, if $A = l$ and $e = 1$ (radian), we have $n = F$.

Thus, the modulus of rigidity of a material may be defined as the *tangential or shearing stress per unit shear, i.e.*, an angle of shear equal to 1 *radian, imagining Hooke's* law to hold good even for a strain as large as this (though, in point of fact, it ceases to be valid in the case of metals for a shear exceeding only 1/200th of a radian).

In case the shear be not proportional to the tangential stress, we have

$$n = \frac{dF/A}{d\theta}$$

where the small increase $d\theta$ in the angle of shear corresponds to a small increase dF/A in tangential (or shearing) stress.

4. Axial modulus. This is defined as longitudinal stress required fo produce unit linear strain, unaccompanied by any lateral strain and is denoted by the Greek letter Z.

It is thus similar to Young's modulus, with the all-important difference that here the lateral strain produced (in the form of lateral contraction) is offset by applying two suitable stresses in directions perpendicular to that of the linear stress. So that the total stress is Young's modulus plus these two perpendicular stresses.

13.8 EQUIVALENCE OF A SHEAR TO A TENSILE AND A COMPRESSIVE STRAIN AT RIGHT ANGLES TO EACH OTHER AND EACH EQUAL TO HALF THE SHEAR

Let a tangential force F be applied to the upper face AB of a cube $ABCD$, of each edge L, with its lower face DC fixed (Fig. 13.4), so that it is sheared through a small angle θ into the position $A'B'$, with its perpendicular diagonals DB and AC extended to DB' and shortened to $A'C$ respectively.

Drop perpendiculars $A'M$ and BN from A' and B on to AC and DB' respectively, so that the extension in diagonal DB is NB' and the compression in diagonal AC is AM.

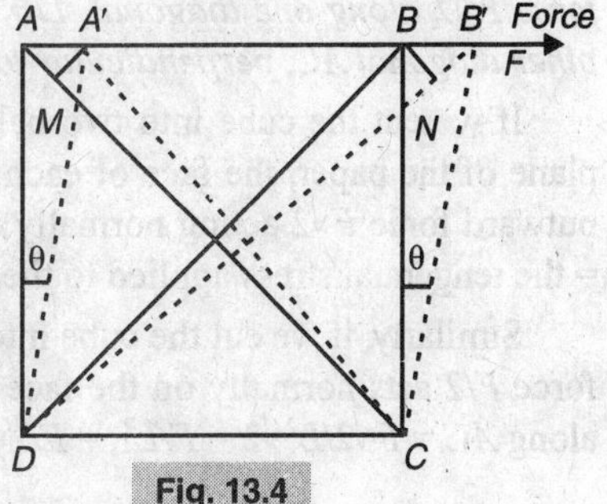

Fig. 13.4

The shear being small, Δs $AM\,A'$ and $BN\,B'$ may be assumed to be right-angled isosceles triangles, so that $NB' = BB' \cos 45° = BB'/\sqrt{2}$.

Since $AB = L$, we have $DB = DN = \sqrt{L^2 + L^2} = L\sqrt{2}$.

$\therefore$ tensile strain slong diagonal DB

$$= \frac{NB'}{DB} = \frac{BB'}{\sqrt{2}(L\sqrt{2})} = \frac{BB'}{2L} = \frac{\theta}{2} \qquad \left[\because \frac{BB'}{L} = \theta\right]$$

Similarly, *compressive strain along diagonal AC*

$$= \frac{AM}{AC} = \frac{AA' \cos 45°}{AC} = \frac{AA'}{\sqrt{2}(L\sqrt{2})} = \frac{AA'}{2L} = \frac{\theta}{2}$$

Thus, the simple shear θ is equal to half a tensile and half a compressive strain at right angles to each other.

13.9 EQUIVALENCE OF A SHEARING STRESS TO AN EQUAL TENSILE AND AN EQUAL COMPRESSIVE STRESS AT RIGHT ANGLES TO EACH OTHER

Again, let a tangential force F be applied to the upper face AB of a cube (Fig. 13.5), of each edge L, with its lower face DC fixed, so that the tangential or shearing stress to which it is subjected is $F/L^2 = F/A$, where A is the area of the upper, and in fact, every face of the cube.

If the cube were free to move, it would move along the direction of F. Since. however, its lower face is fixed, an equal and opposite force F comes into play on this face, to form a couple FL, tending to rotate the cube clockwise, in the case shown.

And since the cube does not rotate, there must be an equal and opposite couple acting on it [as pointed out earlier under § 13.7, (3)] effectively equal to FL, *i.e.*, due to forces F and F acting along the sides AD and CB tending to rotate the cube in the anticlockwise direction in order to keep it in equilibrium.

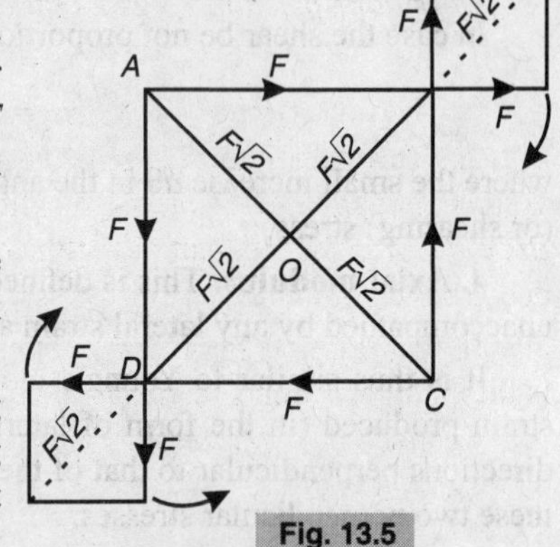

Fig. 13.5

We thus see that a tangential force F applied to one face of the cube gives rise to an equal tangential force (F) on all other faces in appropriate directions, as indicated in the figure.

Now, clearly the resultant of the foreces F and F along AB and CB if $F\sqrt{2}$ along OB and of the forces F and F along AD and CD also equal to $F\sqrt{2}$ along OD, where O is the point of intersection of the diagonals AC and DB of the face $ABCD$. There is thus an *outward pull on diagonal DB, tending to extend its length.*

Similarly, there is an equal inward pull on diagonal AC, tending to shorten its length.

Again, therefore, *a tangential force (F) applied to one face of the cube brings into play a tensile force $F\sqrt{2}$ along one diagonal, DB in this case, and an equal compressive force ($F\sqrt{2}$) along the other diagonal AC, perpendicular to it.*

If we cut the cube into two halves by a plane through diagonal DB and perpendicular to the plane of the paper, the face of each half parallel to DB will have an area $L^2\sqrt{2}.\,L = L^2\sqrt{2}$, with an outward force $F\sqrt{2}$ acting normally on it. So that, *tensil stress along* $DB = F\sqrt{2}/L^2\sqrt{2} = F/L^2 = F/A$ = the tengential stress applied to the upper face of the cube.

Similarly, if we cut the cube into two halves along the diagonal AC, we find that a compressive force $F/2$ acts normally on the face of each half, parallel to AC, and therefore, *compressive stress* along $AC = F\sqrt{2}/L^2\sqrt{2} = F/L^2 = F/A =$ *the tengential stress applied to the upperface of the cube.*

Clearly, therefore, a tangential or a shearing stress is equivalent to an equal tensile stress and an equal compressive stress at right angles to each other.

13.10 WORK DONE PER UNIT VOLUME (OR ENERGY PER UNIT VOLUME IN A STRAIN

Obviously, work has to be done by the applied force in deforming a body, to whatever type of strain it might be subjected. This work done or energy spent remains stored up in the body in the form of potential energy which, in this case, may be called *elastic potential energy, energy of strain* or simply, *strain energy*.

Let us calculate the work done (or the strain energy) per unit volume in the three different cases of strain dealt with above.

1. Longitudinal strain. If F be the stretching force applied (within the elastic limit) to a wire of length L and area of cross-section A, such that it increases in length by l, we have,

$$Y = FL/Al, \text{ whence, } F = YAl/L$$

where Y is the value of *Young's modulus* for the material of the wire.

Clearly, work done for an additional small increase dl in the length of the wire = $F.dl\ (YAl/L).\ dl$.

$\therefore$ work done during the whole increase in the length of the wire from 0 to l, say,

$$W = \int_0^l F.dl = \int_0^l (YAl/L)dl = \frac{1}{2}YAl^2/L = \frac{1}{2}(YAl/L)l = \frac{1}{2}F.l,$$

i.e., work done during stretch of the wire from 0 to $l = \frac{1}{2}$ *stretching force × stretch.*

And since volume of the wire = $L \times A$, we have

work done per unit volume of the wire or strain energy per unit volume of the wir

$$= \frac{1}{2}Fl/AL = \frac{1}{2}(F/A)(l/L) = \frac{1}{2} \text{ stress} \times \text{strain.}$$

2. Volume strain. Let p be the *stress* or *pressure* applied normally over an area A of a body of volume V such that its volume decreases by v. Then, clearly, $K = pV/v$, or, $p = Kv/V$, where K is the *Bulk modulus* for the material of the body, (omitting the – *ve* sign which merely indicates that v is a decrease in volume).

If, therefore, dx be a small movement in the direction of p, work done = $pAdx = p.dv$, where dv is the small additional decrease in volume.

So that, *work done for the whole decrease in volume from* 0 to v,

$$i.e., W = \int_0^v p.dv = \int_0^v \frac{Kv}{V}dv = \frac{1}{2}\frac{Kv^2}{V} = \frac{1}{2}\frac{Kv}{V}v = \frac{1}{2}pv$$

$$= \frac{1}{2} \text{ stress} \times \text{change in volume.}$$

Therefore, *work done (or strain energy) per unit volume* $= \frac{1}{2}pv/V = \frac{1}{2}$ *stress × strain.*

3. Shearing strain. Let the upper face of a cube of each edge L (with its lower face fixed) be sheared through an angle θ *under a tangential force F*, as shown in Fig. 13.6 Then, clearly, $n = F/A\theta$, whence, $F = nA\theta$, where n is the modulus of rigidity of the material of the cube and A, the area of the upper (or any) face of the cube.

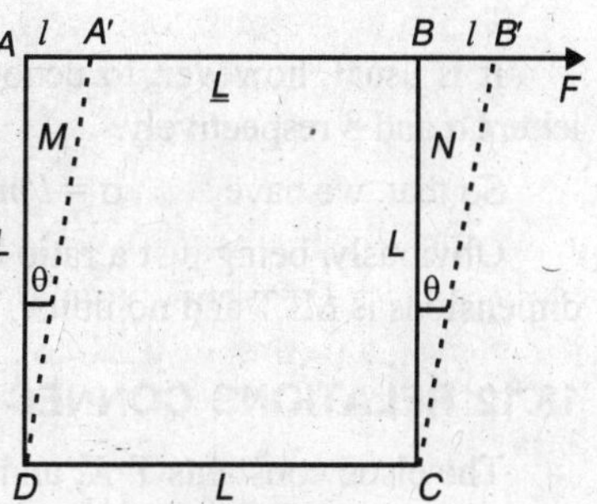

Fig. 13.6

Since $A = L^2$ and $\theta = l/L$, where l is the displacement of each vertical edge of the cube, we have

$$F = nL^2 l/L = nLl.$$

Clearly, work done during a small additional displacement dl of a vertical edge $= Fdl = nLl.dl$. And, therefore,

work done during the whole displacement from 0 to l or during the whole shearing strain θ, *i.e.*,

$$W = \int_0^l nLl.dl = \frac{1}{2}nLl^2 = \frac{1}{2}\frac{F}{Ll}Ll^2 = \frac{1}{2}Fl$$

$$[\because n = F/A\theta = (F/L^2)(L/l)]$$

$$= \frac{1}{2} \textit{ tangential force} \times \textit{displacement.}$$

Since the *volume of the cube* $= L^3$, we have

$$\textit{work done (or strain energy) per unit volume} = \frac{1}{2}Fl/L^3 = \frac{1}{2}(F/L^2)(l/L)$$

$$= \frac{1}{2}(F/A)(\theta) = \frac{1}{2} \textit{stress} \times \textit{strain.}$$

We thus see that in *every type of strain*,

$$\textit{work done per unit volume} = \frac{1}{2} \textit{stress} \times \textit{strain.}$$

13.11 POISSON'S RATIO

It is common knowledge that a wire, on being stretched, becomes *longer* but *thinner*, *i.e.*, although its length increases, its diameter or cross-section decreases. This measn, in other words, that a *linear or tangential* strain, *i.e.*, a strain in the direction of the applied force, also sometimes called *primary strain*, is always accompained by a *lateral strain* or a strain at right angles to the direction of the applied force, also referred to as *secondary strain*. This is true for only a wire but for all bodies, in general.

The ratio between the lateral strain and linear (or tangential) strain due to a given tensile or compressive stress, within the elastic limit, is found to be a constant, called Poisson's ratio for the material of the body in question and is usually denoted by the symbol σ *or, in engineering practice, by l/m. Thus,*

$$\text{Poisson's ratio } \sigma \text{ (or } l/m) = \frac{\textit{Lateral strain}}{\textit{Linear (or tengential) strain}}$$

$$= \frac{\textit{Secondary strain}}{\textit{Primary strain}}$$

It is usual, however, to denote linear (or tengential) and lateral strains per unit stress by the letters α and β respectively.

So that, we have $\sigma = l/m = \beta/\propto$,

Obviously, being just a ratio between two strains, Poisson's ratio is a mere number, having no dimensions is MLT and no units.

13.12 RELATIONS CONNECTING THE ELASTIC CONSTANTS

The elstic constants Y, K, and n, as also the *Poisson's ratio* σ, are all interconnected, as will be seen from the following:

(*i*) **Relation connecting** *Y, K* **and** σ **– (Deformation of a cube).** Consider a unit cube *ABCDEFGH* (Fig. 13.7) with forces T_xT_y and T_z acting normally outwards on its opposite pairs of face's lying along the axes of *x, y* and *z*, respectively.

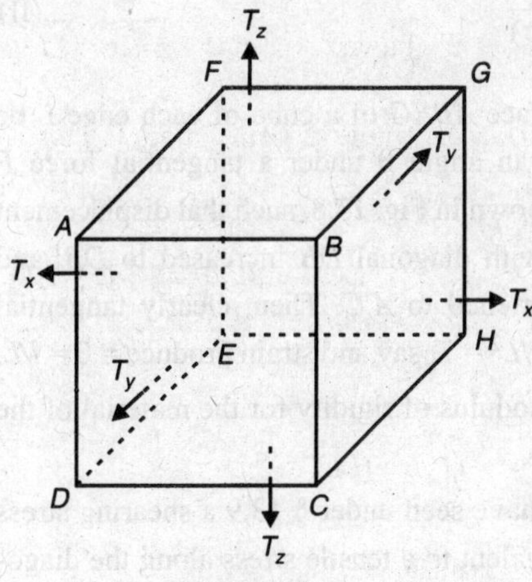

Fig. 13.7

Then, each face of the cube having unit surface area, these forces actually represent the *tensile stresses* on the three pairs of faces respectively, producing elongations along T_x, T_y and T_z and contractions perpendicular to them.

If therefore, α and β be the linear and lateral strains per unit stress respectively, *i.e.*, if α *be the increase strains per unit stress along the direction of the stress* and β, the contraction per unit length per unit stress perpendicular to the direction of the stress, we have elongation produced in edge *AB* due to $T_x = T_x\alpha$ and contractions produced in it due to T_y and T_z equal to $T_y\beta$ and $T_z\beta$ respectively. So that,

length of edge *AB* becomes $1 + T_x\alpha - T_y\beta - T_z\beta$,

Similarly, length of edge *BG* becomes $1 + T_y\alpha - T_x\beta - T_z\beta$,

and length of edge *BC* becomes $1 + T_z\alpha - T_x\beta - T_y\beta$,

So that, the volume of the cube increases to

$$(1+ T_x\alpha - T_y\beta - T_z\beta)\,(1 + T_y\alpha - T_x\beta - T_z\beta)\,(1 + T_z\alpha - T_x\beta - T_y\beta)$$
$$= 1 + (\alpha - 2\beta)\,(T_x + T_y - T_z)$$

neglecting products and squares of the small quantities α and β.

If $T_x = T_y = T_z = T$, clearly,

volume of the cube becomes $1 + (\alpha - 2\beta).\ 3T$.

And, therefore, increase in volume of the cube

$$= 1 + 3T\,(\alpha - 2\beta) - 1 = 3T\,(\alpha - 2\beta).$$

Hence, volume strain set up in the cube $= 3T\,(\alpha - \beta)/1 = 3T\,(\alpha - 2\beta)$, because original volume of the cube = 1.

And, therefore, *Bulk Modulus for the material of the cube,*

$$K = \frac{Stress}{Volume\ strain} = \frac{T}{3T(\alpha - 2\beta)} \quad Or,\ K = \frac{1}{3(\alpha - 2\beta)}$$

If instead of the tension T outwards, a pressure *P* be applied to compress the cube, the decrease in its volume will similarly be $3P\,(\alpha - 2\beta)$, and, therefore, volume strain equal to $3P\,(\alpha - 2\beta)/1$ or $3P\,(\alpha - 2\beta)$.

Again, therefore, Bulk Modulus,

$$K = \frac{Stress}{Volume\ strain} = \frac{P}{3P(\alpha - 2\beta)} = \frac{1}{3(\alpha - 2\beta)} \qquad ....(I)$$

This may be put as $K = \dfrac{1}{3\alpha\,(1 - 2\beta/\alpha)} = \dfrac{1/\alpha}{3(1 - 2\sigma)}$, $[\because \beta/\alpha = \sigma]$.

Clearly, α being the increase per unit length per unit stress, we have strain $= \alpha/1 = \alpha$ corresponding to stress = 1

Therefore, Young's modulus $Y = stress/strain = 1/\alpha$.

Substituting Y for $1/\alpha$, therefore, we have $K = \dfrac{Y}{3(1-2\sigma)}$. ....(II)

(*ii*) **Relation connecting *Y*, *n* and σ.** Let the upper face *ABEG* of a cube of each edge *L* be sheared through an angle θ under a tangential force *F* applied to it, as shown in Fig. 13.8, such that displacement $AA' = BB' = l$, with diagonal *DB* increased to *DB′* and diagonal *AC* shortened to *A′C*. Then, clearly tangential stress applied $= F/L^2 = T$, say and strain produce $= \theta = l/L$.

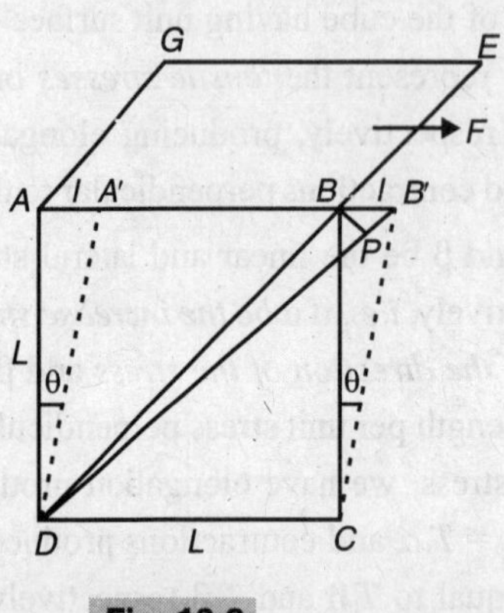

Fig. 13.8

Therefore, modulus of rigidity for the material of the cube, *i.e.*, $n = T/\theta$.

Now, as we have seen under § 13.9 a shearing stress along *AB* is equivalent to a tensile stress along the diagonal *DB* and an equal compressive stress along the diagonal *AC* perpendicular to it. The former clearly increases the length of diagonal *DB* and, sicne the compressive strain along *AC* is accompanied by a lateral strain of the opposite type in a direction perpendicular to it, the compressive stress along *AC* also does so.

If, therefore α and β be the linear and lateral strains per unit stress, we have

increase in length of diagonal DB due to tensile along it

$$= DB \cdot T\alpha = L\sqrt{2} \cdot T\alpha \qquad [\because DB = L\sqrt{2}.]$$

and *increase in its length due to compressive stress along AC*

$$= DB = L\sqrt{2} \cdot T(\alpha + \beta).$$

Therefore, total increase in length of diagonal $DB = L\sqrt{2}\,.\,T(\alpha + \beta)$.

If we drop a perpendicular *BP* from *B* on to *DB′*, we have increase in length of *DB* practically equal to $PB' = BB' \cos BB'P$. Since θ is small, we have *BPB′* a right-angled isosceles triangle, with angle $BB'P = 45°$ and, therefore, $\cos BB'P = \cos 45° = l/\sqrt{2}$.

So that, increase in length of diagonal $DB = l \cos 45° = l/\sqrt{2}$.

We, therefore, have $L/\sqrt{2} \cdot T(\alpha + \beta) = l/\sqrt{2}$, whence,

$$\frac{LT}{l} = \frac{1}{2(\alpha+\beta)} \cdot Or, \frac{T}{l/L} = \frac{1}{2(\alpha+\beta)} \cdot Or, \frac{T}{\theta} = n = \frac{1}{2(\alpha+\beta)} \quad .....III$$

This may be put as $n = \dfrac{1/\alpha}{2(1+\beta/\alpha)}$ *Or*, $n = \dfrac{Y}{2(1+\sigma)}$. IV

(*iii*) **Relation connecting *K*, *n* and σ.** From relation II and IV above, we respectively have

$$Y = 3K(1 - 2\sigma) \text{ and } Y = 2n(1 + \sigma).$$

$\therefore\;\; 3K(1 - 2\sigma) = 2n(1 + \sigma)$, whence, $3K - 2n = \sigma(6K + 2n)$

Or, $$\sigma = \frac{3K - 2n}{6K + 2n} \quad .....V$$

(*iv*) **Relation connecting *Y, K* and *n*.** From relations I and III above,

we have $\alpha - 2\beta = 1/3K$.... (*i*) and $\alpha + \beta = 1/2n$.....(*ii*)

Multiplying relation (*ii*) by 2 and adding to relation (*i*), we have

$$3\alpha = \frac{1}{n} + \frac{1}{3K} = \frac{3K+n}{3Kn}, \text{ whence, } \alpha = \frac{3K+n}{9Kn}.$$

$$\text{And, therefore, } Y = \frac{1}{\alpha} = \frac{9Kn}{3K+n}. \; Or, \frac{9}{Y} = \frac{3K+n}{Kn}.$$

$$\text{Or, } \quad \frac{9}{Y} = \frac{3}{n} + \frac{1}{K}. \qquad \text{...(VI)}$$

Alternatively, as shown under (*iii*) above, $Y = 3K(1 - 2\sigma)$ and $Y = 2n(1 + \sigma)$, whence, we have $1 - 2 = Y\sigma/3K$ and $2(1 + \sigma) = 2 + 2\sigma = Y/n$. Adding the two, we have

$$\frac{Y}{3K} + \frac{Y}{n} = 3 \cdot Or, Y\left(\frac{1}{3K} + \frac{1}{n}\right) = 3 \; Or, \; Y = \frac{9Kn}{3K+n}.$$

$$\text{whence, as above, } \quad \frac{9}{Y} = \frac{3}{n} + \frac{1}{K}.$$

N.B. It may as well be mentioned here that these results do not apply if the material be in the form of a wire. For in the process of being drawn out, the outer layers of the wires become invariably harder than the inner ones and their elastic properties are than considerably altered. Thus, for example, *n* for them is comparatively greater and so is the breaking stress, etc. etc.

13.13 LIMITING VALUES OF POISSON'S RATIO (σ)

We are now in a position to obtain the theoretical limiting values of Possion's ratio σ. For, as we have seen above under § 13.12 (*iii*), $3K(1 - 2\sigma) = 2n(1 + \sigma)$, where, as we know, *K* and *n* are both positive quantities. It follows therefore, that

(*i*) If σ be a positive quantity, the expression on the right hand side in the relation above will be positive. The expression on the left hand side too must therefore be positive. This is, obviously, possible when $2\sigma < 1$ or $\sigma < 1/2$ or 0.5; and

(*ii*) If σ be a negative quantity, the left hand expression in the above relation will be positive and hence the expression on the right hand side too must be positive, and this can be so only if σ be not less than – 1 .

Thus, theoretically, the limiting values of σ are – 1 and 0.5, though in actual practice it lies between 0.2 and 0.4 for most of the materials.

13.14 DETERMINATION OF YOUNG'S MODULUS FOR A MATERIAL

Being the ratio between tensile stress and elongation strain, it should apparently be easy enough to obtain the value of Young's modulus (*Y*) for a given material. Since, however, the extension produced is much too small to lend itself to accurate measurement, different devices are used to overcome the difficulty and these account for the different methods used for determining *Y*.

We shall confine ourselves to two relatively simple methods here.

(*i*) **For a wire.** For a specimen given in the form of a wire, *Y* is usually determined by **Searle's method,** with which the student is perhaps already familiar from his junior classes.

The wire *P* under test is suspended alongside an identical wire *Q*, of the same material, length (*L*) and area of cross section (*A*), (Fig. 13.9), each fastened to an identical metal frame, as shown.

From frame *D* attached to wire *Q* is suspended a constant and sufficiently large weight *W* (which need not be known) just to keep the wire taut and from frame *C* attached to wire *P* is suspended a hanger on which slotted weights can be placed when desired.

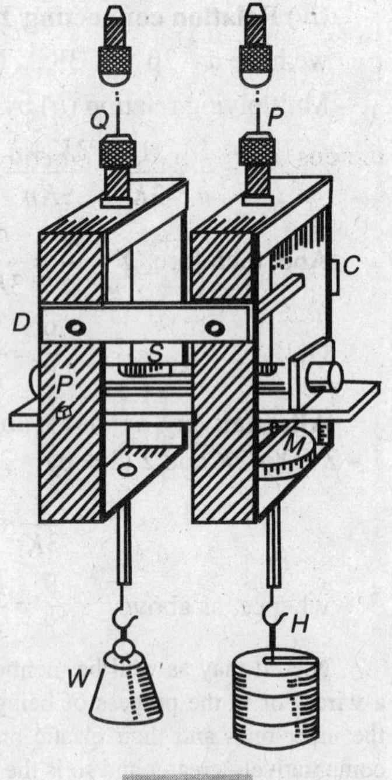

Fig. 13.9

One end of a spirit level, *S.L.*, rests on a point in frame *D* and the other on the tip of a micrometer screw *M*, in frame *C*, as indicated, and it is adjusted to be perfectly horizontal by working the latter up or down until the air bubble lies right in the centre.

Weights are now slipped on to the hanger in equal steps, say, $w = 0.5$ kg each upto a point well within the elastic limit of the material, the stress being never allowed to exceed its maximum or breaking value. Each time due to extension of the wire (p) the spirit level gets disturbed from its horizontal position, to which it is restored back by working the micrometer screw upwards and the distance through which it is moved up (*i.e.*, the extension in the length of the wire) is read on the half-milimeter scale alongside it.

The weights in the hanger are then decreased in the same equal steps w and the spirit level restored to its horizontal position each time by working the micrometer screw downwards and again the distance moved through by it read on the half-millimeter scale.

The mean of all these readings is taken to obtain the true increase in length l of the wire for the given weight or load w added in each step. Then, clearly,

tensile stress applied $= w \times 1000 \times g/A = F/A$, say, and

elongation strain produced $= l/L$.

And, therefore, *Young's modulus* for the material of the wire, *i.e.*,

$$Y = F/A \div l/L = FL/Al$$

and can be easily calculated.

The other wire Q obviously functions as a reference wire, with its length remaining constant all through (due to the constant weight suspended from it). Any yielding of the support or change of temperature during the experiment affecting both the wires equally, the relative increase in lenght of wire P, compared with Q, due to each additional weight w, thus remains quite unaffected.

(*ii*) **For a thick bar.** The elastic properties of wires being different from those of thicker specimens, like bars, of the same materials, (see § 13.6) the methods applicable for the former are not found suitable for the letter.

For thick bars, therefore, we generally use what is called **Ewing's extensometer**, (Fig. 13.10).

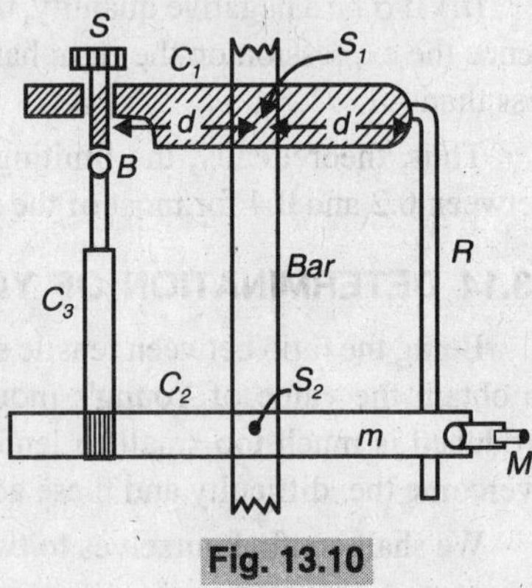

Fig. 13.10

This extensometer essentially consists of two parallel clamp-pieces C_1 and C_2 to which the bar under test can be fixed by means of set-screws S_1 and S_2, the distance between which, and hence the initial length L of the bar, is accurately known.

A micrometer screw S fixed at one end in clamp C_1 has a hollow in its tip which can be made to engage with a ball-point B carried at the top of a vertical clamp C_3 fixed on to C_2, so that the ball point serves as a fulcrum about which the clamp-piece C_1 can be made to turn.

A vertical rod R emanating from the other end of C_1 passes through an axial slot in C_2 and carries a glass plate, with a small horizontal line m marked on it, set in a notch in the portion passing through C_2. A microscope M, fitted with micrometer eye-piece, is also fixed into the slot, as shown, so as to be able to accurately measure any displacement of mark m, which is kept illuminated by light reflected from a mirror.

The micrometer screw S is first moved downwards to just engage with the ball-point B and the position of mark m noted on the micrometer scale of the eye-piece. The bar is then stretched by means of a vertical testing machine, so that it extends downwards, with clamp piece C_1 turning clockwise about the fulcrum B, resulting in downward movement of rod R and hence also of mark m, which is again similarly noted.

The downward displacement of mark m, thus accurately known, is twice the extension of the bar, for the simple reason that R and B being equidistant from the axis of the bar, R and hence m lies twice as far away from the fulcrum (B) as the bar, so that the movement of R or m is twice that of the bar. Let l be the extension of the bar.

Then, clearly, *elongation strain* set up in the bar = l/L.

And, if F be the force applied by the testing machine and A, the area of cross section of the bar, the *tensile stress* applied = F/A.

And, therefore, Young's modulus for the material of the bar, *i.e.*,

$$Y = \frac{F/A}{l/L} = FL/Al,$$

and can be easily evaluated.

The apparatus is sensitive enough to be able to measure extensions of the bar as small as 2.5×10^{-5} *cm* and can be used with both vertical and horizontal testing machines.

13.15 DETERMINATION OF POISSON'S RATIO (σ)

(*i*) **For rubber.** About a metre-long rubber tube R (like a cycle tyre) is closely fitted with rubber bungs (smeared with glue) and metal caps (A and B) at its two ends. The upper cap A is clamped tightly in a wall bracket or a massive stand (Fig. 13.11) and a small weight placed in the scale pan suspended from a hook in the lower cap B, so that the tube hangs vertically with no bends or kinks in it.

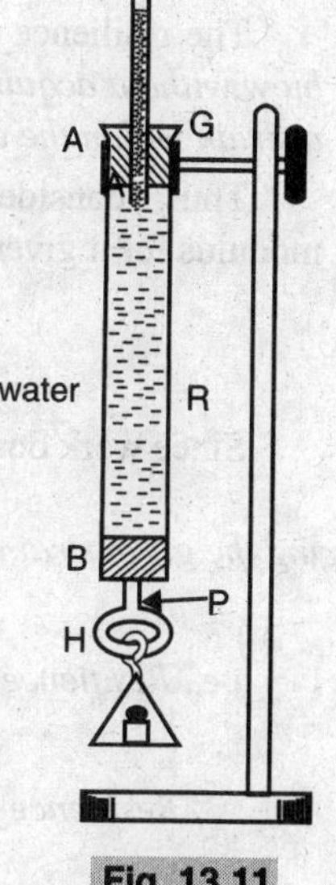

Fig. 13.11

A glass tube G, about half a metre long and of redius r is just inserted into the rubber tube which is then filled with air-free water untile some of it rises in tube G.

When conditions become steady, the positions of the water meniscus in G and a point or pin P carried by hook H are noted with the help of two separate treavelling microscopes. A suitable weight (W) is then placed in the scale pan so that the length of the rubber tube, as also its internal volume increases. Again, when conditions become steady, the positions of the water meniscus and the point or pin P are noted.

Several such readings are taken by increasing the weight in equal steps of w each and the mean increase in length, say, dL, of the tube for a stress $P = W/A$ as also the mean fall dh in the level of the water meniscus in G obtained.

If L be the original length of the rubber tube, clearly, *longitudinal strain* = dL/L. And, if Y be the Young's modulus for the material of the tube, $Y = \dfrac{P}{dL/L}$.

And, since the fall in the level of the water meniscus in G corresponds to increase in volume of the rubber tube R, we have increase in volume of the rubber tube = $(\pi r^2)\ dh = dV$, say. And, therefore, **Bulk modulus** for the material of the tube is given by $K = \frac{P}{3(dV/V)}$, where P is the stress applied along the length of the tube, *i.e.*, **only in one direction** (so that the increase in volume of the tube is one-third of what it would be with an equal stress (P) in all the three directions), and V, the initial volume of the tube (obtained by measuring) the volume of the water filling it completely).

Now, we have the ralation $K = \frac{Y}{3(1-2\sigma)}$.

Substituting for K and Y, therefore, we have

$$\frac{dV}{V} = \frac{dL}{L}(1-2\sigma) \text{ whence, } \sigma = \frac{1}{2}\left(1 - \frac{dV}{V}\cdot\frac{L}{dL}\right).$$

N.B. In case the specimen be given in the form of a cord, we simply obtian the mean increase (*dL*) in its length and the mean decrease (*dD*) in its diameter for a given stress by suspending it from a rigid support and loading and unloading it in equal steps. If *L* and *D* be its initial length and diameter respectively, we have

longitudinal (or linear) strain = dL/L and lateral strain = dD/D.

And, therefore, Poisson's ratio for it, $\sigma = \frac{dD/D}{dL/L} = \frac{dD}{dL}\cdot\frac{L}{D}$.

(*ii*) **For glass**. We proceed here too in the same fashion as in case (*i*) for rubber. Since, however, the change in volume in this case is very much smaller, we use a *capillary tube* in place of tube *G* above. A much better method is the one due to *Cornu*. (see chapter 14.)

13.16 RESILIENCE – PROOF RESILIENCE

The resilience of an elastic body is its *capacity to withstand a mechanical shock or a sudden blow without acquiring a permanent set*. It is measured by the *work done in subjecting the body to a strain within the elastic limit.*

Thus, considering the case of a bar of volume *V*, subjected to a stress *P*, we have Young's modulus for it given by

$$Y = \frac{stress}{strain} = \frac{P}{strain}, \text{whence, } strain = \frac{P}{Y}$$

Since work done per unit volume in a strain $= \frac{1}{2}$ stress × strain, we *have work done in producing the given strain in the bar* $= \frac{1}{2}$ *stress × strain × V*

$$i.e., \textit{ Resilience of the bar} = \frac{1}{2}P\times\frac{P}{Y}\times V = \frac{P^2V}{2Y} = \frac{(stress)^2\times V}{2Y}.$$

$$\therefore \textit{ Resilience per unit volume of the bar} = \frac{P^2}{2Y} = \frac{(stress)^2}{2Y}.$$

The maximum value of the work done, or energy stored up in the body, without its acquiring a permanent set is called proof resilience of the body. So, that, if the maximum stress that can be applied to the bar (considered above) to strain it right up to its elastic limit be P_m,

We have Proof resilience of the bar $= \frac{P_m^{\ 2}V}{2Y}$

Or, *its proof resilience per unit volume* $= \frac{P_m^{\ 2}}{2Y} = \frac{(max.\ stress)^2}{2Y}$.

13.17 TWISTING COUPLE ON A CYLINDER

(*i*) **Case of a solid cylinder or wire.** Let a solid Cylinder (or wire) of length L and radius R be fixed at its upper end and let a couple be applied to its lower end in a plane perpendicular to its length (with its axis coinciding with that of the cylinder) such that it is twisted through an angle θ.

This will naturally bring into play a resisting couple tending to oppose the twisting couple applied, the two balancing each other in the position of equilibrium.

To obtian the value of this couple, let us imagine the cylinder to consist of a large number of hollow, coaxial cylinder, one inside the other and consider one such cylinder of radius x and thickness dx, [Fig. 13.12 (*i*)]. As will be readily seen, each radius of the base of the cylinder will turn through the same angle θ but the displacement (BB') will be the maximum at the rim, progressively decreasing to *zero* at the centre (O), [Fig. 13.12 (*i*) and (*ii*)] indicating that the stress is not uniform all over.

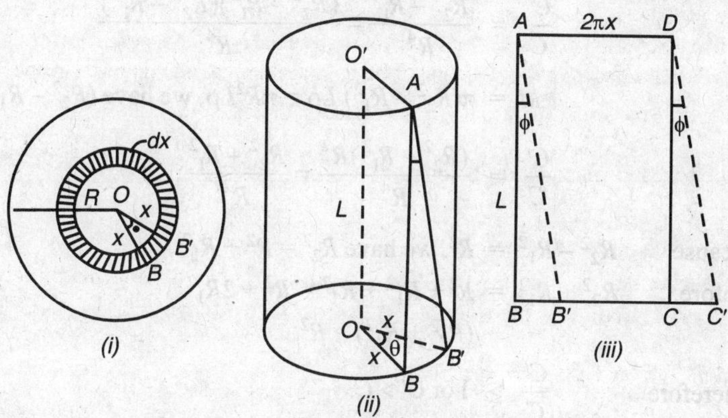

Fig. 13.12

Thus, a straight line AB, initialy parallel to the axis OO' of the cylinder will take up the position AB' or the angle of shear (or shear) = $< BAB' = \phi$. This may be easily visualised if we imagine the hollow cylinder to be cut along AB and spread out when it will initially have a rectangular shape $ABCD$, [Fig. 13.12 (*iii*) and will acquire the shape of a parallelogram $AB'C'D$ after it has been twisted, so that angle of shear = $BAB' = \phi$.

Now, $BB' = x\theta = L\phi$, whence, the shear $\phi = x\theta/L$ and will obviously have the maximum value when $x = R$, *i.e.*, at the outermost part of the cylinder and the least at the innermost.

If n have be the coefficient of rigidity of the material of the cylinder, we have

$$n = \frac{Shearing\ stress}{Shear} \quad \text{or Shearing stress} = n \times \text{Shear.}$$

Or, $$\text{Shearing stress} = n\phi = nx\theta/L.$$

$\therefore$ *Shearing force on face area of the hollow cylinder* = $(nx\theta/L) \times$ *Face area of the cylinder* $= (nx\theta/L) \times 2\pi x dx = (2\pi n\theta/L)\, x^2 dx.$

And the moment of this force about the axis OO of the cylinder

$$= (2\pi n\theta/L)\, x^2 dx . x = (2\pi n\theta/L)\, x^3 dx,$$

$\therefore$ *Twisting couple on the whole cylinder* $= \int_0^R \frac{2\pi n\theta}{L} x^2 dx = \frac{\pi n R^4}{2L}\theta$

Or, *twisting couple per unit twist of the cylinder or wire*, also called **torsional rigidity** of its material, is given by

$$C = \frac{\pi n R^4}{2L}.$$

It will be racalled that we have made use of this relation earlier in discussing the **Torsion pendulum** and **Inertia Table** (§ 7.7.4)

(*ii*) **Case of a hollow cylinder.** If the cylinder be a hollow one, of inner and outer radii R_1 and R_2 respectively, we have

$$\textit{twisting couple on the cylinder} = \int_{R_1}^{R_2} \frac{2\pi n\theta}{L} x^2 dx = \frac{\pi n}{2L}(R_2^{\,4} - R_1^{\,4})\theta.$$

$$\therefore \quad \textit{Twisting couple per unit twist, say, } C' = \frac{\pi n}{2L}(R_2^4 - R_1^4).$$

Now, if we consider two cylinders of the same material, of density ρ, and of the same mass M and length L, but one solid, of radius R and the other *hollow* of inner and outer radii R_1 and R_2 respectively,

We have $$\frac{C'}{C} = \frac{R_2^{\,4} - R_1^{\,4}}{R^4} = \frac{(R_2^{\,2} - R_1^{\,2})(R_2^{\,2} - R_1^{\,2})}{R^4}.$$

Since $$M = \pi(R_2^2 - R_1^2)\, L\rho = \pi R^2 L\rho, \text{ we have } (R_2^2 - R_1^2) = R^2.$$

Or, $$\frac{C'}{C} = \frac{(R_2^{\,2} - R_1^{\,2})R^2}{R^4} = \frac{R_2^{\,2} + R_1^{\,2}}{R^2}.$$

Again, because $R_2^2 - R_1^2 = R^2$, we have $R_2^2 = R^2 + R_1^2$.

And, therefore, $R_2^2 + R_1^2 = R^2 + R_1^2 + R_1^2 = R^2 + 2R_1^2$

i.e., $(R_2^2 + R_1^2) > R^2$.

Clearly, therefore $$\frac{C'}{C} > 1 \text{ or } C' > C.$$

Or, *the twisting couple per unit twist is greater for a hollow cylinder than for a solid one of the same material, mass and length.*

This explains at once the use of hollow shafts, in preference to solid ones, for transmitting large torques in a rotating machinery.

13.18. VARIATION OF STRESS IN A TWISTED CYLINDER

(*i*) **Along the radius.** Referring back to the hollow cylinder of readius x in case (*i*) in § 13.16 above, we have seen how the *shear* ϕ produced in it $= x\theta/L$, where θ is the angle through which the cylinder is twisted.

Obviously, therefore, the shear will be the maximum on the outermost part of the given cylinder, say,

$$\phi_m = R\theta/L.$$

So that, $$\frac{\phi}{\phi_m} = \frac{x\theta/L}{R\theta/L} = \frac{x}{R}. \quad \text{Or, } \phi = \frac{x}{R}\phi_m.$$

i.e., shear at distance c from the axis of the cylinder $= \dfrac{x}{R} \times$ *maximum shear.*

Now, $n = \dfrac{\textit{shearing stress}}{\textit{shear}}$. Or, *shearing stress* $= n \times$ *shear.*

$\therefore$ shearing stress at distance x from the axis $= n\phi$

and maximum shearing stress at distance R from the axis $n\phi_m$.

Again, therefore, $\frac{\textit{shearing stress at distance x}}{\textit{maximumshearing stress}} = \frac{n\phi}{n\phi_m} = \frac{\phi}{\phi_m} = \frac{x}{R}$.

Or, stress at distance x from the axis $= \frac{x}{R} \times$ maximum stress.

Thus, the shearing strain, as also stress, progressively goes on increasing as we proceed outwards from the axis of the cylinder and is, therefore, the maximum at the surface of the cylinder.

(*ii*) **Along the length.** Let us now consider the shearing stress in a plane parallel to the base of the cylinder and at a distance αL from the fixed, end, where $\alpha > 0$ but < 1.

As we have seen, for a cylinder of radius R, the mximum shear $\phi_m = R\theta/L$. Or, $\theta = \phi_m L/R$, showing that for a given cylinder (of radius R), ϕ_m being constant, θ varies as L. Clearly, therefore, the angle of twist of the plane at distance αL from the fixed end will be $\alpha\theta$.

Hence, strain or shear on the surface of the cylinder

$$= R\alpha\theta/\alpha L = R\theta/L.$$

But, θ (from above) $= \frac{L}{R}\phi_m$.

∴ *Shear on the furface of the cylinder* $= \frac{R}{L}, \frac{L}{R}\phi_m = \phi_m$, the same as in the plane at distance L from the fixed end.

And therefore, *shearing stress on the surface of the cylinder* $= n\phi_m$, *the same as in the plane at distance L from the fixed end.*

Thus, *the shearing stress on the surface of the cylinder is quite independent of the distance from either end of it.*

13.19 STRAIN ENERGY IN A TWISTED CYLINDER

As we know, energy per unit volume in any kind of strain $= \frac{1}{2}$ Stress × Strain.

Hence, imagining a solid cylinder of radius R and length L to consist of a number of hollow cylinders, as before, and considering one such hollow cylinder of radius x to be subjected to a shearing stress P so that a shear ϕ is produced in it, we have

strain energy per unit volume of this cylinder (of radius x) $= \frac{1}{2} P\phi$. Since *shearing stress (P)/ shear (φ) = n*, we have $\phi = P/n$.

∴ *Strain energy per unit volume of this cylinder, or, strain energy per unit volume at distance x from the axis of the solid cylinder*

$$= \frac{1}{2}P(P/n) = \frac{1}{2}P^2/n.$$

But, as we have seen above, $P = xP_m/R$, where P_m is the maximum stress on the surface of the solid cylinder (*i.e.*, at distance R from the axis). We, therefore, have

energy per unit volume at distance x from the axis $= \frac{1}{2}\frac{x^2 P_m^{\ 2}}{nR^2}$

If dx be the thickness of the hollow cylinder of radius x, its volume $= 2\pi xLdx$. So that, *energy of the whole hollow cylinder of radius x*

$$= \frac{1}{2}\frac{x^2 P_m^{\ 2}}{xR^2} 2\pi xLdx = \frac{\pi LP_m^{\ 2}}{nR^2}x^3 dx.$$

∴ *Energy of the whole solid cylinder of radius R, i.e.,*

$$E = \int_0^R \frac{\pi L P_m^{\,2}}{nR^2} x^3 dx = \frac{\pi R^2 L}{4n} P_m^{\,2}$$

If the maximum strain corresponding to the maximum stress P_m be ϕ_m, we have $P_m = n\phi_m = nR\theta_m/L$,

where, θ_m is the maximum angle of twist, i.e., its value for the maximum couple

$$C_m = (\pi nR^4/2l)\theta_m.$$

$$\therefore \quad E = \frac{\pi R^2 L}{4n} \cdot \frac{n^2 R^2 \theta_m^{\,2}}{L^2} = \frac{1}{2}\frac{\pi nR^4}{2L}\theta_m \cdot \theta_m = \frac{1}{2}C_m\theta_m.$$

Or, since $C_m = C\theta_m$, where C is the couple per unit twist, we have

work done or strain energy $E = \dfrac{1}{2}C\theta_m\theta_m = \dfrac{1}{2}C\theta_m^{\,2}$.

This is clearly half the strain energy that would be stored up in the cylinder if the stress on it were uniform and equal to its maximum value throughout instead of increasing from zero at the axis to the maximum on the surface of the cylinder [§13.17 (*i*)].

It follows, therefore, that the work done or energy stored up in a cylinder twisted through an angle $\theta = \dfrac{1}{2}C\theta^2$.

13.20 DETERMINATION OF THE COEFFICIENT OF RIGIDITY (*n*) FOR THE MATERIAL OF A WIRE

1. Statical method – (Barton's). The apparatus used is shown in Fig. 13.13, where the wire w, the value of n for the material of which is to be determined, is fixed at its upper end at the torsion head H and at its lower end carries a heavy cylinder C which can be made to turn about the wire as axis (coincident with its own axis of symmetry) by means of a couple applied by two known and equal masses M and M, as shown.

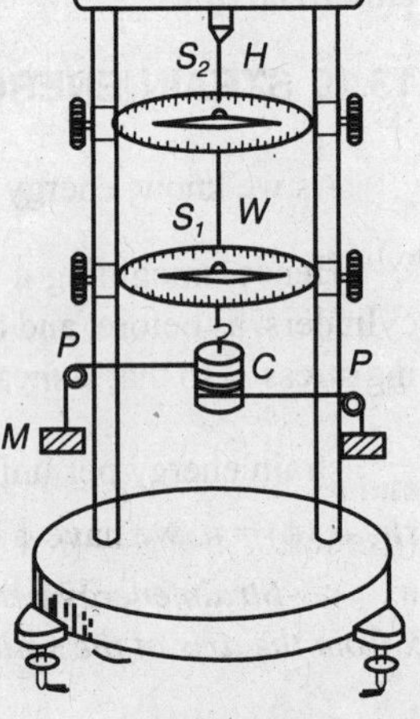

Fig. 13.13

The angle through which the wire is thus twisted can be read on a circular scale, arranged horizontally, over which a pointer attached to the wire moves freely, or better still, by the telescope and scale method.

Actually, two such circular scales, S_1 and S_2, are arranged and the angles of twist θ_1 and θ_2 noted on them. The effective length of the wire used, *i.e.*, L, is then taken to be its length between the two scales and the angle of twist, $(\theta_2 - \theta_1)$. This eliminates any error as to the exact point at which the wire is clamped at the torrsion head.

Clearly, if d be the diameter of the cylinder, we have

twisting couple applied to the wire = Mgd

and restoring couple set up in length L of the wire = $(\pi nR^4/2L)(\theta_2 - \theta_1)$. Since in the position of equilibrium, the two couples balance each other, we have

$$\frac{\pi nR^4}{2L}(\theta_2 - \theta_1) = Mgd, \text{ whence, } n = \frac{2LMgd}{\pi R^4(\theta_2 - \theta_1)}$$

and the value of n can thus be easily obtained.

As can be readily seen, the fourth power of R is involved in the expression for n. Particular care must therefore be taken to measure the radius of the wire accurately.

2. Dynamical method. In this method, usually referred to as Maxwell's vibrating needle method, the time-period of torsional vibration of the suspended body is observed directly, its total mass kept the same throughout and yet its distribution ingeniously altered about the axis of suspension so as to bring about a known change in its moment of inertia about the axis and hence also a change in its time-period.

The so called vibrating needle is a hollow tube of length a, into which can be fitted two hollow and two solid cylinders of equal lengths ($\alpha/4$), one pair on either, side such that, placed end to end,

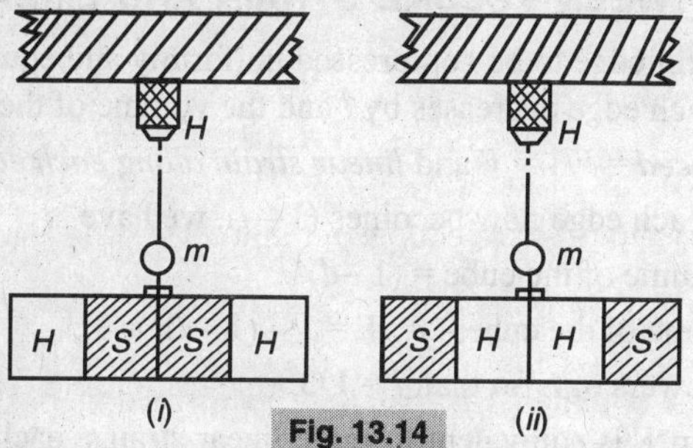

Fig. 13.14

they just completely fill the tube, (Fig. 13.14). Ths tube itself is suspended from a torsion head H by means of the wire under test, of length L and radius R and a small piece of mirror m attached to it to enable the torsional vibrations of the tube to be observed by the telescope and scale method.

The solid cylinders are first placed in the inner position, as shown in Fig. 13.14 (*i*) and the time-period T_1 of the loaded tube determined. The positions of the solid and hollow cylinders are then interchanged (Fig. 13.14 (*ii*)), and time-period T_2 of the tube determined again.

Since the total mass suspended from the wire remains the same, there is no question of any possible change in its torsional rigidity (or restoring couple per unit twist) $C = \pi n R^4/2L$. If, therefore, l_1 and l_2 be the moments of inertia of the loaded tube about the wire as axis in the two cases respectively, we have

$$T_1 = 2\pi\sqrt{I_1/C} \text{ and } T_2 = 2\pi\sqrt{I_2/C}$$

whence, $$T_2^2 - T_1^2 = (4\pi^2/C)(I_2 - I_1) \quad ...(I)$$

To obtain the value of $(l_2 - l_1)$, we note that the *e.g.* of either inner-cylinder lies at a distance $\frac{a/4}{2}$ or $a/8$ and that of each outer cylinder at a distance $\frac{3a/4}{2}$ or $3a/8$ from the axis. So that, if m_1 and m_2 be the masses of a hollow and a solid cylinder respectively, the change from position (*i*) to (*ii*) merely means the shifting of a mass $(m_2 - m_1)$ from a distance $a/8$ to a distance $3a/8$ from the axis on either side. Therefore, in accordance with the principle of parallel axes, we have

$$I_2 = I_1 + 2(m_2 - m_1)\left[\left(\frac{3a}{8}\right)^2 - \left(\frac{a}{8}\right)^2\right] \quad \text{Or, } (I_2 - I_1) = (m_2 - m_1)\,a^2/4.$$

Substituting this value of $(I_2 - I_1)$ in expression I above, we have

$$(T_2^2 - T_1^2) = \frac{4\pi^2}{C}(m_2 - m_1)\frac{a^2}{4} = \frac{4\pi^2 \times 2L}{n\pi R^4}(m_2 - m_1)\frac{a^2}{4}, \text{ which gives}$$

$$n = \frac{2\pi L a^2 (m_2 - m_1)}{(T_2^2 - T_1^2)R^4}.$$

Again, as before, R must be measured most accurately, in view of its 4th power being involved in the expression for n.

N.B. The value of n for the material of the same wire obtained by the dynamical method comes out to be a trifle higher than that obtained by the statical method. This is so because, to some extent, the twist produced depends upon the time for which the twisting couple is applied, so that the time of vibration being short in the dynamical method, θ is invariably smaller for the same couple than in the statical method.

Further, as already pointed out, the outer layers of wires being tougher than the inner ones, the value of n for a thinner wire is always higher than that for a thicker wire of the same material.

13.21 RELATION BETWEEN VOLUME STRAIN AND LINEAR STRAIN

Imagine a cube of unit edge to be compressed uniformly and equally in all the three directions such that the length of each edge decreases by l and the volume of the cube by V. Then, clearly,

volume strain produced $= V/1 = V$ and *linear strain along each edge* $= l/1 = l$.

Since the length of each edge now becomes $(1 - l)$, we have

new reduced volume of the cube $= (1 - l)^3$.

$\therefore$ decrease in volume of the cube, *i.e.*, $V = 1 - (1 - l)^3 = 3l$,

neglecting higher powers of l. So that, $l = V/3$.

Thus a volume strain V is equivalent to three linear strains, each equal to $V/3$ along the three edges of the cube or in mutually perpendicular directions.

13.22 RATIO OF ADIABATIC AND ISOTHERMAL ELASTICITIES OF A GAS

Let the original volume V of a gas under pressure P decrease to $V - dV$ when the pressure is increased to $P + dP$. Then, clearly, *stress applied* $= dP$ and *volume stain produced* $= - dV/V$.

$$\therefore \quad \textit{Bulk modulus } K = \frac{\textit{Stress}}{\textit{Strain}} = -\frac{dP}{dV/V} = -V\frac{dP}{dV}$$

Now, if the gas is compressed under isothermal conditions (*i.e.*, if the temperature remains constant), Boyle's law holds good and $PV = k$, a constant. Or, $P = k/V$, which, on differentiations, gives $-\dfrac{dP}{dV} = \dfrac{k}{V^2}$ and, therefore,

$$-V\frac{dP}{dV} = V\left(\frac{k}{V^2}\right) = \frac{k}{V} = P.$$

Thus, the isothermal elasticity of the gas = its pressure P.

If, on the other hand, the gas is compressed under adiabatic conditions (the temperature not remaining constant), we have $PV^{\gamma} = K$, a constant, or, $P = kV^{-\gamma}$ where γ is the ratio Cp/Cv (between specific heats of the gas at constant pressure and at constant volume). On differentiation, we have

$dP/dV = -\gamma kV^{-\gamma-1} = -\gamma\, kV^{-\gamma}/V = -\gamma P/V$. And, therefore, $-VdP/dV = \gamma P$, *i.e.*, *the adiabatic elasticity of the gas* $= \gamma$ *times its pressure, i.e.*, γP.

$$\text{Clearly, therefore, } \frac{\textit{adiabatic elasticity of the gas}}{\textit{isothermal elasticity of the gas}} = \frac{\gamma P}{P} = \gamma.$$

WORKED EXAMPLES

I–Molduli of Elasticity—Poisson's ratio

Example 13.1 Find the greatest length of a steel wire that can hang vertically without breaking. Breaking stress for steel = 7.9×10^9 dynes/sp. cm. Density of steel = 7.9 gm/c.c

(Callicut 2001)

Solution. Let L be the length of the wire that can hang vertically without breaking. Then, clearly, stretching force on it is equal to its own weight. If, therefore, A be its area of cross section and ρ, its density, we have stretching force on the wire (*i.e., its own weight* $LA\rho g$ and, therefore, *tensile stress applied* $F/A = LA\rho g/A = L\rho g$).

Since this is just equal to the breaking stress, we have $L\rho g = 7.9 \times 10^9$.

whence, length of the wire $L = 7.9 \times 10^9/7.9 \times 981 = 1.02 \times 10^6$ *cm.*

Example 13.2 A mass *M* is suspended from an elastic string so that on pulling the mass down a little and releasing it, it oscillates up and down, executing a S.H.M. It is found that if an additional mass m is added to *M*, the time-period of oscillation changes in the ratio 5:4. Obtain the ratio *m/M*. (*Pune 2003*)

Solution. We know that when a suspended mass is pulled down a little to produce an extension l in an elastic string and then released, it executes a S.H.M. of time period $T = 2\pi\sqrt{l/g}$.

Here, therefore, if l_1 be the extension produced by mass M and l_2, that produced by mass $(M + m)$ and T_1 and T_2, the time-periods in the two cases respectively, we have

$T_1 = 2\pi\sqrt{l_1/g}$ and $T_2 = 2\pi\sqrt{l_2/g}$, so that $l_2/l_1 = T_2^2/T_1^2 = 5^2/4^2 = 25/16$. If Y be the young's modulus for the material of the string, we have

$$Y = MgL/Al_1 = (M + m)\,gL/Al_2, \text{ whence, } (M + m)/M = l_2/l_1 = 25/16.$$

And, therefore, $m/M = (25 - 16)/16 = 9/16$.

Example 13.3 What will be the density of lead under a pressure of 20,000 newtons/*cm*^{2} (Density of lead = 11.4 *gm/cm*^{3} and Bulk modulus of lead = 0.80 × 10^{10} newton/*m*^{2}, (*Madras 2001*)

Solution. We know that Bulk modulus $K = -dP/\dfrac{dV}{V}$, where dP is the *pressure* or the *stress applied* and $-dV/V$, the *volume strain* produced.

$$\therefore \quad -dV = dP.V/K.$$

Since $dP = 2 \times 10^4$ *N/cm*^{2} and $K = 0.8 \times 10^{10}$ *N/m*^{2} $= 0.8 \times 10^{10}/10^4 = 8 \times 10^5$ N/*cm*^{2},

we have $$-dV = 2 \times 10^4\, V/8 \times 10^5 = V/40.$$

Thus, the new volume of lead $= V - V/40 = 39V/40$ *c.c.*

If, therefore, ρ be the new density of lead, its mass $= (39V/40)\rho$ *gm.*

This, must clearly be equal to its initial mass $= V \times 11.4$. We, therefore, have

$$(39V/40) = 11.4V,$$

whence, new density of lead $(\rho) = 11.4 \times 40/39 = 11.69$ *gm/c.c.*

Example 13.4 A uniform glass tube, 2m long and closed at its lower end, is completely filled with water. Its upper end is rigidly clamped and it is stretched downwards. It is found that whereas the length of the tube increases by 0.12 cm, that of the water column in it increases by only 0.08 cm. Obtain Poisson's ratio for the glass of the tube.

Solution. Since the tube itself increases in length by, say, $\Delta L = 0.12m$ and its original length $L = 2\text{m} = 200$ *cm*, the longitudinal strain set up in it $= \Delta L/L = 0.12/200 = 0.0006$.

And if the original diameter of the tube be D and the change in its diameter, ΔD, the lateral strain $= \Delta D/D$.

Now, Poisson's ratio $\sigma = \dfrac{\textit{leteral strain}}{\textit{longitudinal strain}} = \dfrac{\Delta D/D}{0.0006}$. Or, $\Delta D = 0.0006\, D\sigma$.

$\therefore$ diameter of the tube after stretching $= (D - \Delta D) = D\,(1 - 0.0006\sigma)$

Hence area of cross section of the tube after stretching $= \pi D^2\,(1 - 0.0006\sigma)^2/4$

$$= \pi D^2\,(1 - 2 \times 0.0006\sigma)/4 = \pi D^2\,(1 - 0.0012\sigma)/4.$$

$\therefore$ volume of water in the tube $= \dfrac{\pi D^2(1-0.0012\sigma)}{4} \times 200.08\,c.c.$

Since liquids are incompressible, this must be equal to the original volume of water in the tube $= (\pi D^2/4) \times 200$ *c.c.* Thus,

$$\frac{\pi D^2(1-0.0012\sigma)}{4}\times 200.08 = \frac{\pi D^2}{4}\times 200.$$

Or, $200.08 - 0.240\sigma = 200$. Or, $0.24\sigma = 0.8$, whence, $\sigma = 0.8/0.24 = 0.3333$.

The poisson's ratio for the glass of the tube is thus 0.3333.

Example 13.5 (*a*) A wire, 4 metres long and 0.3 mm in diameter, is stretched by a force of 800 gm wt. If the extension in length amounts to 1.5 mm, calculate the energy stored in the wire. (*Punjab*, 2002)

(*b*) Find the work done in joules in stretching a wire of cross section 1sq. mm and length 2 meters through 0.1 mm if Young's modulus for the material of the wire is 2×10^{12} *dynes/cm*^{2}.

Solution. (*a*) Clearly, the energy stored in the wire is equal to the work done in stretching it which, in its turn, is equal to $\frac{1}{2}$ stretching force × stretch, (§ 12.10).

Since stretching force here, *i.e.*, $F = 800$ *gm wt* $= 800 \times 980$ dynes, and stretch or extension produced, *i.e.*, $l = 1.5$ *mm* $= 0.15$ *cm*, we straightaway have

$$\text{work done or energy stored up} = \frac{1}{2}\times 800 \times 980 \times 0.15 = 5.88 \times 10^4 \textit{ ergs}.$$

(*b*) Here, again, work done $= \frac{1}{2}$ *stretching force* (*F*) × *stretch* (*l*).

Since $Y = \dfrac{F/A}{l/L}$, we have $F = \dfrac{YAl}{L}$. And, therefore,

$$\text{work done} = \frac{1}{2}\frac{YAl}{L}.l = \frac{1}{2}\frac{YAl^2}{L} = \frac{2\times10^{12}\times 0.01\times(0.01)^2}{200}$$

$$= \frac{10^4}{2} = 5000 \textit{ ergs} = 5000/10^7 = 5\times 10^{-4} \text{ joules}.$$

Example 13.6 A metal wire of length 3 metres and diameter 1 mm is stretched by a weight of 10 kg. If Young's modulus for its material be 12.5×10^{11} dynes/cm^2 and σ for it equal to 0.26, calculate the lateral compression produced. (*g* = *981 cm/sec*^{2})

Solution. Let L and D be the length and diameter of the wire and ΔL and ΔD, the longitudinal extension and lateral compression produced respectively. Then, clearly,

longitudinal strain $= \Delta L/L$ and *lateral strain* $= \Delta D/D$.

So that, if F be the stretching force applied and A, the area of cross-section of the wire, we have Young's modulus for the material of the wire given by $Y = \dfrac{F/A}{\Delta L/L}$

And therefore, longitudinal strain $\Delta L/L = \dfrac{F/A}{Y} = \dfrac{F}{AY}$.

Now, Poisson's ratio, $\sigma = \dfrac{\textit{lateral strain}}{\textit{longitudinal strain}} = \dfrac{\Delta D/D}{\Delta L/L}$.

Or, $\frac{\Delta D}{D} = \sigma\frac{\Delta L}{L} = \frac{\sigma F}{AY}$ Or, $\Delta D = \frac{D\sigma F}{AY}$.

Here, $D = 1mm = 0.1\ cm$, $\sigma = 0.26$, $F = 10 \times 1000 \times 981$ *dynes.*
$A = \pi R^2 = \pi\ (0.05)^2$ *sqp. cm* and $Y = 12.5 \times 10^{11}$ *dynes/cm*^{2}.

$$\therefore \text{ leteral compression } \Delta D = \frac{0.1 \times 0.26 \times 981 \times 10^4}{\pi(0.05)^2 \times 12.5 \times 10^{11}} = \frac{981 \times 26}{\pi(0.05)^2 \times 12.5 \times 10^{10}}$$

$$= 2.598 \times 10^{-5} \text{ cm.}$$

Example 13.7 A cube of aluminium of side 10 cm is subjected to a shearing force of 10 N. The top surface of the cube is displaced by 0.01 cm with respect to the bottom. Calculate the shearing stress, shearing strain and modulus of rigidity.

Solution. Each side of aluminium cube $L = 10$ cm = 0.1 m

Area of face a = 0.1 × 0.1 = 0.01 m^2

Tangential force $F = 100$ N

Shearing stress $T = \frac{F}{a} = \frac{100}{0.01} = 10^4 \text{ Nm}^{-2}$

Displacement $l = 0.01$ cm = 0.0001 m

Thickness $L = 10$ cm = 0.1m

Shearing strain $\theta = \frac{l}{L} = \frac{0.0001}{0.1} = 10^{-3}$

Modulus of rigidity $\eta = \frac{T}{\theta} = \frac{10^4}{10^{-3}} = \mathbf{10^7\ Nm^{-2}}$

Example 13.8 What force is required to stretch a steel wire $\frac{1}{2}$ sp.cm. in cross-section to double its length ? $Y = 2 \times 10^{11}$ Nm $^{-2}$.

Solution. Given $Y = 2 \times 10^{11}$ Nm^{-2}

Area of cross-section $a = \frac{1}{2}$ sq. cm = 0.5 0 × 10^{-4} m^2

When the length is double; increase in length l = original length L

Now Young's modulus $Y = \frac{FL}{al}$ $\therefore$ $F = \frac{Yal}{L} = Ya$

or Force required, $F = 2 \times 10^{11} \times 0.5 \times 10^{-4} = \mathbf{10^7}$ **Newton**

Example 13.9 A steel wire 1.5 mm in diameter is just stretched between two fixed points at a temperature 40°C. Determine the tension in the wire if the temperature falls to 30°C. Given that for steel α = 0.000012/°C and Y for steel = 20 × 10^{10} Nm^{-2}.

Solution. Here $Y = 20 \times 10^{10}$ Nm^{-2} $\alpha = 0.00012$/°C

If L is the length of the wire at 40°C, then decrease in length at 30°C = $L \times \alpha \times (40 - 30)$

$= L \times 0.000012 \times 10 = 0.00012\ L$

$\therefore$ Longitudinal strain $= \frac{0.000012L}{L} = 0.000012$

Now, stress = $Y \times$ strain = 20 × 10^{10} × 0.000012 = 2.4 × 10^7 Nm^{-2}

Area of cross section $a = \pi r^2 = \pi \times \left(\frac{1.5 \times 10^{-3}}{2}\right)^2 = 1.766 \times 10^{-6} \text{m}^2$

$$\text{Stress} = \frac{F}{a}$$

$\therefore$ Tension in the wire $F = a \times stress = 1.766 \times 10^{-6} \times 2.4 \times 10^{7} =$ **42.4 Newton**

Example 13.10 Calculate the length of the wire that will break under its own weight when suspended vertically. Given breaking stress = 9.8 × 10⁸ Nm⁻², density of wire = 10⁴ kg m⁻³ and g = 9.8 ms⁻².

Solution. When the wire hangs vertically it weight mg acts as a longitudinal force. Let L be the maximum length of the wire that can hang without breaking and a its area of cross-section, then

Weight of wire mg $= L \times a \times \rho \times gN$

$= L \times a \times 10^4 \times gN$

Breaking load = Breaking stress $\times a = 9.8 \times 10^8 \times a\,N$

$\therefore \quad L \times a \times g \times 10^4 = 9.8 \times 10^8 \times a$

or $$L = \frac{9.8 \times 10^8}{9.8 \times 10^4} = 10^4\,m = \mathbf{10\,km}$$

The wire of length 10 km will break under its own weight if the applied stress is greater than the breaking stress. It will not break if the applied stress ≤ the breaking stress.

Example 13.11 A steel wire of length 2.00 m and cross section 1 × 10⁻⁶ m² is held between rigid supports with a tension of 200 N. If the middle of the wire is pulled 5 mm sideways, calculate change in tension. Also calculate change in tension if temperature changes by 5°C. For steel Y = 2.2 ×10¹¹ Nm⁻² and α = 8 ×10⁻⁶ deg⁻¹.

Solution (*i*) Initial length of wire $L = 2m$

Final length of wire shen it is pulled sideways at the centre by 5 mm = 5×10^{-3}m

$$L' = 2\,[1^2 + (5 \times 10^{-3})^2]^{1/2} = 2\,[1 + 25 \times 10^{-6}]^{1/2}$$

$= 2\left[1 + \frac{1}{2} \times 25 \times 10^{-6}\right]$ by applying Binomial theorem and neglecting higher powers of 25×10^{-6} as it is a very small quantity.

$\therefore \quad L' = 2 + 25 \times 10^{-6}$ m

Increase in length $l = L' - L = 25 \times 10^{-6}$ m

Area of cross section of the wire $a = 1 \times 10^{-6}$ m²

Let F be the additional tension in the wire due to increase in length, then

Young's modulus $$Y = \frac{stress}{strain} = \frac{F/a}{l/L} = \frac{FL}{al}$$

or $$F = \frac{Yal}{L} = \frac{2.2 \times 10^{11} \times 10^{-6} \times 25 \times 10^{-6}}{2} = \mathbf{2.75\,N}$$

(*ii*) When the temperature changes by $\theta = 5$°C, the change in length

$$l = L \times \alpha \times \theta = 2 \times 8 \times 10^{-6} \times 5 = 8 \times 10^{-5}\,\text{m}$$

$\therefore$ Change in tension $$F = \frac{Yal}{L} = \frac{2.2 \times 10^{11} \times 1 \times 10^{-6} \times 8 \times 10^{-5}}{2} = \mathbf{8.8\,N}$$

Example 13.12 A wire 0.5 m long and 1 sp. mm in cross section has Young's modulus 1.24 × 10¹¹ N = m⁻². How much work is done in stretching it through 1 mm ? ***(K.U. 2002)***

Solution. $a = 1$sq. mm $= 10^{-6}$ m^2, $l = 1$ mm $= 10^{-3}$ m, $L = 0.5$m

$Y = 1.24 \times 10^{11}$ Nm^2

Work done $W = \frac{1}{2}\frac{Yal}{L}l = \frac{1.24 \times 10^{11} \times 10^{-6} \times 10^{-3} \times 10^{-3}}{2 \times 0.5} = \mathbf{0.124J}$

Example 13.13 If $\eta = 8 \times 10^{11}$ N/m^2 and $Y = 20 \times 10^{11}$ N/m^2 for iron, calculate Poisson's ratio.

Solution. From the relation $Y = 2\eta\,(1 + \sigma)$, we have,

$$\sigma = \frac{Y}{2\eta} - 1 = \frac{20 \times 10^{11}}{2 \times 8 \times 10^{11}} - 1 = \mathbf{0.25.}$$

Example 13.14 A steel wire of length 2.0 m is stretched through 2.0 mm. The cross sectional area of wire is 40 mm^2. Calculate the elastic potential energy stored in the wire in the stretched condition. Young's modulus of steel = 2.0 × 10^{11} N/m^2.

Solution. $L = 2.0$ m, $l = 2.0$ mm $= 2 \times 10^{-3}$ m, $a = 40$ mm^2 $= 40 \times 10^{-6}$ m^2.

$Y = 2 \times 10^{11}$ N/m^2

Elastic potential energy stored = Work done in stretching the wire

$$= \frac{1}{2}Y\frac{al^2}{L} = \frac{1}{2} \times \frac{2 \times 10^{11} \times 40 \times 10^{-6} \times 2 \times 10^{-3} \times 2 \times 10^{-3}}{2} = \mathbf{8\,J}$$

Example 13.15 Calculate the Poisson's ratio for silver. Given Young's modulus for silver it 7.25 ×10^{10} N/m^2 and bulk modulus is 11 × 10^{10} N/m^2. ***(Meerut. U., 2001)***

Solution. $Y = 7.25 \times 10^{10}$ N/m^2 $K = 11 \times 10^{10}$ N/m^2

Now, $Y = 3K\,(1 - 2\sigma)$ $\therefore 1 - 2\sigma = \frac{Y}{3K}$ or $2\sigma = 1 - \frac{Y}{3K}$

$$\therefore \quad \sigma = \frac{1}{2}\left[1 - \frac{Y}{3K}\right] = \frac{1}{2}\left[1 - \frac{7.25 \times 10^{10}}{3 \times 11 \times 10^{10}}\right] = \frac{1}{2}(1 - 0.22) = \mathbf{0.39}$$

Example 13.16 The volume of a solid does not very with pressure. Find Poisson's ratio for the solid. ***(Meerut U., 2003)***

Solution. Young's modulus Y, Bulk modulus K, and Poisson's ratio s are connected by the relation

$$Y = 3K\;(1 - 2\sigma) \text{ or } 1 - 2\sigma = \frac{Y}{3K}$$

Now, bulk modulus $K = \frac{\text{Applied pressure}}{\text{Volumetric strain}} = \frac{P}{v/V}$

As the volume of the solid does not vary with pressure, the volumetric strain in zero or $v/V = 0$

Therefore, $K = \alpha$ (infinity) and $= \frac{Y}{3K} = 0.$

Hence, $1 - 2\sigma = 0$ or $2\sigma = 1$ $\therefore \sigma = \frac{1}{2} = \mathbf{0.5}$

Example 13.17 A gold wire, 0.32 mm in diameter, elongates by 1 mm when stretched by a force of 330 gm wt and twists through 1 radius when equal and opposite torques of 145 dyne cm are applied at its ends. Find the value of Poisson's ratio for gold. (g = 981 *cm/sec^2*).

(Bihar, Bombay)

Solution. Here, clearly, Young's modulus for the material of the wire is given by

$$Y = \frac{F/A}{l/L} = \frac{FL}{Al} = \frac{330 \times 981 \times L}{\pi(0.016)^2 \times 0.1}$$

And, since the couple applied to twist the wire throught 1 radian or the value of torsional couple per unit twist of the wire, *i.e.*, $C = 145$ dyne-cm, we have

$$C = \pi n R^4/2L = 145, \text{ whence, } n = \frac{145 \times 2L}{\pi R^4} = \frac{290L}{\pi(0.016)^4}$$

Now, as we know, $n = \frac{Y}{2(1+\sigma)}$. Or, $1+\sigma = \frac{Y}{2n}$ Or, $\sigma = \frac{Y}{2n} - 1$.

$$\therefore \text{ poisson's ratio } (\sigma) \text{ for gold} = \left[\frac{330 \times 981 \times L}{\pi(0.016)^2 \times 0.1} \bigg/ \frac{2 \times 290L}{\pi(0.016)^4}\right] - 1$$

$$= 1.429 - 1 = 0.429.$$

Example. 13.18 *(a)* A mental disc of 10 cm radius and mass 1 kg is suspended in a horizontal plane by a vertical wire attached to its centre. If the diameter of the wire is 1 mm. its length 1 metre and the period of torsional vibrations is 4 second, find the rigidity of the wire. ***(Punjab, Bombay)***

(b) **A body, suspended symmetrically from the lower end of a wire, 100 cm long and 1.22 mm in diametre, oscillates about the wire as axis with a period of 1.25 sec. If the modulus of rigidity of the material of the wire is 8.0 × 10^{11} dynes per sq. cm, calculate the moment of inertia of the body about the axis of rotation.** ***(I. A. S)***

Solution *(a)* Obviously, the metal disc oscillates as a torsion pendulum about eh wire as axis and its time-period is, therefore, given by $T = 2\pi\sqrt{I/C}$, where I is its moment of inertia about the wire and C, the torsional rigidity (or couple per unit twist) of the wire.

If R' be radius of the disc and M, its mass, we have $I = \frac{1}{2}MR'^2$.

And, if R be the radius of the wire, $C = \pi n R^4/2L$.

So that, $T^2 = \frac{4\pi^2 I}{C} = \frac{4\pi^2 \times \frac{1}{2}MR'^2}{\pi n R^4/2L} = \frac{4\pi M R'^2 L}{nR^4}$. Or, $n = \frac{4\pi M R'^2 L}{T^2 R^4}$

Here, $M = 1$ kg $= 1000$ *gm*, $R' = 10$ *cm*, $L = 100$ *cm*, $T = 4$ *sec* and $R = 1/2 = 0.5$ *mm* $= 0.05$ *cm.*

$$\therefore \text{ rigidity of the wire, } n = \frac{4\pi \times 1000 \times (10)^2 \times 100}{(4)^2 \times (0.05)^4} = 12.56 \times 10^{11}\, dynes/cm^2.$$

(b) Here, again, the body oscillates as a torsion pendulum about the wire as axis with a time-period $T = 2\pi\sqrt{I/C}$, where I is its *M.I.* about the wire or the axis of rotation and C, the torsional rigidity of the wire, So that,

$$T^2 = 4\pi^2 I/C. \quad \text{Or, } I = CT^2/4\pi^2.$$

Since $C = \pi n R^4/2L$, where R and L are the length and radius of the wire respectively, we have

$$I = \frac{\pi n R^4}{2L} \cdot \frac{T^2}{4\pi^2} = \frac{nR^4 T^2}{8\pi L}.$$

∴ substituting the given values of *n, R, L,* and *T*, we have moment of inertia of the body,

$$I=\frac{8\times10^{11}\times(0.061)^4\times(1.25)^2}{8\pi\times100}=6.385\times10^3 \text{ gm-cm}^2.$$

Example 13.19 A shaft of diameter 8 cm and length 5 meters is transmitting power of 8 kilowatts at 300 revolutions per minute. If the coefficient of rigidity of the material of the shaft be 8 × 10¹¹ *dynes/cm²*, find the relative shift between the ends of the shaft. ***(Delhi, 2006)***

Solution. Work done per second = 8 × 1000 × 10^7 = 8 × 10^{10} ergs [∵ 1 watt = 1 joule or 10^7 ergs/sec.

Since work done per second = couple applied × angle turned through in 1 sec and the angle turned through in 1sec = 2π × 300/60 = 10π redians,

we have couple applied × 10π = 8 × 10^{10} radians

whence, couple applied = 8 × 10^{10}/10π = 8 × 10^9/π *dyne-cm.*

If θ be the angle through which the shaft gets twisted, we have couple applied = Cθ = (πnR^4/2L) θ, where *n* is the coefficient of rigidity of the material of the shaft, *R*, its radius and *L*, its length. We, therefore, have

$$\frac{\pi nR^4}{2L}\theta=\frac{8\times10^9}{\pi}, \text{ whence } \theta=\frac{8\times10^9}{\pi}\times\frac{2L}{n\pi R^4}=\frac{8\times10^9\times2\times500}{\pi^2\times8\times10^{11}\times(4)^4}$$

$$= 0.004 \text{ radian.}$$

∴ are through which the shaft is twisted or the shift between its two ends = 0 × length of the shaft = 0.004 × 500 = 2.0 *cm.*

Example. 13.20 What couple must be applied to a wire one metre long, 1 mm in diametre in order to twist one end of it, through 90°, the other end remaining fixed. Rigidity of material of the wire is 2.8 ×10¹⁰ N-m⁻².

Solution. Here l = 1 m; radius a = 0.5 mm = 0.5 × 10^{-3} m

η = 2.8×10^{10} N-m^{-2}, θ = 90° = π/2 radian

Couple per unit angular twist $c=\frac{\eta\pi a^4}{2l}$

∴ Couple for angular twist $\theta=c\theta=\eta\frac{\pi a^4}{2l}\times\frac{\pi}{2}=\frac{\eta\pi^2a^4}{4l}$

$$=\frac{2.8\times10^{10}\times\pi^2\times(0.5\times10^{-3})^4}{4\times1}=43.19\times10^{-4} \text{ N-m}$$

Example 13.21 A circular bar one metre long and 8 mm diameter is rigidly clamped at one end in a vertical position. A couple of magnitude 2.5 Nm is applied at the other end. As a result a mirror fixed at this end deflects a spot of light by 0.15 m on the scale one metre away. Calculate the modulus of rigidity of the bar.

Solution. Here l = 1 m, radius a = 4 mm = 4 ×10^{-3} m

Couple c = 2.5 N-n, η = ?

The spot of light is deflected through 0.15 *m* on a scale on metre away, the angle 2θ through which the reflected ray turns is given by

tan 2θ = 0.15 or 2θ = 8°32′

∴ θ = 4°16′ = 0.0745 rad

Twisting couple $c = \frac{\pi\eta a^4}{2l}.\theta$

or $\eta = \frac{2cl}{\pi a^4\theta} = \frac{2\times2.5\times1}{\pi(4\times10^{-3})^4\times0.0745}$

$= 8.344 \times 10^{10}\ Nm^{-2}$

Example 13.22 A cylindrical bar of length 1m and diameter 8 mm is fixed at one end and the other end is twisted through an angle of 5° by the application of a couple of 2.5 Nm. Calculate the modulus of rigidity of the material of the bar. ***(Kerala U. 2001)***

Solution. $5° = \frac{5\pi}{180} = 0.0873$ rad. $\eta = \frac{2cl}{\pi a^4\theta} = \frac{2\times2.5\times1}{\pi(4\times10^{-3})^4\times0.0873}$

$= 7.12 \times 10^{10}\ Nm^{-2}$

Example 13.23 A power of 6 kilowatts is transmitted by a shaft of length 4 metres and radius 2.5 cm at a speed of 200 revolutions per minute. If the modulus of rigidity of the material is 9 × 10^{10} Nm^{-2}, calculate the relative twist between the ends of the shaft.

Solution. Here $l = 4$ m; $a = 2.5$ cm $= 2.5 \times 10^{-2}$ m

$\eta = 9 \times 10^{10}\ Nm^{-2}$; Power = 6 K. watt = 6000 Js^{-1}

Time of one revolution $= \frac{60}{200} = \frac{3}{10}$ sec

Work done/rev $W = \frac{6000\times3}{10} = 1800J$

If θ is the relative shift between the ends of the shaft and c the couple per unit angular twist, then

$$\frac{1}{2}c\theta^2 = w$$

or $$\frac{1}{2}\frac{\pi\eta a^4}{2l}\theta^2 = 1800$$

$$\theta = \sqrt{\frac{1800\times4\times4}{\pi\times9\times10^{10}\times(2.5\times10^{-2})^4}} = \mathbf{0.51\ radian}$$

Example 13.24. One end of a steel wire of length 0.2 m and radius 2 ×10^{-3} m is fixed. If the work done in twisting the free end of the wire is 3.85 ×10^{-2} J, calculate the angle through which the wire is twisted. Given rigidity modulus of steel = 8.075 × 10^{11} Nm^{-2}.

(M.S.U. Tirunaveli 2007; Bang. U., 2000)

Solution. $c = \frac{\eta\pi r^4}{2l} = \frac{8.075\times10^{11}\times22\times2^4\times10^{-12}}{2\times0.2\times7} = 101.5$

$$\frac{1}{2}c\theta^2 = W \ \therefore \theta^2 = \frac{2W}{c} = \frac{2\times3.85\times10^{-2}}{101.5} = 0.07586\times10^{-2}$$

or $\theta = 0.02754$ rad $= 1.58°$

Example 13.25 A sphere of mass 0.8 kg and radius 3 cm is suspended by a wire 1 m long of radius 0.5 m. If the time for one torsional vibration is 1.23 sec, determine the modulus of rigidity of the wire.

Solution. Here $l = 1$m, $M = 0.8$ kg. $R = 3$ cm $= 3 \times 10^{-2}$ m

$a = 0.5$ mm $= 0.5 \times 10^{-3}$ m, $t = 1.23$ sec

M.I of sphere $I = \frac{2}{5}MR^2 = \frac{2}{5} \times 0.8 \times (3 \times 10^{-2})^2$

$= 2.88 \times 10^{-4}$ kgm²

Now $t = 2\pi\sqrt{\frac{I}{c}} = 2\pi\sqrt{\frac{2Il}{\eta\pi a^4}}$

$\therefore \quad \eta = \frac{8\pi Il}{t^2 a^4} = \frac{8 \times \pi \times 2.88 \times 10^{-4} \times 1}{(1.23)^2 \times (0.5 \times 10^{-3})^4} = 7.654 \times 10^{10}$ N-m⁻²

Example 13.26 A cylindrical metal bar of length 0.24 m and diameter 4 cm is suspended by a wire 0.5 m long such that the axis of the bar is horizontal. The arrangement makes 100 torsional vibrations in 235.9 sec. Determine the co-efficient of rigidity of the material of wire. Given density of material of bar = 9 × 10³ kgm⁻³ and radius of wire = 0.1 cm.

Solution. For cylindrical bar $L = 0.24$ m, $R = 2$ cm $= 2 \times 10^{-2}$ m

Density $\rho = 9 \times 10^3$ kgm⁻³

Volume $V = \pi R^2 L = \pi \times 4 \times 10^{-4} \times 0.24 = 3.016 \times 10^{-4}$ m³

$\therefore$ Mass $M = 3.016 \times 10^{-4} \times 9 \times 10^3 = 2.715$ kg

M.I. of cylindrical bar about an axis passing through its centre and perpendicular to the length

$$I = M\left[\frac{R^2}{4} + \frac{l^2}{12}\right] = 2.715\left[\frac{4 \times 10^{-4}}{4} + \frac{24 \times 24}{12}\right] = 133.04 \times 10^{-4}\ kgm^2$$

Time period $T = \frac{235.9}{100} = 2.359$ sec

Now $T = 2\pi\sqrt{\frac{I}{c}}$ or $c = \frac{4\pi^2 I}{T^2}$ and $c = \frac{\pi\eta a^4}{2l}$

$\therefore \quad \frac{\pi\eta a^4}{2l} = \frac{4\pi^2 I}{T^2}$

or $\eta = \frac{8\pi Il}{T^2 a^2} = \frac{8\pi \times 133.04 \times 10^{-4} \times 0.5}{(2.359)^2\ (1 \times 10^{-3})^4} = \mathbf{3 \times 10^{10}\ Nm^{-2}}$

EXERCISE

I–Moduli of Elasticity—Poisson's ratio

1. (*a*) Define stress, strain and Poisson's ratio.
   (*b*) Define Young's modulus, Bulk modulus and modulus of rigidity. If E, K and n represent these moduli respectively, prove the relation $E = 9nK/(3K + n)$. ***(Allahabad, Poona)***
2. Show that the theoretical limiting values of Poisson's ratio are –1 and 0.5. ***(Agra, Poona,)***
3. Explain the terms:
   (*i*) Elastic limit
   (*ii*) Yield point
   (*iii*) Elastic fatigue.
4. Explain the terms stress and strain. Define Young's modulus Y, the Bulk modulus K, rigidity modulus η and Poisson's ratio σ. Write dimensions of σ.
   (M.D.U. 2003, Meerut U. 2003, Nagpur U. 2001, 2009, K.U. 2000; M.S.U. Tiruneveli 2007; Agra U. 2006; Madurai U. 2003)

5. Define Young's modulus. Show that the Young's modulus Y, modulus of rigidity n and Poisson's ratio σ are related by the equation $Y = 2n(1 + \sigma)$ ***(Agra)***

6. (*a*) Define Young's modulus, Bulk modulus, modulus of rigidity and Poisson's ratio. Obtain the relations connecting these quantities. ***(Agra, Jodhpur. Punjab Vikram,)***

   (*b*) A wire 300 cm long and 0.625 sq. cm in cross section is found to stretch 0.3 cm under a tension of 1200 kg. What is the Young's modulus for the material of the wire? ***(A.M.I.E)***

   [**Ans.** 2.3×10^{12} dynes/cm^2.]

7. A steel wire of length 2.0 *m* and cross-section 1×10^{-2} sq. cm is held between rigid supports with a tension 2×10^7 dynes. If the middle of the wire is pulled 5 mm sideways, calculate the change in tension. Also calculate the change in tension if the temperature changes by 5°C. (For steel, $Y = 2.2 \times 10^{12}$ *dynes/cm*^{2} and $\alpha = 8 \times 10^{-6}$ deg^{-1}). ***(Agra)***

   [**Ans.** 2.75×10^5 dynes; 8.8×10^5 dynes]

8. Find the formula for the work done in stretching a wire and apply it to find the elastic energy stored up in a wire, originally 5 metre long and 1 mm in diameter, which has been stretched by 3/10 mm due to a load of 10 kg. (Take $g = 300\pi$). ***(Bombay)***

   [**Ans.** 1.413×13^5 ergs.]

9. (*a*) Define Young's modulus *Y*, modulus of rigidity *n* and Poisson's ratio σ. Obtian an expression for σ in terms of *Y* and *n* for a uniform and isotropic substance. ***(Bombay; Nagpur; Punjab)***

   (*b*) Define Young's modulus, Bulk modulus and Poisson's ratio and derive a relation between them. ***(Delhi, Punjab)***

10. Calculate the strain in a rod of isotropic material stretched in such a way that all lateral strains are prevented. [**Hint:** $\beta = \frac{\alpha}{2}$ and 6 = 0.5. It is an ideal case]

11. Describe the form of stress-strain graph for a steel wire. ***(Punjab)***

12. (*a*) Show that in any type of strain, work done per unit volume is equal to $\frac{1}{2}$ stress × strain.

    (*b*) Find the ratio between adiabatic and isothermal elasticities of a gas. ***(Poona)***

13. (*a*) Define Poisson's ratio and describe a method for its determination. Derive the formula used. ***(Agra)***

    (*b*) Calculate *n* and σ for silver, given *Y* and *K* for silver = 7.25×10^{11} *dynes/cm*^{2} and 11×10^{11} dynes/cm^2.

    [**Ans.** $n = 2.607 \times 10^{11}$ *dynes/cm*^{2}; $\sigma = 0.39$]

14. (*a*) Explain what you understand by shearing strain. ***(Agra)***

    (*b*) Show that a shear is equivalent to a compression and an extension. Find the work done in stretching a wire and hence deduce an expression for the energy per unit volume of the wire. ***(Madras, B.A)***

15. If *Y*, *K* and σ represent Young's modulus, Bulk modulus and Poisson's ratio respectively, then prove that $K = \frac{Y}{3(1-2\sigma)}$.

    (Purvanchal U., 2006, 2004; Agra U., 2005, 2006 M.D.U 2001; M.S.U Tiruneveli 2007)

16. Show that for a homogeneous isotropic medium $Y = 2\eta\,(1 + \sigma)$ where letters have their usual meaning. ***(Nagpur 2009, Meerut U. 2003; Cal. U. 2003; K.U 2002; M.D.U 2003)***

17. If Y, K, η and σ represent the Young's modulus, bulk modulus, coefficient of rigidity and Poisson's ratio, then derive various relations connecting each other and prove that σ is less than 0.5 and cannot be less than −1. What are the practical limits for Poisson's ratio (σ)?

    (Madurai U. 2003; Kerala U. 2001; Nagpur U. 2001; Indore U. 2001; M.D.U 2001; KU 2001, 2000; Bang U. 2000; Guwahati U. 2000; Gharwal U. 2000)

18. Prove that

$$\frac{3}{Y}=\frac{1}{3K}+\frac{1}{\eta}$$ ***(Purvanchal U. 2006; Agra, 2006)***

19. Show that

$$\sigma=\left(\frac{Y}{2\eta}\right)-1$$ ***(Purvanchal U 2006; Arga 2006)***

20. If Y, η and K represent Youngs modulus, coefficient of rigidity and bulk modulus repectively, then prove that

$$\frac{9}{Y}=\frac{3}{\eta}+\frac{1}{K}$$ ***(Purvanchal U 2007; Agra, 2006)***

21. Describe Searle's method for measuring Young's modulus of a material in the form of a wire. Derive the formula used. ***(Allahabad)***

22. Calculate the value of Young's modulus given $\eta = 2 \times 10^{10}$ N/m^2 and $\sigma = 0.25$. ***(Nagpur U., 2001)*** [**Ans.** 5×10^{10} Nm^{-2}]

23. Calculate Poisson's ratio σ for Brass.
Given $Y = 10 \times 10^{10}$ N/m^2 and $K = 10 \times 10^{10}$ N/m^2
[**Hint:** $Y = 3K(1 - 2\sigma)$] ***(Nagpur U. 2005)*** [**Ans.** 0.33]

24. Poisson's ratio for a material is 0.379 and rigidity is 2.87×10^{-2} *Nm*$^{-2}$, find Young's modulus. [**Ans.** 7.196×10^{-2} *Nm*$^{-2}$]

25. Find the Poisson's ratio of a material whose volume is not changeable at any pressure. ***(Purvanchal U. 2005)***

26. Find the work done in stretching a wire of 1 *sq. mm* cross-section. Young's modulus 2×10^{11} *N/m*^{2} and 2 m long through 0.1 mm. [**Ans.** 5×10^{-4}]

27. A gold wire 0.32 mm in diameter elongates by 1 mm, when stretched by a force of 0.33 kg wt. and twists through 1 radian when equal and opposite torques of 145 *dyne-cm* are applied at its ends. Find the Poisson's ratio for gold. (*given g = 9.8 ms*$^{-2}$.) [**Ans.** 0.427]

28. Describe an experiment for measuring the Young's modulus of a rectangular bar of steel. Deduce the formula you use. ***(Bombay)***

29. A block of soft rubber, 1.5m square, has one face fixed, while the opposite face is sheared through a distance 1.27 cm parallel to the fixed face by a tangential force of 17.7 kg wt. How much work is done per unit volume of the cube to do this ? [**Ans.** 3.92 kgwt.]

30. Show that the torsional rigidity is greater for a hollow cylinder than for a solid one of the same material, mass, length and cross-section area. [**Hint:** Since M.E. greater] ***(D.A.U. 2008; Agra, 2006)***

II–Torsional couple—Torsion pendulum

31. What are torsional oscillations? Derive an expression for the twisting couple per unit angular twist for a hollow cylinder.

32. Explain why a hollow cylinder is stronger than a solid cylinder of the same length, mass and material. ***(Gharwal U. 2001, 2000; K. U 2001, Bang U. 2000)***

33. Deduce an expression to calculate the work done in twisting a cylindrical wire by an angle θ. Prove that a hollow cylinder is stronger than a solid cylinder of same mass and material. ***(M.S.U. Tiruneveli, 2007; D.A.U Agra U. 2007, 2004)***

34. A solid cylinder of radius 5 cm is converted into a hollow cylinder of same mass and length and external radius 7 cm. If the restoring couple per unit radian twist in original cylinder, is C, deduce the same for the new hollow cylinder. [**Ans.** $C' = 2.92\ C$]

35. A circular hollow rod and a circular solid rod of same length and same mass are to be twisted by same amount. Which one will be more difficult ? ***(Purvanchal U. 2004)*** [**Ans.** Hollow cylinder]

36. Two spheres, one hollow and one solid, are of same mass, same external radius and same external appearance. Which one will roll down faster on an inclined plane?

(Purvanchal U. 2004) [**Ans.** Solid sphere rolls down faster than hollow sphere]

37. Two cylinders have the same length and mass and are made of same material; one is solid while the other which is hollow has an external radius twice the internal radius. Compare the torsional rigidities of two cylinders. Show that second cylinder is stronger.

38. Show that shearing strain θ is equivalent to the extensional strain or compressional strain and it is equal to the half of the shearing strain (θ). ***(Purvanchal U. 2005)***

39. (*a*) Explain clearly what you understand by the term rigidity. Calculate the couple required to twist a cylindrical rod of circular cross-section through an angle θ at one end, the other end being kept fixed, and hence deduce an expression for the rigity of the rod. ***(Agra)***

(*b*) Obtain an expression for the couple required to twist one end of a cylindrical rod through 1 radian, the other end being fixed. ***(Vikram)***

40. Distinguish between angle of twist and angle of shear. What is meant by resilience and proof resilience? Show that the shear is always the maximum on the surface of a twisted cylinder or wire.

41. (*a*) Deduce an expression for the moment of the couple required to twist the lower end of a bar of circular cross section by 90°, the upper end being clamped. ***(Agra)***

[**Ans.** $n\pi^2R^4/4L$]

(*b*) Find the amount of work done in twisting a steel wire of radius 1.0 mm and of length 25 cm through an angle of 45°. Given *n* for steel = 8×10^{11} *dynes per cm*^{2}. *(Patna)*

[**Ans.** 15.47×10^5 ergs.]

42. From first principles deduce an expression for the moment of the couple required to twist one end of a hollow cylinder by an angle θ while the other end is held fixed. The internal and external radii of the cylinder are r_1 and r_2 respectively. ***(Agra; Rajasthan)***

43. What fraction of the material would be saved if a solid shaft be replaced by a hollow one which can be twisted to the same extent as the solid shaft by the application of the same couple, its external radius being twice its internal radius. [**Ans.** 0.13.]

44. One end of a wire, 2 mm in diameter and 50 cm in length, is twisted through 0.8 radian. Calculate the shearing strain at the surface of the wire. ***(Agra)*** [**Ans.** 1.6×10^{-3} radian]

45. Derive an expression for the moment of the couple required to twist one end of a cylinder when the other is fixed. Hence find the periodic time of a torsion pendulum. ***(Rajasthan)***

46. A uniform circular disc is suspended by a steel wire and the system is allowed to vibrate torsionally. The periodic time is 4 sec. Find the period if (*i*) the length of the wire is reduced to one half and (*ii*) two particles each having a mass 1/4 times the mass of the disc are placed on diametrically opposite points on the circumference of the disc. ***(Bombay)*** [**Ans.** (*i*) 2.8 sec. (*ii*) 5.6 sec.]

47. A metal bar, soldered to the lower end of a wire, vibrates torsionally. How will the time of oscillation be changed by having (*a*) the linear dimensions of the wire, (*b*) the linear dimensions of the metal bar (*c*) the linear dimensions of both bar and wire ?

[**Ans.** (*a*) *Increased* $\sqrt{2}$ *times; (b) reduced* $4\sqrt{2}$ *times; (c) halved.*]

48. The couple per unit twist for a certain solid cylinder of radius *r* is 10.0×10^8 dyne-cm. Calculate the contribution to this couple due to the central part up to radius *r*/4 and due to the outermost part between radii 3*r*/4 and *r*. ***(Agra)*** [**Ans.** 3.9×10^6 *dyne-cm*; 6.84×10^6 *dyne-cm*.]

49. Describe, with appropriate theory, a method to find the moment of inertia of an irregular body.

(Punjab)

50. How is the modulus of rigidity of the material of a wire determined by the statical method ? Derive the formula used. ***(Bombay, Punjab)***

51. Describe a dynamical method by which the modulus of rigidity of a given specimen of wire may be determined. ***(Punjab, Delhi)***

52. Define modulus of rigidity. Describe, with necessary theory, Maxwell's method for determining it experimentally. ***(Delhi)***

53. A cylindrical metal bar having length 24 cm and diameter 4 cm is suspended by a wire 50 cm long such that the axis of the bar is horizontal .It is observed that the arrangement makes 100 torsional oscillations in 235.9 sec. Determine the coefficient of rigidity of the material of the wire. Density of the material of the bar = 9 *gm/c.c* and radius of the wire = 0.1 cm. ***(Punjab)***

[**Ans.** 3×10^{11} *dynes/cm*^{2}.]

54. A solid and a hollow cylindrical shaft have the same mass per unit length, the latter having an external diameter twice the internal one. Show that the torsional rigidities (*i.e.*, couples per unit twist) as also the maximum strains produced in them by equal twisting couples are as 5:3.

55. (*a*) What is the difference between angle of twist and angle of shear? Deduce an expression for the couple required to twist a uniform solid cylinder by an angle θ.

(D.A.U Agra 2008 Kerala U. 2001; Meerut U. 2005,2002, 2000; M.D.U. 2002; Nagpur U. 2005, 2003)

(b) What is the value of couple for a hollow cylinder of inner radius r_1 and outer radius r_2?

56. Show that couple required per unit angular twist in the case of cylindrical wire is

$$C = \frac{\pi \eta r^4}{2l}$$

(Purvanchal U. 2005; 2004; M.S.U. Tiruneveli 2007)

57. Prove that a shearing stress is equivalent to a linear tensile stress and an equal compression stress mutually at right angles. ***(Agra U. 2005)***

58. Show that the work done (or potential energy) per unit volume in a strained air is $\frac{1}{2}$ (*stress* × *strain*).

(Agra U. 2007)

14 Chapter

BENDING OF BEAMS —COLUMNS

Brief Contents

14.1 BEAM

A rod or a bar of a circular or rectangular cross section, *with its length very much greater than its thickness* (so that there are no shearing stresses over any section of it) is called a *beam*.

Now, a beam may just rest on a support, like a knife-edge or have a small part of it firmly clamped or built into a wall at either end. In the former case, it is called a **supported beam** and in the latter, a built-in or an **encastre beam** or usually, simply, **a fixed beam**.

In a supported beam, obviously, the support can merely exert a force on the beam but in a fixed beam, it can also exert a couple on it.

If the beam be fixed only at *one end* and loaded at the other, it is called a **cantilever**.

A beam or a bar of a homogeneous, isotropic material, *subjected to an axial push or compressive stress,* is, in general, called a **strut** and may be inclined in any direction, including the horizontal and the vertical.

In the *vertical or upright position,* however, a long and slender beam or bar, thus subjected to an axial push or compressive stress, is referred to as **a column, pillar** or **stanchion**.

As will be readily seen, *a column or a pillar is just a vertical strut.*

A beam or a bar, *subjected to a pull or a tensile stress*, is called a **tie**.

14.2 BENDING OF A BEAM—SOME DEFINITIONS

Suppose we have a beam, of a rectangular cross section, say, fixed at one end and loaded at the other (within the elastic limit) so as to be bent a little, as shown in Fig. 14.1, with its upper surface becoming slightly convex and the lower one concave. All the longitudinal filaments in the upper half of the beam thus get extended or lengthened, and therefore under tension, and all those in the lower half get compressed or shortened and therefore under pressure.

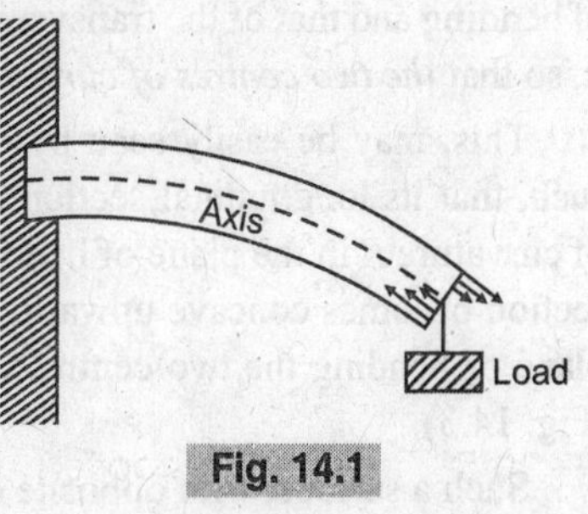

Fig. 14.1

These extensions and compressions increase progressively as we proceed away from the axis on either side (as shown in a rough and ready manner by the lengths of the arrow), so that they are the maximum in the uppermost and the lowermost layers of the beam respectively.

Obviously, there must be a layer between the uppermost and the lowermost layers where the extensions in the upper half change sign to become compressions in the lower half. In this layer or plane, which is perpendicular to the section of the *beam containing the axis*, the filaments neither get extended nor compressed, *i.e.*, retain their original lengths. This layer is therefore called the neutral surface of the beam, shown shaded in Fig. 14.2

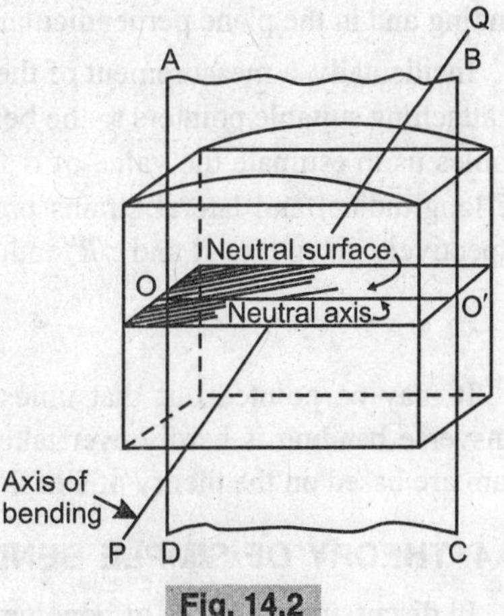

Fig. 14.2

If the material of the beam be homogeneous and isotropic and the bending uniform, the longitudinal filaments all get bent into circular acrs in planes parallel to the *plane of symmetry ABCD* of the beam, which is also, therefore, the **plane of bending**. The centres of curvature of all these arcs lie on a straight line *PQ*, perpendicular to the plane of bending (or the plane of symmetry), which is referred to as the **axis of bending.**

The line of intersection (OO') of the plane of bending and the neutral surface (which are clearly perpendicular to each other) is called the **neutral axis** of the beam. The extensions and compressions of the filaments are directly proportional to their respective distances from *this axis*.

In the unstrained condition of the beam, the neutral surface will obviously be a plane surface. The filament of this surface lying in the plane of symmetry of the bent beam is called the **neutral filament**.

14.3 ANTICLASTIC CURVATURE

In the above discussion, we have tacitly assumed the bending of the beam to be *pure* or simple, *i.e.*, only longitudinal, with no shearing stresses over any section and hence no transverse bending. In actual practice, however, a longitudinal bending is almost invariably accompanied by a transverse bending.

This is really only to be expected. For, the filaments above the neutral axis, undergoing extension, must suffer a lateral contraction, and those below the neutral axis, undergoing compression, must suffer a lateral extension, σ times as large (*See* §13.11), where σ is the *poisson's ratio* for the material of the beam. As a result, if the cross-section of the beam be rectangular, a layer, initially plane and perpendicular to the plane of bending and containing the neutral filament, assumes the *shape of a saddle*, with the radius or curvature of its longitudinal section in the plane of bending and that of the transverse section in the plane perpendicular to it, so that *the two centres of curvature lie on opposite sides of the beam.*

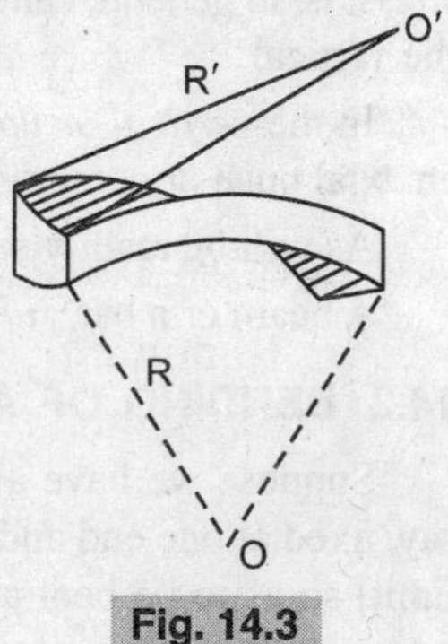

Fig. 14.3

This, may be easily seen by bending a rectangular piece of rubber such, that its longitudinal section is concave downwards with its radius of curvature R in the plane of bending (here the plane of the paper). We shall find that its transverse section becomes concave upwards, with its radius of curvature R' in the plane perpendicular to the plane of bending the two centres of curvature O and O' thus lying on opposite sides of the piece, (Fig. 14.3).

Such a surface, with opposite curvatures of its longitudinal and transverse sections is called an **anticlastic surface,** as opposed to a *synclastic surface* for which the two centres of curvature lie on the same side of the surface as, for example, in the case of a sphere or an ellipsoid.

The opposite curvature acquired by the surface in two perpendicular directions (in the plane of bending and in the plane perpendicular to it) is called **anticlastic curvature**.

Incidentally, a measurement of the two radii of curvature, R and R' (which may easily be done by attaching suitable pointers to the beam and noting the distances and angles transversed by them) enables us to estimate the value of σ for the material of the beam. For, as we shall see in § 13.5, the longitudinal and lateral strains produced in the beam at distance z from the neutral axis are respectively given by z/R and z/R' and, therefore,

$$\sigma = \frac{\textit{lateral strain}}{\textit{longitudinal strain}} = \frac{z/R'}{z/R} = \frac{R}{R'}.$$

It may be pointed out that unless extreme accuracy is called for in any specific case, the transverse bending is hardly ever taken into account and all calculations for the curvature of the beam are based on the theory of simple (or pure) bending, which follows.

14.4 THEORY OF SIMPLE BENDING—ASSUMPTIONS

In discussing the cases of bending that follow we shall concern ourselves with only the theory of simple (pure) bending which makes the following assumptions:

(i) That Hook's law is valid for both tensile and compressive stresses and that the value of Young's modulus (Y) for the material of the beam remains the same in either case.

(ii) That there are no shearing stresses over any section of the beam when it is bent. This is more or less ensured if the length of the beam is sufficiently large compared with its thickness.

(iii) That there is no change in cross-section of the beam on bending. As just explained in § 14.3 above, this is hardly ever true, a rectangular cross-section almost always acquiring an anticlastic curvature and a circular cross-section possibly assuming an oval form. This change in the shape of cross-section may result in a change in its area and hence also in its geometrical moment of inertia I_g.

Any such change is however always much too small compared and is, in general. ignored.

(iv) That the radius of curvature of the neutral axis of the bent beam is very much greater than its thickness. This is invariably true in all cases of bending of beams.

(v) That the minimum deflection of the beam is small compared with its length. This too is true, in general, except in cases like that of a clock spring or strongly bent beams. We shall deal with such a case separately in § 14.8.

14.5 BENDING MOMENT

Let a beam *ABCD* be fixed at the end *AD* and loaded (within the elastic limit) with a weight *W* at the free end *BC** so as to be bent a little and remaining in equilibrium in the position shown (Fig. 14.4).

Consider a section *PBCP′* of the bent beam, cut by a plane *PP′* at right angles to its length and its plane of bending (or its plane of symmetry).

Clearly, the load *W* acting vertically downwards at its free end gives rise to an equal reactional force *W* acting vertically upwards at *P* and the two thus form a couple, tending to bend the section *clockwise*, as indicated by full line arrows. This couple applied due to load *W* is, therefore, called the **bending couple**.

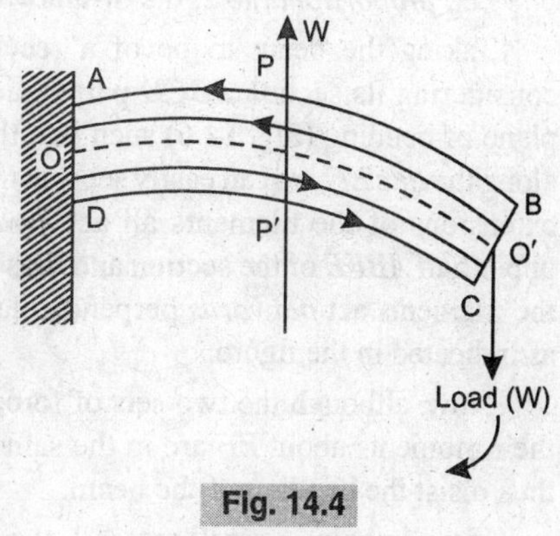

Fig. 14.4

Since the section is in equilibrium, there must be another *equal* and *opposite* couple brought into play on the section due to the tensile and compressive stresses set up in its upper an lower halves respectively. For, the filaments above the neutral axis *OO′* being elongated, and hence in a state of tension, exert on the filaments next to them an *inward pull* (towards the fixed end) and the filaments below the neutral axis being shortened and hence in a state of compression, exert on the filaments next to them an *outward pull* (towards the loaded end), as indicated by the arrowheads in the two halves respectively.

These inward and outward pulls thus form a pair of equal and opposite (non-collinear) forces or a *couple*, tending to bend the section in the opposite direction to that due to that applied or the bending couple *i.e., anticlockwise*, as indicated by the dotted arrows. The moment of this couple is called the **moment of the resistance to bending** for the obvious reason that it opposes or resists the bending of the beam due to the applied couple. Since, however, in the equilibrium position of the beam it is equal in magnitude (though opposite in direction) to the bending couple, it is referred to as the **bending moment** (*M*).

* Taking the weight of the beam itself to be negligible and, therefore, ineffective compared with *W*.

Expression for bending moment. Consider a portion of the beam to be bent into a circular arc, as shown in Fig. 14.5, subtending an angle θ at its centre of curvature C and let the radius of curvature of the neutral axis OO' be R.

Let the original length of a filament (*i.e.*, its length in the unstained or unbent condition of the beam) at a distance z from the neutral axis be ab, *the same as that on the neutral axis,* and let its extended length in the strained or bent condition of the beam be $a'b'$. Then, clearly,

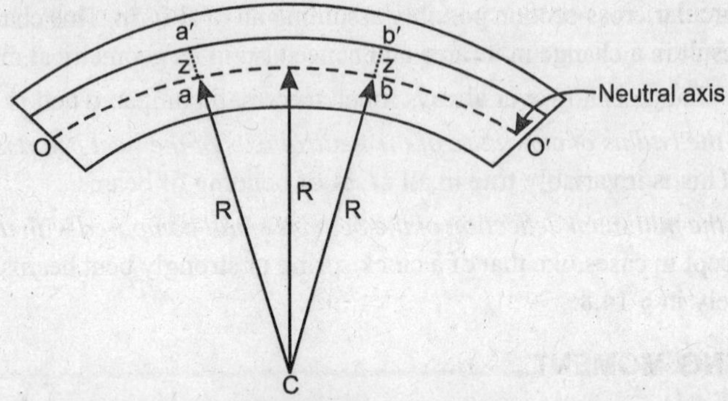

Fig. 14.5

its original length $ab = R\theta$ and *its extended length* $= (R + z)\theta$.

So that, *increase in its length* $= a'b' - ab = (R + z)\theta - R\theta = z\theta$.

$$\therefore \quad \textit{tensite strain} = \frac{\textit{increase in length}}{\textit{original length}} = \frac{z\theta}{R\theta} = \frac{z}{R},$$

i.e., proportional to z, the distance from the neutral axis.

Taking the beam to be of a rectangular cross-section and considering its section *ABCD* perpendicular to its length and the plane of bending (Fig. 14.6) such that the neutral surface meets it along the *line EF*, we can easily see that the internal forces opposing extensions of the filaments all act *inwards* perpendicular to the upper half *ABFE* of the section and those opposing contractions of the filaments act *outwards* perpendicular to its lower half *EFCD*, as indicated in the figure.

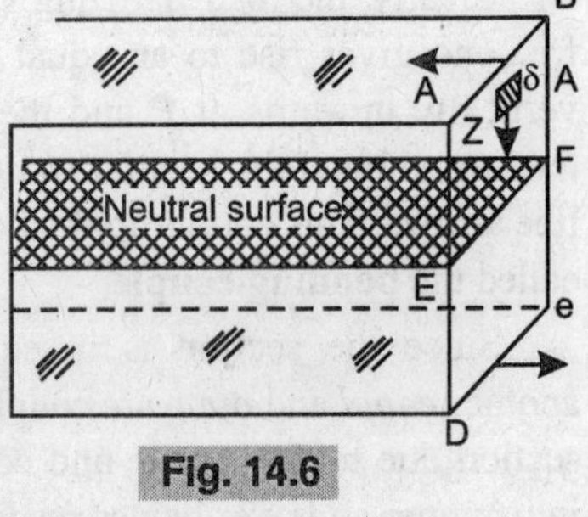

Fig. 14.6

Now, although the two sets of forces are oppositely directed, their moments about *EF* are in the same direction, viz., opposite to that of the bending couple and thus resist the bending of the beam.

If we imagine a small area δ.1 at a distance z from *EF*, the tensile strain there, as we have just seen is given by z/R.

Now, *Young's modulus* for the material of the beam is given by

$$Y = \textit{tensile stress/tensile strain} = \textit{tensile stress}/\frac{z}{R}.$$

$\therefore$ *tensile stress on the small area* $\delta A = Yz/R$, and, therefore, *force on the area* δA = *stress* × *area* $= (Yz/R)\delta A$,

and *moment of this force about EF* $= \dfrac{Yz}{R}\delta A.z = \dfrac{Yz^2}{R}\delta A.$

Since moment of all the forces on elemental are as like δA both in the upper and lower halves of the section act in the same direction, we have

total moment of the forces acting on section ABCD $= \Sigma\dfrac{Yz}{R}\delta A = \dfrac{Y}{R}\Sigma\delta Az^2$. The quantity $\Sigma\delta Az^2$ is called the *geometrical moment of inertia* of the cross-section of the beam, which we may denote by I_g (to distinguish it from the mechanical moment of inertia for which we use the symbol I). It is also called the *second moment of inertia.*

∴ *total moment of all forces about EF,* or the **bending moment of the beam, $M = YI_g/R$.**

The quantity YI_g, which is obviously the external bending moment required to produce a curvature of unit radius in the beam (*i.e.* when $R = 1$), is called **flexural rigidity** of the beam and is clearly a measure of the resistance of the beam of the beam to bending.

Thus, **bending moment of a beam = flexural rigidity/R.**

For a beam of rectangular cross-section, since $I_g = bd^3/12$. where b is the breadth and d, the depth of the beam, we have

$$\text{bending moment } (M) = Ybd^3/12R.$$

And, *for a beam of a circular cross-section,* since $I_g = \pi R^4/4$, where R is the radius of its cross-section, we have

$$\text{bending moment } (M) = Y\pi R^4/4R.$$

14.6 STIFFNESS OF A BEAM

The stiffness of a beam is taken to be the *ratio between the maximum deflection of its loaded end and its spa* and is usually denoted by the symbol $1/n$. For steel girders with a large span, n should lie between 1000 to 2000, and for those with a smaller span, between 500 to 700. For timber beams, it should be 360 or above.

14.7 THE CANTILEVER—(DEPRESSION OF ITS LOADED END)

As already mentioned (§14.1), a beam rigidly fixed at one end and loaded at the other is called a *cantilever.*

We shall discuss *three cases* of bending here. (*i*) When the weight of the *cantilever is ineffective. i.e.,* produces no bending by itself and (*ii*) *when it is effective,* (*iii*) *when the cantilever is uniformly loaded.*

Case (*i*)—(weight of the cantilever ineffective). Let AB be a cantilever of length L, rigidly fixed at the end A and loaded (within the elastic limit) with a weight W at its free end (Fig. 14.7) so as to be bent a little into the dotted position where (the bending being small) end B may be taken to be practically vertically below its earlier position.

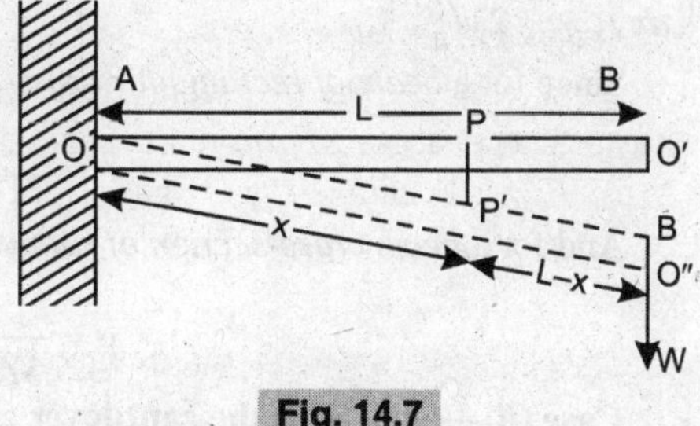

Fig. 14.7

Clearly, the neutral axis OO' of the beam will now take up of the position OO'', so that the depression (or deflection) of the loaded end is $O'O''$.

Considering a section PB of the beam by a plane passing through P a right angles to its length and the plane of bending, at a distance x from the fixed end A, we have

external couple acting on the section due to load $W = W \times P'O'' = W(L - x)$.

This, as we know, is, in the position of equilibrium, balanced by the *bending moment* YI_g/R due to the tensile and compressive stresses set up inside the beam, where Y is the value of *Young's modulus* for the material of the beam, I_g, the geometrical moment of inertia of its cross-section and R, the radius of curvature of the neutral axis of the section at P.

We, therefore, have $\quad W(L - x) = YI_g/R.$

Now, the curvature $\quad 1/R = \dfrac{d^2y/dx^2}{[1+(dy/dx)^2]^{3/2}},$

which, when dy/dx is small (as is usually the case), reduces to $1/R = d^2y/dx^2$, the rate of change of slope. [See worked example I.]

So that, $W(L-x) = YI_g \frac{d^2y}{dx^2}$. Or, $\frac{d^2y}{dx^2} = \frac{W}{YI_g}(L-x)$.

This, on integration, gives $\frac{dy}{dx} = \frac{W}{YI_g}\left(Lx - \frac{x^2}{2}\right) + C_1$,

where C_1 is a constant of integration.

Since end A is fixed, we have $dy/dx = 0$ at $x = 0$ and, therefore, $C_1 = 0$, and we have

$$\frac{dy}{dx} = \frac{W}{YI_g}\left(Lx - \frac{x^2}{2}\right) \qquad ...(i)$$

Integrating once again, we have

$$y = \frac{W}{YI_g}\left(L\frac{x^2}{2} - \frac{x^3}{6}\right) + C_2,$$

where C_2 is another constant of integration.

Again, however, $y = 0$ and $x = 0$ and, therefore, $C_2 = 0$.

And so we have $$y = \frac{WI}{YI_g}\left(\frac{Lx^2}{2} - \frac{x^3}{6}\right), \qquad ...(ii)$$

where y gives the depression or deflection of the beam at a distance x from the fixed end A.

Since the free (or the loaded) end B of the beam is at a distance L from A, we have $x = L$ and, therefore,

depression of the loaded end B is given by

$$y = \frac{W}{YI_g}\left(\frac{L^3}{2} - \frac{L^3}{6}\right) = \frac{W}{YI_g}\cdot\frac{2L^3}{6}.$$

Or, $$y = \frac{WL^3}{3YI_g}.$$

And, *slope of the end B relative to A* (or its inclination to the horizontal) is given by $\tan\theta = \theta = \left(\frac{dy}{dx}\right)_{x=L} = \frac{WL^2}{2yI_g}$.

Since for a *beam of rectangular cross-section of breadth b and depth d*, $I_g = bd^3/12$, we have

$$y = \frac{WL^3}{3Y(bd^3/12)} = \frac{4WL^3}{Ybd^3}.$$

And for a *beam cross-section of radius r*, $I_g = \pi r^4/4$. So that, we have

$$y = \frac{WL^3}{3Y(\pi r^4/4)} = \frac{4WL^3}{3Y\pi r^4}.$$

Case (*ii*)—(weight of the cantilever effective). Considering again the section PB (Fig. 14.7) at distance x from the fixed end, we have, in addition to the load W acting at B, a weight equal to that of the portion $(L-x)$ of the beam also acting at its mid-point. So that, if w be the weight per unit length of the beam, we have an additional weight $w(L-x)$ acting at a distance $(L-x)/2$ from P. And, therefore,

total moment of the external couple applied

$$= W(L-x) + w(L-x)(L-x)/2$$

$$= W(L-x) + \frac{w}{2}(L-x)^2.$$

The beam being in equilibrium, this must be balanced by the *bending moment* YI_g/R. We, therefore, have

$$W(L-x)+\frac{w}{2}(L-x)^2 = YI_g/R = YI_g(d^2y/dx^2),$$

which, on integration yields

$$YI_g\frac{dy}{dx} = W\left(Lx-\frac{x^2}{2}\right)+\frac{w}{2}\left(L^2x-2L\frac{x^2}{2}+\frac{x^3}{3}\right)+C,$$

where C is a constant of integration.

Since at $x = 0$, $dy/dx = 0$, we have $C = 0$.

So that,

$$YI_g\int_0^y dy = W\int_0^L\left(Lx-\frac{x^2}{2}\right)dx+\frac{w}{2}\int_0^L\left(L^2x-Lx^2+\frac{x^3}{3}\right)dx$$

$$= \frac{WL^3}{3}+\frac{wL^4}{8}.$$

Or, since $wL = W_0$, *the weight of the beam*, we have

$$YI_g y = \frac{WL^3}{3}+\frac{W_0L^3}{8}, \text{ whence } y = \left(W=\frac{3}{8}W_0\right)\frac{L^3}{3YI_g}.$$

Thus, *the beam now behaves as though the load (W) at its free end (B) is increased by 3/8 of its own weight.*

Case (*iii*)—(Cantilever uniformly loaded). In this case, if the load on the cantilever be w per unit length (including its own weight), the bending at the section PB of the beam is produced by a load $w(L-x)$ acting at a distance $(L-x)/2$ from P or B, with no load suspended at B (Fig. 14.7).

we, therefore, have

$$W(L-x)(L-x)/2 = \frac{w}{2}(L-x)^2 = YI_g/R = YI_g(d^2y/dx^2),$$

which, on integration, gives $YI_g\dfrac{dy}{dx} = \dfrac{w}{2}\left(L^2x-2L\dfrac{x^2}{2}+\dfrac{x^3}{3}\right)+C,$

where C is a constant of integration.

Since at $x = 0$, $dy/dx = 0$, we have $C = 0$. And, therefore,

$$YI_g\int_0^y dy = \frac{w}{2}\int_0^L\left(L^2x-Lx^2+\frac{x^3}{3}\right)dx.$$

Or,

$$YI_g y = \frac{w}{2}\left(\frac{3L^4}{12}\right) = \frac{wL}{2}\left(\frac{L^3}{4}\right)$$

Since $wL = W$, the total load on the beam (including its own weight), we have

$$y = \frac{WL^3}{8YI_g},$$

i.e., the bending due to the uniformly distributed load W, instead of the whole of it at B, is 3/8 of that in the latter case and hence the stiffness of the beam increases to 8/3 of its value with the entire load at B.

In case there if *no load placed on the cantilever* and *it bends under its own weight*, we have $W = W_0$. So that, in that case,

$$y = \frac{W_0L^3}{8YI_g},$$

14.8 STRONGLY BENT BEAMS—FLEXIBLE CANTILEVER

In the three cases discussed above, the bending of the beam and hence the inclination of its loaded end with its unbent position being small, its curvature ($1/R$) has been taken to be equal to the rate of change of slope, d^2y/dx^2. This is obviously not possible if the beam bends strongly so that this angle of inclination is large. In such a case, as we know the curvature is given by

$$\frac{1}{R} = \frac{d^2y/dx^2}{[(1+dy/dx)^2]^{3/2}}$$

This makes the problem complicated and the differential equations obtained do not admit of an easy solution. However, in some cases, like that of a *flexible cantilever, e.g., a clock spring,* the problem becomes simpler and we shall, therefore, consider only this one case here.

If a clock spring be loosely clamped at a point close to its free end and the free end loaded with a weight W, it is found that as more and more of the spring is passed through the clamp, *keeping the load constant,* the loaded end falls progressively down on account of the large bending of the spring until finally it becomes quite vertical, with the horizontal distance between the loaded end and the clamp now the maximum. Any further length of the spring passed out through the clamp merely hands vertically without any change in this horizontal distance.

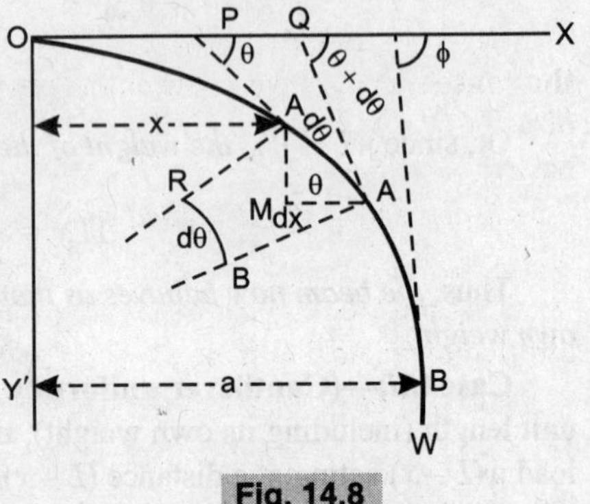

Fig. 14.8

Let OAB, in Fig. 14.8, represent the bent position of the spring, clamped at O and loaded at the free end B, such that the tangents to it and A and B make angles θ and ϕ with its unbent position along OX and their horizontal distances from the clamp are x and a respectively. Then, clearly,

moment of the bending couple at $A = W(a-x) =$ *bending moment* YI_g/R,

where R is the radius of curvature of the spring at A.

Considering another point infinitely close to A, with $AA' = ds$, say, so that the radius of curvature of the spring at A' remains the same (R) as at A, if $d\theta$ be the angle that the two radii make at the centre of curvature, we have

$$d\theta = AA'/R = ds/R. \quad \text{Or} \quad 1/R = d\theta/ds.$$

Draw $A'M$ and AM parallel to the two coordinate axes respectively as to meet in M. Then, since AA' is sensibly straight and in a line with PA, we have

$$\angle PA'M = \angle AA'M = \angle QPA' = \theta$$

and, therefore,
$$\cos\theta = MA'/AA' = dx/ds.$$

So that,
$$W(a-x) = YI_g/R = YI_g\frac{d\theta}{ds} = YI_g\frac{d\theta}{dx}\frac{dx}{ds} = YI_g\cos\theta\frac{d\theta}{dx}.$$

Or,
$$W(a-x)dx = YI_g\cos\theta\, d\theta.$$

Integrating between the limits $x = 0$ and $x = a$, we have

$$\int_0^a W(a-x)dx = YI_g\int_0^\phi \cos\theta d\theta.$$

Or, $W\left[ax - x^2/2\right]_0^a = YI_g\left[\sin\theta\right]_0^\phi$, whence, $Wa^2/2 = YI_g\sin\phi$ ...(*i*)

When the loaded end becomes vertical, $\phi = 90°$ and the horizontal distance a, the maximum, say, a_m. Expression (*i*) therefore becomes

$$Wa_m^2/2 = YI_g, \text{ whence, } a_m^2 = 2YI_g/W$$

and, therefore,
$$a_m = \sqrt{2YI_g/W}. \quad ...(ii)$$

As will be readily seen, either of the two expressions may be used to obtain the value of Y for the material of the spring, if we know ϕ and a in the first, and a_m in the second, case.

14.9 DETERMINATION OF *Y* FOR THE MATERIAL OF A CANTILEVER

(i) Statical method. This consists in noting the depression or deflection (y) of the loaded end of the cantilever for different loads (W) suspended from its free end and plotting a graph between W and y when we obtain a straight line OA passing through the origin, as shown in Fig. 14.9.

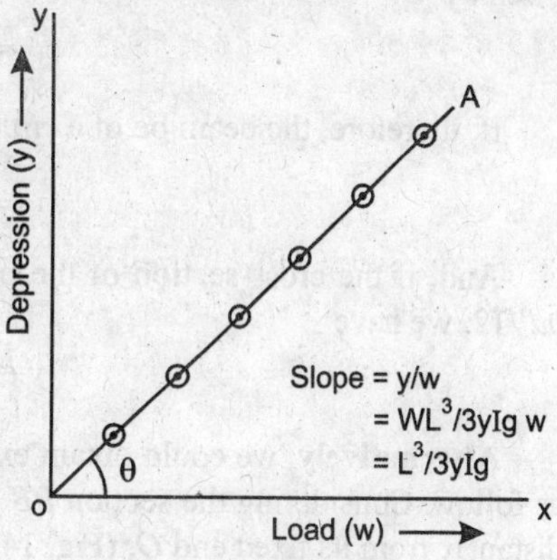

Fig. 14.9

The slope of the straight line graph is clearly $\tan\theta = y/W = WL^3/3YI_g.W = L^3/3YI_g$, whence, knowing L and I_g, the value of Y for the material of the cantilever may be easily obtained.

(ii) Dynamical method—(Transverse vibration of the cantilever). As we know, in the position of equilibrium of a cantilever loaded with a weight W at its free end, we have

displacement of the loaded end, i.e.

$$y = WL^3/3YI_g, \text{ whence, } W = (3YI_g/L^3)y. \quad ...(i)$$

This must obviously be equal to the inertial reaction of the cantilever balancing it and hence directed oppositely to it.

But if m be the *mass* of the weight W and d^2y/dt^2, the acceleration (upwards), we also have

$$\textit{inertial reaction} = -md^2y/dt^2,$$

the –ve sign indicating its direction, *opposite to that of the displacement of mass m* or the free end of the cantilever.

We, therefore, have $-m\dfrac{d^2y}{dt^2} = \dfrac{3YI_g}{L^3}y.$ Or, $\dfrac{d^2y}{dt^2} = -\dfrac{3YI_g}{mL^3}y,$

i.e., $d^2y/dt^2 = -\mu y$, where $3YI_g/mL^3 = \mu$, a constant.

The acceleration of mass m or the free end of the cantilever is thus proportional to its displacement and is directed oppositely to it. It therefore executes a *S.H.M.* of time-period T, given by

$$T = 2\pi\sqrt{\frac{1}{\mu}} = 2\pi\sqrt{mL^3/3YI_g} \quad ...(i)$$

Or, since $y = WL^3/3YI_g = mgL^3/3YI_g$, we have $mL^3/3YI_g = y/g$.

And, therefore, $$T = 2\pi\sqrt{y/g}. \quad ...(ii)$$

This gives us a dynamical method for the determination of Y for the material of the cantilever, particularly a light one whose weight is ineffective, *e.g.*, a *metre stick*. For, plotting a graph between m and T^2, we obtain a straight line passing though the origin, whose slope is given by $4\pi^2L^3/3YI_g$, whence the value of Y may be easily calculated.

14.10 DEPRESSION OF SUPPORTED AND FIXED BEAMS

We shall deal with the two cases separately, restricting ourselves to beams which are supported or fixed in a horizontal plane.

(i) Supported beam, centrally loaded.

(a) When the weight of the beam is ineffective. Let a beam be supported on two knife-edges A and B, distance L apart and loaded in the middle at O with with a weight W, as shown in Fig. 14.10.

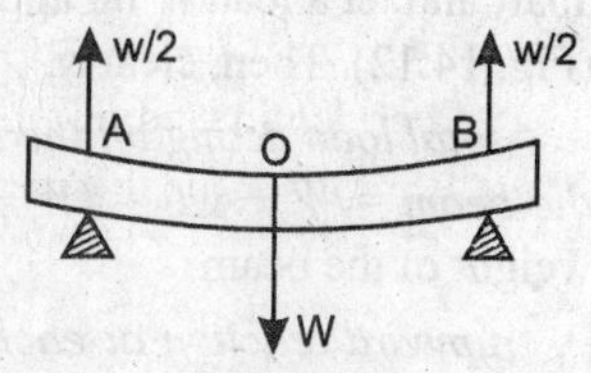

Fig. 14.10

The upward reaction at each knife-edge being $W/2$ and the middle part of the beam being sensibly horizontal, it may be taken to be a combination of two inverted cantilevers OA and OB, each of effective length $L/2$, fixed at O and bending upwards under a load $W/2$ acting at A and B. Clearly, then, the elevation of A or B above O, or the depression of O below A and B is given by

$$y = \frac{(W/2)(L/2)^3}{3YI_g} = \frac{WL^3}{48YI_g}. \quad \ldots(i)[\S \text{ Fig. 14.7}(i)]$$

If, therefore, the beam be of a *circular cross-section*, of *radius r*, so that $I_g = \pi r^4/4$, we have

$$y = \frac{WL^3}{48Y}\left(\frac{4}{\pi r^4}\right) = \frac{WL^3}{12Y\pi r^4}. \quad \ldots(ii)$$

And, if the cross-section of the beam be *rectangular,* of *breadth b* and *depth d*, so that $I_g = bd^3/12$, we have

$$y = \frac{WL^3}{48Y}\left(\frac{12}{bd^3}\right) = \frac{WL^3}{4Ybd^3}. \quad \ldots(iii)$$

Alternatively, we could obtain expression (i) for y directly as follow. Considering the section PB of the cantilever OB, say, distant)x from its fixed end O, (Fig. 14.11) we have

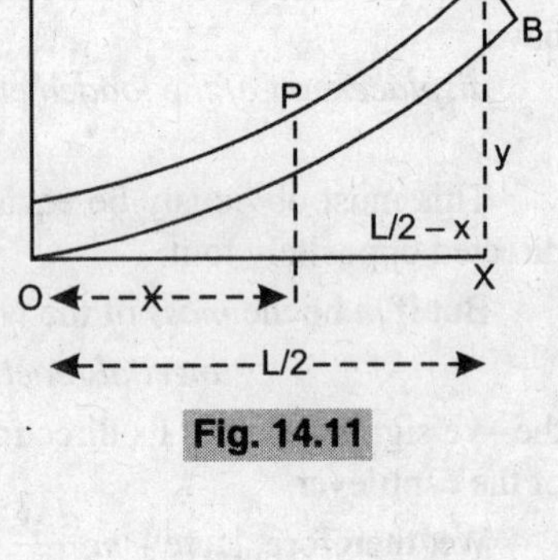

Fig. 14.11

moment of bending couple due to lot

$$W/2 = \frac{W}{2}\left(\frac{L}{2} - x\right)$$

The beam being in equilibrium, must be just balanced by the *bending moment* (or the moment of the resistance to bending). YI_g/R where R is the radius of curvature of the section at P, (§14.5).

We, therefore, have
$$\frac{YI_g}{R} = YI_g\frac{d^2y}{dx^2} = \frac{W}{2}\left(\frac{L}{2} - x\right),$$

which on integration gives
$$\frac{dy}{dx} = \frac{W}{2YI_g}\left(L\frac{x}{2} - \frac{x^2}{2}\right) + C.$$

Since at $x = 0$, $dy/dx = 0$, we have $C = 0$ and, therefore,

$$\frac{dy}{dx} = \frac{W}{2YI_g}\left(L\frac{x}{2} - \frac{x^2}{2}\right). \text{ Or, } dy = \frac{W}{2YI_g}\left(L\frac{x}{2} - \frac{x^2}{2}\right)dx,$$

which, on further integration between the limits $x = 0$ and $x = L/2$, gives

$$y = \frac{W}{2YI_g}\left[\frac{L^3}{16} - \frac{L^3}{48}\right] = \frac{WL^3}{48YI_g},$$

the same expression as (i) above.

And, clearly, slope of : A, B and hence also that of A, relative O (or their angle of integration θ to, the horizontal) is given by

$$\tan\theta = \theta = \left(\frac{dy}{dx}\right)L/2 = \frac{W}{2YI_g}\left(\frac{L^2}{4} - \frac{L^2}{8}\right) = \frac{WL^2}{16YI_g}$$

(b) When the weight of the beam is effective. Let the beam, of weight w per unit length be resting in a horizontal plane on two knifeedges A and B distance L apart and let a load W be applied to it at its mid-point O, (Fig. 14.12). Then, clearly,

total load acting on the beam at 0 = W + *weight of the beam* = $W + wL = (W + W_0)$, where $wL = W_0$, the weight of the beam.

$\therefore$ *upward reaction at each knife-edge* = $(W + W_0)/2$, as shown.

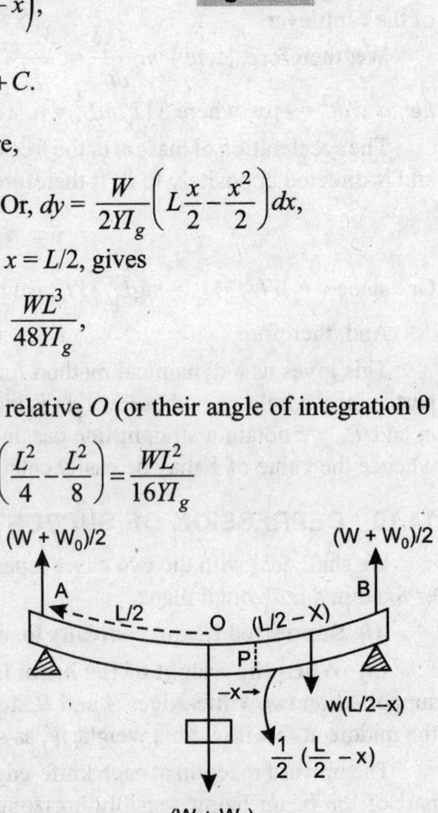

Fig. 14.12

Now, as in case (*a*), so also here, the beam behaves as a combination of two cantilevers *OA* and *OB*, each of length $L/2$ and fixed at 0, with a load $(W + W_0)/2$ acting upwards at their free ends *A* and *B*. The elevation of *A* or *B* above *O* thus gives the depression *y* of the centre *O* of the beam below *A* or *B*.

Considering a section *PB* of the cantilever *OB*, distant *x* from the fixed end *O*, we have *weight of section PB of the beam* $= w\left(\frac{L}{2} - x\right)$, acting vertically downwards midway between *P* and *B*, *i.e.*, at a distance $\frac{1}{2}\left(\frac{L}{2} - x\right)$ from *P* or *B*, as indicated.

Taking moment about *P*, we have

moment of $(W + W_0)/2$ *about* $P = \left(\frac{W + W_0}{2}\right)\left(\frac{L}{2} - x\right)$ *anticlockwise.*

And moment of $w\left[\frac{L}{2} - x\right]$ *about* $P = \frac{1}{2}w\left[\frac{L}{2} - x\right]\left[\frac{L}{2} - x\right] = \frac{w}{2}\left[\frac{L}{2} - x\right]^2$, *clockwise.*

$\therefore$ *resultant moment about* $P = \frac{W + W_0}{2}\left[\frac{L}{2} - x\right] - \frac{w}{2}\left[\frac{L}{2} - x\right]^2$, tending to bend the beam in the anticlockwise direction.

Since the beam is in equilibrium, this must be just balanced by the *bending moments* YI_g/R, where *R* is the radius of curvature of the section at *P*. We therefore, have

$$\frac{YI_g}{R} = YI_g\frac{d^2y}{dx^2} = \frac{W + W_0}{2}\left[\frac{L}{2} - x\right] - \frac{w}{2}\left[\frac{L}{2} - x\right]^2,$$

which, on integration, gives

$$2YI_g\frac{dy}{dx} = [W + W_0]\left[\frac{Lx}{2} - \frac{x^2}{2}\right] - w\left[\frac{L^2x}{4} - \frac{Lx^2}{2} + \frac{x^3}{3}\right] + C.$$

Since at $x = 0$, $dy/dx = 0$, we have $C = 0$ and, therefore, on integrating again between the limits $x = 0$ and $x = L/2$, we have

$$2YI_g y = [W + W_0]\int_0^{L/2}\left[\frac{Lx}{2} - \frac{x^2}{2}\right]dx - w\int_0^{L/2}\left[\frac{L^2x}{4} - \frac{Lx^2}{2} + \frac{x^3}{3}\right]dx$$

$$= [W + W_0]\left[\frac{Lx^2}{4} - \frac{x^3}{6}\right]_0^{L/2} - w\left[\frac{L^2x^2}{8} - \frac{Lx^3}{6} + \frac{x^4}{12}\right]_0^{L/2}$$

$$= [W + W_0]\left[\frac{L^3}{24}\right] - wL\left[\frac{3L^3}{192}\right]$$

$$= \frac{L^3}{24}\left[W + W_0 - \frac{3}{8}W_0\right]. \qquad [\because wL = W_0.]$$

Or, $$y = \frac{L^3}{48YI_g}\left[W + \frac{5}{8}W_0\right]$$

Thus, *the weight of the beam has the effect of increasing the effective load on the beam by 5/8 of its own value.*

(*ii*) Supported beam uniformly loaded. As before, let the beam be resting in a horizontal plane on two knife-edges *A* and *B*, distance *L* apart, (Fig. 14.13). Then, if *w* be the load per unit length the beam (including its own weight), the total load on it is $wL = W$, acting at its mid-point *O* and, therefore, upward reaction at each knife-edge is $W/2$, as shown.

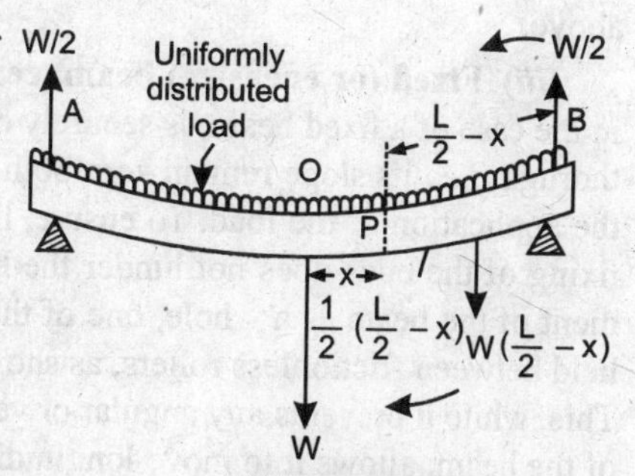

Fig. 14.13

As in cases (*i*) (*a*) and (*b*), the beam behaves as a combination of two cantilevers *OA* and *OB*, each of length *L*/2, with its end *O* fixed and with a load *W*/2 acting upwards at its other end *A* or *B* above the fixed end) gives the depression *y* of the mid-point *O* of the beam below *A* or *B*.

Considering again a section *PB* of the cantilever *OB*, distant *x* from *O*, we have weight of the section *PB*, equal to $w\left[\frac{L}{2}-x\right]$ acting vertically downwards at its mid-point, *i.e.*, at a distance $\frac{1}{2}\left(\frac{L}{2}-x\right)$ from *P* or *B*. We, therefore, have

moment of $\frac{W}{2}$ *(at B) about P* = $\frac{W}{2}\left[\frac{L}{2}-x\right]$, *anticlockwise,* and *moment of* $w\left[\frac{L}{2}-x\right]$ *about* $P=\frac{1}{2}w\left[\frac{L}{2}-x\right]\left[\frac{L}{2}-x\right]=\frac{w}{2}\left[\frac{L}{2}-x\right]^2$, *closckwise.*

∴ *resultant moment about P*, tending to bend the cantilever anticlockwise

$$=\frac{W}{2}\left[\frac{L}{2}-x\right]-\frac{w}{2}\left[\frac{L}{2}-x\right]^2.$$

Since the cantilever is in equilibrium in its bent position, this must just be balanced by the bending moment (or the moment of the resistance to bending) YI_g/R, where *R* is the radius of curvature of the section at *P*. Thus,

$$\frac{YI_g}{R}=YI_g\frac{d^2y}{dx^2}=\frac{W}{2}\left[\frac{L}{2}-x\right]-\frac{w}{2}\left[\frac{L}{2}-x\right]^2,$$ which, on integration gives $2YI_g\frac{dy}{dx}=W\left[\frac{Lx}{2}-\frac{x^2}{2}\right]-w\left[\frac{L^2x}{4}-\frac{Lx^2}{2}+\frac{x^3}{3}\right]+C.$

Since at $x = 0$, $dy/dx = 0$, we have $C = 0$. So that, integrating again between the limits $x = 0$ and $x = L/2$, we have

$$2YI_gy=W\int_0^{L/2}\left[\frac{Lx}{2}-\frac{x^2}{2}\right]dx-w\int_0^{L/2}\left(\frac{L^2x}{4}-\frac{Lx^2}{2}+\frac{x^3}{3}\right]dx$$

$$=W\left[\frac{L^3}{24}\right]-W\left[\frac{3L^2}{192}\right]=\frac{WL^3}{24}\left[1-\frac{3}{8}\right], \qquad [\because wL=W]$$

whence,
$$y=\frac{5}{8}\frac{WL^3}{48YI_g},$$

showing that *the depression y is 5/8 of that when the same load is applied centrally.* In other words, *the stiffness of the beam now increases to 8/5 or 1.6 times its value in the former case.*

If there be *no load placed on the beam,* we have $W = W_0$, the weight of the beam itself and, therefore, $y=\frac{5}{8}\frac{W_0L^3}{48YI_g}$, which thus gives the *depression of the beam when bending under its own weight.* As will be readily seen, we obtain the same expression for *y* by putting $W = 0$ in case (*i*) (*b*) above.

***(iii)* Fixed (or encastre) beam, centrally loaded.** As already pointed out (§ 14.1), each end, in the case of a fixed beam, is securely clamped or built into a wall, so that it remains horizontal all thorugh, *i.e.*, its slope remain zero both before and after the application of the load. To ensure, however, that the fixing of the ends does not hinder the horizontal movement of the beam as a whole, one of the ends is usually held between frictionless rollers, as shown in Fig. 14.14. This, while it prevents any angular or vertical movement of the beam, allows it to move longitudinally.

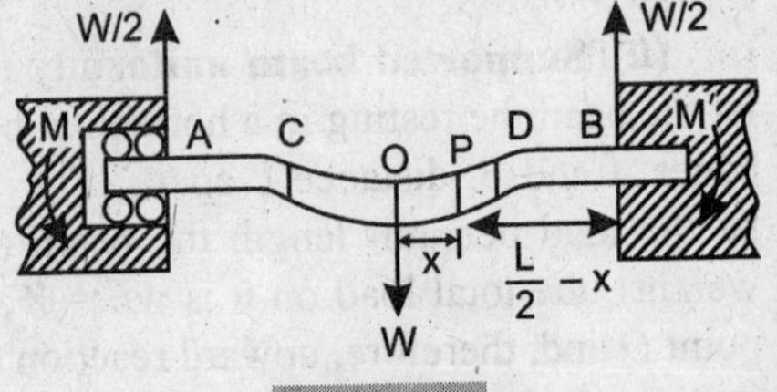

Fig. 14.14

If the beam were simply supported at the ends, as in case (*i*)(*a*), (Fig. 14.10), the centrally applied load would bend the entire beam, *including the ends*, so as to be concave upwards. In order to keep the ends horizontal, as here, therefore, a couple must be applied in the opposite direction to that due to the load. This couple is provided by the clamp or the built-in support and is called the **fixing moment**. The beam being symmetrical, its magnitude is the same at either end, say, M'.

Now, as the load W is applied to the centre O of the beam, it tends to bend the beam into a curve, *concave upwards*, but the fixing moment M', which is effective all over the beam, tends to bend it into a curve concave *downwards*. As a result, the beam assumes a shape such that *its middle part CD is concave upwards and its parts AC and BD between it and the two ends are concave downwards, with well-marked points of inflexion at C and D on either side of, and equidistant from, its centre O and where, obviously, the slope* (*dy/dx*) *is the maximum* (because the curvature of the beam changes sign there).

Again, considering a section PB of the right half of the beam, distant x from its mid-point O and remembering that there is an upward reaction $W/2$ at A and B, we have

moment of the bending couple due to the applied load about P

$$= \frac{W}{2}\left(\frac{L}{2} - x\right).$$

Since the fixing moment M is directed oppositely to it, we have

$$\textit{resultant moment of the bending couple about } P = \frac{W}{2}\left[\frac{L}{2} - x\right] - M'$$

For equilibrium of the beam in its bent position, this must just be balanced by the bending moment (or the moment of the resistance to bending) YI_g/R, where R is the radius of curvature of the section at P. We, therefore, have

$$\frac{YI_g}{R} = YI_g\frac{d^2y}{dx^2} = \frac{W}{2}\left[\frac{L}{2} - x\right] - M', \qquad \ldots(i)$$

which, on integration, gives $YI_g\dfrac{dy}{dx} = \dfrac{W}{2}\left[\dfrac{Lx}{2} - \dfrac{x^2}{2}\right] - M'x + C.$

Since at $x = 0$, $dy/dx = 0$, we have $C = 0$, and therefore,

$$YI_g\frac{dy}{dx} = \frac{W}{2}\left[\frac{Lx}{2} - \frac{x^2}{2}\right] - M'x. \qquad \ldots(ii)$$

Now, at $x = L/2$, *i.e.*, at the end B of the beam also, $dy/dx = 0$. So that,

$$0 = \frac{W}{2}\left[\frac{L}{2}\left(\frac{L}{2}\right) - \frac{(L/2)^2}{2}\right] - \frac{M'L}{2}. \text{ Or, } \frac{M'L}{2} = \frac{W}{2}\left[\frac{L^2}{8}\right]$$

whence, $M' = WL/8.$

Substituting this value of M in relation (*ii*), we have

$$YI_g\frac{dy}{dx} = \frac{W}{2}\left[\frac{Lx}{2} - \frac{x^2}{2}\right] - \frac{WLx}{8}. \qquad \ldots(iii)$$

Therefore, maximum elevation or the elevation of end B above O, or what is the same thing, *depression y of mid-point O of the beam below the ends A and B,* is obtained by integrating expression (*iii*) for the limits $x = 0$ and $x = L/2$. Thus,

$$YI_g y = \frac{W}{2}\int_0^{L/2}\left(\frac{Lx}{2} - \frac{x^2}{2}\right)dx - WL\int_0^{L/2}\frac{x}{8}dx.$$

$$= \frac{W}{2}\left[\frac{Lx^2}{4} - \frac{x^3}{6}\right]_0^{L/2} - WL\left[\frac{x^2}{16}\right]_0^{L/2}$$

$$= WL^3\left(\frac{1}{32}-\frac{1}{96}-\frac{1}{64}\right)=\frac{WL^3}{192}.$$

$$\therefore \quad y=\frac{WL^3}{192YI_g}=\frac{1}{4}\frac{WL^3}{48YI_g},$$

i.e., the depression of the mid-point of the beam is one-fourth of that when it is simply supported at the ends.

This means, in other words, *that the stiffness of the beam, when its ends are fixed, is four times that when the ends are simply supported.*

Further, as we have just seen,

moment of bending couple about P distant x from 0

$$=\frac{W}{2}\left(\frac{L}{2}-x\right)-M'.$$

Now, $M' = WL/8$ and for the mid-point O of the beam, $x = 0$.

∴ *moment of bending couple about the mid-point of the beam*

$$=\frac{W}{2}\left(\frac{L}{2}-0\right)-\frac{WL}{8}=\frac{WL}{8}$$

On the other hand, *when the beam is simply supported at the ends, the moment of the bending couple about the mid-point of the beam.*

$$=\frac{W}{2}\left(\frac{L}{2}-0\right)=\frac{WL}{4}$$

Thus, *fixing the ends of the beam reduces the moment of the bending couple to half the value it would have if the ends are simply supported.* So that, for the same value of the bending couple ($WL/4$), the fixed beam can take twice the load that can be taken by the supported beam. In other words, *the strength of a beam, when fixed, is twice that when it is merely supported.*

Positions of points of inflexation. The positions of the points of inflexion C and D may be easily obtained from the fact that because of the curvature changing sign at these points, the slope dy/dx is the maximum there and hence the rate of change of slope, $d^2y/dx^2 = 0$.

Thus, putting $d^2y/dx^2 = 0$ in relation (*i*) above and substituting the value of $M' = WL/8$, we have

$$0=\frac{W}{2}\left(\frac{L}{2}-x\right)-\frac{WL}{8}. \text{ Or, } \frac{WL}{4}-\frac{WL}{8}=\frac{Wx}{2}, \text{ whence, } x = L/4$$

This gives the point D at a distance $L/4$ from O and hence also $L/4$ from B.

Similarly, point C lies at a distance $L/4$ from O to the left or $L/4$ from A.

The net *m* is thus, in effect, a combination of a central beam of length $L/2$, with a pair of cantilevers, each of length $L/4$, on either side, with the loading as shown in Fig. 14.15.

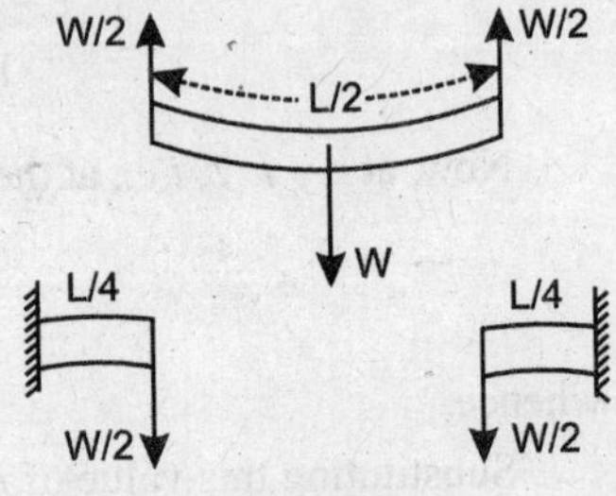

Fig. 14.15

14.11 SHAPE OF GIRDERS

It will be noted that in all the various cases of bending of beams discussed above, the depression of the beam (y) is proportional to W^3/YI_g. Since for a beam of rectangular cross-section, $I_g = bd^3/12$, we have

$$y \propto WL^3/Ybd^3.$$

Thus, for a given load (W), the depression (y) is *directly proportional to* (*its length*)^3 *and inversely proportional to its breadth,* (*depth*)^3 *and the value of Young's modulus* (Y) *for its material.*

For the depression (y) to be small for a given load (W), therefore, the length or span of the girder should be small and its breadth and depth large, as also the Young's modulus for its material.

Since in a supported or fixed beam, the middle portion gets depressed, its upper and lower halves, (above and below the neutral surface) get compressed and extended respectively. These compressions and extensions, and hence the corresponding stresses, are, as we know, the maximum at the upper and the lower surfaces and progressively decrease to zero as we approach the neutral surface from either face. Obviously, therefore, the upper and the lower surfaces of the beam must be stronger than the intervening part. That is why the two surfaces of a girder or iron rails (for railway tracks etc.) are made much broader than the rest of it, thus giving its cross-section the shape of the letter *I*.

This naturally effects a good deal of saving in the material of the girder, without appreciably impairing its strength.

14.12 DETERMINATION OF YOUNG'S MODULUS FOR THE MATERIAL OF A BEAM—METHOD OF BENDING

As can be readily seen, any one of the expressions for the depression (y) of a supported or a fixed been under an applied load may be used to obtain the value of Young's modulus (Y) for its material, if we can accurately measure y for a known load W and if the physical dimensions of the beam (*i.e.*, its length, breadth and depth) be known.

1. Simple Laboratory Method. We use a light beam of a rectangular cross-section for the purpose, supported at its two ends and loaded centrally (case *i*(*a*), § 14.10), when, measuring y, we may use relation (*iii*) to calculate Y for the material of the beam.

The arrangement will be easily understood from Fig. 14.16(*a*) which shows the beam supported symmetrically in the horizontal plane on two knife-edges, placed parallel to each other, a known distance L apart, with the load applied at its mid-point by placing suitable weights in a scale pan, also supported on a knife-edge. The depression y of the mid-point is noted directly on a micrometer screw placed on the beam, as shown or, with greater precision, with the help of a microscope fitted with a micrometer eye-piece, carrying cross wires. [Fig. 14.16(*b*)].

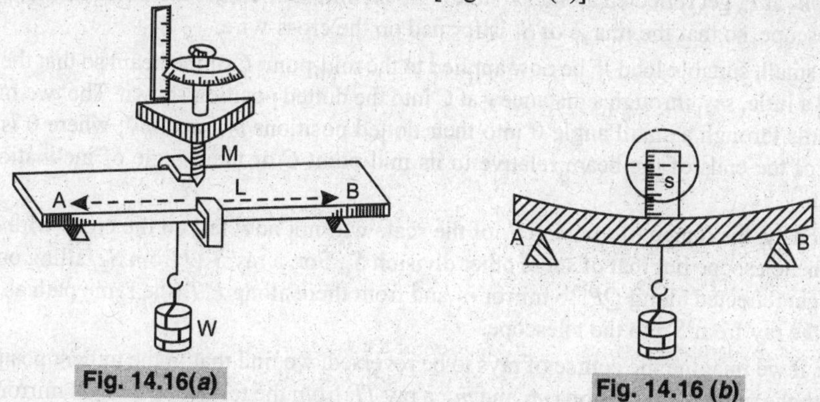

Fig. 14.16(*a*) Fig. 14.16 (*b*)

The procedure consists in first increasing the load in equal steps W and then decreasing it in the same equal steps and noting the values of y in each case. The mean of all these readings is then taken to be the correct value of y for a load W. Then, from the relation $y = WL^3/4\ Ybd^3$ we have $Y = WL^3/4ybd^3$ and the value of Y for the material of the beam thus easily obtained.

The method, though simple enough, suffers from the following drawbacks:

(*i*) *The depression of the beam cannot be measured sufficiently accurately.*

(*ii*) *Fairly large loads are required to be used to produce a measurable depression and the elastic limit may possibly get exceeded, resulting in permanent damage to the beam.*

(iii) *With increasing load applied to the beam, the knife-edges may bite into it, thereby seriously affecting the readings taken.*

All these defect have been removed in *König's method* which we shall now proceed to discuss.

2. König's method. König's devised, in the year 1885, a method in which the depression of the beam is not measured directly but obtained from the slope of its ends or their inclination to the horizontal. This angle of inclination can be measured far more accurately by the scale and telescope method than the depression of the beam. Also much smaller loads can be used, thereby eliminating the possibility of the elastic limit being exceeded or of the knife-edges biting into the beam.

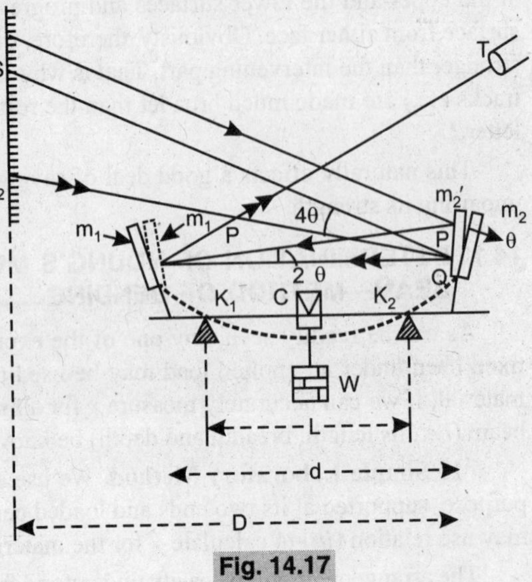

Fig. 14.17

The beam, mounted on two knife-edges K_1 and K_2 distance L apart, carries two plane-mirror pieces m_1 and m_2 near its two ends, a *small equal distance* beyond the knife-edges, such that they are inclined slightly outwards from the vertical (Fig. 14.17.)

A suitable load W can be placed on a hanger pivoted on the beam at its mid-point C (*i.e.*, midway between the two knife edges).

An illuminated translucent scale and a telescope (T) are arranged, as shown, so that a ray of light proceeding from a division on the scale first gets reflected at mirror m_2 and then at m_1 and from there on to the telescope where the image of the scale division is brought into sharp focus on a cross wire of the eye-piece.

To start with, *i.e.*, with no load yet applied to the beam, let a ray S_1P from a scale division S_1 fall on mirror m_2 at P, get reflected along PP' to to fall on mirror m_1 and P and from there, along $P'T$ on to the telescope, so that the image of S_1 is formed on the cross-wire.

Let a small, suitable load W be now applied to the mid-point C of the beam so that the beam gets depressed a little, say, through a distance y at C into the dotted position shown. The two mirrors then turn inwards through a small angle θ into their dotted positions m_1' and m_2', where θ is obviously the slope of the ends of the beam relative to its mid-point C or their angle of inclination with the horizontal.

Obviously, the image of division S_1 of the scale will not now fall on the cross-wire of the eye-piece of the telescope but that of some other division S_2. For, a ray S_2Q from S_2 falling on mirror m_2 at Q will get reflected along QP' to mirror n_1 and from there along $P'T$ (the same path as previously taken by the ray from S_1) to the telescope.

Now, if we imagine the course of rays to be reversed, we find that in the unbent positions of the beam, with the mirrors in positions m_1 and m_2, a ray TP from the telescope falls on mirror m_1 and P', reflected along PP' to mirror m_2 and from there along PS_1 to meet the scale in S_1.

In the bent position of the beam, with the mirrors in position m_1' and m_2', the same ray TP' from T, falling on mirror m_1 at P', is reflected along $P'Q$. Since mirror m_1' has turned through angle θ, the ray $P'Q$ is turned through angle 2θ, *i.e.*, $< PP'Q = 2\theta$. This ray ($P'Q$) now falls on mirror m_2' which too has turned through angle θ, so that the reflected ray QS_2 corresponding to the incident ray $P'Q$, turns through angle 2θ. Since ray $P'Q$ has already turned through angle 2θ due to reflection at m_1, the angle through which the reflected ray QS_2 turns in $2\theta + 2\theta = 4\theta$, *i.e.*, makes an angle 4θ with the first reflected ray PS_1 or with QS, where QS is drawn parallel to PS_1. Thus,

$\angle SQS_2 = 4\theta$ and $\therefore$ distance $SS_2 = 4\theta.(D)$,

where D is the distance between mirror m_2 and the scale.

And, since $\angle PP'Q = 2\theta$, we have $PQ = 2\theta(d) = S_1S$ $\quad [\because QS \parallel PS_1]$

where d is the distance between the two mirrors.

$\therefore$ distance $S_1S_2 = s$, say, between the two scale divisions S_1 and S_2, whose images are received on the cross wire of the telescope eye-piece before and after the bending of the beam respectively, is given by

$$s = S_1S_2 = S_1S + SS_2 = 2\theta(d) + 4\theta(D) = 2\theta(d + 2D),$$

whence,
$$\theta = \frac{s}{2(d+2D)}$$

But, as we have seen in § 14.10, $\theta = WL^2/16YI_g$, where the symbols have their usual meanings. We there have

$$\frac{s}{2(d+2D)} = \frac{WL^2}{16YI_g},$$

whence,
$$Y = \frac{(d+2D)L^2}{8I_g}\left(\frac{W}{s}\right) \quad \text{...(I)}$$

As we know, in the case of a beam of *rectangular cross-section*, $I_g = bd^3/12$ and

$$\therefore \quad Y = \frac{3}{2}\frac{(d+2D)L^2}{bd^3}\left(\frac{W}{s}\right). \quad \text{...}(i)$$

And, in the case of a beam of *circular cross-section*,

$$I_g = \pi r^2/4.$$

So that, in this case, $Y = \dfrac{(d+2D)L^2}{2\pi r^4}\left(\dfrac{W}{s}\right)$ $\quad$ ...(*ii*)

In actual practice, we gradually increase the load (W) and note the corresponding value of s and then plot s against W, when we obtain a straight line graph passing through the origin. The slope of the straight line gives the mean value of (W/s) and this is substituted in relation (*i*) or (*ii*) for Y above, as the case may be.

14.13 DETERMINATION OF ELASTIC CONSTANTS

(*i*) Searle's method for the material or a wire. *G.F.C.* Searle devised, in the year 1900, a simple method for the determination of elastic constants of an *isotropic material in the form of a wire.*

A short length of the given wire (w) is fastened to the mid-points P_1 and P_2 of two identical metal bars AB and CD, suspended from points directly above P_1 and P_2 by means of two equal lengths of *cotton* threads, each about a metre long, (so that the torsional couple set up in the suspension threads may be negligibly small).

Initially the bars, which are chosen to be of a circular or rectangular cross-section, (so that their *M.I.* about their respective suspension threads may be easily obtained from their mass and physical dimensions), lie parallel to each other, with the wire w quite straight and horizontal, as shown in Fig. 14.18(*a*).

To determine the elastic constants for the material of the wire, we then proceed as follows:

(*a*) Determination of *Y*. The ends A and C of the two bars respectively are pulled symmetrically inwards through small equal distances so that the wire gets bent into a circular arc of radius R, as shown in Fig. 14.18(*b*), and then released.

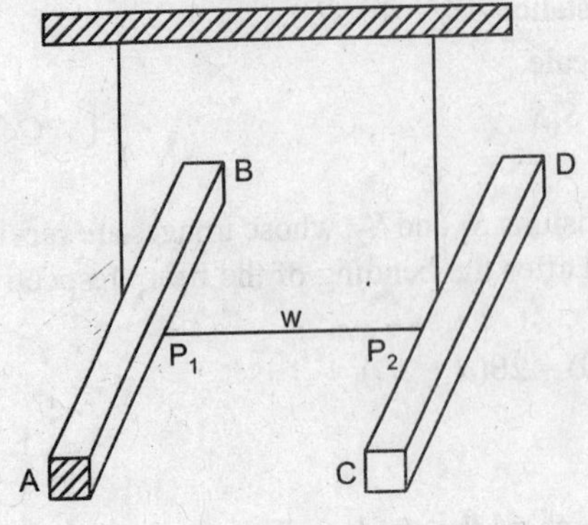

Fig. 14.18 (*a*)

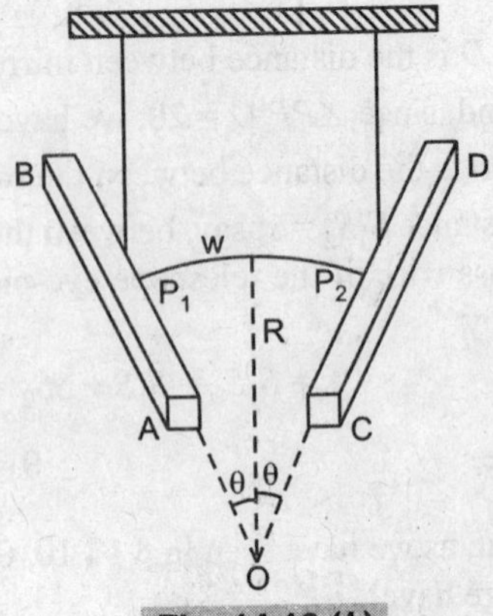

Fig. 14.18 (*b*)

Due to the torque exerted by the wire, the two bars are thus set oscillating in a horizontal plane about their respective suspension threads, with the wire forming an arc first facing one side and then the other, the mid-points of the bars remaining practically at rest and the bending moment at all transverse sections of the wire constant.

If L be the length of the wire and θ, the angle through which each other has been pulled in from its initial position, clearly,

angle subtended by the circular arc at its centre $O = 2\theta$,

and we, therefore, have $L = R.2.\theta$, whence, $R = L/2\theta$.

Now, *bending moment of the wire*, $M = YI_g/R$,

where I_g is the geometrical *M.I.* of the cross-section of the wire, equal to $\pi r^4/4$, (r being the *radius of the wire*).

Substituting the values of I_g and R, therefore, we have

$$M = \frac{Y\pi r^4}{4}.\frac{2\theta}{L} = \frac{Y\pi r^4}{2L}\theta.$$

This being equal to the *restoring couple* acting on each bar, its *equation of motion* is

$$M + Id\omega/dt = 0,$$

where $d\omega/dt$ is the angular acceleration produced in each bar and I, its *M.I.* about the axis through its mid-point and perpendicular to its length, *i.e.*, about its suspension thread.

So that, $Id\omega/dt = -M = -\dfrac{Y\pi r^4}{2L}\theta = -\mu\theta$. Or, $d\omega/dt \propto \theta$ [where $Y\pi r^4/2\,LI = \mu$]

Each bar thus executes a *simple harmonic motion* of a time-period given by

$$T_1 = 2\pi\sqrt{1/\mu} = 2\pi\sqrt{2LI/Y\pi r^4},$$

whence,

$$Y = 8\pi LI/r^4 T_1^2.$$

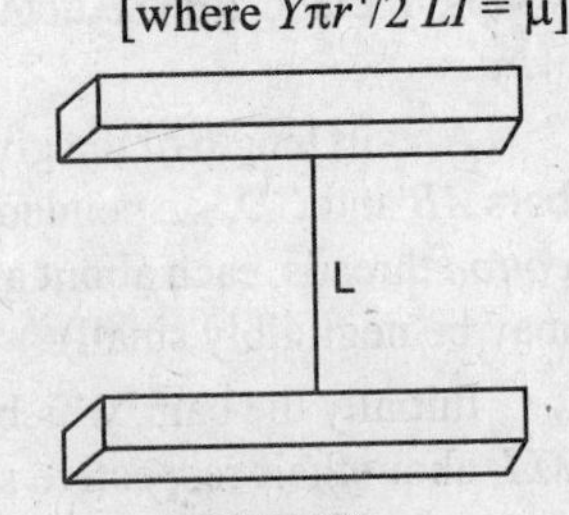

Fig. 14.19

(*b*) Determination of *n*. Removing the suspension threads, one of the bars is clamped horizontally, and the other hangs freely from it at the other end of the wire so as to be free to rotate in the horizontal plane, as shown in Fig. 14.19.

The suspended bar is then turned a little in its own (*i.e.*, horizontal) plane and released, when it executes torsional oscillations about the wire, with its time-period given by

$$T_2 = 2\pi\sqrt{I/C},$$

where C is the torsional couple per unit twist of the wire, equal to $n\pi r^4/2L$.

So that, $T_2 = 2\pi\sqrt{I.2L/n\pi r^4}$, whence, $n = 8\pi LI/r^4T_2^2$ and may be easily evaluated.

(c) Determination of σ. As we know, *Poisson's ratio* $\sigma = (Y/2n) - 1$. Substituting for Y and n, therefore, we have

$$\sigma = \frac{T_2^2}{2T_1^2} - 1 = \frac{T_2^2 - 2T_1^2}{2T_1^2}.$$

(d) Determination of K. The value of *bulk modulus* K for the material of the wire may either be obtained form the relation

$$\frac{9}{Y} = \frac{3}{n} + \frac{1}{K},$$

whence, $K = nY/(9n - 3Y)$ or from the relation $K = Y/3(1 - 2\sigma)$, whence we have

$$K = \frac{8\pi LI}{3r^4(3T_1^2 - T_2^2)}.$$

Thus, all the four elastic constants, Y, n, K and σ, for the material of the wire may be easily obtained.

It will be noted that the method has the merit of (*i*) *requiring only a short length* (*just a few centimetres*) *of the wire* and (*ii*) *giving the value of σ in terms of two accurately measurable quantities T_1 and T_2*, eliminating altogether the chief source of error, namely, the measurement of the radius (r) of the wire.

(*ii*) Cornu's optical method for a glass plate or a metal beam. A sensitive optical method, based on the phenomenon of interference of light, was devised by *Cornu* in the year 1869 for the determination of the elastic constants of a material in the form of a beam. The method is obviously applicable to substances like glass or metals which can take a high polish. It is particularly suited for glass which can be subjected to only small stresses with safety.

The glass plate or the metal beam, with its upper surface highly polished is supported *symmetrically* on two knife-edges K_1 and K_2 in a horizontal plane, with the knife-edges normal to the axis of the plate (or the beam) and an *optically plane* cover glass G placed on it at its mid-point O, [Fig. 14.20].

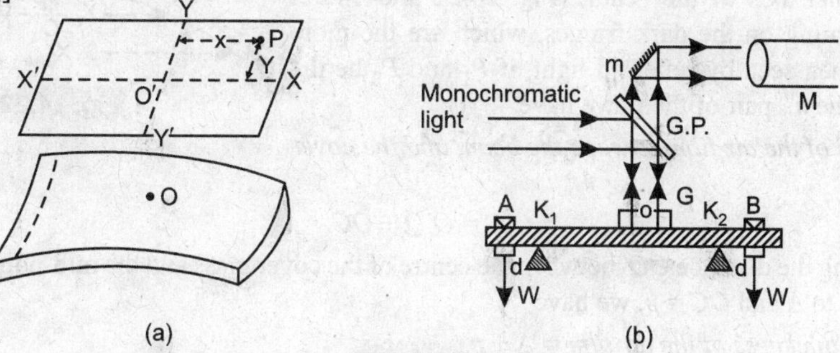

Fig. 14.20

The beam (or the plate) is then subjected to a *uniform bending couple Wd* by suspending equal weights W and W from it at A and B, a little outside the two knife-edges at an equal distance d from them, as shown. Thus loaded, the beam experiences no shear anywhere between the two knife-edges and the bending couple is uniform all over in this portion. It thus undergoes a pure or simple bending about the mid-point O, with its longitudinal axis concave downwards, having a radius of curvature R_1, say.

This, as we know, is accompanied by the transverse axis of the beam acquiring an anticlastic curvature or a curvature in the opposite direction to that of the longitudinal axis, *i.e.*, it becomes concave upwards, as shown in Fig. 14.20(*a*),* having a radius of curvature R_2.

*That the bending couple is uniform between the knife-edges may be seen by taking moments about any arbitrarily

So that, although the mid-point O' of the lower surface of the cover glass still lies vertically above the mid-point O of the upper surface of the beam, the two no longer remain in contact and a thin film air is formed between them.

If, therefore, a parallel beam of monochromatic light from a suitable source like a sodium lamp is allowed to fall normally on the film by reflecting it downwards by means of a glass plate *G.P.*, interference fringes are formed due to reflection of light from the upper and lower surfaces of the film (or, what is the same thing from the lower surface of the cover glass and the upper surface of the beam or the glass plate). These fringes are localised in the film itself and may be observed by means of a long-focus travelling microscope M arranged vertically above or, more conveniently, by deflecting the rays through 90° by means of a plane mirror m and arranging the microscope horizontally to receive them, as indicated in the Figure above.

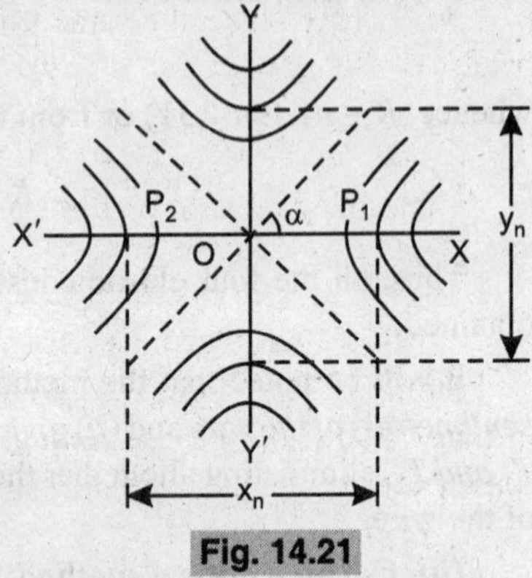

Fig. 14.21

Although the interference fringes formed *in this case* consist of two conjugate sets of rectangular hyperbolae, shown diagrammatically in Fig. 14.21, (see note on the shape of interference fringes formed), their actual shape or the actual position of the centre of fringe system is really quite immaterial for our purpose. The only relevant point is that the distances between any two pairs of conjugate fringes along and across the beam, measured by a horizontal and a vertical travel of the microscope respectively, enable us to obtain the radii R_1 and R_2 of the longitudinal and transverse sections of the beam respectively, and hence to calculate the values of the elastic constants of the material of the beam, as explained hereunder.

Calculations

(*i*) For Poisson's ratio, σ. Considering the conjugate set of hyperbolic fringes formed along the direction of the longitudinal axis of the beam, (Fig. 14.21 and 14.22) and concentrating on the dark fringes, which are the more prominent when seen by reflected light, if P_1 and P_2 be the positions of the nth pair of them, we have

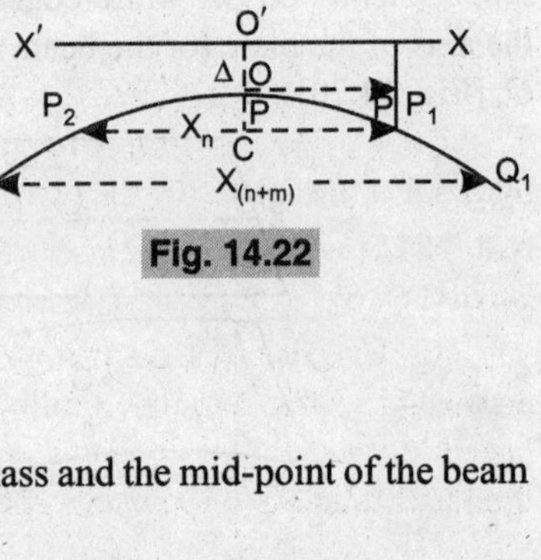

Fig. 14.22

thickness of the air film between the beam and the cover glass

$$= O'C = O'O + OC.$$

Or, putting the distance OO' between the centre of the cover glass and the mid-point of the beam surface equal to Δ and $OC = p$, we have

thickness of the air film $= \Delta + p$.

Now, clearly, $OC(2R_1 - OC) = CP_1 \times CP_2$. Or, $p(2R_1 - p) = (X_n/2)^2$ where R_1 is the radius of curvature of the bent beam, or rather of the neutral axis of its longitudinal section, and $P_1P_2 = X_n$.

Or, $2R_1p - p^2 = X_n^2/4$. Or, neglecting p^2 compared with $2Rp$, we have

$$p = X_n^2/8R_1.$$

So that, *thickness of the enclosed air film* $= \Delta + p = \Delta + X_n^2/8R_1$.

$\therefore$ *path difference for the interfering rays* = 2(*thickness of the air film*)

chosen section P between the knife-edges [Fig. 14.20(*b*)], when we have

resultant moment at section $P = W(AP) - W(K_1P) = W(AP - K_1P) = Wd$,

which is clearly independent of the position of section P, showing that the moment of the bending couple is the same (Wd) at all sections of the beam between the two knife-edges.

$$= 2(\Delta + X_n^2/8R_1) = 2\Delta + X_n^2/8R_1. \quad (i)$$

The case being similar to that of Newton's rings, this path difference for a dark fringe must be equal to a whole number of wavelengths (λ) of the monochromatic light used (usually sodium light).

So that, $$2\Delta + \frac{X_n^2}{4R_1} = n\lambda.$$

Again, if $Q_1Q_2 = X_{(n+m)}$ be the distance between another conjugate pair of dark fringes of the $(n + m)^{th}$ order along the same direction (i.e., along the direction of the longitudinal axis of the beam), we have

$$2\Delta + \frac{X_{(n+m)}^2}{4R_1} = (n+m)\lambda \quad \ldots(ii)$$

Subtracting relation (*i*) from (*ii*) we have

$$\frac{X_{(n+m)}^2 - X_n^2}{4R_1} = m\lambda, \text{ whence, } R_2 = \frac{Y_{(n+m)}^2 - X_n^2}{4m\lambda} \quad \ldots(iii)$$

Similarly, if Y_n and $Y_{(n+m)}$ be the respective distances between a pair of conjugate dark fringes of the nth order and pair of conjugate dark fringes of the $(n + m)^{th}$ order along the direction of the transverse axis of the beam, we have, proceeding exactly as above,

$$\frac{Y_{(n+m)}^2 - Y_n^2}{4R_2} = m\lambda, \text{ whence, } R_2 = \frac{Y_{(n+m)}^2 - Y_n^2}{4m\lambda}. \quad \ldots(iv)$$

So that, $$\frac{R_1}{R_2} = \frac{X_{(n+m)}^2 - X_n^2}{Y_{(n+m)}^2 - Y_n^2}.$$

Thus, since $R_1/R_2 = \sigma$, *Poisson's ratio* for the material *of the beam,* we have

$$\sigma = \frac{X_{(n+m)}^2 - X_n^2}{Y_{(n+m)}^2 - Y_n^2} \quad \ldots(v)$$

Hence, measuring distances X_n and $X_{(n+m)}$ by moving the microscope horizontally and distances Y_n and $Y_{(n+m)}$ by moving it vertically, we can easily determine the value of *Poisson's ratio* for the material of the beam (or the glass plate).

N.B. We may also obtain the value of σ from the angle α from that the asymptotes in Fig. 14.21 make with the x-axis. For, $\sigma = R_1/R_2 = \cot^2\alpha$, where a can be measured by mass of a goniometer eye-piece.

***(ii)* For Young's modulus *Y*.** We know that the bending couple applied to the beam is uniform and equal to Wd. For the equilibrium of the beam in its bent position, therefore, this must be balanced by the bending moment or the moment of the resistance to bending. We, therefore, have for the longitudinal section of the beam,

$$Wd = YI_g\left(\frac{1}{R_1} - \frac{1}{R_0}\right), \quad \ldots(vi)$$

where $1/R_0$ is any slight curvature the beam may possibly have along this section on account of its own weight.

So that, $$YI_g/R_1 = Wd + YI_g/R_0.$$

Or, putting $YI_g/R_0 = \beta$ and substituting the value of R_1 from relation (*iii*) above, we have

$$YI_g \frac{4m\lambda}{X_{(n+m)}^2 - X_n^2} = Wd + \beta.$$

Or $$\frac{4mYI_g\lambda}{d}\left(\frac{1}{X_{(n+m)}^2 - X_n^2}\right) = W + \frac{\beta}{d}.$$

Again, putting $1/(X_{(n+m)}^2 - X_n^2) = x$ and $W = y$, we have

$$y = \frac{4mYI_g\lambda}{d}x - \frac{\beta}{d},$$

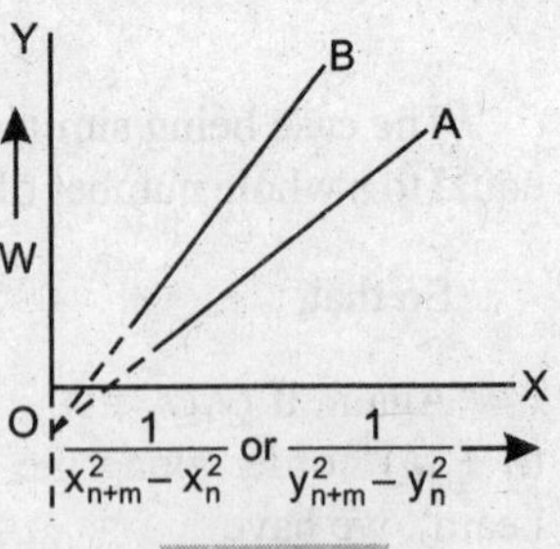

Fig. 14.23

which is the equation to a straight line, of slope $4mYI_g\lambda/d$ and intercepting the y-axis at $-\beta/d$.

If, therefore, we change the values of W in equal steps, obtain the corresponding values of $1/(X^2_{(n+m)} - X^2_n)$ and plot $y = W$ against $x = 1/(X^2_{(n+m)} - X^2_n)$, we obtain a straight line A (Fig. 14.23) intercepting the y-axis at β/d below the origin and having a slope = $4mYI_g\lambda/d$, whence the value of Y for the material of the beam can be easily calculated.

Now, since $R_1 = \sigma R_2$, we may put expression (vi) for Wd in terms of R_2 as

$$Wd = YI_g\left(\frac{1}{\sigma R_2} - \frac{1}{R_0}\right)$$

Or, $$\frac{YI_g}{\sigma}\left(\frac{1}{R_2}\right) = Wd + \frac{YI_g}{R_0} = Wd + \beta.$$

Or, substituting the value of R_2 from relation (iv) above, we have

$$\frac{YI_g}{\sigma}\left(\frac{4m\lambda}{Y^2_{(n+m)} - Y^2_n}\right) = Wd + \beta.$$

Or, $$\frac{4mYI_g\lambda}{\sigma d}\left(\frac{1}{Y^2_{(n+m)} - Y^2_n}\right) = W + \frac{\beta}{d}.$$

Again, putting $1/Y^2_{(n+m)} - Y^2_n) = x$ and $W = y$, we have

$$y = \frac{4mYI_g\lambda}{\sigma d}x - \frac{\beta}{d},$$

which is also equation to a straight line of slope $4mYI_g l/\sigma d$ and intercepting the y-axis at $-\beta/d$.

So that plotting $y = W$ against $x = 1/(Y^2_{(n+m)} - Y^2_n)$, we obtain a straight line B (Fig. 14.23), intercepting the y-axis at β/d below the origin, *i.e.*, at the same point as A, and having a slope = $4mYI_g\lambda/\sigma d$.

Clearly, therefore $$\frac{\textit{slope of A}}{\textit{slope of B}} = \frac{4mYI_g\lambda}{d}\bigg/\frac{4mYI_g\lambda}{\sigma d} = \sigma$$

Thus, the value σ for the material of the beam may also be obtained from the slopes of the two curves A and B.

Now, knowing σ and Y for the material of the beam, we can obtain the other two elastic constants K and n for it from the relations

$$K = Y/3(1 - 2\sigma) \text{ and } n = Y/2(1 + \sigma).$$ [See § Fig. 13.12]

Shape of interference fringes formed. As mentioned already, the actual shape of the interference fringes formed is of no consequence to us. Nevertheless, it may interest the student to see why they assume a hyperbolic shape in the case discussed above and how they may have other shapes as well.

In fig. 14.24, let EF and GH represent the longitudinal and transverse axes of the bent portion of the beam (or the glass plate) between the two knife edges, concave downwards and upwards respectively, with the tangent planes to them (shown dotted) touching the surface of the beam at its mid-point O. And, let $XO'X'$ and $YO'Y'$ represent the longitudinal an the transverse axes respectively of the undersurface of the cover glass.

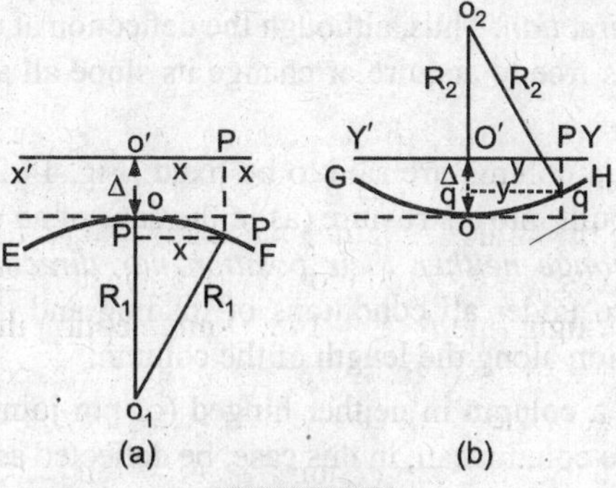

Fig. 14.24

As already pointed out, the mid-point O' of the cover glass lies vertically above the mid-point O of the beam but, in view of the anticlastic curvature of the latter, does not actually touch it. So that, the thickness of the *air film* at O or O' is not zero. Let it be equal to Δ.

And, at a point such as P (coordinates x, y), the thickness of the air film is increased by an amount p on account of the longitudinal curvature of the beam [Fig. 14.24(*a*)] and decreased by an amount q on account of its transverse curvature [Fig. 14.24(*b*)]. Its thickness at P is thus $(\Delta + p - q)$.

Now, from the geometry of Figure (*a*) we have

$$p(2R_1 - p) = x^2. \text{ Or, } 2R_1 p - p^2 = x^2.$$

p^2 being negligibly small compared with R_1, we have $p = x^2/2R_1$.

Similarly, from Fig. 14.24(*b*), we have $q = y^2/2R_2$, where R_1 and R_2, as we know, are the radii of curvature of the longitudinal and transverse sections of the beam respectively.

The thickness of the air film at P is thus $\Delta + (x^2/2R_1) - (y^2/2R_2)$.

Since an interference fringe is really the locus of points for which the optical path difference is the same, *i.e.*, for which the thickness of the air film is the same, we have

$$\Delta + \frac{x^2}{2R_1} - \frac{y^2}{2R_2} = \text{a constant, } k, \text{ say,} \qquad \text{...I}$$

And, therefore, $\dfrac{x^2}{2R_1 k} - \dfrac{y^2}{2R_2 k} = 1.$

Or putting $2R_1 k = a^2$ and $2R_2 k = b^2$, we have $\dfrac{x^2}{a^2} - \dfrac{y^2}{b^2} = 1$

which is the equation to a rectangular *hyperbola*.

The fringes formed are thus hyperbolic in shape, the whole interference pattern consisting of two conjugate sets of rectangular hyperbolae, as shown diagrammatically in Fig. 14.21.

If instead of a cover glass, we place the curved surface of a plano-convex lens of a large radius of curvature r on the surface of the beam, we obtain *Newton's rings* in the unbent position of the beam (as expected) which, on the bending of the beam, assume an *elliptical* or a *hyperbolic* shape according as $R_2 >$ or $< r$. Since, generally, $R_2 > r$, the fringes are elliptical in shape. Further, in the event of r being equal to either R_1 or R_2, we obtain *straight* or *linear* fringes.

14.14 COLUMNS OR PILLARS—EULER'S THEORY

A column or a pillar, as mentioned earlier (§14.1), is just a *long, straight* and *vertical* beam or a bar of *uniform cross-section,* subjected to compressive axial loads. There are three modes of fixation of its ends:

***(i)* Rounded, hinged or pin-jointed.** The ends of a column are said to be rounded, hinged or pin-jointed if they are fitted into a metal socket such as shown in Fig. 14.25(*a*), so that they are *fixed in position but not in direction*. Thus, although the deflection at the ends is always zero, the column is free to acquire or change its slope all along its length.

***(ii)* Fixed.** The ends of a column are said to be fixed [Fig. 14.25(*b*)] if they are clamped tightly or built into a structure (as in the case of an encastré beam), so that *they can change neither their position nor direction*. The deflection at the ends is zero under all conditions of loading and there are well-marked points of inflexion along the length of the column.

***(iii)* Free.** If the end of a column in neither hinged (or pin-jointed) nor fixed, it is said to be free. The column can, in this case, be deflected as well as acquire slope, *i.e.*, *the end can change its position as well as direction.*

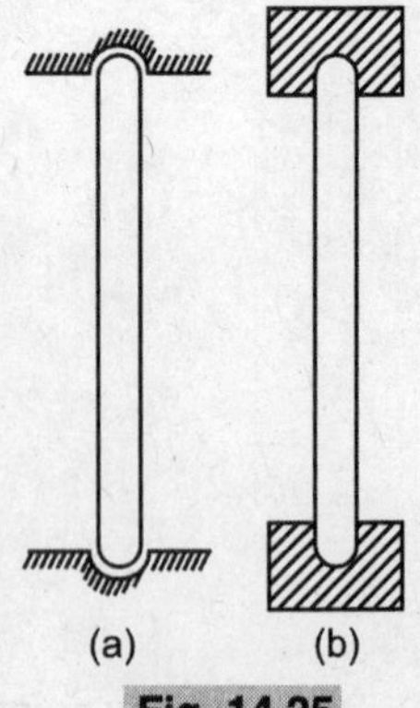

Fig. 14.25

The mode of fixation of the ends of a column has a great bearing on its strength, *i.e.*, its capacity to withstand or resist the thrust due to the axial load placed on it, as we shall see as we proceed along.

Euler's theory. The noted Swiss mathematician **Leonard Euler** propounded, in the year 1757, his *theory of long columns* on the basis of the following assumptions:

(*i*) *The material of the column is homogeneous and isotropic*, (*ii*) *its cross-section is uniform*, (*iii*) *its length very much* (*i.e.*, *at least* 10 *times*) *greater than its cross-sectional or lateral dimensions*, (*iv*) *if pin-jointed, the pin-joints are frictionless and if fixed, the fixed ends are rigid*, (*v*) *the column is initially straight*, (*vi*) *it is loaded axially and* (*viii*) *its own weight is neglected*.

In the articles below, we shall follow Euler's treatment of long columns in accordance with his theory.

14.15 CRITICAL LOAD FOR A COLUMN

Let a *long*, *straight* and vertical column of length L be represented by a strip AB of wood or metal, with its ends rounded or hinged (Fig. 14.26). Let a cylinder C, free to move only vertically between two parallel guides G, G, be arranged at A, such that varying amounts of lead shot or mercury may be placed inside it and any desired load thus applied axially to the column or the strip AB.

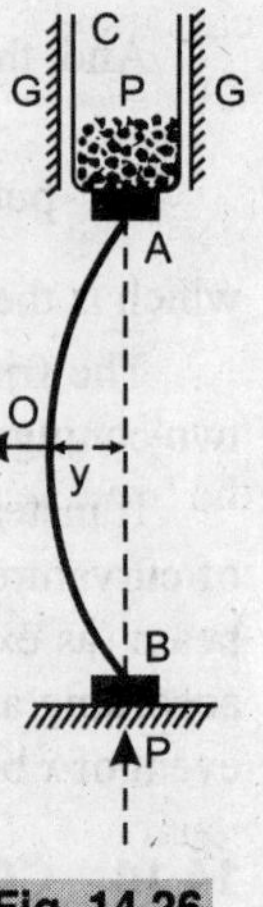

Initially, with no load at A or a load insufficient to bend the column or the strip, if a lateral force f be applied to its mid-point O so as to deflect it through a distance y, it is found that on removal of this force, the column or the strip straightens itself out.

On gradually increasing the load at A, however, we arrive at a certain load P, fixed for the given column, such that on applying the lateral force f, as before, and then removing it, the column no longer straightens out but remains in its bent position with its mid-point O deflected through y. The same is true for any other deflection that may be given to the mid-point of the column (within the elastic limit) by some other lateral force, so long as the load at A remains P.

This maximum load P which a column can support such that, if initially straight, it still remains straight and, if given a slight bend, it remains bent in that very position without tending to bend further, is called the critical, buckling or crippling load for the column.

Fig. 14.26

For a load less than the critical load, the column, if bent, will tend to straighten out and for a load greater than the critical load, it will collapse due to *buckling*, (*i.e.*, bending further or bulging out).

Only under the critical load will the column remain in equilibrium whatever the deflection we may choose to give it within it elastic limit. This may be seen from the following:

Let us consider a column AB, of length L, under a vertical load P_1 (less than its critical load P) and a lateral force f at its mid-point O deflecting it through a distance y [Fig. 14.27(a)].

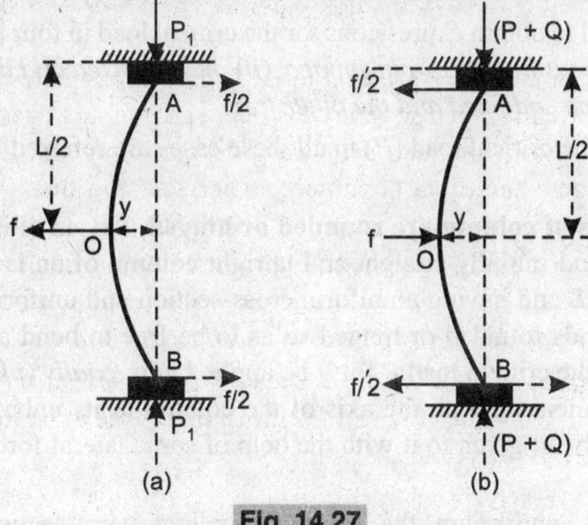

Fig. 14.27

For equilibrium of the column, obviously, the lateral force f must be balanced by two horizontal forces each equal to half its value and directed oppositely to it and A and B, as shown, with the total bending couple with O equal to zero. We, therefore, have

$P_1 y + (f/2)(L/2) + M = 0$, where M is the bending moment or *the moment of the resistance to bending* set up in the column at O.

If R be the *radius of curvature* of the column at O, we have

$M = YI_g/R$, where Y is the *Young's modulus* for the material of the column and I_g, the *geometrical moment of inertia* of its cross-section.

So that, $\quad P_1 y + fL/4 + YI_g/R = 0.$

Now, if we gradually decrease the lateral force f to zero and increase the load P_1 to P, such that the deflection at the mid-point O of the column remains unchanged at y, we have $Py + YI_g/R = 0$, where P is the *critical load* for the column, showing clearly that, deflection y being proportional to curvature $1/R$, the column will continue to be in equilibrium under the critical load for its whatever the deflection given to it within its elastic limit.

If, however, we increase the load on the column beyond its critical value P to, say, $(P + Q)$, as shown in Fig. 14.27(b), we should have for equilibrium of the column

$$(P + Q)y + YI_g/R = 0. \text{ Or, } Py + Qy + YI_g/R = 0.$$

This is obviously, *not possible*, since as we have seen above $py + YI_g/R = 0$, indicating that the bending moment YI_g/R can balance only the part py of the bending couple $(Py + Qy)$. The part Qy of the bending couple thus remains unbalanced and bends the column further beyond y.

In order to restrict the deflection of the column to y, therefore, we shall have to apply a lateral force f', say, at O in the direction opposite to that of f in the first case to balance the part Qy of the bending couple.

Since, again, this lateral force f' may be supposed to be balanced by two horizontal forces, each equal to $f'/2$ directed oppositely to f' at A and B, we shall have

$$Qy + (f'/2)(L/2) = 0. \text{ Or, } Qy + f'L/4 = 0.$$

Now, the bending moment (or the moment of the resistance to bending) is proportional to the deflection of the column only within the elastic limit. Once the elastic limit is crossed, the column acquires a permanent set, though, quite possibly, the bending moment increasing more rapidly beyond the elastic limit, the column may attain a new position of equilibrium under the load $(P + Q)$. If this doesnot come about, however, the column simply collapses due to buckling.

14.16 CALCULATION OF CRITICAL LOAD—EULER'S FORMULAE FOR LONG COLUMNS

We shall now proceed to obtain expressions for the critical load in four possible cases of fixation of columns, *viz.*, (*i*) *both ends hinged or pin-jointed,* (*ii*) *one end fixed and the other pin-jointed,* (*iii*) *both ends fixed* and (*iv*) *one end fixed and the other free.*

The expressions for the critical load (P) in all these cases are referred to as *Euler's formulae.*

(*i*) When both ends of column are rounded or hinged. Let AB (Fig. 14.28) represent a long and initially straight and upright column of an isotropic material, of length L and having a uniform cross-section and uniform elasticity, with both its ends rounded or hinged so as to be free to bend all along its length. And, let the critical load P for it be applied to it *axially* (*i.e.*, with its line of action coinciding with the axis of the column in its unbent position AB) and a small bend given to it with the help of some lateral force applied to it for an instant.

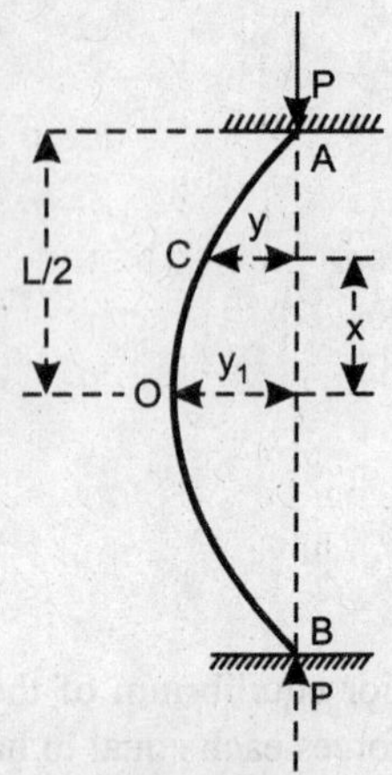

Fig. 14.28

The column being in equilibrium, the bending couple at every section of its is balanced by the bending moment (or the moment of the resistance to bending) there.

Consider the equilibrium of the portion CA of the column, where the point C lies a vertical distance x from its mid-point O and is deflected through a distance y from its initial position.

If the radius of curvature of the column at C be R, we have, for equilibrium,

$$Py + YI_g/R = 0,$$

where Y is the value of Young's modulus for the material of the column and I_g, the geometrical $M.I.$ of its cross-section.

Since the curvature 1/R may, as we know, be taken to be equal to d^2y/dx^2, we have

$$Py + YI_g \frac{d^2y}{dx^2} = 0. \text{ Or, } \frac{d^2y}{dx^2} + \frac{P}{YI_g} y = 0.$$

The solution to this equation is $y = A \sin \lambda x + B \cos \lambda x$, where $\lambda = \sqrt{P/YI_g}$ and A and B are constants.

On differentiating with respect to x, we have

$$dy/dx = A\lambda \cos \lambda x - B\lambda \sin \lambda x.$$

So that, (*a*) at $x = 0$, *i.e. at the mid-point of the column,* $dy/dx = 0$, $\lambda x = 0$ and, therefore, $\sin \lambda x = 0$ and $\cos \lambda x = 1$. Hence, $A = 0$. And if the deflection there be y_1, we have, from relation (*i*) above, $y_1 = B$. And (*b*) with $x = L/2$, *i.e.*, at the end A or B of the column, $y = 0$ and, therefore, from relation (*i*), $0 = B \cos \lambda L/2$. $(\because A \sin \lambda x = 0)$

This clearly means that either B or $\cos \lambda L/2 = 0$, Since, as we have just seen, $B \neq 0$ but equal to y_1, we have

$$\cos \lambda L/2 = 0. \text{ Or, } \lambda L/2 = \pi/2, 3\pi/2, 5\pi/2 \text{ etc,}$$

Ignoring all other values except the first (since they indicate points of inflexion in the column), we have

$$\sqrt{P/YI_g}.L/2 = \pi/2. \text{ Or, } P/YI_g = \pi^2/L^2,$$

whence, **the critical load $P = \pi^2 Y I_g/L^2 = 9.8YI_g/L^2$.**

Thus, for given values of Y and I_g, the smaller the value of $\underline{L}$, *i.e., the shorter the column,* the greater the *critical load for it.*

The critical loads in all other cases can be expressed in terms of the critical load for this type of hinged column. It is, therefore, taken to be a **fundamental case** and the column is referred to as the *fundamental hinged column.*

The length of such a column, for which the critical load is the same as that for any other type of column of length L, is called its *equivalent or effective length* corresponding to the latter and is denoted by the symbol L_e. This enables us to easily compare the strengths of columns with different types of end-fixation with that of this fundamental hinged column of the same length.

***(ii)* When one end of the column is fixed and the other hinged.** Fig. 14.29 represents such a column with its lower end fixed and the upper one hinged and loaded. In order, however, to keep its two ends in the same vertical line, the upper hinged end is constrained to move between two parallel guides G, G.

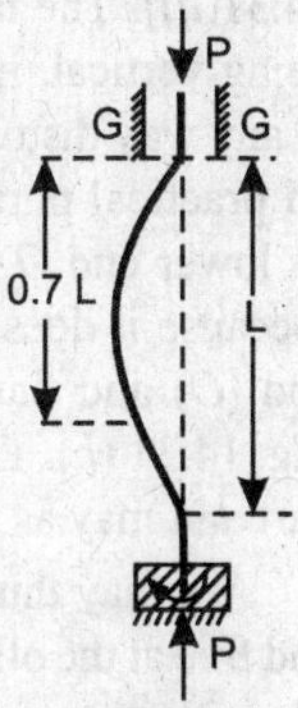

It can be shown that such a column of length L is equivalent to a column of length 0.7 L of the fundamental hinged type [*i.e.*, case (*i*)]. So that, $L_e = 0.7L$. All we have to do to obtain the value of the critical load, therefore, is to substitute L_e for L in the expression for P in case (*i*), when we obtain

$$\textbf{Critical Load } P = \frac{\pi^2 YI_g}{L_e^2} = \frac{\pi^2 YI_g}{(0.7L)^2} \approx \frac{2\pi^2 YI_g}{L^2},$$

which is twice the critical load for a fundamental type of hinged column of the same length (L).

Fig. 14.29

Thus, a column fixed at one end and hinged at the other has twice the strength it will have when hinged at both ends.

***(iii)* When both ends of the column are fixed.** Let the ends A and B of a column of length L be fixed as shown in Fig. 14.30 so that when bent, the tangents at the ends A and B, as also at the mid-point O, are all vertical. The line of action of the resultant load P now no longer coincides with the axis of the column but lies in between the longer coincides with the axis of the column but lies in between the axis (AB) and the mid-point O, cutting the bent column in points C and D, which due to the absence of any bending couple there, are points of opposite flexure.

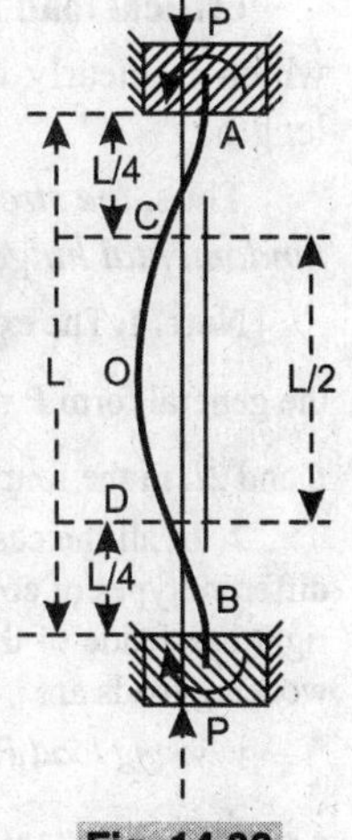

Fig. 14.30

Clearly, at all those points in curves CA and CO of the bent column where the deflections (as measured from the vertical line through C) are equal, the bending couples must also be equal and, since the column has a uniform cross-section, the radii of curvature too at these points must be the same.

Thus, since the slope of the curve at C, as also at A and O, is the same (the tangents there being all vertical), it follows that curves CA and CO are similar and equal. The same being true of curves DB and DO, it is clear that points C, O and D divides the column into four equal parts, so that the length of the bent portion COD is equal to half the length of the entire column, *i.e.*, equal to $L/2$.

Obviously, therefore, the portion COD of the column, the whole of which is bent, behaves like a column, the whole of which is bent, behaves like a column of length $L/2$, with its two ends rounded or hinged (*i.e.*, the fundamental hinged type), carrying a load P at C. So that, the *equivalent or effective length* $L_e = L/2$.

Hence, proceeding exactly as in case (*i*) above, we have

$$\textbf{critical load } P = \pi^2 YIg/L_e^2 = \pi^2 YI_g/(L/2)^2 = 4\pi^2 YI_g/L^2,$$

showing that *the critical load* (P) *is now four times that for the fundamental hinged type of the same length.*

Thus, *a column, with its two ends fixed, has four times as much strength as when its two ends are rounded or hinged.*

(iv) When one end of the column is fixed and the other free. The critical load for the column in this case may be deduced directly from case may be deduced directly from case (*i*) of a column hinged at both ends (the fundamental hinged column) as will be seen from the following:

Let *AB* be a column of length *L'*, with both its ends rounded or hinged, and *P*, the critical load on it [Fig. 14.31(*a*)]. The tangent to the bent column at its mid-point *O* being vertical, if we clamp it tightly, *i.e.*, fix it, at *O* without in any way disturbing the position of the tangent, we have, for all practical purpose, a column *OA*, of length $L'/2 = L$, with its lower end *O* fixed and the upper *A* behaving as a free end (because it does not lie on the vertical line through the fixed end (*O*) and thus suffers lateral displacement), as shown in Fig. 14.31 (*b*). The lower half OB of the column now plays no part and may as well be removed.

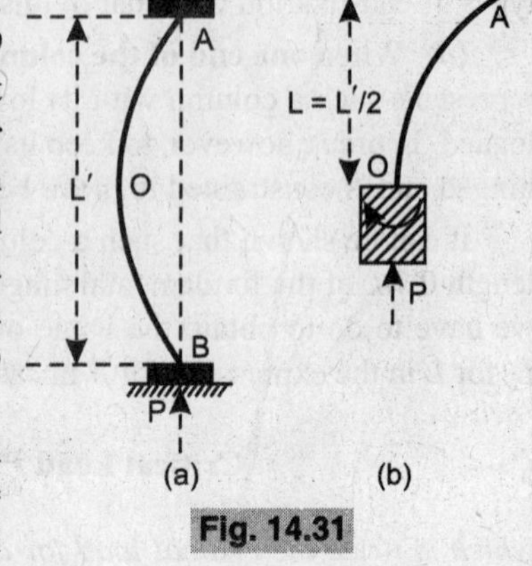

Fig. 14.31

We may thus take a column of length *L*, fixed at one end and free at the other, to be equivalent to a column of length $L' = 2L$, with its two ends rounded or hinged, *i.e.*, the fundamental hinged column. So that, we have

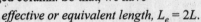

effective or equivalent length, $L_e = 2L$.

∴ *for a column fixed at one end and free at the other* we have

critical load $P = \pi^2 YI_g/L_e^2 = \pi^2 YI_g/(2L)^2 = \pi^2 YIg/4L^2$,

which is clearly one-fourth of the critical load for the fundamental hinged column of the same length.

Thus, *the strength of a column fixed at one end and free at the other in one-fourth of that of the fundamental hinged column* (*or a column hinged at both ends*) *of the same length.*

Note. 1. The expression for the critical load (P) in all the different cases of end fixation may be put in either the general form $P = N\pi^2 YI_g/L^2$ or $P = \pi^2 YI_g/L_e^2$, where *N* is equal to 1, 2, 4 and 1/4 and L_e equal to *L*, 0.7 *L*, $\frac{1}{2}$ *L* and 2*L* in the four cases respectively.

2. In all the cases discussed above, Euler's formulae for *P* give the maximum or the critical load for the different types of columns and *not the working loads* for them. To obtain the working loads we must divide the right hand side of the expression for *P* by a suitable safety factor, *n*, say. So that, the general expressions for working loads are

working load $Pw = N\pi^2 YI_g/nL^2$ or *working load* $P_w = \pi^2 YI_g/nL_e^2$.

14.17 MAXIMUM HEIGHT OF COLUMN OR A PILLAR (OR A TREE)

We have just seen in case (*iv*) of the previous article that the critical load for a column or a pillar, fixed at one end and loaded at the other free end is given by $P = \pi^2 YI_g/4L^2$.

Now, when there is no external load placed on the upper free end of the column, the only load on it is its own weight which acts at its centre of gravity. Since the centre of gravity of a column of uniform diameter and homogeneous composition lies at its mid-point, we have, in effect, a column of length *L*/2, fixed at its lower end and carrying a load equal to its own weight at the upper free end. So that, putting *L*/2 for *L* in the expression for *P* in case (*iv*), we have

$$P = \frac{\pi^2 YI_g}{4(L/2)^2} = \frac{\pi^2 YI_g}{L^2}.$$

All that we have to do, therefore, to determine the maximum length or height of a column or a pillar is to find the value of L corresponding to the critical load P, equal to its own weight.

Thus, P = *weight of the column* = $\pi r^2 L\rho g$, where r is its radius and ρ, the *density* of its material, and $I_g = \pi r^4/4$. And, therefore,

$$\pi r^2 L\rho g = \frac{\pi^2 YI_g}{L^2} = \frac{\pi^2 Y\pi r^4}{4L^2} = \frac{\pi^3 Yr^4}{4L^2}.$$

Or,
$$L^3 = \frac{\pi^3 Yr^4}{4\pi r^2 \rho g} = \frac{\pi^2 Yr^2}{4\rho g},$$

whence,
$$L = \left(\frac{\pi^2 Yr^2}{4\rho g}\right)^{1/3}$$ and can be easily evaluated.

This value of L then gives the maximum length or height of a column which can just support its own weight.

Similarly, if we can imagine a tree to have a uniform area of cross-section all along its length, we can obtain the value of L for its from a knowledge of its diameter (or radius) and the values of ρ and Y for its material. And this gives the maximum height it can attain without collapsing under its own weight.

WORKED EXAMPLES

I–Bending of Beams

Example 14.1. Obtain expression for the radius of curvature of a flat curve in terms of the slope of the curve and use the result to find the value of deflection in the case of a bar fixed horizontally at one end and loaded at the other. ***(Bombay)***

Solution. Let P and Q be two points, distance δx apart on a flat curve OA (Fig. 14.32) such that the radius of curvature of the portion PQ is R, with C as its centre of curvature, and let PD and QE be tangents to the curve at P and Q and and $\angle PCQ = \angle DPE = \theta$.

Then, clearly $PQ = \delta x = R\theta$.

Since θ is the change in slope of the tangents from P to Q, we have

$$\theta = (dy/dx)Q - (dy/dx)P.$$

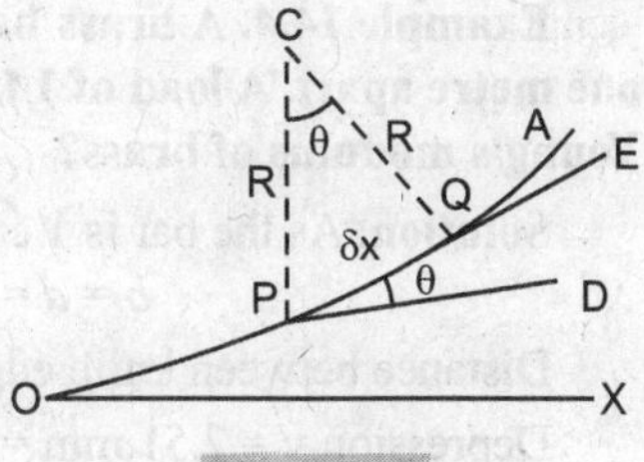

And since the rate of change of slope is d^2y/dx^2, the change in slope from P to Q is also equal to $(d^2y/dx^2)\delta x$, We therefore, have

$\theta = (d^2y/dx^2)\delta x$. And $\therefore\ \delta x = R(d^2y/dx^2)\delta x$, whence, $R(d^2y/dx^2) = 1$. So that, $1/R = d^2y/dx^2$ = *rate of change of slope.*

Fig. 14.32

Thus, if the curvature ($1/R$) be small (as it usually is in the case of bent bars or beams) its value at any point on the curve is given by the rate of change of slope at that point.

For part two of the question, see § 14.7

Example 14.2. A rod of rectangular cross-section having breadth and thickness each 0.5 cm is bent in the form of an arc of radius of curvature 1000 cm. If Young's modulus of the material of the rod is 10^{12} dynes/cm^2 calculate (*i*) stress, strain at the curved surface and (*ii*) bending moment.

Solution. (*i*) When a bar is bent, the tensile strain on any filament at a distance x from the neutral surface is given by

$$\text{strain} = \frac{\text{change in length}}{\text{original length}} = \frac{x}{R}$$

where R is the radius of curvature of the neutral surface.

The neutral surface lies along the middle of the bar.

Thickness of the bar = 0.5 cm = 0.005 m

∴ For the convex surface of the bent bar $x = \frac{0.005}{2} = 0.0025$ m

Radius of curvature of the curved surface R = 1000 cm = 10 m

Hence tensile strain = $\frac{x}{R} = \frac{0.0025}{10} = 0.00025 = 25 \times 10^{-5}$

Young's modulus $Y = 10^{12}$ dynes/cm^2 = 10^{11} Nm^{-2}

∴ Tensile stress = $Y \times$ tensile strain = $10^{11} \times 25 \times 10^{-5} = 25 \times 10^{6}$ Nm^{-2}

(*ii*) Geometrical moment of inertia of the rectangular bar

$$I = \frac{bd^3}{12}$$

Now $b = d = 0.005$ m

$$I = \frac{(0.005)^4}{12} = \frac{625 \times 10^{-12}}{12} = 52 \times 10^{-12}$$

∴ Bending moment = $\frac{YI}{R} = \frac{10^{11} \times 52 \times 10^{-12}}{10} = \mathbf{52 \times 10^{-2}}$ **Nm**

Example 14.3. A steel rod of length 50 cm, width 2 cm and thickness 1 cm is bent into the form of an arc of radius of curvature 2.0 m. Calculate the bending moment. Young's modulus of the material of the rod = 2 × 10^{11} N/m^2. (***Kerala U., 2001***)

Solution. $b = 2$ cm $= 2 \times 10^{-2}$ m; $d = 1$ cm $= 10^{-2}$ m

$$\therefore \quad I = \frac{bd^3}{12} = \frac{2 \times 10^{-2} \times 10^{-6}}{12} = \frac{1}{6} \times 10^{-8}$$

∴ Bending moment = $\frac{YI}{R} = \frac{2 \times 10^{11}}{2} \times \frac{1}{6} \times 10^{-8} = \frac{10^3}{6} = \mathbf{166.67}$ **Nm**

Example 14.4. A brass bar 1 cm square in cross-section is supported on two knife edges one metre apart. A load of 1 kg at the centre of the bar depresses that point 2.51 mm. What is Young's modulus of brass? (***Purvanchal U. 2005***)

Solution. As the bar is 1 cm square

$$\therefore \quad b = d = 1 \text{ cm} = 10^{-2} \text{ m}$$

Distance between knife edges l = 1m

Depression y = 2.51 mm = 2.51×10^{-3} m

Load W = 1 kg wt. = 9.8 N

Now,
$$Y = \frac{Wl^3}{4bd^3y}$$

$$= \frac{9.8 \times 1}{4 \times 10^{-2} \times 10^{-6} \times 2.51 \times 10^{-3}} = \mathbf{9.761 \times 10^{10}\ N\text{-}m^{-2}}$$

Example 14.5. In an experiment the diameter of the rod was 1.26 cm and distance between the knife edges 0.7 m. On putting a load of 0.9 kg at the mid-point, the depression was 0.025 cm. Find Young's modulus of elasticity of the material of rod.

Solution. Here
$$l = 0.7 \text{ m},$$
$$W = 0.9 \text{ kg-wt} = 0.9 \times 9.8 \text{ N}$$
$$r = 0.63 \text{ cm} = 0.63 \times 10^{-2} \text{ m}$$
$$y = 0.025 \text{ cm} = 2.5 \times 10^{-4} \text{ m}$$

Now,
$$Y = \frac{Wl^3}{12\pi r^4 y} = \frac{0.9 \times 9.8 \times 0.7 \times 0.7 \times 0.7}{12\pi \times (0.63 \times 10^{-2})^4 \times 2.5 \times 10^{-4}}$$

$$= \mathbf{20.374 \times 10^{10}\ Nm^2}$$

Example 14.6. Compare the loads required to produce equal depressions for two beams made of the same material and having the same length and weight with only difference that one has circular cross-section while the cross-section of the other is squre. (*Vikram*)

Solution. If l is the length of each bar, ρ its density, r the radius of circular bar and a each side of the face of square bar, then

Mass of square bar $= a^2 l\rho$

Mass of circular bar $= \pi r^2 l\rho$

As, the mass of the bars are equal

$$\therefore \qquad \pi r^2 l\rho = a^2 l\rho$$

$$\text{or} \qquad \pi r^2 = a^2 \qquad \ldots(i)$$

If I_1 is the geometrical *M.I.* of the square bar and I_2 that of the circular bar, then

$$\text{Depression for square bar } y = \frac{W_1}{YI_1} \cdot \frac{l^3}{3} \qquad \ldots(ii)$$

$$\text{and Depreciation for circular bar } y = \frac{W_2}{YI_2} \cdot \frac{l^3}{3} \qquad \ldots(iii)$$

From (*ii*) and (*iii*), we get,

$$\frac{W_1}{I_1} = \frac{W_2}{I_2}$$

$$\text{or} \qquad \frac{W_1}{W_2} = \frac{I_1}{I_2}$$

$$\text{Now} \qquad I_1 = \frac{a^4}{12} \text{ and}$$

$$I_2 = \frac{\pi r^4}{4}$$

$$\therefore \qquad \frac{W_1}{W_2} = \frac{a^4}{12} \times \frac{4}{\pi r^4} = \frac{a^4}{3\pi r^4}$$

$$= \frac{\pi^2 r^2}{3\pi r^4} = \frac{\pi}{3} = \mathbf{1.05}$$

Example 14.7. A square bar of length 1 m and cross-section 1 cm^2 is clamped horizontally at one end and a weight of 1 kgm is applied at the other end. Neglecting weight of the bar calculate the depression of the loaded end. Given $Y = 9.78 \times 10^{10}$ N/m^2 and $g = 9.78$ m/sec^2. (*Nag. U. 2001; M.D.U. 2002*)

Solution. Here $l = 1$m. As it is a square bar $d = b = 1$ cm $= 10^{-2}$ m.

$W = 1$ kgm $= 1 \times 9.78 = 9.78$ N; $Y = 9.78 \times 10^{10}$ Nm^{-2}

$$\therefore \text{ Depression of the loaded end } y = \frac{4Wl^3}{Ybd^3} \text{ for a rectangular bar}$$

$$= \frac{4Wl^3}{Yb^4} \text{ for a square bar}$$

$$= \frac{4 \times 9.78 \times 1}{9.78 \times 10^{10} \times 10^{-8}} = 4 \times 10^{-2} \text{ m} = \mathbf{4\ cm.}$$

Example 14.8. (*a*) A rectangular bar, 2 cm is breadth and 1 cm in depth and 100 cm in length, is supported at the ends and a load of 2 kg is applied at its middle. Calculate the depression if the Young's modulus of the material of the bar is 20 × 10^{11} dynes/cm^2. (*Punjab*)

(*b*) In an experiment, the diameter of the rod was 1.26 cm and the distance between the two knife edges, 70 cm. On putting a load of 900 gm at the middle point, the depression was 0.025 cm. Calculate the Young's modulus for the substance. (*Agra*)

Solution. (*a*) In this case, the depression of the mid-point of the bar supported at its two ends is given by $y = WL^3/48\ YI_g$.

Now, $W = 2 \times 1000 \times 980$ *dynes*, $L = 100 = 10^2$ *cm*, $Y = 20 \times 10^{11}$ *dynes/cm*^{2} and $I_g = bd^3/12 = 2 \times (1)^3/12 = 1/6$. So that, *depression of the mid-point of the bar,*

i.e.,
$$y = \frac{2\times1000\times980\times(10^2)^3}{48\times20\times10^{11}\times(1/6)} = \frac{49}{400} = 0.1225\ cm.$$

(*b*) Here, again, $y = WL^3/48\ YI_g$. And, since $I_g = \pi r^4/4$, we have

$$y = \frac{WL^3\times4}{48Y\times\pi r^4} = \frac{WL^3}{12Y\pi r^4}, \text{ whence, } Y = \frac{WL^3}{12y\pi r^4}.$$

Substituting the given values, therefore, we have

Young's modulus for the material of the rod,

$$Y = \frac{900\times980\times(70)^3}{12\times0.025\times\pi(1.26/2)^4} = 2.039\times10^{12}\ dynes/cm^2.$$

Example 14.9. A wooden bar, 100 cm long and 2.0 cm × 2.0 cm in section, rests horizontally and symmetrically on two knife-edges 60 cm apart. When a weight of 2 kg is suspended from each end of the bar, the centre is elevated through a distance 0.102 cm. Calculate the value of Young's modulus for the material of the bar.

Solution. In Fig. 14.33, let *AB* be the initial position of the bar resting symmetrically on two knife-edges K_1 and K_2, 60 *cm* apart, with 20 *cm* of its projecting beyond the knife-edges on either side.

When a weight of 2 kg is suspended from each end, the bar takes the form *A'B'*, its portion *CD* between the knife edges bending into a circular arc of radius *R* and centre *O*, with its midpoint *E* elevated through a distance *EF* = *y* = 0.102 *cm*.

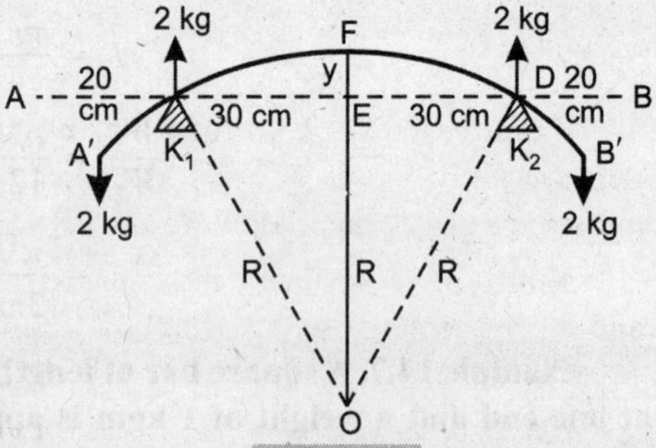

Fig. 14.33

Clearly, *bending couple applied to the bar at either end* = 2 × 1000 × 981 × 20 *dynes-cm*.

The bar being in equilibrium, this must be just balanced by the *bending moment* (or the moment of the resistance to bending), equal to YI_g/R, set up in the bar.

We, therefore, have $YI_g/R = 2 \times 1000 \times 981 \times 20$,

whence, $Y = 2 \times 1000 \times 981 \times 20 \times R/I_g$.

To obtain the value or *R* we observe from the geometry of the figure that

$$CE \times ED = (2OF - y)y. \text{ Or, } 30 \times 30 = (2R - y)y \approx 2Ry.$$

[y^2 being negligibly small.]

Or, $R = 30 \times 30/2y = 30 \times 30/2 \times 0.102$ cm.

And I_g for the bar $= bd^3/12 = b(b^3)/12 = b^4/12 = (2)^4/12 = 16/12 = 4/3\ (cm)^4$ [$\because b = d$]

∴ *Young's modulus for the material of the bar, i.e.,*

$$Y = 2 \times 1000 \times 981 \times 20 \times 30 \times 30 \times 3/2 \times 0.102 \times 4$$
$$= 1.3 \times 10^{11}\ dynes/cm^2.$$

Example 14.10. A steel strip is clamped horizontally at one end. On applying a 500 gm load at the free end, the bending in equilibrium state is 5.0 cm. Calculate (*i*) the potential energy in the strip, (*ii*) the frequency of vibration if the load is disturbed from equilibrium. (Neglect mass of the strip itself). (*Agra*)

Solution. (*i*) We know that the depression of the free and loaded end of a cantilever (its own weight being neglected) is given by $y = WL^3/3YI_g$, whence the load or the force under which the cantilever remains in equilibrium, *i.e.*, $W = (3YI_g/L^3)\,y$.

This must naturally be equal in magnitude, though opposite in sign, to the elastic reaction set up in the strip.

∴ work done in depressing the loaded end through a further distance

$$dy = Wdy = (3YI_g/L^3)ydy.$$

Hence *work done or potential energy stored up in depressing the strip through the whole distance*

$$y = \int_0^y \frac{3YI_g}{L^3} ydy = \frac{3YI_g}{L^3}\cdot\frac{y^2}{2} = \frac{W}{y}\cdot\frac{y^2}{2} = \frac{1}{2}Wy$$

$$= \frac{1}{2} \times 500 \times 980 \times 5 = 12.25 \times 10^5 \textit{ ergs}.$$

(*ii*) We have seen under § 13.9, how the loaded end of a cantilever executes simple harmonic oscillations when disturbed from its equilibrium position and how the time-period of these oscillations is given by $T = 2\pi\sqrt{y/g}$.

Since $y = 5$ cm and $g = 980$ *cm/sec*^{2}, we have $T = 2\pi\sqrt{5/980} = 0.4487$ sec.

Hence *frequency of oscillation*, $n = 1/0.4487 = 2.228 \approx 2.23$ sec.

II–Columns or Pillars

Example 14.11. A uniform bar of circular cross-section, 120 cm long, rests on two knife-edges at its two ends. When it is centrally loaded with a weight of 3 kg, it is depressed through a distance of 1.5 cm. Calculate the critical load for it when used as a column with hinged ends.

Solution. As we know, the depression of the mid-point of a bar or beam, supported at the ends and loaded centrally with a weight W is given by

$$y = WL^3/48\ YI_g, \text{ whence, } YI_g = WL^3/48y.$$

Here, $W = 3 \times 1000 \times 980$ dynes, $L = 120$ cm and $y = 1.5$ cm, So that

$$YI_g = 3 \times 1000 \times 980 \times (120)^3/48 \times 1.5 \textit{ dynes cm}^2.$$

Now, Euler's formula for critical load for a column hinged at both ends is

$$P = \pi^2 YIg/L^2.$$

∴ *critical load for the column, i.e.,* $P = \dfrac{\pi^2 \times 3\times1000\times980\times(120)^3}{48\times1.5\times(120)^2}$ *dynes*

$$= \frac{\pi^2 \times 3\times1000\times980\times120}{48\times1.5\times980\times1000} = \frac{\pi^2\times3\times120}{48\times1.5} \approx 50 \text{ kg}.$$

Example 14.12. Calculate the working axial load for a column, 200 cm in length and 4 cm in diameter, when both ends of the column are (*i*) pin-jointed, (*ii*) fixed. Factor for safety = 4 and *Y* for the material of the column = 20 × 10^{11} dynes/cm^2. (Take g = 1000 cm/sec^2).

Solution. (*i*) The safe working load P_w for a column with hinged or pin-jointed ens is, as we know, given by the relation $P_w = \pi^2 YIg/nL^2$, where n is the factor of safety (*See note* on page 799.)

Since $I_g = \pi r^4/4 = 4\pi$ (cm)^4, we have

safe working load far the column,

$$P_w = \frac{\pi^2 \times 20 \times 10^{11} \times 4\pi}{4 \times (200)^2} = \pi^3 \times 5 \times 10^7 \text{ dynes.}$$

$$= \frac{\pi^3 \times 5 \times 10^7}{1000 \times 1000} = 1550 \text{ kg.}$$

(*ii*) The safe working load for a column with fixed ends is given by

$P_w = 4\pi^2 YIg/nL^2$, which is clearly 4 times that in case (*i*).

∴ *safe working load in this case, i.e.,* $P_w = 4 \times 1550 = 6200$ kg.

EXERCISE

I–Bending of Beams

1. What is meant by a beam? Explain the terms: *neutral surface, neutral axis, flexural rigidity* and *bending moment* of a beam.

2. A steel wire of 1.00 mm radius is bent in the form of a circular arc of radius 50 cm. Calculate (*i*) the bending moment, (*ii*) the maximum stress. (Given Young's modulus for steel = 2×10^{12} dynes/cm²)
(*Agra*) [**Ans.** (*i*) 3.142×10^6 *dyne-cm*, (*ii*) 4×10^9 *dynes/cm²*]
[**Hint.** (*ii*) *stress/strain* = *Y*. ∴ stress, *P*, say = $Y \times$ strain. If *R* be the radius of the bent wire (or rather its neutral axis), strain at distance *z* from the neutral axis = *z/R* (§Fig. 14.5). Since strain is maximum on the surface of the wire, *z* = *r*, the radius of the wire. So that, maximum strain = *r/R* and ∴ *maximum* stress = *Yr/R*.]

3. Obtain, in terms of the bending moment *M*, an expression for (*i*) the longitudinal stress in a beam at a distance *z* from its neutral axis, (*ii*) the maximum stress in the case of (*a*) a cylindrical rod of radius *r* and (*b*) a cylindrical pipe of external and internal diameters d_1 and d_2 respectively.

$$\left[\textbf{Ans. } (i) \frac{M}{I_g z}; (ii)\ (a)\ \frac{4M}{\pi^3}\ (b)\ \frac{32Md_1}{\pi(d_1^4 - d_2^4)}\right]$$

[**Hint.** (*i*) At distance *z* from the neutral axis, stress *P* = *Yz/R* (See Hint under Question 2 above). Now, *bending moment M* = *YIg/R*, whence, $Y/R = M/I_g$.]

$$\therefore \quad P = \frac{M}{I_g} z.$$

(*ii*) Since maximum stress occurs at the surface of a beam, *z* = *r* in case (*a*) and $z = d_1/2$ in case (*b*) Also $I_g = \pi r^4/4$ in case (*a*) and $I_g = \pi[(d_1/2)^4 - (d_2/2)^4]/4$ in case (*b*).]

4. (*a*) What is cantilever? Obtain an expression for the depression at the free end of a thin light beam clamped horizontally at one and loaded at the other. **(*Bombay*)**
(*b*) If in (*a*) above, the beam be of a rectangular cross-section, with breadth *b* and depth *d*, and if the depression of its free end be *y* under a load *W*, show that for the same load, the depression of the free end will be $y' = y(d^2/b^2)$ if the beam be used with *d* as breadth and *b* as depth.
[**Hint.** $I_g = bd^3/12$ in the first case and equal to $db^3/12$ in the second case. Therefore, $y = WL^3/3Y \dfrac{bd^3}{12}$ and $y' = WL^3/\dfrac{db^3}{12}$. So that, $y'/y = d^2/b^2$.

Or $\qquad y = y(d^2/b^2)$.]

5. A cantilever of length 50 cm is depressed by 15.00 mm at the loaded end. Calculate the depression at a distance of 30 cm from the fixed end and deduce the formula used. **(*Agra*)** [**Ans.** 6.48 *mm*]
[**Hint.** (See § 14.7). At the loaded end $y = 1.5 = WL^3/3\ YI_g$, whence, the value of WL^3/YI_g can be obtained. Then, at distance *x* from the fixed end,

$$y = \frac{W}{YI_g}\left(\frac{Lx^2}{2} - \frac{x^3}{6}\right) \text{ and may be easily evaluated.]}$$

6. A cantilever of length *l* is loaded at a point *x*. Calculate the depression of the tip of the cantilever. If the same load is shifted to the tip, what is the depression of the point *x*? **(*Bombay (Supp.)*)**

[Ans. $\frac{Wx^2}{2YI_g}\left(1-\frac{x}{3}\right)$; same.]

[**Hint.** We have *depression at the distance x from the fixed end,*

$$y = \frac{W}{YI_0}\left(\frac{lx^2}{2}-\frac{x^3}{6}\right)$$ [§ 14.7]

$\therefore$ *slope of the curve at* $x_1 = \frac{dy}{dx} = \tan\theta = \frac{W}{YI_g}\left(lx-\frac{x^2}{2}\right).$

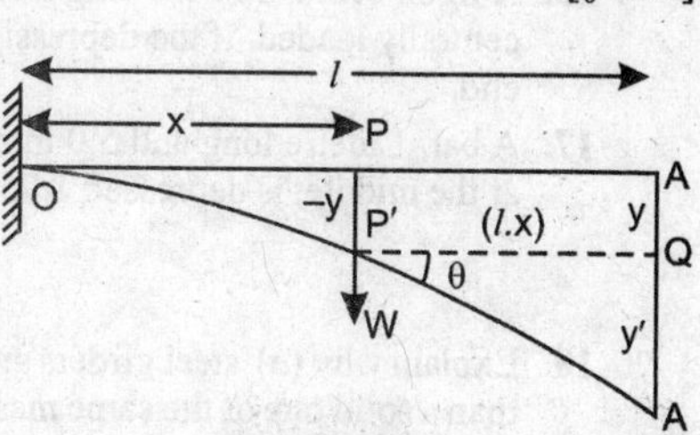

Fig. 14.34

Now, with the load W at P distant x_1 from the fixed end (Fig. 14.34) the depression at P is $PP' = y = Wx^3/3YI_g$, there being no depression beyond P', with the rest of the cantilever ($P'A'$) tangential to the curve at P', making an angle q with the horizontal, where

$$\tan\theta = dy/dx = \frac{W}{YI_g}\left(x^2-\frac{x^2}{2}\right) = \frac{Wx^2}{2YI_g}.$$

$\therefore$ *displacement AA′ of the tip of the cantilever* $= AQ + QA' = y + y' = v + P'Q\tan\theta$

$$= y + (l-x)\tan\theta$$

$$= \frac{Wx^3}{3YI_g} + (l-x)\frac{Wx^2}{2YI_g}$$

$$= \frac{W}{YI_g}\left(\frac{lx^2}{2}-\frac{x^3}{6}\right) = \frac{Wx^2}{2YI_g}\left(l-\frac{x}{3}\right).$$

And, when load W is shifted to the tip of the cantilever, we have *depression at distance x from the fixed end* $= \frac{W}{YI_g}\left(\frac{lx^2}{2}-\frac{x^3}{6}\right) = \frac{Wx^2}{2YI_g}\left(l-\frac{x}{3}\right)$, *i.e.,* the *same as that of the tip in the first case.*]

7. A solid cylindrical rod of radius 6 mm bends by 8 mm under a certain load. Deduce the bending when all other things remaining the same, the beam is replaced by a hollow cylindrical one with external radius 10 mm and internal, 8 mm. ***(Agra(Supp.))*** [**Ans.** 1.756 mm.]

[**Hint.** The length L and the load W being the same in either case, $y \propto 1/I_g$. If, therefore, y and y' be the bendings in the two cases respectively, we hae $y/y' = I_g/I_g'$. And, since $I_g = \pi r^4$ and $I_g' = \pi(r_1^4 - r_2^4)/4$, we have

$$y' = \left(\frac{r^4}{r_1^4 - r_2^4}\right)y.]$$

8. A uniform beam is clamped at one end and loaded at the other. Obtain the relation between the load and depression at the loaded end when (*a*) the weight of the beam can be neglected, (*b*) when the weight of the beam cannot be neglected. ***(Delhi)***

9. (*a*) The end of a strip cantilever depresses 10 mm under a certain load. Calculate the depression unde the same load for another cantilever of the same material, two times in length, two times in breadth and three times in thickness. ***(Agra)*** [**Ans.** *1.48 mm.*]

(*b*) What should be the change in the load if the depression of the strip cantilever is to be maintained at 10 mm but its dimension are halved? [**Ans.** *The load should be halved.*]

10. Give the theory of transverse vibrations of a bar fixed at one end and loaded at the other. ***(I.A.S.)***

11. A light beam of circular cross section is clamped horizontally at one end and a heavy mass is attached at the other end. Find the depression at the loaded end.

If the mass is pressed down a little and then released, show that it will perform *S.H.M.* Explain how from a knowledge of the period of oscillation, the mass and the dimensions of the bar, the value of Young's modulus for the material of the bar may be determined. ***(Madras)***

12. A hollow metal tube, 1 metre long and of internal and external radii 0.60 cm, and 0.80 cm is supported at its two ends and loaded in the middle with a weight of 10 kg. If the depression of its mid-point be 4.96 mm, calculate the value of Young's modulus for its material. [**Ans.** 1.87×10^{12} dynes/cm^2.]

13. A light uniform beam, supported horizontally at the two ends on two knife-edges and loaded at the centre, has at its each end a mirror attached almost normally to its length. show how this arrangement can be used to determine Y for its material. Deduce the necessary formula. ***(Delhi)***

14. Deduce the expression for Young's modulus of the material of a beam supported at its ends and carrying a central load W, when the beam has a weight w per unit length. ***(Delhi)***

15. Describe an interference method for determining Young's modulus for a rectangular glass plate. Prove the necessary formula. ***(Delhi)***

    How may *Poisson's ratio* for the glass of the plate be obtained from the same experiment?

16. A ligtht beam, 100 cm long and of uniform cross section, rests on two knife-edges at its ends and is centrally loaded. If the depression of the mid-point of the beam be 1.0 cm, calculate its slope at other end. **[Ans.** 30×10^{-2} radian.]

17. A bar, 1 metre long and 5.0 mm square in section, supported horizontally at its two ends and loaded at the middle, is depressed 1.96 mm by a load of 100 gm. Calculate Youn's modulus for its material. ($g = 980$ cm/sec^2)
    [Ans. 19.99×10^{11} dynes/cm^2.]

18. Explain why (*a*) steel girders and rails are made in the form of *I*-section; (*b*) a hollow shaft is stronger than a solid one of the same mas, length and material; (*c*) beam of a square cross section is stiffer than one of circular cross-section of the same material, mass and length and that either is most likely to rupture at, or close to, the fixed end.

19. A uniform rod of length 1 m is clamped horizontally at one end. A weight of 0.1 kg is attached at the free end. Calculate the depression of the free end of the rod. The diameter of the rod is 0.02 m. Young's modulus of the material of the rod = 1×10^{10} Nm^{-2} **[Ans.** 4.1 mm]

20. A cylinder of diameter 4 cm and length 5 cm is suspended horizontally by a steel wire of length 100 cm and radius 0.02 cm. Calculate the time oif one vibration. The coefficient of rigidity of steel is 8×10^{11} dynes/cm^2 and the density of lead is 11.4 gms/c.c. **[Ans.** 6.586 seconds]

    [Hint. $M = \pi R^2 l\rho$ and $I = M\left[\frac{R^2}{4} + \frac{l^2}{12}\right]$

    $t = 2\pi\sqrt{\frac{I}{C}} = 2\pi\sqrt{\frac{I.2l}{\eta\pi r^4}}$]

21. Define neutral axis of a beam. ***(Nagpur U. 2009)***

22. Obtain in terms of bending moment M, an expression for the longitudinal stress in a beam at a distance z from the neutral axis. ***(Agra U. 2006)***

23. In case of bending of a rod, Young's modulus only comes into play and not modulus of rigidity even though there is a change in shape. Explain.

24. Explain the term 'Neutral surface' and 'Bending moment' of a beam. ***(Napgur U. 2005)***

25. (*a*) What is a cantilever? Derive an expression for the depression or the loaded end of a cantilever of (*i*) circular cross-section and (*ii*) rectangular cross-section of negligible weight.
    (Meerut U. 2002; K.U. 2002, 2001; M.D.U. 2003; Gauhati U. 2007; M.S.U. Tiruneveli 2007)

    (*b*) Hence derive an expression for the bending of a bar supported a the two ends and loaded in the middle. Describe an experiment to determine Y be bending. ***(Luck. U. 2001; K.U. 2000)***

26. The end of a rectangular cantilever depresses 10 mm under a certain load. Calculate the depression unde the same load, for anotehr cantilever of same material two times in length, two times in width and three times in thickness. ***(Napgur U. 2005)*** **[Ans.** 1.48 mm]

27. Show that the bending moment for a thin uniform bar of rectangular cross-section is

$$\frac{\gamma b d^3}{12R}$$

28. Define a cantilever. Obtain an expression for the depression produced at its free end when the weight of the beam is negligible. ***(M.S.U. Tiruneveli 2007)***

II–Columns or Pillars

29. What is a column or a pillar? What is meant by the critical load for it? Show that under the critical load, a column may be given any deflection within its elastic limit.

30. What are the different types of end-fixation for columns. Clearly point out their basic features.

31. Show that (*i*) a column with fixed ends has four times the strength and (*ii*) a column with one end fixed and the other free has one-fourth the strength of an identical column with both ends hinged.

15 Chapter FLUID MECHANICS VISCOSITY

Brief Contents

INTRODUCTION

Fluid mechanics is the study of fluids (includes liquid, gases and plasmas) and the forces on them. Fluid mechanics can be divided into fluid kinematics, the study of fluid motion and fluid dynamics, the study of the effect of forces on fluid motion, which can be further divided into *fluid statics*, the study of fluids at rest. In other words, fluid mechanics is a branch of *continuum mechanics*, a subject which models matter without using the information that is made out of atoms, *i.e.*, it matters from a macroscopic view point rather than microscopic view point. The study of fluid mechanics goes back at the least to the days of ancient Greece when Archimedes investigated fluid statics and buoyancy and formulated his famous law, known as Archimedes Principle. Rapid advancement in fluid mechanics began with Leonardo da Vinci, Evangelista Torricelli (barometer), Isaac Newton (viscosity) and Blaise Pascal (hydrostatics) and was continued by Daniel Bernoulli (hydrodynamica, 1738). Viscous flow was explored by a multitude of engineers including Poiseuille and Heinrich and further by Claude-Louis Navier and George Gabriel Stokes and gave full justice to the understanding of fluid viscosity.

15.1 LAMINAR OR VISCOUS FLOW

Imagine a liquid in contact with a fixed horizontal surface at its bottom. If a shearing stress be applied to it (as, for example, by placing a glass plate P on its surface and moving it forwards) as indicated in Fig. 15.1 (*a*), it will begin to flow since by its very definition, a liquid cannot permanently withstand a shearing stress.

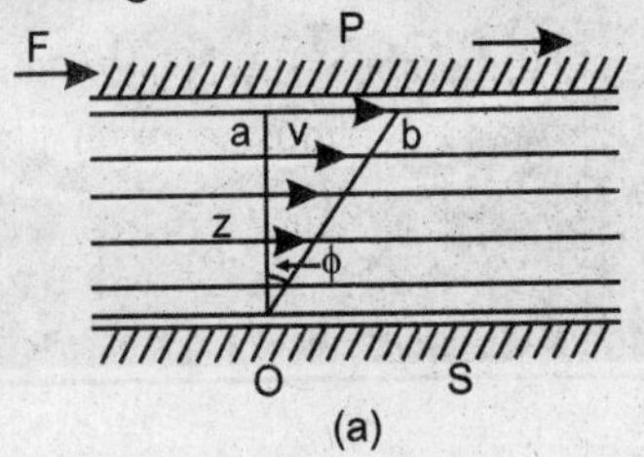

(a)

(b)

Fig. 15.1

If the flow of the liquid be slow and steady, it behaves as though it consists of a number of layers or liminae, one above the other, with the uppermost layer moving the fastest and each succeeding layer slower than the one above it, with the lowermost layer in contact with the horizontal surface remaining at rest. This is indicated in the figure by the lengths of the arrows which represent the magnitudes of the velocities of the different layers.

As will be readily seen, the greater the distance of a layer from the fixed surface or the stationary layer, the greater its velocity; so that, the *velocity-distribution curve* or the *profile* of the flowing liquid in a straight line such as OB, inclined to the vertical.

If the liquid be flowing in a tube or a pipe [Fig. 15.1 (*b*)], the layers are cylindrical in form, one inside the other. Again however, the cylindrical layer or shell in contact with the walls of the tube or pipe remains at rest whereas the one along its axis (and, therefore farthest from the stationary layer) moves the fastest, *i.e.*, the velocity of the layers increases from *zero* at the walls of the tube (or pipe) to a maximum along its axis. The *velocity-distribution curve* or the *profile* of the flowing liquid here is *parabolic* in form, as shown.

Such a liquid-flow in which the different layers or laminae glide over one another at a slow and steady velocity (below its critical velocity), without intermixing, is called a **laminar, streamline** *or* **viscous flow.**

15.2 VISCOSITY

As we have just seen, in a steady or laminar flow of a liquid over a fixed horizontal surface, the uppermost layer moves the fastest and the other layers progressively slower as we proceed downwards, with the lowermost layers remaining at rest.

This clearly shows that as the uppermost layer moves forwards under the shearing stress applied to it, a tangential, *backward dragging force,* frictional in nature, comes into play in between it and the layer next to it, tending to oppose the relative motion between the two. As a result, the second layer moves with the velocity somewhat lower than that of the first.

This process goes on repeating itself down to the lowermost layer in contact with the fixed horizontal surface whose velocity is thus reduced to *zero.*

This tangential backward dragging force, coming into play in between two adjacent layers of a liquid and tending to oppose the relative motion between them, is called the **viscous force** *or the* **viscous drag.**

And, *the property of a liquid which gives rise to such viscous forces or which tends to oppose relative motion between its different layers is called* **viscosity** or **internal friction.**

It follows, therefore, that if a relative velocity between the layers of a liquid is to be maintained, an external force must ber applied to it. In the absence of such outside force, the relative motion between the layers is destroyed and the flow of the liquid ceases.

15.3 NEWTONS'S LAW OF VISCOUS FLOW—COEFFICIENT OF VISCOSITY

Referring back to Fig. 15.1 (*a*), if F be the external force applied to plate P to maintain a laminar or streamline flow of the liquid and v, the velocity of the uppermost layer, distant z from the lowermost or stationary layer, we have *tangential or shearing stress applied* = F/A, where A is the *surface area* of the layer.

And, since in 1 sec, a point a on the layer moves through a distance v to the position b, the *angle of shear* or *shear strain* produced in 1 sec = $< aob = \phi = v/z$.

Newton found that *the shear strain* ϕ *is a function of the shearing stress* F/A and is a measure of the viscosity of the liquid. He termed the ratio between F/A and ϕ as the *coefficient of viscosity* of the liquid, η. So that,

$$\textit{coefficient of viscosity of the liquid, } \eta = \frac{F/A}{\phi}$$

Now, unlike the case of a solid, where the displacement once produced stays constant so long as the shearing stress remains operative, in the present case of a liquid, as pointed out by *Maxwell* (See § 15.4), the liquid breaks down under the shearing stress but the shear is formed again, because the point a on the liquid surface gets displaced through distance v after every one second and a fresh shear ϕ is thus formed at intervals of one second. Thus, ϕ here stands not for shear strain but for the *rate of formation of shear*. And, we therefore, have

$$\textit{coefficient of viscosity, } \eta = \frac{F/A}{\phi} = \frac{\textit{shearing stress}}{\textit{rate of formation of shear}}$$

$$= \frac{F/A}{v/z}$$

Assuming the velocity-distribution curve to be a linear one [as shown in Fig. 15.1(*a*)], *i.e.*, assuming the velocity of the layers of the liquid to vary linearly with distance from the stationary layer, the quantity v/z represents the *rate of change of velocity with distance* (or the *space rate of change of velocity*) in a direction perpendicular to that of the liquid-flow It is called the **velocity gradient** in that direction. So that, we have

$$\eta = \frac{F/A}{\phi} = \frac{F/A}{v/z} = \frac{\textit{shearing stress}}{\textit{velocity gradient}}.$$

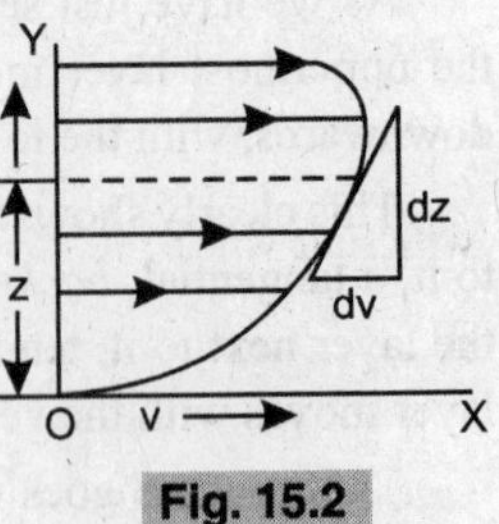

Fig. 15.2

In case the velocity-distribution curve be *not a linear one*, as shown in Fig. 15.1 (*b*), the velocity gradient is given by dv/dz, (Fig. 15.2). And we therefore have

$$\eta = \frac{F/A}{dv/dz}. \text{ Or, } F = \eta A \frac{dv}{dz}.$$

This is known as *Newton's law of viscous flow of a liquid* and is, obviously, applicable only when the flow is laminar or streamline.

Now, in the relation above, if $A = 1$ and $dv/dz = 1$, we have $F = \eta$.

Thus, the *coefficient of viscosity of a liquid may be defined as the tangential force required per unit area to maintain a unit velocity gradient* (*i.e., to maintain unit relative velocity between two layers unit distance apart*) *normal to the direction of flow,* and its value naturally depends upon the nature of the liquid, being greater for thick liquids like *pitch, wax, treacle* etc. than for thin liquids like *water*.

η is quite often referred to as the *absolute viscosity,* simply *viscosity* or *dynamic viscosity* to distinguish it from what is called *kinematic viscosity* which is the *ratio between dynamic viscosity and the density* of the liquid and is usually denoted by the letter v. Thus,

$$\textit{kinematic viscosity}, v = \frac{\textit{dynamic viscosity}}{\textit{density}} = \frac{\eta}{\rho}.$$

The reciprocal of dynamic viscosity (or, simply, viscosity) is called *fluidity*.

Units and dimensions of viscosity

Dynamic viscosity (η). Since $\eta = \dfrac{F}{A(dv/dz)}$, its dimensions in *force, length* and *time* are

$$\frac{F}{L^2\left(\frac{L/T}{L}\right)} = FL^{-2}T.$$

Its unit is the *C.G.S system* is thus 1 dyne cm^{-2} sec or 1 gm cm^{-1} sec^{-1}.

Or substituting the dimensions of F, its dimensions in *mass, length* and *time* are $MLT^{-2}L^{-2}T = ML^{-1}T^{-1}$.

This *C.G.S.* unit of dynamics viscosity is called the **poise** (*P*) after the French scientist *Poiseuille*, whose work on viscosity is important.

A *submultiple of poise, viz.*, the **centipoise** = 10^{-2} *poise* is commonly used, this being nearly the viscosity of water at 20°*C*.

A smaller submultiple, *micropoise* (μP) = 10^{-6} *poise* is also sometimes used.

(*ii*) *Kinematic viscosity* (v). Since $v = \eta/\rho$, its dimensions are

$$\frac{ML^{-1}T^{-1}}{ML^{-3}} = L^2T^{-1}.$$

The C.G.S. unit of kinematic viscosity is thus cm^2 sec^{-1}. It is called the **stokes,** after *Sir G.G. Stokes*, an English scientist. Usually, however, 1 *cm squared per sec* is called a *stoke.*

15.4 VISCOSITY, A FUGITIVE RIGITIDY

We have the relation for *coefficient of viscosity*,

$$\eta = \frac{F/A}{dv/dz} = \frac{tangental\ stress}{velocity\ gradient}, \qquad ...(i)$$

which, it will be readily seen, is very much akin to that for *coefficient of rigidity, viz,*

$$\eta = \frac{F/A}{\theta} = \frac{F/A}{dy/dx} = \frac{tangential\ stress}{displacement\ gradient} \qquad [\because \theta = dy/dx] \quad ...(ii)$$

Maxwell thus perceptively saw in the viscosity of a liquid a striking similarity with the limiting case of the rigidity of a solid when it breaks down under the shearing stress applied. He, therefore, rightly surmised that a liquid too possesses some rigidity but that it quickly breaks down under the shearing strain (or shear) produced by the shearing stress to which it is subjected. The shear, however, is formed over again and this process of breaking down and reformation of shear goes on continually so long as the sharing stress to which it is subjected. The shear goes on continually so long as the sharing stress continues to be applied.

A liquid thus offers only a momentary or a fleeting resistance to a shearing stress and is, therefore, said to possess a fleeting or *fugitive rigidity*.

Taking the rate of breakdown of the shear to be proportional to the shear (θ) itself, we have *rate of breakdown of shear* = $\lambda\theta$, where λ is a constant.

And, clearly *rate of formation of shear* is given by

$$\frac{d\theta}{dt} = \frac{d}{dt}\left(\frac{dy}{dz}\right) = \frac{d}{dz}\left(\frac{dy}{dt}\right) = \frac{dy}{dz} = \phi,$$

where v is the velocity in the same plane.

Obviously enough, for the liquid-motion to be steady, the rates of breakdown and formation of the shear must be the same. We, therefore, have

$$\lambda\theta = dv/dz, \text{ whence, } \theta / \frac{dv}{dz} = 1/\lambda. \qquad ...(iii)$$

From relations (*i*) and (*ii*) above, we have $\eta/n = \theta / \frac{dv}{dz}$.

Substituting for $\theta / \frac{dv}{dz}$ in relation (*iii*), therefore, we have $\eta/n = 1/\lambda$ or $\eta = n/\lambda$, where $1/\lambda$ is called the *time of relaxation*, i.e., the time taken by the shear to vanish, provided no fresh shear is allowed to be formed. Thus, the time t taken by the shear to fall to half its value is given by the relation $\lambda t = \log 2$.

15.5 STEADY OR STREAMLINE AND TURBULENT FLOW—LINES AND TUBES OF FLOW

The flow of a fluid is said to be *steady, orderly, streamline* or *laminar*, if the velocity at every point in the fluid remains constant (in magnitude as well as direction), *the energy needed to drive the fluid* being used up in overcoming the '*viscous drag*' between its layers. In other words, in a steady or streamline flow, each infinitesimally small volume element of the fluid, which we may call a *particle* of the fluid, follows exactly the same path and has exactly the same velocity as its predecessor, *i.e.*, its velocity does not change with time.

Thus, if a fluid flows along a path *ABC* (Fig. 15.3), where *A*, *B* and *C* are points inside the fluid, each new particle arriving at *A* will always have the same velocity $\vec{V}_A$ in a direction tangential to the curve *ABC* at *A*, and the pressure and density will always be the same there. Similarly, the particle arriving at *B* will always have the same velocity $\vec{V}_B$ which may or may not be the same as $\vec{V}_A$. And the same is true for the point *C*.

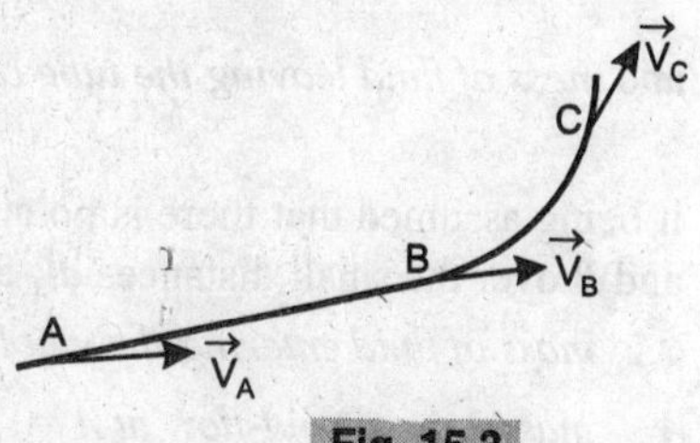

Fig. 15.3

This line ABC along which the particles of the fluid move, one after the other, with their velocities constant at the various points on it and directed along the tangents to these points, is called a **streamline**.

Or, more accurately, we may define a steam line as *a curve tangent to which at any points gives the direction of fluid-flow at that point.* Further, a streamline may be straight or curved according as the lateral pressure on it is the same throughout or different. In the latter case, the pressure is greater on the convex than on the concave side.

The fluid-flow, however, remains steady or streamline if its velocity does not exceed a limiting value, called its *critical velocity*, beyond which the flow loses all steadiness or orderliness and becomes zigzag and sinuous, acquiring what is called *turbulence*. (See § 15.12).

Now, considering an incompressible fluid in steady flow, if we take two areas A and B (Fig. 15.4), normal to the direction of flow and draw streamlines through their boundaries, a tabular portion of the liquid is enclosed by them, as shown. It is called a **tube of flow**.

The sides of the tube of flow being everywhere in the direction of flow, no fluid can possibly cross the sides and must enter and leave only through the ends. *A tube of flow thus functions, in effect, as a pipe of the same shape as its own, with the fluid entering it at one end and leaving at the other.*

15.6 EQUATION OF CONTINUITY OF FLOW

Usually referred to as simply the *equation of continuity*, it is a *fundamental equation of fluid-flow* and is a special case of the general physical law of conservation of matter. For an incompressible fluid it may be deduced as follows:

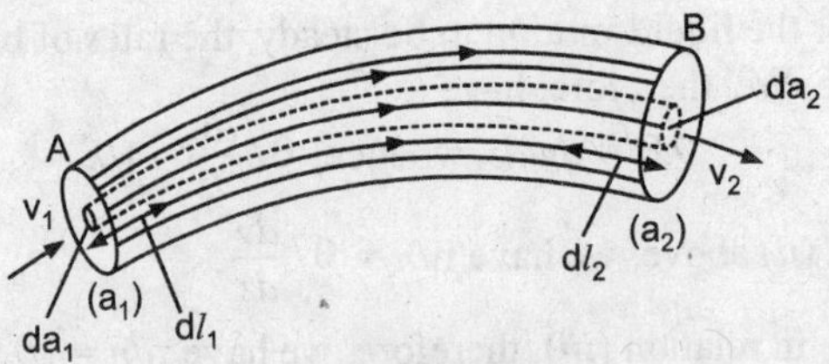

Fig. 15.4

Imagine the fluid to be flowing through a pipe AB, (Fig. 15.4), with a_1 and a_2 as its cross sectional areas at sections A and B.

Then, although the streamlines are all parallel to the axis of the pipe and perpendicular to its cross at every point, the velocity of flow is not necessarily the same at all sections of the pipe. Let is be v_1 at section A and v_2 at section B.

Consider an infinitely narrow tube of flow, shown dotted in the Figure, of cross-sectional areas da_1 and da_2 at sections A and B respectively. Then, if the fluid covers distances dl_1 and dl_2 in time δt at the two ends respectively and if ρ_1 and ρ_2 be the densities of the fluid at A and B, we have

mass of fluid entering the tube of flow per unit time at section A

$$= da_1 dl_1 \rho_1/\delta t = da_1 v_1 \rho_1 \qquad [\because dl_1/\delta t = v_1.]$$

and *mass of fluid leaving the tube of flow per unit time at section B*

$$= da_2 dl_2 \rho_2/\delta t = da_2 v_2 \rho_2, \qquad [\because dl_2/\delta t = v_2.]$$

it being assumed that there is no appreciable change in the cross sections of the tube at sections A and B over the small distances dl_1 and dl_2 respectively.

$\therefore$ *mass of fluid entering the whole section A of the pipe per unit time, i.e.,*

$$\textit{mass rate of fluid-flow at } A = \int_0^{a_1} da_1 v_1 \rho_1 = a_1 v_1 \rho_1$$

and *mass of fluid leaving the whole section B of the pipe per unit time,*

or *mass rate of fluid-flow at B* $= \int_0^{a_2} da_2 v_2 \rho_2 = a_2 v_2 \rho_2.$

Since the fluid is incompressible, $\rho_1 = \rho_2 = \rho$, say, and since there can be no flow across the sides of a tube of flow and there is no 'source' or 'sink' in between the sections A and B to add more fluid or to drain away some of it on its way from A to B, we have, from the law of conservation of matter.

mass of fluid entering section A per second

= mass of fluid leaving section B per second.

Or, $a_1 v_1 \rho = a_2 v_2 \rho$, *i.e.*, $\mathbf{a_1 v_1 = a_2 v_2}$.

This is called the equation of continuity and clearly means that the quantity av remains constant throughout the fluid-flow if it be steady or streamline (for, obviously, what is true of sections A and B of the pipe is equally true for all other sections of it).

Clearly, av is the volume of the fluid flowing across any cross-section of the pipe in unit time. It is, therefore, called the *volume rate of flow,* or, simply the **rate of flow** or the **rate of discharge** (or, also, *volume flux*) and may be denoted by the letter V or Q, the latter being the more appropriate symbol, used in Engineering practice and elsewhere.

Thus, the equation of continuity tells us that the *volume rate of flow of an incompressible fluid, (i.e., a liquid) remains constant throughout the flow, and so does its mass rate of flow of flow* ($av\rho$).

Further, since av = constant, it follows that $v \propto 1/a$, *i.e.*, the *velocity of the fluid-flow at any section of the pipe is inversely proportional to the cross-section of the pipe at that section.*

15.7 ENERGY OF THE FLUID

A fluid in steady or streamline flow may possess any or all of the three types of energy, *viz.*(*i*) *kinetic energy* because of its inertia, (*ii*) *potential energy* because of its position relative to the earth's surface and (*iii*) what is referred to as *pressure energy* because of its pressure; for if work be done o n it against its (hydrostatic) pressure,it can do the same amount of work back for us and thus acquires energy.

Let us obtain the value of each type of energy per unit mass and per unit volume of the fluid.

(*i*) Kinetic energy. If m be the mass of a fluid, of density ρ, flowing with velocity v, its kinetic energy is clearly $\frac{1}{2}mv^2$. And, therefore,

kinetic energy per unit mass of the mass of the fluid $= \frac{1}{2}v^2$.

And, since *mass of unit volume of the fluid = its density* ρ, we have

kinetic energy per unit volume of the fluid $= \frac{1}{2}v^2 \times \rho = \frac{1}{2}\rho v^2$.

(*ii*) Potential energy. If we have a mass m of the fluid at a height h above the earth's surface, its potential energy = mgh. And, therefore

potential energy per unit mass of the fluid = gh,

and *potential energy per unit volume of the fluid*

$= gh \times \rho = \rho gh.$

(*iii*) Pressure energy. Suppose we have a tube of uniform area of cross-section a, containing an incompressible *non-viscous* fluid, with its hydrostatic pressure equal to p. If we introduce an additional mass δm of the fluid into the tube against this pressure so gradually as not to impart any velocity, and hence any kinetic energy, to it and if the mass occupies at length δl of the tube, clearly,

work done on the mass = force × distance $= (pa) \times \delta l$,

Since the work done on mass δm of the fluid forms its pressure energy, we have

pressure energy per unit mass of the fluid = $(pa) \times \delta/\delta m$.

Now, δm = *volume* × *density* = $a\delta l \times \rho$.

So that, *pressure energy per unit mass of the fluid* = $pa\delta/a\delta l\rho = p/\rho$.

And ∴ *pressure energy per unit volume of the fluid*

$$= (p/\rho) \times \rho = p, \text{ its pressure.}$$

15.8 BERNOULLI'S THEOREM

The theorem enunciated by Daniel Bernoulli, in the year 1738, states that the total *energy of an incompressible, non-viscous fluid in steady flow remains constant throughout the flow*. The theorem may be easily deduced as follows:

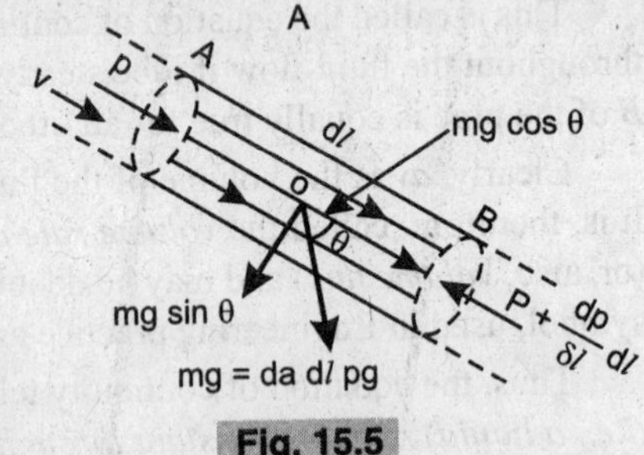

Fig. 15.5

Consider an infinitesimally small portion AB of a tube of flow of length dl (Fig. 15.5), and in view of its small length, let it area of cross portion be assumed to be uniform and equal to da.

Then, if ρ be the density of the fluid (supposed to be incompressible), its mass in portion $AB = m = dadl\rho$. Its weight $mg = da\, dl\rho g$, therefore, acts vertically downwards at its centre of gravity, O, making an angle θ with the direction of flow, as shown. So that, its component $mg \cos\theta$ $= da\, dl\rho g \cos\theta$ acts *in the direction of flow,* with its other component $mg \sin\theta = dadlg \sin\theta$ acting perpendicularly to the wall of the tube, its effect being offset by the lateral thrust due to the adjoining tube of flow.

If p be the pressure on face A of the tube, that on face B will be $p + \dfrac{\partial p}{\partial l} dl$, in the direction shown. And, therefore,

force acting on face A in the forward direction = $p\, da$,

and *force acting on face B in the backward direction*

$$= \left(p + \frac{\partial p}{\partial l} dl\right) da.$$

Hence, *net force acting on mass da dl*ρ *of the fluid in the tube*, say,

$$F = pda - \left(p + \frac{\partial p}{\partial l} dl\right) da + da\, dl\rho\, g \cos\theta.$$

Or, $$F = -\frac{\partial p}{\partial l} dl\, da + da\, dl\rho\, g \cos\theta. \quad \ldots(i)$$

If v be the velocity of the fluid as it enters the tube at A, we have its acceleration = dv/dt, where dt is the time taken by the fluid to cover the length dl of the tube. So that, *force acting on mass da dl*ρ *of the fluid in the tube* is also

$$= (mass)(acceleration), \text{ i.e., } F = dadl\rho\, dv/dt. \quad \ldots(ii)$$

Now, taking the most general case where the velocity, being a function of both distance and time, may change from point to point or from moment to moment, we have

$$dv = \frac{\partial v}{\partial l} dl + \frac{\partial v}{\partial t} dt \text{ and } \therefore \frac{dv}{dt} = \frac{\partial v}{\partial l}\frac{\partial l}{\partial t} + \frac{\partial v}{\partial t}.$$

Or, $$\frac{dv}{dt} = v\frac{\partial v}{\partial l} + \frac{\partial v}{\partial t}.$$

Substituting this value of dv/dt in expression (*ii*) above, we have $$F = da\, dl\rho\left(v\frac{\partial v}{\partial l} + \frac{\partial v}{dt}\right)$$

And, $\cos\theta = -\,\partial h/\partial l$, where h is the vertical height of tube AB from a chosen datum plane. Relation (*i*) above thus becomes

$$da\, dl\rho\left(v\frac{\partial v}{\partial l} + \frac{\partial v}{\partial t}\right) = -\frac{\partial p}{\partial l}dl\, da - dadl\rho g\frac{\partial h}{\partial l}.$$

Or, $$\rho\left(v\frac{\partial v}{\partial l} + \frac{\partial v}{\partial t}\right) = -\frac{\partial p}{\partial l} - \rho g\frac{\partial h}{\partial l}. \quad ...(iii)$$

This is an important equation, applicable to both steady and unsteady fluid-flow and is referred to as **Euler's eqaution**.

In the case of steady or streamline flow, $\partial v/\partial t = 0$ and the other partial derivatives all become total derivatives. so that, relation (*iii*) becomes

$$\rho v dv + dp + \rho g\, dh = 0. \quad \text{Or,} \quad v\, dv + dp/\rho + gdh = 0.$$

Integrating along the streamline, therefore, we have

$$\frac{1}{2}v^2 + \int\frac{dp}{\rho} + gh = constant.$$

This is called **Bernoulli's equation** which, in the case of the fluid being incompressible, and, therefore, ρ, a constant, takes the familiar form

$$\frac{1}{2}v^2 + p/\rho + gh = constant. \quad ...(iv)$$

Or, if we consider *unit volume* of the fluid, i.e., a *mass* ρ of the fluid (because mass of unit volume is the density ρ), we have on multiplying relation (*i*) by ρ,

$$\frac{1}{2}\rho v^2 + p + \rho gh = constant. \quad ...(v)$$

This is *another form of Bernoulli's equation* in terms of pressure, for as will be rapidly seen, every term on the left hand side has the dimensions of *pressure*.

Now, the term $(p + \rho gh)$ represents the pressure of the fluid even if it be at rest. It is, therefore, called *static pressure* of the fluid. And, the term $\frac{1}{2}\rho v^2$ represents the pressure of the fluid in virtue of its velocity v, and is, therefore, called dynamic pressure of the fluid. We thus have

static pressure + dynamic pressure = constant.

Again, on dividing relation (*iv*) by g, we have

$$\frac{1}{2}v^2/g + p/\rho g + h = constant, \quad (vi)$$

which is *yet another form of Bernoulli's equation* in terms of *lengths* or *heads*, as they are called. For, as can be easily seen, each term on the left hand side has the dimensions of *length* or a *height* and hence called a '*head*'. Thus, $\frac{1}{2}\frac{v^2}{g}$, is the velocity head*, $p/\rho g$, the *pressure head*, h, the *gravitational* head. So that, we have

velocity head + pressure head + gravitational head = total head = constant.

15.9 EULER'S EQUATION

For a non-steady flow of a non-viscous and incompressible liquid through a tube, the Euler's equation is

$$\rho\left(V\frac{\partial V}{\partial l} + \frac{\partial v}{\partial t}\right) = -\frac{\partial P}{\partial l} - \rho g\frac{\partial h}{\partial l} \quad ...(i)$$

* Because the fluid must fall through this height to attain the velocity v.

Dividing by ρ and re-arranging the terms, we get

$$\frac{1}{\rho}\frac{\partial P}{\partial l}+v\frac{\partial v}{\partial l}+g\frac{\partial h}{\partial l}+\frac{\partial v}{\partial t}=0 \quad ...(ii)$$

where v is the velocity of the liquid at a cross-section at distance l from the same reference point, ρ is the density of the liquid, $\partial p/\partial l$ is the rate of change of pressure with distance l, $\partial v/\partial l$ is the rate of change of velocity with distance; $\partial h/\partial l$ is the rate of change of vertical height of cross-section and $\partial v/\partial t$ is the acceleration of the liquid at the cross-section.

This equation (*ii*) is the Euler's equation and is applicable to both steady and non-steady flow of liquids.

Derivation of Bernoulli's Theorem

For steady and streamline flow, $\frac{\partial v}{\partial t}=0$

Substituting in Eq. (*ii*), we get

$$\frac{1}{\rho}\frac{\partial P}{\partial l}+v\frac{\partial v}{\partial l}+g\frac{\partial h}{\partial l}=0$$

Integrating *w.r.* to l along streamline flow, we get

$$\frac{1}{\rho}\int\frac{dP}{dl}dl+\int v\frac{dv}{dl}dl+g\int\frac{dh}{dl}dl = constant$$

$$\frac{1}{\rho}\int dP+\int v\,dv+g\int dh = constant$$

$$\frac{P}{\rho}+\frac{1}{2}v^2+gh = constant \quad ...(iii)$$

This is Bernoulli's equation for steady flow of unit mass.

15.10 APPLICATIONS OF BERNOULLI'S THEOREM

Following are some of the application is of Bernoulli's theorem.

15.10.1 Venturimeter

It is an arrangement to measure the rate of flow of a liquid in a pipe, usually that of water in the main of a city water supply (when it is sometimes called the *venturi water meter*) and is based on the *Bernoulli principle* that *in a liquid-flow, the pressure is the maximum where the velocity is the minimum and vice versa.* It was actually devised by an American engineer, *Clemens Herschel*, in the year 1886, but he gave it this name in honour of the Italian philosopher and engineer, **G.B. Venturi,** who had studied the phenomenon of liquid-flow through pipes almost a century earlier, in the year 1791.

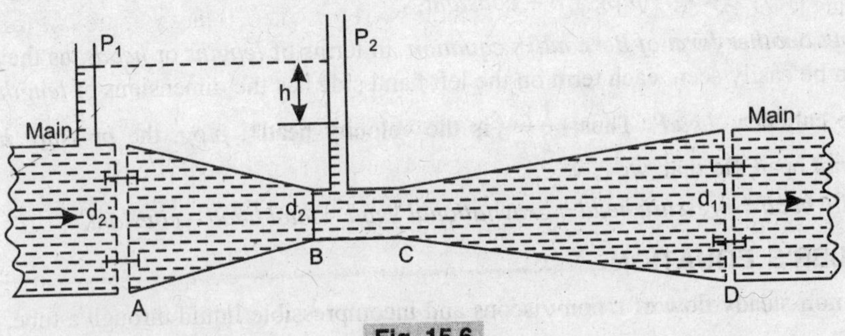

Fig. 15.6

As shown in Fig. 15.6, the venturimeter consists of three distinct parts: (*i*) **a convergent cone *AB***, with its diameter d_1 at its outer end A. tapering down to a much smaller diameter d_2 at its inner end *B*, the slope of its sides being 1 in 4 or 1 in 5, with the angle of convergence between 20° to 30°, (*ii*) **a short horizontal part** *BC*, of a uniform diameter d_2, called the **throat** and (*iii*) **a divergent cone** *CD*, also called the **diffuser**, with diameter d_2 at it inner end *C* and d_1, at its outer end *D*, the same as that of the outer end (*A*) of the convergent cone (*AB*) but the slope of its sides is very much smaller, being 1 in 10 or even 1 in 20, with the angle of divergence, between 5° or 14°, so that it is considerably longer than the convergent cone.

The diameter (d_1) *of the inlet or upstream end A of cone AB and of the outlet or downstream end D of cone CD is actually the same as that of the water Main* in which the rate of flow is to be determined and to which it is connected on either side, as shown. And the ratio of the diameter of the throat to that of the outer end of either cone (or that of the water Main), *i.e.*, d_2/d_1, is called the **throat ratio** and may vary between 1/4 to 3/4, though usually it is 1/2.

The function of the convergent cone *AB* is to reduce the cross-sectional area of the water stream so as to increase its velocity and decrease its pressure difference at the throat, thus bringing about an appreciable pressure between the inlet end *A* of the cone and the throat. The throat ratio (d_2/d_1) must, however, be such that the pressure at the throat does not become negative (*i.e.*, less than atmospheric). For, then, the water gives out its dissolved air and starts vaporising, thereby breaking the continuity of the water stream. And the function of the divergent cone (or the diffuser) *CD* is to change the cross-sectional area of the water stream,and hence also its velocity and pressure, back to the same as at the inlet *A* of cone *AB* or in the water Main.

Thus, whereas in the convergent cone, the water stream gets accelerated at it moves towards the throat, in the divergent cone (or the diffuser) it gets *decelerated* as it moves away from the throat. Now, there is no harm in hastening the acceleration of the stream but hastening its deceleration may result in its breaking away from the walls of the cone due to what is called the 'boundary layer effect,' rolling itself up into vertices and being left behind, forming what is called a '*wake*'. It is precisely to avert this possibility that the slope of the divergent cone is made much more gradual than that of the convergent cone. Even so, *for the measurement of the rate of flow, we always use, as a precautionary measure, the pressure difference between the inlet A of the convergent cone and the throat and never the one between the outlet D of the divergent cone and the throat.*

Another obvious precaution is that *the venturimeter must always be run full of water* or else any air present in it may dirupt the continuity of the water stream.

To measure the pressure difference between the inlet *A* and the throat, two narrow vertical glass tubes, *i.e.*, piezometer tubes*, P_1 and P_2, are fixed right at the end *A*, or better still, in the water main itself, close to the end *A*, and the mid-point of the throat respectively, as shown.

Calculations. The velocity of the water stream being much higher, and hence the pressure much lower, at the throat than at the inlet *A* (or in the main), the height of the water column in tube P_2 is much smaller than that in tube P_1, measured from the axis of the venturimeter (shown dotted) as the datum level. Let the difference between the two be h. Then, if the pressure at *A* (or in the main) be p_1 and that at the throat, p_2, we have

$$p_1 - p_2 = h\rho g, \qquad \ldots(i)$$

where ρ is the density of water, taken to be constant throughout.

And, if a_1 and a_2 be the cross-sectional areas of the end *A* (or the main) and the throat respectively, and v_1 and v_2, the respective velocities of the water stream there, we have, in accordance with the *equation of continuity*,

rate of flow of water stream, $Q = a_1v_1 = a_2v_2$, whence, $v_2/v_1 = a_1/a_2$ ...(*ii*)

Now, in accordance with *Bernoulli's equation*,

$$p_1/\rho + \frac{1}{2}v_1^2 = p_2/\rho + \frac{1}{2}v_2^2.$$

(The venturimeter being horizontal, $h_1 = h_2 = constant$)

* So called, from 'Piezo' meaning 'pressure'.

Or, $\dfrac{p_1}{\rho} - \dfrac{p_2}{\rho} = \dfrac{v_2^2}{2} - \dfrac{v_1^2}{2}$. Or, $p_1 - p_2 = \rho\left(\dfrac{v_2^2 - v_1^2}{2}\right)$

Or, $$h\rho g = \rho\left(\frac{v_2^2 - v_1^2}{2}\right). \qquad [\because \; p_1 - p_2 = h\rho g.]$$

Multiplying and dividing the right hand side of the equation by v_1^2, we have

$$h\rho g = \frac{\rho v_1^2}{2}\left(\frac{v_2^2 - v_1^2}{v_1^2}\right) = \frac{\rho v_1^2}{2}\left(\frac{v_2^2}{v_1^2} - 1\right).$$

Or, substituting for v_2/v_1 from relation (*ii*) above, we have

$$h\rho g = \frac{\rho v_1^2}{2}\left(\frac{a_1^2}{a_2^2} - 1\right) = \frac{\rho v_1^2}{2}\left(\frac{a_1^2 - a_2^2}{a_2^2}\right) \qquad ...(iii)$$

Or, $$v_1^2 = \frac{2hga_2^2}{a_1^2 - a_2^2}, \text{ whence, } v_1 = a_2\sqrt{\frac{2hg}{a_1^2 - a_2^2}}.$$

Hence, **rate of flow of water** through the venturimeter and, therefore, also through the main, *i.e.*,

$$Q = a_1 v_1 = a_1 a_2\sqrt{\frac{2hg}{a_1^2 - a_2^2}}. \qquad ...(iv)$$

The factor $\sqrt{2g/(a_1^2 - a_2^2)}$ clearly depends upon the dimensions of the venturimeter and the value of g at the place. It is, therefore, known for a given instrument at a given place and is called the constant of the *venturimeter*, denoted by the letter C. So that,

rate of flow or rate of discharge, $Q = C\sqrt{h}$.

This gives the *theoretical rate of discharge of water* when we neglect the slight fall in the pressure head between A and B. If we take this too into account, we have

rate of discharge $= kC\sqrt{h}$,

where k is called the coefficient of discharge, its usual value being 0.97.

And thus, *rate of discharge*, $Q = 0.97\,C\sqrt{h}$.

15.10.2 The Pitot Tube

This too is a simple device, based on Bernoulli's theorem, for the measurement of velocities of flowing liquids and hence their rates of flow.

It owes its name to a Frenchman, *Henry Pitot*, who, in the year 1730, happened to dip one end of a bent glass tube into the river *Siene*, at Paris, and observed that water rose into the tube. An open-ended L-shaped tube thus came to be known as a *Pitot tube*. Usually, however, there is only an aperture at the smaller bent end, whereas the other end is quite open. Let us study its working.

Let v be the velocity if the liquid-flow in the direction shown in Fig. 15.7 and let its pressure at any point such as A be p_A. *This pressure of the undisturbed liquid is called it static pressure.*

Now, let a Pitot tube T be immersed into the liquid, with the aperture at its nose B facing the liquid-flow (*i.e.*, with the plane of the aperture normal to the direction of liquid-flow) and lying some distance away from A but on the same streamline with it. The liquid-flow will be brought to a stop at the nose B of the tube, which is, therefore, known as the *stagnation point* of the tube. The whole of the kinetic energy of the liquid will be converted here into potential energy and the liquid will rise into the tube up to a certain height, as shown. This liquid column inthe tube thus measures the *total pressure* or the *stagnation pressure* at B. Let is be p_B.

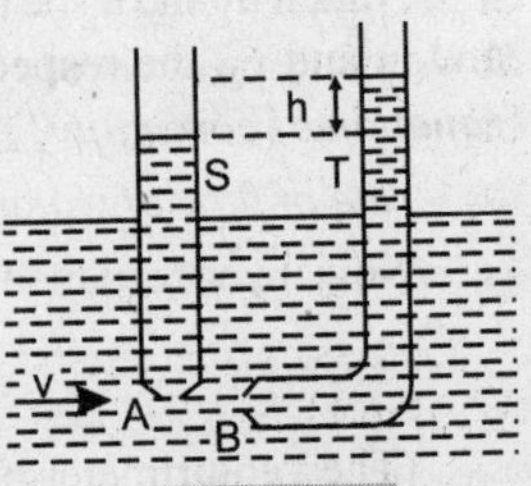

Fig. 15.7

Then, applying *Bernoulli's equation* to points B and A, lying on the same streamline, we have

$$p_A + \frac{1}{2}\rho v^2 = p_B + 0, \qquad [\because \text{ the velocity of the liquid at } B = 0]$$

where ρ is the density of the liquid, supposed to remain constant.

$$\therefore \qquad \frac{1}{2}\rho v^2 = p_B - p_A$$

= *total or stagnation pressure at B – the static pressure at A.*

To determine the static pressure at A, we immerse into the liquid another straight tube S, quite close to T, with the aperture at its lower end lying at A, such that the plane of the aperture is parallel to the liquid-flow. The liquid will also rise into this tube (S) because of the static pressure at A and the height of the liquid column in it will thus measure the static pressure p_A at A. So that, the difference (h) in the levels of the liquid column in T and S will measure $(p_B - p_A)$, *i.e.*,

$$p_B - p_A = h\rho g,$$

and $\therefore$ $\frac{1}{2}\rho v^2 = h\rho g$, whence, $v^2 = 2gh$.

Or, *velocity of liquid-flow*, $v = \sqrt{2gh}$.

The combination of the two tubes S and T, either placed separately, as shown or joined together at the upper ends, rather than tube T alone, is more commonly spoken of as the *Pitot tube.*

And, as can be easily seen, if a be the cross-sectional area of the channel or the pipe at the place where the Pitot tube is placed in it, we have

rate of liquid-flow, $Q = av = a\sqrt{2gh}$.

15.10.3 Lift of an Aeroplane

The wings of the aeroplane are made tapering as shown in fig. 15.8. The upper surface is made convex and the lower surface is made concave. Due to this shape of the wings, the air currents at the top have a large velocity than at the bottom ($v_1 > v_2$). Consequently according to the Bernoulli's equation, the pressure above the surface of the wing is less as compared to the lower surface of the wing. The difference of pressure creates an upward force on the wing, normal to the flow of air. This force provides upward lift for the aeroplane.

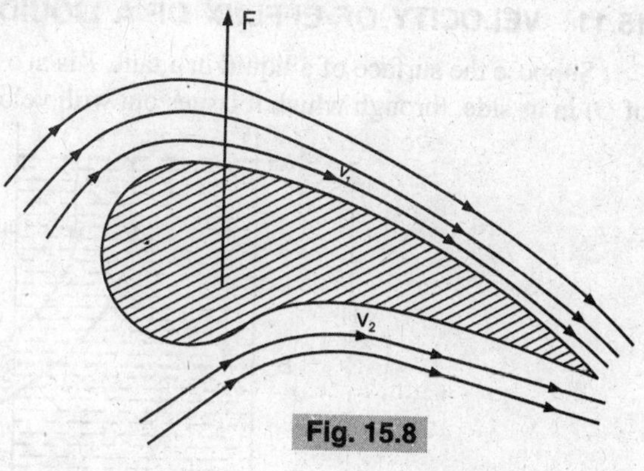

Fig. 15.8

15.10.4 Bunsen Burner

In bunsen burner, the gas enters the base and comes out of the nozzle N. As the cross-section of the nozzle is very small, the velocity of the gas emerging out is very high. Consequently, pressure just above the nozzle decreases. Air from the atmosphere rushes into the burner. The mixture of gas and air moves up in the burner and burns at the top.

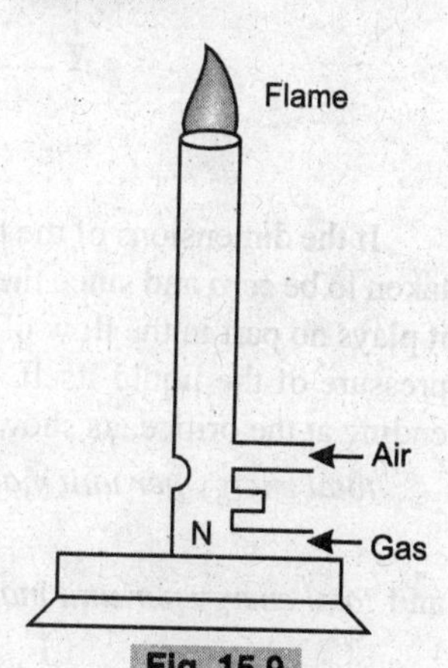

Fig. 15.9

15.10.5 Atomiser or Sprayer

An atomiser consists of an air pump T and a bottle containing liquid to be sprayed (Fig. 15.10). Air is blown through the tube T by compressing a rubber tube fitted at its neck. Air rushes out through the jet (orifice O) with high velocity. The pressure at the orifice O of tube A, according to Bernoulli's theorem, decreases and thereby the liquid rises up in the tube are divided into very fine enormous droplets by high velocity jet.

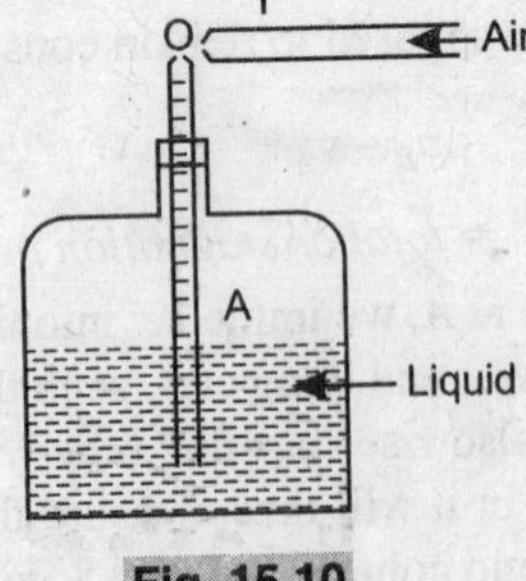

Fig. 15.10

15.10.6 Carburettor

Carburettor is a chamber to mix air and petrol vapour in an internal combustion engine. Air is allowed to enter through a nozzle with large velocity. The pressure is lowered and the petrol is sucked up into the chamber. The petrol vaporizes quickly. The mixed vapours of petrol and air are fed into the carburettor chamber where it burns at the moment spark is produced by spark plug.

15.10.7 Blowing of Roofs

Due to wind, storms or cyclone, the roofs are blown off. When a high velocity wind blows over the roof, a considerably lower pressure at the top of the roof is created. As the pressure on the lower side of the roof is higher, the roofs are easily blown off, without damaging the walls of the building.

15.11 VELOCITY OF EFFLUX OF A LIQUID—TORRICELLI'S THEOREM

Suppose the surface of a liquid in a tank T is at a height h from the orifice O (*i.e.*, from the axis of O) in its side, through which it issues out with velocity v (Fig. 15.11), called its *velocity of efflux*.

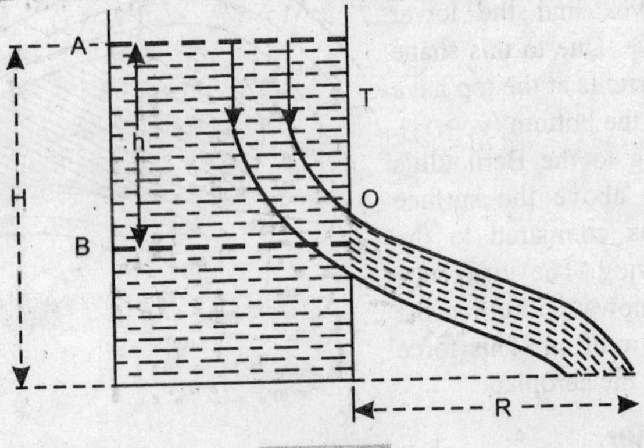

Fig. 15.11

If the dimensions of the tank be sufficiently large, the velocity of the liquid at its surface may be taken to be *zero* and since the pressure there as well as at the orifice O is the same, *viz.*,atmospheric, it plays no part in the flow of the liquid, which thus occurs purely in consequence of the hydrostatic pressure of the liquid itself. So that, considering a tube of flow, starting at the liquid surface and ending at the orifice, as shown, and applying Bernoulli's theorem, we have

total energy per unit mass of the liquid at the surface = *K.E.* + *P.E.* + *Pressure energy*

$$= 0 + gh + 0 = gh,$$

and *total energy per unit mass of the liquid at the orifice*

$$\frac{1}{2}v^2 + 0 + 0 = \frac{1}{2}v^2.$$

Since total energy of the liquid must remain constant in steady flow, in accordance with Bernoulli's theorem, we have

$$\frac{1}{2}v^2 = gh, \text{ whence, } v^2 = 2gh. \text{ Or, } \textit{velocity of efflux}, v = \sqrt{2gh}.$$

Evangelista Torricelli showed in the year 1644 that this velocity is the same as the liquid will attain in falling freely through the vertical height (h) from the surface to the orifice. For then, if v be the velocity attained by the liquid, we have $v^2 - u^2 = 2aS$.

Or, $v^2 - 0 = 2gh$ ($\because$ here, $u = 0$, $a = g$ and $S = h$), whence $v^2 = 2gh$ or $v = \sqrt{2gh}$, the same as the velocity of efflux deduced above.

This is known as **Terricelli's theorem or law,** or the **law of efflux** and may be stated thus:

The velocity of efflux or a liquid issuing out of an orifice is the same as it would attain if allowed to fall freely through the vertical height between the liquid surface and the orifice.

No liquid being free internal friction or viscosity, however, this ideal velocity $v = \sqrt{2gh}$ is never actually attained in practice. The observed velocity is always less than v and is equal to $C_v\sqrt{2gh}$, where C_v is what called the *coefficient of velocity*, its value lying between 0.95 to 0.99 in the case of water, depending upon the '*head*' of water (*i.e.*, depth of the orifice from the water surface) and the shape of the orifice. Its usual value is, however taken to be 0.97 if the orifice to be circular and sharp-edged. So that, *actual or observed velocity of efflux* in the case of water is given by $0.97\sqrt{2gh}$.

Vena Contracta. The liquid entering the orifice O comes not only from a direction perpendicular to its plane but from all sides, as shown in Fig. 15.12, with the streamlines near the edges of the orifice all getting curved, as indicated. And, since on account of inertia, the liquid entering the orifice from the sides still possesses a lateral (*i.e.*, upward or downward) velocity, it continues to move towards the centre of cross-section of the jet until the outward pressure in it is just balanced by the atmospheric pressure on it.

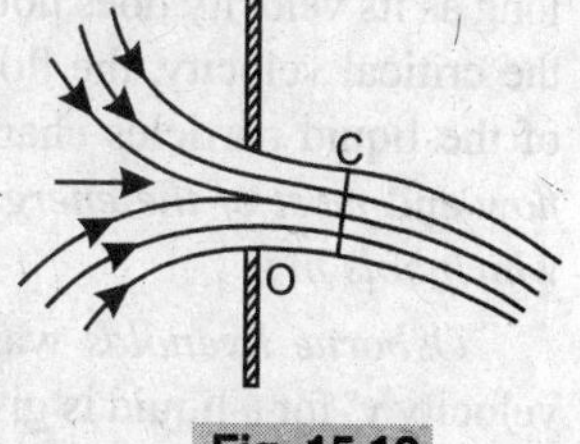

Fig. 15.12

As a result, the cross-section of the jet goes on contracting upto a little distance, equal to about half the diameter of the orifice beyond it, say, up to C, where it acquires its minimum value, forming a short of *neck*, called *contracted vein* or, more commonly, *vena contracta*. The cross-section of the jet remains uniform hereafter, with the stream-lines all parallel to each other and perpendicular to the plane of the orifice, and its velocity remains constant.

Since velocity varies inversely as the cross-section of a tube of flow, it clearly has its maximum value at the *vena contracta,* where the cross-section is the least. It is the velocity which is given by Torricelli's expression $v = \sqrt{2gh}$ for the velocity of efflux of the liquid.

Now, the cross-section of the jet at the vena contracta C is smaller than that of the orifice O. The ratio between the two is referred to as the *coefficient of contraction*, denoted by the symbol C_c. Its theoretical value is $\pi/(\pi + 2) = 0.611$, but it may go up to 0.69, depending upon the '*head*' of liquid and the size and shape of the orifice. For circular and sharp-edged orifices it is very nearly equal to 0.624.

It thus follows that the volume of a liquid issuing out of an orifice in unit time *i.e.*, its *rate of flow of liquid through the orifice* = C_vC_cva, where a is the area of cross-section of the orifice.

And, since $C_vC_c = C_D$, called the *coefficient of discharge*, we have *rate of flow of liquid through the orifice* = $C_D\, a\sqrt{2gh}$. For water, $C_D = 0.62$, so that *rate of flow of water through a circular, sharp edged orifice* = $0.62\, a\sqrt{2gh}$.

Velocity of efflux of a gas. Since a gas issues out of an orifice in a reservoir under adiabatic conditions, we have, from *Bernoulli's equation* for adiabatic flow of a gas,

$$\frac{1}{2}v^2 + \frac{\gamma}{\gamma-1}\frac{p}{\rho} = \frac{1}{2}v_0^2 + \frac{\gamma}{\gamma-1}\frac{P_o}{\rho_o},$$

where, vo, p_o and ρ_o are the ***velocity, pressure*** and ***density*** of the gas inside the reservoir and v, p and ρ their respective values as the gas issues out of the orifice in the reservior, so that v is the *velocity of* efflux of the gas.

Since, obviously, $v_o = 0$, we have

$$\frac{1}{2}v^2 = \frac{\gamma}{\gamma-1}\left(\frac{p_o}{\rho_o} - \frac{p}{\rho}\right). \text{ Or, } v^2 = \frac{2\gamma}{\gamma-1}\left(\frac{p_o}{\rho_o} - \frac{p}{\rho}\right)$$

Because under adiabatic conditions, $p_o/p_o^{\gamma} = p/\rho^{\gamma}$, we have

$$v^2 = \frac{2\gamma}{\gamma-1}\cdot\frac{p_o}{\rho_o}\left[1-\left(\frac{p}{p_0}\right)^{\frac{\gamma-1}{\gamma}}\right],$$

whence, v, *the velocity of efflux of the gas*, may be easily obtained.

15.12 CRITICAL VELOCITY

It has been pointed out earlier (§ 15.6) that the flow of a liquid remains steady or orderly only so long as its velocity does not exceed a certain limiting value for it, called its *critical velocity*. Beyond the critical velocity, the flow loses all its steadiness and orderliness, with the paths and velocities of the liquid particles changing continuously and haphazardly. Such a flow is called a *turbulent flow* and *most of the energy needed to drive the liquid is now dissipated in setting up eddies and whirlpools in it.*

Osborne Ryenolds was the first to have shown experimentally that the value of the critical velocity v_e for a liquid is given by $v_e = k\eta/\rho r$, a relation naturally called *Osborne Reynolds' formula*, where η and ρ stand for the *coefficient of viscosity and density of the liquid respectively*, r for the *radius of the tube* and k is a number, called *Reynold's number*. The value of k being very high, it is usually represented on a logarithmic scale. For narrow tubes, however, it is usually taken to be 1000.

Deduction of the expression for v_e by the method of dimensions. The critical velocity of a liquid depending upon the *coefficient of viscosity* (η) and on the density (ρ) of the liquid as also on the radius (r) of the tube through which it flows, we may put

$$v_e = k\eta^a\rho^b r^c, \text{ where k is dimensionless constant.}$$

Or, $$[LT^{-1}] = [ML^{-1}T^{-1}]^a[ML^{-3}]^b[L]^c = [M^{a+b}L^{-a-3b+c}T^{-a}]$$

So that, $a + b = 0, -a - 3b + c = 1$ and $-a = -1$.

And, therefore, $a = 1, b = -1$ and $c = -1$.

Thus, $v_e = k\eta/\rho r$, where k is *Reynolds' number*.

The critical velocity (v_c) of a liquid flowing through a tube (or pipe) is thus proportional directly to its coefficient (η) and inversely to its density (ρ) and the radius (r) of the tube (or the pipe).

If follows at once, therefor, that the follow of liquids of higher viscosity and lower density through narrow tubes tends to be steady or orderly, whereas that of liquids of lower viscosity and higher density through broader tubes tends to be disorderly or turbulent.

And, since $v_c \propto 1/r$, all liquids, irrespective to their viscosities, flow equally readily through tubes or pipes of wide bores. Thus, in a wide tube, a highly viscous liquid like treacle will flow just as freely as water. A typical example is that of the highly viscous lava flowing freely down the sides of an erupting volcano—its rate of flow being the same as though it were water.

On the other hand, since for a perfectly *mobile* or *inviscid* liquid, $\eta = 0$, its critical velocity v_e too is zero. So that, its flow will always be disorderly or turbulent, howsoever narrow the tube and slow its rate of flow.

It will thus be seen that it is by virtue of its viscosity alone that a liquid can possibly have a smooth, orderly flow, approximating to the streamline flow of a perfect fluid.

15.13 SIGNIFICANCE OF REYNOLD'S NUMBER

We have the relation for critical velocity, $v_e = k\eta/\rho r$. Or, since $\eta/\rho = \nu$, the *kinematic viscosity* of the liquid, we have $v_c = k\nu/r$, whence, the *Reynold's number* $k = v_c r/\nu$, *a pure number* with no dimensions in *MLT*.

Surprisingly enough, Reynolds failed to realise the full implications and importance of this '*group*' constituting the number that bears his name and considered it to be merely a criterion for the critical velocity of a liquid flowing through a pipe or a closed channel.

It was *Lord Rayleigh* who not only pointed out that this '*group*' was a dimensionless quantity or a *numeric* but also that *it really governed all problems on fluid motion in which inertia forces and viscous forces* (*but not gravity forces*) *were operative*; for example, in the case of (*i*) enclosed fluid-flow like the one in pipes, closed channels, pumps or turbines (where the gravity forces are ineffective) and (*ii*) motion of bodies completely immersed in the fluid (where the gravity forces are balanced by buoyant forces), like ordinary vehicles and aeroplanes (immersed in air) and submarines (immersed in water). *It is, in fact, the ratio of the inertia and viscous forces in any given case.*

The expression for it, therefore, is generalised in the form

$$k = v\rho D/\eta \text{ or } k = vD/\nu,$$

where D replaces r and represents the diameter (or radius) of pipes or closed channels in case (*i*) and any particular dimensions, like length or diameter, of the moving body in case (*ii*), and v, the velocity of the fluid-flow or of the moving body.

Rayleigh pointed out that two fluid-flows or motions of two bodies immersed in viscous media are *mechanically* or *dynamically* similar if (*a*) the shapes of the pipes or those of the moving bodies are *geometrically similar*, whatever their actual dimensions and (*b*) the Reynold's number for both is the same, *i.e.*, even if the individual parameters v, ρ, D and η be entirely different for the two pipes or the two bodies, the group $v\rho D/\eta$, as a whole, (constituting the Reynolds' number k), remains the same for either pipe or for either body. When this is so, the fluid-flow, whether steady or turbulent, will be similar in the two bodies will be similar in case (*ii*).

15.14 POISEUILLE'S EQUATION FOR LIQUID-FLOW THROUGH A NARROW TUBE

In deducing an expression for the rate of flow of a liquid through a narrow tube, *Poiseuille* made the following assumptions:

(*i*) *The liquid-flow is steady or streamline, with the streamlines parallel to the axis of the tube.*

(*ii*) *Since there is no radial flow, the pressure, in accordance with Bernoulli's theorem, is constant over any given cross-section of the tube.*

(*iii*) *The liquid in contact with the walls of the tube is stationary.*

All these assumptions are found to be quite valid if the tube be narrow and velocity of liquid-flow really small.

Remembering further that a liquid yields to the smallest shearing stress and taking the tube to be horizontal to eliminate the effect of gravity on the liquid-flow, we may proceed to deduce Poiseuille's equation as follows:

Let a liquid of coefficient of viscosity η be flowing through a narrow horizontal tube of *radius* r and *length* l and when the conditions become steady, let the velocity of flow at all points on an imaginary, coaxial cylindrical shell of the liquid, of radius x, be v (Fig. 15.13) and, therefore, the velocity gradient, dv/dx.

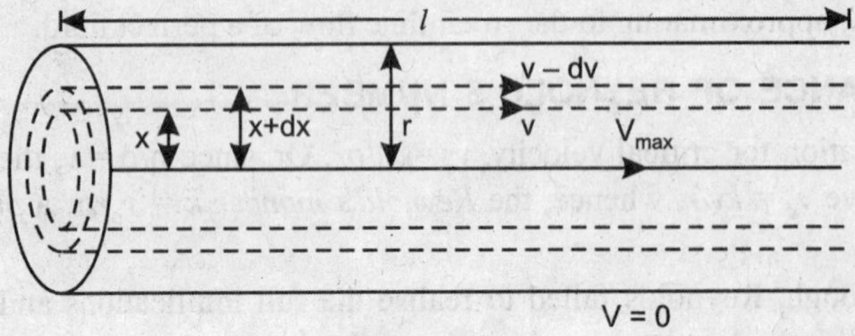

Fig. 15.13

Since the velocity of the liquid in contact with the walls of the tube is *zero* and goes on increasing as the axis is approached, where it is the maximum, it is clear that the liquid layer just inside the imaginary shell is moving faster, and the one just outside it, slower, than it. So that, in accordance with *Newton's law of viscous flow*, the *background dragging force on the imaginary liquid shell* is given by $F = \eta A dv/dx = 2\pi x l \eta dv/dx$, where A is the *surface area* of the shell, equal to $2\pi xl$.

And, if the pressure difference across the two ends of the tube be P, the *force on the liquid shell, accelerating it forwards* $= P \times \pi x^2$, where πx^2 is the area of cross-section of the shell.

For the liquid-flow to be steady, therefore, we must have driving force equal to backward dragging force, i.e., $P \times \pi x^2 = -2\pi x l \eta \; dv/dx$, the $-ve$ sign of the dragging force indicating that it acts in a direction opposite to that of the driving force. We, therefore, have

$$dv = -\frac{P\pi x^2 dx}{2\pi x l \eta} = -\frac{Pxdx}{2\eta l}, \text{ which, on integration, gives}$$

$$v = -\frac{P}{2\eta l}\int x dx = -\frac{P}{2\eta l}\cdot\frac{x^2}{2} + C_1,$$

where C_1 is a constant of integration.

Since at $x = r$, $v = 0$, we have $0 = -\dfrac{Pr^2}{4\eta l} + C_1$. Or, $C_1 = \dfrac{Pr^2}{4\eta l}$.

∴ velocity of flow at distance x from the axis of the tube, *i.e.*,

$$v = -\frac{Px^2}{4\eta l} + \frac{Pr^2}{4\eta l} = \frac{P}{4\eta l}(r^2 - x^2).$$

which, incidentally shows at one that the profile or the velocity distribution curve of the advancing liquid is a parabola [as shown in Fig.15.1(*b*)], the velocity increasing from zero at the walls of the tube to a maximum at its axis.

Now, if we imagine another coaxial cylindrical shell of the liquid, of radius $x + dx$, enclosing the shell of radius x, the cross-sectional area between the two is clearly $2\pi x dx$ and, therefore, volume of the liquid flowing per second through this area is, say, $dQ = 2\pi x dx v$.

Imagining the whole of the liquid inside the tube to consists of such coaxial cylindrical shells, the volume of the liquid flowing through all of them per second *i.e.*, the *rate of flow through the tube, as a whole* say, Q, is obtained by integrating the expression for dQ between the limits $x = 0$ and $x = r$. We thus have rate of liquid flow through the narrow tube, *i.e.*,

$$Q = \int_0^r 2\pi x dx v = \int_0^r 2\pi x \frac{P}{4\eta l}(r^2 - x^2)dx$$

$$= \frac{\pi P}{2\eta l}\left[\frac{x^2 r^2}{2} - \frac{x^4}{4}\right]_0^r = \frac{\pi P}{2\eta l}\left(\frac{r^4}{2} - \frac{r^4}{4}\right) = \frac{\pi P}{2\eta l}\cdot\frac{r^4}{4}.$$

Or, $$Q = \frac{\pi P r^4}{8\eta l} \quad \text{...(I)}$$

whence, $$\eta = \frac{\pi P r^4}{8Ql} \quad \text{...(II)}$$

15.15 POISEUILLE'S METHOF FOR DETERMINING COEFFICIENT OF VISCOSITY OF A LIQUID

The method, suitable only for liquids having a low viscosity, like water, consists in collecting in a weighted beaker the liquid flowing out in a trickle, in a given time t (in sec), from a tall cylinder C through a horizontal capillary tube T of radius r and a known length l, fitted near its bottom, the liquid head h being kept constant by means of an overflow tube O, as shown in Fig. 15.14.

Dividing the mass of the liquid collected in the beaker by its density ρ and the time t, its *rate of flow* Q is obtained. Then, from the relation $\eta = \pi P r^4/8Ql$, (where $P = h\rho g$), the value of η for the liquid can be easily calculated.

Source of error. These are two important sources of error in the simple Poiseuille experiment above:

(*i*) *The liquid-flow all along the length of the capillary flow-tube* (T) *is not uniform or streamline, as assumed.* For, the motion of the liquid where it enters the flow-tube is clearly accelerated and does not become uniform or streamline until after covering a good length of it.

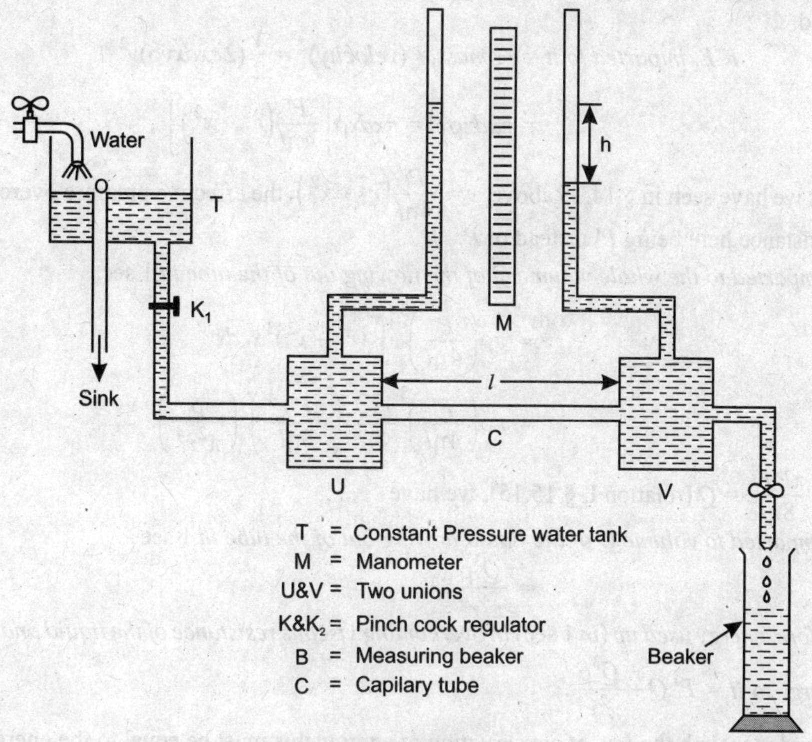

Fig. 15.14

This error is, however, easily eliminated if the *effective length* of the flow-tube is taken to be $(l + \alpha)$ instead of l, where α is almost invariably found to be equal to $1.64r$. *The correction* (α) *is thus quite independent of the length of the tube but depends upon its radius.*

•

This effective length $(l+\alpha) = (1 + 1.64\, r)$ is, therefore, substituted in the place of l in the relation for η.

(ii) *Part of the pressure difference P between the two ends of the flow-tube is used up in imparting kinetic energy to the liquid flowing through the tube;* so that, *only the remainder,* say, P', *is really responsible for overcoming the viscous resistance of the liquid.* In other words, the *effective pressure difference* for our purpose is P', which should, therefore, be substituted for P in the relation for η.

The value of P' can, however, be easily obtained. For, with P as the actual pressure difference between the two ends of the flow-tube, we have

pressure energy per unit volume of the liquid $= P$. [See § 15.8 (*iii*)]

$\therefore$ *Therefore, pressure energy of volume Q of the liquid (flowing out of the tube per second)*

$$= P \cdot Q.$$

The flow-tube being horizontal, this is thus also the *total energy of volume Q* of the liquid to start with.

Of this, a part $P'.Q$ is used up in overcoming the viscous resistance of the liquid in 1 sec (because the liquid flowing out in 1 sec is Q.)

To calculate the kinetic energy imparted to the liquid, we recall that the *volume of liquid flowing per second through the annular space between two cylindrical layers, of radii x and (x + dx) respectively = cross sectional area of the annular space × velocity of the liquid there* $= 2\pi x dx v$,

$\therefore$ *mass of the liquid flowing per sec through this annular space* $= 2\pi x dx v\rho$, where ρ is the *density* of the liquid.

Hence, $$\textit{K.E. imparted to it} = \frac{1}{2}\textit{mass} \times (\textit{velocity})^2 = \frac{1}{2}(2\pi x dx v\rho)v^2$$

$$= \pi x dx \rho v^3 = \pi x dx \rho\left[\frac{P'}{4\eta l}\left(r^2 - x^2\right)\right]^3,$$

because, as we have seen in § 14.15 above, $v = \dfrac{P'}{4\eta l}\left(r^2 - x^2\right)$, the effective pressure overcoming the viscous resistance here being P' instead of P.

$\therefore$ *K.E. imparted to the whole volume Q of the flowing out of the tube in* 1 sec.

$$= \pi\rho\left(\frac{P'}{4\eta l}\right)^3 \int_0^r (r^2 - x^2)^3\, x.\, dx$$

$$= \pi\rho\left(\frac{P'}{4\eta l}\right)^3 \frac{r^8}{8} = \left(\frac{\pi P' r^4}{8\eta l}\right)^3\left(\frac{\rho}{\pi^2 r^4}\right).$$

Since $\dfrac{\pi P' r^4}{8\eta l} = Q$ (relation I, § 15.15), we have

K.E. imparted to volume Q of the liquid flowing out of the tube in 1 sec

$$= \frac{Q^3\rho}{\pi^4 r^4}.$$

Therefore, energy used up (*in* 1 sec) *in overcoming viscous resistance of the liquid and imparting kinetic energy to it* $= P'.Q + \dfrac{Q^3\rho}{\pi^2 r^4}$.

In accordance with the *law of conservation of energy*, this must be equal to the energy initially possessed by the liquid, *i.e.*, $P.Q$. We, therefore, have

$$P \cdot Q = P' \cdot Q + (Q^3\rho/r^2 r^4), \text{ whence, } P' \cdot Q = P \cdot Q - (Q^3\rho/p^2 r^4).$$

Or, $$P' = P - \frac{Q^2\rho}{\pi^2 r^4}.$$

Although the experimental investigations of *Hagenback, Couette* and *Wilberforce*, among others, have shown that this value of P' gives extremely good results, still, for greater accuracy, the value suggested is $P' = P - (kQ^2\rho/\pi^2 r^4)$, where the constant k depends upon the actual form of the apparatus used but is almost always equal to 1 very nearly.

Thus, putting $(kQ^2\rho/\pi^2 r^4) = \beta$, we have $P' = P - \beta$.

It may be noted that this *correction* β *for the effective pressure across the two ends of the tube is also quite independent of the length of the tube but depends upon its radius.*

Substituting P' for P and $(l + \alpha)$ for l in the expression for η, we have

$$\eta = \frac{\pi P' r^4}{8Q(l+\alpha)} = \frac{\pi(P-\beta)r^4}{8Q(l+\alpha)}$$

$$= \frac{\pi\left(P - \dfrac{kQ^2\rho}{\pi^2 r^4}\right)r^4}{8Q(l+1.64r)} = \frac{\pi^2 Pr^2 - kQ^2\rho}{8\pi Q(l+1.64r)}.$$

Or,
$$\eta = \frac{\pi Pr^4}{8Q(l+1.64r)} - \frac{kQ\rho}{8\pi(l+1.64r)}.$$

Now, only if extreme accuracy is aimed at, should the value of k be determined by calibration or else it must always be assumed to be equal to 1. So that, the above expression then becomes

$$\eta = \frac{\pi Pr^4}{8Q(l+1.64r)} - \frac{Q\rho}{8\pi(l+1.64r)}.$$

15.16 ANALOGY BETWEEN LIQUID-FLOW AND CURRENT-FLOW

The rate of flow of a liquid through a capillary tube is, as we know, given by Poiseuille's equation, $Q = \pi P^4/8\eta l$.

If we put $8\eta l/\pi r^4 = R$ and call it effective viscous resistance, we have

$$Q = P/R,$$

which is clearly a relation similar to $I = V/R$ for flow of electric current in accordance with *Ohm's law.*

A liquid-flow through a capillary tube is thus analogous to the flow of electric current through a conductor, with the rate of liquid-flow, Q, corresponding to current or rate of flow of charge, I; the pressure difference P across the two ends of the capillary, to potential difference V across the two ends of the conductor and the '*effective viscous resistance,*' $(8\eta/\pi r^4)$, to electrical resistance R.

This analogy is found to be most helpful in calculating the rates of liquid-flow through capillaries *in series* and *in parallel*, as will be seen from the following:

(*i*) Rate of liquid-flow through capallaries in series. Let two capillaries A and B, of lengths l_1 and l_2 and radii r_1 and r_2 respectively be connected in series, as shown in fig. 15.15 and let a liquid of coefficient of viscosity η flow through them in steady or streamline motion.

Then, since liquids are incompressible, the same volume of liquid that passes through capillary A, in a given time, also passes through capillary B in the same time. In other words, *the rate of liquid-flow through each capillary as also through the combination, as a whole, is the same* (like the flow of current through conductors in series). Let it be Q.

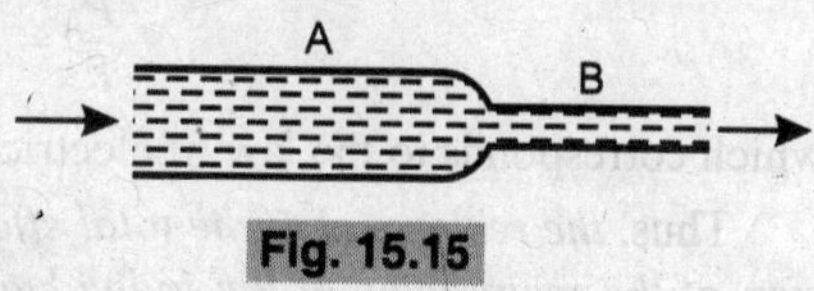

Fig. 15.15

And, let the pressure difference across the capillaries A and B be p_1 and p_2 and that across the combination, as a whole, P. So that,

$$P = p_1 + p_2. \qquad \text{...(I)}$$

If, therefore, R_1 and R_2 be the *effective viscous resistances* for capillaries A and B and R, for the combination, as a whole we have

$$\textit{rate of liquid-flow } Q = \frac{P}{R} = \frac{p_1}{R_1} = \frac{p_2}{R_2}.$$

Or, $$P = RQ, p_1 = R_1Q \text{ and } p_2 = R_2Q.$$

Substituting these values in relation I above, we have

$$RQ = R_1Q + R_2Q. \text{ Or, } R = R_1 + R_2,$$

i.e., the total effective viscous resistance of the combination is equal to the sum of the effective viscous resistances for the individual capillaries,—the same as the law of electrical resistances in series.

Therefore, rate of liquid-flow through the combination, *i.e.*,

$$Q = \frac{P}{R} = \frac{P}{R_1 + R_2},$$

Now $$R_1 = 8\eta l_1/\pi r_1^4 \text{ and } R_2 = 8\eta l_2/\pi r_2^4.$$

$$\therefore \quad Q = \frac{P}{\frac{8\eta}{\pi}\left(\frac{l_1}{r_1^4} + \frac{l_2}{r_2^4}\right)} = \frac{\pi P}{8\eta\left(\frac{l_1}{e_1^4} + \frac{l_2}{r_2^4}\right)}$$

Or, $$Q = \frac{\pi P}{8\eta}\left(\frac{l_1}{r_1^4} + \frac{l_2}{r_2^4}\right)^{-1}.$$

And thus, the rate of liquid-flow through the combination may be easily calculated.

What is true for two capillaries in series, naturally holds equally good for any number of them.

(*ii*) **Rate of liquid-flow through capillaries in parallel.** Let A ad B be two capillaries, of lengths l_1 and l_2 and radii r_1 and r_2 respectively lying in the same horizontal plane and in parallel with each other, as shown in Fig. 15.16 and let a liquid of coefficient of viscosity η be flowing through them in steady or streamline motion.

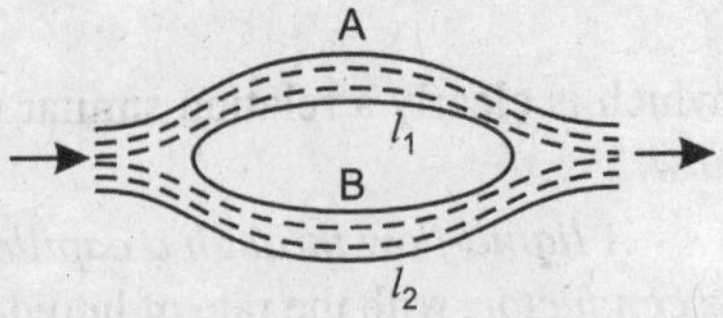

Obviously, the pressure difference across each capillary, as also across the combination, as a whole, will be the same, say, P. The rate of liquid-flow through each capillary will, however, be different. Let it be Q_1 and Q_2 through the two capillaries respectively. Then, if Q be the rate of flow through the combination, we have

Fig. 15.16

$$Q = Q_1 + Q_2. \qquad \text{...(II)}$$

Now, $$Q = P/R, Q_1 = P/R_1 \text{ and } Q_2 = P/R_2,$$

where R is the *total effective viscous resistance* for the combination and R_1 and R_2, the effective viscous resistances for capillaries A and B respectively.

Substituting these values in relation II above, we, therefore, have

$$\frac{P}{R} = \frac{P}{R_1} + \frac{P}{R_2}. \quad \text{Or, } \frac{1}{R} = \frac{1}{R_1} + \frac{1}{R_2}.$$

which corresponds to the law of electrical resistances in parallel.

Thus, *the reciprocal of the total effective viscous resistance for the combination is equal to the sum of the reciprocals of the individual effective viscous resistances for the two capillaries.* The same will, of course, be true for any number of them.

Clearly, rate of liquid-flow through the combination is given by

$$Q = \frac{P}{R} = P\left(\frac{1}{R_1} + \frac{1}{R_2}\right).$$

Or, since $R_1 = 8\eta l_1/\pi r_1^4$ and $R_2 = 8\eta l_2/\pi r_2^4$, we have

$$Q = P\left(\frac{\pi r_1^4}{8\eta l_1} + \frac{\pi r_2^4}{8\eta l_2}\right) = \frac{\pi P}{8\eta}\left(\frac{r_1^4}{l_1} + \frac{r_2^4}{l_2}\right).$$

We could also obtain the same result by substituting the values of Q_1 and Q_2 in relation II above, which also gives

$$Q = \frac{\pi P r_2^4}{8\eta l_1} + \frac{\pi P r_2^4}{8\eta l_2} = \frac{\pi P}{8\eta}\left(\frac{r_1^4}{l_1} + \frac{r_2^4}{l_2}\right)$$

15.17 MOTION OF A BODY IN A VISCOUS MEDIUM

Stokes' Law. It is a common experience that a body falling through a viscous medium always encounters an opposing viscous drag, resulting in absorption of energy by the medium in the form of heat. And, if the motion of the body be fast enough, even eddies and waves may be set up in the medium, absorbing still more energy.

This opposing force or viscous drag increases with velocity of the falling body and, in the case of small bodies, may become just equal to the driving or the motive force on the body, which then attains a constant velocity, called its **terminal velocity**.

Stokes obtained the expression $F = 6\pi r v\eta$ for the retarding viscous drag on a *small and spherical body,* where r is the radius of the body, v, its velocity and η, the coefficient of viscosity of the medium through which it is falling. It is usually referred to as **Stokes' law** and is based on the following assumptions:

(i) That the body is perfectly rigid and smooth; *(ii) that the medium is infinite in extent and homogeneous in so far as the body is concerned* (*i.e., the intramolecular space in the medium is very much smaller than the diameter of the body*); *(iii) that there is no slip between the body and the medium and (iv) that there are no eddies and waves set up in the medium i.e., the body moves through the medium with a small velocity v, not exceeding a certain critical value which Stokes suggested to be* $\eta/\sigma r$ *but which Arnold pointed out later, should not exceed* $0.6\eta/\sigma r$ *in actual practice, where* σ *is the density of the medium.*

Deduction of Stokes' law. The law may be easily deduced by the method of dimensions, as can be seen from the following:

For a slow-moving spherical body, the viscous drag F can possibly depend on (*i*) the *radius* (r) of the body, (ii) its *velocity* (v) and (*iii*) the *coefficient of viscosity* (η) of the medium through which it is falling or moving. So that, we can put $F = Rr^a v^b \eta^c$, k is a constant.

Or, putting the dimensions of the physical quantities involved, we have

$$[MLT^{-2}] = [L]^a\,[LT^{-1}]^b\,[ML^{-1}T^{-1}]^c,$$
$$= M^c\,L^{a+b-c}\,T,^{-b-c} \quad [k \text{ being a number, having no dimensions}]$$

whence, $c = 1,\ a + b - c = 1 \text{ and } -b - c = -2,$

which gives $a = 1,\ b = 1 \text{ and } c = 1.$

So that, $F = krv\eta.$

The value of k, as found experimentally by Stokes was 6π.

And, therefore, $F = 6\pi r v\eta$, which is *Stokes' law.*

Expression for terminal velocity. If ρ be the density of the falling spherical body, its *weight* = *volume* × *density* × $g = \frac{4}{3}\pi r^3 \sigma g$.

∴ *resultant downward force on the body* $= \frac{4}{3}\pi r^3 \rho g - \frac{4}{3}\pi r^3 \sigma g$

$$= \frac{4}{3}\pi r^3(\rho - \sigma)g.$$

When the body attains its terminal velocity v, this downward force on it must be balanced by the the viscous drag F. We, therefore, have

$$F = 6\pi r v\eta = \frac{4}{3}\pi r^3(\rho-\sigma)g, \text{ whence, } v = \frac{4}{3}\pi r^3(\rho-\sigma)g/6\pi r\eta.$$

Or, *terminal velocity of the body,* $v = \dfrac{2}{9}\dfrac{(\rho-\sigma)r^2 g}{\eta}$.

15.18 STOKE'S METHOD FOR THE COEFFICIENT OF VISCOSITY OF A VISCOUS LIQUID—THE FALLING SPHERE VISCOMETER

As can be readily seen, Stoke's relation for the terminal velocity of a tiny sphere falling through at thick liquid can be used to determine the coefficient of viscosity of the liquid, the apparatus used being referred to as the *falling sphere viscometer*.

A tiny sphere of a suitable size (usually a steel ball-bearing or a tiny sphere of wood metal) is dropped centrally into the liquid, contained in a tall and wide jar [Fig.15.17 (*a*)] and the time t taken by it to cover the distance S equal to about 5 cm between two fiducial marks M_1 and M_2, 10 or 12 cm below the top and above the bottom respectively, noted carefully. In view of the small size, the sphere is assumed to have attained its *terminal velocity* v before crossing the first mark M_1; so that, $v = S/t$. Substituting this value in the expression for v, deduced under § 15.21, we have

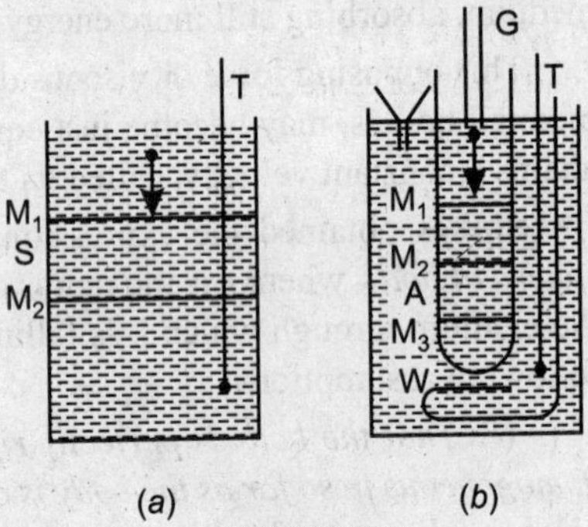

$$\eta = \frac{2}{9}\frac{(\rho-\sigma)r^2 gt}{S},$$

Fig. 15.17

where r is the radius of the sphere, determined accurately with the help of a micrometer screw gauge.

A better form of the viscometer, due to *Gibson* and *Jacobs* is the one shown in Fig. 15.17(*b*), where the tiny sphere is dropped centrally through a glass tube G into a wide test tube A, kept immersed in a water bath whose temperature can be noted to within 0.1°C on a sensitive thermometer placed in it. The time t taken by the sphere to cover the distance S between successive fiducial marks M_1, M_2 and M_3 on the tube, 5 cm apart, is noted.

If the time taken by the sphere to cover the distance S between successive marks decreases (*i.e.*, if its velocity increases) as it falls, a smaller sphere must be tried until the time taken to cover successive marks becomes the same (t). The *terminal velocity* of the sphere is then $v = S/t$ and this substituted in the expression for η above.

Now, since r^2t remains constant for a sphere in a given liquid, the experiment is repeated with spheres of different suitable sizes and a graph plotted between r^2 and $1/t$ which obviously comes to be straight line whose slope gives the mean value of r^2t. This is then substituted in the expression for η.

Corrections to be applied. Stokes' formula for η, as pointed out by *Ladenburg*, is applicable only if the liquid be unbounded in extent and depth. Being contained in a vessel, however, it is clearly bound in extent as well as depth by the wall and the bottom of the vessel respectively, called the '*wall effect*' and the '*end effect*,' and a correction must be applied for each.

(*i*) **Correction for wall-effect.** If v be the observed value of the terminal velocity of the sphere of radius r in a liquid contained in a vessel or jar of radius R, *its value, corrected for the wall-effect* is givn by

$$v = v(1 + 2.4r/R) = S(1 + 2.4r/R)t.$$

(*ii*) **Correction for end-effect.** If μ be the depth of the liquid column in the vessel or the jar and v, the observed terminal velocity of the sphere in it, *its value, corrected for the end-effect* is given by

$$v_\infty = v(1 + 3.3r/\mu) = S(1 + 3.3r/\mu)/t.$$

So that, with both corrections made, the coefficient of viscosity of the liquid is given by the relation,

$$\eta = \frac{2}{9}\frac{(\rho-\sigma)r^2 g}{v(1+2.4r/R)(1+3.3r/\mu)} = \frac{2}{9}\frac{(\rho-\sigma)r^2 gt}{S(1+2.4r/R)(1+3.3r/\mu)}$$

It will be seen at once how, if η for air be known, the method may also be used to determine the radius of a drop falling through it (provided the drop is larger in size than the intramolecular distance off air, when alone Stokes' law remains valid). Indeed, as the student will easily recall, this is how *Millikan* determined the radius of the drop in his famous oil-drop experiment for determining the charge on an electron.

15.19 ROTATION VISCOMETER

The principle and working of a *rotation viscometer* will be understood from the following:

Let *A* be a cylinder, of radius *a*, suspended coaxially, by means of a long and thin suspension wire, inside a cylinder *B*, of radius *b*, clamped on to a table which can be rotated by means of a small electric motor, and let the space between the two be filled with a fluid, say, a liquid, up to a height *l*, say, Fig. [15.18 (*a*)].

As the outer cylinder *B* is rotated with a suitable angular velocity Ω (so as not to cause turbulence in the fluid), its rotation communicates a torque to the stationary cylinder *A*, the magnitude of the torque depending upon the coefficient of viscosity of the fluid.

Representing the two cylinders by the full line circles *A* and *B*, of radii *a* and *b* respectively. [Fig. 15.18 (*b*)], with their common axis perpendicular to the plane of the paper and passing through *O*, let us consider a coaxial cylindrical layer of the fluid of thickness *dr* at a distance *r* from O (shown dotted). If ω be its angular velocity and hence its linear speed, $v = r\omega$, the *viscous drag* on it is, in accordance with Newton's formula, given by F = its area × its coefficient of viscosity × velocity gradient = $2\pi rl\eta\, dv/dr$.

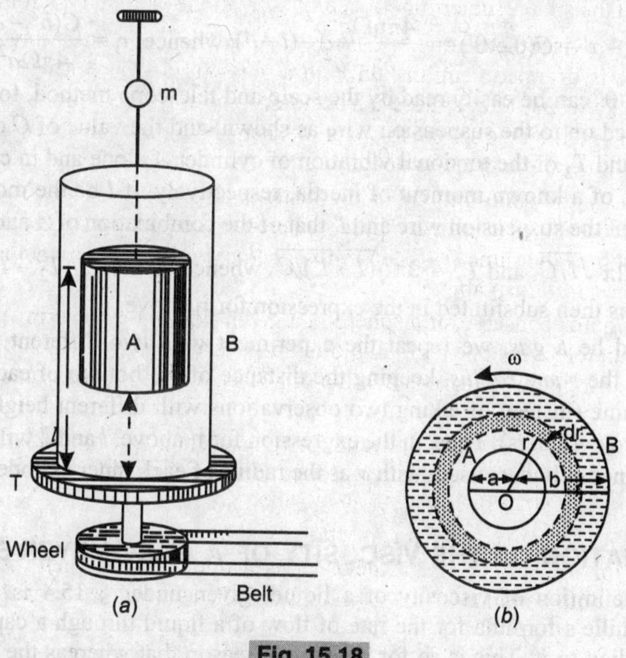

Fig. 15.18

Now, $dv/dr = d(r\omega)/dr = \omega + r\, d\omega/dr$, where ω being a constant quantity, only the second term is operative and the *effective velocity gradient* is thus $r d\omega/dr$. So that, $F = 2\pi rl\eta r\, d\omega/dt = 2\pi r^2 l\eta\, d\omega/dr$.

Hence, *moment of this force or the torque acting on this layer or on the inner cylinder A* (the fluid in between the two being in a steady sate) is given by

$$\tau_1 = 2\pi r^2 l\eta\ d\omega/dr \times r = 2\pi r^3 l\eta\ d\omega/dr.$$

Putting the relation in the form $2\pi l\eta\ d\omega = \tau_1 dr/r^3$ and integrating for the limits $\omega = 0$ and $\omega = \Omega$ and $r = a$ and $r = b$, we have

$$\int_0^{\Omega} 2\pi l\eta d\omega = \tau_1 \int_b^a \frac{dr}{r^3}, \text{ which gives } \tau_1 = \frac{4\pi l\eta\Omega a^2 b^2}{b^2 - a^2}.$$

Here, τ_1 is clearly the torque on the sides of the cylinder A. There is also a torque on its bottom, depending on the radii of the two cylinders and the distance between their bottoms. Let this be τ_2. Then, *total torque on cylinder A* is $\tau = \tau_1 + \tau_2$.

This torque (τ) tends to accelerate the motion of the fluid between the layer and the inner cylinder A and hence also the inner cylinder A (the fluid in between being in a steady state), tending to rotate it through an angle θ, say, until the *restoring torsional couple* $C\theta$, set up in the suspension wire, just balances it (C being the torsional couple per unit twist of the wire). We, therefore, have

$$\textit{total torque } \tau = C\theta = \frac{4\pi l\eta\Omega a^2 b^2}{b^2 - a^2} + \tau_2. \qquad \text{...}(i)$$

To eliminate τ_2, the experiment is repeated with a different height l' of the fluid in between the two cylinders when, since the radii a and b of the cylinders and the distance between their bottoms remain the same as before, τ_2 remains unchanged. If the torque on the sides of the cylinder be now τ_1 and cylinder A rotates through an angle θ', we have

$$\textit{total torque } \tau' = C\theta' = \frac{4\pi l'\eta\Omega a^2 b^2}{b^2 - a^2} + \tau_2. \qquad \text{...}(ii)$$

From relations (*i*) and (*ii*), therefore, we have

$$\tau - \tau' = C(\theta - \theta') = \frac{4\pi\eta\Omega a^2 b^2}{b^2 - a^2}(l - l'), \text{ whence, } \eta = \frac{C(b^2 - a^2)(\theta - \theta')}{4\pi\Omega a^2 b^2 (l - l')}.$$

The angle θ and θ' can be easily read by the scale and telescope method, for which purpose a small mirror m is fixed on to the suspension wire as shown, and the value of C obtained by noting the time-periods T_1 and T_2 of the torsional vibration of cylinder A alone and in combination with a hollow metallic disc, of a known moment of inertia, respectively. If I be the moment of inertia of cylinder A alone about the suspension wire and I' that of the combination of A and the disc, we have

$$T_1 = 2\pi\sqrt{I/C} \text{ and } T_2 = 2\pi\sqrt{(I + I')/C}, \text{ whence, } C = 4\pi^2 I/(T_2^2 - T_1^2).$$

This value of C is then substituted in the expression for η above.

In case the fluid be a *gas*, we repeat the experiment with two different inner cylinders of *different lengths* but the *same radius*, keeping the distance of the bottom of each from that of the outer cylinder the same (instead of taking two observations with different heights of the liquid in between the same two cylinders). Thus, in the expression for η above, l and l' will now stand for the lengths of the two inner cylinders used, with a as the radius of each inner cylinder and b, that of the outer cylinder.

15.20 DETERMINATION OF THE VISCOSITY OF A GAS—MEYER'S FORMULA

Although the definition of viscosity of a liquid, given under § 15.4 is applicable equally well to a gas, Poiseuille's formula for the rate of flow of a liquid through a capillary tube cannot straightaway be applied to it. This is so for the simple reason that whereas the density of a liquid (an almost incompressible fluid) remains practically unaffected by pressure, that of a gas (a highly compressible fluid) varies directly with it. As a result, *in the case of a liquid, both mass and volume of it flowing through any section of a tube in a given time may be assumed to remain constant but in that of a gas, only the mass (and not its volume) may be assumed to remain so.*

So that, if ρ be the density of the gas over a section of the tube over which the pressure may be assume to be uniform and equal to P and if the volume of the gas flowing through the section per second be Q' and its mass m, we have $m = \rho Q = constant$.

And since $\rho \propto P$, we have $P.Q = constant$.

Keeping this essential difference between the two cases in mind, let us proceed to obtain an expression for the rate of flow of a gas through a capillary tube or rather modify Poiseuille's expression for the purpose.

Considering a section or a length dx of the tube at a distance x from its inlet end, if dP be the pressure difference across the section, the volume of the gas flowing through it per second, *i.e.*, its *rate of flow*, is, in accordance with Poiseuille's equation, given by

$$Q = -\frac{\pi(dP)r^4}{8(dx)\eta} = -\frac{\pi r^4}{8\eta}\cdot\frac{dP}{dx},$$

where $-dP/dx$ is the pressure gradient along the section, the –ve sign indicating decrease of pressure with increase of distance from the inlet end.

$$\therefore \qquad P.Q = -\frac{\pi r^4}{8\eta}\cdot\frac{PdP}{dx} = constant.$$

If the volume of the gas entering the tube per second at the inlet end be Q_1 under pressure P_1, we must have $P_1.Q_1 = P.Q$. So that,

$$P_1.Q_1 = -\frac{\pi r^4}{8\eta}\cdot\frac{PdP}{dx}. \quad \text{Or, } P_1.Q_1 dx = -\frac{\pi r^4}{8\eta}\cdot PdP$$

Integrating between the limits $x = 0$ and $x = l$ and $P = P_1$ and $P = P_2$, where l is the length of the tube and P_1 and P_2, the pressures at its inlet and the outlet ends, we have

$$P_1 Q_1 \int_0^l dx = -\frac{\pi r^4}{8\eta}\int_{P_1}^{P_2} PdP. \quad \text{Or, } P_1.Q_1 l = \frac{\pi r^4}{8\eta}\left(\frac{P_1^2 - P_2^2}{2}\right),$$

which gives
$$P_1.Q_1 = \frac{\pi r^4(P_1^2 - P_2^2)}{16\eta l} = P.Q.$$

This is referred to as **Meyer's formula** for the rate of flow of a gas through a capillary tube and enables us to obtain the coefficient of viscosity of the gas.

15.21 RANKINE'S METHOD FOR A GAS AVAILABLE IN SMALL QUANTITIES

Rankine devised, in the year 1910, a method for determining the coefficient of viscosity of a gas, available only in a small quantity, like what are called the rare *gases, argon, krypton, neon* etc.

His apparatus, shown in Fig. 15.19, consists of a closed glass tube system *ABCD*, one metre in length and having a capillary section AB of about 2 mm bore. the rest of the system too is narrow enough (about 3 mm bore) to be able to hold a mercury pellet in position anywhere inside it until forced to move under pressure.

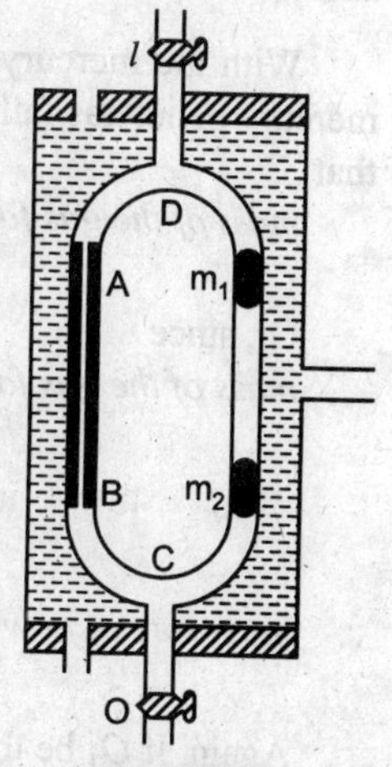

Fig. 15.19

Two reference marks M_1 and M_2 are engraved on the portion *CD*, opposite the capillary section, such that the volume of the portion ADm_1 of the system is equal to that of the portion BCm_2, and the whole system can be kept immersed in a suitable bath to ensure constancy of temperature. The bath is, however dispensed with if the experiment is desired to be performed at the room temperature.

With the tube system initially laid horizontally on the table, the gas inside is under the same uniform pressure P, say, in every part of it. So that, if ρ be the density of the gas under unit pressure, its density under pressure P is ρP. If, therefore, V be the total volume of the gas in the system (ignoring the negligibly small amount inside the capillary portion), its mass is ρPV and this, as we know, must remain constant all through the experiment.

As the tube is held in the vertical position shown, the mercury pellet starts falling gradually under its own weight. The time t taken by it to fall from the upper position, when mark m_1 makes a tangent with its upper meniscus, to the lower position, when mark m_2 is tangential to its lower meniscus, is carefully noted.

Now, in the upper position of the pellet, if V_1 be the volume and P_1, the pressure of the gas above mark m_1, the volume of the gas below mark m_1 will clearly be $(V-V_1)$ and its pressure $(P_1 + mg/a)$, where mg is the weight of the mercury pellet and a, the area of cross section of portion CD of the tube. And, therefore,

mass of the gas above mark $m_1 = \rho P_1 V_1$

and *mass of the gas below mark* $m_1 = \rho(P_1 + mg/a)(V - V_1)$.

The mass of the gas in the system remaining constant, we have

$$\rho PV = \rho P_1 V_1 + \rho(P_1 + mg/a)(V - V_1).$$

Or, dividing throughout by ρV, we have

$$P = P_1\frac{V_1}{V} + (P_1 + mg/a)\left(1 - \frac{V_1}{V}\right) = P_1 + \frac{mg}{a} - \frac{mg}{a}\left(\frac{V_1}{V}\right),$$

whence,

$$P_1 = P - \frac{mg}{a} + \frac{mg}{a}\left(\frac{V_1}{V}\right) \quad \ldots(i)$$

And, *pressure blow mark* m_2, say,

$$P_2 = P_1 + \frac{mg}{a} = P + \frac{mg}{a}\left(\frac{V_1}{V}\right) \quad \ldots(ii)$$

Similarly, in the lower position of the pellet, if the volume of the gas above mark m_2 be V_2 and its pressure P_1', its volume and pressure below mark m_2 will respectively be $(V - V_2)$ and $P_1' + \frac{mg}{a} = P_2'$, say. So that,, proceeding as above, we have

$$P_1' = P - \frac{mg}{a} + \frac{mg}{a}\left(\frac{V_2}{V}\right) \quad \ldots(iii)$$

and

$$P_2' = P_1' + \frac{mg}{a} = P + \frac{mg}{a}\left(\frac{V_2}{V}\right) \quad \ldots(iv)$$

With the mercury pellet at m_1, the mass of the gas below it was $\rho P_2(V - V_1)$ and when the mercury pellet has fallen to position m_2, the mass of the gas below it is $\rho P_2'(V - V_2)$. It is thus clear that

mass of the gas forced through the capillary tube

$$= \rho P_2(V - V_1) - \rho P_2'(V - V_2)$$

Or, since $V = V_1 + V_2$, we have

mass of the gas forced through the capillary tube

$$= \rho P_2 V_2 - \rho P_2' V_1 \quad \ldots(v)$$

$$= \rho\left(P + \frac{mgV_1}{aV}\right)V_2 - \rho\left(P + \frac{mgV_2}{aV}\right)V_1 = \rho P(V_2 - V_1)$$

∴ *mass rate of flow of the gas through the capillary*

$$= \rho P(V_2 - V_1)t. \quad \ldots(vi)$$

Again, if Q_1 be the volume rate of flow of the gas through the capillary tube when the mercury pellet is at m_1, we have, in accordance with *Meyer's formula*

$$\frac{(P_2^2 - P_1^2)\pi r^4}{16\eta l} = P_2 Q_1,$$

where r is the radius and l, the length of the capillary tube.

And, if Q_2 be the *volume rate of flow* of the gas through the capillary tube when the mercury pellet is at m_2. We similarly have

$$\frac{(P_2'^2 - P_1'^2)\pi r^4}{16\eta l} = P_2' Q_2.$$

$\therefore$ Clearly, *average mass rate of flow of the gas* $= \frac{1}{2}\rho(P_2Q_1 + P_2'Q_2)$

Now, $$\frac{1}{2}(P_2Q_1 + P_2'Q_2) = \frac{1}{2}\frac{\pi r^4}{16\eta l}\left[\left(P_2^2 - P_1^2\right) + \left(P_2'^2 - P_1'^2\right)\right]$$

$$= \frac{\pi r^4}{32\eta l}\left[(P_2 - P_1)(P_2 + P_1) + (P_2' - P_1')(P_2' + P_1')\right]$$

$$= \frac{\pi r^4}{32\eta l}\left(\frac{mg}{a}\right)\left[(P_2 + P_1)(P_2' + P_1')\right]$$

$$[\because P_2 - P_1 = P_2' - P_1' = mg/a]$$

$$= \frac{\pi r^4}{32\eta l}\left(\frac{mg}{a}\right)\left[\left(P + \frac{mgV_1}{aV} + P - \frac{mg}{a} + \frac{mgV_1}{aV}\right)\right.$$

$$\left. + \left(P + \frac{mgV_2}{aV} + P - \frac{mg}{a} + \frac{mgV_2}{aV}\right)\right]$$

$$= \frac{\pi r^4}{32\eta l}\left(\frac{mg}{a}\right)\left[2P - \frac{mg}{a}\left(1 - \frac{2V_1}{V}\right) + 2P - \frac{mg}{a}\left(1 - \frac{2V_2}{V}\right)\right]$$

$$= \frac{\pi r^4}{32\eta l}\left(\frac{mg}{a}\right)\left[4P - \frac{mg}{a}\left(2 - 2\frac{V_1 + V_2}{V}\right)\right]$$

$$= \frac{\pi r^4}{32\eta l}\left(\frac{mg}{a}\right)\left[4P - \frac{mg}{a}\left(2 - \frac{2V}{V}\right)\right]$$

$$= \frac{\pi r^4}{32\eta l}\left(\frac{mg}{a}\right)(4P) = \frac{\pi P r^4 mg}{8\eta la}.$$

And, therefore, *mass rate of flow of the gas through the capillary tube*

$$= \frac{\pi P r^4 \rho mg}{8\eta la}. \qquad \ldots(vii)$$

So that, from relations (*vi*) and (*vii*), we have

$$\frac{\rho P(V_2 - V_1)}{t} = \frac{\pi P r^4 \rho mg}{8\eta la}. \quad \text{Or,} \quad \frac{V_2 - V_1}{t} = \frac{\pi r^4 mg}{8\eta la},$$

whence, $$\eta = \frac{\pi r^4 mgt}{8(V_2 - V_1)la}.$$

Clearly, $(V_2 - V_1)/t = Q$, the *volume rate of flow of the gas* through the capillary tube and $mg/a = p$, say, the pressure exerted by the mercury pellet on the gas; whether at m_1 or m_2. We, therefore, have

$$\eta = \frac{\pi p r^4}{8Ql},$$

an expression identical in form with Poiseuille's equation for the *coefficient of viscosity* of a liquid.

Corrections required.

(*i*) We have, in our calculations above, taken the volume of the gas forced through the capillary tube in time t to be $(V_2 - V_1)$, *i.e.*, the volume lying between marks m_1 and m_2. Actually, as will be easily seen, it is only the volume lying between the lower meniscus of the mercury pellet when at m_1 and its upper meniscus when at m_2 that passes through the apillary tube. Thus, the volume of the gas forced through the capillary tube is really $(V_2 - V_1)$ *minus twice the volume of the mercury pellet.* This correction must therefore be applied.

(*ii*) However pure the mercury of the pellet may be, some of it does stick to the wall of the tube, so that the pressure exerted by the mercury pellet on the gas below it (whether at m_1 or m_2) is not really mg/a, as we have assumed, but a little less. A correction for this too is, therefore, called for.

Despite both these corrections, however, the experiment suffers from the basic defect of being a capillary tube method. It is not, therefore, susceptible of any high degree of accuracy such, for instance as required in determining the coefficient of viscosity of air in Millikan's oil drop experiment.

15.22 EFFECT OF TEMPERATURE AND PRESSURE ON THE VISCOSITY OF LIQUIDS

(*i*) **Effect of temperature**. The viscosity of a liquid falls so rapidly with temperature that it becomes meaningless to mention the viscosity of a liquid without specifying its temperature. Thus, for example, the viscosity of water at 10°C has one-third its value at 80°C and that of castor oil falls even more rapidly.

Although several attempts have been made to corelate the viscosity of a liquid with its temperature, no satisfactory relationship between the two has yet emerged.

Slotte was the first to suggest the empirical formula

$$\eta_t = \frac{\eta_0}{1 + at + bt^2},$$

where η_t and η_0 are the viscosities of the liquid at t°C and 0°C respectively and a and b are constants.

This, however, hardly accords with the experimental results obtained.

A modification of it, $\eta_t = A/(1 + Bt)^c$, where A, B and C are constants, is found to be in fairly good agreement with experimental results but *only in the case of pure liquids.* It does not apply to that very important class of liquids, oils, which, as we know, are not pure liquids but mixtures of chemical compounds, difficult to separate.

Andrade, on the basis of his theory of viscosity of liquids, gave, in the year 1934, the relation $\eta V^{\frac{1}{2}} = Ae^{C/T}$, where T is the absolute temperature of the liquid and A and C are constants.

This is good enough as a first approximation and has the additional merit of satisfying Porter's empirical criterion that if T and T_0 be two temperatures at which two liquids have the same viscosity, T/T_0 plotted against T must give a straight line graph.

However, a more rigorous application of Andrade's theory leads to the relation $\eta V^{\frac{1}{2}} = Ae^{C/VT}$ or $Ae^{C\rho T}$, where V is the *specific volume* of the liquid and ρ, its density.

This is found to be application to most liquids, with the exception of that most important of all liquids, *water*, as also some tertiary alcohols.

(*ii*) *Effect of pressure*. No really cogent theory as to the variation of viscosity of a liquid with pressure has yet been advanced.

The one fact that stands established is that pressure produces a much smaller effect than temperature on the viscosity of liquids in general and on that of mobile liquids (*i.e.*, liquids with low viscosity) in particular. Thus, the viscosity of water decreases only marginally with increase of pressure up to a few hundred atmospheres and that of *ether* at 20°*C* increases by only about 60% for an increase of 500 atmospheres of pressure.

In the case of liquids with high viscosity, like *mineral oils*, the change in viscosity with pressure is very much greater, there being as much as a tenfold increase for a rise of 1000 atmospheres in pressure.

Barring the case of water (an exceptional liquid in may other ways), whose viscosity decreases with pressure, the viscosity of all other liquids increases with pressure and the higher the pressure to which they are subjected, the higher the rate of increase of viscosity with pressure.

WORKED EXAMPLES

I–Fluid motion

Example 15.1. A horizontal pipe of a non-uniform bore has water flowing through it such that the velocity of flow is 40 cm/sec at a point where the pressure is 2 cm of mercury column. what is the pressure at a point where the velocity of flow is 60 cm/sec? (Take g = 980 cm/sec^2 and density of water = 1 gm/c.c.).

Solution. Here, $p_1 = 2$ cm *of mercury column* $= 2 \times 13.6 \times 980$ dynes/cm^2, $\rho_1 = \rho_2 = \rho = 1$ gm/c.c., $v_1 = 40$ cm/sec and $h_1 = h_2 = h$.

In accordance with *Bernoulli's equation,*

$$p_1/\rho + gh + \frac{1}{2}v_1^2 = p_2/\rho + gh + \frac{1}{2}v_2^2,$$

where p_2 is the pressure at the second point.

Or, $$\frac{1}{2}(v_2^2 - v_1^2) = (p_1/\rho - p_2/\rho) = p_1 - p_2. \qquad [\because \ \rho = 1 \text{ gm/c.c.}]$$

So that, $$\frac{1}{2}(60^2 - 40^2) = 2 \times 13.6 \times 980 - p_2. \quad \text{Or, } 1000 = 26650 - p_2,$$

whence, $$p_2 = 26650 - 1000 = 25650 \text{ dynes/cm}^2$$
$$= 25650/13.6 \times 980 = 1.925 \text{ cm } \textit{of mercury column.}$$

Example 15.2. Calculate the velocity of efflux of kerosene oil from a tank in which the pressure is 50 lb wt per square inch above the atmospheric pressure. The density of kerosene is 48 lb per c. ft. ***(Bombay)***

Solution. As we know, the *velocities of efflux* $v = \sqrt{2gh}$, where h is the height of the liquid surface from the axis of the orifice.

Now, *pressure due to kerosene at the level of the axis of the orifice*

$$= h\rho g \textit{ poundals/ft}^2 = h\rho \textit{ lb wt/ft}^2.$$

But this is given to be 50 *lb wt/(inch)*^{2} = 50 × 144 *lb wt/ft*^{2}

∴ $hg\rho = 50 \times 144$. Or, $h = 50 \times 144/\rho = 50 \times 144/48$ *ft.*

Hence, *velocity of efflux,* $$v = \sqrt{2gh} = \sqrt{2 \times 32 \times 50 \times 144/48}$$
$$= 97.97 \text{ or } 98 \textit{ ft/sec.}$$

Example 15.3. A water main of 20 cm diameter has a Pitot tube fixed into it and the pressure difference indicated by the gauge is 5 cm of water column. Calculate the rate of flow of water through the main. (Take g = 980 cm/sec^2 and ρ for water = 1 gm/cc).

Solution. Here, *radius (r) of the main* = 20/2 = 10 cm and, therefore,its *area of cross section* $a = \pi r^2 = \pi(10)^2 = 100\pi$ sq cm.

Since, *loss of kinetic energy per unit mass on stoppage of flow* $= \frac{1}{2}v^2$ = *gain in pressure energy per unit mass* $= p/\rho = p/1 = p = 5 \times 1 \times 980$

Or, $v^2 = 10 \times 980$, whence, $v = \sqrt{9800} = 99.0$ cm/sec

$\therefore$ *rate of flow of water through the main*

= *velocity of flow* $\times$ *area of cross section of the main*

= 99 × 100p = 31100 c/c./sec or 31.1 litres/sec

Example 15.4. The diameters of a water main where a venturimeter is connected to it are 20 cm and 10 cm. What is the rate of water flow if the water levels in the two piezometer tubes differ by 5 cm? (g = 980 cm/sec^2).

Solution. As we know, the *rate of flow of water through the main* is given by the relation

$$Q = a_1v_1 = a_1a_2\sqrt{2hg/(a_1^2 - a_2^2)}$$

Here, $a_1 = \pi r_1^2 = \pi(20/2)^2 = 100\pi$ sq cm, $a_2 = \pi r_2^2 = \pi(12/2)^2 = 36\pi$ sq cm and $h = 5$ cm. We, therefore, have

rate of flow of water through the main, i.e., $Q = 100\pi \times 36\pi\sqrt{\dfrac{2\times5\times980}{(100\pi)^2-(36\pi)^2}}$

$$= 3600\pi\sqrt{\frac{9800}{8704}} = 11920 \text{ cc/sec or } 11.92 \text{ or } 12 \text{ litres/sec.}$$

Example 15.5. Calculate the speed at which the velocity head of a stream of water is equal to 0.50 m of Hg.

Solution. Velocity head = $\dfrac{v^2}{2g}$ metres of Hg

Given: Velocity head = 0.50 m of Hg

= 0.50 × 13.6 m of water

$$\therefore \quad \frac{v^2}{2g} = 0.5 \times 13.6$$

$$v^2 = 2 \times 9.8 \times 0.5 \times 13.6 = 9.8 \times 13.6$$

$$v = \sqrt{9.8\times13.6} = \mathbf{11.54\ m/s}$$

Example 15.6. A railway engine is fitted with a tube whose one end is inside a reservoir of water is between the rails. The other end of the tube is 4 m above the surface of water in the reservoir. Calculate the speed of with which the water rushes out of the upper end, of the engine is moving with a speed of 108 km/hr.

Solution. Applying Bernoulli's theorem,

$$mgh_1 + \frac{1}{2}mv_1^2 = mgh_2 + \frac{1}{2}mv_2^2$$

$$gh_1 + \frac{1}{2}v_1^2 = gh_2 + \frac{1}{2}v_2^2$$

$$\frac{1}{2}v_1^2 = g(h_2 - h_1) + \frac{1}{2}v_2^2$$

$$v_1 = \sqrt{2g(h_2 - h_1) + v_2^2}$$

Here $(h_1 - h_2) = 4$ m; $g = 9.8$ m/s^2; $v_2 = 108$ km/hr = 30 m/s

$$v_1 = \sqrt{2\times9.8\times(-4)\times(30)^2}$$

$$v_1 = \sqrt{900 - 78.4}$$

$$v_1 = \mathbf{28.66\ m/s}$$

Example 15.7. Water flows through a horizontal pipe line of varying cross-section. At a point where the pressure of water is 0.5 m of mercury the velocity of flow is 0.25 m/s. Calculate the pressure at another point where velocity of flow is 0.4 m/s. Density of water = 10^3 kg/m^3.

(Nag. U., 2001)

Solution. Here, $P_1 = 0.5$ m of Hg $= 0.05 \times 13.6 \times 10^3 \times 9.8$

$$= 6.664 \times 10^3 \text{ Nm}^{-2}$$

$$v_1 = 0.25 \text{ ms}^{-1}, \quad v = 0.4 \text{ ms}^{-1} \quad P_2 = ?$$

As the pipe is horizontal, according to Bernoulli's theorem

$$\frac{P_1}{\rho} + \frac{v_1^2}{2} = \frac{P_2}{\rho} + \frac{v_2^2}{2}$$

or
$$\frac{6.664 \times 10^3}{10^3} + \frac{0.25^2}{2} = \frac{P_2}{10^3} + \frac{0.4^2}{2}$$

or
$$\frac{P_2}{10^3} = 6.664 + \frac{0.25^2}{2} - \frac{0.4^2}{2}$$

or
$$P = (6.664 + 0.03125 - 0.08)10^3 = 6.61525 \times 10^3 \text{ Nm}^{-2}$$

$$= \frac{6.61525 \times 10^3}{13.6 \times 10^3 \times 9.8} = \mathbf{0.0496 \text{ m of mercury}}$$

Example 15.8. A pipe is running full of water. At a certain point *A* it tapers from 0.6 m diameter to 0.2 m diameter at *B*. The pressure difference between *A* and *B* is 1 m of water column. Find the rate of flow of water through the pipe.

Solution. Let p_1, v_1 be the pressure and velocity at A and p_2 and v_2 the corresponding values at B, then,

$$p_1 - p_2 = 1 \times 10^3 \times 9.8 \text{ Nm}^{-2}$$

Rate of flow at $A = v_1 \times \text{area} = \pi \times 0.3^2 \times v_1 = 0.09\pi\, v_1$

Rate of flow at $B = v_2 \times \text{area} = \pi \times 0.1^2 \times v_2 = 0.01\pi\, v_2$

For a steady flow $0.01\, \pi v_2 = 0.09 \pi v_1$

or $v_2 = 9 v_1$

As the height remains the same, according to Bernoulli's theorem, we have

$$\frac{p_1}{\rho} + \frac{v_1^2}{2} = \frac{p_2}{\rho} + \frac{v_2^2}{2}$$

or
$$\frac{p_1 - p_2}{\rho} = \frac{1}{2}(v_2^2 - v_1^2)$$

or
$$\frac{10^3 \times 9.8}{10^3} = \frac{1}{2}(81 v_1^2 - v_1^2)$$

$\therefore$
$$v_1 = \sqrt{\frac{9.8}{40}} = 0.495 \text{ ms}^{-1}$$

$\therefore$ Rate of flow $= \pi \times 0.09 \times 0.495 = \mathbf{0.14\ m^3\ s^{-1}}$

Example 15.9. Water issues into the air from a horizontal nozzle whose area of cross-section is 0.125 × 10^{-4} m^2. Its speed is such that 1.875 kg emerge in one minute. The water strikes a fixed wall which is at right angles to the nozzle and 0.5 m from it and then falls in a vertical plane. Calculate the vertical distance below the nozzle of the point where the jet strikes the wall and the force which the water exerts on the wall.

Solution. Volume of water flowing out per second $V = \dfrac{1.875}{60 \times 10^3} = 31.25 \times 10^{-6}$ m^3

Area of nozzle $a = 0.125 \times 10^{-4}$ m^2

If v is the velocity with which water issues, then $V = av$

$$v = \frac{V}{a} = \frac{31.25 \times 10^{-6}}{0.125 \times 10^{-4}} = 250 \times 10^{-2} \text{ ms}^{-1}$$

Distance of wall from the nozzle = 0.5 m

$\therefore$ Time taken by water to reach the wall $= \dfrac{0.5}{250 \times 10^{-2}} = 0.2$ sec.

Vertical distance through which water falls in 0.2 sec.

$$= \frac{1}{2} g t^2 = \frac{1}{2} \times 9.8 \times (0.02)^2 = 0.196$$

Hence, the water jet will strike the wall at a point 0.196 m below the nozzle.

Force exerted on wall = Momentum imparted by water in one second

$$= \frac{1.875}{60} \times 250 \times 10^{-2} = \mathbf{7.813 \times 10^{-2}\ N}$$

Example 15.10. A tank contains water to a height H. Calculate the range of flow of water from an orifice at depth $\frac{H}{4}, \frac{H}{2}$ and $\frac{3H}{4}$ from the surface of water. ***(Indore U. 2001)***

Solution. (*i*) *When the orifice is at a depth* $\dfrac{H}{4}$

$$h = \frac{H}{4},\ h' = H - \frac{H}{4} = \frac{3H}{4}$$

Range $$S = 2\sqrt{hh'} = 2\sqrt{\frac{H}{4} \times \frac{3H}{4}} = \frac{\sqrt{3}}{2} H$$

(*ii*) *When the orifice is at a depth* $\dfrac{H}{2}$

$$h = \frac{H}{2},\ h' = H - \frac{H}{2} = \frac{H}{2}$$

Range $$S = 2\sqrt{hh'} = 2\sqrt{\frac{H}{2} \times \frac{H}{2}} = H$$

(*iii*) *When the orifice is at a depth* $= \dfrac{3H}{4}$

$$h = \frac{3H}{4},\ h' = H - \frac{3H}{4} = \frac{H}{4}$$

Range $$S = 2\sqrt{hh'} = 2\sqrt{\frac{3H}{4} \times \frac{H}{4}} = \frac{\sqrt{3}}{2} H.$$

Example 15.11. A flat plate of metal 100 sq. cm. in area rests on a layer of castor oil 2 mm thick whose co-efficient of viscosity is 15.5 poise. Calculate the horizontal force required to move the plate with a speed of 0.03 ms^{-1}.

Solution. Area A = 100 sq. cm. = 10^{-2} m^2, $v = 0.03$ ms^{-1}, $r = 2$ mm $= 0.2 \times 10^{-2}$ m,
η = 15.5 poise = 1.55 deca-poise

Horizontal viscous force $F = -\eta A \dfrac{v}{r} = \dfrac{-1.55 \times 10^{-2} \times 0.03}{0.2 \times 10^{-2}} = -0.2325$ N

$\therefore$ External force required = 0.2325 N

II–Viscosity

Example 15.12. Calculate the mass of water flowing in 10 minutes through a tube 0.1 cm in diameter, 40 cm long if there is a constant pressure head of 20 cm of water. The coefficient of viscosity of water is 0.0089 C.G.S. Units. ***(Agra)***

Solution. We have, from Poiseuille's equation, *volume rate of flow of water* given by

$$Q = \frac{\pi P r^4}{8\eta l} = \frac{\pi \times 20 \times 1 \times 981 \times (0.05)^4}{8 \times 0.0089 \times 40} = 0.1353 \text{ cc/sec.}$$

∴ volume of water flowing out in 10 minutes = 0.1353 × 10 × 60, say, V = 81.18 c.c.

Hence, *mass of water flowing out in 10 minutes* = $V \times \rho$ = 81.18 × 1 = 81.18 gm.

Example 15.13. A cylindrical vessel of radius 7 cm is filled with water to a height of 50 cm. It has a capillary tube 10 cm long, 0.2 mm radius, protruding horizontally at its bottom. If he viscosity of water is 0.01 C.G.S. units and g = 980 cm/sec², find the time in which the level will fall to a height of 25 cm. ***(Punjab)***

Solution. Let h be the height of the water column in the vessel at any given instant and dh, the fall in its height in a small interval of time dt. Then, if A be the area of cross-section of the vessel, we have

rate of flow of water through the capillary tube, i.e., $Q = -A\, dh/dt$,

the –ve sign indicating that h decreases as t increases.

But, as we know, the rate of flow of water through a capillary tube is given by *Poiseuille's equation.* $Q = \pi P r^4/8\eta l$, where $P = h\rho g = hg$ (ρ being the density of water, equal to 1 gm/cc). We, therefore, have

$$-A\frac{dh}{dt} = \frac{\pi h g r^4}{8\eta l}. \quad \text{Or, } dt = -\frac{8\eta l A}{\pi g r^4}\cdot\frac{dh}{h}.$$

And ∴

$$\int_0^t dt = \int_{h_1}^{h_2} -\frac{8\eta l A}{\pi g r^4}\cdot\frac{dh}{h}, \text{ whence, } t = \frac{8\eta l A}{\pi g r^4}\log_e\frac{h_1}{h_2}.$$

Or, putting the value of $A = \pi \times 7^2$, r = 0.02 cm, h_1 = 50 cm and h_2 = 25 cm, we have

$$t = \frac{8 \times 0.01 \times 10 \times \pi \times 7^2}{\pi \times 9.80 \times (0.02)^4} \times 2.3026 \log_{10}\frac{50}{25} = 1.734 \times 10^5 \text{ sec} = 48.16 \text{ hr.}$$

The water level in the vessel will thus fall to 25 cm in 48.16 hours.

Example 15.14. Write down Poiseuille's formula for the rate of flow of a liquid through a capillary tube. From this show that if two capillaries of radii a_1 and a_2, having lengths l_1 and l_2 respectively, are set in series, the rate of flow Q* is given by

$$Q = \frac{\pi P}{8\eta}\left(\frac{l_1}{a_1^4} + \frac{l_2}{a_2^4}\right)^{-1},$$

where P is the pressure across the arrangement and η, the coefficient of viscosity of the liquid. ***(Rajashtan)***

Solution. Let P_1 be the pressure across the first, and P_2 across the second, capillary. So that, $P = P_1 + P_2$ and, therefore, $P_2 = P - P_1$.

Obviously, in accordance with the equation of continuity, *the rate of flow through either capillary will be the same,* say Q and, therefore, from Poiseuille's equation, we have

$$Q = \pi P_1 a_1^4/8\eta l_1 = \pi P_2 a_2^4/8\eta l_2 = (P - P_1)a_2^4/8\eta l_2,$$

whence,

$$P_1 a_1^4/l_1 = P a_2^4/l_2 - P_1 a_2^4/l_2$$

Or,

$$P_1\left(\frac{a_1^4}{l_1} + \frac{a_2^4}{l_2}\right) = \frac{P a_2^4}{l_2}.$$

∴

$$P_1 = \frac{P a_2^4/l_2}{(a_1^4/l_1) + (a_2^4/l_2)} = \frac{P l_1}{a_1^4[(l_2/a_2^4) + (l_1/a_1^4)]}$$

* Here, symbol Q has been substituted for V in the original question.

$$= \frac{Pl_1}{a_1^4}\left(\frac{l_2}{a_2^4}+\frac{l_1}{a_1^4}\right)^{-1}.$$

Substituting this value of P_1 in the expression $Q = \pi P_1 a_1^4/8\eta l_1$, we have

$$Q = \frac{\pi P}{8\eta}\left(\frac{l_1}{a_1^4}+\frac{l_2}{a_2^4}\right)^{-1}.$$

Example 15.15. (*a*) Three capillaries of lengths 8*L*, 0.2*L* and 2*L*, with their radii *r*, 0.2*r* and 0.5 *r* respectively, are connected in series. If the total pressure across the system in an experiment is *p*, deduce the pressure across the shortest capillary. ***(Agra)***

(*b*) Fig. 15.20 below shows two wide tubes *P* and *Q*, connected by three capillaries *A*, *B*, *C* whose relative lengths and radii are indicated. If a pressure *p* is maintained across *A*, deduce (*i*) the ratio of liquid flowing through *A* and *B*, (*ii*) the pressure across *B* and across *C*.

(Agra (Supp.))

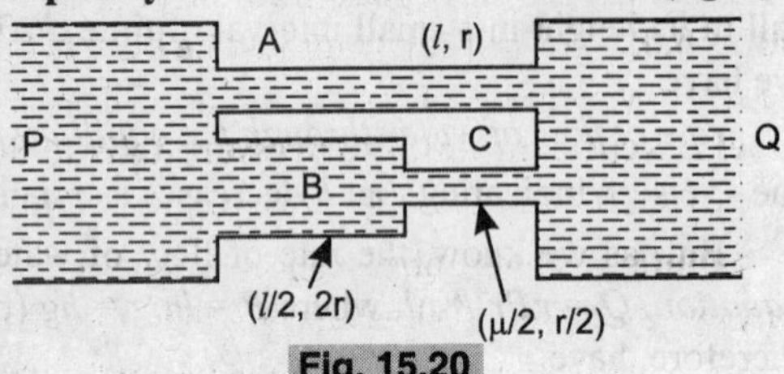

Fig. 15.20

Solution. (*a*) Obviously, the rate of flow of liquid across each capillary is the same. So that, if p_1, p_2 and p_3 be the pressures across the three capillaries respectively, we have, in accordance with Poiseuille's equation,

$$Q = \frac{\pi p_1 r^4}{8\eta(8L)} = \frac{\pi p_2(0.2r)^4}{8\eta(0.2L)} = \frac{\pi p_3(0.5r)^4}{8\eta(2L)},$$

whence, $$\frac{p_1}{64} = \frac{p_2}{1000} = \frac{p_3}{256},$$

which gives $$p_1 = \frac{p_2}{1000}\times 64 = \frac{8}{125}p_2 \text{ and } p_3 = \frac{p_2}{1000}\times 256 = \frac{32}{125}p_2.$$

Now, $$p = p_1 + p_2 + p_2 = \frac{8}{125}p_2 + p_2 + \frac{32}{125}p_2 = \frac{165}{125}p_2.$$

And, therefore, *pressure across the shortest capillary, i.e.*,

$$p_2 = \frac{125}{165}p = 0.7575\,p.$$

(*b*) (*i*) Clearly, *rate of liquid-flow through capillary A* is $Q = \pi pr^4/8\eta l$, and

rate of liquid-flow through B and C is, say, $Q' = \dfrac{\pi p_1(2r)^4}{8\eta(l/2)} = \dfrac{\pi p_2(r/2)^4}{8\eta(l/2)},$

whence, $(2r)^4 p_1 = (r/2)^4 p_2$. Or, $p_2 = 256\,p_1$.

Or, since $p = p_1 + p_2$, we have $p = p_1 + 256\,p_1 = 257\,p_1$.

$\therefore$ *ratio of liquid flowing through A and B* $= \dfrac{Q}{Q'} = \dfrac{\pi pr^4/8\eta l}{\pi p_1(2r)^4/8\eta(l/2)} = \dfrac{257\pi p_1 r^4/8\eta l}{32\pi p_1 r^4/8\eta l} = 257 : 32.$

(*ii*) since $p = 257\,p_1$, we have

Pressure across capillary B, i.e., $p_1 = p/257$

and *pressure across capillary C, i.e.*, $p_2 = p - p_1 = p - p/257 = \dfrac{256}{257}p.$

Example 15.16. A gas bubble of diameter 2 cm rises steadily through a solution of density 1.75 gm/c.c. at the rate of 0.35 cm/sec. Calculate the coefficient of viscosity of the solution. (Neglect density of the gas).

Solution. As we know, the coefficient of viscosity of the solution is given by the relation

$$\eta = \frac{2}{9}\left(\frac{\rho-\sigma}{v}\right)r^2 g.$$

Here, *radius of the bubble*, $r = 2/2 = 1$ cm, *density of the solution*, $\sigma = 1.75$ gm/c.c. *density of the bubble*, $\rho = 0$ (negligible) and *velocity of the bubble*, $v = -0.35$ cm/sec, (because it is directed upwards). We, therefore, have

coefficient of viscosity of the solution,

$$\eta = \frac{2}{9}\frac{\sigma r^2 g}{v} = \frac{2}{9}\times\frac{1.75\times(1)^2\times 981}{0.35} = 1.09\times 10^3 \text{ poise.}$$

Example 15.17. A glass bulb of volume 500 c.c. has a capillary tube of length 40 cm and radius 0.020 cm leading from it. The bulb is filled with hydrogen at an initial pressure of 86 cm of mercury, density 13.6 gm/c.c., and it is found that if the volume of the gas remaining in the vessel is kept constant, the pressure falls to 80 cm of mercury in 25.4 sec. If the height of the barometer is 76 cm and g = 981 cm/sec^2, find the viscosity of hydrogen.

Solution. This is obviously a straight applicationof Searle's method for determining the coefficient of viscosity of a gas and we, therefore, have

$$\eta = \frac{\pi r^4 H\rho g t}{8lV\times 2.3026\log_{10}\left(\frac{h_1}{h_2}\cdot\frac{2H+h_2}{2H+h_1}\right)}$$

Substituting the given values, *viz.*, $H = 76$ cm, $\rho = 13.6$ gm/c.c., $g = 981$ cm/sec^2, $t = 25.4$ sec, $l = 40$ cm, $V = 500$ c.c., $h_1 = 86 - 76 = 10$ cm and $h_2 = 80 - 76 = 4$ cm, we have

coefficient of viscosity of hydrogen,

$$\eta = \frac{\pi(0.02)^4\times 76\times 13.6\times 981\times 25.4}{8\times 40\times 500\times 2.3026\log_{10}\left(\frac{10}{4}\cdot\frac{152+4}{152+10}\right)}$$

$$= \frac{\pi(0.02)^4\times 76\times 13.6\times 981\times 25.4}{8\times 40\times 500\times 2.3026\times 0.3815} = 9.204\times 10^{-5} \textit{ poise.}$$

Example 15.18. Two horizontal capillary tubes *A* and *B* are connected together in series so that a steady stream of fluid flows through them. *A* is 0.4 mm in internal radius and 256 cm long. *B* is 0.3 mm in internal radius and 40.5 cm long. The pressure of the fluid at the entrance is 3 inches of mercury above the atmosphere. At the exit end of *B*, it is atmospheric (30 inches of mercury). What is the pressure at the junction of *A* and *B* if the fluid is (*i*) a liquid (*ii*) a gas?

Solution. Case (*i*) When the fluid is liquid. Let the pressure at the junction of capillary tubes *A* and *B* be *h* inches of mercury, so that

pressure across capillary A is, say, $P_1 = (33 - h)$ *inches of mercury,* and

pressure across capillary B is, say, $P_2 = (h - 30)$ *inches of mercury*.

The two tubes being connected *in series, the volume rate of flow of the liquid is the same through both* and we, therefore, have

$$Q = \frac{\pi P_1 r_1^4}{8\eta l_1} = \frac{\pi P_2 r_2^4}{8\eta l_2}, \text{ whence, } \frac{P_1}{P_2} = \frac{l_1}{l_2}\left(\frac{r_2}{r_1}\right)^4,$$

where l_1, l_2 and r_1, r_2 are the lengths and the radii of the two tubes respectively.

Substituting the values of P_1 and P_2 from above, we have

$$\frac{33-h}{h-30} = \frac{256}{40.5}\left(\frac{0.3}{0.4}\right)^4 = \frac{256}{40.5}\times\frac{81}{256} = 2.$$

Or, $33 - h = 2(h - 30) = 2h - 60$. Or, $3h = 93$, whence, $h = 31$ inches,

i.e., the pressure at the junction of the two capillary tubes is 31 inches *of mercury.*

Case (*ii*) When the fluid is a gas. Here, *the mass rate of flow of the gas through either capillary tube is the same* and we thus have

$$\frac{\pi r_1^4(33^2 - h^2)}{16\eta l_1} = \frac{\pi r_2^4(h^2 - 30)}{16\eta l_2}, \qquad \text{[See § 15.20]}$$

where h, as before, is the pressure in inches at the junction of the two tubes.

We, therefore, have $$\frac{33^2 - h^2}{h^2 - 30^2} = \left(\frac{r_2}{r_1}\right)^4 = 2. \qquad \text{[From above.]}$$

Or, $33^2 - h^2 = 2h^2 - 2 \times 30^2$. Or, $h^2 = (2 \times 30^2 + 33^2)/3 = 2889/3 = 963$,

whence, $h = \sqrt{963} = 31.03$ inches.

Thus, *the pressure at the junction of the two capillary tubes, in this case, equal to* 31.03 inches *of mercury.*

Example 15.19. A horizontal tube of 1 mm bore is joined to another horizontal tube of 0.5 mm bore. Water enters at the free end of the first tube at a pressure equal to 0.5 m of water above the atmospheric pressure and leaves at the free end of the second tube at the atmospheric pressure. Calculate the pressure at the junction of the tubes if the lengths of the tubes are equal.

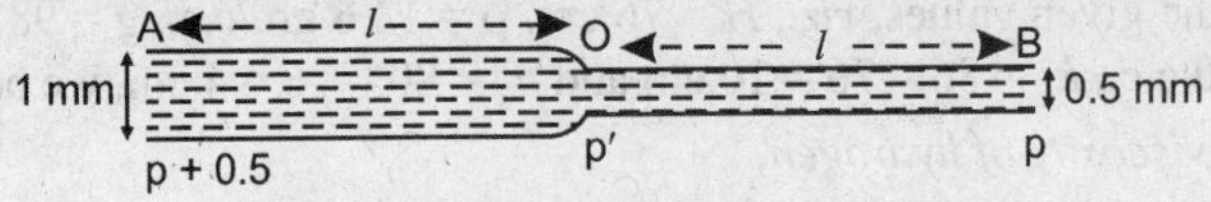

A ← l → O ← l → B
1 mm
0.5 mm
p + 0.5
p′
p

Fig. 15.21

Solution. According to Poiseuille's equation $V = \dfrac{\pi P a^4}{8\eta l}$

If p' is the pressure at the junction O of the two tubes each of length l, then difference of pressure between A and $O = p + 0.5 - p'$

$\therefore$ Volume of water flowing through AO per second $= \dfrac{\pi(p + 0.5 - p')(0.5 \times 10^{-3})^4}{8\eta l}$

Difference of pressure between O and $B = p' - p$

$\therefore$ Volume of water flowing per second through $OB = \dfrac{\pi(p' - p)(0.25 \times 10^{-3})^4}{8\eta l}$

As the two tubes are joined end to end, the volume of water flowing per second through them is the same.

$$\therefore \quad \frac{\pi(p + 0.5 - p')(0.5 \times 10^{-3})^4}{8\eta l} = \frac{\pi(p' - p)(0.25 \times 10^{-3})^4}{8\eta l}$$

or $$p + 0.5 - p' = \frac{(p' - p)}{16}$$

$$17(p' - p) = 8$$

$$\therefore \quad p' - p = \frac{8}{17} = \mathbf{0.47\ m\ of\ water\ column.}$$

Hence, pressure at O is 0.47 m of water column.

Example 15.20. A capillary tube of radius *a* and length *l* is fitted horizontally at the bottom of a cylindrical flask of cross-section area *A*. Initially there is water in the flask up to a height *h*. What time would be required for half the liquid to flow out, if the coefficient of viscosity of the liquid is η?

Solution. According to Poiseuille's equation for volume V of the water flowing through a tube of length l and radius a is given by

$$V = \frac{\pi P a^4}{8\eta l}$$

As A is the area of cross-section of the vessel and h the height of water above the capillary tube.

$\therefore$ Pressure head $P = hg$ [$\because \rho = 1$ for water in C.G.S. system]

Suppose in a small time dt the level of water in the vessel falls through a height dh, then

Volume of water flowing in time $dt = A.dh$

$\therefore$ Rate of flow $V = -A\frac{dh}{dt}$

The negative sign shows that the height decreases with time.

Substituting the value of P and V in (*i*), we have

$$-A\frac{dh}{dt} = \frac{\pi hga^4}{8\eta l} \text{ or } dt = -\frac{8\eta lA}{\pi ga^4}\cdot\frac{dh}{h} \qquad ...(ii)$$

Let t be the time in which the initial height h is reduced to $h/2$, then

$$\int_0^t dt = \frac{8\eta lA}{\pi ga^4}\int_h^{h/2}\frac{dh}{h}$$

$$\therefore \quad t = -\frac{8\eta lA}{\pi ga^4}[\log_e h]_h^{h/2} = \frac{8\eta lA}{\pi ga^4}\left[\log_e h - \log_e\frac{h}{2}\right]$$

$$= \frac{8\eta lA}{\pi ga^4}\log_e 2 = \mathbf{2.3026 \times A\frac{8\eta l}{\pi ga^4}\log_{10} 2}$$

Example 15.21. In the Poiseuille experiment the following observations were made. Volume of water collected in 5 minutes = 40 c.c.; Head of water 0.4 m; length of capillary tube = 0.602 m and radius of capillary tube = 0.52 × 10^{-3} m. Calculate the coefficient of viscosity of water.

Solution. Volume of water collected per second

$$V = \frac{40}{5\times 60}\text{ cm}^3 = \frac{40}{5\times 60}\times 10^{-6}\text{ m}^3 = \frac{2}{15}\times 10^{-6}\text{ m}^3$$

Head of water $h = 0.4$ m

$\therefore$ Difference of pressure $P = h\rho g = 0.4 \times 10^3 \times 9.8 \text{ Nm}^{-2} = 3.92 \times 10^3 \text{ Nm}^{-2}$

Length of capillary tube $l = 0.602$ m

Radius of the capillary tube $a = 0.52 \times 10^{-3}$ m

$$\text{Now, coefficient of viscosity } \eta = \frac{\pi Pa^4}{8lV} = \frac{3.142\times 3.92\times 10^3\times(0.52)^4\times 10^{-12}\times 15}{8\times 0.602\times 2\times 10^{-6}}$$

$$= \mathbf{1.4 \times 10^{-3}\ Nm^{-2}\ (or\ deca\text{-}poise)}$$

Example 15.22. If two capillaries of radii r_1 and r_2 and length l_1 and l_2 are joined in series, derive an expression for the rate of flow of the liquid through the arrangement using Poiseuille's formula.

Solution. According to Poiseuille's formula, the rate of flow V of a liquid through a capillary tube of length l and radius r is given by

$$V = \frac{\pi pr^4}{8\eta l}$$

where p is the pressure difference across the ends of the tube and η the co-efficient of viscosity.

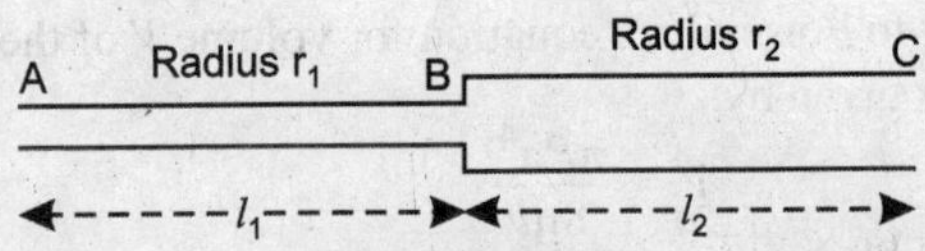

Fig. 15.22

Consider two capillaries of lengths l_1 and l_2 having radii r_1 and r_2 respectively connected in series. If p_1 is the pressure difference between the ends of capillary AB and p_2 that between the ends of the capillary BC, then as the same volume of liquid is flowing through each of the capillaries

$$V = \frac{\pi p_1 r_1^4}{8\eta l_1} = \frac{\pi p_2 r_2^4}{8\eta l_2}$$

So that $$p_1 = \frac{8\eta l_1}{\pi r_1^4} V \text{ and } p_2 = \frac{8\eta l_2}{\pi r_2^4} V$$

If p is the effective pressure across the ends A and C, then

$$p = p_1 + p_2 = \left(\frac{8\eta l_1}{\pi r_1^4} + \frac{8\eta l_2}{\pi r_2^4}\right) V$$

$\therefore$ Rate of flow $$V = \frac{\pi p}{8\eta\left(\frac{l_1}{r_1^4} + \frac{l_2}{r_2^4}\right)}$$

Example 15.23. Two drops of water of the same size are falling through air with terminal velocity 1 ms^{-1}. If the two drops combine to form a single drop, calculate the terminal velocity.

Solution. Let r be the radius of each drop and r_1 that of the combined drop, then

$$4/3\pi r_1^3 = 2 \times 4/3\pi r^3$$

$\therefore$ $$r_1 = 2^{1/3} r$$

If v is the terminal velocity of each drop and v_1 that of the combined drop then according to Stoke's law

$$v = \frac{2r^2(\rho - d)g}{9\eta}$$

and $$v_1 = \frac{2r_1^2(\rho - d)g}{9\eta}$$

$\therefore$ $$\frac{v_1}{v} = \frac{r_1^2}{r^2}$$

$$= \frac{2^{2/3} r^2}{r^2} = 2^{2/3} = \mathbf{1.588\ ms^{-1}} \qquad [\because V = 1\ \text{ms}^{-1}]$$

Example 15.24. Eight drops of water of the same size are falling through air with terminal velocity of 10 m/sec. If the eight drops combine to form a single drop what will the new terminal velocity?

Solution. $\frac{4}{3}\pi r_1^3 = 8 \times \frac{4}{3}\pi r^3$ or $r_1 = 2r$

$$\frac{v_1}{v} = \frac{r_1^2}{r^2} = \frac{2^2 r^2}{r^2} = 4 \text{ or } v_1 = 4 \times 10 = \mathbf{40\ m/s}$$

Example 15.25. A steel ball of radius 2 × 10^{-3} m falls in a vertical column of castor oil. The co-efficient of viscosity of castor oil is 0.7 Nm^{-2} and its density 0.98 × 10^3 kg m^{-3}. The density of steel is 7.8 × 10^3 kg m^{-3} and g = 9.8 ms^{-2}. Find its terminal velocity.

Solution. According to Stokes' formula, the terminal velocity is given by

$$v = \frac{2r^2(\rho - d)g}{9\eta}$$

Now, radius of the ball $r = 2 \times 10^{-3}$ m

Density of steel ball $\rho = 7.8 \times 10^3$ kg m^{-3}

Density of castor oil $d = 0.98 \times 10^3$ kg m^{-3}; g = 9.8 ms^{-2}

Viscosity of castor oil $\eta = 0.7$ Nm^{-2}

$$\therefore \quad v = \frac{2\times(2\times10^{-3})^2(7.8\times10^3 - 0.98\times10^3)9.8}{9\times0.7}$$

$$= \frac{2\times4\times10^{-3}\times6.82\times9.8}{9\times0.7}$$

$$= 84.87 \times 10^{-3} \text{ ms}^{-1}$$

EXERCISE

I–Fluids and Fluid motion

1. Distinguish between streamline and turbulent flow of a liquid and explain the significance of the Reynolds' number. ***(Nagpur 2009, Agra U.2006)***
2. Define viscosity and coefficient of viscosity and give its units.
3. What is critical velocity? How it makes a difference of streamline and turbulent flow.
4. Derive critical velocity by using method of dimensions.
5. Explain the term viscosity and coefficient of viscosity. Give the dimensions of coefficient of viscosity. ***(Bhopal U., 2004; Nag. U., 2009, 2003, 2001; Gharwal U. 2000)***
6. Distinguish between streamline and turbulent flow of a liquid. Discuss briefly the idea or critical velocity and explain the significance of the Reynold's number. ***(Meerut U. 2003; Osm. U. 2004; Nag. U. 2003, 2001; Bang. U. 2000; D.A.U. Agra 2008, 2007, 2006)***
7. State the explain rate of flow of liquid. What is the equation of continuity? ***(D.A.U. Agra 2008)***
8. Show how Bernoulli's theorem is applied to measure the rate of discharge through city water mains. Explain the principle and application of venturimeter. ***(Osm. U. 2004)***
9. Describe the working of a Pitot's tube.
10. Show how the coefficient of viscosity of two liquids may be compared.
11. How does the viscosity vary with temperature and pressure? ***(Meerut U. 2003, Gharwal U. 2000)***
12. State and the prove Bernoulli's theorem. Explain the lifting action of an aeroplane. ***(Nag. U. 2005)***
13. Enunciate Bernoulli's theorem and deduce Bernoulli's equation. Give some simple illustrations of the theorem.
14. What are the different types of energy liquid in streamline flow may possess? Show that they are mutually convertible.
15. What is the *equation of continuity*? Water flows through a horizontal pipe having a tapering bore. The velocity of water is 2 m/sec at the broader end and the pressure is 1 kilo-newton/m^2 less at the narrow end. What is the velocity of water at the latter end? **[Ans.** 6 m/sec.]
16. Enunciate *Torricelli's theorem* and obtain an expression for the *velocity of efflux* of a liquid from a tank. Calculate the velocity of efflux of alcohol from a tall cylinder in which the tall pressure is 2 atmospheres. (*sp. gr.* of alcohol = 0.80). **[Ans.** 15.92 m/sec.]
17. Water is flowing through a horizontal main having a non-uniform bore. The velocity of water is 100 cm/sec at a point in it where the pressure is 7/19th of that of the atmosphere. Calculate the velocity of water at the point where the pressure is half this value. **[Ans.** 251.7 cm/sec]

18. A venturimeter is connected to a horizontal main of radius 20 cm. If radius of the throat of the venturimeter be 15 cm and the difference of water level in the piezometer tubes be 10 cm, calculate the rate of flow of water per hour through the main. [**Ans.** 43.11×10^4 litres/hour.]

19. State Bernoulli's theorem and apply it to obtain an expression for the reduction of pressure when water flows through a constriction in a pipe. Describe the device depending on this theorem for the measurement of liquid-flow. ***(Punjab)***

20. Enunciate Newton's law of viscous flow and deduce from it the definition of coefficient of viscosity of a fluid.

A flat plate of area 20 sq cm is placed on a horizontal surface coated with a layer of glycerine 1 mm thick. What force must be applied to the plate to keep it moving with a speed of 1 cm/sec over the horizontal surface? (Coefficient of viscosity of glycerine = 20 gm cm^{-1} sec^{-1}) [**Ans.** 4000 dynes.]

21. State and prove Bernoulli's theorem for a liquid along a stream line.

(Osm. U., 2004; Nag. U., 2003, 2001; Indore U., 2001)

22. Show that for a liquid in stream line motion

$$\frac{P}{\rho} + gh + \frac{v^2}{2} = \text{constant}$$

23. Give Euler's equation for a non-steady flow or non-viscous and incompressible liquid through a tube. Hence, derive Bernoulli's theorem.

24. Explain the following applications using Bernoulli's theorem:

(*i*) Atomiser

(*ii*) Venturimeter

(*iii*) Bunsen burner

(*iv*) Carburettor

25. What do you mean by equation continuity? Derive it for steady current.

(Agra U. 2004, 2003; S.M.U. Tiruneveli, 2007)

26. Explain the parabolic nature of velocity profile of a streamline flow.

27. Calculate the velocity of efflux and range of flow of a liquid through an orifice in a reservoir.

28. Explain the terms in detail:

(*i*) Coefficient of viscosity

(*ii*) Velocity of efflux

(*iii*) Velocity gradient ***(Purvanchal U. 2004)***

29. What do you mean by Reynol's number? Give its significance. ***(Agra U. 2007)***

30. State Bernoulli's theorem and apply it to obtain an expression for the reduction of pressure when water flows through a constriction in a pipe. ***(M.S.U. Tiruneveli, 2007)***

31. Define critical velocity and Reynold's number. ***(Nagpur Uni. 2009)***

32. Describe any two applications of Bernoulli's theorem. ***(Nagpur Uni. 2009)***

II–Viscosity

33. Define coefficient of viscosity of a liquid. Describe the Poiseuille's method for measuring the coefficient of viscosity of a liquid. Derive the formula used with its two correction terms.

(Purvanchal U. 2004; M.S.U. Tiruneveli 2007; Meerut 2004; D.A.U. Agra 2008)

34. (*a*) Give the necessary theory Poiseuille's method of determining the coefficient of viscosity of a liquid. State clearly the assumptions made.

(*b*) Why is correction of Poiseuille's equation necessary? Obtain the corrected version.

(Bhopal U. 2004; Utkal U. 2003; Nag. U. 2003, 2001; Meerut U. 2003, 2002, 2001, 2000; Indore U. 2001; Guwahati U. 2000; Gharwal U.2000; Purvanchal U. 2006, 2004; Agra U. 2005, 2003)

35. Deduce an expression for the distribution of velocity of a liquid flowing through a uniform capilary tube of circular cross-section. What is the nature of velocity profile?

36. The rate of flow of liquid through a capillary is given by $Q = \pi Pr^4/8\eta l$, with usual notations. Deduce this relation, stating clearly the conditions under which it holds.

Why does the formula fail in the case of a tube of a wide bore?

37. Define coefficient of viscosity of a liquid and find its dimensions. Describe the way in which the different parts of a viscous liquid move when flowing through a fine tube. What changes take place if the motion is increased?

38. In an experiment with Poiseuille's apparatus the following figures were obtained:

Volume of water issuing per min = 7.08 c.c. Head of water = 34.1 cm. Length of tube = 56.45 cm. Radius of the tube = 0.0514 cm.

Find the coefficient of viscosity. ***(Calcutta)***

39. Explain the limitations of Poiseuille's formula for the rate of flow of a liquid through a capillary tube. Why does it fail in the case of a gas?

40. Deduce the expression for the rate of steady flow of a liquid through a capillary tube of circular cross section.

A vessel of cross section 20 sq cm has at the bottom a horizontal capillary tube of length 10 cm and internal radius 0.5 mm. It is initially filled with water to a height of 20 cm above the capillary tube. find the time taken by the vessel to empty one half of its contents, given that the viscosity of water is 0.01 *C.G.S.* units ***(Madras)*** [**Ans.** 9 min 36 sec.]

41. Discuss the effect of (*i*) temperature, (*ii*) pressure on the viscosity of fluids. ***(Agra)***

42. Explain the rotating cylinder method of determining the coefficient of viscosity of a liquid and give its theory. ***(Agra; Poona)***

43. Show that the total viscous resistance of a liquid flowing through a number of capillary tubes in series and in parallel respectively.

44. Three capillaries of the same length but internal radii 3r, 4r and 5r are connected in series and a liquid flows through them in streamline conditions. If the pressure across the third capillary is 8.1 mm, deduce the pressure across the first capillary. ***(Agra (Supp.))*** [**Ans.**6.25 cm]

45. Derive Stoke's formula for the velocity of a small sphere falling through a viscous liquid. Explain how this is utilised to determine the viscosity of a liquid like castor oil. Mention one more application of Stokes's formula. ***(Madras)***

46. Derive Stoke's formula for the velocity of a small sphere falling through a viscous liquid using the method of dimensions. Explain how this is utilised to determine the viscosity of a liquid like castor oil. Mention one more application of Stoke's law. ***(Guwahati U. 2000)***

47. A small spherical drop of radius a, of a material of density r falls from rest in still air of viscosity η. Now,

(*i*) Write down the equation of motion of the drop.

(*ii*) Evaluate the terminal velocity,

(*iii*) Evaluate the time and distance traversed when the drop has acquired 90% of the terminal velocity.

48. Obtain Stokes' law for the motion of a body in a viscous medium from dimensional considerations. ***(Madras 2004)***

49. A water drop of radius 0.01 cm is falling through air. Find its terminal velocity. Neglect the desnity of air. (η for air = 1.8×10^{-4} *C.G.S.* units). Why are cloud particles seen floating in the sky? ***(Poona, 2005)*** [**Ans.**1.2 cm/sec]

50. Two equal drops of water are falling through air with a steady terminal velocity of 5 cm/sec. If the drops coalesce, what will be the new terminal velocity? ***(Ranchi, 2006)*** [**Ans.** 7.98 cm/sec]

51. Determine the radius of the drop of water falling through air, if the terminal velocity of the drop is 1.2 cm/sec. Assume the coefficient of viscosity for air = 1.8×10^{-4} and the density of air = 1.21×10^{-3} gm/sec. ***(Patna, 2001)*** [**Ans.** 0.001 cm. (approximately)]

52. State Stoke's law of viscous force. ***(Nag. U. 2005)***

53. Discuss main sources of errors and the corrections applied in Poiseuille's formula.

54. Derive Poiseuille's formula for the rate of steady flow of liquid through a capillary tube of circular cross-section. why does it fails in the case of a gas? ***(Agra U. 2006)***

55. Discuss the rate of flow of liquid in a capillary tube. Explain the analogy between liquid flow and electric current. ***(M.S.U. Turneveli, 2007)***

56. Three capillaries of lengths 8 l, 0.2 l, 2 l and radii r, 0.2 r and 0.5 $\underline{r}$ respectively are connected in series. If the total pressure across the system is p, deduce the pressure across the shortest capillary.

Hint: $p = p_1 + p_2 + p_3 = \left(\frac{8\eta l_1}{\pi r_1^4} + \frac{8\eta l_2}{\pi r_2^4} + \frac{8\eta l_3}{\pi r_3^4}\right) = 0.7575\, p$

57. What is Stokes' law? A horizontal tube has different cross-sectional areas at points A and B. the diameters of the tube at A and B are 4 cm and 2 cm respectively. The pressure difference between he two points is 8 cm when a liquid of density 8 gm/cm^3 flows through this. Calculate the rate of flow of liquid in the tube (g = 980 cm/sec^2)

Hint: $p = p_1 + p_2 = \frac{8\eta l_1}{\pi r_1^4} + \frac{8\eta l_2}{\pi r_2^4}$ ***(Purvanchal U. 2007)***

58. A venturimeter is connected to a horizontal main of radius 20 cm. If the radius of the throat of the venturimeter be 15 cm and difference of water level in the piezometer tubes be 10 cm. Calculate the rate of flow of water per hour through the main. ***(M.S.U. Tiruneveli, 2007)***

[Ans. 43.11 × 10^4 litre/hour]

59. Water flows through a horizontal capillary tube of 1 mm internal diameter of length 70 cm under pressure of a column of water 30 cm in height. Find the rate of flow of water through the capillary tube $\eta = 10^{-3}$ N-s/m^2. ***(Nagpur Uni. 2008)***

Hint: Rate of flow = $\frac{P\pi a^4}{8\eta l} = \frac{h\rho g\pi a^4}{8\eta l}$

Here $h = 30 \times 10^{-2}$ m, $\rho = 10^3$ kg/m^3, $g = 9.8$ m/s^2, $a = 0.5 \times 10^{-3}$ m, $l = 0.7$ m.

60. A capillary tube of bore 1 mm and length 20 cm is fitted horizontally to sufficiently big vessel kept full of alcohol of density 0.8 gm/c.c. The depth of the centre of the capillary tube below the surface of alcohol is 30 cms. If the viscosity of alcohol is 0.012 poise find the amount that will flow in 5 minutes. **[Ans.** 72.19 c.c.]

61. A water drop is observed to fall through a gas of density 0.001 gm/c.c. with a constant velocity of 980 cm/sec. What is the radius of the drop? The coefficient of viscosity of the gas 2 × 10^{-4} poise.

[Ans. 3 × 10^{-2} cm]

16 Chapter

PRODUCTION AND MEASUREMENT OF LOW PRESSURES (PUMPS AND GAUGES)

Brief Contents

INTRODUCTION

Production and measurement of low pressure without error is a challenging task. For production of low pressure, exhaust pumps like rotary oil pump, molecular pump, diffusion pump are very common. Many techniques have been developed for the measurement of pressure and vacuum. Instruments employed are called pressure gauges or vacuum gauges. A manometer is usually referred to a pressure measuring instrument but limited to measuring pressures near to atmospheric. The term *manometer* is often used to refer specially to liquid column hydrostatic instruments. A vacuum gauge is used to measure the pressure in vacuum—which is further divided into subcategories : high and low vacuum (and sometimes even less called utter-high vacuum). Adaption of most of the common types of pressure transducer can be used for absolute pressure measurement in the vacuum range (less than atmospheric pressure). Special forms of bourdon tubes measure pressures down to 10 *mbar*, manometers and bellows-type instruments measure pressure down to 0.1 *mbar*, and diaphragms can be designed to measure pressures down to 0.001 *mbar*. Other more specialized instruments are also used to measure vacuum pressures. These instruments include the thermo-couple gauge, the Pirani gauge, the thermistor gauge, the Mcleod gauge and the ionization gauge. The construction of a bourdon tube gauge, the construction elements are made of brass. The applicable pressure range of many of the techniques used to measure vacuums have an overlap. Hence, by combining several differal different types of gauge, it is possible to measure system pressure continuously from 10 *mbar* to 10^{-11} *mbar*.

16.1 ABSOLUTE, GAUGE AND DIFFERENTIAL PRESSURES —ZERO REFERENCE

Although no pressure is an absolute quantity, every day pressure measurements, such as for tire pressure in a vehicle, are usually made relative to ambient air pressure. In other cases, measurements are made relative to vacuum or to some other adhoc reference. Where distinguishing between these zero references, the following terms are used:

(*i*) **Absolute pressure** is zero referred against a perfect vacuum, so it is equal to gauge pressure plus atmospheric pressure.

(*ii*) **Gauge pressure** is zero referred against ambient air pressure, so it is equal to absolute pressure minus atmospheric pressure. Negative signs are usually omitted.

(*iii*) **Differential pressure** is the difference in pressure between two points.

The zero reference in use is usually implied by context, and these words are only added when clarification is needed. Tire pressure and blood pressure are gauge pressures by convention, while atmospheric pressures, deep vacuum pressures and altimeter pressures must be absolute. Differential pressures are commonly used in industrial process systems. Differential pressure gauges have two inlet ports, each connected to one of the volumes whose pressure is to be monitored. I=n effect, such a gauge performs the mathematical operation of subtraction through mechanical means and operates on the difference in readings.

Atmospheric pressure is typically about 100 kPa at sea level (or 76 cm of Hg), but is variable with attitude and weather. If the absolute pressure of a fluid stays constant, the gauge pressure of the same fluid will vary as atmospheric pressure changes. For example, when a car drives up a mountain (atmospheric air pressure decreases), the (gauge) tire pressure goes up. Some standard values of atmospheric pressure such as 101.325 kPa or 100 kPa have been defined and some instruments use one of these standard values as a **constant zero reference** instead of the actual variable ambient air pressure. This impairs the accuracy of these instruments, especially when used at high altitudes. As mentioned above, the absolute pressure measurement is one that is referred to absolute vacuum.

The best example of an absolute referenced pressure is **atmospheric** or **barometric pressure**. To produce an absolute pressure sensor, the manufacturer will seal a high vacuum behind the sensing diaphragm.

The pressure units are related as under:

	Pascal (Pa)	Bar (bar)	Atmosphere (atm)	Torr (Torr)
1 Pa	$\equiv$ N/m^2	10^{-5}	9.8692×10^{-6}	7.5006×10^{-3}
1 bar	100,000	$\equiv 10^{-6}$ dyne/cm^2	0.98692	750.06
1 atm	101,325	1.01325	$\equiv$1 atm	760
1 torr	133.322	1.3332×10^{-3}	1.3158×10^{-3}	$\equiv$1 Torr, $\cong$1 mm Hg

Example reading: 1 Pa = 1 N/m^2 = 10^{-5} bar = 9.8692×10^{-6} atm = 7.5006×10^{-3} torr.

The SI unit for pressure is pascal (Pa), equal to one Newton per square metre (N-m^{-2} or Kg. m^{-1}. s^{-2}). Atmospheric pressures are usually stated using. Kilopascal (KPa) or atmosphere (atm), except in American mateorology where the hectopascal (hPa) and millibar (mbar) are preferred.

16.2 EXHAUST PUMPS AND THEIR CHARACTERISTICS

An exhaust pump, as its very name indicates, is a device to exhaust or remove air, gas or vapour from a vessel. Before dealing with the different types of exhaust pumps, it is better to familiarize ourselves with the terminology associated with them as also with the characteristics of a good exhaust pump.

(*i*) **Exhaust pressure.** An exhaust pump must necessarily have (*a*) an *inlet, intake* (or *fine*) *side* which is connected to the vessel desired to be exhausted and (*b*) an *outlet* or *exhaust side* into which the air, gas or vapour drawn from the vessel is expelled.

The pressure on the exhaust side is referred to as the exhaust pressure. It may just be atmospheric pressure if the exhaust side is open to the atmosphere or may be reduced to a fraction of the atmospheric pressure by means of an auxiliary(pump, called the '*rough*' or the '*backing pump*'. The *fore-vacuum* thus created, greatly facilities the exhausting process. In general, therefore, the higher the degree of vacuum desired to be produced, the lower must be the exhaust pressure.

(*ii*) **Attainable vacuum.** The lowest limit to which the pressure in a given vessel can be reduced is called the *attainable vacuum*. While it naturally varies from pump to pump, it depends a good deal on the *correct amount* of exhaust pressure. For, an unduly low exhaust pressure may well reverse the direction of flow of the gas, which may thus start leaking back from the exhaust to the intake side, *i.e.*, into the vessel. Connecting tubes of wide bores also help improve the degree of attainable vacuum, since the resistance to the flow of gas through them is then small.

(*iii*) **Speed of the pump.** The speed of a pump may best be defined as *the relative rate of reduction of pressure in a given volume of gas or vapour.*

Thus, if the attainable pressure with the help of a given pump be P_0 and the pressure in the vessel, of volume V, connected to it be p at any given instant, we have

rate of reduction of pressure in the vessel, i.e.,

$$-dp/dt = S(p - p_0)/V, \qquad \ldots(i)$$

whence

$$-dp\,(p - p_0) = S\,dt/V, \qquad \ldots(ii)$$

where S is is the *speed of the pump* at pressure p.

So that, if p_1 and p_2 be the values of the pressure in the vessel at instants t_1 and t_2 respectively, we have

$$\int_{p_1}^{p_2} \frac{dp}{(p-p_0)} = \int_{t_1}^{t_2} S\frac{dt}{V}. \text{ Or, } \log_e \frac{p_1-p_0}{p_2-p_0} = \frac{S}{V}(t_2-t_1),$$

which gives
$$S = \frac{V}{t_2-t_1}\log_e\left(\frac{p_1-p_0}{p_2-p_0}\right) \quad ...(iii)$$

This is referred to as **Langmuir's equation for the speed of a pump,** since it was he who drew attention to the fact that *the limiting value of attainable pressure* (p_0) *is never zero,* or that *perfect vacuum is quite unattainable by means of an exhaust pump.*

If, however, p_0 be negligibly small, the equation reduces to

$$S = \frac{V}{t_2-t_1}\log_e\frac{p_1}{p_2}. \quad ...(iv)$$

This is called **Gaede's equation for the intrinsic speed of a pump.**

If $p_1/p_2 = e$ and $(t_2-t_1) = 1$ *sec*, we clearly have $S = V$.

Thus, *the intrinsic speed of a pump may be defined as the volume in which it can reduce the pressure to* $1/e^{th}$, *or about* 36.79%, *of its instantaneous value in* 1 *second.*

If we take the attainable vacuum to be perfect, *i.e.,* if $p_0 = 0$, relation (*i*) above reduces to

$$-\frac{dp}{dt} = S.\frac{p}{V}, \text{ whence, } S = -\frac{V}{p}.\frac{dp}{dt}$$

This is called the *speed of exhaust* or the *pumping speed, E.*

Thus, *exhaust* or *pumping speed,* $E = -\dfrac{V}{p}.\dfrac{dp}{dt}$ ... (*v*)

Now, if dV be the small volume of gas or vapour (measured at pressure p) extracted from the vessel, *i.e.*, from a volume V, in time dt, we have

$$pV = (p-dp)(V+dV), \text{ whence, } dV = -Vdp/p$$

[neglecting $dp\,dV$ as a very small quantity.

So that,
$$\frac{dV}{dt} = -\frac{V}{p}.\frac{dp}{dt} = E. \quad ... (vi)$$

The *exhaust or the pumping speed* of a pump may thus be defined as *the rate of change of volume of the gas or vapour in the given vessel at a given instant,* (*i.e., the volume of gas or vapour removed from the vessel per second*) the volume being measured at the pressure of the gas or vapour at that very instant.

If we substitute the value of dp/dt as obtained from relation (i) in expression (v) for E, we have

$$E = -\frac{V}{p}\left[-\frac{S}{V}(p-p_0)\right] = \frac{S(p-p_0)}{p}.$$

Or,
$$E = S\left(1-\frac{p_0}{p}\right) \quad ... (vii)$$

From relation (*vii*), it is thus clear that

(*a*) when the pump just starts working, $p >> p_0$ and, therefore, p_0/p is negligibly small or zero, so that $E \approx S$, *i.e., to start with, the pumping speed of an exhaust pump is practically the same as its intrinsic speed;*

(*b*) as $p \to p_0$, E gradually decreases and approaches zero; *i.e., the pumping speed of the pump is zero at the lowest attainable pressure.*

When designing a pump, therefore, care should be taken to see that not only does it produce high vacuum but has also as high a pumping speed as possible at all pressures.

Let us now proceed to consider the different types of exhaust pumps.

16.3 ROTARY OIL PUMPS

(*i*) **Gaede's rotary oil pump.** The main parts of the pump are shown in Fig. 16.1, where *S* is a hollow steel chamber or *stator*, inside which rotates eccentrically a strong and massive electrically driven shaft *S*, called the *rotor*, such that it is always in contact with a certain peripheral point of the stator, such as *P*. On either side and close to the point of contact *P* lie the *inlet I* and the *outlet O* for the gas or vapour to enter and leave the stator, with the outlet fitted with a spring-operated valve *V*.

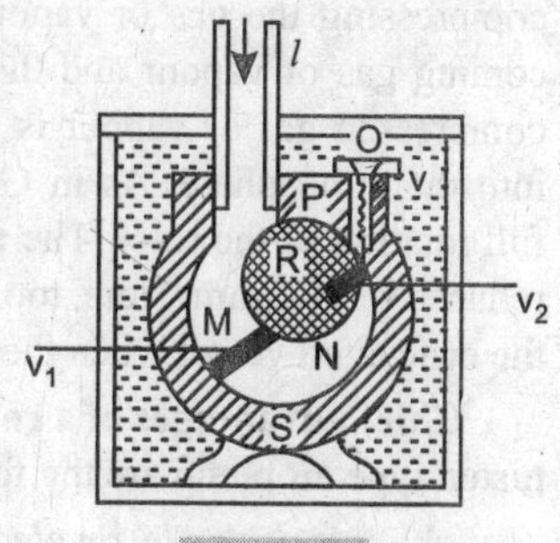

Fig. 16.1

A slot, cut diametrically across the rotor, carries two sliding rods or discs, called the *vanes*, V_1, V_2 with one or more springs between them which keep them pressed against the wall of the stator. This is further ensured by the centrifugal force on the vanes due to the high-speed rotation of the rotor. The space between the rotor and the stator is thus divided into two separate and air or gas-proof compartments.

The pump is kept immersed in a special type of oil, called *vacuum oil*, which (*i*) *provides automatic lubrication*, (*ii*) *prevents leakage of or gas vapour into the high vacuum created* and (*iii*) *ensures efficient cooling of the pump.*

As the electric motor is switched on and the rotor starts rotating in the direction indicated, the space on the inlet side of the chamber goes on increasing and that on the outlet side decreasing correspondingly. The gas or vapour from the vessel connected to the inlet *I* is thus continually drawn into the former and that in the latter goes on getting compressed. When the pressure of this compressed gas or vapour is high enough, it forces open the outlet valve *O* and escapes out into the atmosphere. All this operation is completed in one full rotation of the rotor and goes on repeating itself as the rotor continues to rotate, until the pressure in the vessel is reduced to 10^{-3} mm. A special *self-sealing oil-valve* prevents the gas or vapour being sucked back into the evacuated vessel when the pump stops working.

(*ii*) **Cenco Hyvac or rotary oil pump.** This is a later type and perhaps a trifle more efficient. In construction, it in almost similar to the Gaede type, with one important difference that instead of two vanes inside the rotor, there is only one vane here (*V*) outside the rotor, which is kept pressed against it by a stout spring *s*, as shown in Fig. 16.2. The rotor here too is driven by a separate electric

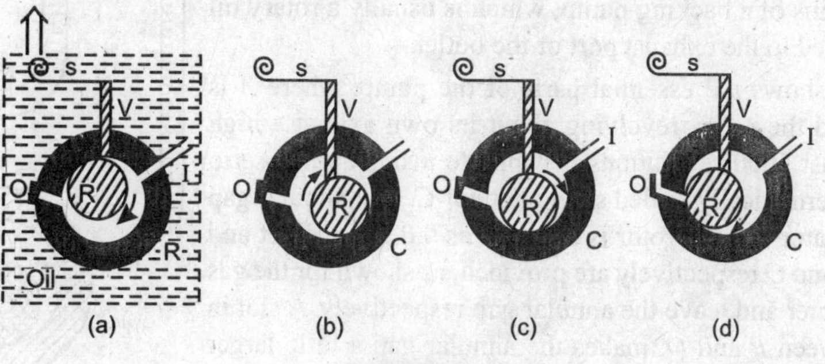

Fig. 16.2

motor and rotates eccentrically inside the stator, so as to be in contact with its wall at one point or another. And, like the Gaede pump, it is also kept immersed in vacuum oil.

The vessel to be exhausted is connected to the Inlet *I*, with the rotor in the position shown in Fig. 16.2 (*i*), and the electric motor started. As the rotor starts rotating in the direction indicated by the arrow, it takes up the successive positions shown in Fig. 16.2 (*ii*), (*iii*) and (*iv*), thus progressively compressing the gas or vapour, with the vane *V* cutting off all communication between the in-coming gas or vapour and that already present and being compressed. When the pressure of the compressed gas or vapour is sufficiently high, it forces open the outlet valve *O* and escapes out into the atmosphere. As in Gaede's pump, so also here, this entire process is completed in one full rotation of the rotor. The process goes on repeating itself until the pressure inside the vessel is reduced to 10^{-4} mm. Here, too, a self-sealing oil valve prevents the gas or air being sucked back into the evacuated vessel when the pump stops working.

Chief advantages of a rotary oil pump. The advantages of a rotary oil pump over the ordinary piston type air pump are the following:

1. *It is driven by an electric motor and the whole operation is thus quick and automatic, with no man power needed.*

2. *Due to a much higher speed of rotation of the rotor than is possible manually, it can produce a much higher degree of vacuum.*

3. *Its being kept immersed in oil automatically ensures its efficient cooling and lubrication as also prevents leakage of the gas or vapour into the vacuum prouduced.*

4. *It can operate directly from the atmospheric pressure and no forè-vacuum is thus necessary.*

5. *It is small and compact in size and occupies much less space.*

6. *It can also be used as a compression pump. For, if a vessel be connected to the outlet O of the pump, the out-coming gas or vapour can be compressed into it.*

16.4 MOLECULAR PUMP

A molecular pump works on the principle that if the linear dimensions of the annular gap between a rapidly rotating surface and the surrounding stationary surface be smaller than the mean free path λ of the gas molecules, there are much fewer collisions amongst the molecules themselves than those between the molecules and the walls of the gap. Under such conditions, as shown by *Knudsen*, the molecules acquire the *drift velocity* of the rotating surface and this velocity then remains unaffected by any subsequent collisions among the molecules.

A molecular pump, however, can not operate directly from the atmosphere and the necessary fore-vacuum has therefore to be created by means of a backing pump, which is usually a rotary oil pump, connected to the exhaust port or the outlet.

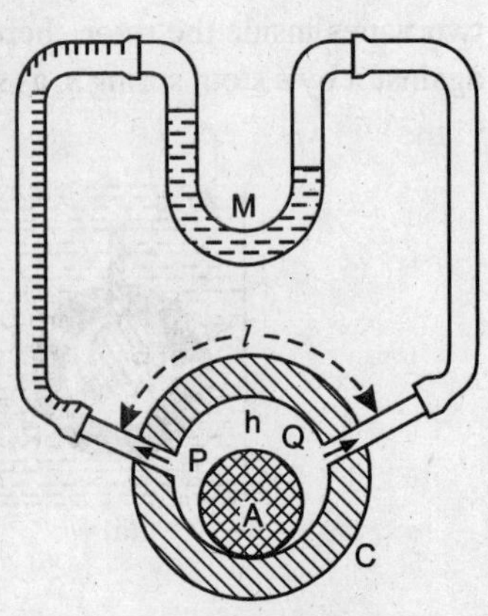

Fig. 16.3

Fig. 16.3 shows the essential parts of the pump, where *A* is cylinder, called the *rotor*, revolving about its own axis at a high speed of at least 5000 revolutions per minute inside and close to the wall of a hermetically sealed shell or stator *C*. The annular gap between the stator and the rotor is as small as 0.03 mm. Inlet and outlet ports *P* and *Q* respectively are provided, as shown for the gas or vapour to enter and leave the annular gap respectively. A slot in the stator between *P* and *Q*, makes the annular gap a little larger there than elsewhere. The inlet port *P* is connected to the vessel to be exhausted and a backing rotary oil pump to the exhaust port *Q*. The necessary fore-vacuum is created by working the oil pump and the rotor set in motion by means of an induction motor. As the rotor rotates at a high speed in the direction shown, the gas molecules in the annular space, rebounding from the walls of the gap and falling into the wide part between P and Q are dragged along with the rotor from P to Q, where they are ejected out. A pressure difference is thus created between P and Q, as indicated by the manometer M. More molecules therefore enter the gap through P, are dragged along from P to Q and then escape out. In this manner, a vacuum of the order of 10^{-6} mm is created in the vessel in the course of just a few minutes.

In the **Gaede type of the pump**, there are a set of twelve *slots* or *grooves* along the surface of the rotor, their depths increasing progressively from about 6 mm to 15 mm. Fitting into these are a set of projections on the stator wall, the clearance between the two being 0.03 mm. As the rotor rotates, the gas or vapour is swept along this small clearance.

In the **Holweck type of the pump**, although there are slots or grooves on the stator, there are no corresponding projections on the rotor and the clearance between the two is even less than 0.03 mm.

The working of these pumps depends upon both the fore-vacuum created and the rate of rotation of the rotor. Thus, the *Gaede type of* pump can create a vacuum of 10^{-6} mm in just a few minutes with a fore-vacuum of about 2 mm and a rotor speed of 10,000 *rev/min*.

And, the *Holweck type* does even better and can create a vacuum of 10^{-7} mm with a fore-vacuum of only 15 mm and a rotor speed of just 4500 *rev/min*.

The drawbacks of a molecular pump are that (*i*) *there are recurring mechanical troubles* on account of the very small clearance between the rotor and the stator and (*ii*) while there is no problem in the case of gases and vapours, slowly vaporising substances like mercury or any traces of grease present make the working of the pump difficult.

16.5 DIFFUSION PUMP

Originally devised by *Gaede*, in the year 1915, this speed pump has, with some modifications, proved to be the very best among mechanical pumps and has almost completely replaced all the rest. It cannot, however, operate directly from the atmospheric pressure but requires a fore-vacuum ranging from 20 mm to 10^{-2} mm.

The principle underlying the pump is that in a mixture of gases, the diffusion of a gas occurs from a region where its partial pressure is higher to that where it is lower, irrespective of the total pressure in the two regions.

The vessel F to be exhausted is connected up, as shown in Fig. 16.4 to a wide tube AB through a narrow connecting tube CD, having a cylindrical slit at D. The necessary fore-vacuum is created by means of a rotary oil pump connected to the side tube T and a stream of easily condensable vapour is passed through AB in the upward direction as indicated by the arrow.

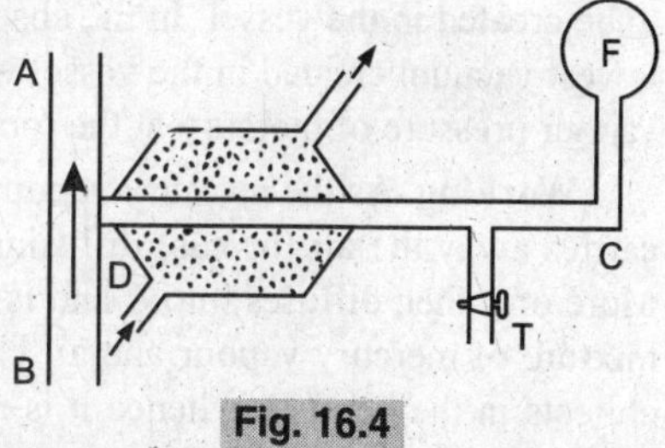

Fig. 16.4

The partial pressure of the gas being greater at the end C of the tube than at the end D, diffusion of the gas occurs from C into AB, where it is swept away by the vapour stream. Again, therefore, the partial pressure of the gas is less at D than at C, so that more of the gas diffuses into AB and is carried away by the vapour stream. This goes on so long as the partial pressure of the gas remains greater at C than at D, with the result that the pressure in vessel F goes on falling progressively. Since the partial pressure of the vapour is higher in tube AB than in CD, it tends to diffuse along DC, thus driving the gas diffusing from C into AB backwards. This back-diffusion of the vapour and the gas not only reduces the speed of the pump but also sets a limit to the attainable vacuum in vessel F. It is, therefore, prevented by (*i*) making the aperture at C very narrow (about 0.1 mm in width) and (*ii*) cooling tube *CD* by circulating cold water around it, as shown, so as to condense the vapour into its liquid before it can reach the vessel. The liquid is then transferred back to the boiler.

Gaede showed theoretically and later confirmed experimentally that the speed of the pump is the maximum when the width of the aperture at *C* is of the same order of magnitude as the mean free path of the molecules in the back-streaming vapour.

Since diffusion as well as condensation play their parts in the working of the pump, such pumps are also referred to as *diffusion-condensation pumps* or even *condensation pumps*.

(*i*) **Warran model.** A simple and common form of the pump was designed by the *Warran* in the year 1923 and is shown in Fig. 16.5. It is made of pyrex glass and all in one piece. Mercury is boiled in the conical flask *A* and its vapour rises up in tube *B*, lagged with asbestos (to prevent condensation) and issues out at *J* in the form of a parallel jet into a broader tube *C*, kept cooled by circulating cold water through a jacket *W* around it. An inlet *I* and an outlet *O* are provided in tubes *C* and *T*, as shown. The vessel to be exhausted is connected to the former and a backing pump to the latter.

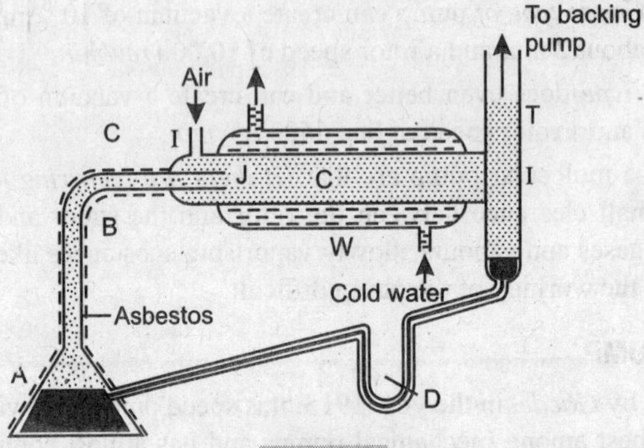

Fig. 16.5

In view, however, of the fact that the vapour pressure of mercury is not low enough at the room temperature, a '*vapour trap*' is interposed between the inlet *I* and the vessel, as indicated in Fig. 16.6. The trap is cooled by liquid air or solid-CO_2 in alcohol, contained in a Dewar flask, so that the vapour pressure of mercury falls to a value lower than the vacuum desired to be created in the vessel. In the absence of the trap, obviously, the lowest vacuum created in the vessel will be of the same order as the vapour pressure of mercury at the room temperature, *viz.*, 10^{-3} mm.

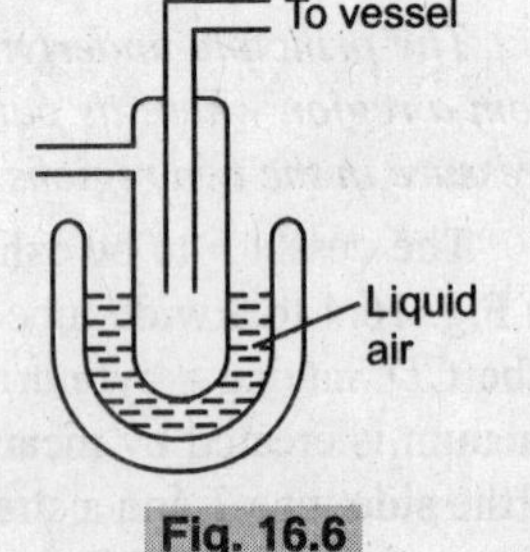

Fig. 16.6

Working. As the mercury vapour issues out of *J* into tube *C*, it carries away the air (or gas) diffusing from the vessel into tube *C*. More of it then diffuses into *C* and is similarly carried away. As the mixture of mercury vapour and air pass through tube *T*, the vapour gets condensed and the liquid collects in the bend *D*, whence it is returned back to the flask *A*, and the air (or gas) is swept out by the backing pump. The process goes on repeating itself and if the vapour jet be parallel and of a width of about 8 mm and the backing pump quite efficient, a pressure as low as 10^{-7} mm can be produced in the vessel fairly quickly.

Since mercury vapour, once it gets into the vacuum system, can cause serious trouble, liquids like *Apiezon oils, Butyl phthalate* or even 10% *paraffin with Butyl phthalate*, are now increasingly used in place of mercury. All these liquids have a low vapour presure, of the order of 10^{-6} mm at the room temperature and no '*vapour trap*' need be used with them. Also, the speed of the pump increases appreciably. But the temperature of oil has to be carefully regulated such that its vapour pressure never exceeds 1 mm, since at higher temperatures it gets oxidised and forms an oil of high viscosity and high vapour pressure.

Theoretically, there is no limit to the vacuum that can be created by the pump, for, the air (or gas) must go on diffusing from the vessel into tube C, until its partial pressure in the vessel is reduced to zero. In actual practice, however, some back-streaming vapour finds its way into the vessel and this ideal state of affairs is never really attained.

(*ii*) **Kaye-Backhurst Model.** It is a one stage, high speed pump, all made of steel, (Fig. 16.7), its speed being due to its rather large dimensions.

Mercury vapour from the boiler rises up in the central tube and issues out through holes in its upper part into the annular space between two deflectors D_1 and D_2. From there, it emerges in the form of a jet and carries along with it the gas (or air) diffusing from the vessel, through the inlet at the top into the space between the upper deflector D_2 and the outer casing AB. The casing being kept cooled by circulating cold water around it, as indicated, the vapour condenses and returns back to the boiler through tube C, while the gas (or air) is swept out by the backing pump. The pressure in the vessel thus falls progressively and ultimately attains the value 10^{-6} mm, with a fore-vacuum of 1.5 mm.

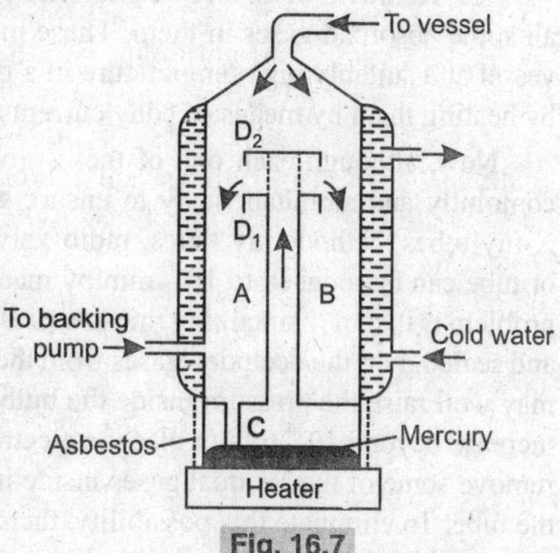

Fig. 16.7

Diffusion pumps may be used in series, each pump, in turn, carrying the evacuation process a step further than the last and thus a low pressure may be easily and more rapidly obtained. They are, therefore, commonly used for the evacuation of X-ray tubes, and wireless valves and other allied industrial purposes.

Their only disadvantages are that (*i*) their exhaust speed is relatively slow and (*ii*) a careful regulation of the density of mercury vapour is absolutely necessary if the maximum speed is to be achieved.

16.6 OTHER METHODS OF PRODUCING LOW PRESSURES

The following is a brief account of the various methods for the reduction of pressure beyond 10^{-6} mm, upto which a diffusion pump is quite satisfactory.

1. Sorption process. This process consists in connecting system to be evacuated to a tube containing some coconut charcoal, freshly heated under reduced pressure and cooled by liquid air, when gases like carbon dioxide, nitrogen and ammonia are absorbed by the charcoal. Similarly, for the absorption of hydrogen, palladium or platinum black may be used in place of coconut charcoal. Pressures as low as 10^{-7} mm may thus be easily obtained. For still further reduction of pressure, the process may be used in conjunction with a suitable backing pump.

2. Electrical process. This consists in removing the gas atoms by ionising them either by bombarding them by electrons obtained by thermionic emission or by passing a slow electric discharge through the gas. The ions thus produced get deposited on the wall of the vessel which is kept properly cooled.

3. Thermal Process. This depends upon the fact that certain gases, like nitrogen, disappear slowly in the presence of a glowing tungsten filament. This explains how high vacuum continues to be maintained in our incandescent lamps.

4. Chemical process of 'flashing' or gettering. This method was suggested by *Soddy* in the year 1907 and consists in suddenly vaporising an electropositive metal like magnesium, barium or calcium by placing a pellet of the chosen metal on a tungsten filament, through which a momentary high current is passed. The metal burns with a flash and gets vaporised. Most of the vapour forms a shining mirror-like deposit on the wall of the vessel and the rest forms chemical compounds with the gases present. These chemical compounds have all a very low vapour pressure and the deposit formed on the wall continues to function as a high speed pump, as it were, so that not only is a high vacuum produced but it continues to be maintained. Soddy himself used calcium for the purpose, though commonly magnesium and barium (or their alloy) are used. Such '*gas hungry*' metals are called *getters*; hence the name of the process, '*gettering*'.

5. Removal of absorbed gases. The walls of a glass vessel and the metal parts inside it have all some absorbed gases in them. These may be released or removed either by 'baking, the whole vessel at a suitably high temperature in a gas or electric oven or by making the metal parts red hot by heating them by means of eddy currents at radio frequencies. The process is called '*de-gassing*'.

Now, although each one of these processes is independent of the other, they are often used conjointly and simultaneously to ensure good evacuation. As an example may be cited the case X-ray tubes, cathode ray tubes, radio valves etc. As we know, the pressure inside the glass bulb or tube can be reduced to 10^{-6} mm by means of a diffusion pump so long as it is in operation. The problem is that of maintaining this low pressure once the bulb or the tube is separated from the pump and sealed. For, the occluded gases from the walls of the bulb (or the tube) and the metal parts therein may well raise the pressure inside the bulb. In no case, however, should the pressure be allowed to increase beyond 10^{-4} mm or else the electrons emitted by the hot tungsten filament of the bulb may remove some of the residual gases inside it (by ionisation) and thus alter the very characteristics of the tube. To eliminate this possibility, therefore, the bulb is first *de-gassed* in the manner explained above, while the pump is still operating, so that the occluded gases may be removed by the pump.

And, to ensure that the pressure in the bulb (or the tube) does not, at any time later, cross the upper limit of 10^{-4} mm, the bulb is subjected to the process of gettering, which ensures the maintainance of pressure at the requisite level, so that, the X-ray or the cathode ray tube, thus treated, needs no further attention.

16.7 EXPERIMENTAL DETERMINATION OF THE SPEED OF A PUMP

(*i*) **Constant volume method.** This is a direct application of the expression $S = \frac{V}{t_1 - t_2} \log_e \frac{p_1}{p_2}$ for the speed of a pump, deduced in § 16.1 (*iv*), the more exact relation (*iii*) being not necessary in view of p_0 being vanishingly small under the conditions of the experiment.

The pump whose speed is to be determined is connected to a large vessel, of volume V and the pressure of the gas or air inside it noted just before the pump starts working and at frequent intervals thereafter, its volume remaining constant at V throughout.

If p' be the pressure at $t = 0$ and p at $t = t$, we have

$$S = \frac{V}{t} \log_e \left(\frac{p'}{p}\right) \quad \text{or,}\ t = \frac{V}{S} \log_e \left(\frac{p'}{p}\right).$$

Or, $$t = 2.3026 \frac{V}{S} (\log_{10} p' - \log_{10} p)$$

$$= 2.3026 \frac{V}{S} \log_{10} p' - 2.3026 \frac{V}{S} \log_{10} p.$$

Since 2.3026 $(V/S) \log_{10} p'$ is a constant in a given experiment, we may put it equal to C.

So that, $$t = C - 2.3026 \frac{V}{S} \log_{10} p.$$

If, therefore, we plot t against $\log_{10} p$, we obtain a straight line graph so long as the speed of the pump is independent of pressure. The speed of pump, S, may thus be easily obtained from the slope of this straight line.

(ii) **Constant pressure method.** This is the method commonly used for determining the speed of the present day high speed pumps since the speed of such pumps depends a great deal on pressure.

The method is due to *Gaede* and as its very name suggests, the pressure of the gas (or air) in the vessel is kept constant by supplying gas (or air) to it at the same rate at which it is being exhausted from it by the pump. This *volume-rate of supply of the gas (or air) to the vessel then straightaway gives the speed of the pump.*

The procedure consists in mounting a large spherical glass bulb A, (Fig. 16.8), of about 1 litre capacity, immediately above the pump and linked to it by the shortest possible tube; for, the bigger the dimensions (*i.e.,* length and diameter) of the link or the tube, the greater the fall in the actual speed of the pump. The bulb is fitted with a needle valve N at the top to regulate the supply of gas (or air) to it. A long, horizontal and fine capillary tube BC (of 1 to 2 mm bore), with a mercury pallet D inside it and an oil manometer $O.M.$ are also connected to the needle valve, as shown.

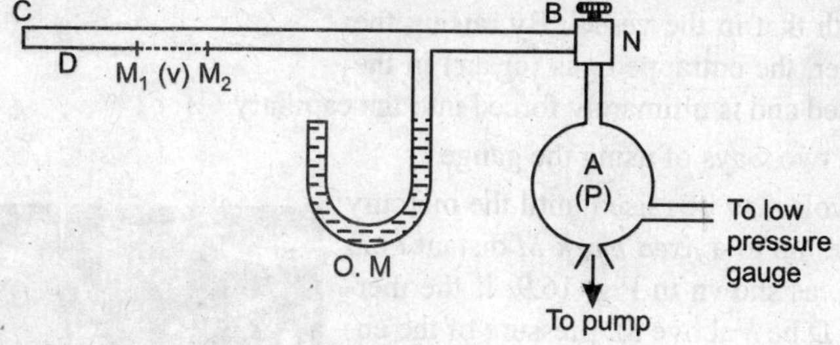

Fig. 16.8

The oil used in the manometer must have a low vapour pressure, and the most suitable for the purpose is found to be *tetrahydronaphthalene* ($C_{10} H_{12}$)

By suitably adjusting the needle valve, the supply of the gas (or air) to bulb A is so regulated that the pressure inside it remains constant at the desired value, as noted on a low pressure gauge connected to the bulb.

The gas (or air) is supplied to the bulb, through needle valve N, at a pressure slightly lower than that of the atmosphere, as indicated by the oil manometer $O.M.$ The rate of supply of the gas (or air) can be easily determined by observing the time t taken by the mercury pellet D to cover the distance between two fiducial marks M_1 and M_2 etched on the capillary BC.

Suppose the volume between the marks M_1 and M_2 is v and the pressure in the capillary, p_1. Then if P be the (constant) pressure inside the bulb, the volume V of the gas (or air) supplied to it in the same time t (that the mercury pellet takes to cover the distance $M_1 M_2$) is given by the relation $PV = pv$, assuming Boyle's law to hold. So that,

$$V = \frac{pv}{P} \text{ and hence the speed of pump, } S = \frac{V}{t} = \frac{pv}{Pt}.$$

16.8 PRESSURE GAUGES

A pressure gauge is a device to measure the pressure produced by a pump. Here, we shall consider only a few important gauges used to measure low pressures produced by exhaust pumps.

1. **Method Gauge.** This is the most commonly used gauge for the measurement of low pressures up to 10^{-5} mm and was devised by *Mcleod* in the year 1874.

As shown in Fig. 16.9 (*a*), it consists of a cylindrical bulb B, ending at the top in a closed capillary tube CA and connected at the bottom to a reservoir of mercury R by means of a flexible rubber tubing T, A side-tube $DEFI$ emerges immediately below the bulb, with the portion EF vertical, to which is attached a capillary tube D of an identical bore with the capillary CA. This counterbalances the depression of the mercury column in CA, for the same depression is produced in the mercury column in capillary D.

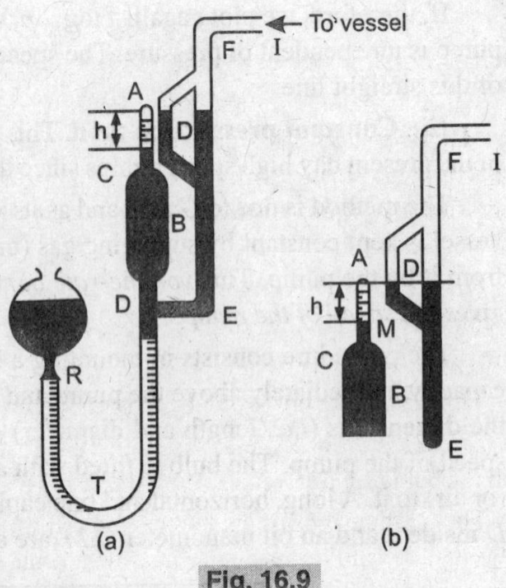

Fig. 16.9

The vessel in which the pressure is desired to be determined is connected to the gauge at I and the reservoir lowered until the mercury falls to a level below the bend at D. The gas or air in the vessel thus fills the bulb B, the tube EF and the capillary D at the same pressure p cm as that in the vessel.

The reservoir is now raised and mercury rises up in the bulb, the tube EF and the capillary D. Some of the gas or air is thus trapped in the bulb, with no communication with that in the vessel. By raising the reservoir still further, the entrapped gas (or air) in the bulb gets compressed and is ultimarely forced into the capillary CA.

Now, there are two ways of using the gauge.

(*i*) The reservoir may be raised until the mercury in capillary CA rises up to a *fixed mark M* distant l cm say, from its top A, as shown in Fig. 16.9. If the mercury level in EF or D be h above M, pressure of the entrapped gas (or air) in capillary CA is $(h + p) \approx h$, since p is negligible compared with h. And, if v be the volume per centimetre length of the capillary, the volume of this gas or air is vl. So that, if V be the volume of the whole of the bulb B up to the bend E, including that of the capillary CA, we have, in accordance with Boyle's law,

McLeod Pressure Gauge

$$pV = h\,(vl), \text{ whence, } p = \frac{h(vl)}{V},$$

whence, p, the pressure in the vessel can be easily calculated.

Since $p \propto h$, the scale is a linear or uniform one and can be arranged alongside the tube EF to make the gauge direct reading.

(*ii*) The reservoir is raised until the mercury in capillary D rises up to the level of the top A of capillary CA, as shown in Fig. 16.9 (*a*). Then, clearly, the pressure of the gas in the capillary CA is h, where h is the difference of the mercury levels in the two capillaries CA and D, and its volume = hv. Again, therefore, in accordance with Boyle's law,

$$pV = (hv)\, h = h^2 v, \quad \text{whence, } p = h^2 v/V$$

and may be easily calculated.

Since here $p \propto h^2$, the scale is a non-uniform or non-linear one and is, in fact, parabolic. It, therefore, opens out or spreads out as the pressure decreases. The obvious advantage of this is that *the accuracy of the gauge increases at lower pressures*. This is a great point in favour of using the gauge in this manner. The gauge can be made direct reading by placing the scale alongside the capillary CA.

Though quite an efficient gauge, so much so that practically all other gauges are calibrated with reference to it, it suffers from a number of drawbacks, among which may be listed the following:

(*i*) It behaves erratically in the presence of easily condensable vapours (because they do not obey Boyle's law). This can, however, be remedied by interposing a liquid air trap between the gauge and the vessel in which the pressure is to be determined to rapidly remove such vapours. Even otherwise, the liquid air trap must be used to prevent any mercury vapours from entering the evacuated vessel.

(*ii*) The mercury which remains in contact with a large length of the rubber tubing is likely to get contaminated by the sulphur present in the rubber. Moreover, air may diffuse through the rubber tubing and may find its way to the gauge.

This has, in recent years, been remedied by replacing the rubber tubing by one of stainless steel.

(*iii*) It is rather large and unwieldy and it is very inconvenient to raise or lower the reservoir with such a large amount of mercury in it.

This difficulty too has been removed in the improved form of the gauge, shown in Fig. 16.10, where the reservoir has been dispensed with altogether. Instead, tube *D* is made longer, is fitted in one mouth of a Woulff's bottle *W* and dipped in mercury contained in the bottle. In the other mouth of the bottle is fitted a tube *N* connected through a two-way stop-cock *S* to a sodalime tower *T* and a tube *L* leading to a backing pump. The tower has a packing of cotton wool as a safeguard against particles of soda lime getting into the gauge. To the top of the tower is connected a long capillary tube *J* through a small rubber tubing provided with a spring-clip.

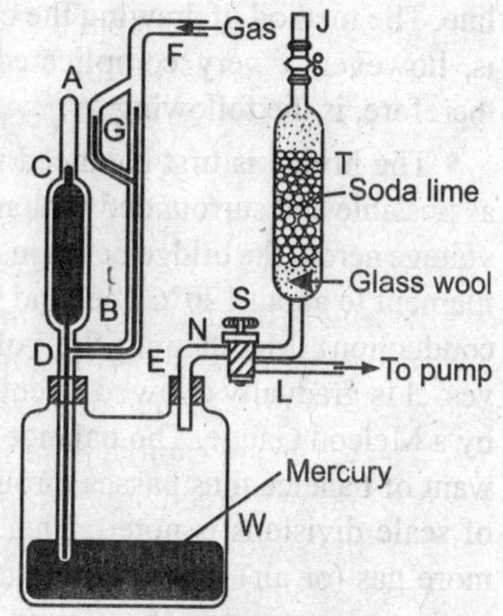

Fig. 16.10

The Woulff's bottle is first put in communication with the pump and the whole of the mercury thus comes down into the bottle, the pressure being the same as produced by the pump and obviously very much lower than that of the atmosphere. The stop-cock is now turned to disconnect the pump and to partially connect the bottle and the tower. The air from outside thus gradually enters the bottle, deprived of its moisture by the sodalime. The pressure on the mercury in the bottle increases and some of it rises up in *D*. The gauge may then be used in one of the two ways, explained above.

Despite all the improvements made, the Mcleod Gauge still suffers from the inherent defects of being unwieldy, and the inability to give a continuous record of pressure-changes. Then, the use of the liquid air trap adversely affects the speed of the pump, and the readings obtained do not truly give the pressure inside the vessel. And, in any case, its readings in the last lap of its range, *viz.*, 10^{-4} to 10^{-5} mm, are hardly ever reliable.

2. **The Pirani gauge.** It is a well known fact that whereas at high and ordinary pressures, the thermal conductivity of a gas (K) is quite independent of pressure, at pressures below 10^{-2} mm, it is directly proportional to pressure, *i.e.*, K is a linear function of p. This fact was first used by *Warburg*, in 1907, for the measurement of low pressures and forms the basis of the *Pirani gauge*.

Construction. In construction, it is very much like the cage-type incandescent lamp. The essential requirements are that (*i*) the filament should have a high coefficient of increase of resistance with temperature, so that even a small change in its temperature may result in an appreciable change in its resistance, (*ii*) the heat-loss along the filament-support should be as small as possible and (*iii*) the distance between the filament and the wall of enclosing glass bulb must remain unaltered. The filament is, therefore, of tungsten or platinum wire, of a diameter of about 0.06 mm, a glass rod (a poor conductor of heat) is used as the support and the filament is kept taut by taking it round glass beads, as shown in Fig. 16.11 so that the longer portions of the filament are equidistant from the wall of the bulb. The bulb is open at the lower end which can be connected to the vessel in which the pressure is to be measured.

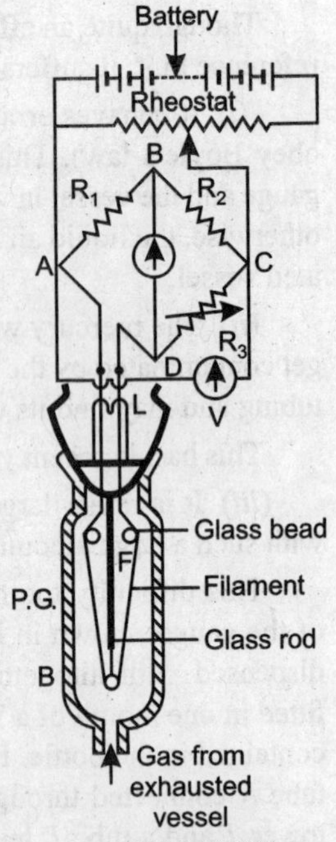

Fig. 16.11

With change in pressure of the gas between the filament and the wall of the bulb, the rate of conduction of heat across the gas changes. The results in a change in the temperature of the filament and hence a change in its resistance. The change in the resistance of the filament is measured. It gives the change in conductivity of the gas and hence, indirectly, the pressure of the gas.

A calibration curve is drawn between resistance of the filament (measured by a Wheatstone's bridge) and the pressure of the gas (measured by Mcleod Gauge). The pressure corresponding to any resistance of the filament can then be read off directly from the curve, which is a straight line. The method of drawing the calibration, curve suggested by Campbell is, however, a very complicated one. The procedure usually adopted, therefore, is the following:

The bridge is first balanced with the gauge exhausted as completely as possible and surrounded with melting ice (*i.e.*, a thermostat at 0°*C*), the voltage across the bridge being just sufficient to raise the temperature of the filament to about 120°*C* (beyond which heat is lost more by radiation than conduction). Maintaining the voltage constant, the gas (or air) from the vessel is gradually allowed to enter the gauge. The pressure in the gauge increases and is measured by a Mcleod Gauge. The balance of the bridge is naturally upset and a current corresponding to the want of balance thus passes through the galvanometer. The deflection in the galvanometer in terms of scale divisions is noted. This is repeated for each small increase of pressure due to more and more gas (or air) entering the gauge. A graph is then plotted between pressure and the deflection in the galvanometer. It is found to be almost a straight line. From this graph, then, the pressure corresponding to any deflection in the galvanometer can be read straightaway.

The range of the gauge is rather small, from 10^{-2} to 10^{-5} mm. But, because of its almost instant action, it is very useful for measuring pressure fluctuations. The chief **drawbacks** of the gauge are that (*i*) *it is quite unsuitable for use with organic vapours, for they 'poison' the filament;* (*ii*) *it is not an absolute gauge and has to be calibratede against a Mcleod or any other absolute gauge,* (*iii*) *it is not suitable for measurement of pressures below* 10^{-3} mm, for, then, heat loss occurs mostly by radiation rather than conduction, (*iv*) *in the range* 10^{-3} to 10^{-5} mm, *it requires some manual adjustment, which obviously cannot be made reliably*. This has, however, been remedied by Scott, in 1939, by including a triode valve in the circuit of the gauge, making its working both smooth and automatic.

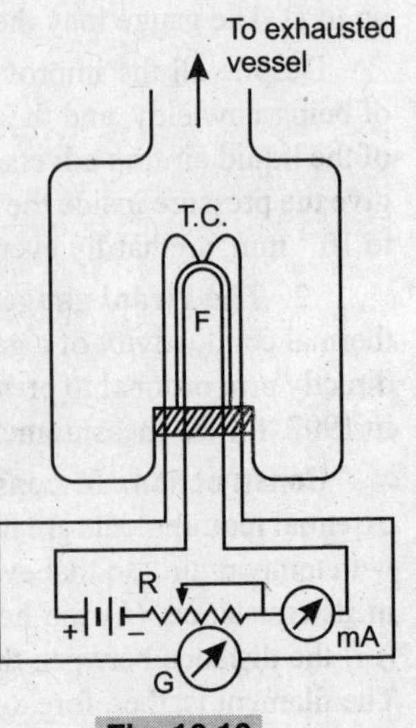

Fig. 16.13

3. **Thermocouple Gauge.** It is just a *variation of the Pirani gauge*. Here, the hot junction of a thermocouple T.C. (Fig. 16.12) say, *iron - constantan, chromel - alumel* or *anti-mony bismuth* or any other—is attached to the mid-point of the filament which consists of a short ribbon of constantan. The cold junction of the thermocouple is connected to a sensitive galvanometer. From the deflection in the galvanometer the thermo-emf developed in the thermocouple isobtained and hence the temperature of the hot junction. The temperature of the hot junction depends upon the thermal conductivity

of the gas between the thermocouple or the filament and the wall of the bulb, the outerside of which is maintained at $0°C$. The whole upper part of the gauge is enclosed in a small chamber, with an opening at the top through which it can be put in communication with the vessel in which the pressure is desired to be determined.

From the temperature of the filament we can obtain the conductivity of the gas which at low pressures (below 10^{-2} mm), as we know, is directly proportional to its pressure. So that, the pressure inside the evacuated vessel can thus be determined indirectly.

It has the same range as the Pirani gauge and is similarly calibrated against a Mcleod or any other absolute gauge.

4. **Ionization Gauge.** This gauge is based on the fact that at pressures below 10^{-3} mm, the ionization current varies linearly with pressure.

The construction of the gauge is more or less similar to that, of a triode valve. The tungsten filament is here supported on a glass rod R (Fig. 16.13), in the manner indicated, with a co-axial grid G of tungsten or molybdenum, around it. A nickel or silver coating on the inner side of the enclosing glass bulb functions as the plate P. A platinum wire w, sealed on to the plate, connects it to the external circuit. To prevent any metal film (from the filament or the plate) getting deposited on the glass rod (thereby causing inter-electrode leaks), glass collars C, C are provided, as shown. These can freely move along the rod and thus remove any metal film formed. The bulb is open at the top and is put in communication with the evacuated vessel in which the pressure is to be measured.

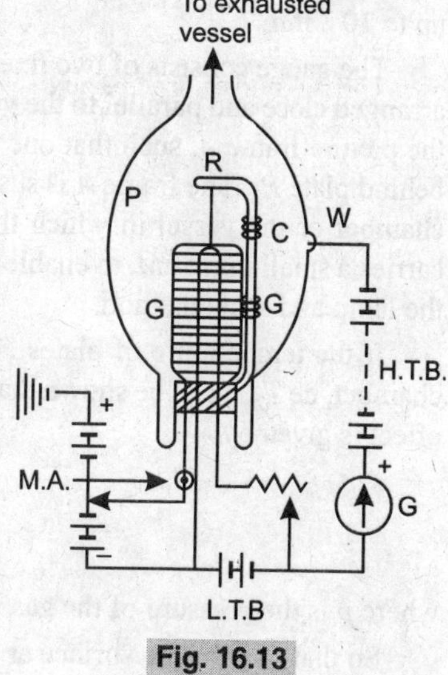

Fig. 16.13

The grid is given a positive potential with respect to the filament and the plate is connected to the negative terminal of a high tension battery, *H.T.B.*, of about 120 volts, with a galvanometer included in the circuit.

The electrons emitted by the filament (on being heated by the current from the low tension battery *L.T.B.*) are strongly attracted by the grid. Due to their momentum, however, quite a few of them get past the grid and ionise the gas between the grid and the plate. The positive ions, thus released are collected by the plate, any electrons reaching it being repelled. The ionization current thus produced is indicated by the galvanometer.

This gauge too is not an absolute one and has to be calibrated against a Mcleod or some other absolute gauge. Once calibrated, the galvanometer is replaced by a micrometer, graduated in pressure units, to straightaway give the pressure of the gas. It has certain clear advantages over the Mcleod gauge. Thus, *(i) it can measure much lower pressures, in the range* 10^{-3} *to* 10^{-7} *mm, (ii) it can be used with both, vapours and gases, (iii) it is much smaller in size, and can be placed quite close to the vessel being evacuated.*

Its sensitivity, however, depends upon the nature of the gas, the arrangement of its electrodes and the electric circuit employed.

Hot Cathode Ionization Gauge

5. **Knudsen Gauge.** This is perhaps the simplest and the most efficient gauge developed up to date and has been

successfully used to measure the lowest pressures yet produced.

It is based on the principle of *radiometric effect,* which may be defined as the *mechanical force exerted between two surfaces very close to each other and maintained at a difference of temperature. The effect manifests itself only when the mean free path of the gas molecules is longer than the distance between the two heated surfaces or a heated surface and a wall.* This means, obviously, that the effect is possible only at very low pressures.

Kundsen showed that if a cold plate be suspended close and parallel to a hot plate in a vessel in which the pressure is below 10^{-3} mm, the cold plate gets deflected due to the bombardment by the molecules rebounding from the hot plate. If the dimensions of the plates be very much larger than the distance between them and if this distance be smaller than the mean free path of the gas molecules, the deflecting repulsive force on the cold plate is proportional to the gas pressure right up to 10^{-7} mm.

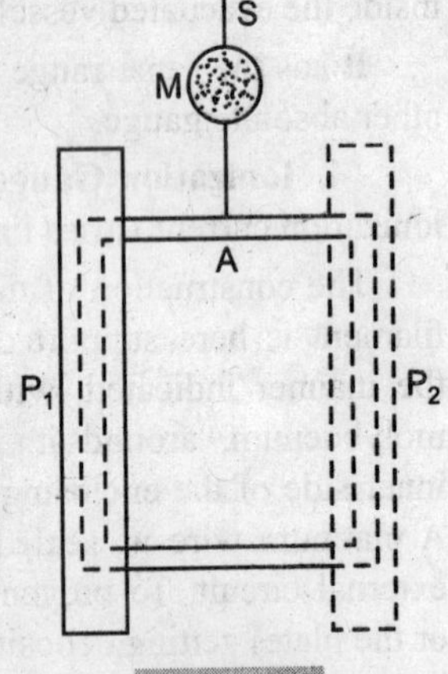

Fig. 16.14

The gauge consists of two fixed metal plates P_1 and P_2 (Fig. 16.14) arranged close and parallel to the vertical strips of a metal framework in the picture frame *A*, such that one strip lies in front of P_1 and the other behind plate P_2. The frame *A* is suspended by a fine quartz fibre *S* in the chamber or the vessel in which the pressure is to be determined, and carries a small mirror *M*, to enable the deflection of *A* to be observed by the lamp and scale method.

If the temperature of plates P_1 and P_2 be T_1 and that of the two strips, and hence also of the chamber, be T_2, it can be shown that the force acting per unit area on the two strips due to radiometric effect is given by

$$F = \frac{p}{4}\left(\frac{T_1 - T_2}{T_2}\right), \qquad \dots (i)$$

where *p* is the pressure of the gas in the chamber of the vessel.

So that, if α be the surface area of each strip, the force acting on it is $F. \alpha$.

Since these forces acting on the two strips are *equal, opposite* and *parallel*, they constitute a couple, tending to rotate the frame *A* about the susqension fibre *S* and the moment of this deflecting couple is $C = F\,\alpha \times 2\,r$, where *r* is the distance of each strip from the axis of suspension.

As the frame *A* tends to rotate about the suspension axis or the quartz fibre *S*, an opposing or restoring couple is set up in the quartz fibre, tending to bring the frame back to its original position. The frame, therefore, oscillates about the quartz fibre and ultimately comes to rest, say, after deflection θ from its initial position, where the two couples balance each other. If τ be the torsional couple per unit twist of the suspension fibre, the torsional couple $= \tau\,\theta$. We, therefore, have $F\,\alpha \times 2\,r = \tau\,\theta$, whence, $F = \tau\,\theta/2\,\alpha\,r$.

Substituting this value of *F* in relation (*i*) above, we have

$$\frac{\tau\theta}{2\alpha r} = \frac{\rho}{4}\left(\frac{T_1 - T_2}{T_2}\right),$$

whence
$$p = \frac{2\tau\theta}{\alpha r}\cdot\frac{T_2}{T_1 - T_2}. \qquad \dots (ii)$$

If *I* be the moment of inertia of frame *F* about the suspension axis we have $t = 2\pi\sqrt{I/\tau}$, where *t* is the time-period of oscillation of the frame. So that, $\tau = 4\pi^2 I/t^2$. Substituting this value of τ in relation (*ii*), we, therefore, have

$$p = \frac{8\pi^2 I}{\alpha r t^2} \cdot \frac{T_2}{T_1 - T_2}.$$

The pressure p in the vessel can thus be obtained.

The gauge has the following advantages over others:

(*i*) It is an absolute gauge; (*ii*) it gives a continuous indication of pressure in the vessel, (*iii*) it is unaffected by outside influences, (*iv*) it is compact and stable and yet sensitive at low pressures, down to 10^{-7} mm. In fact, as mentioned earlier, even much lower pressures have been measured by it; (*v*) it can be used with all kinds of vapours and gases; (*vi*) it does not require the use of objectionable liquids, like mercury.

If cannot, however, be used to measure pressure above 10^{-3} mm, for then, the mean free path of the molecules become comparable with the distance between the plates.

16.9 DETECTION OF A LEAKE A VACUUM SYSTEM

The following are some of the simple method used for the purpose :

1. In case of an all-glass system, a spark discharge from a small induction coil (or a Tesla coil) may be used. One terminal of the induction coil may be connected to a metal piece in direct communication with the system and the other may be connected to a long copper wire attached to a glass rod. Holding the rod, the wire may be moved all over the portion suspected of a leak. In case of a pinhole leak anywhere, a small spark passes through the hole and the general intensity of the discharge in the system increases.

2. In the case of a glass-metal or an all-metal system, the above procedure cannot be adopted. Instead, some form of a discharge tube is attached to the system and its parts suspected of a leak painted with alcohol or acetone. Its vapour enters the system through the leak and the colour of the discharge from pink to pale blue, this being the colour associated with the presence of carbon compounds, in the region of the discharge. The trouble with these vapours is that they may pass into the backing pump and, later reappear in the system when the pump is in action and the coil gets hot.

It is, therefore, advisable to use carbon dioxide instead, which can later be easily removed. A jet or CO_2 is, therefore, directed over the suspected of the system. In case of a leak, the gas enters the system and its presence, and hence that of the leak, directed by the change in the colour of discharge, as before.

3. In case the leak be so small that a discharge cannot be maintained, one of the way, mentioned hereunder, is adopted.

(*a*) An *ionisation gauge* may be attached to the system, which will show at once the entry of any vapours into the system through a leak.

(*b*) A jet of hydrogen may be directed over the parts under test which will diffuse much more readily into the system than air. A Pirani gauge (sensitive to hydrogen) attached to the system will thus show a sudden and a marked change in its readings.

(*c*) In case the pressure be very low, in the range 10^{-6} to 10^{-7} mm, a mass spectrography may be included in the system and a helium steam passed over the suspected part. The presence of a heilum line in the spectrograph will be clear indication of a leak.

EXERCISE

1. Explain what is meant by the speed of an exhaust pump. How many it be determined experimentally? **(*Delhi*)**
2. Describe, with a neat diagram, the principle and working of a rotary pump. Mention the order of vacuum it produces. **(*Delhi*)**
3. Describe and explain the working of the Cenco-Hyvac rotary pump. How is the pressure so produced measured? **(*Madras, 1965, Vikram*)**
4. Describe the construction and working of a rotary oil pump. How much vacuum can be produced by the pump? **(*Lucknow*)**
5. Describe, with a neat diagram, the construction of a mercury vapour pump and explain its working. Why does it need a backing pump? **(*Delhi*)**
6. Give an account of the construction and working of a good diffusion pump. Explain with the help of a diagram how such a pump is utilized to obtain a high vacuum.
   Describe a method of measuring accurately low pressures. **(*Punjab (supp)*)**
7. Describe, with a neat diagram, the construction and working of a diffusion condensation pump. What order of vacuum can it reach? Why is a backing pump necessary for its working?
8. Describe the principle, construction and working of diffusion pump and also a gauge which can measure the low pressure produced. **(*Delhi*)**
9. Define the speed of a vacuum pump. Describe a vacuum pump which can produce vacuum of the order of 10^{-6} mm of mercury. **(*Delhi*)**
10. (*a*) Write notes on (*i*) Mcleod gauge to measure pressure below 0.25 mm of Hg.
11. Describe with a neat diagram the construction and working of (*a*) any modern high vacuum (*b*) a gauge which can measure the low pressure this pump produces. **(*Agra, Madras*)**
12. Explain the working of (*i*) a Pirani gauge; (*ii*) a thermocouple gauge.
13. Explain the principle and working of the Kundsen gauge. What is the range of pressures for which it can be used? What are its points of superiority over other forms of gauge?
14. Write an essay on the production and measurement of low pressures.
15. (*a*) Explain the construction and working of an ionization gauge.
    (*b*) Explain how leaks in a vacuum system may be detected.